Scott Foresman - Addison Wesley

Science Insights
Exploring Matter and Energy

Teacher's Edition

About the Authors

Michael DiSpezio, M.A.

Michael DiSpezio is a science consultant who conducts workshops for educators throughout the United States. He taught and chaired the science departments of two independent schools in Cape Cod, Massachusetts. Mr. DiSpezio is a former marine biologist and a frequent contributor to NSTA journals. He currently resides in North Falmouth, Massachusetts.

Marilyn Linner-Luebe, M.S.

Marilyn Linner-Luebe has been a science writer and editor since 1985. She taught physical science for fourteen years and chemistry for one year at Fulton High School in Fulton, Illinois. Ms. Linner-Luebe has a master's degree in journalism, specializing in science communication, from Boston University. She currently resides in Clinton, Iowa.

Marylin Lisowski, Ph.D.

Marylin Lisowski is a professor of science education at Eastern Illinois University in Charleston, Illinois. She has taught biology, earth science, and elementary science. In addition to teaching, Dr. Lisowski leads international expeditions and field programs for high school students and teachers. Dr. Lisowski, who has been recognized as an Ohio Science Teacher of the Year, is also one of Florida's Honor Science Teachers.

Gerald Skoog, Ed.D.

Gerald Skoog is a professor of science education and the supervisor of science teachers at Texas Tech University in Lubbock, Texas. Dr. Skoog has taught biology and chemistry and has been a director of several science curriculum and training projects. He served as president of the National Science Teachers Association in 1985 and 1986.

Bobbie Sparks, M.A.

Bobbie Sparks is K–12 Science Consultant for the Harris County Schools in Houston, Texas. Ms. Sparks has taught science for sixteen years, including biology and middle school life and earth science. She has also supervised K–12 science teachers. Ms. Sparks is active in local, state, and national science organizations.

Scott Foresman
Addison Wesley

Editorial Offices: Menlo Park, California • Glenview, Illinois
Sales Offices: Reading, Massachusetts • Atlanta, Georgia • Glenview, Illinois
Carrollton, Texas • Menlo Park, California
http://www.sf.aw.com

Front cover photographs: Telegraph/FPG International (earth); Jeff Foott/Bruce
Coleman Inc. (honeycomb); Telegraph/FPG International (integrated chip wafer);
Gareth Hopson for Addison-Wesley (geode).

Back cover photograph: Telegraph/FPG International (integrated chip wafer).

ISBN 0-201-33286-8

2 3 4 5 6 7 8 9 10—VH—02 01 00 99

Teacher's Edition Contents

Reviewers and Consultants

Content Reviewers

Farzan Abdolsalami
Assistant Professor
Trinity University
San Antonio, TX

Randall Bryson
Middle School Science Coordinator
Durham Academy
Durham, NC

John Caferella
Science Programs Supervisor
Community School District 10
Bronx, NY

Catherine K. Carlson
Science Department Chairperson
Parkhill/Richardson Intermediate
    School District
Dallas, TX

Anita Gerlach
Chemistry/Physics Teacher
Santa Fe High School
Santa Fe, NM

Karen G. Jennings
Chemistry Instructor
Lane Technical High School
Chicago, IL

George Moore
Science Coordinator
Midwest City Public Schools
Midwest City, OK

Gary Vitta
Superintendent of Schools
West Essex Regional Schools
North Caldwell, NJ

Miriam R. Weiss
Director of Science/Technology
Community School District 11
Bronx, NY

Richard A. Williams
Chemistry Instructor
Winter Haven High School
Winter Haven, FL

Multicultural Consultants

William Bray
Stanford University
Stanford, CA

Gloriane Hirata
San Jose Unified School District
San Jose, CA

Joseph A. Jefferson
Ronald McNair School
East Palo Alto, CA

Martha Luna
McKinley Middle School
Redwood City, CA

Peggy P. Moore
Garnet Robertson Intermediate School
Daly City, CA

Steven Oshita
Crocker Middle School
Burlingame, CA

Modesto Tamez
Exploratorium
San Francisco, CA

Participants

Chapter Opener Participants

Anna Rufus
Iroquois Center for Math/Technology
Grand Rapids, MI

Ben Burnett
El Toro High School
El Toro, CA

Thomas F. Koscuik
Edmond North Mid-High
Edmond, OK

Sue Trafton and Rich Marvin
Barnstable Summer School
Hyannis, MA

Cindy Stevens
Bair Middle School
Sunrise, FL

Nancy Schlack
Sullivan High School
Chicago, IL

Candy Henderson
Northside School
Midway, KY

Judy Bryant
Tuckahoe Middle School
Richmond, VA

Mike Wilson
North Garland High School
Garland, TX

Brad Manor
Open School
Saint Paul, MN

Cassie Soeffing
Axtell Park Middle School
Sioux Falls, SD

Robert W. Hofacker
Stivers Middle School
Dayton, OH

John P. Norton
Sage Park Middle School
Windsor, CT

Ed Mueller
Shattuck Junior High
Neenah, WI

Anita Gerlach
Santa Fe High School
Santa Fe, NM

Randall D. Bryson
Durham Academy
Durham, NC

John Straw
Carman-Ainsworth Junior High
Flint, MI

John J. Sullivan
Milton High School
Milton, MA

Gloria Yost
Albert Einstein Middle School
Sacramento, CA

Joyce Keemer Peterson
Wakefield High School
Arlington, VA

John Rozeboom
South High School
Minneapolis, MN

John Zlatnik
Washington High School
Fremont, CA

Sally Shaffer
Indiana Area Junior High
Indiana, PA

Catherine K. Carlson
Parkhill Junior High, Richardson ISD
Garland, TX

Jane E. Capiello
Bethlehem Central Middle School
Delmar, NY

Science Insights *Program Rationale and Goals*

Science Insights *has been developed to meet the science learning needs of the early adolescent. To support the teacher in anticipating the special needs of this student,* Science Insights *contains a balance of features and teacher assistance that are geared to these needs.*

This early adolescent student...

▶ Needs frequent **motivation** to focus attention in an increasingly distracting environment.

▶ Students will be motivated by the dynamic and accurate **visual learning program**, the engaging writing, and the special features that speak to their interests.

▶ Is beginning to see **integration** of ideas and processes but is still not able to generalize easily.

▶ **Integration** of the sciences and of other subjects is used throughout the program.

▶ Needs **activities** and hands-on experiences to channel energy and enrich learning.

▶ An active, hands-on approach to science within the student text and within other program materials is employed to involve all students and meet the needs of different learning styles.

▶ Requires special support to learn how to work with others **cooperatively**.

▶ Teachers are provided with strategies to encourage students to work **cooperatively**.

▶ Is **self-oriented** and wants to see how learning affects personal issues and the future.

▶ Emphasis on **Science, Technology, and Society** in every section shows students that science affects them and their future.

▶ Needs special help in learning how to make **decisions** in a world that is beginning to provide more and more options.

▶ Questioning format and activity strategies in every section encourage **decision-making** development.

Explore Visually

Themes

Cooperative Learning

Multicultural Perspectives

Portfolio

Connections

Program Overview

Science Insights—Exploring Matter and Energy
Student Edition

Science Insights—Exploring Matter and Energy
Teacher's Edition

Supplementary Materials
Teacher's Resource Package

A resource of more than 700 blackline masters that can be used to review, reteach, reinforce, integrate, enrich, and assess.

▶ *Section Activities*
A comprehensive series of student worksheets that includes vocabulary and section reviews, and reteach and enrich worksheets that can be used to meet the needs of different student ability levels.

▶ *Skills Worksheets*
A series of student worksheets that stress science process skills, language arts and writing skills, and decision-making skills while reinforcing science content and concepts.

▶ *Integrated Resource Book*
Student worksheets that encourage students to explore the thematic, interdisciplinary, and intra-science connections of science concepts.

▶ *Spanish Supplement*
Spanish translations of the chapter summaries and the glossary.

▶ *Assessment Program—Chapter and Unit Tests*
Each chapter has two test versions. Chapter Test A has standard multiple-choice, true/false, modified cloze, and fill-in-the-blanks type questions. Each Chapter Test B has a skill-based and extended answer format.

Science Insights—Exploring Matter and Energy
Laboratory Manual
Student Edition
Annotated Teacher's Edition

More than 40 hands-on exploratory and decision-making laboratory investigations and surveys.

Overhead Transparency Package

Contains 96 color transparencies, 24 blackline transparencies, and the Overhead Transparency Teacher's Guide. The Teacher's Guide includes teaching strategies for using the color transparencies, overhead blackline master transparencies, and correlated student worksheets.

Science Skills and Techniques Manual
Student Edition
Annotated Teacher's Edition

More than 50 worksheets and activities that stress basic science skills and laboratory techniques.

Computer Software

SelecTest is a flexible test-generating computer program with a bank of more than 700 questions.

Test File

A printed version of the test questions used in the SelecTest.

Spaceship Earth Video

A 25-minute video that stresses connections between people, their environment, and technology. Relevant to students from its music to its message.

Ancillary Options

Optional materials that can be used with *Science Insights—Exploring Matter and Energy* are:

▶ *Multiculturalism in Mathematics, Science, and Technology*

▶ *One-Minute Readings: Issues in Science, Technology, and Society*

▶ CEPUP Modules

▶ *Living Textbook:* Popular videodisc series, barcoded in the Teacher's Edition, available from Optical Data.

See the Difference, Feel the

From the beginning of each unit, Science Insights motivates and challenges students.

Motivate

Dynamic color photography stimulates student interest right from the start.

Creative ▶ *Writing*

Lots of opportunities for you to integrate creative writing throughout each unit.

UNIT OVERVIEW

Unit 1 provides an introduction to the study of science, a survey of force and motion, and a discussion of the relationship of force and motion to energy. Chapter 1 introduces science skills and methods. It also describes some of the tools and technologies used in physical science research. Chapter 2 explores the relationship between motion and energy. Frames of reference, motion, and acceleration are discussed. Finally, the chapter

defines energy, compares potential and kinetic energy, and introduces the law of conservation of energy. Chapter 3 examines the relationship between force, motion, and gravity. The chapter relates force and friction to each of Newton's three laws of motion. A discussion of universal forces closes the chapter. Chapter 4 discusses forces in fluids, fluid pressure, and the relationships among gravity, weight, buoyancy, and density. The chap-

ter closes with a presen[t...] differences in moving fl[...] nation of how heavier-th[...] Chapter 5 focuses on [...] and energy. The chap[...] power, shows how to [...] mechanical advantag[...] machine, and describ[...] machines. Finally, the[...] the Law of Conserva[...] Energy.

Introducing the Unit

Directed Inquiry

Have students examine the photograph. Ask:

▶ How can scientists learn how water striders walk across water? (Scientists learn by observing the water striders and/or by conducting experiments.)

▶ What information can scientists obtain by studying the circles, or dimples, around the strider's feet? (They can see where the strider's feet touch the water, and determine the amount of stress each foot exerts on the water's surface.)

▶ What tools or technologies might help scientists in their study of water striders? (They might use a video recorder, special photographic techniques like the one shown in the photograph, and so on. Accept all reasonable answers.)

Writing About the Photograph

Ask students to think about factors involved in walking on water without sinking. Have students imagine that they must cross a lake. They have no boat and can't swim. Their only resource is a stand of saplings. Have students discuss how they might build a frame that would allow them to cross the water.

UNIT 1

Unit 1 Forces, Motion, and Energy

Chapters

1 Studying Science
2 Motion and Energy
3 Forces and Motion
4 Forces in Fluids
5 Work, Machines, and Energy

xvi

Excitement, Enjoy the Results

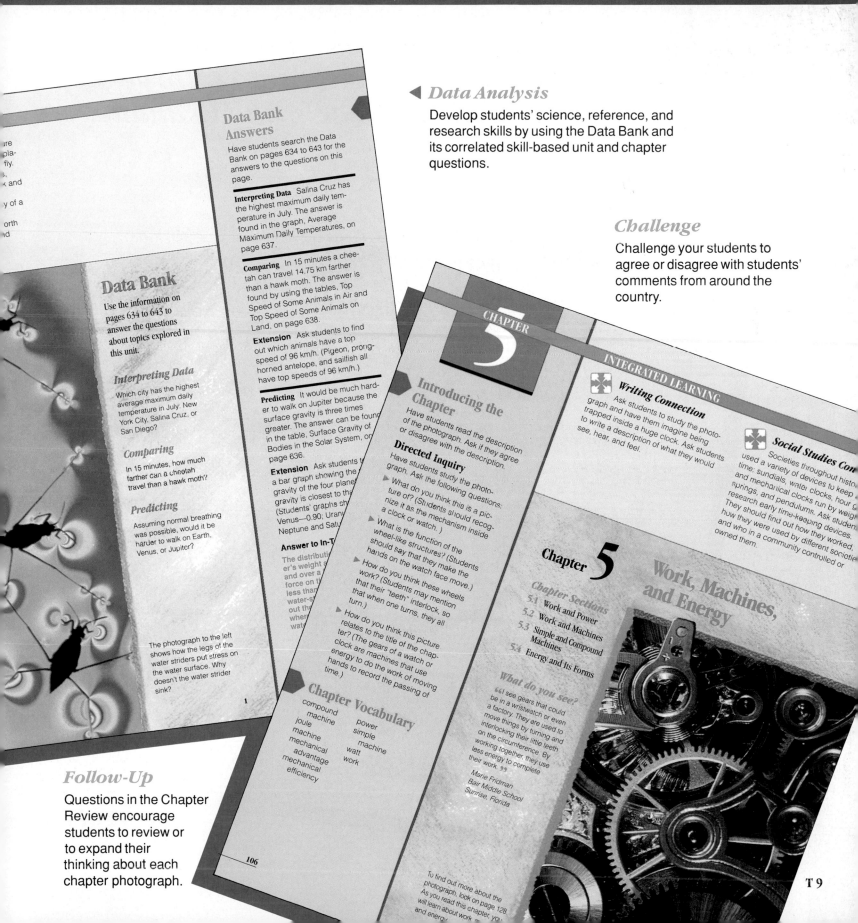

Data Analysis

Develop students' science, reference, and research skills by using the Data Bank and its correlated skill-based unit and chapter questions.

Challenge

Challenge your students to agree or disagree with students' comments from around the country.

Follow-Up

Questions in the Chapter Review encourage students to review or to expand their thinking about each chapter photograph.

Data Bank

Use the information on pages 634 to 643 to answer the questions about topics explored in this unit.

Interpreting Data

Which city has the highest average maximum daily temperature in July: New York City, Salina Cruz, or San Diego?

Comparing

In 15 minutes, how much farther can a cheetah travel than a hawk moth?

Predicting

Assuming normal breathing was possible, would it be harder to walk on Earth, Venus, or Jupiter?

The photograph to the left shows how the legs of the water striders put stress on the water surface. Why doesn't the water strider sink?

1

Data Bank Answers

Have students search the Data Bank on pages 634 to 643 for the answers to the questions on this page.

Interpreting Data Salina Cruz has the highest maximum daily temperature in July. The answer is found in the graph, Average Maximum Daily Temperatures, on page 637.

Comparing In 15 minutes a cheetah can travel 14.75 km farther than a hawk moth. The answer is found by using the tables, Top Speed of Some Animals in Air and Top Speed of Some Animals on Land, on page 638.

Extension Ask students to find out which animals have a top speed of 96 km/h. (Pigeon, pronghorned antelope, and sailfish all have top speeds of 96 km/h.)

Predicting It would be much harder to walk on Jupiter because the surface gravity is three times greater. The answer can be found in the table, Surface Gravity of Bodies in the Solar System, on page 636.

Extension Ask students t... a bar graph showing the ... gravity of the four planet... gravity is closest to th... (Students' graphs sh... Venus—0.90; Uran... Neptune and Satu...

Answer to In-T...

The distributi... er's weight a... and over a... force on th... less than... water-s... out th... wher... wat...

106

Introducing the Chapter

Have students read the description of the photograph. Ask if they agree or disagree with the description.

Directed Inquiry

Have students study the photograph. Ask the following questions:

▶ What do you think this is a picture of? (Students should recognize it as the mechanism inside a clock or watch.)

▶ What is the function of the wheel-like structures? (Students should say that they make the hands on the watch face move.)

▶ How do you think these wheels work? (Students may mention that their "teeth" interlock. Ask that when one turns, they all turn.)

▶ How do you think this picture relates to the title of the chapter? (The gears of a watch or clock are machines that use energy to do the work of moving hands to record the passing of time.)

Chapter Vocabulary

compound machine
joule
machine
mechanical advantage
mechanical efficiency
power
simple machine
watt
work

INTEGRATED LEARNING

Writing Connection

Ask students to study the photograph and have them imagine being trapped inside a huge clock. Ask students to write a description of what they would see, hear, and feel.

Social Studies Con...

Societies throughout histo... used a variety of devices to keep... time: sundials, water clocks, hour g... and mechanical clocks run by weig... springs, and pendulums. Ask studen... research early time-keeping devices. They should find out how they worked... how they were used by different societie... and who in a community controlled or owned them.

Chapter 5

Work, Machines, and Energy

Chapter Sections

5.1 Work and Power
5.2 Work and Machines
5.3 Simple and Compound Machines
5.4 Energy and Its Forms

What do you see?

❝I see gears that could be in a wristwatch or even a factory. They are used to move things by turning and interlocking their little teeth on the circumference. By working together, they use less energy to complete their work.❞

Marie Fridman
Bair Middle School
Sunrise, Florida

To find out more about the photograph, look on page 128. As you read this chapter, you will learn about work m... and energy...

T 9

Integrate Learning in Every

Science Insights works for you by organizing each section into a three-step lesson: Motivate, Teach, and Evaluate.

Integrated Learning

Bring themes, science and subject connections, and multicultural perspectives into each lesson.

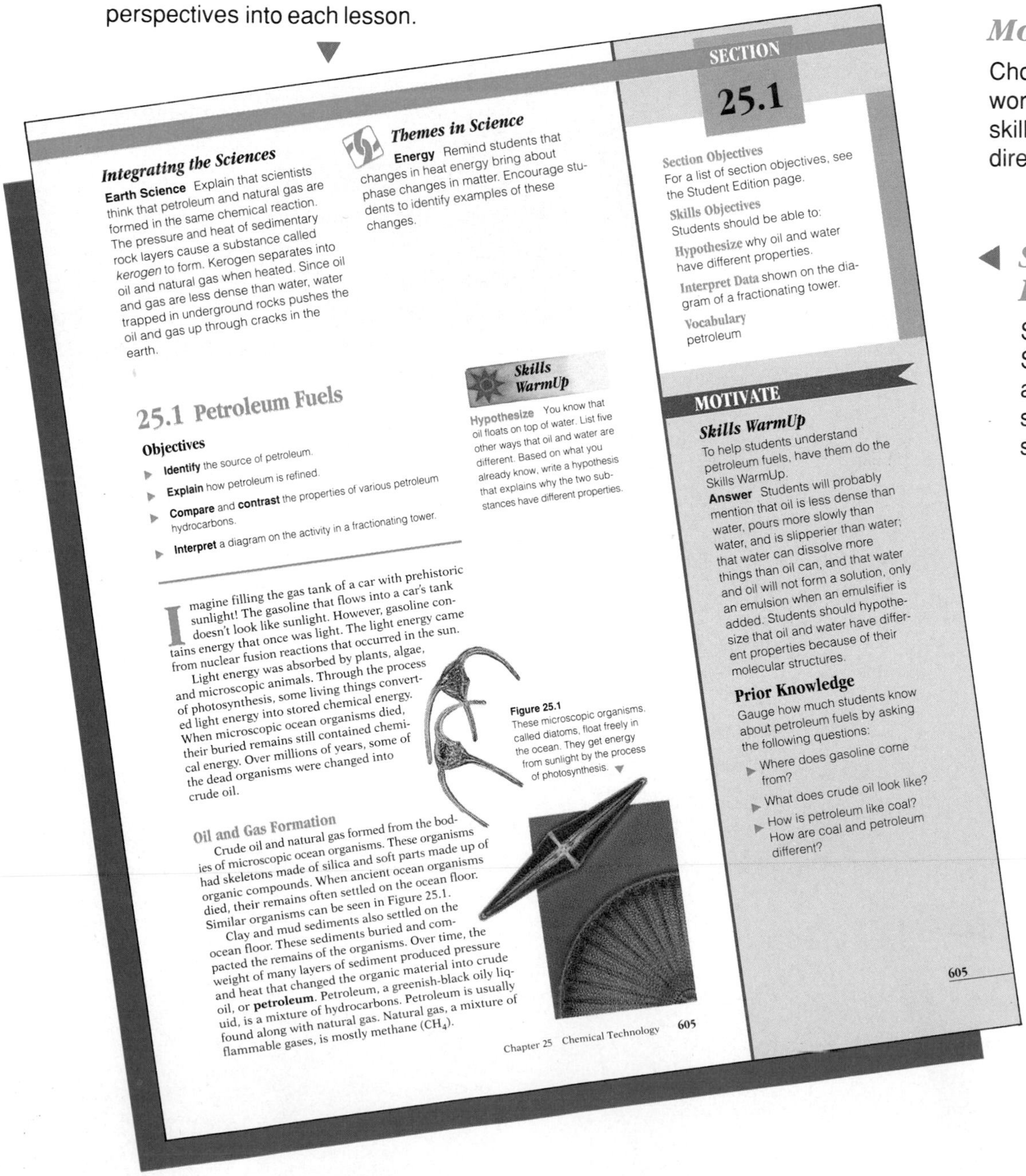

▼

(reproduction of Teacher's Edition page)

Integrating the Sciences
Earth Science Explain that scientists think that petroleum and natural gas are formed in the same chemical reaction. The pressure and heat of sedimentary rock layers cause a substance called *kerogen* to form. Kerogen separates into oil and natural gas when heated. Since oil and gas are less dense than water, water trapped in underground rocks pushes the oil and gas up through cracks in the earth.

Themes in Science
Energy Remind students that changes in heat energy bring about phase changes in matter. Encourage students to identify examples of these changes.

25.1 Petroleum Fuels

Objectives
▶ **Identify** the source of petroleum.
▶ **Explain** how petroleum is refined.
▶ **Compare** and **contrast** the properties of various petroleum hydrocarbons.
▶ **Interpret** a diagram on the activity in a fractionating tower.

Skills WarmUp
Hypothesize You know that oil floats on top of water. List five other ways that oil and water are different. Based on what you already know, write a hypothesis that explains why the two substances have different properties.

I magine filling the gas tank of a car with prehistoric sunlight! The gasoline that flows into a car's tank doesn't look like sunlight. However, gasoline contains energy that once was light. The light energy came from nuclear fusion reactions that occurred in the sun.

Light energy was absorbed by plants, algae, and microscopic animals. Through the process of photosynthesis, some living things converted light energy into stored chemical energy. When microscopic ocean organisms died, their buried remains still contained chemical energy. Over millions of years, some of the dead organisms were changed into crude oil.

Figure 25.1
These microscopic organisms, called diatoms, float freely in the ocean. They get energy from sunlight by the process of photosynthesis. ▼

Oil and Gas Formation
Crude oil and natural gas formed from the bodies of microscopic ocean organisms. These organisms had skeletons made of silica and soft parts made up of organic compounds. When ancient ocean organisms died, their remains often settled on the ocean floor. Similar organisms can be seen in Figure 25.1.

Clay and mud sediments also settled on the ocean floor. These sediments buried and compacted the remains of the organisms. Over time, the weight of many layers of sediment produced pressure and heat that changed the organic material into crude oil, or **petroleum**. Petroleum, a greenish-black oily liquid, is a mixture of hydrocarbons. Petroleum is usually found along with natural gas. Natural gas, a mixture of flammable gases, is mostly methane (CH_4).

Chapter 25 Chemical Technology   **605**

SECTION
25.1

Section Objectives
For a list of section objectives, see the Student Edition page.

Skills Objectives
Students should be able to:

Hypothesize why oil and water have different properties.

Interpret Data shown on the diagram of a fractionating tower.

Vocabulary
petroleum

MOTIVATE

Skills WarmUp
To help students understand petroleum fuels, have them do the Skills WarmUp.
Answer Students will probably mention that oil is less dense than water, pours more slowly than water, and is slipperier than water; that water can dissolve more things than oil can, and that water and oil will not form a solution, only an emulsion when an emulsifier is added. Students should hypothesize that oil and water have different properties because of their molecular structures.

Prior Knowledge
Gauge how much students know about petroleum fuels by asking the following questions:

▶ Where does gasoline come from?
▶ What does crude oil look like?
▶ How is petroleum like coal?
▶ How are coal and petroleum different?

605

Motivate

Choose the strategy that works best for students—from skills development activities to directed-inquiry questions.

◀ Skills Development

Skills WarmUp and Skills WorkOut activities focus students on science skills and methods

◀ Prior Knowledge

Find out how much science knowledge students bring to each chapter.

Lesson

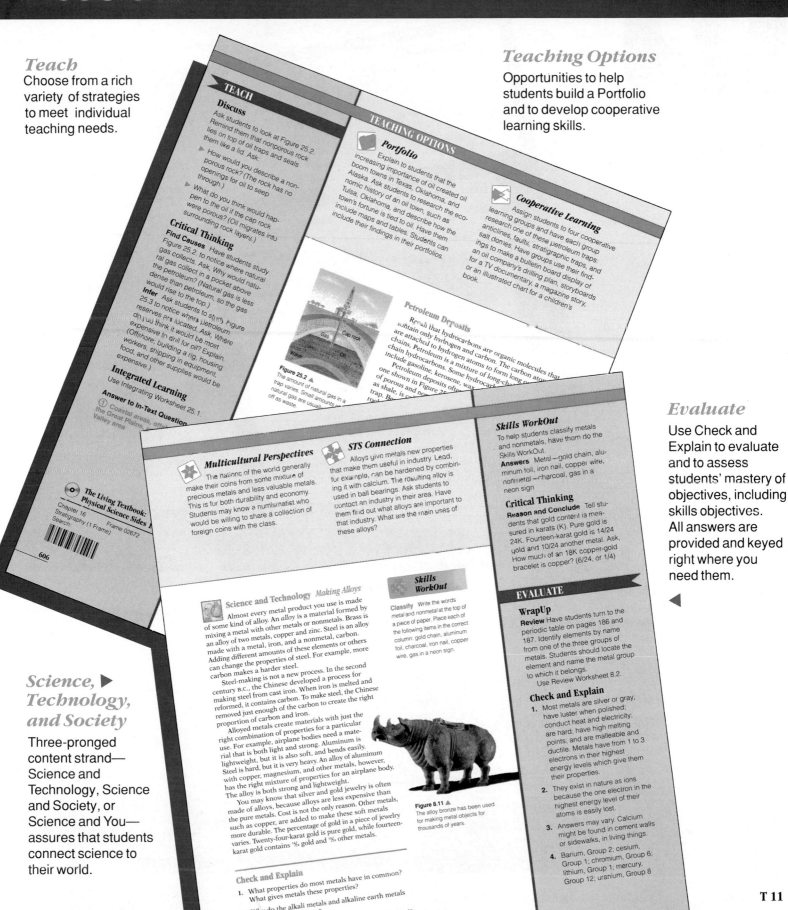

Teach
Choose from a rich variety of strategies to meet individual teaching needs.

Teaching Options
Opportunities to help students build a Portfolio and to develop cooperative learning skills.

Evaluate
Use Check and Explain to evaluate and to assess students' mastery of objectives, including skills objectives. All answers are provided and keyed right where you need them.

Science, ▶ Technology, and Society
Three-pronged content strand—Science and Technology, Science and Society, or Science and You—assures that students connect science to their world.

TEACH

Discuss
Ask students to look at Figure 25.2. Remind them that nonporous rock lies on top of oil traps and seals them like a lid. Ask:
▶ How would you describe a non-porous rock? (The rock has no openings for oil to seep through.)
▶ What do you think would happen to the oil if the cap rock were porous? (Oil migrates into surrounding rock layers.)

Critical Thinking
Find Causes Have students study Figure 25.2 to notice where natural gas collects. Ask, Why would natural gas collect in a pocket above the petroleum? (Natural gas is less dense than petroleum, so the gas would rise to the top.)
Infer Ask students to study Figure 25.3 to notice where petroleum reserves are located. Ask, Where do you think it would be most expensive to drill for oil? Explain. (Offshore; building a rig, housing workers, shipping in equipment, food, and other supplies would be expensive.)

Integrated Learning
Use Integrating Worksheet 25.1.
① **Answer to In-Text Question** Coastal areas, often the Great Plains, Valley area

The Living Textbook:
Physical Science Sides
Chapter 16
Stratigraphy (1 Frame)   Frame 02672
Search.

606

TEACHING OPTIONS

Portfolio
Explain to students that the increasing importance of oil created boom towns in Texas, Oklahoma, and Alaska. Ask students to research the economic history of an oil town, such as Tulsa, Oklahoma, and describe how the town's fortune is tied to oil. Have them include maps and tables. Students can include their findings in their portfolios.

Cooperative Learning
Assign students to four cooperative learning groups and have each group research one of these petroleum traps: anticlines, faults, stratigraphic traps, and salt domes. Have groups use their findings to make a bulletin board display of an oil company's drilling plan, storyboards for a TV documentary, a magazine story, or an illustrated chart for a children's book.

Figure 25.2 ▲
The amount of natural gas in a trap varies. Small amounts of natural gas are usually ___ off as waste.

Petroleum Deposits
Recall that hydrocarbons are organic molecules that contain only hydrogen and carbon. The carbon atoms are attached to hydrogen atoms to form long chains. Petroleum is a mixture of long-chain hydrocarbons. Some hydrocarbons include gasoline, kerosene, wax ___. Petroleum deposits often ___ one shown in Figure 25 ___ of porous and non ___ as shale, is ___ trap. Be ___

Multicultural Perspectives
The nations of the world generally make their coins from some mixture of precious metals and less valuable metals. This is for both durability and economy. Students may know a numismatist who would be willing to share a collection of foreign coins with the class.

STS Connection
Alloys give metals new properties that make them useful in industry. Lead, for example, can be hardened by combining it with calcium. The resulting alloy is used in ball bearings. Ask students to contact an industry in their area. Have them find out what alloys are important to that industry. What are the main uses of these alloys?

Skills WorkOut
To help students classify metals and nonmetals, have them do the Skills WorkOut.
Answers Metal—gold chain, aluminum foil, iron nail, copper wire, nonmetal—charcoal, gas in a neon sign

Critical Thinking
Reason and Conclude Tell students that gold content is measured in karats (K). Pure gold is 24K. Fourteen-karat gold is 14/24 gold and 10/24 another metal. Ask, How much of an 18K copper-gold bracelet is copper? (6/24, or 1/4)

Science and Technology *Making Alloys*

Almost every metal product you use is made of some kind of alloy. An *alloy* is a material formed by mixing a metal with other metals or nonmetals. Brass is an alloy of two metals, copper and zinc. Steel is an alloy made with a metal, iron, and a nonmetal, carbon. Adding different amounts of these elements or others can change the properties of steel. For example, more carbon makes a harder steel.

Steel-making is not a new process. In the second century B.C., the Chinese developed a process for making steel from cast iron. When iron is melted and reformed, it contains carbon. To make steel, the Chinese removed just enough of the carbon to create the right proportion of carbon and iron.

Alloyed metals create materials with just the right combination of properties for a particular use. For example, airplane bodies need a material that is both light and strong. Aluminum is lightweight, but it is also soft, and bends easily. Steel is hard, but it is very heavy. An alloy of aluminum with copper, magnesium, and other metals, however, has the right mixture of properties for an airplane body. The alloy is both strong and lightweight.

You may know that silver and gold jewelry is often made of alloys, because alloys are less expensive than the pure metals. Cost is not the only reason. Other metals, such as copper, are added to make these soft metals more durable. The percentage of gold in a piece of jewelry varies. Twenty-four-karat gold is pure gold, while fourteen-karat gold contains ¹⁴⁄₂₄ gold and ¹⁰⁄₂₄ other metals,

Skills WorkOut
Classify Write the words metal and nonmetal at the top of a piece of paper. Place each of the following items in the correct column: gold chain, aluminum foil, charcoal, iron nail, copper wire, gas in a neon sign.

Figure 8.11 ▲
The alloy bronze has been used for making metal objects for thousands of years.

Check and Explain
1. What properties do most metals have in common? What gives metals these properties?
2. Why do the alkali metals and alkaline earth metals exist in nature as ions?
3. **Infer** Where might you find calcium in your school?
4. ___ iodic table to determine the ___

EVALUATE

WrapUp
Review Have students turn to the periodic table on pages 186 and 187. Identify elements by name from one of the three groups of metals. Students should locate the element and name the metal group to which it belongs.
Use Review Worksheet 8.2.

Check and Explain
1. Most metals are silver or gray, have luster when polished; conduct heat and electricity; are hard; have high melting points; and are malleable and ductile. Metals have from 1 to 3 electrons in their highest energy levels which give them their properties.
2. They exist in nature as ions because the one electron in the highest energy level of their atoms is easily lost.
3. Answers may vary. Calcium might be found in cement walls or sidewalks, in living things.
4. Barium, Group 2; cesium, Group 1; chromium, Group 6; lithium, Group 1; mercury, Group 12; uranium, Group 8

193

T 11

Build Science and Decision-

Activities

Laboratory activities promote hands-on science experiences.

Cooperative Learning

Each activity is organized by task so that you can choose to use a traditional laboratory approach or assign cooperative learning groups.

Teaching Options

Build students' understanding with a prelab discussion. Strategies and safety tips ensure safe and successful completion of each lab activity.

SkillBuilder ▶

Enrich chapter concepts with additional skills practice and hands-on activities.

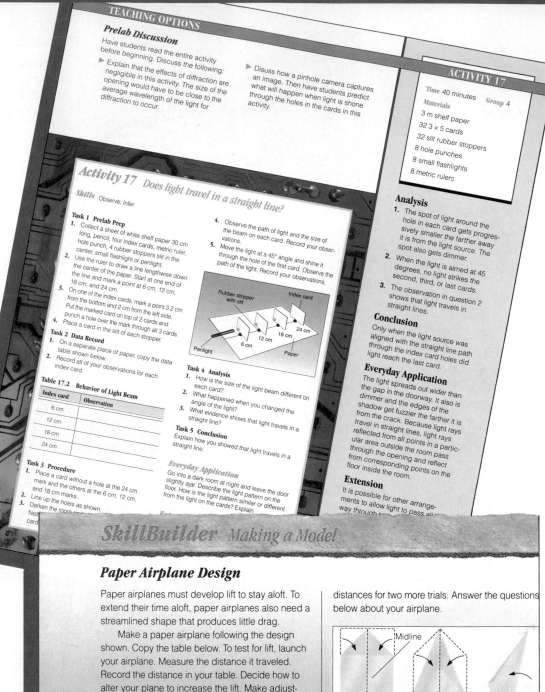

TEACHING OPTIONS

Prelab Discussion

Have students read the entire activity before beginning. Discuss the following:

▶ Explain that the effects of diffraction are negligible in this activity. The size of the opening would have to be close to the average wavelength of the light for diffraction to occur.

▶ Disuss how a pinhole camera captures an image. Then have students predict what will happen when light is shone through the holes in the cards in this activity.

ACTIVITY 17

Time 40 minutes Group 4

Materials

3 m shelf paper
32 3 × 5 cards
32 slit rubber stoppers
8 hole punches
8 small flashlights
8 metric rulers

Activity 17 *Does light travel in a straight line?*

Skills Observe; Infer

Task 1 Prelab Prep

1. Collect a sheet of white shelf paper 30 cm long, pencil, four index cards, metric ruler, hole punch, 4 rubber stoppers slit in the center, small flashlight or penlight.
2. Use the ruler to draw a line lengthwise down the center of the paper. Start at one end of the line and mark a point at 6 cm, 12 cm, 18 cm, and 24 cm.
3. On one of the index cards, mark a point 3.2 cm from the bottom and 2 cm from the left side. Put the marked card on top of 2 cards and punch a hole over the mark through all 3 cards.
4. Place a card in the slit of each stopper.

Task 2 Data Record

1. On a separate piece of paper, copy the data table shown below.
2. Record all of your observations for each index card.

Table 17.2 Behavior of Light Beam

Index card	Observation
6 cm	
12 cm	
18 cm	
24 cm	

Task 3 Procedure

1. Place a card without a hole at the 24 cm mark and the others at the 6 cm, 12 cm, and 18 cm marks.
2. Line up the holes as shown.
3. Darken the room and shine the flash ... card ...

4. Observe the path of light and the size of the beam on each card. Record your observations.
5. Move the light at a 45° angle and shine it through the hole of the first card. Observe the path of the light. Record your observations.

Rubber stopper with slit
Index card
24 cm
12 cm 18 cm
6 cm
Penlight
Paper

Task 4 Analysis

1. How is the size of the light beam different on each card?
2. What happened when you changed the angle of the light?
3. What evidence shows that light travels in a straight line?

Task 5 Conclusion

Explain how you showed that light travels in a straight line.

Everyday Application

Go into a dark room at night and leave the door slightly ajar. Describe the light pattern on the floor. How is the light pattern similar or different from the light on the cards? Explain

Analysis

1. The spot of light around the hole in each card gets progressively smaller the farther away it is from the light source. The spot also gets dimmer.
2. When the light is aimed at 45 degrees, no light strikes the second, third, or last cards.
3. The observation in question 2 shows that light travels in straight lines.

Conclusion

Only when the light source was aligned with the straight line path through the index card holes did light reach the last card.

Everyday Application

The light spreads out wider than the gap in the doorway. It also is dimmer and the edges of the shadow get fuzzier the farther it is from the crack. Because light rays travel in straight lines, light rays reflected from all points in a particular area outside the room pass through the opening and reflect from corresponding points on the floor inside the room.

Extension

It is possible for other arrangements to allow light to pass all the way through ...

SkillBuilder *Making a Model*

Paper Airplane Design

Paper airplanes must develop lift to stay aloft. To extend their time aloft, paper airplanes also need a streamlined shape that produces little drag.

Make a paper airplane following the design shown. Copy the table below. To test for lift, launch your airplane. Measure the distance it traveled. Record the distance in your table. Decide how to alter your plane to increase the lift. Make adjustments to your plane. Test for lift and record the distance. Continue to adjust, launch, and record

distances for two more trials. Answer the questions below about your airplane.

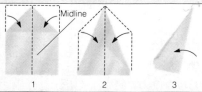

Midline
1 2 3

1. Which adjustment most affected the lift of your plane?
2. Discuss how you could adjust your plane to increase drag.
3. Draw your plane and label the forces affecting your plane when it flies.
4. Compare the forces of gravity and lift affecting your plane.

Testing for Lift on a Paper Airplane

Trial	Adjustment	Distance Flown (m)
1		
2		
3		

Making Skills

Consider This

Should Breakwaters and Wave Barriers Be Built?

Walk barefoot along the edge of the surf and you can feel the sand shifting constantly beneath your feet. The movement of the water causes the sand to move. Waves, tides, and water currents cause the natural formation and erosion of beaches.

Breakwaters and wave barriers are long walls built near harbors or along the shoreline. Breakwaters and wave barriers protect areas such as harbors, recreational areas, and private homes from erosion by forcing incoming waves to break farther from the shore. Breakwaters also prevent damage to the harbor during heavy storms.

Consider Some Issues By changing wave action and redirecting water currents, these barriers cause sand deposits and beach erosion elsewhere. These changes affect the ecology of the shoreline. Often the habitat of wildlife is destroyed.

Construction costs of break-

Should nature be left to take its course or should people interfere with the natural processes?

Write About It Write a paper

◀ *Consider This*

Decision-making skills are developed about issues related to science—encouraging students to write about them or debate them.

Career Corner: Optician

Who Makes and Fits Your Glasses?

Suppose you have a prescription for new eyeglasses or contact lenses. You can purchase your new glasses or contact lenses from an optician. An optician makes the glasses or contact lenses you need according to your eyeglass prescription.

The optician will also measure and record the distance between the center of one pupil to the center of the other pupil. This distance is important to make sure your new lenses form a sharp, clear image. She can help you to

The optician will order lenses that match your prescription. She cuts the lenses to fit your frames. Once your eyeglasses are made, the optician adjusts them to make sure your glasses fit properly.

To work as an optician requires good math skills and the ability to make accurate measurements. You should have an interest in both physical and life sciences. You should also

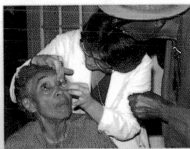

job training as opticians. Others receive formal training in a trade school. Many states require candidates to take a state board exam to obtain a medical assurance certificate before they can practice as an optician.

Career Corner ▶

Open up a wide range of career opportunities for students.

Historical Notebook

Boat Design in Polynesia

For thousands of years, the people of the South Pacific have built a special type of boat, an outrigger. The boat's main body, or hull, is long and narrow like a canoe. The hull usually attaches to one or two logs alongside. The crew sits within the hull and propels the boat using paddles like you would in a canoe.

Another Polynesian boat design consists of two hulls joined by a central platform. Sails are mounted on the central platform. The double-hulled design is very stable, so these boats can sail in strong winds. While sailing downwind, the long, narrow hulls rise in the water. The boat sails very fast because there is less hull surface in contact with the water. Ancient Polynesians used these double-hulled voyaging canoes to colonize the islands in a vast area of the South Pacific. The Hawaiian Islands were colonized by these early explorers about 1000 A.D.

1. Compare an outrigger to a canoe. Explain how they are alike and how they are different.

2. Research the water routes traveled by the ancient Polynesians. Make a map of their travels across the Pacific.

3. Make models of an outrigger and a double-hulled voyaging canoe. Locate and identify the forces acting on each boat.

◀ *Historical Notebook*

Focus students' attention on people in science, the evolution of scientific theories, and contributions from diverse cultures.

Develop Science Concepts with

A Math Appendix enhances the text material

Symbols ▶

An alphabetical listing of the math symbols used throughout the book.

Formulas ▶

Formulas are listed by chapter to provide the students with a quick reference.

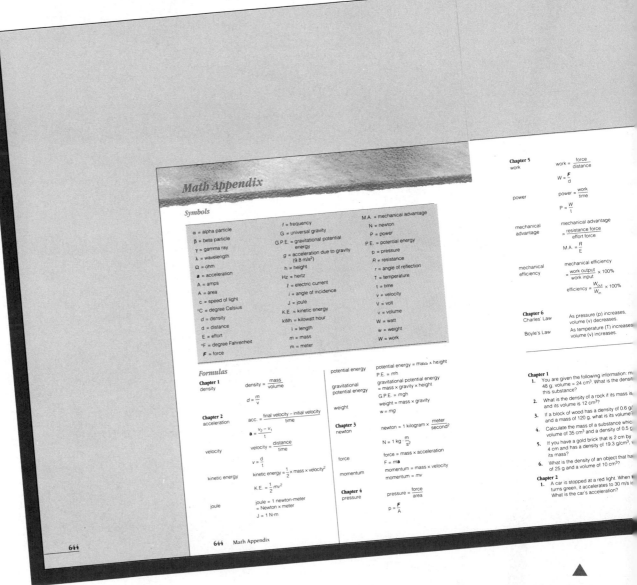

Math Appendix

Symbols

α = alpha particle
β = beta particle
γ = gamma ray
λ = wavelength
Ω = ohm
a = acceleration
A = amps
A = area
c = speed of light
°C = degree Celsius
d = density
d = distance
E = effort
°F = degree Fahrenheit
F = force

f = frequency
G = universal gravity
G.P.E. = gravitational potential energy
g = acceleration due to gravity (9.8 m/s²)
h = height
Hz = hertz
I = electric current
i = angle of incidence
J = joule
K.E. = kinetic energy
kWh = kilowatt hour
l = length
m = mass
m = meter

M.A. = mechanical advantage
N = newton
P = power
P.E. = potential energy
p = pressure
R = resistance
r = angle of reflection
T = temperature
t = time
v = velocity
V = volt
v = volume
W = watt
w = weight
W = work

Formulas

Chapter 1
density

$$\text{density} = \frac{\text{mass}}{\text{volume}}$$

$$d = \frac{m}{v}$$

Chapter 2
acceleration

$$\text{acc.} = \frac{\text{final velocity} - \text{initial velocity}}{\text{time}}$$

$$a = \frac{v_2 - v_1}{t}$$

velocity

$$\text{velocity} = \frac{\text{distance}}{\text{time}}$$

$$v = \frac{d}{t}$$

kinetic energy

$$\text{kinetic energy} = \frac{1}{2} \times \text{mass} \times \text{velocity}^2$$

$$K.E. = \frac{1}{2} mv^2$$

joule

$$\text{joule} = 1 \text{ newton-meter}$$
$$= \text{Newton} \times \text{meter}$$
$$J = 1 \text{ N·m}$$

potential energy

$$\text{potential energy} = \text{mass} \times \text{height}$$
$$P.E. = mh$$

gravitational potential energy

$$\text{gravitational potential energy} = \text{mass} \times \text{gravity} \times \text{height}$$
$$G.P.E. = mgh$$

weight

$$\text{weight} = \text{mass} \times \text{gravity}$$
$$w = mg$$

Chapter 3
newton

$$\text{newton} = 1 \text{ kilogram} \times \frac{\text{meter}}{\text{second}^2}$$

$$N = 1 \text{ kg} \cdot \frac{m}{s^2}$$

force

$$\text{force} = \text{mass} \times \text{acceleration}$$
$$F = ma$$

momentum

$$\text{momentum} = \text{mass} \times \text{velocity}$$
$$\text{momentum} = mv$$

Chapter 4
pressure

$$\text{pressure} = \frac{\text{force}}{\text{area}}$$

$$p = \frac{F}{A}$$

Chapter 5
work

$$\text{work} = \frac{\text{force}}{\text{distance}}$$

$$W = \frac{F}{d}$$

power

$$\text{power} = \frac{\text{work}}{\text{time}}$$

$$P = \frac{W}{t}$$

mechanical advantage

$$\text{mechanical advantage} = \frac{\text{resistance force}}{\text{effort force}}$$

$$M.A. = \frac{R}{E}$$

mechanical efficiency

$$\text{mechanical efficiency} = \frac{\text{work output}}{\text{work input}} \times 100\%$$

$$\text{efficiency} = \frac{W_{out}}{W_{in}} \times 100\%$$

Chapter 6
Charles' Law

As pressure (p) increases, volume (v) decreases.

Boyle's Law

As temperature (T) increases, volume (v) increases.

Chapter 1
1. You are given the following information: mass = 48 g; volume = 24 cm³. What is the density of this substance?
2. What is the density of a rock if its mass is ___ and its volume is 12 cm³?
3. If a block of wood has a density of 0.6 g/___ and a mass of 120 g, what is its volume?
4. Calculate the mass of a substance which ___ volume of 35 cm³ and a density of 0.5 g___
5. If you have a gold brick that is 2 cm by ___ 4 cm and has a density of 19.3 g/cm³, ___ its mass?
6. What is the density of an object that ha___ of 25 g and a volume of 10 cm³?

Chapter 2
1. A car is stopped at a red light. When ___ turns green, it accelerates to 30 m/s ___ What is the car's acceleration?

▲ Practice Problems

Problems connect concepts to real life situations.

T 14

Math

and integrates physical science and mathematics.

Develop Thinking Skills

Problems help students develop the thinking skills used throughout the text.

Answers

Answers are printed in the margins for quick reference.

▼

Enrich

▲

Practice problems can be used to enrich or to challenge.

$°F = \frac{9}{5}°C + 32$

$°C = \frac{5}{9}(°F - 32)$

heat = mass × specific heat × temperature change

heat = m × specific heat × ($T_2 - T_1$)

current = $\frac{voltage}{resistance}$

$I = \frac{V}{R}$

electric power = volt × current

$P = VI$

volt = current × resistance

$V = IR$

energy = power × time

energy = Pt

speed = frequency × wavelength

speed = $f\lambda$

angle of incidence = angle of reflection

$i = r$

...ook a car trip with your family to visit rela-
...who live 750 km away. The trip took 8 h.
...was your average speed in km/h?

...u travel 50 km due east in 2 h, what is your
...city?

...ain goes from 20 m/s to 40 m/s in 5 min.
...at is the train's acceleration in m/s²?

...ain takes 10 min to slow down to 10 m/s from
...m/s. What is its acceleration?

...e traffic on the highway you are traveling
...oves at 90 km/h. At this rate, how long will it
...ke you to travel 450 km?

...a runner maintains a speed of 2.5 m/s, how far
...an he run in 15 s? In an hour?

...ou pedal your 20 kg bicycle at 3 m/s. What is
...he kinetic energy of your bicycle?

...ou are pedaling your bicycle at 3 m/s. If you add
...your mass in kg to the 20 kg bicycle, what is the kinetic
...energy of both you and the bicycle?

Answers to Practice Problems

Chapter 1
1. 2 g/cm³
2. 3 g/cm³
3. 200 cm³
4. 17.5 g
5. 463.2 g
6. 2.5 g/cm³

Chapter 2
1. 2 m/s²
2. 93.75 km/h
3. 25 km/h
4. 0.07 m/s²
5. – 0.05 m/s²
6. 5 h
7. 37.5 m; 9000 m
8. 90 kg · m/s
9. Answers will average 300–360 kg · m/s.

Chapter 3
1. 686 N
2. 60 kg
3. 1000 m/s²
4. 2000 m/s²
5. 150 000 kg · m/s
6. 50 000 kg · m/s
7. 10.50 kg
8. 40 m/s

Chapter 4
1. 75 N
2. 4 N/m²
3. 0.4 m²
4. 8750 N/m²
5. 250 000 N/m²

Chapter 5
1. 2 J
2. 0.4 W
3. 3000 J
4. 6400 J
5. 100 N
6. 4500 J; 150 W
7. 200 W
8. M.A. = 3
9. 280 N
10. 80 N
11. 67%
12. 500 N
13. 6000 J; 75%

Chapter 6
1. 9 mL
2. 18 mL
3. divided by 2

Chapter 2 *Continued*
10. 9 m/s
11. 0.08 kg
12. 600 m
13. 11 760 kg · m/s
14. 617.4 N
15. 102.9 N

Chapter 3
1. 686 N
2. 60 kg
3. 1000 m/s²
4. 2000 m/s²
5. 150 000 kg · m/s
6. 50 000 kg · m/s
7. 10.50 kg
8. 40 m/s

Chapter 4
1. 75 N
2. 4 N/m²
3. 0.4 m²
4. 8750 N/m²
5. 250 000 N/m²

Chapter 5
1. 2 J
2. 0.4 W
3. 3000 J
4. 6400 J
5. 100 N
6. 4500 J; 150 W
7. 200 W
8. M.A. = 3
9. 280 N
10. 80 N
11. 67%
12. 500 N
13. 6000 J; 75%

Chapter 6
1. 9 mL
2. 18 mL
3. divided by 2

---

10. While ice skating, a 50 kg student has a kinetic energy of 2025 J. What is the student's velocity?

11. A baseball thrown at a velocity of 40 m/s has a kinetic energy of 64 joules, what is its mass?

12. A ball has a potential energy of 150 kg m and a mass of 0.25 kg. How high is the ball from the ground?

13. What is the gravitational potential energy of a 60 kg skier at the top of a hill that is 20 m high?

14. A rock has a mass of 63 kg. What is its weight on the earth?

15. Suppose you took a rock with a mass of 63 kg to the moon where the gravitational force is 1/6 that of the earth. What would the rock weigh on the moon?

Chapter 3
1. What is a person's weight in newtons if she has a mass of 70 kg?

2. If a person weighs 588 N, what is his mass?

3. Imagine that you throw a baseball that weighs 0.1 kg with a force of 100 N, what is the acceleration of the baseball?

4. An arrow leaves the bow with a force of 500 N. The mass of the arrow is 250 g. What is its acceleration?

5. A 5,000 kg car is moving with a velocity of 30 m/s, what is its momentum?

6. What is the momentum of a 2,500 kg boulder rolling down a hill at a velocity of 20 m/s?

7. A rolling ball has a velocity of 5 m/s and a momentum of 250 kg m/s. What is the mass of the ball?

8. A train has a momentum of 400 000 kg m/s and a mass of 10,000 kg. What is its velocity?

Chapter 4
1. If a pressure of 15 N/m² is applied over an area of 5 m², what is the force?

2. You are given the following information: Force = 20 N; Area = 5 m². Find pressure.

3. Find the cross-section area of a concrete piling if the force required to drive it into the ground is 10 N with a pressure of 25 N/m².

4. A person weighing 350 N is standing up. The area of the bottom of her feet is 0.04 m². What pressure is being exerted onto the ground, in N/m²?

5. A bullet hits a target with a force of 500 N. The hole it leaves has an area of 0.002 m². What pressure did the bullet apply to the target?

Chapter 5
1. If Maria uses 4 N of force to lift a box onto a shelf 0.5 m high, how much work did she do?

2. Joanne did 2 J of work in 5 s. How much power did she use?

3. How much work is required to push a 300 N box 10 m across the floor?

4. Suppose you weigh 300 N and you carry your books, which weigh 20 N, to your class on the fourth floor. Each flight of stairs is 5 m high. How much work did you do?

5. If a person does 200 J of work by lifting a box 2 m off the floor, how much does the box weigh?

6. A 450-N person ran up a flight of stairs which was 10 m high. How much work did the person do? If it took 30 s, what was the person's power?

7. What is the power of a motorboat that can do 5000 J of work in 25 s?

8. What is the mechanical advantage of a lever if the effort force is 15 N and the resistance force is 45 N?

9. A lever has a mechanical advantage of 7. If John applies 40 N of effort force, how much resistance force can he overcome?

10. If a machine has a mechanical advantage of 3, how much effort force is required to overcome a resistance force of 240 N?

11. If you need to put 12 N of work into a machine to get 8 N of work out, what is the mechanical efficiency of this machine?

12. A machine has an efficiency of 80%. If you need to get a work output of 400 N, how much work must you put in?

13. A machine can lift 1,500 kg to a height of 4 m, but it uses 8,000 J to do so. What is the work output of the machine? What is its mechanical efficiency?

Chapter 6
1. You are given the following information: initial pressure) × (initial volume) = (final pressure) × (final volume); initial pressure = 3.0 N/m²; initial volume = 12 mL; final pressure = 4.0 N/m². Calculate the final volume.

2. If a sample of gas has an initial volume of 30 mL at a pressure of 1.2 N/m², what is the final volume if the pressure is increased to 2.0 N/m², assuming no change in the temperature?

3. If you double the pressure on a specific amount of gas, what happens to its volume, assuming there is no temperature change?

---

4. If the volume of a 50 mL sample of gas at 2.1 N/m² of pressure is reduced to 30 mL, what is the final pressure?

5. Suppose you use all of the air from a filled balloon to blow up a toy that is only one half the size of the balloon. How will the pressure inside that toy compare to the original pressure in the balloon?

Chapter 9
1. If today's air temperature is 41°F, what is the air temperature in °C.

2. What is the approximate temperature in °F of 20°C?

3. You take your temperature with a thermometer that measures in degrees Celsius. Your temperature is 40°C. Are you sick? What is your temperature in °F?

4. A radiator with a mass of 50 kg has an initial temperature of 95 °C and a final temperature of 50°C. Its specific heat is 448 J/kg°C. How much heat energy did it give off?

5. How much heat is required to raise the temperature of 0.5 kg of water from 20°C to 30°C? The specific heat of water is 4,190 J/kg°C.

6. How much heat is needed to raise the temperature of 2 kg of copper by 5°C (specific heat of copper = 387 J/kg °C)

7. A 10 kg mass of an unknown substance gives off 180 200 J/kg°C of heat when it cools 20° C. What is its specific heat?

8. How much heat is needed to raise the temperature of 0.05 kg of iron from 20°C to 35°C? (specific heat of iron = 448 J/kg °C)

Chapter 11
1. What is the current used by a toaster that has a resistance of 12 ohms and uses 120 volts?

2. What is the resistance of a light bulb if it uses 0.5 amps of current and 110 volts?

Motivate with Features that

Unique page formats that draw in and engage students.

Explore ► Visually

Suggested teaching questions that encourage students to explore and to study the visual elements of their texts.

Visual Learning

Carefully rendered and colorful illustrations work with the text to help sharpen students' understanding of science content and processes. Here, the visual helps students better understand the theme—Patterns of Change/Cycles.

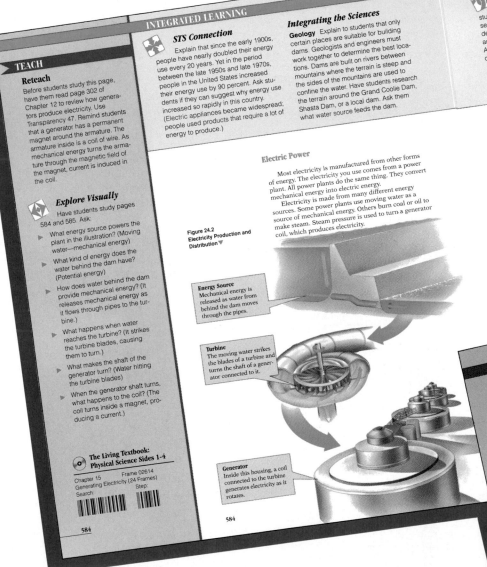

INTEGRATED LEARNING

STS Connection
Explain that since the early 1900s, people have nearly doubled their energy use every 20 years. Yet in the period between the late 1950s and late 1970s, people in the United States increased their energy use by 90 percent. Ask students if they can suggest why energy use increased so rapidly in this country. (Electric appliances became widespread; people used products that require a lot of energy to produce.)

Integrating the Sciences
Geology Explain to students that only certain places are suitable for building dams. Geologists and engineers must work together to determine the best locations. Dams are built on rivers between mountains where the terrain is steep and the sides of the mountains are used to confine the water. Have students research the terrain around the Grand Coolie Dam, Shasta Dam, or a local dam. Ask them what water source feeds the dam.

Themes in Science
Stability and Equilibrium Remind students that according to the law of conservation, energy is neither created nor destroyed. It is changed from one form to another or transferred to other objects. Ask students how the production and use of electricity shows the law of conserva-

TEACH

Reteach
Before students study this page, have them read page 302 of Chapter 12 to review how generators produce electricity. Use Transparency 47. Remind students that a generator has a permanent magnet around the armature. The armature inside is a coil of wire. As mechanical energy turns the armature through the magnetic field of the magnet, current is induced in the coil.

Explore Visually
Have students study pages 584 and 585. Ask:

► What energy source powers the plant in the illustration? (Moving water—mechanical energy)

► What kind of energy does the water behind the dam have? (Potential energy)

► How does water behind the dam provide mechanical energy? (It releases mechanical energy as it flows through pipes to the turbine.)

► What happens when water reaches the turbine? (It strikes the turbine blades, causing them to turn.)

► What makes the shaft of the generator turn? (Water hitting the turbine blades)

► When the generator shaft turns, what happens to the coil? (The coil turns inside a magnet, producing a current.)

The Living Textbook:
Physical Science Sides 1-4

Chapter 15   Frame 02614
Generating Electricity (24 Frames)
Search: Step:

584

Electric Power

Most electricity is manufactured from other forms of energy. The electricity you use comes from a power plant. All power plants do the same thing. They convert mechanical energy into electric energy.

Electricity is made from many different energy sources. Some power plants use moving water as a source of mechanical energy. Others burn coal or oil to make steam. Steam pressure is used to turn a generator coil, which produces electricity.

Figure 24.2
Electricity Production and Distribution ▼

Energy Source
Mechanical energy is released as water from behind the dam moves through the pipes.

Turbine
The moving water strikes the blades of a turbine and turns the shaft of a generator connected to it.

Generator
Inside this housing, a coil connected to the turbine generates electricity as it rotates.

584

Electric power plants normally serve large Study Figure 24.2 to learn how electricity is p and supplied to homes and industry. Some of electric energy must be transported great dis Electricity travels quickly and efficiently thr voltage wires called transmission lines. Like of roads, power lines carry electricity to far and businesses in your community.

Step-down transformers
reduce voltage where high-voltage lines connect with low voltage lines.

tion. (
beco
move
in th
cha
elec
sou

SCIENCE AND LITERATURE CONN

About the Literary Work
"Blue Tights" was adapted from the novel Bl Tights by Rita Williams-Garcia, copyright 19 Rita Williams-Garcia and Bantam Books. Re by permission of Rita Williams-Garcia and Books.

Description of Change
Detailed passages were edited from a t of the text for the sake of readability. Th has been kept as true to the original a

Rationale
This vocabulary and syntax are too entry-level Limited English Proficier However, the story itself is appropr dent level.

Vocabulary
kalimba, contralto, gourd, engre

Teaching Strategie

Directed Inquiry
After students finish reading Relate the story to the scie discussing the sensations during the ceremony. Ask

► What are some examp sound and light to su (In devices such as ...sang...joyously"; a the drum within her

► What sources of so the "stage magic" the colors reflecte the signs and sh

► How do the diffe instruments aff may vary. High the congas ar more energy eardrums. Pe duced by h which "sen

Science and Literature Connection ►

Integrate language arts into the science classroom. Literary excerpts from notable authors and diverse cultures help students appreciate the application of science to their everyday lives.

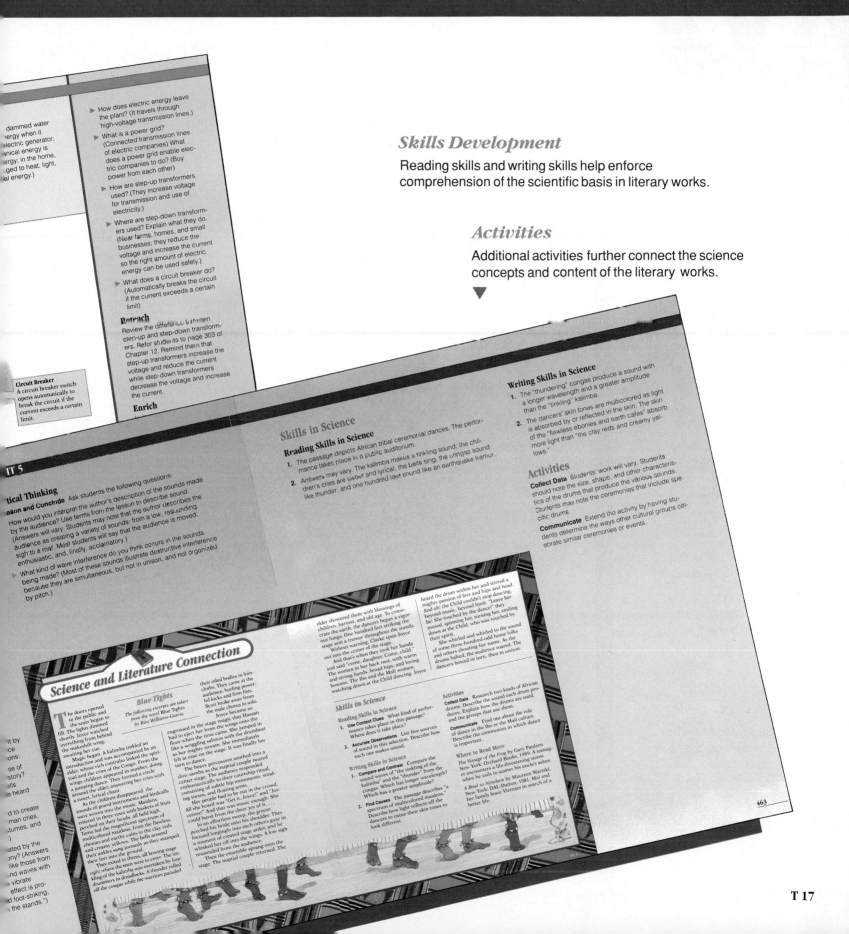

Skills Development

Reading skills and writing skills help enforce comprehension of the scientific basis in literary works.

Activities

Additional activities further connect the science concepts and content of the literary works.

▼

How does electric energy leave the plant? (It travels through high-voltage transmission lines.)

What is a power grid? (Connected transmission lines of electric companies) What does a power grid enable electric companies to do? (Buy power from each other)

How are step-up transformers used? (They increase voltage for transmission and use of electricity.)

Where are step-down transformers used? Explain what they do. (Near farms, homes, and small businesses, they reduce the voltage and increase the current so the right amount of electric energy can be used safely.)

What does a circuit breaker do? (Automatically breaks the circuit if the current exceeds a certain limit)

Reteach

Review the difference between step-up and step-down transformers. Refer students to page 303 of Chapter 12. Remind them that step-up transformers increase the voltage and reduce the current while step-down transformers decrease the voltage and increase the current.

Circuit Breaker
A circuit breaker switch opens automatically to break the circuit if the current exceeds a certain limit.

Enrich

UNIT 5

Critical Thinking

Reason and Conclude Ask students the following questions:

How would you interpret the author's description of the sounds made by the audience? Use terms from the lesson to describe sound. (Answers will vary. Students may note that the author describes the audience as creating a variety of sounds: from a low, resounding sigh to a roar. Most students will say that the audience is moved: enthusiastic, and, finally, acclamatory.)

What kind of wave interference do you think occurs in the sounds being made? (Most of these sounds illustrate destructive interference because they are simultaneous, but not in unison, and not organized by pitch.)

Skills in Science

Reading Skills in Science

1. The passage depicts African tribal ceremonial dances. The performance takes place in a public auditorium.

2. Answers may vary. The kalimba makes a tinkling sound; the children's cries are sweet and lyrical; the bells sing; the congas sound like thunder; and one hundred feet sound like an earthquake tremor.

Writing Skills in Science

1. The "thundering" congas produce a sound with a longer wavelength and a greater amplitude than the "tinkling" kalimba.

2. The dancers' skin tones are multicolored as light is absorbed by or reflected in the skin. The skin of the "flawless ebonies and earth cafes" absorb more light than "the clay reds and creamy yellows."

Activities

Collect Data Students' work will vary. Students should note the size, shape, and other characteristics of the drums that produce the various sounds. Students may note the ceremonies that include specific drums.

Communicate Extend the activity by having students determine the ways other cultural groups celebrate similar ceremonies or events.

Science and Literature Connection

Blue Tights

The following excerpts are taken from the novel Blue Tights by Rita Williams-Garcia

The doors opened to the public and the seats began to fill. The lights dimmed shortly. Joyce watched everything from behind the makeshift wing, awaiting her cue.

Magic began. A kalimba tinkled an introduction and was accompanied by an elder, whose rich contralto linked the spiritual and the cries of the Congo. From the wings children appeared in number, doing a jumping dance. They formed a circle around the elder, answering her cries with a sweet, lyrical chant.

As the children disappeared, the sounds of gourd instruments and birdcalls were woven into the music. Maidens entered in three rows with baskets of fruit perched on their heads, all held high. Tamu led the magnificent spectrum of multicolored maidens, from the clay reds ebonies and earthy cafés to the flawless and creamy yellows. The bells around their ankles sang joyously as they stamped their feet into the ground.

They exited in threes, all bowing single file right where the men were to center. The tinkling of the kalimba was overtaken by four drummers in dreadlocks. A thunder rolled off the congas while the warriors paraded their oiled bodies in loincloths. They came at the audience, hurling powerful kicks and firm fists. Scott broke away from the male chorus to solo.

Joyce became so engrossed in the stage magic that Hassan had to eject her from the wings onto the floor when the time came. She jumped like a wriggling salmon with the drumbeat as her mighty stream. She immediately felt at ease on the stage. It was finally her turn to dance.

The heavy percussion soothed into a slow samba as the nuptial couple neared center stage. The audience responded enthusiastically to their courtship ritual, consisting of subtle hip movements, winding torsos, and floating arms.

"Get her people had to be out in the crowd. All she heard was "Get it, Joyce!" and "Joyceeeee!" And that was music enough. She could burst from the sheer joy of it. . . .

In an effortless sweep, the groom perched his bride onto his shoulder. They focused longingly into each other's gaze in a moment of created stage ardor, and he whisked her off into the wings. A low sigh resounded from the audience.

Then the ensemble sprang onto the stage. The nuptial couple returned. The elder showered them with blessings of children, harvest, and old age. To consecrate the earth, the dancers began a vigorous funga. One hundred feet striking the stage sent a tremor throughout the stands.

Without warning, Clarke spun Joyce out into the center of the stage. And that's when they took her hands and said "come, daughter. Come, child." The women in her back root, with warm and strong hands, broad hips, and loving bosoms. The Ibo and the Mali women, watching down at the Child dancing. Joyce heard the drum within her and stirred a mighty passion of feet and hips and head. And oh! the Child couldn't stop dancing, beyond music, beyond limit. "Leave her be! She touched by the dance!" they mused, spinning her, turning her, smiling down at the Child, who was touched by their spirit.

She whirled and whirled to the sound of some three-hundred-odd home folks and others shouting her name. As the drums halted, the audience roared. The dancers bowed in turn, then in unison.

Skills in Science

Reading Skills in Science

1. **Use Context Clues** What kind of performance takes place in this passage? Where does it take place?

2. **Accurate Observations** List five sources of sound in this selection. Describe how each one makes sound.

Writing Skills in Science

1. **Compare and Contrast** Compare the sound waves of "the tinkling of the kalimba" and the "thunder" from the congas. Which has longer wavelength? Which has a greater amplitude?

2. **Find Causes** The passage describes "a spectrum of multicolored maidens." Describe how light reflects off the dancers to cause their skin tones to look different.

Activities

Collect Data Research two kinds of African drums. Describe the sound each drum produces. Explain how the drums are used, and the groups that use them.

Communicate Find out about the role of dance in the Ibo or the Mali culture. Describe the ceremonies in which dance is important.

Where to Read More

The Voyage of the Frog by Gary Paulsen. New York: Orchard Books, 1989. A teenager encounters a life-threatening storm when he sails to scatter his uncle's ashes.

A Boat to Nowhere by Maureen Wartski. New York: DAL-Dutton, 1981. Mai and her family leave Vietnam in search of a better life.

463

Organize Lessons at a Glance

Two-page interleaf section with everything

Advance Planner

Reminders about special preparations for the chapter—keyed to the page where you'll need them.

Skills ▶ Development

An overview of the skills developed in each chapter.

Individual Needs

Suggestions for the special requirements of students.

CHAPTER 5

Overview

This chapter addresses work, machines, and energy. Work and power are defined in the first section. The second section explains how to determine the mechanical advantage and the efficiency of a machine. The third section describes six simple machines and defines a compound machine. The final section of the chapter discusses various forms of energy and defines the Law of Conservation of Mass and Energy.

Advance Planner

▶ Supply samples of electric bills for TE page 111.

▶ Provide 2-L plastic soft drink bottles, with caps, for TE page 115.

▶ Obtain a mechanical model of the inner ear for TE page 117.

▶ Collect hot plate, teakettle, toy car or pinwheel, plastic drinking straws, strips of cloth, scissors, and masking tape for SE Activity 5, page 126.

Skills Development Chart

Sections	Calculate	Classify	Communicate	Compare and Contrast	Define Operationally	Infer	Measure	Observe	Predict
5.1 Skills WarmUp Skills WorkOut Practice Problems	●		●	●	●				●
5.2 Skills WarmUp Practice Problems	●					●			
5.3 Skills WarmUp SkillBuilder		● ●							
5.4 Skills WarmUp Activity			●			● ●	●	●	

Individual Needs

▶ **Limited English Proficiency Students** Photocopy the figures on pages 108 and 116 to 119 with the labels masked. Draw arrows to the important parts of each figure. Have students make labels from strips of index cards and place the labels in the correct place on the photocopies. Have them refer to the text to check the placement of the labels. For each of the machines shown on pages 116 to 119, students can make a label telling the kind of machine and give an example of each. Students should remove and save the labels, then review the chapter by repeating the exercise.

▶ **At-Risk Students** Provide pictures of simple machines for the group. Have students identify all the machines in each picture by name. Have students label each machine on the pictures. Encourage them to use the textbook as a reference. Have students discuss how each machine works.

▶ **Gifted Students** Invite students to do a study of Einstein's famous equation, $E = mc^2$. They should try to answer questions such as the following: How did scientists compare mass and energy before Einstein's theory? What are the processes by which mass can be converted into energy? Encourage students to make a visual display to present their findings.

Resource Bank

▶ **Bulletin Board** Place the title *Energy Conversion* at the top of the bulletin board. Attach several pictures that represent energy being converted from one form to another. Make a number of labels for each of the five forms of energy listed in Section 5.4. Also, make labels that show arrows only. Have volunteers label each picture with energy labels linked by arrow labels to show the energy conversion involved. Encourage them to include as many steps in the conversion as possible. For example, for a picture of a person exercising, the labels should be chemical energy→mechanical energy→heat energy.

106A

CHAPTER 5 PLANNING GUIDE

Section	Core	Standard	Enriched
5.1 Work and Power pp. 106–111			
Section Features Skills WarmUp, p. 107 / Skills WorkOut, p. 108	●	●	●
Blackline Masters Review Worksheet 5.1 / Reteach Worksheet 5.1	● ●	● ●	●
Laboratory Program Investigation 9 / Investigation 10	●	●	
5.2 Work and Machines pp. 112–115			
Section Features Skills WarmUp, p. 112 / Career Corner, p. 114	●	●	●
Blackline Masters Review Worksheet 5.2 / Integrating Worksheet 5.2	●	●	●
5.3 Simple and Compound Machines pp. 116–121			
Section Features Skills WarmUp, p. 116 / SkillBuilder, p. 120	●	●	●
Color Transparencies Transparencies 9, 10, 11, 12	●	●	●

Section	Core	Standard	Enriched
Blackline Masters Review Worksheet 5.3 / Skills Worksheet 5.3a / Skills Worksheet 5.3b / Integrating Worksheet 5.3	● ● ● ●	● ● ● ●	●
Ancillary Options *One-Minute Readings,* pp. 101–102	●	●	●
Overhead Blackline Transparencies Overhead Blackline Master 5 and Student Worksheet	●	●	●
Laboratory Program Investigation 11		●	●
5.4 Energy and Its Forms pp. 122–126			
Section Features Skills WarmUp, p. 122 / Activity, p. 126	●	●	●
Blackline Masters Review Worksheet 5.4 / Skills Worksheet 5.4a / Skills Worksheet 5.4b / Vocabulary Worksheet 5	● ● ● ●	● ● ● ●	● ●
Ancillary Options *Multicultural Perspectives,* pp. 123, 124	●	●	●
Color Transparencies Transparency 13	●	●	●

◀ *Chapter Planning Guide*

Teaching options at a glance. Program resource materials keyed directly to section content and concepts.

Student ability recommendations help you make decisions about what materials to use to meet students' abilities and needs.

Bibliography

The following resources can be used for teaching the chapter. See page T-46 for supplier codes.

Audio-Visual Sources

(video unless noted)

The Lever. Film. BFA.

Simple and Compound Machines: How They Work. AIMS, QE.

Simple Machines. Filmstrip. EB.

Work and Play Made Easier: Using Simple Machines. Film. MF.

Work and Power. Filmstrip. EB.

Software Resources

Momentum and Work. Apple II, IBM/PC. COM.

Work and Machines. Apple II, IBM PC, Macintosh. QE.

Work and Energy. Apple II. J & S.

Library Resources

The Diagram Group. Comparisons. New York: St. Martin's Press, 1980.

Lafferty, Peter. Energy and Light. New York: Gloucester Press, 1989.

Macauley, David. The Way Things Work. Boston, Houghton Mifflin Company, 1988.

Sherwood, Martin, and Christine Sutton. The Physical World. New York: Oxford University Press, 1988.

106B

Themes in Science

Themes are like trellises—they provide support and structure. By using a thematic approach to teaching, you can help students relate science concepts to their lives, both in and out of the classroom. The goal of using themes to teach science is to help students understand the important ideas in science and the connections among those ideas.

Defining Themes

Using a thematic approach to teaching is not new, but different teachers may have different definitions of the word *theme*. Themes are sometimes defined as topics, such as when someone explains that the theme of a lesson is *heat*. This topical approach can be very useful to students and teachers. In this text, however, themes are defined as links between the major concepts or ideas in science. Since there are many ways to link ideas, there is no one official list of themes in science. See the chart on page T-21 for a list and descriptions of the themes used in *Science Insights*.

Using a Thematic Approach

The volume of scientific information has grown so large that it is impossible to teach students every fact that has been discovered. Too often, though, science curricula present science as a long string of unconnected facts and activities. A thematic approach to science allows students to derive a sense of how the big ideas in science relate to one another. You may wish to use themes to help students integrate different branches of science, connect science concepts with other disciplines, or relate science to their lives and society.

While it is not necessary for students to memorize themes, it is useful to pose questions that encourage students to analyze concepts in the light of specific themes. The following is a list of some questions that can be used in classroom discussions for each of the themes used in *Science Insights:*

- ▶ **Diversity and Unity** How are these forms of matter alike? How are they different?
- ▶ **Energy** What role does energy play in this change? How has energy flowed through this system?
- ▶ **Evolution** How have advances in our knowledge of electricity led to changes in how we use it? How have new discoveries led to rapid change in technical fields?
- ▶ **Patterns of Change/Cycles** How is this form of energy converted to another form? What patterns do you see in the way all matter changes phase?
- ▶ **Scale and Structure** What are the levels of organization in matter? How does the molecular structure of a compound affect its chemical characteristics?
- ▶ **Stability and Equilibrium** What is and isn't changing in the process we are studying? What keeps the process from changing?
- ▶ **Systems and Interactions** How do the parts of this system work together? How would changing one part of this system affect the other parts?

Themes and *Science Insights*

Themes are often used to enhance the presentation of concepts in *Science Insights*. Material in the student text is presented thematically, with various themes weaving in and out of the prose. For example, the chapters describing forces, motion, energy, and changes in matter all incorporate the themes of stability and equilibrium. Teacher's Edition margin notes provide strategies for using themes that are appropriate for a particular concept. These include references to themes that unify an entire chapter. For example, Chapter 5, which describes work and power, begins with a reference to the theme Systems and Interactions. Themes also relate specific concepts, as in Chapter 16, when the theme Diversity and Unity helps link ideas about various kinds of music and sound energy.

Themes in Science Insights

Addison-Wesley's *Science Insights* series focuses on
seven themes. They do not represent all possibilities.

Diversity and Unity	Throughout the sciences, diverse kinds of structures—living and nonliving—are described. Yet, despite great diversity—such as of chemical structures, diversity of life, and of geological formations—there is unity. For example, microwaves, X-rays, and visible light are all different forms of energy on the same electromagnetic spectrum.
Energy	The theme of energy is the central concept to all of science. Life processes, physical and chemical changes, interactions, and the forces that cause natural cycles and change the earth's features all involve energy.
Evolution	In the most general sense, evolution can be defined as change through time. In addition to living and nonliving things, scientific knowledge also evolves, or changes, over time.
Patterns of Change/Cycles	Patterns of change are an essential feature of the natural world. It is useful to understand that changes occur as trends or as cycles, and that not all changes are predictable. Trends are relatively steady patterns, such as heat moving from a warm location to a cool location. Cycles, such as the water cycle, are repeating patterns.
Scale and Structure	Scientists study the natural world at the microscopic as well as macroscopic levels. While much analysis is done by observing the smallest parts of objects, often it is necessary to observe structures as parts of systems. For example, atoms have electric and magnetic properties that provide important applications in the field of electronics.
Stability and Equilibrium	Stability and equilibrium refer to the ways that things do not change. All forces are balanced in a system at equilibrium. The conservation of mass in a chemical reaction and homeostasis in living organisms are examples of stability and equilibrium.
Systems and Interactions	In science, natural systems range from the chemical systems in chemical reactions, to ecosystems, to the solar system. Within every system, there are many kinds of interactions.

Thematic Matrices in Science Insights

Theme	Chapter 1	Chapter 2
Diversity and Unity	All scientists, regardless of their field of study, search for knowledge about the natural world using the same basic science skills.	
Energy	Energy production, energy forms—light, heat, sound, and motion—and energy transfer are central to the study of physical science.	Energy is needed for any change in motion to take place. It is possible to observe the effects of energy even if the energy itself is not observable.
Evolution	Scientific ideas about the natural world have changed over time.	
Patterns of Change/ Cycles	New discoveries often effect changes in scientific theories.	Energy can be converted into different forms.
Scale and Structure	Scientists observe matter at different levels. Some scientists study galaxies while others study subatomic particles.	Descriptions of motion depend upon the observer's frame of reference.
Stability and Equilibrium		
Systems and Interactions	Scientists from different branches of science often work together to solve a single problem.	A change in forces acting on a motionless object or acting on an object moving at constant speed may cause the system of forces to become unbalanced. The object will accelerate as a result of the unbalanced forces.

Chapter 3	Chapter 4	Chapter 5
Every action in the universe is the result of the action of one or more of the universal forces.	Fluids, like all other kinds of matter, exert a force on the objects with which they come in contact.	• Energy may change from one form to another but is neither created nor destroyed. • Simple machines working together can perform a single task.
• Energy applied to a moving object changes its speed, direction, or both. • In any system momentum is conserved.	Energy is required both to overcome the force of gravity and to move objects from one place to another.	Energy is the ability to do work.
All matter, from atoms to movement by the stars, is subject to the same principles of motion.	The effect of forces on fluids changes according to principles described by Bernoulli, Archimedes, Pascal, and others.	Machines can change energy from one form to another.
Unless acted upon by a force, objects in motion stay in motion and objects at rest stay at rest.	The hydraulic force acting on an object increases proportionally through a system.	Machines can do a large amount of work with a small amount of force.
• Gravity is a force by which energy affects motion. • The motion of an object is the result of a system of forces, whether balanced or unbalanced, acting on that object.	In fluids, the upward or buoyant force acts in opposition to the force exerted by gravity.	Machines make doing work easier but do not change the amount of work done or energy needed.
	Moving fluids result in pressure differences. In air, these differences can support heavier-than-air objects.	• Machines can change the size and direction of a force needed to do work. • The human body can detect several forms of energy through its senses.

Thematic Matrices in Science Insights continued

Theme	Chapter 6	Chapter 7
Diversity and Unity	All matter in the universe is made of atoms. The diversity of matter depends on how a small number of different atoms combine with one another.	Different atoms of the same element can vary in the number of neutrons in the nucleus. Each isotope of the same element has the same number of protons and acts similarly in chemical reactions.
Energy	The phases of matter are distinguished by the energy of their particles.	Energy bonds exist between the atoms in a compound.
Evolution	Chemical changes have played an important part in changing the earth's surface over long periods of time.	Atoms of one element can become atoms of a different element by a process of radioactive decay.
Patterns of Change/ Cycles	Matter that gains or loses energy may change phase.	Atoms of elements combine chemically to produce compounds that have unique characteristics.
Scale and Structure	The arrangement of particles in a substance may determine its properties.	The simplest substance and the most complex organism are both made from some arrangement of the 106 different kinds of atoms.
Stability and Equilibrium	The stability of the atoms in an element or compound depends on the energy in the bonds.	The charge of each atomic particle in an element determines an element's stability.
Systems and Interactions	Substances may react with one another, or with energy, to produce new substances.	Interactions of matter form new substances during chemical reactions.

Chapter 8	Chapter 9	Chapter 10
All elements are made of atoms; different kinds of atoms have different numbers of protons.	Each kind of phase change is accompanied by a change in the amount of heat.	All heating systems rely on three methods of heat transfer: conduction, convection, and radiation.
The energy of electrons differs from one energy level to another.	The amount of heat energy in a substance is directly related to the motion of the molecules in the substance.	Refrigeration absorbs energy as the liquid changes to vapor and releases energy as the vapor changes to liquid.
The development of the periodic table progressed as knowledge about the atom increased.		
• The physical and chemical properties of atoms repeat as the atomic number increases. • The position of an element in the periodic table is determined by its atomic number.	• Heat energy always flows from an area of higher temperature to an area with lower temperature. • Different substances conduct heat at different rates.	A cooling system demonstrates that heat flows from areas or objects that are hot to areas or objects that are cold.
The number and arrangement of electrons in an atom determines the properties of that element.	Temperature is a measure of the average movement of molecules in a substance; internal energy is the total amount of energy a substance contains.	
The number of electrons in the outermost occupied energy level of an atom determines its stability.	The energy exchanged between the sun and the earth creates a stable atmosphere on the earth.	The human body maintains a relatively constant body temperature: perspiration cools the body; metabolic processes warm the body.
The periodic table is a systematic numbering of elements that is used to predict how different elements will interact.	Changes in temperature in a system are related to changes in pressure.	Heating and cooling systems transfer heat into and out of buildings. Heat loss if directly proportional to the difference between the indoor and outdoor temperature.

Thematic Matrices in Science Insights *continued*

Theme	Chapter 11	Chapter 12
Diversity and Unity	The two kinds of electric charge are the result of a loss or gain of electrons.	In a magnetic material, the atoms are grouped together as domains that have north and south poles.
Energy	Electricity is a form of energy.	Magnetic force can be converted to electric energy and then to mechanical, light, thermal, or sound energy, or back into magnetic energy.
Evolution	Relatively recent advances in electronics have led to great changes in how electricity is used.	
Patterns of Change/ Cycles	Electricity can change to other forms of energy.	Moving electric charges produce magnetic effects. The direction of the electric charges affects how a magnet will act.
Scale and Structure	Electricity and electromagnetism rely on the electrons and properties of atoms.	Galvanometers, voltmeters, and ammeters measure small amounts of electric current.
Stability and Equilibrium	As a charge moves through a circuit, work is done.	Magnetic forces work in a consistent manner either to pull objects together or to push objects apart.
Systems and Interactions	Resistance is the force that opposes moving electrons.	Electromagnetic induction occurs whenever there is motion between a current-carrying wire and a magnetic field. The direction and speed of motion affect the direction and strength of the electric current produced.

Chapter 13	Chapter 14	Chapter 15
All electronic devices control the movement of current.	• All waves carry energy and have properties of wavelength, frequency, speed, and amplitude. • Waves can move vertically or horizontally to the direction of motion.	
Electronic devices convert electric energy into light, sound, and heat energy.	A wave model for the motion of energy can be used to predict the location of a wave, what happens as wave energy moves through different media, and how wave energy interacts.	Energy from a vibrating object moves as a compression wave through a matter as sound.
The development of diodes, rectifiers, and transistors has led to great changes in the field of electronics.		
Increased miniaturization of diodes, rectifiers, and transistors has led to new technologies.		Sound wave frequency is measured in cycles per second, or hertz.
	Wavelength is the distance between two consecutive crests of a transverse wave or between two consecutive compressions in a longitudinal wave.	• As the distance from a sound source increases, the intensity of a sound decreases. • The size and shape of an acoustical space can affect the behavior of sound waves.
	Wavelength, frequency, and speed of waves are related mathematically.	
• In vacuum tubes, electrons move across a gap in response to a potential difference. • In transistors and semiconductors, electrons move in response to differences in atomic energy levels.	Reflection, diffraction, and refraction result from a wave's interaction with an object. During all interactions, waves behave in a manner that can be predicted.	The interaction of sound waves with their surroundings, and with other sound waves, causes sound waves to refract.

Thematic Matrices in Science Insights *continued*

Theme	Chapter 16	Chapter 17
Diversity and Unity	All sound, music, and musical instruments rely on sound energy. The variety of sounds results from the manipulation and combination of sound's frequency, intensity, and timbre.	Light is both an electromagnetic wave that does not require a medium, and a particle that is emitted from an atom when electrons change energy levels.
Energy	Sound is heard by living things when energy vibrating the bones in the ear is interpreted by the brain.	Light is a form of energy that is emitted as electrons in an atom change energy levels.
Evolution		
Patterns of Change/ Cycles		Colors in the visible spectrum always appear in the same order, and combinations of colored light produce predictable colors.
Scale and Structure	• The parts of the human ear are small and delicate yet function with the precision of much larger objects. • Sound waves of relatively short wavelengths—ultrasonic waves—are useful in detecting smaller objects.	Light waves make up a small portion of the electromagnetic spectrum, which is arranged in order of wavelength and frequency.
Stability and Equilibrium		Light travels at a constant speed of about 300,000 m/s through a vacuum.
Systems and Interactions	Many characteristics of sounds, such as pitch, intensity, rhythm, melody, harmony, and quality, interact to create music.	• The interaction of light waves with materials determines whether materials appear transparent, translucent, or opaque. • The colors an organism sees depend on reflected light and the organism's ability to see the reflected light.

Chapter 18	Chapter 19	Chapter 20
Light refracts as it passes through a lens and converges or diverges. A variety of images—real, virtual, larger, or smaller than the object—can be produced.	Nearly four million different kinds of compounds have the carbon atom as a component.	All chemical reactions, regardless of their type, produce new substances and a redistribution of energy.
Light energy is emitted from a luminous object and illuminates objects that reflect light.	Electrons in an atom are arranged in energy levels characterized by a specific number of electrons in each level.	A balanced chemical equation accounts for the total mass and energy involved in a chemical reaction. All chemical reactions require some amount of activation energy.
Plants have evolved ways to use sunlight to produce usable energy. Animals have evolved organs sensitive to light that allow them to see.		
	Electrons always move to the lowest available energy level.	During any chemical reaction, substances change in ways that can be predicted.
The structure of the eye is similar in all animals; variations depend on each creature's environment and survival needs. The predictable interactions of light and lenses produce images that are different in scale yet preserve structure.	Atoms measure about a billionth of a meter in diameter. In that volume there is a nucleus surrounded by electrons. It is the electrons that participate in forming chemical bonds. The size of ions varies with atomic number.	
	Atoms are most stable when their outermost occupied energy level is completely filled. Bonding—in either covalent or ionic bonds—is one way that atoms fill their outermost energy levels.	The atoms present in the reactants are also present in the products of a chemical reaction.
Light interacts with flat as well as reflective surfaces to form images. The size and location of the object and the characteristics of the reflecting surface can be used to predict the size, location, and orientation of the image.	The arrangement of ionic solids in an orderly three-dimensional repeating pattern is called a crystal lattice.	Increasing the temperature of a system, the concentration of the reactants, or the reactant's surface area increases the rate of reaction.

Thematic Matrices in Science Insights *continued*

Theme	Chapter 21	Chapter 22
Diversity and Unity	All substances have at least one solvent and at least one solute.	• All the living organisms contain carbon compounds. • Animals differ from plants and other organisms in the ways they use the sun's energy.
Energy		• The energy source for all living things is the sun. • Carbohydrates, lipids, and proteins provide energy to the human body.
Evolution		
Patterns of Change/ Cycles	Water always moves from an area of greater concentration of water molecules to an area of lesser concentration of water molecules.	
Scale and Structure	The size of the suspended particles determines if a mixture is homogeneous or heterogeneous.	The structure of the carbon atom allows it to form a ring or a straight or branched chain, as well as single, double, or triple bonds.
Stability and Equilibrium	• A solution is a stable homogeneous mixture. • The body keeps the pH of blood stable between 7.35 and 7.45 by regulating the amount of carbon dioxide in the blood.	
Systems and Interactions	• Solutions can be made by combining forms of matter in any of their phases—solid, liquid, or gas. Each kind of solution is homogeneous. • When an acid and a base combine, a salt and water are formed.	Energy from the sun absorbed by plants is converted during photosynthesis and stored in the chemical bonds of glucose. During respiration, oxygen reacts with glucose, the chemical bonds break, and energy is released.

Chapter 23	Chapter 24	Chapter 25
In transmutation, one element changes into another element by giving off alpha and/or beta particles.	Both renewable and nonrenewable natural resources may become unavailable if they are not used wisely.	Diverse use of petroleum affects the standard of living throughout the world.
Energy is released during nuclear fission, which occurs during radioactive decay, or during fusion, which occurs when atomic particles combine.	The prime energy source of both renewable and nonrenewable energy is the sun.	Changes in heat energy bring about phase changes in matter.
The half-life, or decay rate, of some radioactive elements can be used to date prehistoric life forms.		
• Many elements go through natural radioactive decay. Many more decay artificially. • Atoms decay by giving off alpha particles, beta particles, or gamma rays.	Nutrients and energy are recycled naturally in the environment.	The way humans use chemical technology can cause changes in the environment.
		The arrangement of electrons in hydrocarbon molecules determines the chemical properties of petrochemicals.
Atoms with unstable nuclei release energy, or matter, until the forces inside the nucleus are balanced and the atom is stable.	The production and use of electricity demonstrates the law of energy conservation.	A stable environment is dependent on the quality of air, water, and land.
Energy binds the protons and neutrons in a nucleus to one another. If that bond is broken, energy or matter is released from the atom's nucleus.		Changes in one part of the environment affect other parts of the environment.

Skills in Science

The study of science involves more than the absorption of information. Inquiry, investigation, and discovery are also part of a scientist's work. Educators have observed that students need to develop process skills and critical thinking skills as they study science. By developing skills as well as concepts, students will be prepared for life both in and out of the classroom.

As students use process skills, they will also use particular critical thinking skills and a pattern may emerge linking these two types of skills.

Observe Observing is a skill that is fundamental to all learning. As students study science, they need to extend their senses using tools such as microscopes or hand lenses.

Classify Classifying is the grouping of objects or events according to an established scheme. When classifying, students should be able to perceive similarities and differences among objects. Classifying is both a critical thinking skill and a process skill.

Infer When students infer, they make evaluations and judgements based on past experiences. The skill of inferring may involve identifying cause-and-effect relationships from events observed, identifying the limits of inferences, and testing the validity of inferences. Inferring also relates to the critical thinking skills Find Causes and Reason and Conclude.

Predict When students predict, they formulate an expected result based on past experience. Students learn that it takes repeated observations of an event to predict the next occurrence of that event. Predicting is a critical thinking skill and a process skill.

Measure Measuring involves direct or indirect comparison of an object with arbitrary units. In science classrooms, the SI system of units is generally used. Measure is also related to the critical thinking skill Compare and Contrast.

Communicate Communicating involves an exchange of information. The exchange can involve speaking, listening, writing, reading, or creating a visual display. Communication is a common thread that runs through all critical thinking skills.

Define Operationally An operational definition is a statement about an object or phenomenon based on one's experience with it. Define Operationally is related to the critical thinking skill Generalize.

Hypothesize When students hypothesize, they formulate a statement that can be tested by experiment. Hypothesizing relates to the critical thinking skills Generalize and If...Then Arguments.

Make Models Models can be physical or mental representations that explain an idea, object, or event. Making models is related to the critical thinking skill Reason by Analogy.

Estimate The skill of estimating generally involves an indirect means of measuring. Estimating requires students to make mental comparisons between physical objects or lengths of time. Estimating is related to the critical thinking skill Compare and Contrast.

Control Variables As part of designing experiments, students need to identify factors that may affect the outcome of an event. They must then decide how to manipulate one factor while holding other factors constant. Controlling variables relates to the critical thinking skill Find Causes.

Collect Data The skill of collecting data includes gathering information in a systematic way and recording it.

Interpret Data Three skills are included in this category—Read a Graph, Read a Table, and Read a Diagram. When students read a graph, table, or diagram, they must explain the information presented in that graphic form and/or use it to answer questions.

Applying Skills in *Science Insights*

In *Science Insights—Exploring Matter and Energy,* process skills and critical thinking skills are emphasized and integrated throughout the text. Students are given many opportunities to develop their skills. These opportunities range from informal to formal activities and investigations that use process and critical thinking skills. In Chapter 1, students learn how to apply eleven key process skills as they study science. The following features in *Science Insights* also stress the use and application of various skills.

Process Skills and Critical Thinking Skills

Skills WarmUp

A Skills WarmUp activity appears in the margin of every section. It focuses students' attention on specific skills. The Skills WarmUp is usually a simple pencil and paper activity or discussion that leads students into the main topic of the section. For example:

▶ *Skills WarmUp, Chapter 6, page 140* Students compare the solid, liquid, and gas phases of water. The WarmUp reinforces the skills of comparing and contrasting. In addition, cooperative learning is emphasized.

Skills WorkOut

Skills WorkOut activities appear in the margins throughout the text. Students mainly do hands-on activities and research, extending the process skills they have learned. For example:

▶ *Skills WorkOut, Chapter 6, page 149* Students define physical and chemical change by applying a familiar observation. The WorkOut reinforces the skills of comparing and interpreting data.

Check and Explain

Each section ends with four Check and Explain questions. The third and fourth questions require that students apply critical thinking or process skills. The questions are tied to the objectives.

Chapter Review

Two sections of the Chapter Review require students to use both process and critical thinking skills. They include Check Your Understanding and Develop Your Skills. All skills are in boldface.

SkillBuilders

There are 20 SkillBuilders in *Science Insights.* The SkillBuilder focuses on a specific process skill, but other skills are required as well. For example:

▶ *SkillBuilder, Chapter 5, page 120* Students investigate compound machines by studying an imaginary invention. The SkillBuilder reinforces the skills of observing and classifying. In addition, students make models of compound machines.

Activities

There are 25 activities in *Science Insights,* one for each chapter. All activities emphasize the process skills that students use while doing the activity.

Decision-Making Skills

Consider This

After reading about the two sides of an issue related to science in a Consider This feature, students must decide where they stand on the issue. They then communicate their opinions orally by debating the issue with classmates. Students also express their opinions in essays or editorials.

Research Skills

Historical Notebook

In the Historical Notebook feature, students read about a historical technological development in science or prominent people in science history. Students answer questions about the feature, then research a related topic or find out more about the subject of the feature.

Data Bank

Data Bank questions are presented in both the Chapter Review and Unit Opener pages. As students research answers to data bank questions, they use a variety of process skills, including predicting, inferring, classifying, and reading a diagram or table.

Skills Matrix

Chapters	Observe	Compare and Contrast	Classify	Infer	Predict	Measure/Calculate	Communicate	Define Operationally	Hypothesize	Make a Model	Make a Graph	Collect/Organize Data	Interpret Data	Generalize	Reason/Conclude	Research
Chapter 1	▲	■	▲■	■		▲■	▲			■			▲■			
Chapter 2	▲	■	▲	▲■		▲■					■		▲■			
Chapter 3	▲■	▲	■	▲■	■	▲■		■		■		▲	■	■	▲	
Chapter 4	▲	▲■		▲■	▲■				▲				■	■	■	
Chapter 5			▲■	▲■	▲■	■	■		▲				■			
Chapter 6	▲	▲	▲■			■			▲	▲■	■		■			
Chapter 7		▲■	▲	▲■	■	■	▲	■		▲■	▲■		■		■	▲
Chapter 8			▲■	▲■	▲		■		■			▲■	■	■		
Chapter 9	▲	■		■		■	■	■	▲	▲■			■	■		
Chapter 10	▲	■	▲■	▲■						■			■		▲	
Chapter 11	▲	▲■		■	▲■	■	■		▲	▲		▲	▲■	▲		
Chapter 12		■	▲	▲■	■					▲		▲	■			
Chapter 13	▲	■	▲■	■			▲■					▲	■	■		▲
Chapter 14	▲	▲■		▲■	■				■	▲						
Chapter 15	▲	■		▲■	▲			■		▲■			■	▲■		
Chapter 16	▲	■	▲	▲■	■					■			■			
Chapter 17	▲	■		■	■	■			■	▲			■	▲		
Chapter 18	▲■	▲■	▲	▲■	▲	▲■				■		▲	■			
Chapter 19		▲■	▲	■	■					▲■			■	■		
Chapter 20		■	▲■	▲	■		▲■		▲	▲■	■		■		■	
Chapter 21	▲	▲■	▲■		■	■	▲	▲	■	■			■			
Chapter 22		▲■	■	■	■				■	■			■			
Chapter 23		■	▲■	▲■	■	■	▲■			■	■		▲■	■		
Chapter 24	▲	■		▲■		▲	■	■	▲		▲	■	■			▲
Chapter 25	▲	■	▲	■			■		▲	■			▲	■		

Integrated Learning

Integrated learning not only makes teaching and learning more fun, it helps students synthesize concepts and integrate skills.

Most middle schools and junior high schools are structured in such a way that fragmentation of the curriculum is obvious. Students have several teachers—each of whom specializes in teaching a particular subject in isolation of other subject areas. Teachers have observed that this approach may not be the best way to serve the early adolescent's educational needs. Instead, presenting an integrated approach to learning can help students synthesize concepts and coordinate experiences. In an integrated approach, teams of teachers work together to integrate the subjects that they teach. Integrated learning can often answer the age-old student question, "Why do I have to learn this?"

Integrating the Curriculum

A commitment to integrate the curriculum requires planning—sometimes months in advance. For integrated learning to be successful, all teachers must be involved and informed. While it may not be practical to integrate all lessons in a given school, some lessons can be integrated or individual teachers can implement integration into individual lessons within their classrooms. Ideally, integrated learning in science should occur at three levels:

► Integrating other sciences

► Connecting science to other disciplines

► Integrating science, technology, and society

Integrating the Sciences

Within *Science Insights—Exploring Matter and Energy*, several strategies are used to help teachers integrate and make connections. For example:

Section 4.3 Forces in Moving Fluids In Chapter 4, students explore forces in fluids, such as buoyancy and hydraulic pressure. Section 4.3 uses Bernoulli's principle to illustrate how birds' bodies are adapted for flying, integrating **physics** and **life science.**

Section 6.3 Changes in Matter Within this section, **chemistry** and **earth science** are integrated. Students learn that chemical weathering in rocks helps shape the earth's surface.

Margin notes throughout the **Teacher's Edition** provide numerous strategies and suggestions for integrating the sciences. For example, in Chapter 15 page 365, a health integration explains a simple technique based on resonance that physicians use to check a person's lungs.

Integrated Resource Book

This unique resource provides science integration worksheets that are correlated to the student text, covering topics from chemistry to physics to environmental science.

An Interdisciplinary Approach

Various components in *Science Insights* have been developed to help teachers make connections across curricula. In the **Student Edition,** features such as Skills WorkOut, Consider This, Historical Notebook, SkillBuilder, and Science and Literature connect science content, events, and concepts to language arts skills, literature, and mathematics.

Margin notes throughout the **Teacher's Edition** include strategies for making interdisciplinary connections.

Science, Technology, and Society

Within the Student Edition of *Science Insights,* each section concludes with a Science, Technology, and Society subsection.

In the Teacher's Edition, margin notes also stress STS Connections, providing additional resources for integration and relevancy.

Multicultural Perspectives

The demographics of the United States are changing rapidly. The school-age population of the nation's largest cities is becoming more and more ethnically diverse. A multicultural perspective has become essential in education as students prepare for membership in these diverse communities.

Building Multicultural Awareness

Multicultural education is a process through which students learn to respect ethnic and cultural diversity. Through this process, students can gain a global perspective on the universal role of science in the world. Multicultural education includes the history and accomplishments of people of all heritages, particularly those who have been underrepresented in the past, such as people of African, Asian, Native-American, Pacific-Island, and Hispanic backgrounds.

Many of the techniques that you use in your classroom already are well suited to a program that includes multicultural perspectives. In particular, cooperative learning, hands-on activities, and cross-curricular strategies are effective approaches to content that combine science concepts and multicultural understanding.

Here are some suggestions to help you incorporate multiculturalism into your science curriculum:

▶ Tell students about the contribution to science and technology of people from diverse ethnic and cultural backgrounds.

▶ Invite members of the community who are scientists to speak to students about careers in science and technology.

▶ Provide opportunities for students to work in cooperative groups that are balanced with respect to gender, race, and ethnic background.

▶ Provide examples to students of how science applies to the daily lives of all people.

▶ Allow students to develop projects based on their own cultural experiences.

Multiculturalism in *Science Insights*

You will find that multiculturalism is infused throughout the *Science Insights* program.

Student Edition The Student Edition includes many text references and visuals that stress cultural diversity. In addition, Asian, African, Native-American, Pacific-Island, and Hispanic people are represented in illustrations and photographs. For example:

Chapter 4, page 94 In a Historical Notebook feature, students learn about the Polynesian boats called outriggers, which are specially designed to be fast and stable. A photograph of an outrigger accompanies the text.

Teacher's Edition You will also find specific strategies for teaching multiculturalism in the Teacher's Edition margin notes, under the head Multicultural Perspectives. For example:

Chapter 5, page 116 Archaeologists' theories about the types of machines used by the pyramid builders of ancient Egypt are included for discussion.

Chapter 16, page 392 While studying how musical instruments make sound, a teaching strategy suggests that students describe instruments from three different cultures that belong to one musical family—stringed, wind, or percussion.

Ancillaries References to Addison-Wesley's *Multiculturalism in Mathematics, Science, and Technology: Readings and Activities* are provided in the Teacher's Edition. This book offers a variety of multicultural readings and activities appropriate for grades 7 to 12 in a blackline master format. The lesson topics, covering a diverse multicultural spectrum, combine the vision and experiences of 12 multicultural educators throughout the United States.

Cooperative Learning in the Science Classroom

When people cooperate on a task, they often achieve surprising results.

Cooperative learning is an approach to teaching that involves building a cooperative climate in the classroom as well as structuring specific group activities. To accomplish a cooperative task, students work in small learning groups. Often students find that in sharing information with team members, they come to a better understanding of the science concepts they are studying. Process and critical thinking skills are extended as students become aware of the methods teammates use to solve a problem.

Cooperative Learning Groups

Cooperative learning groups should range in number from two to six. The ideal group size for a cooperative learning activity, however, is four. Once a cooperative learning group has been established, the cooperative group should remain together until the assigned activity has been completed. If a cooperative learning group is having difficulty working together socially or keeping on task, do not dissolve the group. It is important to keep the group intact so that students within the group will learn the social interaction skills necessary to solve problems or to complete tasks effectively through cooperation and collaboration.

Suggested Roles in Cooperative Groups

Here are some suggested roles.

Principal Investigator The Principal Investigator is responsible for managing the tasks within the activity and ensuring that all members understand the goals and content of the activity. The Principal Investigator should read instructions, check results, and ask questions of the teacher. Also, the Principal Investigator should facilitate group discussions.

Materials Manager The Materials Manager is responsible for assembling and distributing the materials and equipment needed. As an activity progresses, the Materials Manager is responsible for assembling and operating equipment, as well as checking the results of the activity. The Materials Manager is also responsible for insuring that all equipment is cleaned and returned.

Data Collector The Data Collector is responsible for gathering, recording, and organizing the data. The Data Collector also is responsible for coordinating the certification of the data among all group members and reporting the results of an activity either in writing or orally to the class or to the teacher. If information is being gathered on a master table on the chalkboard, the Data Collector is responsible for recording the data on the chalkboard.

Timekeeper The Timekeeper is responsible for keeping track of time, for safety, and for monitoring noise level. The Timekeeper must also observe and record the group's social interactions and encourage group members to discuss the activity as well as check the results.

Collaborative/Social Skills

Social skills are basic to the cooperative learning process. You should assign a specific social skill for each cooperative learning task. For example, if the activity requires students to hold a debate, the social skill for the activity can be *listening carefully*. Other cooperative group skills include the following:

▶ Taking turns
▶ Sharing resources
▶ Encouraging participation
▶ Treating others with respect
▶ Providing constructive feedback
▶ Resolving conflict
▶ Explaining and helping without simply giving answers

Self-Evaluation

Encourage students to become actively involved in the evaluation process by providing time for them to reflect on the activity.

Exploring Science Visually

In the science classroom, visual learning strategies have become just as important as the written word. No longer are visuals just pretty pictures. They convey and expand information in a way that helps students learn.

Visual learning is the pedagogical strategy for the 1990s. The strategy employs a distinct correlation between the prose of a text and the illustrations— both photography and art. The integration of prose and visuals enables the graphics to be conveyors of content and concepts. By using visual learning in textbooks and in classroom experiences, the learning process can be enhanced. Visual learning motivates students and makes the content more relevant to them. It also helps students zero in on concepts. Besides its motivational and relevancy aspects, visual learning also helps to promote a number of skills that are essential in the educational environment and in daily life.

Visual Learning and Skills Development

The following is a list of skills that can be developed and strengthened by using visual learning strategies.

▶ Recognizing color cues that signal important information

▶ Understanding symbols and their uses

▶ Recognizing color cues that indicate connections between ideas

▶ Analyzing and interpreting observations

▶ Reading graphs, charts, and maps

▶ Comparing and contrasting

▶ Identifying and labeling

▶ Comprehending difficult concepts

Visuals in the Diverse Classroom

Think about the opportunities that visual learning offers the diverse student population in today's classrooms. In a single classroom, you may be teaching students with limited proficiency in English, as well as students who are at-risk or gifted. How do you meet the diverse needs of all these students? Visual learning is part of the answer. Because visuals are a universal language, visual learning provides opportunities for all learners. Integrated prose, diagrams, photographs, art, and maps provide students with broader educational materials, empowering students to approach the content in a way that best suits their individual needs.

Visual Learning in *Science Insights*

Color Cues In Chapter 7, Elements, Compounds, and Mixtures, the symbols for every element are color cued; for example, the symbol for oxygen is always represented in red. This color scheme is consistent throughout the text.

Understanding Symbols and Their Uses Many symbols are used throughout the *Science Insights* text, including safety symbols and symbols in everyday life.

Analyzing and Interpreting Observations

Explore Visually is a teaching strategy used throughout the Teacher's Edition that can be used to encourage students to explore the text graphics.

Integration of Prose and Visuals Here are several examples of the various ways in which visual learning is employed in *Science Insights:*

pages 74–75 Gravity and the Solar System
Concepts related to gravitational force within the solar system are developed as a two-page spread that integrates art, a table, and prose.

pages 264–265 Lightning
The physics of lightning is presented in a dynamic two-page visual spread that includes content blocks directly correlated to the illustration.

Concept Mapping

Concept mapping offers a visual representation of relationships, linking concepts in a way that is highly effective in helping students synthesize new information.

Each student connects concepts differently. Therefore, constructing a concept map with a partner or a team gives students valuable experience in comprehending and communicating the meanings of scientific concepts and terms. Whether used to interpret textbook passages or as a problem-solving tool, concept mapping when paired with cooperative learning leads to lively classroom discussion.

Using Concept Maps in Your Classroom

Here are some strategies for introducing students to concept mapping and making concept maps part of the learning environment:

▶ Create a large concept map of the year's lessons for the bulletin board.

▶ List familiar and unfamiliar words from a new lesson and ask students if they can connect the words based on what they already know.
▶ Have students show their concept maps on the chalkboard and explain how the concepts link.
▶ Before testing, have students review and revise concept maps they have already made.
▶ Use concept mapping as a way to let students assist in planning the year's course of study.

Concept Mapping in *Science Insights*

Addison-Wesley's *Science Insights* provides concept mapping opportunities in the Make Connections section of each Chapter Review. In each of the first chapters in a unit, students copy a concept map on a separate sheet of paper, then complete the map by writing the correct term in the empty spaces. With each successive chapter in a unit, the concept maps become more challenging. In the last chapter of each unit, students create their own concept maps using terms listed in the Make Connections section.

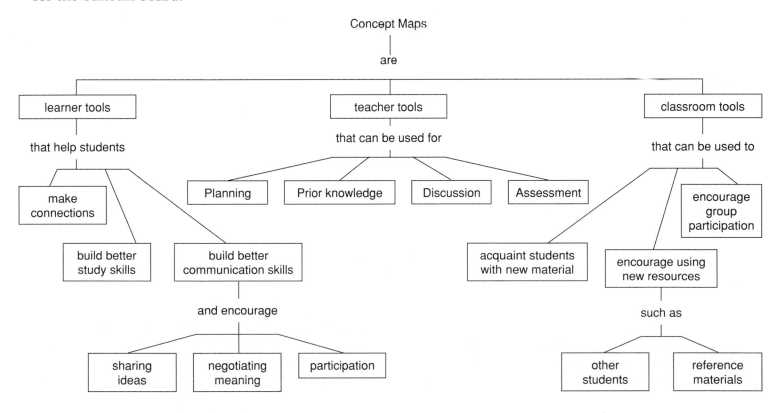

Portfolio Assessment

Portfolio assessment can be an exciting, experimental, and evolving tool for both the student and the teacher.

Portfolio assessment derives its name and approach from the collection of work and achievements usually assembled by artists, designers, and architects. A portfolio is meant to illustrate the true scope of the talents of the professional. In the educational forum, portfolio assessment enables the student and teacher to work together to assemble and to complete the student's best work during a given period of time, usually for a marking period.

With portfolio assessment, the emphasis is placed on overall achievement rather than numerical test scores. Portfolio assessment stresses what students can do rather than what they cannot do. Also, portfolio assessment allows students to remove materials from their portfolios and revise them.

Benefits for Students, Teachers, and Parents

Portfolios motivate students to gauge their own growth. By comparing drafts and finished work, students can see a graphic record of their progress—which can only enhance their self-esteem and make them receptive to further challenges. Instead of measuring themselves against their classmates, they learn to take pride in their own strengths and weaknesses and in personal improvement.

Teachers can use portfolios to communicate more effectively with parents. A portfolio allows parents to browse through a representative collection of their child's work during conferences. Instead of a mere summary of test results, the portfolio reveals an actual legacy of the student's learning experiences.

Contents of the Portfolio

Portfolios can contain any items that students have negotiated with teachers to include. Students should date each piece of work they place in their portfolios and provide a brief description of the assignment and an explanation of the choice.

Students should be encouraged to include various drafts and preliminary stages, as well as finished products, to demonstrate progress. Interesting or humorous mistakes are also appropriate items for a portfolio—particularly if the student adds an analysis or revision of the error. Some suggested materials for portfolios are:

▶ Photographs of any work too large to fit in a portfolio.

▶ Diagrams, tables, graphs, or charts

▶ Audiotapes/videotapes

▶ Projects, laboratory investigations, and activities

▶ Computer printouts

▶ Science journal excerpts

▶ Statements about goals

Portfolios in the Classroom

It will help you to give some thought as to where portfolios will be kept. Both teachers and students will need easy access to the portfolios, and of course the portfolios will take up a good deal of space. Students will also be curious about your system for assessing portfolios. You may wish to get students to help you address both questions.

Portfolios and *Science Insights*

Throughout the Teacher's Edition, suggestions are provided for materials, projects, and so on that students may wish to place in a portfolio. These suggestions can be presented to students. Encourage students to plan ahead and suggest ways to revise their work if necessary.

Portfolio suggestions are a frequent feature of the Teacher's Edition. Here is an example of a portfolio suggestion from the text: Ask students to imagine they are stranded on a deserted tropical island or on a snowy mountain top. Have them write a journal entry describing how knowledge from the various branches of science would help them to survive.

Individual Needs

Every day, classroom teachers face the challenge of a diverse student population with individual students bringing to the educational forum unique sets of abilities, needs, and learning styles.

A Positive Learning Environment

In an effort to provide all students with a positive educational environment with optimum opportunities for success, the following strategies may help teachers structure learning for diverse student populations, especially for those students with different ability levels and those students with limited English proficiency (LEP):

► Provide tools, such as picture dictionaries and other visual learning resources.

► Encourage a variety of responses during discussions, including speaking, drawing, demonstrating, and writing.

► Use hands-on activities and demonstrations to reinforce concepts.

► Speak clearly and slowly using body language and gestures.

► Relate and incorporate various cultural content into discussions. Stress relevant examples.

► Check for understanding and comprehension frequently.

► Use cooperative learning groups for activities and investigations and actively encourage individuals to participate within their groups.

► Use a variety of combination visual/verbal aids to create a language-rich classroom environment.

► Approach concepts in several different ways and provide relevant, common examples.

Ability Levels

In *Science Insights,* the various components of each chapter and the supplements have been designated for use by core, standard, and enriched students. The leveling of the components and supplements is presented as suggestions. Based upon individual students, classroom management, and teaching styles, the components and supplements may be used in different levels, as deemed necessary by the teacher.

Limited English Proficiency Students

Science presents a challenge to LEP students at three levels—overcoming a language barrier, achieving mastery in science, and addressing social concerns as students interact with their peers and teachers. The following teaching strategies are designed to help teachers create a positive and rewarding educational environment for LEP students:

► Create audiocassettes for each chapter that model language patterns.

► Use newspapers, magazines, and library research to provide connections between school and the larger world.

► Use illustrations with labeling exercises to build vocabulary.

► Have students keep a "dictionary" of key terms and words that includes the term in English, the term in their native language, and the definition. Attaching drawings or photographs next to the terms or words is also helpful.

► Encourage LEP students to use an English–primary language dictionary.

► Use remedial or average vocabulary and skills worksheets.

► Provide opportunities for LEP students to communicate nonverbally.

Master Materials List

Most of the activities in *Science Insights—Exploring Matter and Energy* have been designed for use with commonly available materials. The quantities shown are based on a class of 30 students with the recommended student grouping found in the Teacher's Edition. When ordering, adjust quantities for your class size and activity groupings. Quantities shown for nonconsumable equipment used in more than one activity reflect the largest quantity needed for any of the activities.

All activities are optional. Your equipment needs will vary, depending on the activities you elect to do. To help you determine your specific needs, each item is referenced by activity number to the activity or activities in which it is required. Readily available materials such as tap water and notebook paper are not listed.

Addresses of science materials suppliers follow the materials list.

Item	Quantity	Chapter Activities	SkillBuilders
alcohol, rubbing	500 mL	22	
assorted items: rice grains, staples, thread	60 ea	1	
bags, plastic, self-locking, thick	15	25	
bags, plastic, self-locking, 1-L size	30	6	
bags, small cloth or heavy paper	7	23	
baking soda	250 g	6, 21	19.2
balance, equal arm	8		6.2
balloons	30	11	
balloons, 2 different sizes	15 ea	2	
balls, aluminum and steel, same diameter	15 ea	3	
balls, table tennis	6	14	
beakers, 250 mL	15	20	
bells	40	16	
bottle tops	50	16	
bottles, 2-L plastic soda with caps	15	4	
boxes, shoe	8–15	16, 24	
boxes, individual cereal or similar	15	1	
broom handles, wooden	8	16	
Bunsen burners	15	9, 19, 20	
buttons, coat	40	16	
cans, coffee	20	10	
cans, small metal with lids	8	16	
cardboard, 26 x 40 cm sheets	15	15	
cards, 7.5 x 12.5 cm index	20	16, 17	
circuit setups	7	19	
dry cell, bulb and socket, wires	7 sets	19	
clay, modeling	0.5 kg	3	
clocks, stopwatches, or watches	8	2, 9, 19	

Item	Quantity	Chapter Activities	SkillBuilders
cloth, flannel, polyester, wool, 10 x 10 cm	15 ea	11	
cloth strips	8	5	
cloves, whole	150	22	
coat hangers	15	7	
coins	400	23	
common objects, about the size of an apple	40		3.1
containers, small glass	4	21	
cord, heavy, 30-cm pieces	8	16	
cotton balls	15	11	
cups, measuring	7	19	
cups, plastic foam	60	9	6.2
cylinders, graduated	20	7, 10	
detergent, liquid dishwashing	250 mL	7	
dictionary	30	8	
droppers	15	4	6.2
dry cells, 6-V	15	12	
fishing line	400 m	2	
foil, aluminum	2 rolls	10, 24	
funnels	8	16	
glue	8	1	
glycerin	750 mL	7	
hole punches	8	1, 17	
hot dogs	15	24	
hot plates	8	5	
ice cubes	20	10	
insulated electrical wire	30 m	12	
jars, to hold 200 mL	60	7, 25	
jars, small with lids	30	22	
labels, adhesive	90	7, 22	
lenses, hand	15	18	19.2
litmus paper, red and blue	50 ea	21	
magazines	8	13	
magnesium sulfate ($MgSO_4$)	100 g		19.2
metal forks	8	16	
metal bolts,	15	9	
metal nuts,	15	9	
metal trays	8	16	
metal washers, heavy	12	14	
meter sticks	15	2	
nails, iron, small	15	20	

Item	Quantity	Chapter Activities	SkillBuilders
nails, iron , large	15	12	
needles	15	1	
newspaper	4	10	
packing material, polystyrene	4 L	10	
paper clips, boxes	15	12	
paper clips, large metal	15	9	
paper fasteners	100	16	
paper plates	16	16	
paper, construction	30 sheets		7.1
paper, graph tracing	30 sheets	13	
paper, plain white	15 sheets	18	
paper, white shelf	3 m	17	
pencils or pens, assorted colors	30–45	13	
pencils	15	9	
penlights or small flashlights	8	17	
pens, marking	15	9	
pins, safety	10	16	
pins, straight	30		7.1
plastic containers, identical with lids	20	10	
ramps, 2 grooved of equal length	30	3	
rubber bands	50	16	
rubber hose, 30 cm	8	16	
rubber stoppers, slit	32	17	
rulers, metric	15	3, 14, 17, 18	
safety goggles	30	25	
salt (NaCl)	250 g	6, 19	19.2
salt substitute (KCl)	100 g		19.2
samples, at least 4 substances	100 mL ea	21	
sawdust	2 L	10	
seeds or beads	0.5 kg	16	
scissors	8	1, 2, 5, 16	
skewers, long wooden	15	24	
socks	8	16	
solution, 4% borax	100 mL	25	
solution, copper sulfate solution ($CuSO_4$)	500 mL	20	
solution, phenol red	500 mL	6	
solution, phenolphthalein	100 mL	21	
solution, white glue 50%	300 mL	25	
spring scale	8		3.1
sponges	15	10	

Item	Quantity	Chapter Activities	SkillBuilders
stirring rods	14	19	
stones, smooth round	100	16	
straws, jumbo plastic	30	1	
straws, plastic	150	2, 5, 16	7.1
string	500 cm	11, 14	3.1
sugar	200 g	19, 20	
sunglasses, polarized	15		17.1
tape, masking	8 rolls	1, 5, 16	
tape, transparent	8 rolls	2, 12, 13, 14	
teakettles	8	5	
test tubes and holders	15	19, 20	
thermometers, Celsius	15	9	
ticking clocks, watches, or timers	15	15	
tongs	15	9	
tongue depressors	60	1, 16	
toothpicks	60	1	
toy cars	8	5	
tubes, identical cardboard	60	15	
tubs, table spread	6	14	
vials with lids	30	6	
vinegar, colorless	100 mL	21	
walnut shells	40	16	
water, distilled	2.5 L	19, 21	
yarn	1 skein	16	

Science Suppliers

Equipment Suppliers

Analytical Scientific
11049 Bandera Rd.
San Antonio, TX 78250

Arbor Scientific
P.O. Box 2750
Ann Arbor, MI 48106-2750

Carolina Biological Supplies
5100 W. Henrietta Rd.
Charlotte, NC 20391

Central Scientific Co.
3300 CENCO Parkway
Franklin Park, IL 60131

Cuisenaire Co. of America
10 Bank St.
White Plains, NY 10606

Fisher Scientific Co.
4901 W. LeMoyne Ave.
Chicago, IL 60651

Learning Alternatives, Inc.
2305 Elm Rd., NE
Cortland, OH 44410

Learning Things, Inc.
68A Broadway
P.O. Box 436
Arlington, MA 02174

Nasco
901 Janesville Ave.
Fort Atkinson, WI 53538

Northwest Scientific Supply Co., Inc.
4311 Anthony Ct., #700
P.O. Box 305
Rocklin, CA 95677

Sargent-Welch Scientific Co.
7300 N. Linder Ave.
Skokie, IL 60077

Audiovisual Distributors

AIMS Media
6901 Woodley Ave.
Van Nuys, CA 91405-4878

Churchill Films (CF)
662 N. Robertson Blvd.
Los Angeles, CA 90069

Coronet Films & Video (C/MTI)
108 Wilmot Rd.
Deerfield, IL 60015

Encyclopaedia Britannica Educational Corp. (EB)
425 N. Michigan Ave.
Chicago, IL 60611

Films Incorporated (FI)
5547 N. Ravenswood Ave.
Chicago, IL 60640-1199

Guidance Associates (GA)
P.O. Box 3000
Mt. Kisco, NY 10549

Human Relations Media (HRM)
175 Tomkins Ave.
Pleasantville, NY 10570

Media Center
2175 Shattuck Ave.
Berkeley, CA 94704

The Media Guild
11722 Sorrento Valley Rd., Suite E
San Diego, CA 92121

National Film Board of Canada
1251 Avenue of the Americas, 16th Floor
New York, NY 10029

National Geographic Society (NGSES) Educational Services
17th and M Sts., NW
Washington, DC 20036

Optical Data
30 Technology Dr.
Warren, NJ 07059

TVO Video
1443 W. Franklin St., Suite 206
Chapel Hill, NC 27516

Videodiscovery, Inc. (VID)
1700 Westlake Ave. N., Suite 600
Seattle, WA 98109-3012

WINGS for Learning
P.O. Box 66002
Scotts Valley, CA 95066

Software Distributors

Educational Software Institute (ESI)
4213 South 94th St.
Omaha, NE 68127

Learning Services (LS)
P.O. Box 10636
Eugene, OR 97440

Educational Resources (ER)
1550 Executive Dr., P.O. Box 1900
Elgin, IL 60121

Chapter Bibliography Supplier Codes

AIMS = Activities that Integrate Math & Science, Fresno, CA.
AVNA = Audio Visual Narr. Arts, Pleasantville, NY.
BFA = BFA Educational Media, New York, NY.
C/MTI = Coronet/MTI Film & Video, Deerfield, IL.
CES = Cross Educational Software, Rustin, LA.
CM = Cabisco Mathematics, Burlington, NC.
COM = COMPress, Fairfield, CT.
CSWS = The Council for Solid Waste Solutions, Washington, DC.

EI = Estes Industries, Penrose, CO.
EQ = EduQuest/IBM, Atlanta, GA.
FA = Falcon, Wentworth, NH.
FM = Focus Media, Inc., Garden City, NY.
IBM = IBM, Atlanta, GA.
J & S = J & S Software, Port Washington, NY.
JF = Journal Films, Evanston, IL.
JWW = J. Weston Walch, Portland, ME.
LCA = Learning Corp. of America, New York, NY.
LHS = Lawrence Hall of Science, University of California Berkeley, CA.

MF = Macmillan Films, Mount Vernon, NY.
MMI = MMI Corp., Baltimore, MD.
PF = Pyramid Films & Video, Santa Monica, CA.
QE = Queue, Fairfield, CT.
SC = Sunburst Communications, Pleasantville, NY.
SFAW = Scott Foresman - Addison Wesley, Reading, MA.
SVE = Society for Visual Education, Chicago, IL.
T-L = Time-Life Video, New York, NY.
UL = United Learning, Niles, IL.
V = Vernier, Portland, OR.
WN = Ward's Natural Science Establishment, Inc., Rochester, NY.

Scott Foresman - Addison Wesley

ScienceInsights
Exploring Matter and Energy

Authors

Michael DiSpezio, M.A.
Science Consultant
North Falmouth,
Massachusetts

Marilyn Linner-Luebe, M.S.
Former Science Teacher
Fulton High School,
Fulton, Illinois

Marylin Lisowski, Ph.D.
Professor of Education
Eastern Illinois University
Charleston, Illinois

Bobbie Sparks, M.A.
K–12 Science Consultant
Harris County Department
  of Education
Houston, Texas

Gerald Skoog, Ed.D.
Professor and Chairperson
Curriculum and Instruction
Texas Tech University
Lubbock, Texas

Scott Foresman
Addison Wesley

Editorial Offices: Menlo Park, California • Glenview, Illinois
Sales Offices: Reading, Massachusetts • Atlanta, Georgia • Glenview, Illinois
Carrollton, Texas • Menlo Park, California
http://www.sf.aw.com

Content Reviewers

Farzan Abdolsalami
Assistant Professor
Trinity University
San Antonio, Texas

Randall Bryson
Middle School Science
    Coordinator
Durham Academy
Durham, North Carolina

John Caferella
Science Programs Supervisor
Community School District 10
Bronx, New York

Catherine K. Carlson
Science Department
    Chairperson
Parkhill/Richardson
    Intermediate School District
Dallas, Texas

Anita Gerlach
Chemistry/Physics Teacher
Santa Fe High School
Santa Fe, New Mexico

Karen G. Jennings
Chemistry Instructor
Lane Technical High School
Chicago, Illinois

George Moore
Science Coordinator
Midwest City Public Schools
Midwest City, Oklahoma

Gary J. Vitta
Superintendent of Schools
West Essex Regional Schools
North Caldwell, New Jersey

Miriam R. Weiss
Director of
    Science/Technology
Community School District 11
Bronx, New York

Richard A. Williams
Chemistry Instructor
Winter Haven High School
Winter Haven, Florida

Multicultural Reviewers

William Bray
Stanford University
Stanford, California

Gloriane Hirata
San Jose Unified School
    District
San Jose, California

Joseph A. Jefferson
Ronald McNair School
East Palo Alto, California

Martha Luna
McKinley Middle School
Redwood City, California

Peggy P. Moore
Garnet Robertson
    Intermediate
Daly City, California

Steven Oshita
Crocker Middle School
Burlingame, California

Modesto Tamez
Exploratorium
San Francisco, California

Front cover photographs: NASA (Earth), Jeff Foott/Bruce Coleman Inc. (honeycomb), K. Murakami/Tom Stack & Associates (integrated chip wafer), Gareth Hopson for Addison-Wesley (geode).

Back cover photograph: K. Murakami/Tom Stack & Associates (integrated chip wafer).

ISBN 0-201-33285-X

Contents

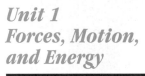

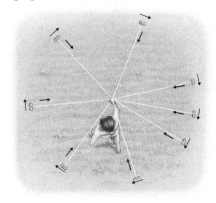

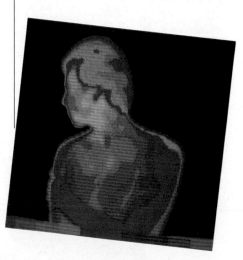

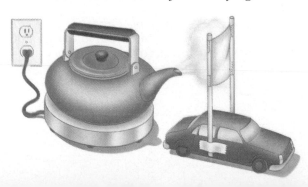

Unit 2
Particles of Matter

page 132

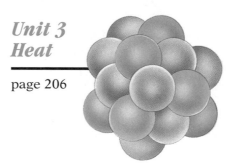

Unit 3
Heat

page 206

Unit 4
Electricity and
Electromagnetism

page 254

Unit 5
Waves, Sound, and Light

page 332

Unit 6
Interactions of
Matter

page 464

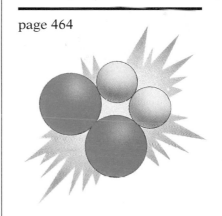

Contents   **vii**

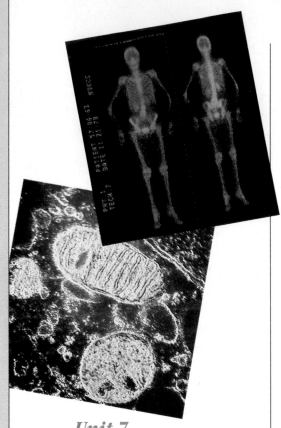

Unit 7
Technology and Resources

page 580

Features

Hands-On Science

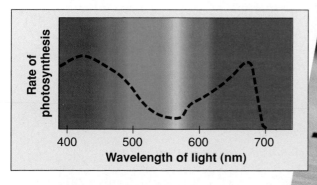

Integrated Science Activity Links

Concept Mapping...

Reading a science textbook is not like reading a magazine or a story. You may not need to work hard to understand a story. You may not need to remember a story for a long time, either. But when you read science, you are reading to learn something new. You will need to think about what you read. You will also need to remember as much as you can. You may just *read* a story, but you will need to *study* your textbook.

Build a Concept Map

One way to help you study and remember what you have learned is to organize the information in the chapter visually. You can do this by making concept maps. In a concept map, the main ideas are identified by a word or phrase enclosed in a box. When these boxes are linked, you can better understand the meanings of the ideas by seeing how the concepts are connected to one another. To build a concept map, follow the steps below.

Identify

1. Identify the concepts to be mapped. They may come from a short section of your book, directions from an activity, or a vocabulary list. List the concepts on a separate sheet of paper or on small cards.

Decide

2. Decide which concept is the main idea. Look for ways to classify the remaining concepts. You may want to list or rank the concepts from the most general to the most specific. For example, "energy resources" is general, and then "renewable" and "conserved" are more specific concepts.

Organize

3. Place the most general concept at the top of your map. Link that concept to the other concepts. Draw a circle or square around each concept.

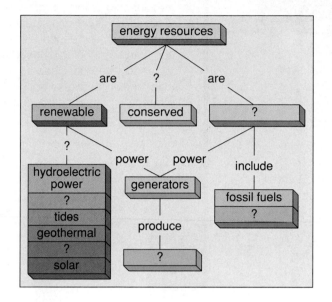

Choose

4. Pick linking words for your map that identify relationships between the concepts. Linking words should not be the concepts themselves. Label all lines with linking words that explain how each pair of concepts relate to one another.

Create

5. Start making your map by branching one or two general concepts from your main concept. Add other, more specific, concepts to the general ones as you progress. Try to branch out. Add two or more concepts to each concept already on the map.

Connect

6. Make cross-links between two concepts that are already on the map. Label all cross-links with words that explain how the concepts are related. Use arrows to show the direction of the relationship.

As you build a concept map, you are doing two things. First, you are automatically reviewing what you already know. Second, you are learning more. Once you have a completed map, you can use it to study and test yourself.

You will often find that several different maps can be made from the same group of concepts.

Introducing the Unit

Directed Inquiry

Have students examine the photograph. Ask:

▶ How can scientists learn how water striders walk across water? (Scientists learn by observing the water striders and/or by conducting experiments.)

▶ What information can scientists obtain by studying the circles, or dimples, around the strider's feet? (They can see where the strider's feet touch the water, and determine the amount of stress each foot exerts on the water's surface.)

▶ What tools or technologies might help scientists in their study of water striders? (They might use a video recorder, special photographic techniques like the one shown in the photograph, and so on. Accept all reasonable answers.)

Writing About the Photograph

Ask students to think about factors involved in walking on water without sinking. Have students imagine that they must cross a lake. They have no boat and can't swim. Their only resource is a stand of saplings. Have students discuss how they might build a frame that would allow them to cross the water.

Unit 1 provides an introduction to the study of science, a survey of force and motion, and a discussion of the relationship of force and motion to energy. Chapter 1 introduces science skills and methods. It also describes some of the tools and technologies used in physical science research. Chapter 2 explores the relationship between motion and energy. Frames of reference, motion, and acceleration are discussed. Finally, the chapter defines energy, compares potential and kinetic energy, and introduces the law of conservation of energy. Chapter 3 examines the relationship between force, motion, and gravity. The chapter relates force and friction to each of Newton's three laws of motion. A discussion of universal forces closes the chapter. Chapter 4 discusses forces in fluids, fluid pressure, and the relationships among gravity, weight, buoyancy, and density. The chap-

Unit 1

Forces, Motion, and Energy

Chapters

1 Studying Science
2 Motion and Energy
3 Forces and Motion
4 Forces in Fluids
5 Work, Machines, and Energy

ter closes with a presentation of pressure differences in moving fluids and an explanation of how heavier-than-air objects fly. Chapter 5 focuses on work, machines, and energy. The chapter defines work and power, shows how to determine the mechanical advantage and efficiency of a machine, and describes six simple machines. Finally, the chapter sets forth the Law of Conservation of Mass and Energy.

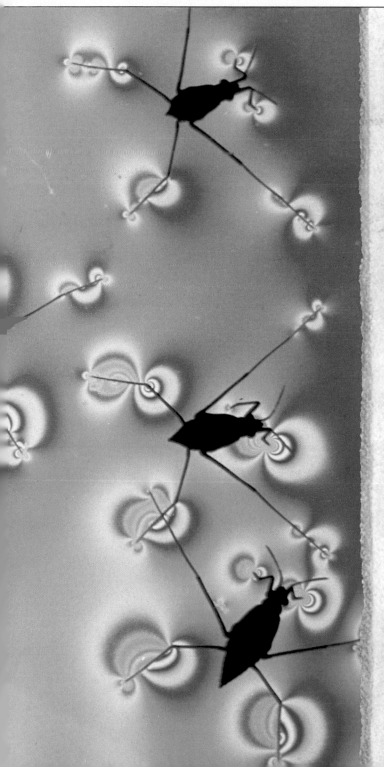

Data Bank

Use the information on pages 634 to 643 to answer the questions about topics explored in this unit.

Interpreting Data

Which city has the highest average maximum daily temperature in July: New York City, Salina Cruz, or San Diego?

Comparing

In 15 minutes, how much farther can a cheetah travel than a hawk moth?

Predicting

Assuming normal breathing was possible, would it be harder to walk on Earth, Venus, or Jupiter?

The photograph to the left shows how the legs of the water striders put stress on the water surface. Why doesn't the water strider sink?

Data Bank Answers

Have students search the Data Bank on pages 634 to 643 for the answers to the questions on this page.

Interpreting Data Salina Cruz has the highest maximum daily temperature in July. The answer is found in the graph, Average Maximum Daily Temperatures, on page 637.

Comparing In 15 minutes a cheetah can travel 14.75 km farther than a hawk moth. The answer is found by using the tables, Top Speed of Some Animals in Air and Top Speed of Some Animals on Land, on page 638.

Extension Ask students to find out which animals have a top speed of 96 km/h. (Pigeon, pronghorned antelope, and sailfish all have top speeds of 96 km/h.)

Predicting It would be much harder to walk on Jupiter because the surface gravity is almost three times greater. The answer can be found in the table, Surface Gravity of Bodies in the Solar System, on page 636.

Extension Ask students to make a bar graph showing the surface gravity of the four planets whose gravity is closest to that of Earth. (Students' graphs should show Venus and Uranus—each 0.92; Neptune—1.20; Saturn—1.06.)

Answer to In-Text Question

The distribution of the water strider's weight among his four feet and over a large area causes the force on the water's surface to be less than its surface tension. The water-strider doesn't sink. Point out the lines of stress that form where the insect's legs meet the water.

Overview

This chapter introduces students to the study of science. The first section presents science skills, and discusses the use of scientific methods during experiments. The second section describes the units of the SI measurement system used in scientific study. The third section explores types of graphs and their uses. The last section describes various tools and technologies scientists use in physical science research.

Advance Planner

▶ Supply posterboard, paint, felt tip pens, and old magazines for TE page 6.

▶ Collect magazines that include scaled-down patterns for TE page 9.

▶ Provide balances, boxes, oranges, books, paper clips, and tissue paper for TE page 13.

▶ Collect magazines and newspapers for TE pages 17, 19, and 20.

▶ Obtain plastic drinking straws, boxes, wooden depressors, assorted small items, hole punch, needles, toothpicks or broom straws, and masking tape for SE Activity 1, page 26.

Skills Development Chart

Sections	Calculate	Classify	Collect Data	Communicate	Estimate	Graph	Interpret Data	Measure	Model	Observe
1.1 Skills WarmUp Skills WorkOut				●			●			
1.2 Skills WarmUp Skills WorkOut Practice Problems	●				●			●		
1.3 Skills WarmUp SkillBuilder		●				●				
1.4 Skills WarmUp Activity			●	●				●	●	●

Individual Needs

▶ **Limited English Proficiency Students** Have students write all the science process skills on pages 3 to 5 and the bold-face vocabulary terms on pages 3 to 7 in their science portfolios. You may wish to have them include any other unfamiliar words in their journals as well. For each term they list, have them leave several blank lines. Ask students to define each term using their own words. Then ask them to write a sentence or two describing the difference between the following pairs of terms: *constant* and *variable, hypothesis* and *fact.*

▶ **At-Risk Students** Ask students to list in their science portfolios the science skills given on pages 3 to 5. Have them leave at least a half page after each skill and then define each in their own words. Then have students work in pairs to think of examples of how that skill is used in everyday life. Point out that activities like making a cake, playing ball, and delivering papers may use one or more of the science process skills.

▶ **Gifted Students** Ask each student to choose a scientific tool shown on pages 22 to 23 or other similar tool that interests them. Have them do research to find out how the tool works, what it is used for, and what areas of science or technology are most likely to use it. You may also suggest that they find out if any of the tools were used to make scientific discoveries. Encourage students to share their findings with the class. They may prepare a bulletin board or present an oral report with pictures and diagrams showing the results of their research.

Resource Bank

▶ **Bulletin Board** Prepare two headings for the bulletin board: *SI Units of Measurement* and *Examples.* In the first section, list the units introduced in Section 1.2. Under each unit, attach an object, or a picture of an object, that illustrates the unit. For example, a meter-long piece of cord string could represent a meter, a small paper clip could represent a gram. Encourage students to bring in examples of everyday items that could also represent each unit. Attach the examples to the *Example* section of the board. Allow students to identify which unit the object represents. Objects that can't conveniently be hung can be labeled and placed on a table or shelf near the board.

Section	Core	Standard	Enriched	Section	Core	Standard	Enriched
1.1 Science Skills and Methods pp. 3–10				**Laboratory Program** Investigation 2 Investigation 3	• •	• •	• •
Section Features Skills WarmUp, p. 3 Skills WorkOut, p. 5	• •	• •	• •	**1.3 Graphing** pp. 17–20			
Blackline Masters Review Worksheet 1.1 Skills Worksheet 1.1 Integrating Worksheet 1.1	• • •	• • •	•	**Section Features** Skills WarmUp, p. 17 SkillBuilder, p. 18	•	• •	• •
Overhead Blackline Transparencies Overhead Blackline Master 1 and Student Worksheet	•	•	•	**Blackline Masters** Review Worksheet 1.3 Skills Worksheet 1.3 Integrating Worksheet 1.3 Reteach Worksheet 1.3	• • •	• • • •	• •
Color Transparencies Transparencies 1, 2	•	•	•	**Ancillary Options** *Multiculturalism in Mathematics, Science, and Technology, pp. 31–34*	•	•	•
Laboratory Program Investigation 1		•	•	**1.4 Science Tools and Technology** pp. 21–26			
1.2 Measuring with Scientific Units pp. 11–16				**Section Features** Skills WarmUp, p. 21 Career Corner, p. 24 Activity, p. 26	• • •	• • •	• • •
Section Features Skills WarmUp, p. 11 Skills WorkOut, p. 15	• •	• •	• •	**Blackline Masters** Review Worksheet 1.4 Integrating Worksheet 1.4 Vocabulary Worksheet 1	• • •	• • •	•
Blackline Masters Review Worksheet 1.2 Skills Worksheet 1.2	• •	• •					
Ancillary Options *One-Minute Readings, pp. 122–123*	•	•	•				

Bibliography

The following resources can be used for teaching the chapter. See page T-46 for supplier codes.

Library Resources

DeBruin, Jerry. *Scientists Around the World.* Carthage, IL: Good Apple, Inc., 1987.

The Diagram Group. *Comparisons.* New York: St. Martin's Press, 1980.

Technology Resources

Internet

PLANETDIARY at *http://www.planetdiary.com*
• Learn more about astronomy in *Astronomy/Space* by clicking on *Phenomena Backgrounders* and *Current Phenomena*.

Software

All about Science I. Mac, Dos. ESI.
Big Science Ideas Systems. Mac, Win. LS.
Graph Power. Mac. LS.

CD-ROMs

An Odyssey of Discovery for Science Insights: Have students explore the activities *Shadow Watch, Data From Space,* and *Dig It* on the Earth and Space Disk. Have them explore *Genes and Traits, Paramecia, Aquarium,* and *Nerve Express* on the Living Science Disk. SFAW.

Laserdiscs

Living Textbook. (See barcodes on pages in this chapter.) Optical Data.

Videos

Basic Math for the Study of Science. CM.
Powers of Ten. PF.
Scientific Notation. CM.

Audio-Visual Resources

Exploring the Scientific Method. Filmstrip. NGSES.

Writing Connection

Have students imagine that someone took a photograph of the wood when it was part of a growing tree. Have them write a description of the scene that would be shown in such a photograph.

Integrating the Sciences

Earth Science Ask students what kind of conditions might be most suitable for petrified wood to form from fallen trees. (Plants are most likely to become petrified wood or mineral fossils if they are buried rapidly by mud or volcanic ash.)

Introducing the Chapter

Have students read the description of the photograph. Ask if they agree or disagree with the description.

Directed Inquiry

Have students study the photograph. Ask:

▶ How would you describe the image in the picture? (Students will mention the different colors, the rings, and its resemblance to a log or tree trunk.) What do you think this is a picture of? (A log changed to stone; fossil wood)

▶ How do you think this change took place? (Over the course of time the wood was replaced by minerals from the earth.)

▶ What are the thinking skills you used to answer the questions about this photograph? (Students may mention looking carefully at the picture, comparing what they see to what they know, and grouping it with things it looks like.)

▶ What kinds of scientists would be most interested in studying petrified wood? Why? (Paleontologist, biologist, climatologist; to determine age, then the types of flora and climate during that area and period)

Chapter Vocabulary

constant
controlled
  experiment
cubic meter
data
density
kilogram

liter
mass
meter
scientific notation
variable
volume

Chapter 1 Studying Science

Chapter Sections

1.1 Science Skills and Methods

1.2 Measuring with Scientific Units

1.3 Graphing

1.4 Science Tools and Technology

What do you see?

❝This is petrified wood. It is a piece of a tree that over many years has slowly lost its inner material and has been replaced by minerals from the earth. It is as hard as rock and is made of many colors which are the minerals. By using carbon-14 dating you could probably find out its exact age.❞

Mike Monsilovich
Indiana Area Junior High
Indiana, Pennsylvania

To find out more about the photograph, look on page 28. As you read this chapter, you will learn about science and how to study matter and energy.

1.1 Science Skills and Methods

Objectives

▶ **Identify** and **use** science skills.

▶ **Describe** a controlled experiment.

▶ **Apply** a scientific method.

▶ **Make a model** of a safety symbol.

▼ **ACTIVITY**

Communicating

Sense of Place

What is your favorite place? Picture the place in your mind, and then write what you **see**, feel, taste, hear, and smell. Exchange your description with a partner, and see if you can guess each other's unknown place.

SKILLS WARMUP

What is science? If you look up the definition of the word science in a dictionary or in a science book, you will see words that give you clues. These words are *knowledge*, *skills*, *experiment*, and *systematize*. *Systematize* means "to organize in an orderly way." Science is a way to gather and organize information about the natural world. When you do science, you gather information about the thing you want to study by using such skills as observing and experimenting. You organize the information in an orderly way in order to figure out its meaning. Science is also a collection of facts and theories about the world around you.

Science Skills

To gather information, or **data**, you use many different skills. These skills are sometimes called science process skills. As you read about science process skills, you'll discover that they're not mysterious or difficult. Science process skills aren't reserved for science classes. In fact, you already use many of these skills every day!

Observe The most direct way to gain knowledge about something in nature is to observe it. When you observe, you use one or more of your senses to get information about your surroundings. Your senses are sight, touch, taste, smell, and hearing. Your ability to observe can be extended by using tools such as microscopes, telescopes, thermometers, and rulers. Look at the objects in Figure 1.1. List as many observations as you can about each object. Which sense did you use most often? ①

Figure 1.1 ▲
Do you think the people who design new skateboards and roller blades use science skills? ②

Chapter 1 Studying Science 3

3

Skills Development

Infer To help students think about observation and inference, tell this story: Four blind people, who had never heard of an elephant, met one in a jungle. To learn about the beast, each person carefully felt a different part of it: one explored the elephant's trunk; the second a leg; the third a tusk; and the fourth the tail. Ask students to imagine how each might have described an elephant from handling just one part. Have them tell what science skills these people used to decide what the elephant was like. (Each used observation and inference.) Invite students to draw conclusions about the point the story makes about science processes. (Even careful observations can lead to wrong inferences, if there isn't enough data. Combining observations may lead to better inferences.)

Answers to In-Text Questions

① **Students can probably infer that in general the symbols are warnings of safety hazards. They probably can infer the meanings of most of them as given in Table 1.1 on page 6.**

② **There are 64 blocks and 18 crystals in Figure 1.3.**

**The Living Textbook:
Physical Science Sides 1-4**

Chapter 1   Frame 00600
Pan Balance (1 Frame)
Search:

**The Living Textbook:
Physical Science Side 1**

Chapter 43   Frame 42457
Making Inferences: Lifting Weights
(Movie)
Search: Play:

Portfolio

To reinforce the concept that science process skills aren't used only in science classrooms, have students keep a journal in which they record the ways in which they use each of the science process skills in daily life. For example, students may use measuring when they mix water with juice concentrate. They may use predicting when they plan outdoor activities. They may use classifying when they sort laundry. Later have students analyze the results of their observations and determine which skills they use most often.

Figure 1.2 ▲
What can you infer about these symbols? ①

Infer When you apply reason to explain an observation, you make an inference, or infer. You often can make more than one inference to explain an observation. You probably can infer several things about the drawings in Figure 1.2. For example, you could infer that they represent safety hazards, or precautions you should take. You could also infer that one of the drawings represents fire. The shape of the symbol helps you infer its meaning. You use your past experience to associate fire with the shape of the symbol.

Estimate When you estimate, you make a careful guess. Estimating skills are used when exact measurements aren't needed or can't be obtained. Perhaps getting exact measurements is impossible or too time consuming. You base estimates on the knowledge you already have. You can estimate many things including speed, distance, size, or time.

Measure When you need exact information about an observation, you measure. Measurements describe an observation exactly by comparing it to standard units. Measurements include both a number and a unit. The number of things in a group, the size of an object, the speed of a car, and your height and weight are all things you can measure.

Predict When you predict, you state what you think might happen in the future. Predictions are based on past experiences and observations. Therefore, you can state how and why something will occur. Predictions always include reasons why.

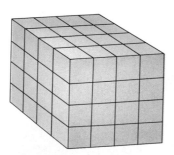

Figure 1.3
Estimate the number of blocks in the cube above and the number of crystals in the photograph. Count the number of blocks and crystals for a more exact measurement. Compare your numbers. ▶ ②

Integrating the Sciences

Geology Geologists classify rocks into three basic types according to how they were formed. *Igneous* rocks are rocks that are formed when molten rock from inside the earth moves toward the cooler outside surface and hardens. Over millions of years, *sedimentary* rocks form as layers of sediments, organic remains, and chemical deposits that are buried and compacted by the pressure of the overlaying deposits. *Metamorphic* rocks are formed by heat, pressure, and chemicals that modify or completely change the features of the original rock.

Use Integrating Worksheet 1.1.

◄ **Figure 1.4**
What are some different ways to classify these rocks? ③

Classify When you classify, you group things together based on how they are alike. You can group things in many different ways. You group things by size, color, shape, texture, or any other characteristic. In science, chemical substances are classified by how they react with other substances. Rocks are classified by how they form. Living things, or organisms, are classified into groups that share common ancestors.

Hypothesize When you state a hypothesis (hy PAHTH uh sihs), or hypothesize, you suggest an answer to a problem. Your answer is based on information that you know. Think of a hypothesis as an explanation or an idea that states why something may always occur. Once you state a hypothesis, you can test it by observing, studying, or experimenting. Your observations, research, or the results of experiments should support your hypothesis. If they don't, you need to think about your hypothesis again and state a new one.

Record and Organize Careful record keeping is an important part of science. During activities and investigations, you should record all your observations, measurements, predictions, and so on. Often you want to organize the data you collect in some way. You can record and organize data in a number of ways, such as using tables, charts, graphs, diagrams, and flow charts.

Analyze After data are recorded and organized, you need to analyze it. When you analyze data, you look for trends or patterns. You also look to see whether or not your data support your inference, prediction, or hypothesis.

Life Science
L I N K

List the following organisms: lizard, whale, tiger, snake, cat, alligator, and lion. Write at least two physical characteristics of each organism. Classify these organisms according to their characteristics.

1. Divide the organisms into two groups, based on similar characteristics.

2. Then divide each of those groups into two groups, again based on characteristics.

How is classification the same in all sciences?

A C T I V I T Y

▼ ACTIVITY
Interpreting Data

Index Patterns

Examine the index of this book. How is the data organized? Can you uncover any patterns among entries? Why aren't the entries made according to the numerical order of the page numbers?

SKILLS WORKOUT

Skills WorkOut

To help students understand more about interpreting data, have them do the Skills WorkOut.

Answers The data in the index consist of topics organized alphabetically. Subdivisions of main topics are listed under them in alphabetical order. Page numbers for each topic are listed in numerical order. Entries are not listed in order of page numbers because it would be time consuming to find all references to one topic.

Extension Ask students to compare the organization of the table of contents to that of the index. How does it differ? (The contents lists chapters and their main parts in order by page numbers.) What does the table of contents tell about the book that the index doesn't? (How information is organized)

Answer to In-Text Question

③ The rocks in Figure 1.4 can be classified by such things as size, shape, color, texture, weight, hardness, how they formed, and what chemical substances they contain.

Answer to Link

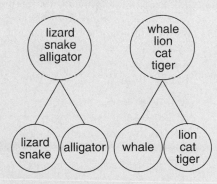

Classification is the grouping of things, any things, based on similarities.

 The Living Textbook:
Physical Science Sides 1-4

Chapter 17   Frame 03099
Data Table: Planets (1 Frame)
Search:

TEACH ▪ *Continued*

Directed Inquiry

Have students study the three general guidelines presented in the text at the top of the page, as well as those listed in Table 1.1. Ask them some or all of the following questions:

▶ How could you summarize the three general guidelines at the top of page 6? (Answers may vary. A possibility is "Be clean, neat, and well organized in the laboratory.")

▶ What is the reason for the first two guidelines under Plant Safety? (Plants often have spines or thorns. Even edible plants can have poisonous parts.)

▶ Why should you point test tubes away from yourself and others when heating substances in them? (Heating can cause substances to boil and overflow and occasionally can cause the test tube to break.)

▶ Why is it important not to mix or taste chemicals? (Chemicals that are harmless by themselves can be caustic, explosive, or poisonous when mixed. They can cause serious injury if inhaled or tasted.)

▶ What are the reasons for the electrical safety warnings? (Worn and loose electrical elements expose people to flowing current, which causes shocks and burns. Water can conduct electricity. Overloaded circuits lead to power failures and fires.)

▶ Which science skills did you use in answering these questions? (Students probably will answer observing, inferring, predicting, and hypothesizing.)

Art Connection

Have students create a safety poster to display in the science classroom. Provide materials such as posterboard, paints, felt-tip pens, old magazines, and paste. Have students choose one of the rules from Table 1.1 or one of the general safety guidelines to make a poster that clearly communicates the appropriate information using words, symbols, and images.

Language Arts Connection

Have students find the everyday definitions of the words *constant* and *variable*. Then have them compare the everyday meanings of each term with its scientific use.

Safety Skills

Your science classroom must be a safe place in which to work and to learn. When you are in the laboratory, always follow these general safety guidelines.

▶ Do not chew gum, eat, or drink in the laboratory.

▶ Read carefully through the activity before you begin. Reread each procedure before you do it.

▶ Clean up your laboratory work area after you complete each activity.

Study the guidelines in Table 1.1. By following these guidelines, you can help make your science laboratory a safe place.

Table 1.1   Laboratory Safety

 Plant Safety
▶ Use caution when collecting or handling plants.
▶ Do not eat or taste any unfamiliar plant or plant parts.
▶ If you are allergic to pollen, do not work with plants or plant parts without a gauze face mask.

 Eye Safety
▶ Wear your laboratory safety goggles when you are working with chemicals, open flame, or any substances that may be harmful to your eyes.
▶ Know how to use the emergency eyewash system. If chemicals get into your eyes, flush them out with plenty of water. Inform your teacher.

Heating Safety
▶ Turn off heat sources when they are not in use.
▶ Point test tubes away from yourself and others when heating substances in them.
▶ Use the proper procedures when lighting a Bunsen burner.
▶ To avoid burns, do not handle heated glassware or materials directly. Use tongs, test-tube holders, or heat-resistant gloves or mitts.

 Clothing Protection
▶ Wear your laboratory apron. It will help protect your clothing from stains or damage.

 Poison
▶ Do not mix any chemicals unless directed to do so in a procedure or by your teacher.
▶ Inform your teacher immediately if you spill chemicals or get any chemicals on your skin or in your eyes.
▶ Never taste any chemicals or substances unless directed to do so by your teacher.
▶ Keep your hands away from your face when working with chemicals.

 Animal Safety
▶ Handle live animals with care. If you are bitten or scratched by an animal, inform your teacher.
▶ Do not bring wild animals into the classroom.
▶ Do not cause pain, discomfort, or injury to an animal. Be sure any animals kept for observations are given the proper food, water, and living space.
▶ Wear gloves when handling live animals. Always wash your hands with soap and water after handling live animals.

 Fire Safety
▶ Tie back long hair when working near an open flame. Confine loose clothing.
▶ Do not reach across an open flame.
▶ Know the location and proper use of fire blankets and fire extinguishers.

 Glassware Safety
▶ Check glassware for chips or cracks. Broken, cracked, or chipped glassware should be disposed of properly.
▶ Do not force glass tubing into rubber stoppers. Follow your teacher's instructions.
▶ Clean all glassware and air dry them.

 Electrical Safety
▶ Use care when using electrical equipment.
▶ Check all electrical equipment for worn cords or loose plugs before using them.
▶ Keep your work area dry.
▶ Do not overload electric circuits.

 Sharp Objects
▶ Be careful when using knives, scalpels, or scissors.
▶ Always cut in the direction away from your body.
▶ Inform your teacher immediately if you or your partner is cut.

Cooperative Learning

Have students work in cooperative learning groups to develop an experiment that determines if the air inside a plastic bag gets hotter when the bag is in the sun coming through a window or in the sun outside the building. Students should state a hypothesis and identify the control, variable, and any predictions they make.

Experiments

What's the best way to learn about something? If you said to ask questions, you're on the right track. Every day you ask questions to get information. In science, you also learn by asking questions and getting answers. A good way to get answers in science is to do experiments.

How would you begin your experiments? When you carefully plan a series of activities, steps, or procedures, you are off to a good start. Experiments need to be carefully designed to

▶ observe how something behaves.

▶ investigate an observation.

▶ test an idea, prediction, hypothesis, or even an inference.

▶ get an answer to a question.

When you plan and design an experiment, be sure that the experiment can be repeated exactly. If your experiment is well planned, anyone can repeat the experiment and get the same results. Scientists repeat experiments to check their data and conclusions.

Most experiments are **controlled experiments**. A controlled experiment has two test groups—the control group and the experimental group. The control group is a standard by which any change can be measured. In the experimental group, all the factors except one are kept the same as those in the control group. The factors that are kept the same are **constants**. The factor that is changed by the person doing the experiment is the **variable**. Read the captions describing the controlled experiment shown in Figure 1.5. What is the variable? ①

Figure 1.5   A Controlled Experiment ▼

Hypothesis: Adding salt to water will increase the temperature at which water boils.

| Each beaker has the same amount of distilled water. | Each beaker of water was heated at the same setting. | Salt was added to the experimental beaker. |

The water in both beakers was stirred for one minute.

A thermometer measured the temperature of boiling water in both beakers.

The unsalted water boiled at 100°C. The salted water boiled at a higher temperature. Do the observations support the hypothesis? Write a conclusion.

Class Activity

Present the following hypothesis: Water expands when it freezes. Ask each student to design a simple experiment to test this hypothesis. Have them write descriptions of their experiments, including materials and step-by-step directions. If possible, ask them to try the experiments at home and to write a conclusion.

Critical Thinking

Reason and Conclude   Ask students to explain why, in a controlled experiment, all the factors in each group except one (the variable) are kept the same. (If all factors but one are the same, then a difference in results between the groups must be due to the variable.)

Directed Inquiry

Have the students study the controlled experiment shown in Figure 1.5. Ask them some or all of the following questions:

▶ What will happen if a thermometer touches the bottom of the beaker, instead of being surrounded by the liquid? (It will indicate the temperature of the beaker bottom, not the liquid.)

▶ Why is it important for both beakers to have the same amount of water? (In a controlled experiment only one variable is different. In this case, it is the salt. Everything else is kept constant.)

Answers to In-Text Questions

① The variable in Figure 1.5 is the presence of salt in the water.

② The observations do support the hypothesis. A possible conclusion would be, "Adding salt to water makes the water boil at a higher temperature."

TEACH ▪ *Continued*

Discuss

Ask students to discuss what might happen if scientists were unable to exchange information and ideas across national boundaries. (Much scientific work would be done more than once; people might not be able to complete work that depended on information from another country.) As a current example, recent contact with scientists of the former USSR revealed that oceanographers had not heard of some basic earth science developments over the last 30 years. For example, they were not aware of the evidence for sea floor spreading, plate tectonics, and mountain building known to western scientists since the late 1950s and early 1960s.

Class Activity

Ask students to think of a science problem or question and write a description of an experiment that will solve it. They should use the steps in Figure 1.6, with the exception of *analyze data* and *conclude*. If they wish, students may use an experiment they have already done. In this case, they can describe the last two stages.

The Living Textbook: Physical Science Sides 1-4

Chapter 17   Frame 03308
Scientific Method (2 Frames)
Search: Step:

8

 Multicultural Perspectives

Have students pick an important series of experiments such as Bernardo Houssay's experiments involving diabetes mellitus, George Washington Carver's research into uses for agricultural products, or Marie and Pierre Curie's work with radioactive elements. Ask students to identify the steps that the scientists used to design their experiments. Have students present their findings in the form of a flow chart like the one shown on this page.

Methods of Science

Does science have one method to approach any problem, experiment, or issue? The answer is both yes and no. You may know the phrase *scientific method* used to describe how scientists find out about the natural world. This method refers to systemized testing of ideas, inferences, predictions, and hypotheses.

The best method for studying science is not a rigid set of steps like those in a cooking recipe. Many different ways are used to study, investigate, and think about scientific problems. An exchange of ideas and information is also part of scientific methods.

To help you think about scientific methods, read Figures 1.6 and 1.7. They show a model for designing and planning an experiment and a model for decision making. These models will help you as you do the activities in this book as well as in your everyday life.

Figure 1.6   Designing and Planning an Experiment

State the Problem
What do you want to find out? State the problem as a question. Make the question as specific as possible.

Hypothesize
What do you think is the cause of the problem you are studying? State a logical answer to your question. This answer, which is your hypothesis, should give one possible explanation for the cause.

Plan Your Experiment
The goal of an experiment is to test your hypothesis. What is the variable? What will be the control? Write a clear step-by-step procedure so that another person can repeat the same process exactly.

Make a Prediction
From your hypothesis, make and record a prediction about the outcome of your experiment.

Gather and Organize Data
What kinds of data will you collect: measurements, observations, or estimates? Will you use graphs, tables, and drawings to organize the data?

Analyze Data
Do you see any trends or patterns in the data? Do the data support your hypothesis or prediction? Do you need more information?

Conclude
State your conclusion based on your data. Your data should either support your conclusion or lead you to another hypothesis. Have any new questions or problems come up?

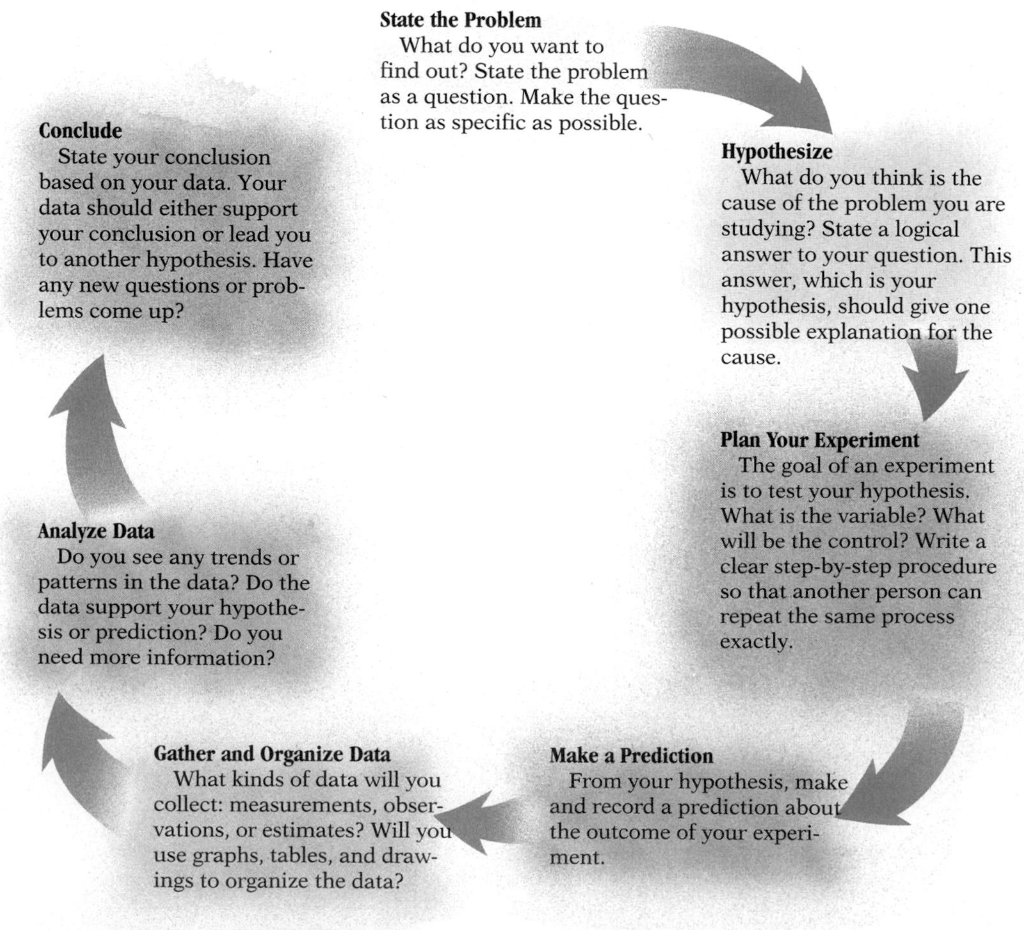

STS Connection

Because computers are such powerful model-building tools, scientists and engineers use computer-generated models to test hypotheses. For example, scientists trying to discover why dinosaurs became extinct have used computer-simulated climates to test theories about the effects of climatic change on dinosaurs. Engineers use computer-generated models to predict how cars will be affected by wind resistance. Astronomers use computers to develop theories about how galaxies were formed. Ask students how computer-generated models would be useful for these experiments. (Computers are especially useful for studying systems that cannot be observed directly, or would be very costly or dangerous to observe directly. Computer programs are capable of applying physics principles to a model system, thereby controlling conditions and variables.)

Figure 1.7   Decision Making ▼

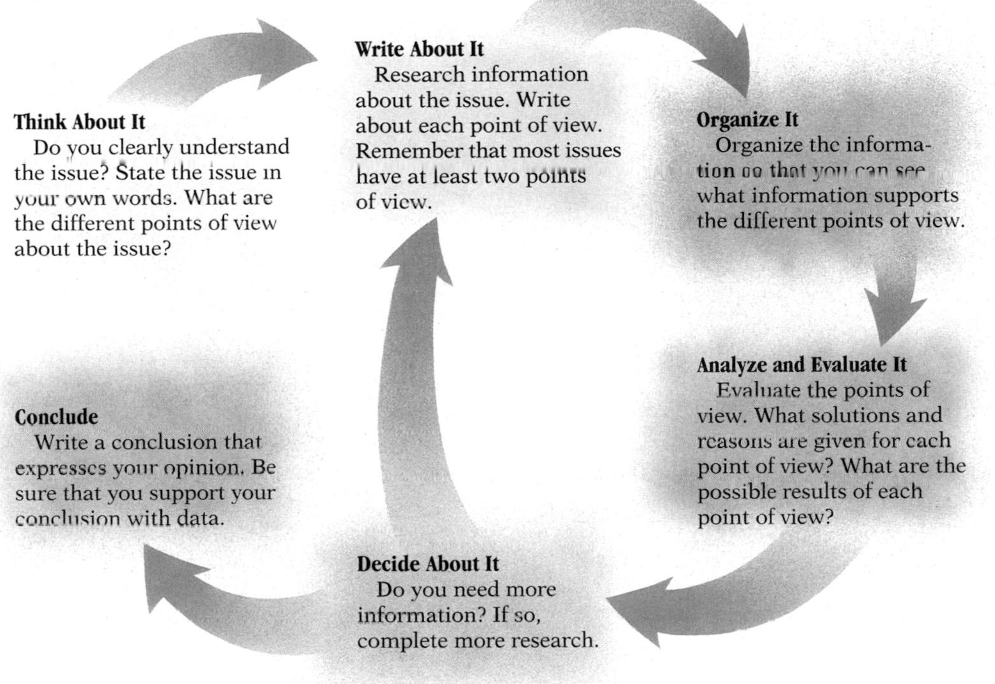

Think About It
Do you clearly understand the issue? State the issue in your own words. What are the different points of view about the issue?

Write About It
Research information about the issue. Write about each point of view. Remember that most issues have at least two points of view.

Organize It
Organize the information so that you can see what information supports the different points of view.

Analyze and Evaluate It
Evaluate the points of view. What solutions and reasons are given for each point of view? What are the possible results of each point of view?

Conclude
Write a conclusion that expresses your opinion. Be sure that you support your conclusion with data.

Decide About It
Do you need more information? If so, complete more research.

Facts, Theories, and Laws

A fact is a true statement. In science, facts can be based on observations, studies, tests, and experiments.

The gathering of facts is an important part of developing a good hypothesis. Once a hypothesis has been thoroughly tested and no contradictions have been found, it may be incorporated into a law or theory.

A scientific law describes how an event occurs. It can be used to make accurate predictions. Scientific laws are sometimes stated in mathematical terms.

A theory describes why an event occurs. It is often an explanation of a law or set of laws. Unlike facts, both laws and theories are subject to change. As new hypotheses are tested, laws and theories are often redefined.

Models in Science

Did you ever notice the tiny parts on a model car or airplane? Even the wheels and lights are scaled to fit on these small copies. There is a mathematical ratio between the measurements of the parts on the model and those on the real object. Suppose a model airplane is built to a scale of 1 centimeter (cm) to 1 meter (m). Each centimeter on the model equals 1 m on the airplane.

There are many types of scale models. Some models are drawings, such as diagrams and maps. Often models are built from real materials and are working models of the real object. Mental models are used to imagine what something would look like. All models are plans from which real objects can be built.

Critical Thinking

Decision Making   Present the following scenario to the class: You live in a town which does not have a program for recycling its trash. You are a member of the town council and will have to vote for or against a proposal to recycle in a few weeks. Right now, you are uncertain about how to vote. Ask each class member to think about making this decision, applying each of the first four steps shown in Figure 1.7. Then have a discussion in which students contribute their information and ideas to a class list. Finally, have each student complete the last two steps in writing. Take a class vote.

Class Activity

To help students understand the idea of scale in models, ask each to measure an object's length in a book or magazine picture. Then have them find out the actual size of the object and determine the picture's scale. For example, if the object is 10 cm long in the picture and 20 m long in real life, the scale is 1 cm to 2 m. Suggest students research magazines like *Popular Science, Woodcraft, Family Circle,* and others that have scaled-down patterns in them.

 **The Living Textbook:
Physical Science Sides 1-4**

Chapter 15   Frame 02426
Earth's Magnetic Field Model (2 Frames)
Search: Step:

9

TEACH ▪ Continued

Research

Have the class work in groups. Each group can prepare an oral report with graphics on a science research group in a university, company, or government agency. They can get facts by talking to people and reading. The report doesn't need to be detailed, but it should indicate the purpose of the group and the responsibilities of the members.

EVALUATE

WrapUp

Reinforce Have students work in pairs to devise a graphic organizer to present the controlled experiment in Figure 1.5 in terms of the seven steps in Figure 1.6. For each step, the students should also list the science skills needed (pages 3 to 5).

Use Review Worksheet 1.1.

Check and Explain

1. Answers may vary. Some possible responses follow: Observe—watching rain fall; estimate—estimating the time to walk to school; measure—standing on a scale.

2. A control functions as a standard by which any change can be measured.

3. Answers may vary. Students' responses should reflect some of the decision-making steps outlined on page 9.

4. Answers may vary. Check students' art to see that symbols clearly communicate the safety message.

Themes in Science

Diversity and Unity NASA employs scientists from diverse fields to work together in space exploration. Ask students why different kinds of scientists are needed in space programs. (Diverse science knowledge is needed.) Have students find out how the following scientists are involved in aerospace: aeronautical engineers, mechanical engineers, biologists, physicians, nutritionists, meteorologists, physicists, and astronomers.

Language Arts Connection

The meanings of the Greek prefixes used in SI relate to multiples of ten. Have students find the meanings of the prefixes listed in Table 1.3. Ask students to name common words that use each prefix. (Examples: kilobyte, hectare, decade, century, millennium, millipede, microcomputer)

Science and Society *Science Communities*

In many pictures of scientists, you often see the scientist working alone in a laboratory. Nothing could be further from the truth! Science is done by people working together, not by individuals working alone.

A research group is the basic unit of a science community. Each research group is made up of people who share an interest and knowledge in the same problem. Each person works on a different piece of the scientific puzzle being studied. Group members hold discussions, plan experiments, and share their knowledge and ideas with each other, as shown in Figure 1.8.

Researchers form a worldwide scientific community based on common interests. They form a network that shares information and holds national and international meetings. They contribute to each other's research by repeating experiments and reviewing published articles.

The large scientific community includes organizations such as research institutes, industrial laboratories, university science departments, and government science agencies. These organizations provide places for scientists to form research groups. Many organizations are an important part of the scientific community. Libraries and companies that make technical equipment provide many services and tools. Museums and schools teach the public about science and prepare students for science careers. Your science class is part of the world scientific community!

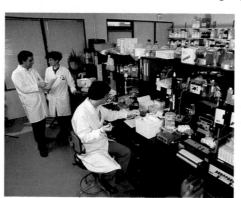

Figure 1.8 ▲
These scientists are part of a research group. Why do you think scientists work together?

Check and Explain

1. Identify three skills and explain how you used them today.

2. Explain why a control is necessary in an experiment.

3. **Apply** How would you use scientific methods to decide if a chemical plant should be located near a river?

4. **Model** Design a safety symbol to use in your school.

Portfolio

Have students reproduce Table 1.3 in their portfolios. They should add a column showing the decimal for each unit. For example: micro-, 1/1 000 000, μ, 0.000001. After you complete pages 14 and 15, have them add a column showing scientific notation for each. Students should keep this table in their portfolios.

1.2 Measuring with Scientific Units

Objectives

▶ **Identify** the base units used in the SI system.

▶ **Explain** the use of scientific notation.

▶ **Compare** volume, mass, and density.

▶ **Measure** length, mass, and temperature using SI units.

D id you know that your feet get bigger during the day? Although this may be hard to believe, it's true. When you are standing or sitting, the earth's gravity pulls blood and other body fluids down to your feet. By the end of the day, your feet are slightly bigger. People discovered this change by making and comparing measurements of foot length and width.

You describe measurements in terms of numbers and units. The system of measurement used throughout most of the world today is the *Systemé International d'Unités*, or SI. It is also called the metric system.

Several basic SI units are shown in Table 1.2. Unlike other systems of measurement, SI units are based on multiples of ten. Calculations are made by multiplying or dividing by ten. To change quantities, you simply move the decimal point. Prefixes such as *kilo-* or *centi-* indicate units larger or smaller than the basic SI units. Some of these prefixes are shown in Table 1.3.

Table 1.3 Prefixes Used in SI

Measurement	Unit	Symbol
kilo	1,000	k
hecto-	100	h
deca-	10	da
deci-	1/10	d
centi-	1/100	c
milli-	1/1,000	m
micro-	1/1 000 000	μ

▼ **ACTIVITY**

Measuring

Finger Ruler

The width of your thumb can be a unit of measure.

1. Using the width of your thumb, mark off ten units on a folded piece of paper.

2. Measure your book and your desk with this ruler.

3. Compare measurements with your classmates. Infer why this unit of measure would not be useful.

SKILLS WARMUP

Table 1.2 SI Units

Measure	Name of Unit	Symbol
Length	Meter	m
Mass	Kilogram	kg
Time	Second	s

Skills Objectives
Students should be able to:

Measure length, mass, and temperature using SI and other units of measurement.

Estimate the size of objects that would require scientific notation to write their measurements.

Compare and Contrast volume, mass, and density.

Vocabulary
meter, volume, cubic meter, liter, mass, kilogram, density, scientific notation

MOTIVATE

Skills WarmUp

To help students understand measurement and the importance of standardized units, have them do the Skills WarmUp.

Answer Students should find some variation when they compare measurements.

Misconceptions

Students often confuse mass and weight. They may think that kilograms and grams are measures of weight. Use the image of an astronaut in a weightless environment to reinforce the effect of gravity on weight. Focus on how weight decreases as gravity decreases but mass remains constant.

 The Living Textbook: Physical Science Sides 1-4

Chapter 17   Frame 03148
Metric System (2 Frames)
Search: Step:

TEACH

Enrich

Ancient people used the *cubit* as the basic unit of length. A cubit is the distance from the tip of the elbow to the tip of the middle finger. Have students determine the length of a cubit in centimeters, using their own forearms as the cubit standard. Ask them why this unit of measurement would not work as a scientific unit of measurement. (Forearms are not all the same length.)

Skills Development

Make Models Have students make paper models representing the volume of a cubic meter, cubic centimeter, liter, or milliliter. Students can construct paper cubes by cutting and folding strips of paper. They can also cut paper cartons or cups to make their models.

**The Living Textbook:
Physical Science Sides 1-4**

Chapter 1   Frame 00586
Kilometer Road Sign (1 Frame)
Search:

**The Living Textbook:
Physical Science Sides 1-4**

Chapter 1   Frame 00624
Meniscus of Mercury (1 Frame)
Search:

STS Connection

Explain to students that the standard meter was first introduced as a unit of measure in France in 1799. (It was supposed to equal one ten-millionth of the distance from the North Pole to the equator, but the original measurements were not quite accurate.) The length of the standard meter was engraved on a metal bar and kept at the International Bureau of Weights and Measures near Paris. As scientists developed the need for more precise measurements, a more precise standard had to be developed. Now the standard meter is based on the wavelength of light given off by krypton-86. One meter equals 1,650,763.73 wavelengths of radiation, which corresponds to the electromagnetic spectrum of krypton-86.

Length

The basic SI unit of length is the **meter** (m). One meter is about the distance between a doorknob and the floor. The SI measuring tool that you'll be using in class is a metric ruler.

A ruler is divided into smaller units. Notice that the metric ruler in Figure 1.9 is marked in units called centimeters (cm). A centimeter is 1/100 of a meter. Your little finger is about 1 cm wide. Each centimeter is divided into ten smaller units called millimeters (mm). A dime is about 1 mm thick.

To measure long distances, units of 1,000 meters are used. These units are called kilometers (km). If you walk or run two and one-half times around a stadium track, you travel about 1 km.

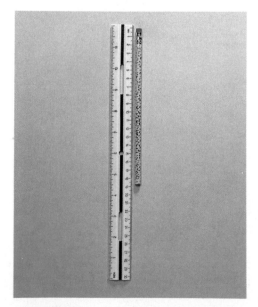

Figure 1.9 ▲
You will measure many distances that are less than 1 meter. The numbers on the right of this ruler represent centimeters.

Volume

Take a deep breath. As your lungs fill with air, you can feel your chest expand. This change in your lung size is an increase in **volume**. Volume is the amount of space that something occupies.

The SI unit of volume is the **cubic meter** (m^3). One cubic meter is the space occupied by a box 1 m × 1 m × 1 m. To measure smaller volumes, the cubic centimeter (cm^3) is used. A convenient unit for everyday use is the **liter** (L). In the United States, soft drinks come in plastic 2-L containers.

A graduated cylinder is used to measure liquid volumes. Look at the cylinder in Figure 1.10. The units marked on its scale are milliliters (mL). There are about 20 drops of water in each 1 mL.

In a graduated cylinder, the liquid surface curves downward to form a *meniscus* (mehn IHS kus). To measure liquid volume accurately, read the scale at eye level at the lowest part of the meniscus.

Figure 1.10 ▲
You can measure liquid volume with a graduated cylinder. To read, observe the surface level of the liquid at eye level.

Integrating the Sciences

Astronomy The mass of an astronaut is the same on the moon as it is on the earth. However, weight is dramatically different. Weight is affected by the force of gravity. The gravitational force is different for each of the bodies in the solar system. Have students compare the force of gravity on the earth to the force of gravity on the moon. (Acceleration due to gravity on the earth is 9.8 m/s². Acceleration due to gravity on the moon is about 1.57 m/s².)

Mass and Weight

Did you know that an object weighs slightly less on top of a mountain than it does at sea level? That's because an object's weight depends upon the force of gravity. Because gravity is measurably less on a mountain top, things weigh less there.

Although the weight of an object varies with the force of gravity, its **mass** does not. Mass is the amount of matter that an object contains. An object's mass always stays the same no matter where the measurement is taken.

The basic SI unit of mass is the **kilogram** (kg). In the laboratory, you will use a unit equal to 1/1,000 kg, called a gram (g). The cap of a pen has a mass of about 1 g.

To determine an object's mass, you use a tool called a balance, similar to the one shown in Figure 1.11. A balance allows you to compare an unknown mass with a known mass. When the arm of the balance is level, the two masses are equal.

Figure 1.11 ▲
The kilogram is the basic unit for mass in the metric system. What unit would you use to measure the mass of an eraser? ①

Density

Mass is related to another important quantity called **density**. Density tells you how much matter is packed into a given volume. The units of density are grams of matter per cubic centimeter (g/cm³). For example, steel has a density of 7.8 g/cm³. This means that each cm³ of steel contains 7.8 g of matter. Oak wood has a density of 0.9 g/cm³. This means that each cubic centimeter of oak contains 0.9 grams of matter.

Density is a characteristic that can be used to identify a substance. Also, an object's density determines whether it will float or sink in water. Water has a density of 1 g/cm³. Materials with densities greater than 1 g/cm³ will sink in water. Materials with densities less than 1 g/cm³ will float. What do you think happens when an object with a density of 1 g/cm³ is put into water? ②

Figure 1.12 ▲
The number of cc, or mL, the water level rises is equal to the volume of the submerged object, which has an irregular shape.

Class Activity

Have students practice using a balance to find the mass of several objects. Provide balances. Collect two equal-size paper boxes with lids, two oranges, a textbook, and a paper clip. Each box must be large enough to hold the textbook. Prepare one mystery box by placing tissue paper and an orange in one of the boxes. Have students weigh the other paper box, a textbook, a paper clip, and a small orange. Then have them weigh the mystery box and identify the object inside the box.

Skills Development

Predict Have students predict the volume of objects with various shapes, then test their predictions using displacement.

Reteach

As a visual and tactile reference, inform students that a brick has a mass of about 1 kilogram and a paper clip has a mass of about 1 gram.

Answers to In-Text Questions

① Grams would be used to measure the mass of an eraser.

② The object will neither sink nor float because only water has a density of 1 g/cm³.

**The Living Textbook:
Physical Science Sides 1-4**

Chapter 1   Frame 00597
Various Balances (4 Frames)
Search: Step:

**The Living Textbook:
Physical Science Side 2**

Chapter 19   Frame 03447
Measuring Densities (Movie)
Search: Play:

TEACH ▪ *Continued*

Research

Have students use reference materials to research the major scientists in thermometry—the science of measuring temperature: Galileo, Daniel Gabriel Fahrenheit, Anders Celsius, and William Thomson (Lord Kelvin). They can put their information on a timeline that shows the historic development of thermometers.

Enrich

Students can relate scientific notation to the math concept of exponents, or "powers" of numbers. Explain that 1.0×10^8 means that the 10 is raised to the eighth power and then multiplied by 1. Ten to the eighth power is $10 \times 10 \times 10 \times 10 \times 10 \times 10 \times 10 \times 10$, or 100 000 000, and is written 10^8. So 1.0×10^8 in standard form is 100 000 000. Likewise, 2.0×10^8 is 10 to the eighth power multiplied by 2. The exponent indicates the number of places to move the decimal point when you write the number in standard form. For example, to write the number 5.34×10^6 in standard form, move the decimal point 6 places to the right; it is written 5 340 000.

Answer to Link

Mercury	5.8×10^7 km
Venus	1.08×10^8 km
Earth	1.50×10^8 km
Mars	2.28×10^8 km
Jupiter	7.78×10^8 km
Saturn	1.426×10^9 km
Uranus	2.87×10^9 km
Neptune	4.497×10^9 km
Pluto	5.914×10^9 km

All of these numbers are very big. Scientific notation can be used to express very small numbers as well.

The Living Textbook:
Physical Science Sides 1-4

Chapter 1   Frame 00590
Various Thermometers (5 Frames)
Search: Step:

STS Connection

Thermometers work because physical characteristics, such as the volume and length of certain substances, change as temperature changes. For example, a standard liquid thermometer works because the liquid expands and contracts with changes in temperature. Have students investigate other types of thermometers, such as bimetallic and electrical thermometers, and explain how they work.

Integrating the Sciences

Earth Science Time is measured in terms of the earth's rotation. One hour equals 15° of rotation. Discuss standardized time—its origin, its use, and worldwide time differences.

Figure 1.13 ▲
On the Celsius scale, water freezes at 0°C and boils at 100°C.

Astronomy
L I N K

Large quantities are often described as "astronomical." This description is related to the huge distances between objects in space.

1. Find the distance of each of the planets in the solar system from the sun, in km.

2. Write each number in scientific notation.

What do all of these numbers have in common?

A C T I V I T Y

Temperature

When you are healthy, your normal body temperature is about 98.6 degrees Fahrenheit (F). On the Celsius scale, which is used internationally and in science, your normal body temperature measures about 37 degrees Celsius, or 37°C.

Temperature is measured with a thermometer like the one in Figure 1.13. Most classroom thermometers are made from a thin glass tube that is filled with a liquid. As the liquid heats up, it expands and moves up the tube. The sides of the glass tube are marked in Celsius degrees. Two important reference marks on the Celsius scale are the boiling point of water, which is 100°C, and the freezing point of water, which is 0°C.

Time

The basic SI unit of time is the second (s). Amounts of time less than one second can be measured in milliseconds (ms). One ms is 1/1,000 of one s. You probably know other units of time, such as minutes, hours, days, and years. There are 60 seconds in a minute, 60 minutes in an hour, 24 hours in a day, and 365 days in a year. These units have been adopted into the SI system and unlike other units are not based on multiples of ten.

Scientific Notation

Suppose you want to write the distance between two stars. It might be 20 000 000 000 000 km. The diameter of a microscopic organism could be about 0.000001 m. Scientists often work with very long numbers. To save time, they write these numbers in **scientific notation**.

In scientific notation, a number is written as the product of two numbers. The first number is between 1 and 10. The second number is 10 and has a small number, called an exponent (ehks POHN uhnt), written above it. For example, 20 000 000 000 000 km is written 2×10^{13} km. The exponent tells you that the decimal point is really 13 places to the right of the 2.

How would you write 0.000001 m? In scientific notation, the diameter of the organism would be written 1×10^{-6} m. The negative exponent (–6) tells you how many decimal places there are to the *left* of the 1.

Integrating the Sciences

Astronomy Tell students that astronomers must estimate and measure the vast distances of space. To do so they use the light-year, a unit based on time and distance. One light-year equals the distance light travels through a vacuum in one year, or about 9.46 trillion km. The star nearest the earth (besides the sun) is 4.3 light-years away. Ask students to calculate this distance in kilometers. (About 40.678 trillion km) Then have them write their answers using scientific notation. (4.0678×10^{13} km)

Unit Calculations and Measurements

When you do calculations involving measurements, you must keep careful track of the units. You also need to check your answers to be sure they make sense. This process is so important that it has been given the name *dimensional analysis*.

Sometimes you need to convert one unit to another. A fraction, called a conversion factor, shows how one kind of unit relates to another. The measurement on the top of the conversion factor equals the measurement on the bottom. For example, 100 cm equals 1 m. You can write: 1 m/100 cm or 100 cm/1 m.

To convert a measurement, you multiply the measurement by the appropriate conversion factor. For example, suppose your friend's height is 170 cm. How many meters is 170 cm?

First write down the value given. Write the conversion factor with the unit you want on top. Then multiply:

Sample Problems

1. How do you write 2.79×10^{-4} mm as a standard numeral?

   Plan The negative sign on the exponent means you move the decimal point to the left.

   Gather Data The number is 2.79×10^{-4} mm.

   Solve Move the decimal point four spaces to the left. Compare your result to the correct answer: 0.000279 mm.

2. How would you convert 250 mL into L?

   Plan The conversion factor must relate to both the units mL and L.

   Gather Data 250 mL = ? L   1,000 mL = 1 L

   Solve Arrange the conversion factor with L on top. Cancel like units. Then multiply.

   $$250 \text{ mL} \times \frac{1 \text{ L}}{1,000 \text{ mL}} = \frac{250 \text{ L}}{1,000} = 0.25 \text{ L}$$

Practice Problems

1. Write the following measurements in scientific notation:

   a. 1 000 000 000 000 000 000 000 km

   b. 45 000 000 000 L

   c. 0.000000000000000001 mm

   d. 0.000000000372 mg

2. Write the following measurements as standard numerals:

   a. 9.46×10^{12} km

   b. 3×10^{10} cm/sec

   c. 1.5×10^{-5} mm

   d. 2.6×10^{-11} m

3. Do the following unit conversions:

   a. 10 m to km

   b. 2,000 g to kg

   c. 10 kg to mg

Apply

Have students use the SI units of measure to determine whether any parts of the following items are standardized: pencils, dollar bills, paperback books, size 7 shoes, soda cans, hairbrushes, and paper clips. Ask them to explain why some parts of some items may be standardized while others may not. (Exact sizes are more important with some items than with others.)

EVALUATE

WrapUp

Reinforce Have students work in cooperative groups. Ask groups to find in the classroom an object or event that would be measured by each unit listed on Table 1.2 on page 11.

Use Review Worksheet 1.2.

Check and Explain

1. Length, meter; volume, cubic meter; mass, kilogram; density, grams per cubic centimeter; temperature, degrees Celsius; time, seconds; amounts that are larger or smaller are based on multiples of ten.

2. Scientists and mathematicians often work with very large or very small numbers. Scientific notation saves time in science and math calculations.

3. Density is the amount of matter within a given volume of space. To compute density, you need measurements for mass and volume.

4. Answers may vary. Check to see that students have chosen appropriate tools to measure their objects. Room temperature should be recorded in degrees Celsius.

✦ STS Connection

Clothing design is not the only area in which measurements of the human body are important. Ergonomics, or human-factor engineering, also makes use of such measurements to design products such as office furniture, cameras, and space suits. Ergonomics is the study of humans and their work environments in order to design tools and workplaces that are efficient and suited to people's needs. Ergonomics combines the work of several scientific disciplines and technologies, including anatomy, psychology, engineering, and physics. Have students find examples of how ergonomics has been used in the design of products familiar to them.

170 cm × 1 m/100 cm. The next step is to cancel out like units, in this case, cm. The equation will be 170×1 m/100. The last step is to multiply and divide. The answer is 1.7 m. Work through the practice problems to better understand how to use dimensional analysis and conversion factors.

**Table 1.4
Standard Garment Sizes**

Size (cm)			
Teen Boys	**Small**	**Medium**	**Large**
Chest	81	89	93
Waist	69	74	76
Hip	83	90	94
Neck	35	37	38
Sleeve	74	79	81

Size (cm)			
Misses	**Small**	**Medium**	**Large**
Bust	83	91	102
Waist	64	71	81
Hip	88	97	107
Back Waist	41	42	43

▣ Science and You   *Designer Fit*

Do you like to shop in a mall? All the items you see there were designed and constructed to exact measurements. Exact measurements make it possible for industries to use standardized sizes. Designers use standard sizes so that manufacturing and using products will be easier.

The diameter of the jack for the headphone in your personal stereo is standardized. Any brand of headphone can be plugged into your personal stereo and it will work. Any brand of AA dry cells will work in your personal stereo because dry cells are standardized also.

When you shop for clothing, you know that certain sizes will fit you because clothing sizes are standardized. Table 1.4 shows the standard for determining clothing sizes for boys and misses. Clothing sizes are based on data collected about human body measurements. The data are based on a certain range of sizes for most of the population. The international clothing industry uses this information to set size standards.

Check and Explain

1. Identify the basic SI units for length, volume, mass, density, temperature, and time. How are amounts much larger and smaller than the basic units named?

2. Explain why scientific notation is used in science and math.

3. **Compare** Explain how volume, mass, and density relate to each other.

4. **Measure** Using the appropriate SI measuring tools and SI units, measure the length and mass of a classroom object and the room temperature.

Math Connection

Have students use a compass and a protractor to determine how the exact portion of a circle is shown on a circle graph when the fractions used are 1/3, 1/6, 1/4, and 1/8. (120°, 60°, 90°, 45°) Have students draw the circle graph.

1.3 Graphing

Objectives

▶ **Describe** three types of graphs.

▶ **Identify** the parts of a line graph.

▶ **Analyze** data and plan a graph.

▶ **Classify** data by how it can be graphed.

▼ **ACTIVITY**

Classifying

Graph of Choice

Think about all the different kinds of data that you could collect about birds or some other kind of living thing. What data do you think could be shown in a graph? What data couldn't be shown in a graph?

SKILLS WARMUP

You've probably seen many different kinds of graphs in newspapers, magazines, and even on television news reports. What is a graph? Basically a graph is a picture of data. You can think of a graph as a picture of a data table. Some data tables contain a lot of information. It may take some time to figure out what all the data means. However, a graph makes it easier to understand this information.

Graphs show numerical data in diagram form. Graphs are useful tools for presenting information. They make it easy to identify trends and patterns quickly, sometimes at a glance.

Kinds of Graphs

Three kinds of graphs are circle graphs, bar graphs, and line graphs. All three types let you compare numerical data. Each kind of graph, however, shows numerical data in a different way. Each is best suited for showing a certain kind of data.

Circle Graphs If you think of how a pie is cut into pieces, you have a mental model of a circle graph. A circle graph is a circle divided into parts. This kind of graph makes it easy to compare how one part relates to the whole amount. You can see quickly what fraction, percentage, share, or proportion of the whole each part represents.

① Look at the circle graph in Figure 1.14. At a glance, you can tell what percent of oxygen gas is present in air. How does the percentage of oxygen gas compare to the percentage of nitrogen gas? You can use a series of circle graphs to show change over time.

Gases in Air

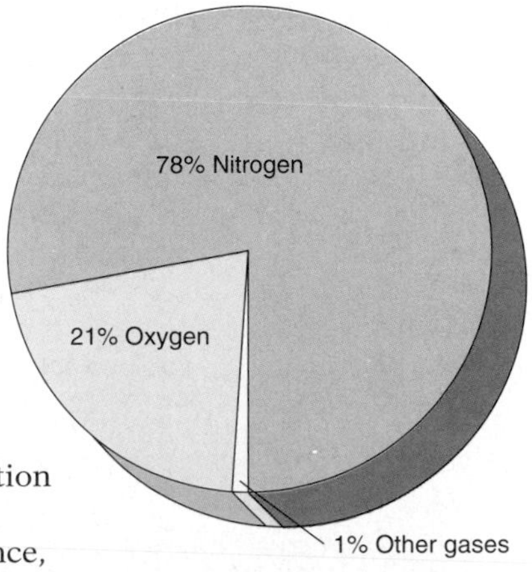

78% Nitrogen

21% Oxygen

1% Other gases

Figure 1.14 ▲
What two gases make up most of the air? Which of the two is there more of? ②

Section Objectives
For a list of section objectives, see the Student Edition page.

Skills Objectives
Students should be able to:

Classify data by how it can be graphed.

Interpret Data from data tables.

Make Graphs using data from data tables.

Classify graphs based on how they present data.

MOTIVATE

Skills WarmUp
To help students understand the kind of data that can be graphed, have them do the Skills WarmUp.
Answer Answers may vary, but students could graph data to compare species' size, life span, distribution, and so on. Data on appearance and behavior can't be graphed.

Prior Knowledge
Gauge how much students know about graphing by asking, Where have you seen graphs used before? How are they used?

Portfolio
Have students collect examples of bar graphs, circle graphs, and line graphs from magazines or newspapers. Have students write a brief explanation on how to interpret each graph. After students read *Science and Society* on page 20, have them examine the graphs in their portfolios to determine if any are misleading.

Answers to In-Text Questions

① There is about 3.5 times more nitrogen than oxygen.

② Nitrogen and oxygen; there is more nitrogen.

Apply

Have students collect data on the number of male and female graduates from their school over the last six years. Have them make a bar graph to show both groups. Ask students to discuss the changes that occurred in both groups over six years.

SkillBuilder

Answers

1. Circle graph; the data are proportions of a whole.

2. Bar graph; the data are comparable quantities that change over time.

3. *x*-axis: years 1910–1990 at twenty-year intervals; *y*-axis: population figures 0–300,000 at intervals of 100,000.

The reports should explain the usefulness of circle graphs for showing parts or proportions of a whole, such as time spent at various daily activities, and the usefulness of bar graphs for comparing quantities, such as the number of people in various age groups.

Ancillary Options

If you are using the blackline masters from *Multiculturalism in Mathematics, Science, and Technology*, have students read about Celestino Beltran on pages 31 and 32. Complete pages 32 through 34.

Answer to In-Text Question

① **Washington, DC; Fairbanks, AK**

STS Connection

Point out that energy companies sometimes give consumers information about monthly energy consumption in the form of a bar graph. Ask students what advantages bar graphs have over tables for showing that type of information. (Easy to read, easy to compare the amount of energy used from month to month and the cost to the consumer)

Geography Connection

Have students locate the cities listed in the bar graph on a map or globe. Ask them to hypothesize about the reasons for the differences in highest annual temperatures. (Latitude, climate zones)

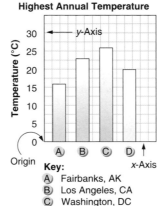

Highest Annual Temperature

Key:
Ⓐ Fairbanks, AK
Ⓑ Los Angeles, CA
Ⓒ Washington, DC
Ⓓ Portland, ME

Figure 1.15 ▲
Which city has the highest yearly temperature? Which has the lowest? ①

Bar Graphs The wide columns on a bar graph are used to compare measurements, such as weight, height, and length, about groups or individual items. Bar graphs also let you compare quantities and change over time. The bar graph in Figure 1.15 shows the highest yearly temperatures in four North American cities. You can easily see which city is the hottest and which is the coolest.

Notice that the bar graph is drawn on graph paper. At the left side of the graph, a scale shows temperature in degrees Celsius. The label for each column is shown at the bottom of the graph. The labels on this graph are letters keyed to the names of the cities.

When you make a bar graph, you need to decide on the scale by looking at the highest and lowest numbers in your data. On this graph, the scale ranges from 0°C to 30°C. Notice that the scale includes values larger than the hottest temperature. Also, each numbered division is equal to 5°C. All bar graphs have a scale and equally numbered divisions.

SkillBuilder *Making a Graph*

What Kind of Graph

When you make a graph, the first step is to determine what kind of graph to use. What you want to show and the kind of data you have determine which graph is the most useful. A circle graph is useful for showing parts or proportions of a whole. A bar graph is useful for comparing quantities and change over time. A line graph is good for comparing two sets of data or for showing changes and trends over time. Study the data tables at the right before answering the following questions.

1. What kind of graph would you use for the data table showing the composition of concrete? Explain your choice.

2. What kind of graph would you use for the data table showing U.S. population changes since 1910? Explain your choice.

3. Identify the scales you would use on the *x*- and *y*-axes on your graph for question 2.

Composition of Concrete	
Substance	**Percentage**
Sand	33
Aggregate	43
Cement	16
Water	8

U.S. Population by Year	
Year	**Population**
1910	91,972,266
1930	122,775,046
1950	150,697,361
1970	203,302,031
1990	248,709,873

4. Make a graph for each data table shown. For each graph, use labels, scales, and titles as needed.

Write a short report on the two types of graphs you have prepared. Give examples of other possible data that could be shown with each type of graph.

Line Graphs One of the most useful graphs is the line graph. Line graphs are useful for comparing sets of numerical data. They also show change and patterns, or trends in data. This type of graph can help you answer "if-then" questions by showing how one variable changes in relation to another. One common use of a line graph is to show how a variable changes over time.

Look at the growth data for the twins Rosa and Raul in Table 1.5. The variable in the first column is age in years. The second and third columns list height measurements in centimeters taken each year from age 5 to age 18. A graph of the data in Table 1.5 shows how the height of the twins Rosa and Raul changed over the years.

Look at the graph in Figure 1.16. The horizontal line on the bottom of the graph is the *x*-axis. The vertical line is the *y*-axis. The point where the *x*- and *y*-axes meet is called the origin. To make a graph of Table 1.5, use the years from 5 to 18 as *x*-values. Mark a scale showing height in centimeters on the *y*-axis.

To build a line graph of each data set, you place a dot on the graph for each pair of *x*- and *y*-values. For example, for Rosa's data set, the first *x*-value is age 5, and the *y*-value is 108 cm. The dot for this data is placed directly across from the *y*-value and directly above the *x*-value.

When all the data are presented as points on the graph, draw a line to connect all the points as shown in Figure 1.16. This line is called a *curve*. Notice that the curve shows the growth pattern of Rosa to her adult height. Raul's data are added to the graph in the same way. Study the graph. You can see that between certain years Rosa or Raul grew much more rapidly than between other years.

Table 1.5   Growth Data

Age (Years)	Height (cm) Rosa	Raul
5	108	120
6	112	123
7	116	126
8	121	129
9	126	134
10	131	139
11	138	143
12	145	147
13	150	151
14	155	155
15	158	159
16	161	168
17	163	176
18	164	183

Growth Data for Raul and Rosa

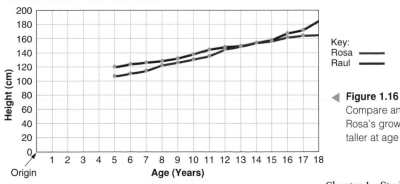

Key:
Rosa —
Raul —

◀ **Figure 1.16**
Compare and contrast Raul and Rosa's growth patterns. Who is taller at age 8? At age 14? ②

TEACH ▪ Continued

Critical Thinking

Evaluate Sources Find graphs that present similar data from sources with different purposes or viewpoints, such as graphs showing airplane fatalities from groups wanting tighter airline regulations and from the airline companies. Have students consider the reliability of the graphs and specify reasons for their judgements on the credibility of the sources.

EVALUATE

WrapUp

Portfolio Ask students to bring in examples of graphs from newspapers and magazines. Have small groups discuss why each type of graph was used for the data it shows.

Use Review Worksheet 1.3.

Check and Explain

1. Circle graphs—relate a part of something to its whole; bar graphs—compare measurements, quantities, and changes over time; line graphs—compare two or more sets of numerical data and show changes, patterns, trends.

2. Line graphs should include labels for the *x*- and *y*-axes. Students' tables should be organized so that all the data for the *x*-axis are grouped in one column and data for the *y*-axis are in another column.

3. Answers may vary; students will probably say that the scale will show a range from −5° or −10° to +20°, and the equal divisions will be 5°.

4. Circle graph

Answers to In-Text Questions
① **The bottom graph**
② **The top graph**
③ **The top graph**

Language Arts Connection

Have students write directions for how to read a bar graph critically. Have students imagine that the reader of these directions has no experience with reading or understanding bar graphs. Remind students to organize their information as a logical series of steps.

Social Studies Connection

Graphs are often used to present information relevant to the social sciences. Ask students which type of graph they would use to show each of the following kinds of data: world population from 1500 to the present (Bar or line); the populations of the world's five largest cities (Bar); the proportion of the world's population that speaks each of the world's major languages (Circle).

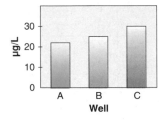
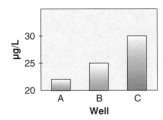

Figure 1.17 ▲
Always study data carefully. Information displayed in graphs and tables may be misleading.

Science and Society *Take a Second Look*

You often see graphs in newspapers, in magazines, and on television. For example, if you were reading a magazine article that compared how many people quit smoking cigarettes each year since 1975, you would probably find a graph. Graphs are an effective tool for showing trends and patterns at a glance. If the same information were presented in a data table, it would take more time to analyze it and you still might not see the pattern.

Although graphs are easy to understand, they can sometimes give you a false impression. Graphs are often used to sway public opinion. Look at the pair of bar graphs in Figure 1.17. Both graphs show the amount of a chemical found in the water samples from three wells. The same information was put on two different graphs. Which graph gives you the impression that the contamination in well B is twice that of well A? ①

Study the graphs carefully. Compare the scales on the *y*-axis of both graphs. The graph on the top shows a spread of 30 µg/L. The graph on the bottom shows a spread of only 10 µg/L. Yet both graphs show exactly the same data! Which graph is the most effective for comparing the chemical in the three wells? Which ② graph gives the most realistic picture of the chemical in the wells? ③

Check and Explain

1. Name three kinds of graphs. Describe each kind.

2. Make a drawing of a simple line graph and label its parts. Show your data in a table.

3. **Analyze** The highest annual temperatures of four cities are shown in a bar graph on page 18. If the lowest temperatures are −5, 15, 18, −3 degrees Celsius, what scale would you use on the bar graph? What would be the equal divisions?

4. **Classify** What kind of graph would you use if you wanted to show what proportion of your time you spent sleeping, eating, going to school, working, playing, and watching television? Give reasons for your choice.

SECTION

1.4

1.4 Science Tools and Technology

Objectives

▶ **Describe** the connections in science.

▶ **Give examples** of technological tools.

▶ **Compare** science and technology.

▶ **Infer** why tools influence science research.

▼ **ACTIVITY**

Observing

School Tools

Identify three examples of tools used in your classroom. Explain how each is used. Are the tools used for everyday activities, scientific investigations, or both?

SKILLS WARMUP

Have you ever wondered what your fingernails are made of? Why a light turns on when you flip a switch? How television and radio signals reach your home? These questions all involve matter and energy. Physical science is the study of matter and energy and how they affect each other. Matter is the "stuff" that everything in the universe is made of. Energy causes matter to interact.

Connections in Science

The study of matter can be identified as two connected sciences, chemistry and physics. Chemistry is the study of matter and its changes. Chemistry can explain why a cake rises, how acid rain forms, and how your body uses food. Physics is the study of energy and how it affects matter. Physics can explain how a bicycle and telephone work, how birds and airplanes fly, and why stars shine.

Science has many divisions. For example, biochemistry is the chemistry of living things. The study of energy and matter in stars is called astrophysics. Geophysics is the physics of the earth, its atmosphere, and its oceans.

Science research explores why and how things happen in the natural world. Technology is the use of science principles to help solve practical problems. Sometimes technology is referred to as *applied science*. Engineering is an applied science based on physical science principles. It focuses on using and developing technology.

Figure 1.18 ▲
The *Gossamer Albatross* is a human-powered airplane. Which science can explain its ability to fly? ④

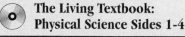

TEACH

Explore Visually

Have students study the photographs on pages 22 and 23. Ask:

▶ Which of these tools have you used? (Many students will have used a computer.)

▶ What does a wind tunnel help engineers study? (The effect of moving fluids on designs and materials)

▶ What do all these tools have in common? (They greatly increase a scientist's ability to observe objects or systems.)

▶ What is a common purpose of all these instruments? (They study something that can't be examined with the unaided eye.)

▶ What do the spectroscope, the gas chromotograph, and the electrophoresis gel have in common? (They are used to identify an unknown.)

The Living Textbook: Physical Science Side 3

Chapter 29   Frame 15011
Atomic Spectra (Movie)
Search: Play:

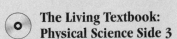

The Living Textbook: Physical Science Side 3

Chapter 48   Frame 38566
Computer Graphics (Movie)
Search: Play:

STS Connection

The spectroscope is a spectrometer to which a telescope has been attached. A spectrometer is a tool that divides light given off by a substance into a spectrum and displays it for study. When a substance is heated to a high temperature, the atoms or molecules of that substance produce a spectrum. Because each substance has its own unique spectrum, technicians can use spectrometers to identify unknown substances. Ask students to find ways that spectrometers are used. (To identify a substance that is polluting a river, to determine the composition of an unknown metal found at an archaeological site, and to find out what kind of matter is contained in a planet or star.)

Tools and Technology

Because the physical world includes objects you can see or touch, many physical science discoveries were made using simple tools. For example, the speed of light was measured with rotating mirrors on two mountaintops. The newest physical science research often involves things that are too far away or too small to be detected by the unaided senses. Some of the tools that make it possible to observe these things are shown here.

Computer
◀ The rapid calculations done by a computer can help people identify things that are too tiny or too distant to see. A computer can help a chemist see the structure of a chemical. Physicists can test their hypotheses with computer models. Engineers use computers to test designs.

Spectroscope
◀ The spectrogram produced by a spectroscope indicates what kind of matter makes up a star or other object in space.

Particle Accelerator ▶
To study how matter and energy interact, physicists "shoot" tiny particles of matter at other particles in a particle accelerator. When the tiny particles hit the other particles at high speed, energy is transferred and new particles may be created.

Integrating the Sciences

Biology Students may be interested to know more about how electrophoresis works. Electrophoresis relies on the ability of biological molecules to carry electric charges that are negative or positive. When the molecules are placed in a solution that conducts electricity, the negative-ly charged molecules move in one direction and the positively charged molecules move in another. The molecules also move at different rates so that eventually they separate into bands of pure substances. The pure substances are used for medical and chemical purposes.

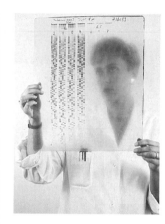

Electrophoresis Gel ▶

Biochemists use electricity to separate the proteins and nucleic acids that make up living things. A sample of a living material is placed on an electrophoresis (ee LEHK troh for EE sihs) gel layer. The gel layer is put into a liquid that conducts electricity.

As electricity separates the proteins or nucleic acids, a pattern of bands forms. Pure substances can be isolated from a single band, or the band pattern can be used for identification.

Gas Chromatograph ▲

A gas chromatograph (kroh MA toh GRAF) is an important tool for chemists. An unknown substance is injected into a heating chamber. The different kinds of matter in the substance vaporize, one by one, and travel through the machine's tubing. As it travels, each substance "peaks" on an attached recorder or computer. The height of the peaks is used to identify each substance.

Radiotelescope

◀ Many objects in the universe send out radio waves. Instruments called radio telescopes receive these waves. Astrophysicists use radiotelescopes to "listen" to outer space.

Wind Tunnel ▶

To study the effects of moving fluids such as water or air, high winds are sent through a wind tunnel. Engineers use wind tunnels to test different designs and materials under extreme conditions.

TEACH ▪ Continued

Portfolio

Ask students to imagine they are stranded in the jungle, on a deserted tropical island, on a snowy mountain top, or in some other isolated place. Have them write a journal entry describing how knowledge from the various branches of science would help them to survive. Ask them to give specific examples. Have students keep the journals in their portfolios.

Career Corner

Research Have students research one of the professions. Then ask them to explain in what way scientific knowledge and skills are used to do the work of that profession. Ask them to give specific examples. Have students use reference materials. Encourage them to interview a person in that profession, if possible.

**The Living Textbook:
Physical Science Side 4**

Chapter 10   Frame 01823
Chopping Wood with an Axe (1 Frame)
Search:

**The Living Textbook:
Physical Science Side 4**

Chapter 22   Frame 07588
Purifying Gold (Movie)
Search: Play:

STS Connection

Physical science has many specialized branches, such as astrophysics, geophysics, and physical chemistry. Have students learn about these and other branches of physical science and the careers related to each branch. Have them present their information in the form of a chart like the one shown on this page.

Career Corner

What Careers Use Scientific Skills and Knowledge?

Many different careers require some use of science. Artists and musicians, as well as building contractors and marine biologists, use science knowledge and skills in their work. The table at the right shows some branches of science and several careers related to each branch.

Each major branch of science includes a large body of knowledge. The main sciences can be divided into more specialized branches. For example, mechanics is a specialized branch of physics. Physiology is a specialized branch of biology.

Careers in Science		
Branch	**Study**	**Careers**
Biology	All living things	Animal trainer, environmental specialist, food scientist
Chemistry	Different substances and the changes they undergo	Chef, food scientist, chemist, materials scientist
Mechanics	The action of forces on objects	Mechanical engineer, machinist, construction worker
Physics	Properties, changes, and interactions of matter and energy	Electrician, civil engineer, materials scientist, physical therapist
Physiology	Functions and life processes of living things	P.E. teacher, optician, physician, physical therapist

Science and Technology *Prehistoric Tech*

When you hear the word *technology*, you probably think of computers, lasers, compact disks, or other modern inventions. Actually, technology based on the principles of physical science is ancient. The stone tools made about 1.9 million years ago in Africa are one example.

The technology in a stone ax is a simple machine called a wedge. Because a wedge is wide at one end and narrow at the other, it can be used to exert a strong force on a small area. The force applied to a wedge is transferred to the narrow edge. As a result, an ax cuts easily through many materials.

The development of this ancient technology probably started with an observation. Ancient people may have observed that wedge-shaped stones cut their feet or foot coverings. When they needed to cut something, they probably remembered the sharp stones and used one for cutting. When natural wedge-shaped stones

◄ **Figure 1.19**
A gold ring of Pharaoh Ramses II (1290-1224 B.C.), and a stone cutting tool made by *Homo habilis.*

were not available, they experimented with making their own. Perhaps they discovered how to make an even better cutting tool, like the one in Figure 1.19. A stone hand ax like this one, made by *Homo habilis,* could cut through wood, animal hide, or bone.

Between 1.6 and 0.4 million years ago, people learned to control and use fire for cooking and heating. Many other technologies became possible once fire was controlled. Metals such as iron, silver, and gold could be obtained by heating rocks that contained ores. Bowls made of clay could be fired into waterproof containers and used as cooking pots. Precious metals could be worked into jewelry.

Check and Explain

1. What are two connected sciences that study matter and energy? Give examples of topics studied by each science.

2. Describe a tool used by scientists to study something too far away to see. Describe a tool used to study something too tiny to see.

3. **Compare** How are science and technology different? How are they alike?

4. **Infer** How might the kind of tools available influence science research?

Time 60 minutes   **Group** pairs

Materials

30 jumbo plastic straws

15 small boxes

45 wooden depressors

assorted small items (rice grains, staples, thread)

hole punch

scissors

glue

needles

toothpicks

masking tape

Analysis

1. After moving the balance, the straw might have to be rebalanced and recalibrated.

2. Examples of variables: Actual mass of disks might not be 50 mg, or the balance does not move freely.

Conclusion

Students should demonstrate an understanding of calibration and of the process of finding the mass of an unknown by comparing it to a known mass. The discussion of data should be consistent with the students' actual results.

Extension

An object that is too heavy would overload the balance and tip it. Balances must be designed to measure within a specific range, and be able to withstand the weight of objects above their range.

Prelab Discussion

Have students read the entire activity. Discuss the following points before beginning:

▶ Remind students that the slits cut in the box should be the same distance apart.

▶ Students will need to find an approximate balance point before sticking the pin through the straw.

▶ A broomstraw may be substituted for the toothpick.

▶ If necessary, students can put a groove in each tongue depressor to stabilize the needle.

Activity 1 *How do you make a microbalance?*

Skills   Measure; Model; Collect Data

Task 1   Prelab Prep

1. Collect the following items: hole punch, 2 jumbo plastic straws, single-size cereal box (or other small box), scissors, 3 wooden depressors, toothpick, glue, needle, masking tape, and pencil.

2. Gather small items to test your scale, such as a blade of grass, rice grain, staple, or thread.

3. Prepare your "disk-units" for measuring mass. Use the hole punch to make 10 to 15 plastic disks from one straw. These are your standard masses (50 mg each).

Task 2   Data Record

1. Prepare a three-column data table. Label the columns as follows: *Object*, *Mass in Disks*, *Mass in Milligrams*.

2. You will measure and record the mass of each item in disk-units. Then, convert and record the mass of each item in milligrams.

Task 3   Procedure

1. Close the top of the cereal box. Cut out the front of the box. **Caution! Handle sharp objects with care.** It should look like a miniature shoebox without a lid. Make two parallel cuts about 0.5 cm deep in each long edge of the box. Fit one depressor into each of these cuts as shown in the figure at right.

2. Cut off a small section of straw no longer than $3/4$ the width of the box. Cut a section out of one end to form a small scoop.

3. Glue a portion of the toothpick into the other end of the straw. The toothpick will act as a pointer on the scale as shown in the figure at the right.

4. Push the needle through the straw at a point between the middle and the toothpick end.

5. Balance the needle and straw on the depressors. If the straw doesn't balance, reposition the needle in the straw until it does balance.

6. Use tape to fasten the last depressor to the balance as shown. This is the scale.

7. Add one plastic disk at a time to the scoop. With a pencil, mark the position of the toothpicks's tip on the scale after each disk is added. These marks are 50-mg calibrations.

8. Use the calibrated balance to determine the mass of each small item you gathered. Record the mass of each item.

Task 4   Analysis

1. What would you have to do to use your balance after moving it to a new location? Explain.

2. What variables could affect the accuracy of your balance?

Task 5   Conclusion

Write a report explaining how your balance worked. Discuss your data.

Extension

Explain why your balance is only good for measuring very small masses. What can you infer about balance design and manufacturing processes from your model?

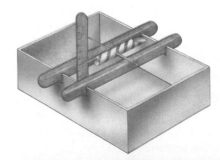

Chapter 1 Review

Concept Summary

1.1 Science Skills and Methods
▶ Scientists use many skills. They observe, infer, estimate, measure, predict, classify, hypothesize, record, organize, and analyze.
▶ Scientists perform experiments to gather data about nature.
▶ Scientific theories and laws may change.
▶ Scientists use models to represent the part of nature they study.

1.2 Measuring with Scientific Units
▶ Scientists measure length, volume, mass, density, temperature, and time with standard SI units.
▶ Scientific notation is used to express very large and very small numbers.

1.3 Graphing
▶ Circle graphs show how parts of something make up a whole.
▶ Bar graphs compare one aspect of several different things.
▶ Line graphs show data defined by two variables.

1.4 Science Tools and Technology
▶ Technology applies science principles to solve problems.
▶ Matter and energy are studied in two connected sciences, chemistry and physics. Other divisions of these sciences extend into the areas of life science and earth science.
▶ Scientists use tools, both simple and complex, to gather data about the world.

Chapter Vocabulary

data (p. 3)	variable (p. 7)	cubic meter (p. 12)	kilogram (p. 13)
controlled experiment (p. 7)	meter (p. 12)	liter (p. 12)	density (p. 13)
constant (p. 7)	volume (p. 12)	mass (p. 13)	scientific notation (p. 14)

Check Your Vocabulary

Use the vocabulary words above to complete the following sentences correctly.

1. Many drink containers use the SI unit ____ to measure their volume.

2. Very large or very small numbers are written using ____ .

3. In a controlled experiment, a factor that is kept the same is a ____ .

4. Scientists use science process skills to gather ____ , or information.

5. The kilogram and gram are units of ____ .

6. The factor that is changed by a person doing a controlled experiment is the ____ .

7. A space 1m × 1m × 1m is one ____ .

8. The ratio of an object's mass to its volume is the object's ____ .

9. To do a ____ , you must have two test groups, an experimental group and a control group.

10. The distance between a doorknob and the floor is about one ____ .

11. In SI, the unit used to measure mass is ____ .

12. The amount of space matter occupies is its ____ .

Write Your Vocabulary

Write sentences using each vocabulary word above. Show that you know what each word means.

Check Your Vocabulary
1. liter
2. scientific notation
3. constant
4. data
5. mass
6. variable
7. cubic meter
8. density
9. controlled experiment
10. meter
11. kilogram
12. volume

Write Your Vocabulary
Students' sentences should show that they know the meaning of each word as well as how to use it in a sentence.

Use Vocabulary Worksheet for Chapter 1.

Check Your Knowledge

1. Meter, cubic meter, gram, degree Celsius
2. Determine the density of the object. If the density of the object is less than 1 g/cm³, it will float.
3. The control in an experiment provides a standard, or point of comparison, against which changes can be measured.
4. a. graduated cylinder
   b. centimeter ruler
   c. thermometer
   d. stopwatch
5. Scientists protect their eyes by wearing safety goggles.
6. A wind tunnel is used to study the effects of moving fluids, like air or water, on objects.
7. False; line
8. True
9. False; 10
10. False; sometimes
11. True
12. True
13. True

Check Your Understanding

1. A circle graph presents the parts of a whole, or 100 percent.
2. a. observe, predict
   b. observe, infer, conclude
   c. measure, predict, estimate
3. Constant: volume of water, mass of sugar; variable: temperature of water
4. a. circle
   b. line
5. Mike observes that petrified wood is pictured and infers its physical characteristics and the process by which it was created.
6. a. 9.0×10^{-7}
   b. 1.3×10^{10}
7. a. 0.00023
   b. 7 000 000

Chapter 1 Review

Check Your Knowledge

Answer the following in complete sentences.

1. What are the basic units of length, volume, mass, and temperature in the metric system?

2. Without placing an object in water, how can you determine if it will float?

3. What is the function of a control in an experiment?

4. What instrument would you use to measure the following?
   a. The volume of water in a jar
   b. The width of this book
   c. The temperature of ocean water
   d. The amount of time it takes to run 100 m.

5. How do scientists protect their eyes during laboratory activities?

6. What is a wind tunnel used for?

Determine whether each statement is true or false. Write *true* if it is true. If it is false, change the underlined term(s) to make the statement true.

7. <u>Circle</u> graphs have *x*- and *y*-axes.

8. To measure volume in a graduated cylinder, you read the level of the <u>lowest</u> point of the meniscus.

9. SI units are based on multiples of <u>100</u>.

10. Scientific facts <u>never</u> change.

11. A number written in scientific notation is a <u>two-part</u> expression.

12. A conversion factor is written as a <u>fraction</u>.

13. <u>Computers</u> help scientists calculate rapidly, test hypotheses, or see the structure of a chemical.

Check Your Understanding

Apply the concepts you have learned to answer each question.

1. Why must all parts of a circle graph add up to 100 percent?

2. **Application** Which skill or skills could you apply to each statement? Explain.
   a. There are heavy dark clouds in the sky. It's going to rain.
   b. The mailbox is empty—either I didn't get mail today or the letter carrier has not delivered the mail.
   c. The container can hold 2 L of milk.

3. In an experiment on how temperature affects the rate at which sugar dissolves, what factor(s) should remain constant? What factor(s) will vary?

4. **Application** What kind of graph—circle, bar, or line—would you use to show each of the following kinds of data?
   a. The percentage of students in your class with brown eyes.
   b. The height of a tree in the park on January 1 for the past 15 years.

5. **Mystery Photo** The photograph on page 2 shows petrified wood. Petrified wood is a fossil formed when minerals replace natural wood fibers. Read Mike's response on page 2. List the science skills he uses to answer the question, "What do you see?"

6. Write each number below in scientific notation.
   a. 0.000 000 9
   b. 13 000 000 000

7. Write each number expressed below as a standard numeral.
   a. 2.3×10^{-4}
   b. 7×10^{6}

Develop Your Skills

1. a. 1000 g

   b. 2000 mL

   c. 1000 mm

2. a. 17%

   b. 8 times

3. a. None; January

   b. New York City; The curve of New York City's monthly average temperatures rises and falls the most frequently and steeply.

Make Connections

1.

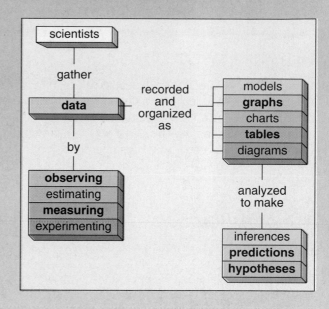

2. Student designs should include the meaning of the symbol they are working from.

3. Student reports will vary, but all should show an effort to explain why their subject's work is considered a scientific contribution.

Develop Your Skills

Use the skills you have developed in this chapter to complete each activity.

1. Calculate Complete the following metric conversions.

  a. 1 kg = _____ g

  b. 2 L = _____ mL

  c. 10 dm = _____ mm

2. Interpret Data The circle graph below shows land use in the United States.

  a. What portion of land is farmland?

  b. The amount of forestland is how many times greater than the amount of urban area?

Land Use in the United States

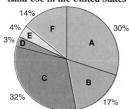

Key:
A = Grassland and pasture
B = Farmland
C = Forestland
D = National and state parks
E = Urban areas
F = Other

3. Data Bank Use the information on page 637 to answer the following questions:

  a. In what month was the highest average temperature for 2 cities? The lowest average temperature?

  b. What city has the most variable weather in a year? How can you tell?

Make Connections

1. Link the Concepts Below is a concept map showing how some of the main concepts in this chapter link together. Only part of the map is filled in. Copy the map. Using words and ideas from the chapter, complete the map.

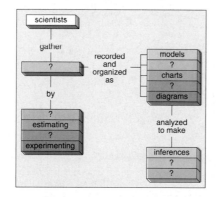

2. Science and Art Choose a common symbol that you have seen. Develop a new symbol that shows the same idea.

3. Science and Social Studies Many of the modern methods of science are based on the ideas or work of scientists who lived many centuries ago. Find out the names of some important scientists who lived before 1800. Choose one and write a report about her or his contributions to science.

Overview

This chapter explores the relationship between motion and energy. The perception and measurement of motion is described, frames of reference are introduced, and the distinctions between speed, velocity, and acceleration are addressed. The chapter's final section defines energy, compares potential and kinetic energy in relation to motion, and presents the Law of Conservation of Energy.

Advance Planner

▶ Find examples of artwork for TE page 31.

▶ Provide stopwatch for TE page 35.

▶ Provide newspaper, weather maps, and a world map or globe for TE page 38.

▶ Supply string and rubber erasers for TE page 43.

▶ Obtain a stringed instrument and a picture of an Alexander Calder mobile for TE page 46.

▶ Provide a dry-cell, any size, for TE page 49.

▶ Collect fishing line, scissors, balloons of two sizes, drinking straws, meter sticks, and stopwatches for SE, page 50.

Skills Development Chart

Sections	Calculate	Classify	Collect Data	Communicate	Control Variables	Infer	Interpret Data	Observe	Research
2.1 Skills WarmUp								●	
Practice Problems	●								
Skills WorkOut	●								
Historical Notebook				●					●
2.2 Skills WarmUp						●			
SkillBuilder	●			●			●		
Practice Problems	●								
Skills WorkOut							●		
2.3 Skills WarmUp		●							
Activity	●		●	●	●				

Individual Needs

▶ **Limited English Proficiency Students** Have students write the word *speed* at the top of a page in their science portfolios. Have them copy the equation for speed (page 34), then write out the terms used in the equation: *speed, distance, time.* Next, ask students to write definitions for the terms. Finally, they should write the equation in words. (For example, *speed equals distance divided by time.*) Have them repeat this procedure for *acceleration* (page 34) and *kinetic energy* (page 47) on new pages in their science portfolios. At the bottom of each page, have them add a statement about how a baseball moves. The statement should use the terms defined on the page.

▶ **At-Risk Students** Invite students to work in groups to design a sculpture or machine with moving parts to illustrate the concepts in Section 2.3 on the energy of motion. Give them materials, such as balls of various sizes and masses, string, wire, springs, inclined planes, wheels, and water. If possible, students should build their sculptures and demonstrate them to the class. As they work, ask questions that help students to build an awareness of the concepts of frame of reference, motion, speed, acceleration, velocity, and energy.

▶ **Gifted Students** Have students research the water wheel. They should explore the development and use of different kinds of water wheels, such as a paddle wheel, overshot, undershot, Pelton, and Frances water wheels. Have them build models of some water wheels and identify the variables that affect the speed of each. Ask them to use their models to identify the potential and kinetic energy associated with each type of wheel.

Resource Bank

▶ **Bulletin Board** Put the titles *Problems in Motion* and *Energy* at the top of the bulletin board. Find two or three pictures showing objects in motion and hang them on the board. Beneath each picture write a word problem that the picture could illustrate. Ask students to add their own pictures with original word problems to the bulletin board. When students have finished, use the board to review the mathematical concepts in the lessons.

Section	Core	Standard	Enriched	Section	Core	Standard	Enriched
2.1 Motion pp. 30–38				**Overhead Blackline Transparencies** Overhead Blackline Master 2 and Student Worksheet	•	•	•
Section Features Skills WarmUp, p. 31 Skills WorkOut, p. 37 Historical Notebook, p. 37	•	• • •	• • •	**Laboratory Program** Investigation 4	•	•	•
Blackline Masters Review Worksheet 2.1 Skills Worksheet 2.1 Integrating Worksheet 2.1a Integrating Worksheet 2.1b	• • •	• • • •	• • •	**2.3 Energy of Motion** pp. 45–50			
Color Transparencies Transparencies 3a, 3b	•	•	•	**Section Features** Skills WarmUp, p. 45 Activity, p. 50	• •	• •	• •
2.2 Acceleration pp. 39–44				**Blackline Masters** Review Worksheet 2.3 Vocabulary Worksheet 2	• •	• •	
Section Features Skills WarmUp, p. 39 Skills WorkOut, p. 44 SkillBuilder, p. 41	•	• • •	• •	**Color Transparencies** Transparency 4	•	•	•
Blackline Masters Review Worksheet 2.2 Skills Worksheet 2.2	• •	• •	•	**Laboratory Program** Investigation 5 Investigation 6	• •	• •	• •

Bibliography

The following resources can be used for teaching the chapter. See page T-46 for supplier codes.

Library Resources

Apfel, Necia H. It's All Elementary: From Atoms to the Quantum World of Quarks, Leptons, and Gluons. New York: Lothrop, Lee & Shepard Books, 1985.

Brancazio, Peter J. Sport Science. New York: Simon and Schuster, 1984.

Gardner, Robert. Science in Sports. New York: Franklin Watts, 1988.

White, Jack R. The Hidden World of Forces. New York: Dodd, Mead & Company, 1987.

Technology Resources

Internet

PLANETDIARY at http://www.planetdiary.com
- Discover more about astronomy in Astronomy/Space by clicking on Phenomena Backgrounders and Current Phenomena.
- Learn more about the atmosphere in Atmosphere by clicking on Phenomena Backgrounders.
- Review geological and meteorological news in Current Phenomena.

Software

All about Science I. Mac, Dos. ESI.
Big Science Comics. Mac, Win. ER.
Learning All About Motion. Mac, Dos. LS.
Superstar Science. Mac, Win. LS.

CD-ROMs

hip Physics. Mac. ESI.

Laserdiscs

Living Textbook. (See barcodes on pages in this chapter.) Optical Data.
Physics at the Indy 500. VID.

Videos

The Forms of Energy. FM.
The Law of Falling Bodies. FI.
Mass, Momentum, Energy. FI.

Audio-Visual Resources

Attraction of Gravity. Film. BFA.

Writing Connection

Have students imagine that they are moving around in the scene shown in the photograph. Have them write a story about what they might feel and see inside the maze. Allow time for some of the students to read their stories aloud.

Introducing the Chapter

Have students read the description of the photograph. Ask if they agree or disagree with the description.

Directed Inquiry

Have students study the photograph. Ask:

▶ Do you think that the photograph shows a real or an imaginary scene? Why do you think so? (This is a photograph of a real scene, but because it was done with a time exposure, it has an unreal appearance.)

▶ What kind of structures do you see in the photograph? (There are several stairways and many walls making up a maze.)

▶ What do you notice first about the photograph? (The many lines of light)

▶ What in the photograph shows energy? (Light has energy. The people at the top of the stairs have potential energy.)

▶ Identify any signs of motion in the photograph. (The lines of light suggest that people are carrying lights down the stairs and around the maze.)

▶ Why do you think this photograph is used with a chapter on motion and energy? (The time exposure captures motion; the image gives an impression of both motion and energy.)

Chapter Vocabulary

acceleration	kinetic energy
centripetal	potential energy
acceleration	speed
deceleration	velocity
energy	

Chapter 2   Motion and Energy

Chapter Sections

2.1   Motion

2.2   Acceleration

2.3   Energy of Motion

What do you see?

66 It looks like a maze with people carrying lights through the maze. The photographer left the shutter open on the camera and exposed the film for a long time causing the moving lights to become lines. The standing people have potential energy, while the 'moving' lines have kinetic energy. 99

Jim Emmons
El Toro High School
El Toro, California

To find out more about the photograph, look on page 52. As you read this chapter, you will learn about motion and energy.

Themes in Science

Stability and Equilibrium
Because the description of any event depends upon the observer's frame of reference, objects that appear stationary to one observer may appear to be in motion to another observer. The study of motion requires an understanding of frames of reference.

Use Integrating Worksheet 2.1a.

Art Connection

Show students examples of paintings that show motion such as Winslow Homer's *The Gulf Stream,* Giacomo Balla's *Dynamism of a Dog on a Leash,* or any of Leroy Neiman's sports paintings. Have students discuss which artworks show motion with the most energy. Ask students to explain their choices.

Section Objectives
For a list of section objectives, see the Student Edition page.

Skills Objectives
Students should be able to:

Observe the motion of objects in relation to a reference point.

Calculate speed as distance over time.

Graph distance-time data.

Vocabulary
speed, velocity

2.1 Motion

Objectives

▶ **Compare** frames of reference.

▶ **Distinguish** between speed and velocity.

▶ **Calculate** when a moving object will arrive at a given point.

▶ **Make a graph** to solve a distance-time problem.

▼ **ACTIVITY**

Observing

Point of Reference

Select an object in the classroom or in the school yard as a reference point. Describe the motion of objects or people in relation to the reference point chosen.

SKILLS WARMUP

Imagine you are traveling across the ocean on a ship. You see another ship getting closer, as shown in Figure 2.1. Are both ships moving or is only the ship you are on moving? There is another possibility as well. The ship you are on could be stationary and the other ship could be moving toward you. As time passes, the distance between the ships gets smaller so it's clear at least one ship must be moving. But which one—or is it both?

Frame of Reference

It isn't always easy to decide when objects are moving. Clues are often given by looking at other objects in your surroundings. Normally you think of walls or signs as not moving, or as being stationary. You judge motion in relation to these apparently stationary objects. When you do this, you use the walls or signs as a *frame of reference*. A frame of reference is a place or object that you assume is fixed. You observe how objects move in relation to that frame of reference.

Frames of reference also move relative to each other, which may cause confusion. Suppose you are seated on a bus that is parked close to another bus. The bus you are on starts to move backward. As you look out the window you might be fooled into thinking that you remain stationary while the other bus moves forward. Because your frame of reference is moving it is easy to be confused.

The perception of motion depends on the observer's frame of reference. From your frame of reference, you're not moving as you sit and read this book. To an observer in outer space, you are a passenger on a planet moving around the sun. You are moving over 100 times faster than a jet plane!

Figure 2.1 ▲
There is no way to tell which ship is moving.

MOTIVATE

Skills WarmUp
To help students understand reference points for motion, have them do the Skills WarmUp.
Answer Students should notice that the description of a motion depends on frame of reference.

Misconceptions
Students sometimes think that speed and velocity are the same. Ask students to listen to weather forecasts for three or four days. Have them pay close attention to the description of the wind in the forecasts. Then have the class discuss the components of velocity. Discuss why velocity may often be a more useful measurement than speed alone when describing winds.

**The Living Textbook:
Physical Science Side 2**

Chapter 34   Frame 29923
Relative Motion (Movie)
Search: Play:

TEACH

Explore Visually

Have students study Figure 2.2. Ask:

▶ Imagine you are the girl observing the bus. Describe the motion of each object that you can see. (The girl sees the bus moving toward her, then away. She sees the ball moving forward and downward.)

▶ Describe the motion observed by one of the boys in the drawings. How does the motion appear to be different to the other boy? (Both see the ball moving straight down. The boy looking backward can see the landscape outside the bus moving away; the other boy sees the landscape moving toward him.)

▶ How would the earth's movement appear to the astronauts? (It would be constantly rotating.)

▶ What are *up* and *down* directions to the astronauts? Why? (*Up* and *down* are meaningless to the astronauts because they are not influenced by the earth's gravity, which provides a frame of reference for vertical movement.)

The Living Textbook: Physical Science Sides 1-4

Chapter 9   Frame 01681
Frame of Reference (6 Frames)
Search: Step:

The Living Textbook: Physical Science Sides 1-4

Chapter 9   Frame 01687
Ball Dropped in Moving Car (4 Frames)
Search: Step:

Cooperative Learning

Have students work in cooperative groups to plan and perform a skit that demonstrates different frames of reference. For example, students might take roles such as a dog, a train conductor, a train passenger, and a railroad crossing guard. The skit's action might include the conductor chasing the dog through a moving train. Other class members should describe the motion the train passenger would see, and the motion the crossing guard would see as the train moves past the railroad crossing.

An Earth Event You use the earth's surface as your frame of reference most of the time. However, you experience moving frames of reference when you ride in a vehicle, such as a car, a bus, or an elevator. If the vehicle moves at a constant speed, events in that frame of reference occur just as if you were not moving. For example, suppose you toss a ball up in the air as you ride in a moving bus. To you, the ball goes up and comes down just as if you were not moving. To an observer who is not in your moving frame of reference, it will look as though the ball is also moving forward (see Figure 2.2).

Figure 2.2
Frames of Reference ▽

Two people with the same frame of reference see the motion of an object the same way. Both boys on the bus see the ball drop straight down.

Two people with different frames of reference see an object's motion differently. To a bystander, the ball moves in two directions—forward with the bus and down toward its floor.

Integrating the Sciences

Astronomy For centuries, astronomers described the motion of the stars, the sun, and the planets as circular orbits around the earth. In the 16th century, Copernicus proposed that the stars and the planets—including earth—moved in orbits around the sun. Why might an observer confined to the earth have difficulty in seeing the sun as the center of the orbits? (To an observer on the earth, the sun appears to move.)

A Space Event Objects in space can be used as a frame of reference, just as they are on the earth. An object used as a frame of reference in space could be a planet, moon, star, or a space vessel. To an observer in space, the earth's shape is very different from the one you experience every day. You experience the earth as a flat, nonmoving surface. From outer space, the earth appears as a rotating sphere revolving around the sun.

Away from the earth's surface and the pull of the earth's gravity, directions such as "up" and "down" are no longer relevant. Events that seem impossible on the earth can occur in space.

During a space walk, two astronauts might have two completely different frames of reference. Each astronaut might say the other is upside down. They would both be right!

Using the shuttle as a frame of reference in space, the earth is a rotating sphere beneath the astronauts.

In the astronaut's frame of reference, there may not be a sunset or a sunrise.

Critical Thinking

Predict Ask students to predict what the classroom would look like to a student who turned in a circle like a ballet dancer or an ice skater. (The room would appear to turn in the direction opposite to that in which the person was turning.) Allow one or two volunteers to take turns testing the students' prediction.

Class Activity

Have four students stand in front of the class. Give the rest of the class one minute to observe them, then have the seated students close their eyes. The four students should change position, change an article of clothing, or move in some way. Have the seated group open their eyes and discuss what changed and how they know. Discuss what they used as a frame of reference to determine movement.

Discuss

Tell students that as the earth spins, the stars move in circular paths across the sky. Remind them that in the Northern Hemisphere, the North Star Polaris is directly over the North Pole and doesn't change position relative to the earth. Have students discuss how the North Star was used by ships at sea. (Answers may vary, but students should indicate that in the absence of physical landmarks, the North Star provided a frame of reference for a ship's movement.)

 **The Living Textbook:
Physical Science Sides 1-4**

Chapter 9   Frame 01607
Revolution of Earth (1 Frame)
Search:

Reteach

Copy the speed calculation on this page onto the chalkboard. Have students circle the conversion factor. (60 min/1 h)

Discuss

You may wish to write a selection of speeds and velocities, such as 10 km/h, 4 ft/s east, 20 m/h north, 4000 km/s up and 32 ft/s, on the chalkboard before asking the following:

▶ Which selections indicate velocity? (4 ft/s east, 20 m/h north, 4000 km/s up)

▶ What can you add to make 10 km/h and 32 ft/s velocities? (Direction, such as forward, north, or west)

▶ Which units can be used to predict where an object will be in 10 minutes? (Units of velocity)

▶ Make a generalization about velocity that is not true for speed. (All velocities indicate a direction.)

Answers to In-Text Questions

① **The image of the cyclist is blurred indicating that the cyclist moved in relation to the camera. In contrast, the road sign is clear, indicating it did not move in relation to the camera.**

② **The wind is blowing southwest.**

③ **40 km/h southwest**

**The Living Textbook:
Physical Science Sides 1-4**

Chapter 17	Frame 03354
Speed (2 Frames)	
Search:	Step:

Language Arts Connection

In our everyday speech, we use a number of colorful comparisons to describe speed. Ask students to think of examples and discuss what they mean. Offer a few examples to get them started: ". . . as quick as a wink . . . ," ". . . a mile a minute . . . ," ". . . a snail's pace . . . ."

Art Connection

Have students study Figure 2.3. Ask them to draw a picture showing a person or object in a fixed position and the background moving. Have students explain how this situation could occur.

Figure 2.3 ▶
How can you tell that the cyclist is moving and the road sign is in a fixed position? ①

Measuring Motion

How would you describe the motion taking place in Figure 2.3? Although you can see that a cyclist passed a road sign, you don't really have much information about the cyclist's motion. To describe the motion further, you measure the cyclist's **speed**. Speed is the distance an object travels per unit of time. To calculate its speed, you divide the distance the bike travels by the time it travels.

$$\text{speed} = \frac{\text{distance}}{\text{time}}$$

Speed is sometimes expressed in kilometers per hour (km/h). If the cyclist rode her bike 8 km to school in 20 min, you can calculate her speed in km/h as follows:

$$\text{speed} = \frac{8 \text{ km}}{20 \text{ min}} \times \frac{60 \text{ min}}{1 \text{ h}} = \frac{24 \text{ km}}{\text{h}}$$

An object's speed doesn't indicate all there is to know about its motion. The direction of motion is also important. An object's speed together with its direction of motion is called **velocity** (vuh LAHS uh tee). For example, the cyclist's velocity might be 24 km/h south. People often use the word *speed* when they mean *velocity*. Since a moving object always travels in some direction, velocity is a more precise term for describing motion.

Wind is often described in terms of its velocity. What would be the velocity of the wind in Figure 2.4 if it blows ③ at 40 km/h? Meteorologists use wind-velocity measurements to help predict weather.

Figure 2.4
This weather vane indicates wind direction. Which direction is the wind blowing? ▼ ②

Constant Speed

A moving object that doesn't change its speed travels at constant speed. Constant speed means equal distances are covered in an equal amount of time. Suppose you and a friend want to run around a track at constant speed for half an hour. How can you check to see if your speed is constant? You can use a stopwatch to measure how long it takes to run each lap. Your measurement can be even more accurate if you measure how long it takes to travel very short distances of equal length. If all the times are the same, your speed must be constant.

Look at the graph in Figure 2.5. Notice that in 2 s the car travels 20 m and in 4 s, it travels 40 m. The speed is constant at 10 m/s. On the graph, the curve for constant speed appears as a straight line. At this speed, the car will travel 100 m in 10 s.

The steepness of the curve indicates how fast the car is moving. A greater speed has a steeper line. Suppose another car travels 100 m in 12 s. How would this speed curve look on the graph? ④

Average Speed

A marathon course usually winds through city streets and up and down hills. Because the conditions of the course change, marathon runners can't keep a constant speed during a 42-km race.

A distance-time graph for a marathon runner is shown in Figure 2.6. Notice that the curve representing speed isn't straight. The graph shows that the runner traveled 10 km in the first half hour and less than 5 km in the second half hour. If a runner has changing speeds, what is his speed during the entire race?

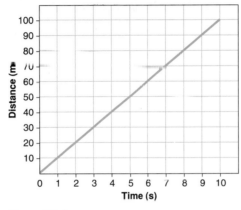

Figure 2.5 ▲
A distance-time graph of a car traveling at constant speed forms a straight line.

Figure 2.6
A distance-time graph of a marathon shows that the runner's speed was not constant. ▼

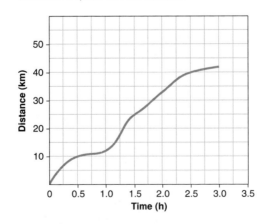

To find the speed of the runner during the entire race, you need to calculate his *average* speed. Average speed is equal to the total distance of the course divided by the runner's total time. What was the average speed of the marathon runner? ⑤

TEACH ▪ Continued

Practice Problems

Class Activity Reinforce the process used to answer the sample problem. Copy the distance calculation from step 2 onto the chalkboard. Have students compare the calculated distance to the distance that the teens wish to travel, shown on the map. Ask, Will the teens be home before dark? (No; they'll be 15 km from home at sundown.)

Apply Have students work on practice problems 1 to 5. Review the answers, and how to arrive at each, as a class.

Answers

1. 100 m ÷ 50 s = 2 m/s, **2.** time = 4,500 m ÷ 2.5 m/s; time = 1,800 s, 2.5 m/s × 60 s/min × 60 min/h × 1 km/1000 m = 9 km/h **3.** distance = speed × time; distance = 3 m/s × 35 s = 105 m; distance = 3 m/s × 60 s/min × 60 min = 10 800 m **4.** Downstream: subtract the velocity of the stream from the clocked speed of the kayak; 2.5 m/s − 1.5 m/s = 1.0 m/s, so the kayak was paddled at 1.0 m/s. Upstream: add the velocity of the stream to the desired speed of the kayak to get the paddling velocity; 1.0 m/s + 1.5 m/s = 2.5 m/s, the kayak must be paddled at 2.5 m/s to overtake downstream velocity and travel upstream at 1.0 m/s. **5.** 7.5 km ÷ 5 h = 1.5 km/h. **6.** time = distance/speed = 270 km/60 km/h = 4.5 h; it would take the family 4.5 hours to drive home; speed = distance/time = 270 km/3 h = 90 km/h; the family would need to travel 90 km/h to arrive home in 3 hours.

Enrich

Assign additional problems on this concept from Math Appendix pages 645 and 646.
    Use Enrich Worksheet 2.1.

Math Connection

Students may occasionally forget to convert units properly. Ask students to solve this speed problem: If a snail crawls at a speed of 3 cm/s, how long would it take to cross a 1.5-m wide path? (Time = distance/speed; distance = 150 cm; 150 cm/3 cm/s = 50 s)

Social Studies Connection

Have students find out about world records for speed and distance for aircraft, cars, boats, or Olympic events. They may find it interesting to discover just how many categories of world records there are. For example, while there are five absolute world records in aeronautics, dozens of records are held within the seven classes for aircraft.

Sample Problems

1. A group of teens traveled 150 km by car to a beach resort. If the driving time was 2 h, what was the average speed their vehicle traveled during the trip?

Plan To find the average speed, divide the distance by the time.

Gather Data distance = 150 km; time = 2 h

Solve $\text{speed} = \dfrac{\text{distance}}{\text{time}}$

$$\text{speed} = \frac{150 \text{ km}}{2 \text{ h}} = \frac{75 \text{ km}}{\text{h}}$$

2. The teens used a map like the one shown below. The sun would be setting in an hour and a half. They wanted to reach home before dark. If they drove at 90 km/h, how far could they travel in 1.5 h?

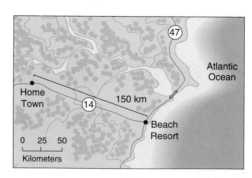

Plan To determine the distance the group could travel, multiply the speed of the car by the time remaining before dark.

Gather Data $\text{speed} = \dfrac{90 \text{ km}}{\text{h}}$; time = 1.5 h

Solve distance = speed × time

$$\text{distance} = \frac{90 \text{ km}}{\text{h}} \times 1.5 \text{ h} = 135 \text{ km}$$

Practice Problems

1. A kayak races 100 m in 50 s. What is its speed?

2. At the speed of 2.5 m/s, how many seconds will it take the kayak to run a 4,500 m course? What is the speed of the kayak in kilometers per hour?

3. When a kayak races downstream, its speed is clocked at 3 m/s. How far does the kayak travel in 35 s? In 1 h?

4. The river in problem 3 was flowing downstream at a velocity of 1.5 m/s. How fast was the kayak being paddled? In order to travel upstream at a speed of 1.0 m/s, how fast must the kayak be paddled?

5. A family backpacking at Yosemite National Park took 5 h to climb a mountain trail 7.5 km long. What was the family's average speed?

6. When it was time to leave the park, the family could only drive at 60 km/h in the mountains. How long would it take them to travel the 270 km to their home? How fast would they have to travel to make the trip in 3 h?

Integrating the Sciences

Astronomy On the earth, we identify one day as the time it takes the earth to complete one turn on its axis. Our clocks are based on the earth's 24-hour day. Have students look up the length of the days on other planets in earth time. (Mercury—59 earth-days, Venus—243 days, Mars—25 h, Jupiter—10 h, Saturn—10 h, Uranus—16 h, Neptune—18 h, Pluto—6.4 days; all are earth-days or earth-hours.)

Multicultural Perspectives

Albert Einstein is most famous for his equation $E = mc^2$ and the theory of special relativity. However, Einstein's work was also fundamental to quantum theory, atomic theory, and general relativity; and he accomplished most of it while working as a clerk in the Swiss patent office. Encourage students to learn more about Einstein by reading one of the many biographies available about his life and work.

Skills WorkOut

To help students understand relativity and space-time, have them do the Skills WorkOut.

Answer Change the speed of light from m/s to km/min: 300 000 000 m/s × 0.001 km/m × 60 s/min = 18 000 000 km/min. Use the equation: time = 149 000 000 km/ 18 000 000 km/min = 8.28 min; light takes 8.28 minutes, or about 8 minutes, to travel from the sun to the earth. 5:21 P.M. – 8 min is 5:13 P.M., the time at which the light left the sun.

Relativity and Space-Time

You know that observations of motion depend on your frame of reference. Yet experiments with light show that the speed of light is always the same, regardless of the motion of the light source or the motion of the observer! To understand this, think about a rocket docked on the earth and another rocket traveling directly toward the sun at great speed. The light from the sun reaches each rocket at the same speed of 300 000 000 m/s.

The constant speed of light is the basis of Albert Einstein's special theory of relativity. He reasoned that space and time are connected into one whole, called space-time. You are constantly traveling through this combination of space and time. When you stand still, you travel only through time. When you move, you travel through space and time. If you could move at close to the speed of light, you would travel quickly through space and slowly through time.

▼ ACTIVITY

Calculating

Sunlight Travel Time

The sun is 149 million km from the earth. If light travels 300 000 000 m/s, how many minutes does it take light from the sun to reach the earth? If you see the sun set at 5:21 p.m., what time did the sunlight actually leave the sun?

SKILLS WORKOUT

Enrich

Introduce the concept of space-time. Students who watch science fiction TV programs may have heard of the space-time continuum; ask if they have any ideas about what that means. Explain that everyone in the class is moving through time at a rate of 24 hours per day. Even if they remain motionless, they are still moving through space with reference to any point outside the planet.

Historical Notebook

Research Have students work in small groups to prepare reports about one of the theories of motion. Ask each group to choose a motion theory, such as in the *Mo Ching*, Aristotle's ideas, or a theory about motion from any other culture. Remind students that their reports should include a description of the theory and any experiments that support the theory.

Answers

1. Answers will vary. Experiments should include a carefully considered control.

2. Galileo's experiments showed that an object moving horizontally continues to move at the same speed unless a force opposes it. This confirmed the *Mo Ching's* statement that motion won't stop without an opposing force.

Historical Notebook

Motion Changes with the Times

About 2,300 years ago, philosophers in China wrote about motion in a book called the *Mo Ching*. They wrote: "Motion stops due to an opposing force. If there is no opposing force, the motion will never stop."

About the same time, the Greek philosopher Aristotle wrote that horizontal motion was "unnatural." He thought that a push or a pull was needed to start and to keep something in horizontal motion. He also thought heavy objects fall at a faster rate, or acceleration, than lighter objects do. Aristotle's ideas about motion were widely accepted for more than 1,900 years.

During the 1500s, Galileo questioned the ideas of Aristotle. He reasoned that if two bricks of the same mass fall at the same rate, side-by-side, they ought to fall at the same rate even when cemented together. In 1589, according to an often-repeated, unverified story, Galileo did an experiment from the Leaning Tower in Pisa, Italy. Galileo is supposed to have dropped two cannonballs of different masses at the same time from the top of the tower. Both cannonballs reached the ground at about the same time. Whether he actually did the experiment or not, his reasoning was correct.

Galileo also did experiments that showed that an object moving horizontally continues to move at the same speed unless a force opposes it. Galileo's experiments confirmed the ideas stated thousands of years earlier in the *Mo Ching*.

1. Design an experiment to test Aristotle's hypothesis that heavy objects fall faster than lighter objects.

2. How did Galileo's experiments support the philosophers' ideas on motion in the *Mo Ching*?

WrapUp

Review To help students understand the idea of relative motion and rest, have them think of an object they see at rest.

▶ Ask them to imagine observing the object from two different frames of reference.

▶ Have them describe the object's motion from each frame of reference.

▶ Have students repeat the exercise for an object in motion. (Answers will vary but students should indicate that the description of the object they chose depends on the frame of reference of the observer.) Use Review Worksheet 2.1.

Check and Explain

1. A frame of reference is usually fixed and is used to describe the motion of objects relative to it. Examples will vary.

2. The velocity of the bird includes the direction the bird is moving.

3. time = 400 km/20 km/h = 20 h

4. Check student art for accuracy. The straight line curve should pass through (10, 1), (20, 2), (30, 3), (40, 4), and (50, 5). The cyclist reaches the destination at 5:00 P.M.

Answer to In-Text Question

① **The plane flying east, with the wind, will travel faster and arrive first.**

The Living Textbook:
Physical Science Sides 1-4

Chapter 9   Frame 01608
Sun's Path (1 Frame)
Search:

Geography Connection

Provide a world map or globe for the class. Have students use the map or globe to explain why the European Space Agency launches many of its eastbound rockets from locations in South America rather than locations in Europe. (Because the earth rotates fastest at the equator, launches at or near the equator can take full advantage of the earth's rotation. Nearly all of South America is closer to the equator than most parts of Europe.)

Integrating the Sciences

Meteorology The rotation of the earth affects the movement of storms across the United States. Have students collect weather maps from a local newspaper for five days. Have them study the movement of major high and low pressure systems across the country. Ask how the storm path relates to the earth's rotation.

Science and Technology *Flight*

You and everything on the earth move with the planet. The earth makes one complete rotation every 24 hours. You can observe this motion as the sun appears to move across the sky each day. The sun may seem to be moving, but it's actually you on the earth that is moving! Locations near the equator move faster than those near the north and south poles. A point on the equator has to travel 40 000 km to make one complete rotation. In contrast, a point at the north or south poles does not move during one rotation.

The earth's rotation creates patterns of wind over its surface. The effect of these winds on airplane flight must be taken into account by pilots and navigators. The winds blow west to east over most of the United States. Westbound planes usually fly into the wind, while eastbound planes fly with the wind. Look at Figure 2.7. Which plane will arrive first? The plane flying from Los Angeles to New York travels east—the same direction as the prevailing winds. The eastbound plane flies faster due to the wind and will arrive first.

At Cape Canaveral in Florida, the earth turns toward the east at about 1,470 km/h. Rockets and space shuttles are launched from this site toward the east, in the same direction that the earth rotates. Because the speed of the earth's rotation adds to the launch speed, the rocket can reach its orbital velocity in less time.

Figure 2.7 ▲
Both planes will cover the same number of miles between New York and Los Angeles. If the departure time is the same for both planes, which one will reach its destination first? ①

Check and Explain

1. How is a frame of reference used to determine the motion of an object? Give two examples.

2. How is the velocity of a bird in flight different from its speed?

3. **Calculate** How long does it take a migrating whale traveling at 20 km/h to travel 400 km?

4. **Make a Graph** At noon, a cyclist starts riding at a constant speed of 10 km/h. Make a graph that shows the distance traveled every hour until 5:00 p.m. What time would the cyclist reach a destination 50 km away?

2.2 Acceleration

Objectives

▶ **Define operationally** the acceleration of an object.

▶ **Relate** motion in a circle to acceleration.

▶ **Contrast** acceleration and constant speed.

▶ **Make a graph** showing acceleration.

▼ **ACTIVITY**

Inferring

Pacing Yourself

1. Choose an exercise, such as running in place.
2. Begin at a slow pace. Increase to a medium pace. Then increase to a fast pace.

As you increase the pace of exercising, what do you think happens to the rate of your heartbeat and your use of oxygen?

SKILLS WARMUP

Imagine you are competing as a speed skater at the Winter Olympics. You feel the excitement mount as you wait for the signal to begin the race. You are off to a fast start on the open stretch of ice. You gain speed with every stride. You think nothing can stop you. As you approach the curve, you slow down to keep your balance during the change in direction. Then once more you speed up to keep your lead.

During practice, you learned that three changes in speed were the key to winning the race: speed up whenever possible, slow down with control when necessary, and change direction as smoothly as possible. When you mastered these three things, you were ready to compete.

Change in Velocity

You experience changes in velocity many times every day. Each time you take a step, you change the velocity of your body. When you write, the velocity of your hand moving across the paper changes. You are probably most familiar with the velocity changes of a moving bus or car. For example, a moving bus changes direction and speed when it turns a corner or pulls over to the curb. To let off passengers or to pick them up, the bus slows to a stop. The bus then starts up again.

In real-life situations, the rate at which a velocity change occurs is very important. For example, if a velocity change occurs too quickly on a moving bus, the passengers can be thrown from their seats. If the velocity changes are slower, they get a smooth, even ride. The rate at which velocity changes occur is called **acceleration**.

Figure 2.8 ▲
To move around the curve, in what direction will the skater next place her right foot? ②

Discuss

Have students study the text and graphs on this page. To help them grasp the concept of acceleration, ask the following:

▶ How do you calculate acceleration? (Divide the change in velocity by the amount of time.)

▶ Will the curve on the distance vs. time graph of positive acceleration be a curved or a straight line? Explain. (Curved; a straight line would mean the distance moved was the same during every unit of time.)

Portfolio

Have students look for examples of acceleration in their life. For two or three days have them record occurrences of positive and negative acceleration they observe. Students can record this information in their portfolios.

Answers to In-Text Questions

① **The acceleration is greatest during the first second when the slope of the straight line segment is steepest.**

② **The car had the greatest negative acceleration during the first 3 seconds (Seconds 0 to 3).**

③ **The curve on the negative acceleration graph progresses downward, while the curve on the positive acceleration graph progresses upward. Both graphs show the change in velocity as a curve.**

The Living Textbook:
Physical Science Sides 1-4

Chapter 9   Frame 01664
Average Acceleration Graphs (2 Frames)
Search: Step:

STS Connection

Abrupt acceleration, like the acceleration experienced by jet pilots and astronauts, can cause the blood to collect in parts of the body. This can result in insufficient blood flow to the brain and loss of consciousness. Pressure suits, or *g* suits, counteract the effects of abrupt acceleration. Encourage interested students to use reference sources on aviation medicine to learn how these suits help pilots and astronauts.

Math Connection

Have students use the information in the SkillBuilder table to make a bar graph. For each second, make a bar showing the total distance covered. Ask students which graph, the bar graph or the line graph, is more useful for predicting speed after 6 seconds. Which is more useful for showing distance traveled between seconds 3 and 4? (Line; bar)

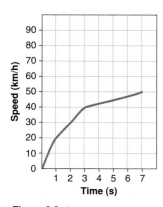

Figure 2.9 ▲
A graph of positive acceleration. When is the acceleration the greatest? ①

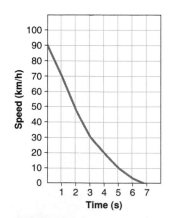

Figure 2.10 ▲
A graph of negative acceleration. During what 3 second interval does the fastest deceleration occur? ②

To calculate acceleration, you divide the change in velocity by the amount of time. Since you divide velocity in units of meters per second (m/s) by the time in seconds (s), the units for acceleration are meters per second per second, or meters per second squared (m/s²).

$$\text{acceleration} = \frac{\text{final velocity} - \text{starting velocity}}{\text{time}}$$

Suppose you ride a bike on a straight path to school at a velocity of 4 m/s. As you get closer, you hear the school bell. In 3 s, you speed up to 10 m/s. How would you calculate your acceleration? First, calculate the change in velocity, and then divide by the time involved.

$$\text{change in velocity} = \text{final velocity} - \text{starting velocity}$$
$$= \frac{10m}{s} - \frac{4m}{s} = \frac{6m}{s}$$

$$\text{acceleration} = \frac{\text{change in velocity}}{\text{time}} = \frac{\frac{6m}{s}}{3s} = \frac{\frac{2m}{s}}{s} = \frac{2m}{s^2}$$

Positive Acceleration To think about positive acceleration, imagine you are in a car waiting at a stoplight. The car is temporarily motionless. The light turns green, the driver steps on the accelerator, and the car speeds up. As the car moves faster, you feel the change in motion as your body is pushed back against the seat. The car's speedometer shows an increase in speed.

A speed-time graph of positive acceleration is shown in Figure 2.9. Notice this curve is made up of several distinct straight-line sections. For instance, during the first second, the straight line shows that the speed increases from 0 km/h to about 20 km/h. The acceleration during this time is constant. Notice the slope of the straight-line section changes. The changing slope of each section indicates a different acceleration. The graph shows three different accelerations.

Negative Acceleration To think about negative acceleration, imagine a car slowing down. The car's velocity decreases over a certain amount of time. This type of velocity change is also called **deceleration**.

You can graph negative acceleration just as you graph positive acceleration. The graph in Figure 2.10 shows negative acceleration. How does the curve differ from the curve for positive acceleration? How is it similar? ③

Cooperative Learning

Have students work in cooperative groups of four to practice a brief mime performance in which people are shown traveling together in a bus, train, or spacecraft. Ask students to judge which group exhibited the effects of acceleration the most effectively.

Anyone who drives a car has to make sure its brakes are working properly so the car will decelerate quickly. Suppose the driver of a car moving at 80 km/h brakes suddenly. If the car comes to a full stop after moving only 40 m, an accident may safely be avoided. If it stops after moving 52 m, it may not!

Change in Direction Turning the steering wheel of a moving car changes the direction of the car. Whenever direction of a moving object changes, the velocity of the object changes. Any change in velocity is acceleration—even if the speed of the object remains the same.

Look at Figure 2.11. Do the paths of the automobiles indicate that acceleration is taking place? The curved paths, where the direction is changing, clearly show acceleration. Remember, a change in direction is a change in velocity, and thus is acceleration.

Figure 2.11 ▲
A time-lapse photo taken at night showing the paths of automobiles.

SkillBuilder Calculating

A Racer's Acceleration

Suppose you are a race car driver. At the beginning of the race, all of the cars start from rest and accelerate straight down the race track before reaching the first corner. Your car's speed after the first few seconds is given in the table. Use the data in the table to plot a speed-versus-time line graph.

1. Look at your speed-versus-time graph. Is the acceleration constant? Explain.

2. What information do you need to calculate your car's acceleration?

3. Calculate the acceleration during the following periods: 0-1 second, 1-2 seconds, 2-3 seconds, and 3-4 seconds.

4. During what period is the acceleration the greatest? The least?

Time and Speed Data	
Time (s)	Speed (m/s)
0	0
1	8
2	16
3	22
4	26

5. Calculate your car's average acceleration over the first four seconds of the race.

6. Your friend is also in the race, and her car has an acceleration of 7.0 m/s^2 over the first four seconds. After four seconds, who will be in the lead—you or your friend?

Skills Development

Define Operationally Ask students to form a definition of acceleration by describing velocity changes that they have experienced. (Answers will vary but students should include motion changes—slower, faster, start, stop—and change of direction as part of their definitions.)

Have students test their definitions by presenting the descriptions of motion such as: came to a stop, sped away, 20 km/h north, moved in a circle, or bounced along. Ask: Which descriptions include acceleration? (All except 20 km/h north)

SkillBuilder

Class Activity Ask students to list the information needed in a computer program that calculates acceleration. What data would the user have to supply? (The program would include the acceleration formula. The user would have to input data giving the velocities and time interval.)

Answers
1. No. Constant acceleration would produce a linear graph.

2. Final velocity, starting velocity, and time.

3. 8 m/s^2, 8 m/s^2, 6 m/s^2, and 4 m/s^2 respectively.

4. Greatest: 0–2 s, Least: 3–4 s

5. $\dfrac{26 \text{ m/s} - 0 \text{ m/s}}{4 \text{ s}} = 6.5 \text{ m/s}^2$

6. The friend will be in the lead.

**The Living Textbook:
Physical Science Sides 1-4**

Chapter 17   Frame 02786
Acceleration: Definition and Formula
(2 Frames)
Search: Step:

TEACH ▪ *Continued*

Practice Problems

Research Ask students to use reference materials such as nature books, videos, and magazines to find out more about a cheetah's motion. Have them find how many seconds it takes a cheetah to reach its top speed. Have them compute the cheetah's initial velocity, final velocity, and acceleration.

Apply Work through the sample problem with students. Ask them to do practice problems 1 through 4 at their desks, alone, or in groups. Then review with the class the answers, and how to arrive at them.

Answers

1. $(6 \text{ m/s} - 12 \text{ m/s}) \div 3 \text{ s} = -2 \text{ m/s}^2$

2. $(0 \text{ m/s} - 10 \text{ m/s}) \div 3 \text{ s} = -3.3 \text{ m/s}^2$

3. $(12 \text{ m/s} - 4 \text{ m/s}) \div 4 \text{ s} = 2 \text{ m/s}^2$; $(18 \text{ m/s} - 12 \text{ m/s}) \div 6 \text{ s} = 1 \text{ m/s}^2$, the speedboat's acceleration decreased by 1 m/s^2.

4. $(9.0 \text{ m/s} - 0 \text{ m/s}) \div 0.5 \text{ s} = 18 \text{ m/s}^2$

Enrich

Assign additional problems on this concept from Math Appendix pages 645 and 646.

Integrating the Sciences

Life Science A cheetah's long stride, as long as 6 m, gives it great speed. As it runs, a cheetah's hind legs reach ahead of its front legs. The unusual footing is possible, in part, because of the cheetah's flexible spine. Have students use biology books and other references to find other animals with special structures that allow them to move at great speeds through water and air.

Meteorology Wind is classified in categories from calm to hurricane force. Have students find out the speed, in knots, of each category used by meteorologists. (The Beaufort wind speed scale rates a windspeed of less than 1 knot as calm; 11 to 16 knots as a moderate breeze; and 63 knots and above as hurricane force.)

Sample Problem

A cheetah moves from 0 km/min to 1.8 km/min in 4 s. What is the cheetah's acceleration?

Plan To determine the acceleration of the cheetah. First calculate the change in velocity in units of m/s. Next divide by the time required in seconds.

Gather Data

$$\text{starting velocity} = \frac{0 \text{ km}}{\text{min}} = \frac{0 \text{ m}}{\text{s}}$$

$$\text{final velocity} = \frac{1.8 \text{ km}}{\text{min}} \times \frac{1000 \text{ m}}{1 \text{ km}} \times \frac{1 \text{ min}}{60 \text{ s}}$$

$$= \frac{30 \text{ m}}{\text{s}}$$

$$\text{time} = 4 \text{ s}$$

Solve $\text{acceleration} = \dfrac{\text{change in velocity}}{\text{time}}$

$$\text{change in velocity} = \frac{30 \text{ m}}{\text{s}} - \frac{0 \text{ m}}{\text{s}} = \frac{30 \text{ m}}{\text{s}}$$

$$\text{acceleration} = \frac{30 \text{ m/s}}{4 \text{ s}} = 7.5 \text{ m/s}^2$$

Practice Problems

1. The velocity of water flowing over Lava Falls is 12 m/s. After going over the falls, the water slows to 6 m/s in 3 s. What is the acceleration of the water?

2. The winner of a track race ran at a speed of 10 m/s. As shown on the graph below, the runner took 3 s to slow down and come to a complete stop. What was the runner's acceleration?

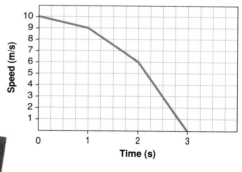

3. A speedboat goes from 4 m/s to 12 m/s in 4 s. What is the speedboat's acceleration? During the next 6 s, the speed of the boat increases to 18 m/s. How much did the speedboat's acceleration change?

4. A leaf is blown from a tree. Half a second after being blown from the tree, the leaf's speed is 9.0 m/s. What is the leaf's acceleration?

Figure 2.12 ▲
The people on this amusement-park ride experience centripetal acceleration.

Motion in a Circle

The amusement-park ride shown in Figure 2.12 moves in a circle. At some point, the ride moves at a constant speed. However, at constant speed the ride is still accelerating! Recall that acceleration is a change in velocity that results from speeding up, slowing down, or changing direction. An object moving in a circle or a curve is constantly changing direction. Therefore, the object is accelerating. Acceleration associated with motion in a circle is called **centripetal** (sehn TRIHP uh tuhl) **acceleration**. Centripetal acceleration is always toward the center of the circle.

When you go around a sharp curve in a car, you experience centripetal acceleration. Your body tends to keep going in a straight line, but your seat belt pushes you toward the center of the curve. As a result, your direction of motion is constantly changing.

To see how centripetal acceleration works, try this. Fasten a small, rubber eraser to the end of a string. Watch what happens when you twirl the eraser around on the string, as shown in Figure 2.13. The tension on the string pulls the eraser toward the center of its path and keeps it from flying off in a straight line. The velocity continuously changes as the eraser follows a circular path.

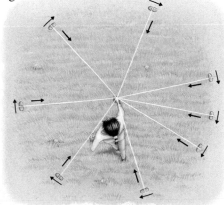

Figure 2.13 ▲
What would happen to the eraser if the girl let go of the string? Why?

TEACH ▪ Continued

Skills WorkOut

To help students understand skid length and drag factor, have them do the Skills WorkOut.
Answer 109 km/h

EVALUATE

WrapUp

Reteach Draw a concept map on the chalkboard. Have students insert terms such as *speed, direction, velocity, acceleration,* and *centripetal acceleration.* Ask students to give an example for each term.

Use Review Worksheet 2.2.

Check and Explain

1. By a change in speed, by a change in direction

2. The centripetal force always acts in a direction toward the center of the rotation of the swing. The centripetal force keeps you moving in an arc.

3. A car moving at constant speed and in the same direction has no acceleration, a car moving at constant speed but changing direction has acceleration.

4. Check students' art for accuracy. The curve should be a straight line passing through (0 s, 0 m/s) and (6 s, 6 m/s). 4 m/s

Answer to Link

Answers will vary depending on student weights. A 150-lb student exerts 667 N of force. The force necessary to slow this student down is a whopping 9340 N.

Writing Connection

Have students write a short story in which the investigator uses skid marks and a chart to determine which of several witnesses is telling the truth about an automobile accident.

STS Connection

Automobile tire tread patterns are designed for special purposes. Have students research tire design and answer these questions: What is the difference between snow tires and other kinds of tires? What is the purpose of a steel belt? What are plies? (Snow tires have extra deep grooves; the steel belt puts as much tread on the road as possible; plies are layers in the tire body.)

▼ ACTIVITY

Interpreting Data

Speed from Skids

The skid length from a car involved in an accident was measured at 59.4 m. The car's drag factor was 0.80. How fast was the car going? Refer to Table 2.1 for help in calculating the speed of the car.

SKILLS WORKOUT

Life Science LINK

When a car crashes head-on, it slows down quickly. Without seatbelts, the people in the car will continue to move through space at the same speed the car was traveling. At 50 km/h, the force necessary to slow a person down and prevent injury is about 14 times a person's weight.

1. Weigh yourself in pounds.

2. Convert your weight in pounds to the force you exert in newtons by multiplying it by 4.448.

3. Calculate the force necessary to slow you down in a collision at 50 km/h.

ACTIVITY

Science and Society *Skid-Mark Evidence*

Police and insurance investigators use skid marks to determine the velocity of cars at the time of an accident. With a table similar to the one below, they can determine how far a vehicle slides before stopping completely. A car slides farther on wet or oily pavement than it does on dry pavement. In Table 2.1, the total of all the factors that affect deceleration is expressed as the "drag factor." The drag factor is shown as a decimal at the top of the table. The skid length is shown in the column at the left.

Table 2.1   Distance Needed to Stop

Drag Factor	0.60	0.65	0.70	0.75	0.80
Skid Length (m)	Speed (km/hr)				
53.3	90	93	98	101	104
54.9	92	95	98	103	106
56.4	93	97	100	104	108
57.9	93	98	101	105	109
59.4	95	100	103	106	109

The investigator locates the length of the skid mark in the left column. He then locates the drag factor column across the top of the table. The row for the skid length meets the drag factor column at a number that tells the speed of the car at the time of the accident!

Check and Explain

1. Name two ways an object's velocity can change.

2. Explain how centripetal force affects a person on a playground swing.

3. **Compare and Contrast** Compare the motion of a car going in a straight line with constant speed to that of a car turning with constant speed.

4. **Make a Graph** Make a speed-time graph to show a boat's acceleration of 1.0 m/s^2 for 6 s. How much did its speed increase between 2 s and 6 s?

2.3 Energy of Motion

Objectives

▶ **Define** energy.

▶ **Explain** the law of conservation of energy.

▶ **Compare** and **contrast** potential energy and kinetic energy.

▶ **Infer** the gravitational potential energy of everyday objects.

A bird swoops down from a tree to pick up crumbs you tossed out for it. You are almost knocked over as your dog chases a cat across the yard. Fortunately, you recover in time to race inside to answer the telephone. In each example, changes in motion take place. Identify the changes in motion that occur in Figure 2.14. ①

Changes in motion occur constantly in the world around you. Cars move on busy highways. Tons of rock hurtle down mountainsides. Underground water is brought to the surface for crop irrigation. What gives the cars, rocks, and water the ability to move?

Energy and Change

A car won't run without the energy it obtains from burning gasoline. Your body can't move unless you have energy from food. Any change in motion requires **energy**. Energy

◀ **Figure 2.14**
What are the energy sources for the motion changes shown in this photograph? ②

Apply

You may wish to bring a guitar, ukulele, or other stringed instrument to class. To help students understand potential energy, ask the following:

▶ Do the strings have any potential energy of their own? Explain. (No, they can't move without receiving energy from another source.)

▶ How can the strings get energy? (Answers may vary, but students should indicate that someone or something will have to pluck or strum the strings.)

▶ What will happen as the strings receive energy? How will you know that energy has been transferred to the strings? (The strings will move; they will make sounds.)

Portfolio

Ask students to collect pictures from magazines or newspapers, or to draw pictures of objects with potential energy. Have them write captions for each picture that describe the objects' potential energy. (For example, a picture of a forest shows potential energy as fuel.)

Answer to In-Text Question

① **Answers will vary. Samples: swings contain potential energy (they can be pulled back and will swing forward), fuel that heats homes and the school contains potential energy.**

The Living Textbook:
Physical Science Sides 1–4

Chapter 17	Frame 02986
Energy (2 Frames)	
Search:	Step:

46

Art Connection

Alexander Calder (1898–1976) was an innovative sculptor best known for his mobiles. Calder's mobiles are groups of brightly colored shapes designed to move as the air around them moves. If possible, show students a picture of one of Calder's mobiles. Ask students to identify the source of energy that allows the mobiles to move. (Moving air; springs; touch.)

Integrating the Sciences

Life Science Every living thing needs energy to live, grow, and reproduce. To get that energy, people and animals eat and digest food. A green plant, however, does not get its food from other sources. Instead, green plants use energy to make their own food. Ask students where they think green plants get the energy they need to make their food. (Plants use light energy to process chemicals and make their own food.)

Figure 2.15 ▶
As the archer releases the bowstring, energy is transferred to the arrow.

is the ability to do work. When work is done, a change occurs. You might say that energy is the source of change.

An unwound spring in a music box has no energy with which to make sound. Suppose you wind the spring into a tight coil. As the spring unwinds, it releases energy that causes a cylinder inside the music box to rotate. Steel pins on the rotating cylinder pluck metal teeth that make sounds.

The archer in Figure 2.15 uses energy to pull the bow's string toward her. When she lets go, energy in the bent bow transfers to the arrow, and the arrow moves forward. The changes in the music box and in the bow-and-arrow involve two types of energy—potential energy and kinetic energy.

Potential Energy Stored energy is called **potential energy**. An object in an elevated position, such as a car on a hill, has potential energy. If its brakes fail, the car would roll down the hill releasing its potential energy. An object in a stretched or compressed position also has potential energy. The compressed spring in the music box and the stretched bow of the archer release this energy when they return to their resting positions.

Substances that can be burned also contain potential energy. For example, energy from the sun is stored in gasoline, wood, and plants. When these substances are burned, their potential energy is released.

You use potential energy many times a day. As your body digests food, it releases the food's potential energy. You use this energy to move. Name some other kinds of potential energy you use. ①

Kinetic Energy A flying arrow and a moving bus have the same type of energy. They have energy of motion. Energy of motion is called **kinetic** (kih NEHT ihk) **energy**. Kinetic energy is written K.E.

The amount of kinetic energy depends on the moving object's mass and velocity. To calculate kinetic energy, you multiply one half of the object's mass by the square of its velocity.

$$\text{kinetic energy} = \frac{\text{mass} \times \text{velocity}^2}{2}$$

$$\text{K.E.} = \frac{mv^2}{2}$$

Do you have more kinetic energy when you walk up stairs or when you run? By looking at the equation, you see that kinetic energy depends on an object's velocity. When you run, you move faster than when you walk up stairs. Your mass does not change. Therefore, you have more kinetic energy when you run.

Mass also affects kinetic energy, as shown in Figure 2.16. A bowling ball and a basketball travel at the same velocity. The speed of the two balls is the same, but the bowling ball has more mass and thus more kinetic energy.

Figure 2.16 ▲
If the mass of the bowling ball is 4 kg and its velocity is 5 m/s, how much kinetic energy does it have? ②

Conservation of Energy Potential energy and kinetic energy can change from one into the other. The potential energy of the wrecking ball in Figure 2.17 changes into kinetic energy during a portion of each swing. When the ball is at the top of its swing, it only has potential energy. When the ball is released, its potential energy changes to kinetic energy. The kinetic energy of the ball is used to break the structure apart.

A child uses kinetic energy to wind the spring in a mechanical toy. Each turn of the key puts more tension on the spring, and adds potential energy. When the spring can't be wound further, the child releases the toy. The potential energy in the toy's spring changes to kinetic energy as the toy moves about.

Energy cannot be created or destroyed. This is known as the *law of conservation of energy*. Energy can change into other forms, but the total amount of energy never changes. For example, energy can transfer to another object, increasing the object's kinetic energy. However, the total amount of energy remains the same.

Figure 2.17 ▲
At what point does the wrecking ball have the greatest amount of kinetic energy? ③

TEACH ▪ *Continued*

Explore Visually

Have students study this page. Ask the following questions:

► Which rocks in the rock slide have potential energy? (The rocks at the top of the hill, and the falling rocks)

► Which rocks in the rock slide have kinetic energy? (The falling rocks)

► Can the rocks at the bottom of the hill ever have potential energy again? Explain. (Yes, if there were another hill they could move down, or if they were moved back to the top of the cliff.)

► What other forms of energy are involved in the rockslide? (Heat, sound)

► Do the rocks speed up as they fall? Why or why not? (Yes, because of the acceleration of gravity)

► What other objects in the picture have potential energy? Why? (The trees at the top of the hill, because they too could fall or be burned as fuel.)

Answers to In-Text Questions

① A tree at the bottom of the cliff, because the rock has maximum kinetic energy at the bottom

**The Living Textbook:
Physical Science Sides 1-4**

Chapter 9   Frame 01529
Acceleration Caused by Gravity
(4 Frames)
Search: Step:

Integrating the Sciences

Earth Science The hills used by skiers are often classified by their grade, or how steep they are. Beginners' slopes are generally short with a gentle slope. Advanced slopes are generally long and may be quite steep. Have students consult reference sources to research how the degree of slope is determined by geologists.

Gravity and Energy

Think about a rock perched at the top of a steep cliff. Does the rock have energy? What kind?

Just like a car on a hill, you can say that the rock has potential energy because of its elevated position. The amount of the rock's potential energy is determined by both its position on the cliff and the force of gravity. How much energy the rock stores depends on the force with which gravity pulls on the rock as well as how far the rock has to travel before resting. Potential energy due to elevated position is called gravitational potential energy (G.P.E.).

As a rock falls, its gravitational potential energy changes to kinetic energy. Because of the force of gravity, a rock speeds up as it falls. Its kinetic energy increases because more of its gravitational potential energy changes into kinetic energy. As the rock hits bottom, it has maximum kinetic energy and zero gravitational potential energy. Which would receive greater damage when hit by the falling rock: a tree near the top of the cliff or one at the bottom? ①

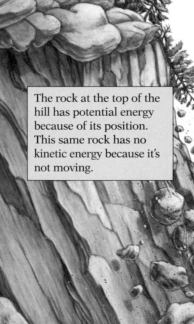

The rock at the top of the hill has potential energy because of its position. This same rock has no kinetic energy because it's not moving.

▪ Figure 2.18
Energy Conversion
in a Rockslide

The falling rock still has some potential energy, but some of its potential energy has changed to kinetic energy. As the rock loses potential energy, it gains kinetic energy.

A fallen rock has lost all its potential energy. It no longer has a position from which to fall. The fallen rock has no kinetic energy because it has stopped moving.

Integrating the Sciences

Environmental Science Building dams allows people to harness the energy of falling water. Dams also change the geography and ecology of an area by creating a lake where none existed before. There are many uses for the water harnessed by the dam—including irrigating crops, boating, and fishing. Ask students to discuss what happens to land and habitats as lakes form behind dams.

Multicultural Perspectives

The agriculture of Southeast Asia relies on the technology of the water wheel. Rice farmers irrigate their rice paddies with water that has been raised up from a lower paddy to a higher one by water wheels. Use a diagram to show how a water wheel is used. Ask, How is this different from using a water wheel to grind grain? (The kinetic energy of an animal or a motor replaces the kinetic energy of falling water.)

Science and Technology *Great Potential*

Around 4,600 years ago, the people of ancient Egypt began to use the potential energy of water stored behind dams. The largest of these dams was 97 m wide, 14 m high, and 55 m thick. Its core was made of impermeable clay, and the mass of the rock fill on each side totaled 90,000 metric tons. The ancient Egyptians originally built dams for flood protection. They also released water over the dam's spillway, changing potential energy into the kinetic energy of flowing water. Workers used the flowing water in transport canals to move construction materials to build the pyramids and other ancient monuments.

Other ancient people used the energy of falling water. Over 2,000 years ago in Greece, people used the kinetic energy of falling water to turn water wheels. The kinetic energy of the turning wheel was used to grind grain into flour. The water wheels used in China about 3,000 years ago were similar to the water wheels used by the Greeks.

Today people use the energy from falling water to produce electricity. Typically, enough water is stored behind a dam to produce continuous power. As the water falls, its potential energy changes to kinetic energy. The kinetic energy makes the turbines rotate. The rotating turbines generate electricity.

Look at the dam in Figure 2.19 and notice the high vertical drop of the water. Why is the dam constructed this way? The higher the dam, the more potential energy the water has.

Figure 2.19 ▲
How is the water wheel like the dam? ③

Check and Explain

1. What is energy?

2. How is an arrow shot from a bow an example of the law of conservation of energy?

3. **Compare and Contrast** How are potential energy and kinetic energy different? How are they similar?

4. **Infer** A person on a trampoline can go higher with each bounce. Explain how gravity affects the amount of energy available for each succeeding jump.

Time 40 minutes   **Group** 2–3

Materials

80 m fishing line

scissors

tape

90 balloons of two different sizes

30 straws

8 meter sticks

8 stopwatches

Prelab Discussion

Have students read the entire activity. Have them work in groups of four to make and test the balloon rockets. Discuss the following points before beginning:

▶ Ask students to predict the effects of varying the mass of the balloon, the amount of air in the balloon, the slope of the line, and any variables not mentioned, such as the length of the straw in contact with the line.

▶ Remind students to be careful not to pull on the fishing line, but to keep the line taut.

Analysis

1. Student answers may vary. Variables include the mass of the balloon, the amount of air in the balloon, and the slope of the line.

2. Answer should agree with the recorded data.

3. Answer should agree with the recorded data.

Conclusion

The following factors should increase speed: balloon with lower mass, larger volume of air, steeper downward slope of the line.

The following should decrease the speed: heavier balloon, smaller volume of air, shallower downward slope.

Extension

Calculated speed will depend on student's results. Encourage students to record predictions before changing a variable.

Activity 2   *How can you change the speed of a rocket?*

Skills   Control Variables; Collect Data; Calculate

Task 1 Prelab Prep
1. Collect the following items: fishing line, scissors, tape, balloon, straw, meter stick, watch to measure seconds, pencil, paper.
2. Cut a length of fishing line the width of the classroom. Attach one end of the fishing line to a table or chair. Inflate the balloon.
3. With tape, attach the balloon to the straw, as shown in the drawing. Deflate the balloon.

Task 2 Data Record
1. On a separate sheet of paper, draw a table like the one shown.
2. Record all data collected. Double check all your calculations.

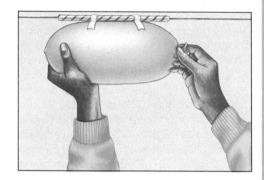

Table 2.2   Speed Measurements

Trial	Variable Changed	Distance (m)	Time (s)	Speed (m/s)
1				
2				
3				

Task 3 Procedure
1. Hold the straw so the neck of the balloon faces you. Thread the free end of the fishing line through the straw.
2. Measure the distance from the end of the balloon to the attached end of the fishing line. Record the distance in meters.
3. Inflate the balloon. Pinch shut the neck of the balloon. Hold one end of the fishing line.
4. Release the inflated balloon. Record the time in seconds it takes for the balloon to reach the other end of the fishing line.
5. Calculate the speed of the balloon. Record the speed in your data table.

6. Change the mass of the balloon, the amount of air in the balloon, or the slope of the fishing line. Record each variable you change.
7. Repeat steps 3 and 4. Record the speed for each trial in your table.

Task 4 Analysis
1. What variables did you change on your balloon rocket?
2. What produced the lowest speed?
3. What produced the greatest speed?

Task 5 Conclusion
Write a paragraph describing how the speed of a balloon rocket is affected by the balloon's mass, amount of air, and slope of movement.

Extension

Calculate the speed of the balloon if it moved half as fast as the fastest speed. Change one variable at a time until your balloon rocket travels at half its fastest speed.

Everyday Application

Apply the results of your findings to discuss how a jet airplane might control its flight speed and the angle of a climb.

Chapter 2 Review

Concept Summary

2.1 Motion
▶ The motion of an object varies depending upon the frame of reference of the observer.
▶ The distance an object moves per unit of time is its speed.
Speed = distance/time. Velocity is a combination of speed and direction.
▶ An object moving at constant speed travels the same distance in each unit of time. A distance-time graph of constant speed is a straight line.
▶ If the object's speed varies with time, the curve on a distance-time graph doesn't form a straight line. An object's average speed is calculated by dividing the distance traveled by the total amount of time.

2.2 Acceleration
▶ Acceleration is the rate at which velocity is changing.
▶ An object moving in a circle changes direction, so it accelerates. Centripetal acceleration produces circular motion.

2.3 Energy of Motion
▶ Energy may be defined as the ability to do work.
▶ Energy of position or stored energy is potential energy.
▶ Energy of motion is kinetic energy.
▶ Potential and kinetic energy can change from one to the other. The law of the conservation of energy states that energy is not created or destroyed.

Chapter Vocabulary

speed (p. 34)	deceleration (p. 40)	potential energy (p. 46)
velocity (p. 34)	centripetal acceleration (p. 43)	kinetic energy (p. 47)
acceleration (p. 39)	energy (p. 45)	

Check Your Vocabulary

Use the vocabulary words above to complete the following sentences correctly.

1. A cup resting on a table has _____ .

2. The distance you travel per unit of time is called _____ .

3. An object that speeds up, slows down, or changes direction is undergoing _____ .

4. A crawling baby has _____ .

5. The speed and direction of motion of an object is its _____ .

6. When you ride on a merry-go-round, you experience _____

7. The slowing down of a galloping horse is _____ .

8. The ability to do work is _____ .

Pair each numbered word with a vocabulary term. Explain in a complete sentence how the words are related.

1. Circle	6. Position
2. Direction	7. Motion
3. Change	8. Time
4. Slower	9. Rate
5. Work	10. Transfer

Write Your Vocabulary

Write sentences using the vocabulary words above. Show that you know what each word means.

Check Your Vocabulary

1. potential energy
2. speed
3. acceleration
4. kinetic energy
5. velocity
6. centripetal acceleration
7. deceleration
8. energy

1. Centripetal acceleration: An object moving in a circle has centripetal acceleration.
2. Velocity: The velocity of an object is its direction and its speed.
3. Energy: Energy is the ability to cause change.
4. Deceleration: When an object decelerates, its speed is reduced or slower.
5. Energy: Energy is the ability to do work.
6. Potential energy: An object has potential energy by virtue of its position.
7. Kinetic energy: An object in motion has kinetic energy.
8. Speed: The amount of distance covered in a certain time is speed.
9. Speed: Speed is the rate at which the distance traveled changes.
10. Energy: Energy can be transferred from one object or form to another.

Write Your Vocabulary

Students' sentences should show that they know the meaning of each word as well as how to use it in a sentence.

Use Vocabulary Worksheet for Chapter 2.

Check Your Knowledge

1. Calculate the speed of an object by dividing the distance it covers by the amount of time it took to cover that distance.

2. To describe an object's velocity, you must know its speed and its direction.

3. A frame of reference is a point or object that you assume is fixed. The earth and a building are examples.

4. Constant speed means that speed does not change over a particular distance. Average speed is simply the total distance of a trip divided by the time it took, even though the speed may have changed from moment to moment.

5. An increase in speed, a decrease in speed, and a change in direction are three types of acceleration.

6. Potential energy is stored energy, kinetic energy is energy of motion.

7. Energy cannot be destroyed; it can only be changed from one form into another.

8. acceleration

9. frame of reference

10. position

11. time

12. speed

13. change in velocity

Check Your Understanding

1. From the earth, the satellite and the shuttle are both moving in the same direction, but the satellite is moving faster. From the satellite, the earth and the shuttle are moving in the opposite direction. From the shuttle, the earth is moving in the opposite direction, and the satellite is moving faster and in the same direction.

2. Speed = distance/time; speed = 10 000m/1800s = 5.6 m/s

3. The object is slowing down or accelerating in the negative direction.

4. The wind will blow the plane off course to the east. The pilot should compensate for the wind by flying in a northwest direction.

5. a. Student drawing showing the path of the skateboarder

   b. At the top of the first hill, the skateboarder has potential energy. As the skateboarder coasts downhill, the potential energy is converted to kinetic energy, until, at the bottom, all the energy is kinetic. As the skateboarder coasts up the next hill, the kinetic energy is converted back into potential energy.

6. a. and b. Areas of acceleration in speed are indicated by relative brightness, while the path of an individual line shows acceleration by change in direction wherever it turns. Locations where person stopped show a larger, brighter spot of light. Students' answers should indicate that they have made these inferences.

Chapter 2 Review

Check Your Knowledge

Answer the following in complete sentences.

1. How do you calculate the speed of a moving object?

2. What information do you need to describe a moving object's velocity?

3. What is a frame of reference? Give two examples.

4. How are constant speed and average speed different?

5. Give examples of three different kinds of acceleration.

6. What is the difference between potential and kinetic energy?

7. Can energy be destroyed? Explain.

Choose the answer that best completes each sentence.

8. The rate of velocity change is called (constant speed, average speed, acceleration, centripetal acceleration).

9. An object's motion depends on the observer's (mass, velocity, energy, frame of reference).

10. Potential energy is due to an object's (weight, position, motion, mass).

11. To determine the speed of a moving object, divide the distance it travels by (mass, time, acceleration, deceleration).

12. The kinetic energy of a moving object depends on the object's mass and (energy, weight, speed, gravity).

13. To calculate acceleration, divide the (starting velocity, change in velocity, final velocity, rate of change) by the time in seconds.

Check Your Understanding

Apply the concepts you have learned to answer each question.

1. As the space shuttle orbits the earth, a satellite traveling in the same direction passes beneath it. Describe this event from the frame of reference of the earth, the space shuttle, and the satellite.

2. **Calculate** World-class athletes can run 10 000 m in 30 min. What is their average speed in meters per second?

3. The acceleration of a moving object is -4 m/s^2. Explain what is happening to the object's motion.

4. **Application** A pilot takes off from Denver and wants to head north. The winds are blowing west to east. What direction should the pilot fly so the plane travels north?

5. **Critical Thinking** A skateboarder at the top of a steep hill coasts downhill and makes it to the top of the next hill.

   a. Draw a picture of what happened.

   b. Analyze this event in terms of potential and kinetic energy. Label your drawing using these terms.

6. **Mystery Photo** The photograph on page 30 shows a time exposure of a people maze, as seen from above. As people walk through the maze, their flashlights form lines of light on the photograph.

   a. Each line of light represents the path of one person's journey through the maze. Select one path and describe the person's journey through the maze in terms of velocity and acceleration.

   b. Identify areas where motion slows or stops completely.

Develop Your Skills

1. a. Distance travelled at each instant.

    b. Cyclist A traveled the greatest distance; Cyclist C the least

    c. Cyclist B reached the highest speed; Cyclist C, the lowest; all three traveled at a constant speed for some or all of the time.

    d. Cyclist B had a flat tire—the graph is a horizontal line for part of the time, indicating that cyclist B stopped completely.

2. a. 0.5 x 18 km/h = 9 km

    b. 0.6 km /72 km/h = 0.5 min

    c. Acceleration = change in velocity/time;
       runner—18 km/h = 5 m/s; 5 m/s /10 s = 0.5 m/s^2; swimmer—
       8 km/h = 2.2 m/s; 2.2 m/s /10 s = 0.2 m/s^2

Make Connections

1.

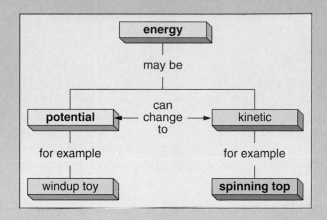

2. Common methods of navigation included using the sun and stars, direction of ocean currents, and landmasses.

3. Student speeds will vary. Make sure they use the correct procedure for determining speed.

4. Student projects will vary.

5. The average speed will depend on the different modes of transportation chosen.

Develop Your Skills

Use the skills you have developed in this chapter to complete each activity.

1. **Interpret Data** The distance-time graph below shows the motion of three cyclists.

   a. What does each line on the graph represent?

   b. Which cyclist traveled the most distance? The least distance?

   c. Which cyclist traveled at the greatest speed? The slowest speed? At constant speed?

   d. Which cyclist had a flat tire? How do you know?

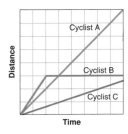

2. **Data Bank** Use the information on page 638 to answer the following questions.

   a. How far can a honeybee travel in 30 min?

   b. A jack rabbit runs at top speed to a hiding place 600 m away. How long does it take to get there?

   c. If a running human reaches top speed in 10 s, what is the acceleration? If the swimming human reaches top speed in the same amount of time, what is the acceleration? Compare the accelerations and explain any differences.

Make Connections

1. **Link the Concepts** Below is a concept map showing how some of the main concepts in the chapter link together. Only parts of the map are filled in. Copy the map. Using words and ideas from the chapter, complete the map.

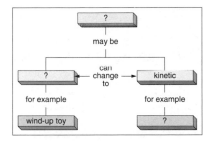

2. **Science and Social Studies** Before the invention of modern navigational instruments, people from many different cultures traveled the open ocean. As a group project, research the navigation methods of several different seafaring cultures. Give a class presentation on your findings.

3. **Science and Math** With a friend, measure a distance of 100 m. Time each other as you each run and walk that distance. Calculate each other's speed in meters per second.

4. **Science and Art** Sculptures that have moving parts are called kinetic sculptures. Design your own kinetic sculpture and describe its motion.

5. **Science and You** Plan a trip to a location 4,800 km east of your home. Research how much time the entire trip will take. What will be your average speed?

Overview

This chapter addresses the relationship between force and motion. It opens with a discussion of force, motion, and gravity that includes a definition of friction. Sections 2, 3, and 4 cover Newton's laws of motion. These sections discuss force and friction, mass and acceleration, and action and reaction forces. The chapter closes with a discussion of universal forces.

Advance Planner

▶ Supply five apple-sized objects for SE page 57.

▶ Obtain Eadward Muybridge's photos for TE page 59.

▶ Obtain balloons for SE, and a bathroom scale for TE page 70.

▶ Obtain a tide table for TE page 76.

▶ Obtain an old telephone or radio for TE page 77.

▶ Collect grooved ramps or grooved rulers, modeling clay, and metal balls for SE Activity 3, page 80.

Skills Development Chart

Sections	Calculate	Collect Data	Communicate	Compare and Contrast	Infer	Observe	Predict	Reason and Conclude
3.1 Skills WarmUp				●				
Skills WorkOut	●							
SkillBuilder			●				●	
Skills WorkOut				●				
3.2 Skills WarmUp				●				
3.3 Skills WarmUp				●				
Consider This			●					
Practice Problems	●							
Skills WorkOut		●						
3.4 Skills WarmUp						●		
3.5 Skills WarmUp								●
Activity			●		●	●	●	

Individual Needs

▶ **Limited English Proficiency Students** Have students divide a page from their science portfolios into three columns. As they study, students can list boldface terms and other unfamiliar words in the first column. Have students use the glossary or dictionary to find the definition for each term. Ask them to write these definitions in the second column. As students read each section, have them draw a picture or diagram in the third column that represents the words.

▶ **At-Risk Students** Write the titles of the three chapter sections on the chalkboard. Have students copy each title onto a page in their science portfolios. As students read each section, have them find a photograph in a magazine or newspaper that relates to the main idea or concepts in each subsection—except the Science and You, Science and Society, and Science and Technology features. Have them write a sentence that tells how the photograph connects to the content in the subsection.

▶ **Gifted Students** In the 1600s, the German astronomer Johannes Kepler discovered three laws that accurately described the motions and orbits of planets. Ask students to do some research to learn what these laws are and how they describe planetary motion and orbits. From their research students should learn to define *ellipse*. Encourage students to make models that illustrate Kepler's laws for a classroom display.

Resource Bank

▶ **Bulletin Board** Divide the bulletin board into three columns. Title the first *Newton's First Law;* the second, *Newton's Second Law;* and the third, *Newton's Third Law.* Invite students to hang pictures that illustrate each law in the appropriate column. Encourage them to use creative choices. They should number each picture as a key to discussion or science journal entries.

▶ **Field Trip** At the conclusion of the chapter, arrange to take students to a carnival or amusement park so they can analyze the rides in terms of the forces and motion they learned about. While they are there, have them list as many examples of forces, gravity, the laws of motion, and universal forces as they can. Have them make diagrams of what they saw that illustrate how the forces were applied.

CHAPTER 3 PLANNING GUIDE

Section	Core	Standard	Enriched	Section	Core	Standard	Enriched
3.1 Forces, Motion, and Gravity pp. 54–59				**Blackline Masters** Review Worksheet 3.3 Reteach Worksheet 3.3	● ●	● ●	●
Section Features Skills WarmUp, p. 55 Skills WorkOut, p. 56 Skills WorkOut, p. 58 SkillBuilder, p. 57	● ● ● ●	● ● ● ●	● ● ●	**Ancillary Options** *One-Minute Readings,* pp. 76–77	●	●	●
Blackline Masters Review Worksheet 3.1	●	●		**Laboratory Program** Investigation 7	●	●	●
Overhead Blackline Transparencies Overhead Blackline Master 3 and Student Worksheet	●	●	●	**3.4 Third Law of Motion** pp. 70–72			
3.2 First Law of Motion pp. 60–63				**Section Features** Skills WarmUp, p. 70	●	●	●
Section Features Skills WarmUp, p. 60	●	●		**Blackline Masters** Review Worksheet 3.4 Skills Worksheet 3.4	● ●	● ●	
Blackline Masters Review Worksheet 3.2 Skills Worksheet 3.2 Integrating Worksheet 3.2	● ● ●	● ● ●	●	**3.5 Universal Forces** pp. 73–80			
Ancillary Options *One-Minute Readings,* p. 72	●	●	●	**Section Features** Skills WarmUp, p. 73 Activity, p. 80	● ●	● ●	● ●
3.3 Second Law of Motion pp. 64–69				**Blackline Masters** Review Worksheet 3.5 Skills Worksheet 3.5 Integrating Worksheet 3.5 Vocabulary Worksheet 3	● ● ●	● ● ● ●	●
Section Features Skills WarmUp, p. 64 Consider This, p. 67 Skills WorkOut, p. 69	● ● ●	● ● ●	● ● ●	**Color Transparencies** Transparency 5	●	●	●

Bibliography

The following resources can be used for teaching the chapter. See page T-46 for supplier codes.

Library Resources

The Diagram Group. Comparisons. New York: St. Martin's Press, 1980.

Gardner, Robert. Famous Experiments You Can Do. New York: Franklin Watts, 1990.

Sherwood, Martin, and Christine Sutton. The Physical World. New York: Oxford University Press, 1988.

Technology Resources

Internet

PLANETDIARY at *http://www.planetdiary.com*
- Explore topics in astronomy in *Astronomy/Space* by clicking on *Phenomena Backgrounders* and *Current Phenomena.*
- Learn more about health in *Health* by clicking on *Phenomena Backgrounders* and *Current Phenomena.*
- Discover more about radioactivity in *Radioactivity* by clicking on *Phenomena Backgrounders.*

Software

Forces & Motion. Mac, Win. ESI.
Learning All About Force and Motion. Mac. LS.
What's the Secret? Mac, Win. ESI.

CD-ROMs

An Odyssey of Discovery for Science Insights: Have students try the activity *Shadow Watch* on the Earth and Space Disk, and the activity *Nerve Express* on the Living Science Disk. *SFAW.*

hip Physics. Mac. ESI.

Laserdiscs

Living Textbook. (See barcodes on pages in this chapter.) Optical Data.

Newton's Laws of Motion: Demonstrations of Mass, Force, and Momentum. AIMS.

Videos

Lets Move It: Newton's Laws of Motion. FM.

Audio-Visual Resources

Forces and Motion. Filmstrip with cassette. NGSES.

Writing Connection

After discussing the photograph of the Ferris wheel, ask students to imagine a similar picture of a speeding roller coaster. Have them write a paragraph explaining how the photograph of the roller coaster would be different from that of the Ferris wheel. Suggest that students include a simple diagram in their written explanation.

Math Connection

The formula for the circumference of a circle is $2\pi r$. Have students determine the distance they would travel on a Ferris wheel if it had a diameter of 12 meters and went around 20 times. (about 754 meters)

Introducing the Chapter

Have students read the description of the photograph. Ask if they agree or disagree with the description.

Directed Inquiry

Have students study the photograph. Ask:

▶ What does this photograph show? (Students will probably answer a Ferris wheel.)

▶ Does the photograph capture the Ferris wheel at rest or in motion? (In motion)

▶ Which part of the photograph shows the most detail? Why? (The part of the Ferris wheel that is standing still shows the most detail. The long exposure captured anything in motion as a blur.)

▶ What does the picture have to do with forces and motion? (Students should mention that the force of a motor is necessary both to start and maintain motion, as well as to stop it.)

Chapter Vocabulary

force	newton
friction	nuclear forces
inertia	terminal velocity
momentum	universal forces

 **The Living Textbook:
Physical Science Sides 1-4**

Chapter 10	Frame 01782
Force of Jet/Rocket Engines (3 Frames)	
Search:	Step:

Chapter 3   Forces and Motion

Chapter Sections

3.1 Forces, Motion, and Gravity

3.2 First Law of Motion

3.3 Second Law of Motion

3.4 Third Law of Motion

3.5 Universal Forces

What do you see?

❝The photograph looks like a Ferris wheel. It looks like it's going really fast because of the blurred lines and colors. It also almost looks like rings belonging to a planet. But because of the ladder coming out of the center, it isn't.❞

*Meike Lampe
North Mid High School
Edmond, Oklahoma*

To find out more about the photograph, look on page 82. As you read this chapter, you will learn about forces and motion.

Themes in Science

Energy The motion of the Ferris wheel changes direction, speed, or both when energy is applied. Have students discuss the kinds of energy that are involved in a ride on the Ferris wheel. (Kinetic and potential as well as heat, light, and sound)

Integrating the Sciences

Life Science After discussing Figure 3.1, explain that the skeletal muscles of the body apply forces in pairs. One muscle in each pair contracts to bend a joint and bring a limb closer to the body. The other muscle in the pair is lengthened when pulled. Have students bend their arms at the elbow, holding their upper arm muscles. Ask them to feel which muscle contracts as they bend the arm and which contracts as they straighten the arm.

Section Objectives
For a list of section objectives, see the Student Edition page.

Skills Objectives
Students should be able to:

Compare forces that act in everyday situations.

Calculate the mass of an object.

Estimate weight in newtons

Observe how gravitational force acts on falling coins.

Vocabulary
force, newton, friction, terminal velocity

3.1 Forces, Motion, and Gravity

Objectives

▶ **Identify** some forces that act in everyday situations.

▶ **Determine** the force of gravity in SI units.

▶ **Generalize** about how friction affects motion.

▶ **Observe** projectile motion in everyday objects.

▼ **ACTIVITY**

Comparing

Know Your Strength

Explain the difference in the amount of strength you use to lift a bag of groceries, to hold an apple, and to push a heavy box of books.

SKILLS WARMUP

M oving through the air in a 76-m circle probably sounds like something you have never done. Actually, if you have ever ridden on a Ferris wheel, that is exactly what you were doing. Part of the thrill of the ride is stopping 76 m in the air. However, you knew the wheel would return you to the ground.

A Ferris wheel is driven by the motor attached to it. The motor applies energy to the huge wheel. Energy provides the push that starts the Ferris wheel moving and keeps the wheel in motion. Energy is also needed to stop the wheel.

Forces Around You

When you walk into the wind, you can feel it push against you. When you ride in a car, you push against the seat as the car turns a corner. You are constantly affected by some kind of **force**. A force is any push or pull. An applied force can start, stop, or change the direction of an object. For example, to push the wheelbarrow, the man in Figure 3.1 must first apply force to lift it. He must then apply force in another direction to push the wheelbarrow. He applies a different amount of force to each handle as he pushes the wheelbarrow around the corner in order to keep it from tipping over. To determine the amount of force applied on an object, you need to know the mass and acceleration of the object.

Other forces are acting on the man and the wheelbarrow. In order to maintain his balance, the man's muscles apply forces that keep him from falling over. Identify the forces on the wheelbarrow if all the plants were moved to the front. How would the force that's applied by the man change, if the load were three-10 kg sacks of sand?

Figure 3.1 ▲
How do the forces on the wheelbarrow handles change after the man turns the corner? ②

MOTIVATE

Skills WarmUp
To help students understand forces, motion, and gravity, have them do the Skills WarmUp.
Answer The least amount of force is needed to support the weight of the apple. Force is needed to put the bag of groceries in motion as well as to support it. The most force must be used to set the box of books in motion, because of its weight and the friction against the floor.

Prior Knowledge
Gauge how much students know about forces, motion, and gravity by asking the following questions:

▶ How do you think force and motion are related?

▶ Why is gravity called a force?

▶ When you throw a ball, what happens to it and why?

Answers to In-Text Questions

① **The force would have to increase.**

② **After the turn, all forces are equal.**

TEACH

Skills WorkOut

To help students understand how mass and weight relate, have them do the Skills WorkOut.
Answer The mass of the book is 1.5 kg.

Explore Visually

Have students study Figure 3.2. Ask:

▶ How do objects with different amounts of mass affect the spring of a spring scale? (Objects with a large amount of mass stretch the spring farther than objects with a small amount of mass.)

▶ What causes the weight of an object? (The force that gravity exerts on the object)

▶ In what units is weight measured on the spring scale? (In newtons)

▶ What does the spring scale show about the force of gravity? (That it is a downward force)

Portfolio

The force of gravity has been used historically in different kinds of mechanisms. For example, the weights in a cuckoo clock are used to drive the gears that make the clock work. Have students find out how gravity is used in such a mechanism and make a drawing that shows how it works.

The Living Textbook: Physical Science Side 2

Chapter 43   Frame 42457
Lifting Weights in Zero Gravity (Movie)
Search: Play:

Integrating the Sciences

Astronomy The force of gravity on the earth is determined by the planet's mass. Similarly, the moon's smaller mass results in a force of gravity one-sixth that of the earth. Students may have seen videotapes from the Apollo missions demonstrating this fact. Refer students to the Data Bank table on page 636, Surface Gravity of Bodies in the Solar System.

▼ **ACTIVITY**

Calculating

Mass vs. Weight

You can determine the mass of an object by dividing its weight by 9.8 m/s². What is the mass of your book if its weight is 15 N?

SKILLS WORKOUT

Force and Gravity

The amount and direction of most forces can be measured. A spring scale is one kind of instrument used to measure force. The spring scale, shown below, measures the force of gravity on an object. When you hang an object from a scale, the spring stretches according to the amount of force acting on it. The greater the force, the further the spring will stretch.

The SI unit for force is called a **newton**. The newton is named for Sir Isaac Newton, the scientist who explained how force and motion are related. One newton (N) is the amount of force needed to cause a 1-kg mass to accelerate at a rate of 1 m per second for each second of motion. This is about the same as the force a small mouse sitting on a table exerts on the table. You write one newton as

$$1N = 1 \text{ kg} \times \frac{1 \text{ m}}{\text{sec}^2}$$

The weight of an object depends on the force that pulls the object toward the earth. Weight is calculated by multiplying an object's mass by the acceleration due to gravity. Since this acceleration on the earth is 9.8 m/s², the weight of a 1-kg object is 9.8 N.

Figure 3.2
Force of Gravity Measurement ▶

The force of gravity on an object is measured by attaching it to a spring scale.

Objects with a large amount of mass stretch the spring farther than do objects with less mass. The force of gravity exerted on an object is called the weight of the object.

Weight is measured in newtons. Some spring scales are calibrated to show the force of gravity in newtons.

The spring scale shows that gravity is a downward force. It also shows that weight is the downward force of gravity on an object.

Falling Objects

If you drop a feather and a coin at exactly the same time from a second story window, which one will reach the ground first? You might predict that the coin will be first. Recall that the acceleration of gravity is 9.8 m/s^2. If no other force acts on them, both the feather and the coin should accelerate at 9.8 m/s^2 throughout their fall. However, you know this is not what actually happens.

What kind of force might act differently on the feather and the coin? Look at Figure 3.3. Both objects are falling through air. When an object moves through air, its motion is opposed by the force of **friction**. Friction occurs when the surfaces of any kind of matter move past each other.

Friction from the air affects the motion of a falling object by acting against the force of gravity. A falling object gains speed until the force from air friction, which acts upward, equals the downward force of gravity. When the upward and downward forces are equal, the object

Figure 3.3 ▲
What forces are acting on both objects that affect the speed of the falling feather and the coin? ①

SkillBuilder *Measuring*

Force in Newtons

You have some idea of how much force to apply to lift a medium-size apple. Your idea allows you to estimate its weight, or force, in newtons. Although every apple doesn't exert the same amount of force, an average apple exerts a force of about 1 N. Use an apple as a standard to estimate in newtons the weight of other objects.

1. Make a chart like the one shown to record your predictions and measurements.

2. Collect 5 small common objects about the size of an apple or smaller. Lift each object and predict how much each one weighs in newtons. Record your predictions on the chart.

3. Attach a string to an object and hang it from a spring scale that measures in newtons. Weigh the object and record your measurement.

Measurement in Newtons

Object	Predicted Force (N)	Measured Force (N)
1		
2		
3		
4		
5		

4. Repeat step 3 for each object.

5. How did your predictions compare with the actual measurements? Explain any differences.

Write a short paragraph discussing how this method of measurement could be useful in some kind of everyday situation.

The Living Textbook: Physical Science Sides 1-4

Chapter 9   Frame 01529
Acceleration Due to Gravity (4 Frames)
Search: Step:

The Living Textbook: Physical Science Side 2

Chapter 38   Frame 36688
Acceleration of Falling Objects (Movie)
Search: Play:

TEACH ▪ Continued

Skills WorkOut

To help students compare the results of dropping objects with different densities, but with the same area, have them do the Skills WorkOut.

Answer Students should find that the time it takes each object to drop varies according to the amount of surface area that faces down. Flat objects generally fall faster edge first than they do flatside first.

Reteach

Pose the following situation to students: Suppose two sky divers jump out of a plane one right after the other. If the second sky diver wants to catch up with the first, what should this person do—scrunch up into a ball or spread out? Why? (Scrunch up; it would make the surface area smaller and the sky diver will fall faster.)

Skills Development

Classify Have students make a list of sports that involve projectile motion. (Diving, gymnastics, and games that have a ball of some kind involve projectile motion.)

Answers to In-Text Questions

① **Decreasing the surface area of an object will decrease the force of air friction acting on it, and increase its terminal velocity.**

② **No; throwing harder only affects the ball's horizontal motion.**

The Living Textbook: Physical Science Side 2

Chapter 39   Frame 38584
Objects Falling on Earth and Moon (2 Movies)
Search: Play:

Integrating the Sciences

Earth Science During volcanic eruptions, enormous forces push materials up and out of the volcano. The projectile motion of the materials is a combination of a small horizontal force and a great upward push, both from the volcano; and the downward force of gravity. The force of gravity causes the larger materials to fall to the earth within 2 km of the volcano. However, for the lighter volcanic dust released from the volcano, wind and air currents are strong enough to overcome the force of gravity, hold the dust aloft, and increase the horizontal component of the dust's motion. Have students draw a picture of a volcano that indicates where most of the materials from an eruption might fall. Ask them to draw and label the horizontal and vertical motions of the ejected materials.

▼ **ACTIVITY**

Comparing

Free Fall

Collect four flat objects made of paper, cloth, plastic, and metal. The objects should have about the same area.

1. Drop each object from the same height.

2. Time how long it takes each object to reach the ground.

Compare the results and explain any differences.

SKILLS WORKOUT

reaches **terminal velocity**. At terminal velocity, an object's velocity is constant.

All falling objects reach terminal velocity if given enough time. However, the time required to reach terminal velocity varies. Dense objects with little surface area, such as coins, must fall for several seconds before reaching terminal velocity. Less dense objects with a lot of surface area, such as a feather, reach terminal velocity much faster. The average velocity of a falling coin is greater than that of a feather. Therefore, the coin reaches the ground before the feather does. How would changing the shape of an object affect its terminal velocity? ①

Projectile Motion

If you throw a ball for your dog to fetch, the ball follows a curved path to the ground. This path is an example of *projectile motion*. Look at Figure 3.4. The girl throws the ball horizontally but the ball follows a curved path.

The ball also responds to the force of gravity. The ball's projectile motion is a combination of the downward motion produced by gravity and the horizontal motion produced by the thrower. This combination of horizontal and vertical motion causes the ball to follow a curved path.

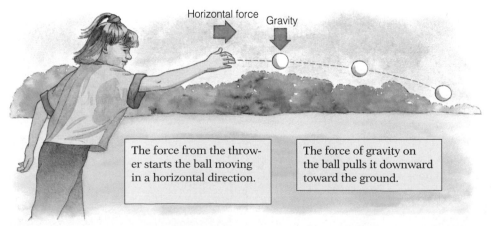

The force from the thrower starts the ball moving in a horizontal direction.

The force of gravity on the ball pulls it downward toward the ground.

Figure 3.4 ▲
If the girl throws the ball harder, the ball will go farther horizontally. Does the distance the ball drops change if the ball is thrown harder? Explain. ②

Art Connection

Today, with the help of video processors, moving images can be stored in computers to be analyzed in minute detail. The study of motion was not always so easy. Before motion pictures, for example, a horse's gallop was captured on film by a series of snapshots. These shots were taken by a line of bulky cameras activated by trip-wires that the horse ran through. You may wish to show students some of the series photographs done by Edward de Muybridge.

Science and You *The Curve Ball*

Anyone who is familiar with baseball has probably heard of a curve ball. A pitcher throws a curve ball to confuse the batter because the path of a curve ball is difficult to judge, and the batter frequently swings and misses. Curve balls, which appear to "break" as they approach the batter, are often referred to as "breaking balls."

What causes a curve ball to break away from the normal path of a pitched ball? The answer becomes clear once you study the forces that are acting on the ball. First, the pitcher applies a force to get the ball moving. Then, as the ball travels through the air, the force of gravity acts on it. These forces combine to produce the gradually arcing path taken by most thrown objects.

Why does a curve ball "break"? A curve ball "breaks" because it has an additional force acting on it. The ball is thrown so it spins as it travels through the air. The spin produces an unbalanced air-pressure force around the ball, causing it to break away from its normal path. The batter judges the path of the ball and swings to hit it. However, it is difficult for the batter to see the spin on the incoming baseball. Instead of hitting the ball, the batter misses it completely! The unexpected spin on the ball has fooled the batter.

Figure 3.5 ▲

Here, a pitcher has just thrown a curve ball. You can see the ball on its way to the batter.

Check and Explain

1. Give two examples of force.

2. Describe how you can use a spring scale to measure the force of gravity on an object.

3. **Generalize** How does friction affect a flat sheet of paper falling through air? How would friction affect a crumpled ball of paper? Make a generalization about friction and falling objects.

4. **Observe** Place two coins next to each other on the edge of a table. Push both coins off the table at the same time. Apply more force to one of the coins. Which coin hits the ground first? Why?

WrapUp

Reinforce Ask students what would happen if an airplane dropped a package. Invite them to show what would happen in drawings. Have them discuss the effect of the forces acting on the motion of the package. (The package will continue moving horizontally in the same direction as the plane, but the package cannot overcome gravity, which will pull it down. Its two paths of motion are horizontal and vertical.)

Use Review Worksheet 3.1.

Check and Explain

1. Examples: pushing a lawn-mower, pushing a door open

2. Answers may vary. The spring scale measures weight in newtons. The weight of an object is a measure of the force of gravity on an object.

3. Air friction will slow down the fall of a flat sheet of paper because the paper has little density and much surface area. A ball of paper is denser than a flat sheet and has less surface area, so it will fall faster than the flat sheet.

4. The coins hit the ground at the same time; horizontal velocity and downward acceleration are separate components of motion, so both fall the same distance at the same rate.

 The Living Textbook: Physical Science Sides 1-4

Chapter 9   Frame 01524
Photos of Balls in Motion (4 Frames)
Search: Step:

Section Objectives
For a list of section objectives, see the Student Edition page.

Skills Objectives
Students should be able to:

Infer how forces act on each other.

Observe Newton's first law of motion.

Vocabulary
inertia

MOTIVATE

Skills WarmUp

To help students understand Newton's first law of motion, have them do the Skills WarmUp.
Answer The forces are equal but are being exerted in opposite directions, so they are balanced. There is no motion.

Prior Knowledge

Gauge how much students know about Newton's first law of motion by asking:

▶ What causes motion?

▶ What causes motion to stop?

▶ What is friction?

Decision Making

If you have classroom sets of *One-Minute Readings*, have students read Issue 42 "Newton's Laws and the Existence of God" on page 72. Discuss the questions.

Answer to In-Text Question

① The applied force pulling the disc out of the stack is not great enough to overcome the inertia of the discs stacked above it.

Themes in Science

Stability and Equilibrium Point out that the behavior of objects at rest and the behavior of objects in motion are examples of stability and equilibrium. Reinforce students' natural awareness of Newton's first law by asking them to describe what might happen in a classroom in which the law did not apply. (Nothing would stay in one place—including the students themselves.)

▼ ACTIVITY

Inferring

Arm in Arm

Suppose two students are arm wrestling, and neither can bring the other's arm down. What can you infer about the forces being exerted?

SKILLS WARMUP

Figure 3.6
Why do the disc boxes at the top of the stack stay in place when the girl pulls out the lower one?

▼ ①

3.2 First Law of Motion

Objectives

▶ **State** Newton's first law of motion.

▶ **Identify** inertia and explain how it affects motion.

▶ **Define operationally** how friction occurs in an everyday situation.

▶ **Observe** Newton's first law of motion.

Suppose you decide to listen to your favorite cassette on the tape player. When you look through the stack of tapes, you notice the cassette you want is at the bottom. You grasp the cassette and yank on it quickly. To your surprise, the rest of the stack doesn't fall over. The tapes remain in a vertical stack. The only tape that really moved horizontally was the one you yanked on.

Inertia

As early as the fourth century B.C., people in China knew about laws of motion. However, their knowledge did not spread outside of China. Newton is recognized as the first person to state laws about the relationship between motion and forces.

Newton observed that an object at rest stays at rest until an outside force causes it to move. He also observed that an object in motion continues to move in the same direction until a force stops it or changes its direction. Newton stated his observations as the first law of motion.

> An object at rest will remain at rest and an object in motion will remain in motion unless acted upon by an outside force.

Objects at Rest When you sit in a chair, many forces act on your body. The pressure of the atmosphere pushes on you and gravity pulls you toward the earth. You sit comfortably, because your body pushes outward with equal force against the atmospheric pressure. Your chair pushes up against the force of gravity to keep you from falling to the ground. All the forces acting on you are balanced.

Portfolio

Students might have trouble accepting Newton's first law of motion. Tell them that scientists from Aristotle's day up to the seventeenth century thought that an object in motion would tend to move in a circle. Their reasoning was based on facts such as, the circle is the most perfect of geometric figures and the planets move in circles. Newton argued that the gravitational force of the sun's mass keeps the planets in their circular paths and pre-vents them from following a straight line into space.

Encourage students to think about Newton's first law by keeping a Force and Motion journal. Have them record their observations of objects at rest, applied forces, and objects in motion. Remind them to consider activities that occur in the classroom, in sports, and at home. They should review their journals as they learn more about Newton's laws.

As you sit, your body obeys Newton's first law of motion. Your body is at rest, and it will remain at rest until some outside force moves it. Your body resists change. You have **inertia** (ihn ER shuh).

The word *inertia* comes from the Latin word *iners*, meaning "idle." Inertia is the tendency of an object to resist any change in motion. To overcome your inertia and move out of the chair, you must apply some kind of force to your body. Until you apply a force to overcome inertia, the forces acting on your body cancel each other out.

Objects in Motion The first law of motion also applies to objects in motion. For example, when you pedal a bike, you accelerate to make the bike move forward. Notice in Figure 3.7 that the rider is no longer pedaling. However, because of their inertia, the bike and the rider keep moving forward in the same direction. Inertia can be overcome only by the application of some type of force. The bike will slow as forces of air resistance and friction act on it. Other forces could result from pushing the pedals, turning the handlebars, or using the brake.

Friction

What would the world be like if every object set into motion continued to move until it hit another object? The bus would go right past the bus stop. A kicked soccer ball would continue to roll. Fortunately when matter rubs against other matter, the motion creates friction. Friction acts in the direction opposite to the motion of an object.

Newton's first law states that objects in motion stay in motion unless they are acted upon by an outside force. Friction is an outside force that resists motion when two surfaces come in contact. The surfaces can be between two objects or between an object and air or water.

Recall the falling feather and coin as they moved through air. It was the upward force of friction from the air that slowed the feather. Friction is present whenever objects slide, roll, or rub against another material. For example, if you kick a soccer ball on flat ground, friction between the ball and the ground slows and stops the ball.

Figure 3.7 ▲
What would happen to the rider if the bike slowed to a complete stop? What force would be acting on the rider? ②

Skills Development

Infer Ask students, What would happen if the brakes on the bicycle fail? (The rider would be unable to stop and might lose control.) What might happen if the brakes are applied suddenly and the rear brakes fail? (If the front brakes grab, the bike and the rider would probably be thrown sideways or even over the handlebars.)

Critical Thinking

Reason and Conclude Ask students to consider how friction interacts with motion. Discuss perpetual motion and have students reason why an object set in motion will eventually come to a stop.

Answer to In-Text Question

② The rider would have to balance the bike or put one or both feet on the ground to keep from falling over. Gravity is the force acting on the rider.

 The Living Textbook: Physical Science Side 2

Chapter 35   Frame 30647
Newton's Laws Applied to Car Crash (Movie)
Search: Play:

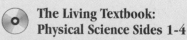 

 The Living Textbook: Physical Science Sides 1-4

Chapter 9   Frame 01669
Inertia Example (1 Frame)
Search

TEACH ▪ *Continued*

Directed Inquiry

Have students study the photographs on this page. Ask:

▶ How would the ground surface influence the runner's decision on when to start her slide? (On a rough surface she would want to start her slide later than she would on a smooth surface.)

▶ Which surface of the boat is subject to a greater amount of fluid friction, the deck or the hull? Why? (The hull of the boat, because water is a denser fluid than air is.)

▶ What effect does the tire tread have on rolling friction? (The tread increases rolling friction.)

▶ How does the tire tread affect stopping? (The heavier tread will create more sliding friction. Also, water and loose material move into the tread when stopping, so the sliding surfaces have less lubrication.)

Answers to In-Text Questions

① **A smooth surface**

② **The wide tire**

**The Living Textbook:
Physical Science Sides 1-4**

Chapter 9   Frame 01750
Sliding Friction (3 Frames)
Search: Step:

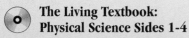

**The Living Textbook:
Physical Science Sides 1-4**

Chapter 9   Frame 01717
Fluid Friction (5 Frames)
Search: Step:

Integrating the Sciences

Earth Science Geologists have determined that the earth's crust is composed of moving plates. The plates either pass one another, slide over one another, or move apart. In certain locations, the start-and-stop motion we recognize as earthquakes is the result of movement at the plate boundaries.

Multicultural Perspectives

In discussing rolling friction and bicycles, mention that in the Netherlands, where nine out of ten people own a bike, the government provides thousands of bicycles for public use. These special bicycles can be used by anyone at any time. Each bike is painted white, and the saddle and handlebars are adjustable.
Use Integrating Worksheet 3.2.

Types of Friction

Friction affects every object on the earth. When you slide a box across the floor, the force of friction opposes your effort. Without friction, you wouldn't be able to walk without slipping and falling down. You wouldn't be able to write because your pencil would slip off the page. Friction even affects boats and airplanes as they move through fluids, such as water or air.

Sliding Friction

When two solid surfaces slide over each other, sliding friction acts between them. The weight of the object and the type of surface it moves over determine the amount of sliding friction present between the two objects. A heavy object exerts more pressure on the surface it slides over, so the sliding friction will be greater.

Sliding friction keeps the baseball player from passing the base. Which kind of surface causes less sliding friction, a smooth surface or a rough one? ▼ ①

Fluid Friction ▲

Air, water, and oil are all fluids. When the boat in the photo sails through the water, fluid friction from both the air and the water opposes its motion. Fluid friction also occurs when an object falls through the air.

Rolling Friction ▶

When an object rolls over a surface, the friction produced is called rolling friction. The force needed to overcome rolling friction is much less than that needed to overcome sliding friction.

The tread on a tire affects the amount of rolling friction to be overcome. Which tire in the photograph will create more rolling friction? ②

To show the versatility of a technologically developed lubricant, give progressive clues to help your students identify a well-known friction-reducer:

▶ The soft, waxy material is used for stoppers for chemical bottles and for electrical insulation.

▶ The polymer reduces friction and is applied to hand-saw and power-saw blades.

▶ It doesn't scorch and is not flammable.

▶ A thin coating of the material on pots and pans prevents food from sticking. (The polymer is a fluorocarbon resin with the trademark name Teflon®.)

Science and Technology *Friction Control*

Friction keeps tires on the road, and it slows down a tossed ball. Friction also slows down motion inside a machine. As machine parts rub against one another, friction causes them to wear out. Worn-out parts can be expensive and dangerous. Too much friction between the moving parts in a car can cause it to break down.

Several techniques are used to reduce friction in machine parts. One technique is to use ball bearings. A ball bearing is a smooth, round ball. It is placed between two surfaces in a machine. The ball rolls as the surfaces move past each other. Friction is directed onto the very small surface that contacts the rolling ball rather than directly onto the two larger surfaces. Friction is reduced as rolling friction replaces sliding friction.

Imagine two books rubbing against one another. The book covers will wear away because of friction. If you place several marbles between the two books, they can still slide past one another. The marbles reduce friction, so the covers will not wear as quickly.

Usually ball bearings are used in sets. Some are sealed into a part. Some are greased to reduce friction even more. You probably use something that has ball bearings in it. Roller skate and skateboard wheels, bicycles, and car parts all use ball bearings to reduce friction.

Another method of controlling friction is to use fluids. The fluid can be a liquid film or a gas, such as air, trapped between the machine parts. The fluid keeps surfaces from making direct contact and reduces friction. The oil in a car engine reduces wear on the engine parts.

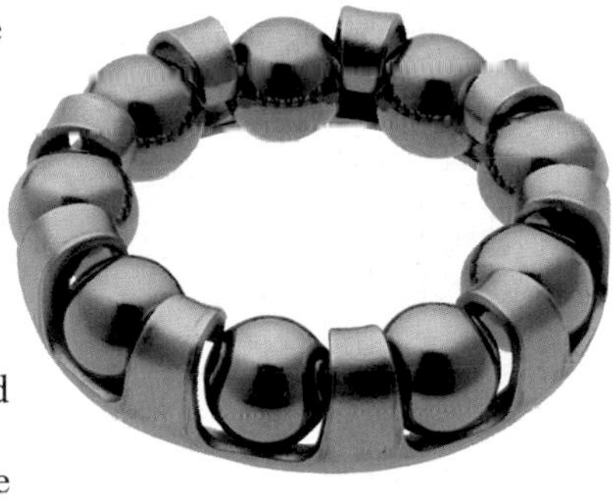

Figure 3.8 ▲

Why do you think these ball bearings are set inside the casing? ③

Check and Explain

1. What is Newton's first law of motion?

2. Explain how a dog overcomes inertia when it gets up after napping on the floor.

3. **Define Operationally** Explain how friction works to keep bicycle tires from sliding on the road.

4. **Observe** Identify two examples each of an object at rest and of an object in motion. Use examples of things in your school. Explain how Newton's first law applies to each example.

SECTION

3.3

Section Objectives
For a list of section objectives, see the Student Edition page.

Skills Objectives
Students should be able to:

Compare and Contrast the accelerated motion in two different size, rolling objects.

Collect Data about gas usage in cars.

Make a Model to demonstrate centripetal force.

Vocabulary
momentum

MOTIVATE

Skills WarmUp

To help students understand how friction acts on different sized objects, have them do the Skills WarmUp.
Answer The quarter should slide first because it has less friction to overcome.

Prior Knowledge

Gauge how much students know about mass, acceleration, and motion by asking the following questions:

- What does it mean to accelerate?
- What is required to make an object accelerate?
- Why is it hard to stop when you run downhill?

Answer to In-Text Question

① Maria will accelerate more quickly because she has less mass.

INTEGRATED LEARNING

Themes in Science

Systems and Interactions The behavior of a moving object is the result of a system of forces, whether balanced or unbalanced, acting on that object. Have students identify all the forces acting on a stationary object, such as a desk. Then ask a volunteer to walk across the classroom and have students identify all the forces acting on the moving student.

ACTIVITY

Comparing

Friction Race

1. Place a quarter and a flat eraser at one end of a book that is lying flat.
2. Slowly raise the end of the book, creating an incline for the objects to slide down.

Which object slides first? Why?

SKILLS WARMUP

3.3 Second Law of Motion

Objectives

- **State** Newton's second law of motion.
- **Calculate** the force of a moving object by using information about its mass and acceleration.
- **Identify** the relationship between momentum, mass, and velocity.
- **Make a model** to show how force acts during circular motion.

Suppose you are sitting in a rowboat on a sandy beach. Your friends get behind the boat and push it toward the water. The force of their push and the force of friction of the sand on the boat act against each other. Your friends push with a greater force than the friction force of the sand. The boat moves because the two opposing forces are unbalanced. When two opposing forces are unbalanced, the combined, or net, force is determined by subtracting the smaller force from the larger one.

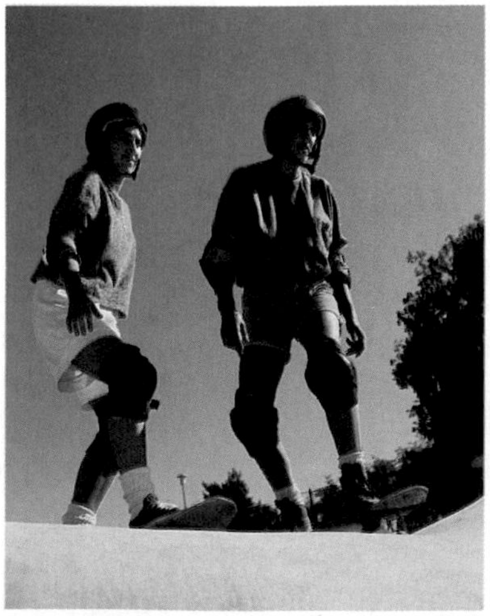

Figure 3.9 ▲
Assuming both girls apply equal force, why will Maria accelerate faster? ①

Accelerated Motion

The two skateboarders in Figure 3.9 wait for a signal to begin racing. When they hear the signal, both racers start to move at the same time. Assuming that they both use the same amount of force, Maria, the lighter racer, accelerates faster than Christine, the heavier racer. Although Newton never saw either racer, he explained why this happens.

Since Christine has more body mass, she accelerates more slowly than Maria. Christine must use more force to match Maria's acceleration. Newton understood that force, mass, and acceleration are related. He showed that the motion of an object changes, or accelerates, when a force acts on it. If you know the mass and the acceleration of an object, you can determine the force. This relationship is stated in Newton's second law of motion.

The net force on an object equals its mass times its acceleration.

Figure 3.10 ▲
What would have to happen for both carts to have the same acceleration?

Force, Mass, and Acceleration

A direct relationship exists between force (f), mass (m), and acceleration (a). The boy in Figure 3.10 applies the same amount of force to both carts. Notice that each cart has a different acceleration. Because more mass was added to the cart on the right, its acceleration is less. For both carts to have the same acceleration, how much mass must be added to the cart on the left? ②

A change in force also affects acceleration. Suppose the boy applies more force to the cart. If the mass doesn't change, the acceleration of the cart will increase.

Newton's second law can also be applied to the amount of gas needed to accelerate a car. A car with a large amount of mass requires a large force to accelerate. Since this force is supplied by gas, a large car requires more gas to accelerate than a small one does.

Graphing Acceleration

Graphs can help you understand relationships between force and acceleration and between mass and acceleration. Look at the graph in Figure 3.11. The graph shows the relationship between force and acceleration during a dog-sled race. Notice that as the force the dogs apply to the sled increases, the acceleration of the sled also increases. In most dog-sled races, more than one dog pulls a sled. How would each dog affect the acceleration of the sled? ③

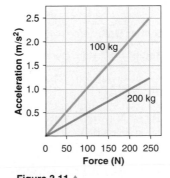

Figure 3.11 ▲
How does the acceleration of the 200 kg sled compare to the acceleration of the 100 kg sled? ④

TEACH ▪ *Continued*

Practice Problems

Work through the sample problem with students. Then have them do the practice problems.

Answers

1. Force = mass × acceleration; force = 40 kg × 2.5 m/s²; force = 100 kg × 1 m/s². Since 1 N = 1 kg × 1 m/s², the force is 100 N.

2. Force/mass = acceleration; 90 N/60 kg = acceleration; 1.5 N/kg = acceleration. Because 1 N = 1 kg × 1 m/s², then 1 m/s² = 1 N/1 kg = 1 N/kg. The unit m/s² equals the unit N/kg, so the acceleration of the cart is 1.5 m/s².

3. Force = mass × acceleration; force = 60 kg × 2.5 m/s²; force = 150 kg × m/s². Since 1 N = 1 kg × 1 m/s², the force is 150 N. To find the additional force, the initial force must be subtracted from the final force: 150 N – 90 N = 60 N.

Enrich

Assign additional problems on force, mass, and acceleration. See Math Appendix page 646.

Answer to In-Text Question

① The greater the mass, the slower the acceleration of the sled. The sled with the 100-kg mass is accelerated at twice the rate of the sled with the 200-kg mass.

Language Arts Connection

Introduce the new terms that have to do with the study of motion in physical science:

▶ Mechanics—the study of motion

▶ Dynamics—the study of the size of the various forces that cause motion

▶ Kinematics—the study of relationships between the components of motion, such as velocity, time, and acceleration

Have students think of related terms, such as *mechanism*, *cinema*, and *dynamo*.

The graph also shows the effect of force and mass on acceleration. One sled, with its load, has a mass of 100 kg. The other sled, with its load, has a mass of 200 kg. Compare the slope of the two curves. How does mass affect the acceleration of each sled? ①

Using Newton's Second Law

Imagine that you are trying to push a stalled car. Your friends come to help. Your force, plus that of your friends, causes the car to move. As you apply more force, the car accelerates. However, if people get into the car, the total mass of the car increases, and the car slows down.

Even without doing calculations, Newton's second law helps you understand how force, mass, and acceleration are related. Recall Newton's formula for the second law of motion.

$$\mathbf{force = mass \times acceleration}$$
$$\mathbf{acceleration = \frac{force}{mass}}$$

Sample Problem

A dog has a mass of 20 kg. If the dog is pushed across the ice with a force of 40 N, what is its acceleration?

Plan Use Newton's second law to find the acceleration.

force = mass × acceleration

Gather Data force = 40 N   mass = 20 kg

Solve $\frac{force}{mass}$ = acceleration

$$\frac{40\ N}{20\ kg} = \frac{2\ N}{kg}$$

Since 1 N is the amount of force that accelerates a 1–kg mass by 1 m/s²,

1 N = 1 kg × 1 m/s². Therefore,

1 m/s² = 1 N/1 kg = 1 N/kg

The unit m/s² equals the unit N/kg, so acceleration of the dog is 2 m/s².

Practice Problems

1. Suppose a student pushes a cart of groceries with a 40-kg mass. How much force does he use if the cart accelerates 2.5 m/s²? What units are used in the answer? Show how to convert to those units in your calculation.

2. A bag of charcoal has a mass of 10 kg. Two bags were added to the cart of groceries mentioned in problem 1. If the student pushes with a force of 90 N, what is the acceleration of the cart? Show how to convert to the correct units in your calculation.

3. If the acceleration of the cart with the added mass of the two bags of charcoal is increased to 2.5 m/s², how much additional force must be applied to the cart? Show how to convert to the correct units in your calculation.

Themes in Science
Patterns of Change/Cycles

Momentum is transferred from one object to another during a collision. The energy of impact in a head-on collision is equal to the combined kinetic energy of the colliding objects. Early automobiles were equipped with window glass. As speed capability increased, high-impact safety glass was used and portions of the car were designed to crumple on impact to protect the passengers.

Math Connection

Point out that the world's fastest-moving insect is called the blue botfly and has been known to fly at speeds exceeding 200 km/h. Ask students, If a blue botfly has a mass of 1 g and a momentum of 0.007 kg m/s, how fast is it flying? (7 m/s—Convert grams to kilograms.)

Momentum

A rolling marble can be stopped more easily than a bowling ball moving at the same velocity. Both objects have inertia of motion, or **momentum**. However, the bowling ball has more momentum than the marble. The momentum of a moving object is related to its mass and velocity. A moving object has a large momentum if it has a large mass, a large velocity, or both. The formula for momentum is

$$\textbf{momentum} = \textbf{mass} \times \textbf{velocity}$$

Momentum doesn't change unless the velocity or mass changes. However, momentum can transfer from one object to another. For example, when a ball rolling across a pool table hits another ball, some of the momentum of the first ball transfers to the second ball.

Consider This

Should Seat Belts and Air Bags Be Required?

Most states require that seat belts be worn. By federal law, all new cars must have air bags. Both seat belts and air bags use physics principles to save lives.

When a moving car stops quickly, inertia tends to keep the passengers moving forward. Seat belts apply a force that tries to counteract this forward motion, hopefully preventing a serious injury.

Following a front-end collision, an air bag fills the space between the passenger and the dashboard. The air bag allows the passenger's head and upper body to decelerate more slowly, helping to prevent injury.

For some people, seat belts are inconvenient or uncomfortable. They feel seat belt laws interfere with their freedom of choice. These people believe that if they drive safely, seat belts are unnecessary.

While air bags increase the cost of new cars, many consumers have been happy to absorb the additional cost in the name of safety.

Think About It Does the risk of personal injury outweigh the inconvenience of using seat belts and the cost increase of air bags?

Write About It Write a paper stating your position on the use of seat belts and air bags.

Class Activity

Ask students to choose a sports activity to demonstrate the transfer of momentum. Examples might include collisions that occur during tennis, baseball, soccer, and between players. In each instance, ask students how momentum was transferred from one object to another. (The tennis ball, baseball, and soccer ball changed direction and probably speed. One player may fall after colliding with another.)

Decision Making

If you have classroom sets of *One-Minute Readings,* have students read Issue 45 "Accelerated Motion Equations and Highway Safety" on pages 76 and 77. Discuss the questions.

Consider This

Research Have students find out about the crash tests of cars involving dummy drivers. Have them explain the role of momentum and inertia when the dummy drivers are "injured." Then have students explain how seat belts, air bags, padded dashboards, and speed limits affect the forces of motion and injuries in a crash.

Write About It Have students provide their research sources as part of their reports.

 The Living Textbook: Physical Science Sides 1-4

Chapter 17   Frame 03160
Momentum (2 Frames)
Search: Step:

 The Living Textbook: Physical Science Sides 1-4

Chapter 9   Frame 01459
Transfer of Momentum (6 Frames)
Search: Step:

Explore Visually

Have students study Figure 3.12 and the information on this page. Ask:

▶ How does the centripetal force on sharp curves change if there is an increase in the car's acceleration? (Centripetal force increases.)

▶ What happens to the centripetal force on sharp curves if there is a decrease in the car's acceleration? (Centripetal force decreases.)

▶ If the tire applies less friction than is necessary on the curve, how would the car move? (The car would move in a straight line or skid sideways.)

▶ **Infer** Why do racing cars have wide tires? (The friction created by the wide surface area of the tires helps to keep the car on the track and provides centripetal force.)

Answer to In-Text Question

① Turning the car somewhat toward the center provides centripetal force because there is friction between the tires and the road in the direction of the turn.

Reteach

Use Reteach Worksheet 3.3.

The Living Textbook: Physical Science Side 2

Chapter 36   Frame 32889
Newton's Law of Rotation:
Gyroscope (Movie)
Search: Play:

Art Connection

Both aerospace designers and science fiction writers have come up with ingenious ways to make use of centripetal force in space stations. Have students design their own space stations. Have them indicate what forces provide gravity and stability in their space station designs.

Forces in Circular Motion

You learned that an object moving in a circle has centripetal acceleration. If you twirl an eraser on a string, the tension on the string pulls the eraser toward the center, causing a continuous change in direction. The inward tension on the string is *centripetal force*. Centripetal force is a center-directed force that causes an object to follow a circular path. Look at Figure 3.12. How does centripetal force apply to the cars to keep them moving around a curved track? ①

**Figure 3.12
Centripetal Force** ▼

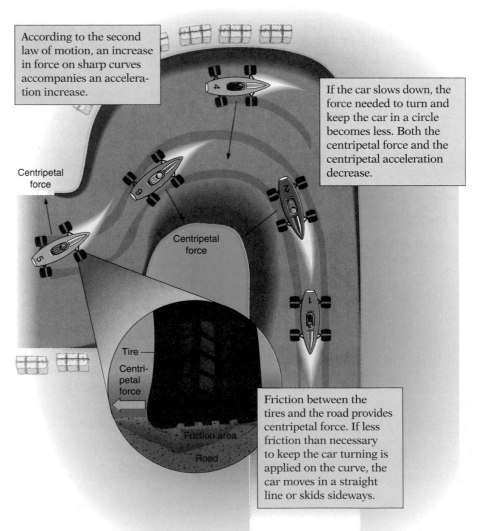

According to the second law of motion, an increase in force on sharp curves accompanies an acceleration increase.

If the car slows down, the force needed to turn and keep the car in a circle becomes less. Both the centripetal force and the centripetal acceleration decrease.

Centripetal force

Centripetal force

Tire
Centripetal force
Friction area
Road

Friction between the tires and the road provides centripetal force. If less friction than necessary to keep the car turning is applied on the curve, the car moves in a straight line or skids sideways.

Integrating the Sciences

Earth Science If the processes necessary to produce coal and petroleum began today, it would be thousands of years before the process was complete. However, by the year 2000, modern society will have used 80 percent of the known deposits of petroleum—and most of that was used in the last 34 years! Have students discuss actions they can take to help conserve this nonrenewable resource.

Science and Society *More Miles for the Size*

When gasoline cost less than fifty cents a gallon, many people had large cars that got low gas mileage. Some people liked the feel of a large car on the road. Others thought large cars were more comfortable and safer.

When the price of gasoline suddenly increased in the 1970s, people began calling the large cars "gas guzzlers." Small cars were more economical and more practical. Soon there were fewer large cars on the highways. Why would the size of the car affect gas mileage?

Gas mileage is the number of kilometers a car travels for each liter of gasoline the engine uses. The second law of motion explains why a large car uses more gasoline than a small one. Consider how much force is needed for a car with a mass of 1,000 kg to accelerate 3 m/s^2. You know that force is equal to mass times acceleration; therefore, 1,000 kg × 3 m/s^2 = 3,000 N. How does this compare with the force needed for an 800-kg car? It takes ② more energy to move a car with a mass of 1,000 kg than it does to move one with a mass of 800 kg.

Gasoline is used much faster in the larger car. Gasoline is made from oil, which is an unrenewable resource. It makes sense to conserve oil resources. In addition, gasoline exhaust causes air pollution. Driving a car with better gas mileage benefits air quality.

Efforts are being made to develop cars that use other types of fuel, such as alcohol and solar power. The resources needed for some of these fuels are renewable. For example, plant fiber is used to make alcohol that is suitable for automobile engines. Solar-powered cars may some day be practical due to new advances in solar technology.

Check and Explain

1. How does a change in the force applied to an object affect its acceleration?

2. If an eagle and a bumble bee are both traveling at 16 km/hr, which has more momentum? Explain.

3. **Calculate** A 28-kg meteor hits the surface of the moon at 130 km/s. What is the meteor's momentum?

4. **Make a Model** Develop a model to illustrate the force needed to keep an object moving in a circle.

▼ **ACTIVITY**

Collecting Data

Gas Usage

Using the information from advertisements in magazines, newspapers, and brochures, determine the make of car that uses the least amount of gas per kilometer. Why do you think automobile manufacturers advertise gas usage statistics?

SKILLS WORKOUT

Skills WorkOut

To help students collect data about gas usage in cars, have them do the Skills WorkOut.

Answer Gas usage statistics allow the potential buyer to consider the overall value of the car in terms of savings on fuel.

Enrich

Have students use reference books to find out what gasohol is (a mixture of gasoline and ethanol) and what the different sources are for the alcohol used in making the fuel.

EVALUATE

WrapUp

Portfolio Have students collect photographs or pictures from magazines or newspapers that represent acceleration. Ask them to write a paragraph for each picture that identifies the force causing the acceleration. They should note anything else about force, mass, and acceleration shown by the picture.

Use Review Worksheet 3.3.

Check and Explain

1. Force, mass, and acceleration are related. The greater the force applied to an object, the greater the acceleration, if the mass remains constant.

2. An eagle; momentum is the product of mass times velocity; the eagle has more mass.

3. 3 640 000 kg·m/s

4. Answers may vary. Students' models should exhibit centripetal force.

Answer to In-Text Question

② The force needed for an 800-kg car is 2400 N. (800 kg x 3 m/s^2 = 2400 kg x m/s^2, or 2400 N)

Integrating the Sciences

Life Science Octopus and squid make use of Newton's third law of motion. An octopus or squid moves by first drawing water into its body. Then the animal forcefully squeezes water out of its body through an opening behind its head. The force of the expelled water moves the animal in the opposite direction. Ask students to design a method of transportation that relies on Newton's third law.

Themes in Science

Systems and Interactions In any system, total momentum is conserved. The momentum caused by a reaction force always equals the momentum caused by the action force.

Section Objectives
For a list of section objectives, see the Student Edition page.

Skills Objectives
Students should be able to:

Observe Newton's third law of motion by blowing up a balloon and observing its motion when they let it go.

Infer how Newton's third law of motion applies to everyday life.

MOTIVATE

Skills WarmUp

To help students understand the third law of motion, have them do the Skills WarmUp.

Answer With the opening downward, the balloon moves upward. Next, the balloon will move horizontally away from the end from which the air is escaping. The direction of motion is opposite the direction of the escaping air.

Class Activity

Use a bathroom scale to show that force is exerted on the ground when a person walks. Have a student volunteer step on the scale. Record the reading. Then record the reading *as the student steps off the scale.* Compare the two readings. Repeat the two measurements and discuss the results.

Answer to In-Text Question

① **The rockets move upward because a force pushes them in that direction. The upwardly directed force is the reaction force to the force the exhaust gases exert in a downward direction .**

▼ **ACTIVITY**

Observing

Balloon Moves

Blow up a balloon. Hold the balloon with the opening downward and let go. In what direction does the balloon move? Blow up the balloon again. Hold the balloon horizontally. In what direction does the balloon move when you let go? Explain why the balloons don't move in the same direction.

SKILLS WARMUP

Figure 3.13
Look carefully at the photo. Why does the space shuttle move
① upward?

3.4 Third Law of Motion

Objectives

▶ **Describe** Newton's third law of motion.

▶ **Distinguish** between balanced and unbalanced forces.

▶ **Predict** how forces interact in everyday situations.

▶ **Infer** how the third law of motion is applied.

uppose you are watching the liftoff of a space shuttle. You hear a deafening roar and see burning gases shooting from the exhaust vents of the rockets. At that moment, the space-shuttle system moves slowly upward. You can infer from Figure 3.13 that the force for the liftoff comes from the burning gases pushing against the shuttle rockets. Why does the shuttle system move in the opposite direction of the gases?

Equal and Opposite Forces

The forces on the space shuttle are similar to the forces in a collision between two tennis balls. When the balls collide, they are propelled in opposite directions. The rockets of the space shuttle force burning gases downward through the exhaust vents. In response to these downward forces, the shuttle system moves upward. The motion of the space shuttle demonstrates Newton's third law of motion.

> When one object exerts a force upon a second object, the second object exerts an equal and opposite force upon the first object.

An easy way to understand the third law of motion is to say that every action has an equal and opposite reaction. You can see equal and opposite forces interact when you blow up a balloon and then let it go. Air shoots out of the neck of the balloon as it moves in the opposite direction. The force propelling the balloon is equal and opposite to the force of the air leaving the balloon.

Forces and Newton's Third Law Notice what happens in Figure 3.14 when the diver jumps down on the diving board. The board springs back and forces the diver into the air. The action force exerted on the board by the diver is accompanied by a reaction force by the board on the diver. The force of the diver on the board is equal and opposite to the force of the board on the diver.

If the action and reaction forces are equal and opposite, why don't they cancel each other out? As you know, when equal forces push on an object in opposite directions, the object doesn't move. The secret to realize is that here the action and reaction forces act on *different* objects. The diver moves because the diving board exerts a net, or unbalanced, force on him. The diving board moves because the diver exerts a net force on it.

Observing Newton's Third Law The crew team in Figure 3.15 uses Newton's third law of motion to move its boat. When an oar is put into the water, the water exerts an equal force on both sides of the oar. However, when the members pull on their oars, the oars push against the water. The water pushes back on the oars with an equal and opposite force. The boat moves in the opposite direction of the oars with a force that is equal to that of the oars as they push against the water.

Figure 3.14 ▲
How will the force of the diving board affect the diver's performance?

Figure 3.15 ▲
The crew members try to produce the greatest possible unbalanced force.

WrapUp

Review Ask students to come up with examples of everyday situations that involve Newton's third law of motion. The examples in the text will guide them. Have them draw or diagram their examples and use labels to show the pairs of forces and the interaction between them.
   Use Review Worksheet 3.4.

Check and Explain

1. When one object exerts a force upon a second object, the second object exerts an equal and opposite force upon the first object.

2. Answers may vary. The racquet exerts an equal and opposite force on the tennis ball that causes the ball to reverse direction.

3. The force on the boat causes it to move away from the river-bank. The force exerted by the jumper makes the boat move instead of the jumper, who falls before reaching the bank.

4. An example of the third law at work is each foot pushing off the ground; the push is the action force, and the ground pushes back with an equal and opposite force. The walker moves forward.

The Living Textbook:
Physical Science Sides 1-4

Chapter 8	Frame 01413
Fireworks (2 Frames)	
Search:	Step:

Cooperative Learning

Have students work in teams to make poster collages of cartoons that show the laws of motion. They should work together to add captions to their posters explaining the various examples of motion.

Portfolio

Students can learn more about rocketry by drawing and labeling various rocket-propulsion systems. For each drawing, have students write brief explanations of what the drawing shows and how the drawing relates to the third law of motion. Students may wish to add these drawings to their portfolios.

Science and Technology
From Fireworks to Outer Space

About 500 years before Newton, the Chinese were putting his third law of motion into practice. They were making rockets! The Chinese invented the rocket around A.D.1150.

   Whenever you see a fireworks display, you see one of the first uses of rocket technology. The ancient Chinese developed fireworks for religious festivals. The bright lights and bursting sound were said to "make the devils jump." Beginning in the thirteenth century, the Chinese used rockets extensively. The rockets burned an explosive black powder that propelled them into the air.

   All rockets require fuel that produces rapidly expanding gases. The gases exert a large amount of force against the inside of the rocket. The expanding gases escape out the back of the rocket. The force of the escaping gases thrusts the rocket forward. A large amount of thrust is needed to propel a rocket into space.

   Rocket fuels became very important as space exploration and technology developed. Rockets burn fuel very rapidly. Liquid fuels that work well in automobile or ship engines are heavy and can't be used in space rockets. Also fuel needs oxygen to burn. There is no oxygen in outer space. Some rockets carry an oxygen supply into space. Modern space rockets also use solid fuels, which when mixed together, release oxygen and burn.

Figure 3.16 ▲
The shape, color, and size of a fireworks display depends on the chemicals used to make them.

Check and Explain

1. What is Newton's third law of motion?

2. Explain how action and reaction forces are important in a tennis game.

3. **Predict** What are the action and reaction forces acting when someone jumps from a canoe to a riverbank? Explain why the jumper often falls into the water.

4. **Infer** Explain how Newton's third law of motion is at work when you walk.

Integrating the Sciences

Earth Science To help students understand how the force of gravity depends on distance and mass, ask them to make the following comparison: How does the weight of an object change as it moves above or below the earth's surface? (Greatest at the earth's surface; less below, because less of the earth's mass is exerting gravitational force; also less above, because object and the earth are farther apart)

Themes in Science

Diversity and Unity Every action in the universe happens as a result of one of the universal forces, or as a result of a combination of them.

Section Objectives
For a list of section objectives, see the Student Edition page.

Skills Objectives
Students should be able to:

Reason and Conclude about the forces acting on common objects.

Generalize on the effect of gravity on matter.

Classify common activities according to universal forces.

Vocabulary
universal forces, nuclear forces

3.5 Universal Forces

Objectives

▶ **Identify** the four universal forces.

▶ **Describe** how each universal force affects everyday experiences.

▶ **Generalize** on the importance of universal forces.

▶ **Classify** everyday forces according to the types of universal forces.

▼ **ACTIVITY**

Reasoning

Common Forces
Give a reason why each of the following happens.
♦ A ball that rolls off the table falls to the floor.
♦ A cabinet door with a magnet on the latch stays closed.
♦ Clothes from a dryer cling to each other.

SKILLS WARMUP

If you travelled through the universe, you would experience several kinds of force. However, even on the most distant planets, you would still be subjected to the same four forces that exist on Earth. These four forces—gravitational, electromagnetic, strong and weak nuclear force—are called the **universal forces**. Table 3.1 compares the strength of the universal forces.

Gravitational Force

Objects of any size are pulled toward each other by gravitational force. You don't notice the gravitational force between small objects because it is the weakest of the universal forces. The strength of the gravitational force depends on the amount of mass in an object and the distance between objects. Planets, stars, and galaxies are so large that their gravitational force affects other objects in space.

Gravity keeps the planets in orbit around the sun and the stars in orbit in their galaxies. The gravitational force of the earth on the moon keeps the moon in its orbit around the earth. The gravitational force of the moon on the earth causes the ocean tides to rise and fall.

Table 3.1 Universal Forces

Force	Relative Strength	Acts Upon
Gravitational	1	All matter
Weak nuclear	10^{27}	Nuclear particles
Electromagnetic	10^{38}	Charged particles
Strong nuclear	10^{40}	Nuclear particles

◀ **Table 3.1**
Notice that gravitational forces are by far the weakest of the universal forces.

MOTIVATE

Skills WarmUp

To help students understand universal forces, have them do the Skills WarmUp.
Answer The ball rolls off the table because it is acted upon by gravity pulling it toward the earth. (Gravitational) The magnet is attracted by another magnet or a magnetic metal. (Electromagnetic) Tumbling in the dryer gives clothes different electrical charges on their surfaces. (Electromagnetic)

Prior Knowledge

Gauge how much students know about universal forces by asking the following questions:

▶ What force keeps the earth moving around the sun?

▶ What do lightning and static cling have in common?

Explore Visually

Have students study the diagram and information about the planets in the solar system on these pages. Ask:

▶ Which planet's surface gravity is more than twice as great as the earth's gravity? How many times greater is it? (Jupiter; 2.54 times greater than the earth's gravity)

▶ Which planets are between Earth and the sun? (Mercury and Venus)

▶ Which planets are beyond Earth? (Mars, Jupiter, Saturn, Uranus, Neptune, and Pluto)

▶ What would happen if a spaceship came very close to a planet? Why? (The gravitational force of the planet would cause the spaceship to go into orbit around the planet.)

▶ On what objects do the planets exert a gravitational force like the sun does on them? (Planets exert a gravitational force on everything in the universe. Moons orbit planets just as planets orbit stars, for example.)

The Living Textbook:
Physical Science Sides 1-4

Chapter 9   Frame 01594
Planetary Orbit (1 Frame)
Search:

The Living Textbook:
Physical Science Sides 1-4

Chapter 9   Frame 01658
Centripetal Force (1 Frame)
Search:

Multicultural Perspectives

About 1800 years ago, the Greek astronomer Ptolemy, gave the first known description of the motion of the planets: circular paths with the earth at the center. In the early sixteenth century, Polish astronomer Copernicus revised the description, indicating that the sun was at the center of the planets' orbits. In the early seventeenth century, German astronomer Johannes Kepler combined his knowledge of ellipses, learned from Greek geometers, with the observations of Denmark's Tycho Brahe. Kepler suggested that the planets' orbits were elliptical rather than circular. Finally, in the late seventeenth century, English mathematician Sir Isaac Newton developed precise formulas to describe the motion of the planets.

Gravity and the Solar System

Newton proposed that the sun exerts a gravitational force on the earth and its moon, as well as on all the other planets. Gravitational force keeps the earth and other objects in the solar system in orbit around the sun. Each planet moves in an elliptical orbit around the sun.

Figure 3.17
The Planets in the Solar System ▼

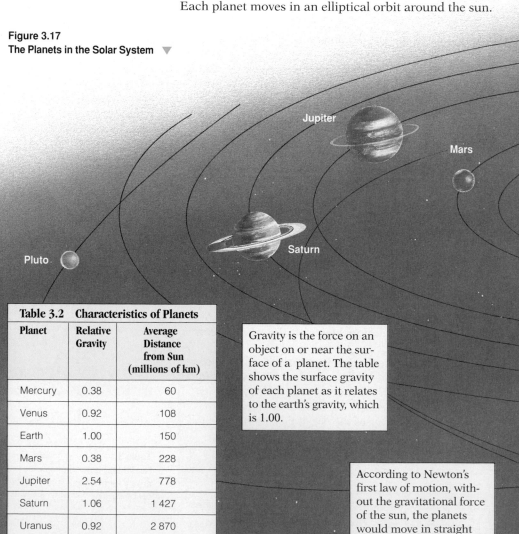

Gravity is the force on an object on or near the surface of a planet. The table shows the surface gravity of each planet as it relates to the earth's gravity, which is 1.00.

According to Newton's first law of motion, without the gravitational force of the sun, the planets would move in straight lines at constant speed. The planets would leave the solar system.

Table 3.2	Characteristics of Planets	
Planet	**Relative Gravity**	**Average Distance from Sun (millions of km)**
Mercury	0.38	60
Venus	0.92	108
Earth	1.00	150
Mars	0.38	228
Jupiter	2.54	778
Saturn	1.06	1 427
Uranus	0.92	2 870
Neptune	1.20	4 497
Pluto	0.07	5 900

Integrating the Sciences

Earth Science Discuss with students planetary rotation and the earth's colder seasons in temperate latitudes when the earth is closest to, not farthest from, the sun along its elliptical course. Emphasize that the energy of sunlight depends on the angle at which the sun strikes a surface.

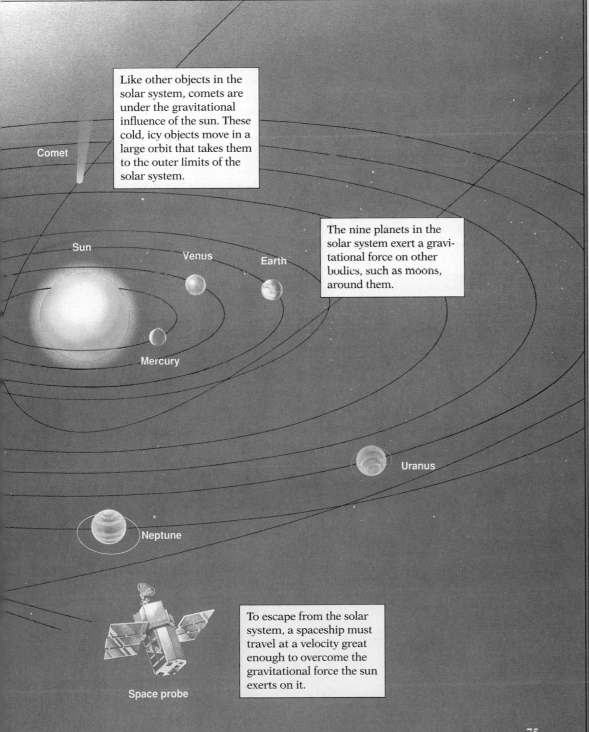

Like other objects in the solar system, comets are under the gravitational influence of the sun. These cold, icy objects move in a large orbit that takes them to the outer limits of the solar system.

The nine planets in the solar system exert a gravitational force on other bodies, such as moons, around them.

To escape from the solar system, a spaceship must travel at a velocity great enough to overcome the gravitational force the sun exerts on it.

Comet

Sun

Venus

Earth

Mercury

Uranus

Neptune

Space probe

▶ **Communicate** Use Newton's second law of motion to explain how the planets stay in orbit around the sun. (The large gravitational force of the sun acts as a centripetal force and causes the planets to travel in orbit around the sun.)

Portfolio

Demonstrate how to draw an ellipse on the chalkboard. Have students draw an ellipse on paper using a pencil, two pushpins, and a length of string. Then have students use the same materials to draw a circle. (Use only one pushpin at the center, and tie the pencil to the other end of the string.) Have them write a comparison of the shape of the two figures and put their drawings and explanations in their portfolios.

Integrated Learning

Use Integrating Worksheet 3.5.

 The Living Textbook: Physical Science Sides 1–4

Chapter 17   Frame 03183
Orbits of Heavenly Bodies (1 Frame)
Search:

TEACH ▪ *Continued*

Research

Have students obtain a tide table from the library, a marina, or a newspaper. Have them relate the tides to the phases of the moon and write a brief report on their findings.

Directed Inquiry

Have students study Figure 3.18. Ask:

▶ Why are the tides stronger when the sun and the moon are in line? (The gravitational forces of the sun and moon act together to pull on the surface waters of the earth in the same direction.)

▶ What causes the neap tides? (The sun pulls the surface waters in one direction and the moon pulls at a right angle to the sun's pull.)

The Living Textbook: Physical Science Side 2

Chapter 37   Frame 34300
Law of Gravitation (Movie)
Search: Play:

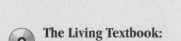

The Living Textbook: Physical Science Sides 1-4

Chapter 9   Frame 01556
Relative Weights (1 Frame)
Search:

STS Connection

As you discuss Figure 3.18, point out that people have relied on tides throughout history for fish farming. The uses for tides continue to become more varied. Among the world's highest tides are those of Canada's Bay of Fundy, which swell to over 8 meters. The city of Annapolis, Nova Scotia, harnesses some of this tidal power to produce electricity. The tides also sweep oxygen-rich waters into the region and clear away waste and potentially harmful algae. As a result, a profitable fish farming industry has been produced, and the region raises Atlantic salmon prized for its beauty and flavor.

Law of Universal Gravitation   Newton's law of universal gravitation states that every object in the universe attracts every other object. For example, the earth's gravitational force on your body pulls you toward the ground. That's why you don't float in the air.

The gravitational force between two objects depends on the mass of each object and on the distance between them. The gravitational force between ordinary objects on Earth is extremely small. For example, the gravitational force between two buildings is too small to measure. However, the gravitational force between the earth and the moon is easily measured, because both objects have a large amount of mass.

Gravitational force is also affected by distance. Though Saturn is almost as massive as Earth, its gravitational pull has no visible effect on this textbook. This is because Saturn is so far away. The earth's gravitational pull is, however, quite noticeable. Try dropping the book on your toes!

The Earth-Moon System   Newton realized the gravitational force that applies to objects on the earth also applies to the moon. He proposed that the moon travels around the earth because the earth pulls on the moon.

Newton also predicted that objects on the moon would weigh less than they do on the earth. Because the moon is eighty-one times less massive than the earth, Newton reasoned that the force of gravity on the moon would be less. The astronauts who visited the moon proved Newton's theory correct. If you weigh 490N on the earth, you weigh about one sixth of 490N, or 81.5N, on the moon.

The earth and the moon are affected by each other's gravitational force. As the moon orbits the earth, the moon pulls on the surface waters of the earth. The gravitational pull of the moon causes the ocean waters nearest the moon to bulge. You know these bulges as tides.

Figure 3.18
The combined gravitational force of the sun and the moon (top) produces large spring tides. Small neap tides (bottom) occur when the gravitational force of the moon and the earth is at right angles. ▼

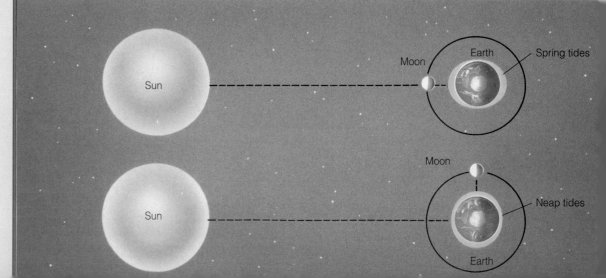

STS Connection

Bone tissue is unique in its ability to regenerate itself. Researchers are studying the possibility that the rate and quality of bone regeneration can be improved by applying a magnetic field to the area around the broken bone. Studies suggest that the treatment encourages healing by duplicating the minute magnetic fields that naturally envelope bone. These fields are referred to as *biomagnetic*.

Integrating the Sciences

Life Science Five hundred species of fish are capable of producing an electric pulse. An electric ray fish, for example, can produce a pulse of 60 volts. The electric catfish from Africa can produce a pulse of 300 volts, and the electric eel of South America has an electric strike force of more than 500 volts. This fascinating adaptation functions in both capturing prey and in perception.

Figure 3.19
Electromagnetic force not only lights this city, it also helped to build it. How is electricity used in construction? ①

Electromagnetic Forces

Electromagnetic forces are really two different forces that are closely related—electric force and magnetic force. Both of these forces may attract or repel.

Electric force exists between charged particles. Objects with opposite charges attract each other, and objects with like charge repel each other. The electric force is much stronger than the gravitational force.

You are constantly being affected by electric force. Electric force causes some objects to come together and others to stay apart. It holds together the particles that make up all matter—the foods you eat, the clothes you wear, and everything around you.

You can't actually see electric force. You can only see what it does. Electric force causes static cling in your dryer. It creates lightning during a thunderstorm. The electric force creates electricity. Think of how electricity affects your daily life.

Magnetic force is similar to electric force. The magnetic force acts between two magnets. Magnetic force attracts or repels just as electric force attracts and repels.

You are probably familiar with the magnetic force. A magnet in a cabinet door uses the attractive force to help it remain closed. Very large magnets can lift an automobile. Magnets move the maglev train in Figure 3.20 along its track.

Magnetic force and electric force interact in motors and other devices. For example, carbon granules in the receiver of your telephone change the sound of your voice into electric signals. These electric signals travel through the wires from your home to that of your friend. A magnet in your friend's telephone receiver changes the electric signals back into the sound of your voice.

Figure 3.20
The magnets moving this train can be seen along the outer edges of the track. ▼

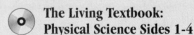
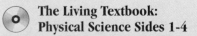

TEACH ▪ *Continued*

Enrich

In referring to Figure 3.21, you may wish to explain the process of radioactive dating. Carbon-14 is a radioactive atom of carbon that is present in a certain amount in living plants and animals. Since it changes into nitrogen at a constant rate after the death of the organism, carbon-14 is used to date plant and animal material. Measuring the amount of carbon-14 in a sample as compared to other carbon atoms and applying a formula gives the approximate age of the sample.

Critical Thinking

Reason and Conclude Have students think about the disposal of radioactive materials in the manner shown in Figure 3.22. Ask what may happen if the barrels begin to leak. (Radioactive materials can migrate and eventually enter the ground water.)

The Living Textbook:
Physical Science Sides 1-4

Chapter 4   Frame 00930
Nuclear Force Diagrams (2 Frames)
Search: Step:

The Living Textbook:
Physical Science Side 1

Chapter 25   Frame 33313
Fission and Fusion (Movie)
Search: Play:

Integrating the Sciences

Environmental Science The process of glass formation, called *vitrification*, may soon provide an effective way to treat nuclear waste. The process uses electrical energy to convert contaminated materials into glass. Temperatures in the range of 1400°C to 2000°C are necessary to melt the soil, heavy metals, and waste materials. The process also reduces the volume of the waste materials by as much as 30 percent. Invite students to discuss the issue of how to handle and dispose of extremely hazardous wastes.

Nuclear Forces

All matter is made of tiny particles called atoms. An atom is composed of electrons orbiting around a nucleus of protons and neutrons. Forces that act on the nucleus are called **nuclear forces.**

The *strong nuclear force* holds the nucleus together. Without the strong force, the protons and neutrons in the nucleus would fly apart. The strong force acts only over extremely short distances, but it is quite powerful. When a nucleus that has been held together by the strong force comes apart, huge amounts of energy are released. This energy can be used to produced electricity or a nuclear explosion.

The other important force in the nucleus is the *weak nuclear force*. As its name implies, the weak force is slightly weaker in strength than the strong force. The weak force also acts only over a short range, but it affects all particles, not just protons and neutrons. The weak force can cause a neutron to decay into a proton, an electron, and a third particle called antineutrino.

All particles that decay in the above manner are called radioactive. Measurement of radioactive decay can be used to reveal the age of a fossil. Some kinds of nuclear decay release harmful radiation that can affect people and the environment.

Figure 3.21 ▲
With special equipment, the scientist is able to determine the amount of radioactive elements in ancient artifacts.

Figure 3.22 ▶
Burying radioactive materials in pits like this one is a temporary means of disposal.

Integrating the Sciences

Life Science   Electric impulses travel through skeletal muscles as well as cardiac muscles. Researchers have duplicated this current and are seeking ways to apply it to assist paralyzed patients. During paralysis, the normal pathway traveled by electric impulses is broken. The electric message that signals movement does not reach the muscle. With the help of tiny computer processors, a paralyzed patient can trigger an impulse directly to the affected muscle. The pulse produces muscle contractions that simulate normal movement. While not all patients can benefit from this functional electric stimulation (FES), some patients have learned to write, drive, and even walk again.

Science and Technology
Reading Your Heartbeat

The cells of your nervous system carry nerve impulses. These impulses pass through nerve cells as an electric charge. Usually electric activity is measured with an electric meter. Perhaps you have watched someone use such a meter to test the electric charge in a battery.

Electric activity in your body can be measured in a similar way. Your heartbeats begin with an electric impulse passing through the heart's muscle cells. The electric current generated in the heart spreads throughout your body. When a machine called an electrocardiograph is attached to your skin, the electric current can be picked up and recorded.

The graph in Figure 3.23 is called an electrocardiogram, or EKG reading. EKG readings have three distinct waves. Each wave shows electric activity increasing then decreasing in different parts of the heart. Doctors use EKG readings to detect abnormal heartbeats.

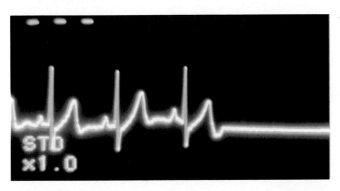

◀ **Figure 3.23**
The top of the wave on the electrocardiogram indicates when the heart muscle contracts. What area indicates that the heart muscle is at rest? ①

Check and Explain

1. Name the four universal forces.

2. Explain the roles of the universal forces when you heat food in an electric oven.

3. **Generalize**   State why the gravitational force is important to every object in the universe.

4. **Classify**   List some activities taking place in your classroom. Classify each activity according to the universal force that applies to it.

Skills Development

Infer   Ask students to explain what must happen in order for the electrocardiogram readout to occur. (The electric impulse must be translated to a motion in the pen that gives a reading.)

EVALUATE

WrapUp

Portfolio   Divide students into four groups and assign one of the universal forces to each group. Ask each group to imagine and discuss what would happen if their force were suddenly "switched off" on the earth. Have the individual members present their group's ideas in a variety of forms, such as oral descriptions, short stories, poems, and drawings. Encourage students to be creative.
Use Review Worksheet 3.5.

Check and Explain

1. Gravitational, electromagnetic, strong and weak nuclear forces

2. Gravity keeps the food in one place; electromagnetic operates the oven; nuclear force holds the atoms together in the particles of food.

3. The gravitational force acts on and between every object.

4. Answers may vary. Students' lists should note each of the four universal forces. Sitting in a chair—gravitational force; lighting—electrical force; cupboards held shut—magnetic force; glow-in-the-dark watch—nuclear force.

Answer to In-Text Question

① The flattened area between the up-and-down waves shows when the heart muscle is at rest.

Time 60 minutes **Group** pairs

Materials

30 grooved ramps

0.5 kg modeling clay

15 rulers

15 steel balls

15 aluminum balls (same diameter as steel balls)

Analysis

1. No. Both should get to the bottom at the same time.

2. The steel ball

3. Variables include the slope and dimension of the ramps, and the mass of the balls.

4. By using both ramps for each ball you eliminate the possibility that one ramp is faster. This is the control in the experiment.

5. Gravitational force, air resistance (fluid friction); Students may also identify rolling friction.

Conclusion

Students should conclude that objects having different masses but the same surface area accelerate downward at the same rate.

Everyday Application

Students might suggest that they would not have used the ramp for the heavy boxes because the heavy boxes would move too fast down the ramp. Now they should expect both the light and heavy boxes to travel down the same ramp at the same rate of acceleration. The heavy boxes will hit the bottom with more force, however.

Extension

Students might expect there to be an obvious difference because of the tennis ball's greater surface area. At a height of only 3 m, however, there is little difference.

Prelab Discussion

Have students read the entire activity before beginning. You may substitute balls of other materials, such as marbles and plastic balls of the same diameter. Discuss the difference between falling objects and objects that roll down a ramp.

▶ Slope and friction between the ramp and the ball are important. The surface of each ramp should slope at the same angle and have the same smoothness.

▶ Rotation of the ball; the circumferences must be the same, so the diameter of both balls must be the same.

Activity 3 Do heavier objects fall faster than lighter objects?

Skills Predict; Observe; Infer

Task 1 Prelab Prep

1. Collect the following items: 2 metal or wood grooved ramps of equal length, clay, ruler, steel ball and aluminum ball with the same diameter, and 2 books.

2. Determine which ball has more mass.

Task 2 Data Record

1. On a separate sheet of paper, draw the data table shown.

2. Predict which ball will take the least amount of time to roll down one of the ramps. Record your prediction.

3. Record your observations about the speed of the two balls in the data table.

Table 3.3 Trial Observations

Ramp A Trial	Which ball reaches bottom first?	
	Prediction	**Actual**
1		
2		
3		
Ramp B Trial		
1		
2		
3		

Task 3 Procedure

1. Set up the two ramps, *A* and *B*, side-by-side. Raise one end of each ramp 5 cm. Support the raised end with a book.

2. With the clay, make a stop at the bottom of each ramp.

3. Place one ball at the top of each ramp. Hold the balls in place with the ruler.

4. Release the balls at the same time by quickly raising the ruler. Listen for the sound of the metal balls striking the clay stop. In your data table, record which ball, if either, reached the bottom first.

5. Repeat steps 3 and 4 two more times. Record your results.

6. Reverse the balls used on each of the ramps in order to control for differences in your ramps. Repeat steps 3 and 4 three times. Record your results.

Task 4 Analysis

1. Does one ball consistently reach the end of the ramp before the other ball? If so, which one?

2. Which ball has more mass?

3. Identify the variables in this activity.

4. Why was it important to release the balls at the same time?

5. What forces act on the balls as they roll down the ramp?

Task 5 Conclusion

Write a short paragraph explaining what happens when objects of different masses fall at the same time.

Everyday Application

Suppose you want to move some very heavy boxes and some light boxes down a ramp. Explain how this activity might help you to decide which boxes to move down the ramp.

Extension

If you dropped a table-tennis ball and a steel ball from 3 m above the floor, would there be a difference in their falling time? Try it. Explain your observations.

Chapter 3 Review

Concept Summary

3.1 Forces, Motion, and Gravity
▶ Forces transfer energy to an object.
▶ Gravity determines weight.
▶ The SI unit for force is the newton.
▶ Friction is a force that opposes motion.

3.2 First Law of Motion
▶ Newton's first law of motion states an object at rest stays at rest and an object in motion stays in motion unless acted on by an outside force.
▶ The inertia of a resting or moving object can be overcome by an outside force.
▶ The types of friction include sliding, rolling, and fluid friction.

3.3 Second Law of Motion
▶ Newton's second law of motion states that force equals mass times acceleration.

▶ The acceleration of an object is directly affected by any change in its mass or in the force applied to it.

3.4 Third Law of Motion
▶ Newton's third law of motion states that for every action exerted on an object an equal and opposite reaction results.
▶ When the forces on an object are unbalanced, motion occurs.

3.5 Universal Forces
▶ The universal forces are gravitation, electromagnetism, and nuclear.
▶ Gravitational force is the attraction between objects in the universe.
▶ Electric force and magnetic force depends on the charges of objects.

Chapter Vocabulary

force (p. 55)	friction (p. 57)	inertia (p. 61)	universal forces (p. 73)
newton (p. 56)	terminal velocity (p. 58)	momentum (p. 67)	nuclear forces (p. 78)

Check Your Vocabulary

Use the vocabulary words above to complete the following sentences correctly.

1. The force that opposes motion is _____ .
2. When the upward and downward forces on a falling object are equal, the object reaches _____ .
3. When your body is at rest, you have _____ .
4. A push or pull that starts or stops the motion of an object or changes its direction is called a(n) _____ .
5. Gravitation, electromagnetic, and strong and weak nuclear forces are _____ .
6. The force that holds the particles in the nucleus together is the _____ .
7. The SI unit for force is _____ .

Identify the word or term in each group that does not belong. Explain why it does not belong with the group.

8. universal force, electromagnetic force, gravitational force
9. weak force, strong force, sliding force
10. electric, magnetic, centripetal
11. sliding, rolling, momentum
12. terminal velocity, constant acceleration, friction

Write Your Vocabulary

Write sentences using the vocabulary words above. Show that you know what each word means.

Check Your Vocabulary

1. friction
2. terminal velocity
3. inertia
4. force
5. universal forces
6. strong nuclear force
7. newton
8. universal force: Universal force is a general term that includes electromagnetic and gravitational forces.
9. sliding force: The sliding force is not one of the universal forces.
10. centripetal force: Electric and magnetic are forces between objects; centripetal force is the force required to make an object move in a circle.
11. momentum: Sliding and rolling are types of friction; momentum is a property of a moving object.
12. constant acceleration: Terminal velocity is reached because of friction between the object and the air.

Write Your Vocabulary

Students' sentences should show that they know the meaning of each word as well as how to use it in a sentence.

Use Vocabulary Worksheet for Chapter 3.

Check Your Knowledge

1. Terminal velocity is the velocity at which the force of gravity pulling down on a falling object is exactly balanced by the force of air resistance pushing upward, resulting in the object falling at a constant velocity.

2. $a = F/m$; $a = 40\ N/70\ kg = 0.57\ m/s^2$

3. The force of gravity from the moon causes tides on the earth.

4. Centripetal force is a force that causes an object to move in a circular path.

5. The weight of an object is a result of the force of gravity on the object.

6. A thrown ball follows a curved path because of the force of gravity on the ball.

7. The force of your muscles on the pedals and handlebars; the force of your weight on the seat; the force of friction from the pavement pushing on the tires; the force of gravity on the bike

8. False; acceleration

9. True

10. False; first

11. True

12. True

13. True

14. True

Check Your Understanding

1. The earth exerts a gravitational force on all objects and the ones near its surface fall toward it.

2. A toy car moving over sandpaper will accelerate more slowly because there will be a greater friction force opposing its motion.

3. The larger the force applied to a given mass, the greater its acceleration.

4. If the chair disappeared, there would no longer be a force pushing up on the person to balance the force of gravity pulling down, and the person would accelerate toward the earth.

5. 5 kg x 400 m/hr = 5 kg x 0.11 m/s = 0.55 kg ·m/s. Anything that is moving has a greater momentum than something that is at rest (velocity = 0).

6. Sliding friction: a hockey puck on ice; rolling friction: a golf ball on a putting green; fluid friction: a fish moving through the water

7. The ball exerts a force on the wall; the wall exerts an equal and opposite force back on the ball, causing the ball to rebound.

8. They both act by attracting or repelling.

9. From the values given, Jupiter probably has the greatest mass, assuming that the masses of the planets are directly related to their radii. Remember that gravitational force is also dependent on the radius of an object.

10. The force acting on the Ferris wheel to keep it rotating is a turning force applied by the motor. If the motor stopped, the wheel would stop rotating.

Chapter 3 Review

Check Your Knowledge
Answer the following in complete sentences.

1. What is terminal velocity?

2. Calculate the acceleration of a 70-kg mass on a swing if you push it with a 40-N force.

3. How does the force of gravity from the moon affect the earth?

4. What is centripetal force?

5. How is gravity related to the weight of an object?

6. What causes a ball to follow a curved path when you throw it?

7. List three different kinds of force you use when you ride your bike.

Determine whether each statement is true or false. Write *true* if it is true. If it is false, change the underlined word to make the statement true.

8. According to the second law of motion, force is equal to mass times <u>speed</u>.

9. The force that holds the <u>nucleus</u> together is the strong nuclear force.

10. Newton's <u>third</u> law of motion could be called the law of inertia.

11. According to Newton's second law, acceleration <u>decreases</u> as mass increases.

12. <u>Momentum</u> can transfer from one object to another object.

13. The electric force and the <u>magnetic</u> force are both a result of charged particles.

14. The acceleration of the earth's gravity is <u>9.8m/s²</u>.

Check Your Understanding
Apply the concepts you have learned to answer each question.

1. Why do objects fall toward the surface of the earth?

2. Predict how a toy car moving over sandpaper will accelerate compared to the same car moving over marble? Explain the reason for your prediction.

3. Explain how the acceleration of a mass changes if the force applied to it increases or decreases.

4. What would happen if the chair you are sitting on disappeared? Explain.

5. Calculate the momentum of a 5-kg fish swimming at 400 m/hr. Which would have more momentum: a 5-kg fish swimming at 400 m/hr or a 25-kg fish at rest?

6. Give an example of each type of friction: sliding friction, rolling friction, and fluid friction.

7. **Application** A handball is hit hard against a concrete wall. Use Newton's third law of motion to explain what happens and why.

8. In what way are electric force and magnetic force similar?

9. **Application** If the surface gravity of Jupiter is 2.54, Earth 1.00, Pluto 0.23, and Saturn 1.06, which planet probably has the most mass? Explain.

10. **Mystery Photo** The curved lines of light in the photograph on page 54 are from a Ferris wheel moving in a circle. What force is acting on the Ferris wheel to keep it moving in a circle? What is the source of this force? If this force were removed, what would happen to the motion?

Develop Your Skills

1. a. Object D fell fastest; object A fell slowest.
   b. Object A experiences more fluid friction.
2. a. You would jump farthest on Pluto.
   b. You would jump the least distance on the sun; of all the planets, you would jump the least distance on Jupiter.
   c. The surface gravity varies among the planets because their masses and diameters vary.
3. Accept any logical design. Check for pertinent variables and effective controls.

Make Connections

1.

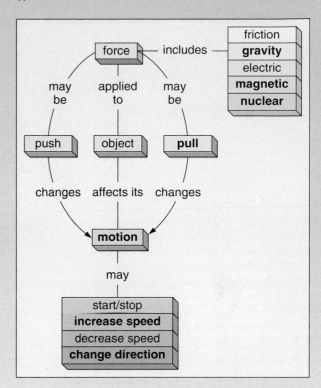

2. Answers will vary, but may include: friction between the ball and a player's hand or glove that keeps the ball from slipping out; friction between the players' shoes and the ground, providing traction; or any other example of two surfaces coming in contact with each other.
3. Collages will vary. In checking student examples of the third law, ask students to identify the pair of equal and opposite forces illustrated in each picture.
4. Answers will vary depending on the student's weight.

Develop Your Skills

Use the skills you have developed in this chapter to complete each activity.

1. **Interpret Data** The graph below shows data about four objects dropped to the ground from the same height at the same time.

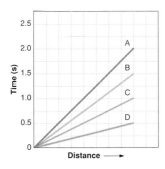

a. Which object fell fastest? Slowest?

b. Suppose object A and C have the same mass. Which object experiences the most fluid friction?

2. **Data Bank** Use the information on page 636 to answer the following questions.

a. Imagine you jumped straight up on each of the solar-system bodies listed in the table. On which planet would you jump the highest?

b. On which solar-system body would you jump the least distance?

c. Why does the distance you could jump vary with each planet?

3. **Design an Experiment** There are many ways to reduce friction in moving parts, such as using oils, greases, air flow, water, and ball bearings. Design an experiment to test which friction-reducing method works best.

Make Connections

1. **Link the Concepts** Below is a concept map showing how some of the main concepts in this chapter link together. Only parts of the map are filled in. Copy the map. Using words and ideas from the chapter, complete the map.

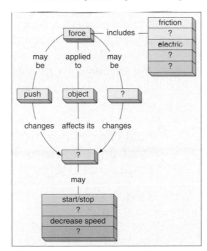

2. **Science and P.E.** Identify the types of friction that take place during a softball game. Explain how each type of friction you identify applies to the softball game.

3. **Science and Art** Using pictures from magazines, make a collage that illustrates Newton's third law of motion.

4. **Science and You** Use your weight on the earth to determine your weight on the moon, on Jupiter, on Saturn, and on Pluto.

Overview

The nature of forces in fluids and fluid pressure are presented in this chapter. Fluid pressure is defined in the first section. A discussion of the relationship between gravity, weight, and buoyancy follows in the second section. The relationship between density and buoyant force is explored. In the last section, pressure changes in moving fluids are described and used to explain how a heavier-than-air object can fly.

Advance Planner

▶ Provide milk cartons for SE page 86.

▶ Supply glasses, water, and drinking straws for TE page 87.

▶ Provide eggs and cooking oil for TE page 91.

▶ Obtain waterproof clay for SE page 93.

▶ Provide a balance, screws, paper clips, erasers, and rulers for TE page 93.

▶ Collect magazines and newspapers for TE pages 88, 94, and 100.

▶ Collect droppers and 1-L plastic soft drink bottles, with caps, for SE Activity 4, page 96.

Skills Development Chart

Sections	Communicate	Compare and Contrast	Hypothesize	Infer	Model	Observe	Predict	Research
4.1 Skills WarmUp				●				
Skills WorkOut		●						
4.2 Skills WarmUp							●	
Skills WorkOut			●					
Historical Notebook		●			●			●
Activity	●	●		●		●		
4.3 Skills WarmUp						●		
SkillBuilder		●		●				

Individual Needs

▶ **Limited English Proficiency Students** Tape record the definitions and pronunciations of the chapter's boldface terms. Tell students which figures and definitions in the text illustrate the term. Have them use the tape recorder to listen to the information about each term. Then have students define the terms using their own words. Have them make their own tape recordings of their definitions. They can use this tape to review important concepts in the chapter.

▶ **At-Risk Students** Ask students to write each of the section titles on a separate page in their science portfolios. Have them choose four important ideas in each section and copy these onto their portfolio pages. Then have them link the ideas together in a concept map, drawing, or short story.

▶ **Gifted Students** Invite students to design, build, and fly a kite. If possible, have them fly their kites for the class and explain the principles involved in the flight. Students who have trouble getting the kites to fly should identify, analyze, and explain the problem.

Resource Bank

▶ **Bulletin Board** Along the left side of the bulletin board, place a vertical scale that starts with a deep ocean trench and ends at the edge of the earth's atmosphere. The scale should show distance above and below sea level, as well as the different fluid pressure at each level. You may want to use colored construction paper to distinguish water, land, and atmosphere. Encourage students to fill the rest of the bulletin board with pictures of life forms that exist at the different levels as well as boats, planes, and anything else that illustrates forces in fluids. Have them add labels that explain the forces acting upon or being used by the things illustrated.

▶ **Field Trip** Arrange a visit to an airport, harbor, or shipyard. Encourage students to observe and ask questions about the buoyancy and motion of various kinds of aircraft or ships.

Section	Core	Standard	Enriched
4.1 Fluid Pressure pp. 85–90			
Section Features Skills WarmUp, p. 85 / Skills WorkOut, p. 86	• •	• •	•
Blackline Masters Review Worksheet 4.1 / Integrating Worksheet 4.1a / Integrating Worksheet 4.1b	• • •	• • •	• • •
Overhead Blackline Transparencies Overhead Blackline Master 4 and Student Worksheet	•	•	•
4.2 Buoyancy pp. 91–96			
Section Features Skills WarmUp, p. 91 / Skills WorkOut, p. 93 / Historical Notebook, p. 94 / Activity, p. 96	• • • •	• • • •	• • • •

Section	Core	Standard	Enriched
Blackline Masters Review Worksheet 4.2 / Reteach Worksheet 4.2 / Skills Worksheet 4.2 / Integrating Worksheet 4.2	• • • •	• • • •	• • •
Laboratory Program Investigation 8	•	•	•
Color Transparencies Transparencies 6, 7	•	•	•
4.3 Forces in Moving Fluids pp. 97–102			
Section Features Skills WarmUp, p. 97 / SkillBuilder, p. 99	• •	• •	• •
Blackline Masters Review Worksheet 4.3 / Skills Worksheet 4.3 / Integrating Worksheet 4.3 / Vocabulary Worksheet 4	• • • •	• • • •	• • • •
Color Transparencies Transparency 8	•	•	•

Bibliography

The following resources can be used for teaching the chapter. See page T-46 for supplier codes.

Library Resources

Cobb, Vicki, and Kathy Darling. Bet You Can! Science Possibilities to Fool You. New York: Avon Books, 1980.

Cobb, Vicki, and Kathy Darling. Bet You Can't! Science Impossibilities to Fool You. New York: Avon Books, 1980.

The Diagram Group. Comparisons. New York: St. Martin's Press, 1980.

White, Jack R. The Hidden World of Forces. New York: Dodd, Mead & Company, 1987.Mead & Company, 1987.

Technology Resources

Internet

PLANETDIARY at *http://www.planetdiary.com*
- Learn more about the atmosphere in *Atmosphere* by clicking on *Phenomena Backgrounders*.
- Review geological and meteorological news in *Current Phenomena*.
- Discover more about animals in *Fauna* by clicking on *Phenomena Backgrounders*.

Software

Eyewitness Virtual Reality: Bird. Win. ER.
Greatest Paper Airplane. Mac, Win. ESI.

Laserdiscs

Living Textbook. (See barcodes on pages in this chapter.) Optical Data.
Physics of Flight. VID.

Videos

Exceeding Man's Reach. MMI.

Writing Connection

Encourage students to imagine the force of water moving in a whirlpool. Have them imagine what that force would do to a small boat or a swimmer in the area. Ask students to write a story about a canoe trip during which they meet up with one of these natural forces.

Integrating the Sciences

Earth Science Explain that a whirlpool moves in a clockwise direction in the Northern Hemisphere and in a counter-clockwise direction in the Southern Hemisphere. At the equator a whirlpool can move in either direction. This phenomenon is caused by the rotation of the earth and is called the Coriolis effect.

Introducing the Chapter

Have students read the description of the photograph. Ask if they agree or disagree with the description. Ask what changes they might make in the description. Encourage any students who have seen a whirlpool to share the experience with the class.

Directed Inquiry

Have students study the photograph. Ask:

► What is this a photograph of? (Students may identify the image as water flowing down a drain or as a whirlpool.)

► How would you describe the movement of the water? (It is moving in a downward spiral in a clockwise direction.)

► What do you think would happen to a leaf caught in this swirl of water? (It would be swept in circles and pulled downward with the spiraling water.)

► How do you think the picture is related to the subject of this chapter? (It shows an example of a fluid—water—whose motion clearly exerts a force.)

Chapter Vocabulary

airfoil	lift
buoyant force	pressure
drag	thrust
fluid	

Chapter 4 Forces in Fluids

Chapter Sections

4.1 Fluid Pressure

4.2 Buoyancy

4.3 Forces in Moving Fluids

What do you see?

❝Water is going down the drain. It is moving like this because there is a hole in the sink and it is pulling the rest of the water. If I were in the middle of this, I would be pulled down the drain.❞

Emily McCormick
Barnstable School
Hyannis, Massachusetts

To find out more about the photograph, look on page 104. As you read this chapter, you will learn about forces at work in fluids.

Themes in Science

Diversity and Unity Fluids, like all other kinds of matter, exert a force on the objects around them. Ask students to describe the fluid forces acting on a fully inflated bicycle tire. (Air inside the tire is pushing outward. The tire is pushing against the air inside it. Air outside the tire is pushing against the tire with the force of atmospheric pressure.)

Patterns of Change/Cycles Point out that some units, such as *newton* and *pascal,* are named after scientists. Blaise Pascal (1623–1662), a French physicist, was the first to point out that fluid in a container exerts equal pressure in all directions. Pascal's interests reached beyond his study of fluids. He was also a mathematician and a philosopher. Encourage students to research Pascal's work in other fields.

Section Objectives
For a list of section objectives, see the Student Edition page.

Skills Objectives
Students should be able to:

Classify gases as fluids.

Observe the effects of fluid pressure.

Predict changes in air and water pressure.

Vocabulary
fluid, pressure

4.1 Fluid Pressure

Objectives

▶ **Define** pressure and explain how it is measured.

▶ **Identify** examples of fluid pressure.

▶ **Predict** the effects of fluid pressure in land and water environments.

▼ ACTIVITY

Inferring

Fluid Air

Fill your cheeks with air so they puff up. What happens when you open your mouth a little? Why? What fluid forced your cheeks outward?

SKILLS WARMUP

What tools do you need to fix a flat tire on a bicycle? One of the tools you probably need is an air pump. By attaching the air pump to the tire stem, you form a passageway for air to flow into the tire. Air is a **fluid**. A fluid is any substance that can flow. People often think of fluids as liquids, such as water or oil. But a gas, like air, is also a fluid.

As you operate the air pump, the tire fills with air. You observe the tire expand and become firmer. How do you know when the tire has enough air? By squeezing the tire, you can judge the amount of air it contains. If the tire feels soft, you keep on pumping. If the tire feels too hard, you let out some air.

Pressure

When you squeeze a bicycle tire, you feel an opposing force. The force comes from billions of air particles striking the inside of the tire. Look at Figure 4.1. The air particles inside the tire are in constant motion. As they move about, the air particles collide with the tire's walls. The force of all the collisions spreads over the tire's inner surface, pushing the wall of the tire outward.

A force exerted on a surface is called **pressure**. To calculate pressure, you divide the force by the area over which it is applied.

$$\text{pressure} = \frac{\text{force}}{\text{area}}$$

Remember force is measured in newtons. When you divide force (N) by area in square meters (m^2), you get an answer in units of newtons per square meter (N/m^2). The official SI unit of pressure, the pascal (Pa), is equal to 1 N/m^2.

Figure 4.1
Air particles pushing against the tire's inner surface produce pressure. What happens if you put too much air in the tire? ▶ ①

MOTIVATE

Skills WarmUp
To help students understand fluid pressure, have them do the Skills WarmUp.
Answer Air escapes from your mouth because the air pressure that was keeping your cheeks puffed is greater than the air pressure outside your mouth. Air is the fluid that forced your cheeks outward.

Misconceptions
Students are likely to think that air pressure exists only when the wind blows. Help them to recognize that the atmosphere constantly exerts pressure. You may wish to use the analogy of the continual pressure swimmers feel as they swim under water.

Answer to In-Text Question
① **Too much air pressure in the tire could cause it to burst.**

⊙ **The Living Textbook:
Physical Science Sides 1-4**

Chapter 9   Frame 01723
Pressure Diagram (1 Frame)
Search:

TEACH

Skills WorkOut

To help students understand fluid pressure, have them do the Skills WorkOut.

Answer Water pressure in the carton is greatest at the bottom of the carton. The lowest hole will spout water the fastest and farthest. The middle hole will spout water more slowly and less far. The top holes will spout water the slowest and least far.

Explore Visually

Have students study pages 86 and 87. Ask the following questions:

▶ Which of the following places would have the most oxygen: at sea level, on top of a 5 km mountain, or sky-diving at an altitude of 6 km? Why? (At sea level; oxygen is more concentrated at lower altitudes.)

▶ Which object is influenced by greater air pressure, the ship or the jet aircraft? Why? (The ship; air pressure is greater at sea level than in the air.)

▶ How does the ozone layer protect the earth? (It filters out harmful amounts of UV light.)

Portfolio

Have students keep a record of the air pressure, temperature, and weather conditions for eight to ten days. Have them make a chart that shows which days the atmospheric pressure changed. Ask them to use this data to make a generalization about the relationship between atmospheric pressure and other weather conditions. (Atmospheric pressure changes before and after storms.)

Home Economics Connection

When the surrounding air pressure is less than the air pressure at sea level, water boils at a temperature lower than 100°C. Ask: How does the boiling point of water change with the altitude? (The boiling point is lower at high altitudes.) How does the time needed to boil a potato change with altitude? (The potato will take longer to cook at high altitudes because the water temperatures will be less than 100°C.)

Math Connection

Explain to students that barometric pressure is measured in units called millibars (mb). On a mercury barometer, 1 mb = 7.50×10^{-2} cm of mercury; also, 1 mb = 100 Pa. Weather reporters give barometric pressure in inches of Hg. Ask: How many mb is in 30 inches of Hg? (1013 mb) How many Pa? (101 600 Pa, 101.6 kPa) What is today's barometric pressure in mb? In Pa? (Answers will vary.)

▼ ACTIVITY

Comparing

Fluid Pressure

Collect the following items: a milk carton, a pin, and tape.

1. Using the pin, make three small holes at different levels in the milk carton.

2. Tape the holes closed, and fill the carton with water.

3. Place the carton over a sink and remove the tape.

Compare the flow of water from each hole.

SKILLS WORKOUT

Figure 4.2
Atmospheric Pressure ▼

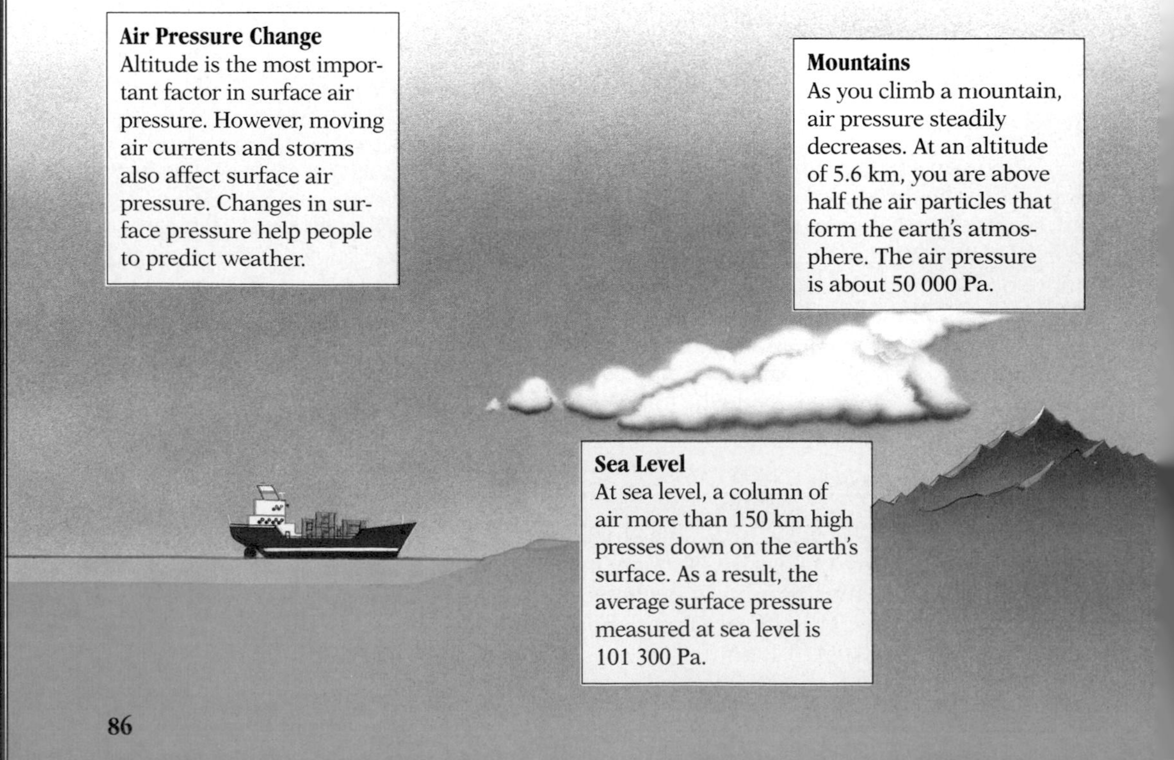

Air Pressure Change
Altitude is the most important factor in surface air pressure. However, moving air currents and storms also affect surface air pressure. Changes in surface pressure help people to predict weather.

Fluid Pressure in the Environment

Do you ever feel your ears "pop" when you ride in a plane or elevator? Or feel a sharp ear pain when you swim underwater? These experiences result from fluid pressure in the environment. Air and water are the most common fluids on the earth's surface. As you move up or down in air or water, the pressure around you changes. The change may be too small for you to notice. However, your eardrums sometimes detect small pressure changes.

Pressure and the Atmosphere You live at the bottom of an ocean of air, the atmosphere. The air that makes up the earth's atmosphere is a mixture of gas particles. The gas particles are pulled toward the earth by the force of gravity. The weight of air causes atmospheric pressure.

Air exerts a downward force on the earth's surface. Over the earth's entire surface, the average pressure produced by the atmosphere is about 100 000 Pa. Look at Figure 4.2. It describes pressure conditions at different locations on or near the earth's surface.

Mountains
As you climb a mountain, air pressure steadily decreases. At an altitude of 5.6 km, you are above half the air particles that form the earth's atmosphere. The air pressure is about 50 000 Pa.

Sea Level
At sea level, a column of air more than 150 km high presses down on the earth's surface. As a result, the average surface pressure measured at sea level is 101 300 Pa.

Integrating the Sciences

Environmental Science In the lower atmosphere, ozone is produced as a result of the reaction between sunlight and automobile exhausts. Have students find out how ozone affects the environment and what can be done to change the amount of ozone produced. (It irritates the eyes and the respiratory system, it can damage rubber and plastic, and it may damage plants and animal tissue; decrease auto exhaust emissions.) Explain that while ozone is a pollutant at the earth's surface, it acts as a sunscreen in the upper atmosphere. It limits the amount of UV light striking the earth.

Imagine an area measuring one square meter (1 m^2). Such an area has about enough room for you and your school desk. Above you and your desk is a column of air about 150 km high. The force of the column of air pressing down on each square meter of the earth's surface is nearly equal to the weight of a school bus! Why aren't you crushed by this great force? Although you can't feel it, air pressure pushes on you from all directions. But the pressure of the fluids inside your body pushes back with the same amount of force. The forces on your body are balanced.

If you travel upward in the air column, the air pressure around you changes. The air column above you gets shorter, and the air gets thinner. Since fewer gas particles are around you and above you, the air pressure is lower. Eventually, you rise to an altitude that has almost no air or other gas particles. The absence of matter is called a vacuum. Space is a near vacuum, which begins at an altitude of about 150 km above the earth's surface.

150 km

50 km

Ozone Layer
A layer of ozone gas at an altitude of 20–50 km shields the earth against harmful ultraviolet radiation. The air pressure in the ozone layer is less than 100 Pa.

Edge of Space
At an altitude of 150 km, air contains so few gas particles that the pressure approaches zero. Beyond 150 km is space. Space contains about one hydrogen molecule per cubic centimeter.

20 km

11 km

6 km

Aircraft
Jet aircraft travel at an altitude of 11 km. The air pressure there is only about 25 000 Pa. People can't survive breathing such thin air, so high-flying aircraft have pressurized cabins.

0 km

87

Skills Development

Infer Explain to students that athletes often prefer to train at high altitudes in places such as Denver, Colorado. Training at high altitudes can be more effective than training at sea level. Ask, How do you think high-altitude training affects the athletes' bodies? (Answers may vary. Example: Because there is less oxygen at high altitudes, the athletes' bodies compensate by producing more oxygen-carrying cells. Explain that this adaptation usually takes about three days.

Reteach

Use a glass of water and a drinking straw to reinforce the concept of atmospheric pressure. Have a volunteer drink water through the straw. Discuss the following:

▶ Ask students to explain how air pressure is involved in moving water through the straw. (Sucking reduces the air pressure in the straw. The atmospheric pressure pushes down on the liquid in the glass, forcing it up into the straw.)

▶ Ask students to explain why water will pour from a bottle that is partially tipped faster than one that is turned completely upside down. (As water leaves the partially tipped bottle, air is free to move inside, keeping the air pressure balanced inside and outside the bottle. If the bottle is turned completely upside down, the air pressure inside will be less than the air pressure outside. An air bubble forms and must move to the top of the fluid inside the bottle to equalize the pressure before more water will run out.)

 **The Living Textbook:
Physical Science Sides 1-4**

Chapter 17   Frame 03406
Vacuum (2 Frames)
Search: Step:

87

TEACH ▪ *Continued*

Class Activity

Have the class create a mural of a marine biome. Several students could provide information about the organisms that live in sunlit water, twilight water, and water without sunlight. Others could organize the information and design the mural. Students doing the drawing or painting could present it to the class, explaining the pictures and any captions.

Research

Ask students to use magazines, videos, and reference books to write a report on the methods and equipment used to explore one of the ocean regions shown on pages 88 and 89. A periodical called *Oceanus* contains this information and is available from the Woods Hole Institute at Woods Hole, MA. Remind students that their report should include information about any special techniques or equipment used for exploring the ocean depths.

Explore Visually

Have students study pages 88 and 89 and answer the following questions:

▶ Which area of the ocean is home to organisms that withstand pressure changes of as much as 200 000 Pa daily. (Intertidal)

▶ How deep is the continental shelf? What is the pressure at the ocean bottom? (200 m; 2 million Pa)

Integrated Learning

Use Integrating Worksheet 4.1a.

Answer to In-Text Question

① The pressure will increase.

Integrating the Sciences

Marine Biology The marine biome is characterized by different creatures living at different depths of the ocean. Plankton drift in the upper levels of the waters over the continental shelf, where an array of giant kelp and seaweeds provide hiding places for many fish species. The plankton are food for zooplankton, which are planktonic animals only slightly larger than plankton, and nekton, which are fishes and other swimming organisms. These organisms provide all the food for the organisms that live deep below the ocean's surface. In these deep regions, among the sediments and other substrates, live bottom-dwelling organisms called *benthos*.

Use Integrating Worksheet 4.1b.

Pressure and the Ocean Suppose you take a trip beneath the ocean's surface. You bring along a pressure gauge to compare the water pressure at different depths. The drumlike membrane of a pressure gauge responds to pressure changes much as your eardrum does. As the pressure outside the container changes, the membrane moves. A dial attached to the membrane records the pressure in pascals.

Using your gauge, you observe that pressure at the water's surface is equal to about 100 000 Pa. Your gauge shows the air pressure at sea level. When you place your gauge 1 cm beneath the water's surface, you observe a pressure increase of about 100 Pa. As you go deeper into the water, the pressure increases. More particles of matter are above and around the gauge.

The particles that make up water are packed more closely together than the particles in air. Water is denser than air. So, water exerts more force per unit area than air does. How do you think the pressure will change as you go to the bottom? ①

Figure 4.3
Water Pressure Beneath the Ocean ▼

Intertidal Zone
Near shore, the water level changes with the tides. Organisms living here experience constant changes in water pressure. In one day, the pressure can vary as much as 200 000 Pa!

Continental Shelf
The shelf is a nearly level extension of the continent. The shelf is up to 200 m deep. Organisms living on the deepest part of the shelf must withstand water pressure of 2 million Pa.

Integrating the Sciences

Oceanography Tell students that light penetrates the ocean to a depth of only 100 m. The light is brightest from the surface to a depth of 1 m. Only 16 percent of the light reaches to 10 m, and about 1 percent reaches to 100 m. Ocean water below 100 m is without light. Encourage students to make a diagram or chart that shows marine organisms that live in each depth. Students may want to keep their diagrams in their portfolios.

Answer to Link

The streams go the same distance, because the pressure of the water above the water coming out of each carton is the same. Pressure depends on depth, not surface area or volume.

If you continue to descend in the ocean, the water pressure builds rapidly. At a depth of about 10 m, your gauge indicates an increase of about 100 000 Pa. A water column 10 m high exerts as much pressure as all of the earth's atmosphere! The total pressure is equal to the air and water pressure combined. So, at 10 m, the pressure is about 200 000 Pa, twice the pressure at sea level.

Marine organisms, like those in Figure 4.3, have adapted to withstand the water pressure where they live. Most of these organisms have water-saturated tissues that enclose air spaces that aren't easily compressed. Deep-water organisms live at great pressures without being crushed, but they can't survive a trip to the low-pressure surface. What do you think happens to tissues of the fish? ②

The viperfish is one deep-water organism that can adjust to depths. During the day, it stays at depths of 1.5 km to 2.5 km where water pressure ranges from 15 to 25 million Pa. At night, it moves up to a depth of 500 meters to feed where prey is more plentiful and water pressure is about 5 million Pa.

Oceanography
L I N K

Collect the following items: an 8-oz milk carton, a half-gallon milk carton, scissors.

1. Make a hole in each milk carton about 2 cm from the bottom.

2. Working over a sink, cover the holes in each carton with one finger.

3. Have a partner fill each carton with water to about 5-cm deep.

4. Take your fingers away from the holes. Which stream goes farther? Explain

A C T I V I T Y

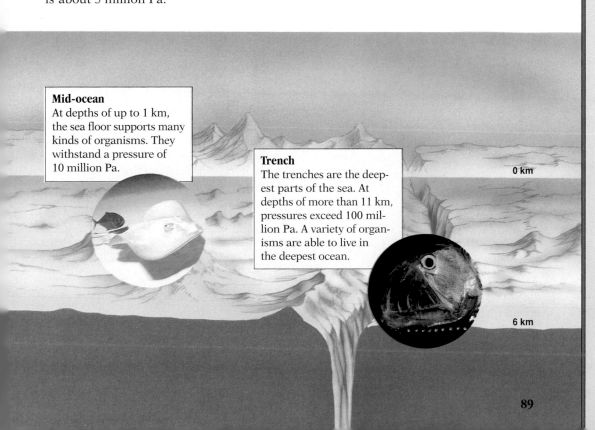

Mid-ocean
At depths of up to 1 km, the sea floor supports many kinds of organisms. They withstand a pressure of 10 million Pa.

Trench
The trenches are the deepest parts of the sea. At depths of more than 11 km, pressures exceed 100 million Pa. A variety of organisms are able to live in the deepest ocean.

0 km

6 km

▶ Where do ocean organisms that can withstand pressures of 10 million Pa live? (Mid-ocean)

▶ What are the deepest parts of the sea? How much pressure is exerted there? (Trenches; the pressure is greater than 100 million Pa at depths of 11 km.)

Skills Development

Make a Graph Have students compare the pressure at different altitudes and ocean depths. Ask them to use pages 86 and 87 to make a graph showing pressure at sea level, and at 5 km, 11 km, and 20 km above sea level. Have students use pages 88 and 89 to make a graph showing pressure at sea level and 10 m, 500 m, and 1500 m below sea level.

Interpret Data Ask students to use their graphs to determine where pressure changes occur more rapidly—when moving up higher into the atmosphere, or deeper beneath the ocean. (Deeper beneath the ocean)

Apply

Draw two diagrams on the chalkboard: one representing a large, shallow lake, such as Lake Erie, and another representing a smaller, but deeper lake, such as Lake Ontario. Ask students which lake has greater water pressure at its deepest point. (Ontario, the smaller, deeper lake, because pressure is greater with depth, not volume)

Answer to In-Text Question

② **When the external pressure is less on tissues, the air pockets expand and burst, killing the fish.**

 The Living Textbook: Physical Science Sides 1-4

Chapter 9   Frame 01730
Barometric Pressure (1 Frame)
Search:

EVALUATE

WrapUp

Reinforce Have students imagine being suddenly transported to the edge of the atmosphere. Have them describe the kind of device they would need to protect them. Next have them discuss the kind of device they would need to protect them if they were instantly transported to 1 km below the surface of the ocean.

Use Review Worksheet 4.1.

Check and Explain

1. Fluid pressure is the force exerted by a fluid, such as a liquid or gas, over a given area.

2. Answers will vary. Possible answers: air in a bicycle tire, water at a depth of 10 m.

3. The tire will function best if it is inflated so the internal pressure is 200 kPa or 200 000 N/m².

4. There is a very slight decrease in air pressure as you leap upward from the diving board. As you enter the water, the water pressure increases the farther you descend.

Answer to In-Text Question

① The brakes would fail. The lack of fluid pressure would prevent the fluid in the cylinders from pushing against the pistons, and the brake pads would not push against the wheel.

The Living Textbook: Physical Science Sides 1-4

Chapter 10   Frame 01869
Hydraulic Cylinders/Pistons (4 Frames)
Search: Step:

INTEGRATED LEARNING

STS Connection

Point out to students that several familiar devices such as gasoline pumps, fire extinguishers, vacuum cleaners, and scuba gear rely on pressure differences to work. Have students sketch one of these devices. Students' sketches should show where pressure differences can occur, what happens if pressures are different, and what happens if the pressures are balanced.

Figure 4.4 ▶
Follow the path of pressure through the brake system. What happens if there is a break in the fluid line? ①

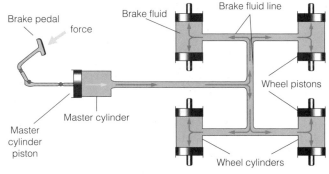

Science and Technology
Putting on the Brakes

A car's braking system uses fluid pressure to allow a driver to stop a moving car with just one foot! Study Figure 4.4. The driver puts on the brakes by applying a pushing force to the brake pedal. The brake pedal moves a metal rod attached to a piston. A piston is a "plug" that can slide snugly inside a cylinder, or tube. As the piston slides into the master cylinder, it presses on the fluid inside. Under pressure, the fluid exits the cylinder and flows into the brake line. The high-pressure fluid then moves evenly throughout the system.

The brake line connects the master cylinder to a smaller cylinder near the hub of each wheel. Pressurized fluid from the brake line enters each wheel cylinder through a small opening. Within each cylinder, the high-pressure fluid pushes against the pistons. The pistons move forcefully out of the cylinders, pushing a brake pad against the spinning car wheel. The friction between the brake pad and the wheel slows the car down.

Check and Explain

1. What is fluid pressure?

2. Give two examples of fluid pressure.

3. **Reason and Conclude** An automobile tire has "200 kPa" written on its side. What does this mean?

4. **Predict** What changes in both air and water pressure occur on your body as you leap from a diving board?

4.2 Buoyancy

Objectives

▶ **Explain** buoyant force.

▶ **Compare** and **contrast** density and buoyancy.

▶ **Predict** whether an object will float in water.

Think about a hot air balloon. These colorful craft seem to float effortlessly through the skies. How can they do this? You may have heard them described as being "lighter than air."

These balloons take advantage of the fact that hot air is less dense than cool air. The hot air balloon rises, carrying a basket filled with passengers up into the sky.

From what you learned about forces, you probably know that the rising motion of the balloon is caused by unbalanced forces. The air beneath the balloon exerts more force on it than the air above. When the balloon reaches an altitude where the forces are equal, it stops rising.

Buoyant Force

What force makes an object float in air or in water? Look at the iceberg in Figure 4.5. Two forces act on the iceberg. The downward force is gravity. Recall that the force gravity exerts on an object is equal to the object's weight. The upward force acting on the iceberg is the **buoyant force**. The buoyant force opposes gravity.

Consider an object completely submerged underwater. If the weight of the submerged object is greater than the buoyant force, the object will sink. If the weight is less than the buoyant force, the object will rise to the surface and float. When the weight of the submerged object is equal to the buoyant force, the object will remain at the same level, and neither sink nor rise.

Any object that is floating on the surface has come to a point of equilibrium. A point of equilibrium is where all the forces are balanced. This means that the force of gravity is equal to the buoyant force. The iceberg in Figure 4.5 is in equilibrium.

Force of gravity

Buoyant force

Figure 4.5 ▲
The buoyant force acts against the force of gravity.

Directed Inquiry

Have students study Figure 4.6. Explain that the direction and size of the arrows represent the forces acting on each block. Ask the following questions:

► What does the arrow pointing down on each cube represent? (The force of gravity)

► What does the arrow pointing upward on each cube represent? (Buoyant force)

► On which cube is the force of gravity the greatest? The least? (Center; left)

► On which cube is the buoyant force the greatest? The least? (Left; center)

► On which cube are the force of gravity and the buoyant force equal? (The cube on the right)

► Which cube is the most dense? How do you know? (The cube in the center, because it is farthest down in the liquid)

Enrich

Explain how Archimedes' principle affects objects in water. Ask students to suppose that the weight in the water of an alligator on the bottom of a pond is 200 N. It displaces 100 N of water. Ask students if the alligator weighs less in the water than it does on land. (Yes) What is the alligator's weight out of water? (200 N + 100 N = 300 N)

Skills Development

Infer Ask students, If you drop a marble into a glass of water, does the buoyant force increase or decrease as the marble sinks to the bottom? (Neither. The buoyant force is the same at all depths.)

Language Arts Connection

Explain to students that there are several legends and stories about Archimedes. Have students refer to an encyclopedia or another reference source to learn about Archimedes. Students should focus on his work for King Hiero, his weapon designs, or the Archimedean screw. Ask students to write and perform a skit about one of the Archimedean legends or stories.

Answer to Link

The fish with the largest hollow would have floated the highest because its buoyant force was least.

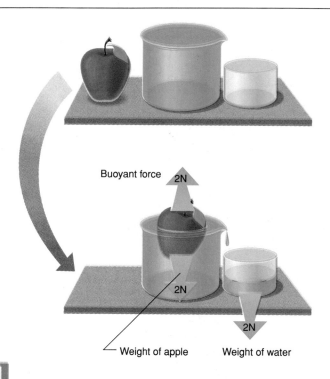

Figure 4.6 ▶
A floating apple displaces its own weight in water.

Life Science
LINK

Fishes have organs called swim bladders that are similar to balloons. Inflating or deflating their bladders changes their buoyancy in the water. Collect the following items: plastic clay, a large container or sink full of water, and three small balloons.

1. Divide your clay into three clumps. Out of each of the clumps, make hollow "fishes."

2. Put one balloon in each of the three fishes. Blow up and knot the balloons.

3. Put your fishes in water to see how they float.

Which fish floated the highest in the water? Why?

ACTIVITY

Archimedes' Principle

More than 2,000 years ago, the Greek mathematician and inventor Archimedes observed a relationship between the buoyant force and the fluid displaced by an object. According to legend, when he stepped into his bathtub, he noticed that the water level rose. He later reasoned that the weight of the fluid displaced would be equal to the buoyant force. For example, if an object immersed in water displaces a volume of water that weighs 4.9 N, then a buoyant force of 4.9 N acts on the object.

As you know already, the buoyant force on a floating object is equal to the weight of the object. Archimedes' principle then tells you that any floating object displaces its own weight in water. Look at Figure 4.6 When an apple is placed in a full glass of water, the water that spills over is equal to the apple's weight.

Archimedes' principle applies to all fluids, including air. At sea level, one cubic meter (1 m³) of air has a weight of about 12 N. So, a balloon that occupies 1 m³ has a buoyant force of 12 N acting upon it.

Cooperative Learning

Have students work in cooperative groups to make a data table on the density of common small objects, such as screws, paper clips, erasers, and plastic spoons. Have them use a balance and a ruler, or displacement to find the volume of each object. Students may wish to keep the data table in their portfolios.

Density and Buoyancy

To predict whether an object will sink or float, you need to consider its density. Recall that mass measures how much matter an object contains. To find the density of an object, you divide its mass by its volume. The density of a substance is one of its properties. The density of liquid water is 1 g/cm^3. The density of solid steel is 7.8 g/cm^3. Cooking oil's density is 0.82 g/cm^3. Balsa wood has a density of about 0.12 g/cm^3.

Any object with a density greater than 1 g/cm^3 will sink in water. For example, a steel bolt sinks because the bolt's density is greater than that of water. The weight of the steel is greater than the buoyant force of the water it displaces. But an object with a density less than 1 g/cm^3 will float in water. For example, a block of balsa wood floats because the wood's density is less than that of water. The buoyant force that the water exerts on the wood is equal to the wood's weight.

Buoyancy can also be observed between fluids of different densities. The density of cooking oil is less than the density of water. When you combine oil and water, the oil floats in a layer at the mixture's surface. You can see what happens when you combine substances with different densities in Figure 4.7. Which substance is the least dense? Which substance is the most dense? ②

Figure 4.7
Density Differences ▼

Balsa wood 0.12 g/cm^3

Ethyl alcohol 0.79 g/cm^3

Cooking oil 0.82 g/cm^3

Polyethylene plastic 0.92 g/cm^3

Colored water 1.0 g/cm^3

Neoprene® rubber 1.23 g/cm^3

Corn syrup 1.38 g/cm^3

Steel 7.8 g/cm^3

▼ **ACTIVITY**

Hypothesizing

Clay Float

1. Obtain some waterproof clay.

2. Design a shape out of the clay that will float in water.

3. Test your design by putting your shape in a sink of water.

What happened to the clay? Explain your results.

SKILLS WORKOUT

Balsa wood has the lowest density of all the substances, so it floats at the top. The other materials arrange themselves in order of density.

Liquids form layers. Each solid floats at the top of a denser liquid layer.

Steel and corn syrup have the highest densities. They rest on the bottom.

Skills WorkOut

To help students understand density and buoyancy, have them do the Skills WorkOut.
Answer Answers may vary. Experiments and reported results should show an understanding of density and buoyancy. For example, a clay ball with an air pocket may have greater buoyancy than a solid clay ball of the same size.

Critical Thinking

Reason and Conclude Tell students a mixture of salt and water has a greater density than plain water. Show how a Neoprene® rubber stopper floats in a glass of saltwater. Ask, What can you conclude about the density of the saltwater? (The density must be greater than 1.23 g/cm^3.)

Directed Inquiry

Have students study Figure 4.7 and read about density and buoyancy. Ask the following questions:

▶ Why is the polyethylene plastic at the bottom of the cooking oil layer? (It's more dense than cooking oil and less dense than water.)

▶ Is Neoprene® rubber more or less dense than water? (More)

▶ What would happen if you pushed the balsa wood to the bottom of the beaker and let go? (It would rise to the top.)

▶ What would happen if you put a much smaller piece of Neoprene® rubber in the beaker? (It would sink to the same level as the piece already in the beaker.)

Answer to In-Text Question

② **Balsa wood is least dense; steel is most dense.**

 The Living Textbook: Physical Science Side 2

Chapter 19   Frame 03447
Density (Movie)
Search: Play:

Reteach

Draw diagrams on the chalkboard to show how a fish can rise or sink in water. Explain that as the swim bladder expands, the volume of the fish increases. However, because the mass of the fish remains the same, the density of the fish decreases. Since the fish has greater volume, it is more buoyant. It displaces more water, and rises. When the fish expels the gases from the swim bladder, its volume decreases and its density increases. The fish displaces less water, is less buoyant, and sinks.

Reteach

Use Reteach Worksheet 4.2.

Prior Knowledge

Gauge how much students know about boats by asking:

► What parts of a boat can you name?

► What is a plimsoll line?

► Why is a plimsoll line important in shipping?

Historical Notebook

Portfolio Have the students collect pictures of boats from different cultures. Ask students to explain how each design affects buoyancy and performance. They can add these pictures to their portfolios.

Answers

1. Both boats have long, narrow hulls and are paddled. The outrigger is balanced alongside the hull.

2. Maps may vary, but should be based on actual routes.

3. Models may vary. Voyaging canoes are steered by paddling. Forces should include wind, current, and paddling.

Answer to In-Text Question

① **By changing the fish's density.**

94

Integrating the Sciences

Life Science Tell students that ocean water has different densities at different locations. These densities depend on the temperature of the water as well as the amount of salt in the water. Waters of different densities sink and rise, forming ocean currents. Have students place an ice cube containing food coloring in a still glass of warm water. Have students describe the currents they see as the ice melts.

Multicultural Perspectives

Explain to students that some villages in China are built almost entirely on the water. These people live, work, and shop in virtual floating villages. Encourage students to discuss the special needs and concerns they would have if they lived on such a houseboat. (Answers might include lack of electricity or weather conditions.)

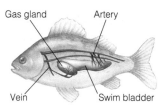

Figure 4.8 ▲
How does its swim bladder help the fish rise or sink in the water? ①

What can you say about objects that don't float? They are too dense. To float, you need to reduce an object's density. Since density is weight divided by volume, you can reduce the weight while keeping the volume the same. Or, you can increase the volume while keeping the weight the same. The purpose of a life jacket is to increase volume while adding very little to a person's weight.

Many types of bony fishes change the density of their bodies to help them rise and sink in their water environment. Look at the diagram of a bony fish in Figure 4.8. These fishes have a balloonlike organ, the swim bladder. An inflated swim bladder increases the fish's volume. This lowers the density of the fish's body relative to the surrounding water. So, the fish rises. To move downward, the fish increases the density of its body by deflating the swim bladder. A gas gland helps control the movement of gases between the fish's bloodstream and the swim bladder.

Historical Notebook

Boat Design in Polynesia

For thousands of years, the people of the South Pacific have built a special type of boat, an outrigger. The boat's main body, or hull, is long and narrow like a canoe. The hull usually attaches to one or two logs alongside. The crew sits within the hull and propels the boat using paddles like you would in a canoe.

Another Polynesian boat design consists of two hulls joined by a central platform. Sails are mounted on the central platform. The double-hulled design is very stable, so these boats can sail in strong winds. While sailing downwind, the long, narrow hulls rise in the water. The boat sails very fast because there is less hull surface in contact with the water. Ancient Polynesians used these double-hulled voyaging canoes to colonize islands in a vast area of the South Pacific. The Hawaiian Islands were colonized by these early explorers about 1000 A.D.

1. Compare an outrigger to a canoe. Explain how they are alike and how they are different.

2. Research the water routes traveled by the ancient Polynesians. Make a map of their travels across the Pacific.

3. Make models of an outrigger and a double-hulled voyaging canoe. Locate and identify the forces acting on each boat.

Explain to students that researchers use submarines and other submersible crafts to study ocean depths. Have students use references to learn about submersibles such as the *Alvin* and bathyscaphes such as the *Kriestel.* Remind students to focus on how the craft can rise and sink in the ocean. Have them include information about how the craft can withstand the pressures of great ocean depths.

Science and Technology
Making Steel Float

What happens when you drop a steel nail into water? The nail sinks. The density of steel is greater than the density of water. So why does a steel ocean liner float?

Ship designers know that flotation depends upon the craft's average density. Both the steel hull and the air trapped in the hull must be considered. A ship with a large volume of trapped air has an average density less than the density of water. As a result, the heavy steel ship floats easily.

The density difference between a craft and water can vary. Look at the ships in Figure 4.9. If the density difference is large, the craft extends high above the water's surface like the ship on the right does. A high-floating craft tends to rock and is easily capsized. The rocking motion can make the passengers seasick. If the density difference is small, the hull may not extend very far above the surface. High waves are likely to swamp the craft.

A submarine is designed to have nearly the same density as ocean water. When special tanks, called ballast tanks, fill with ocean water, the weight of the submarine increases. The submarine's average density increases also, so the craft sinks. When air replaces the ocean water in the ballast tanks, the submarine's density decreases, and the submarine rises.

Figure 4.9 ▲
Why is the ship on the right higher in the water than the ship on the left?

Check and Explain

1. Describe the forces acting on a floating object.

2. What is Archimedes' principle?

3. **Compare and Contrast** How are density and buoyancy similar? How are they different?

4. **Predict** Which items will float in water: canoe, flower petal, brick, or roller skate? Explain.

Time 40 minutes   Group pairs

Materials

15 droppers

15 1-L plastic soda bottles with caps

Analysis

1. The dropper sank.

2. The air bubble got smaller.

3. The dropper rose back to the top.

Conclusion

Water is not compressible, but air is. When the bottle is squeezed, the water transmits the pressure from the squeeze to the air bubble, compressing it. As the air bubble compresses, water flows into the dropper, making the dropper more dense and less buoyant than it was.

Extension

The dropper is not likely to sink. The total pressure of the squeeze will be distributed over a larger area of contact between air and water. As a result, the air bubble in the dropper will not compress enough to cause it to sink.

Everyday Application

When the float is pushed down, a valve opens, allowing water to flow into the tank. The function of the float is to turn off the water when the tank has refilled after a flush.

Prelab Discussion

Have students read the entire activity. Discuss the following points before beginning:

▶ Have students make predictions about what will happen and why.

▶ Compare the compressibility of air and water.

▶ Ask why it is important for there to be as little air as possible trapped in the bottle.

▶ If the dropper does not move up and down, have students recheck the tightness of the lid, or have them change the size of the air bubble in the dropper.

Activity 4 *How can you control an object's buoyancy?*

Skills Observe; Infer

Task 1 Prelab Prep
Collect the following: a glass dropper, 1-L plastic soda bottle with a screw cap, and water.

Task 2 Data Record
1. Draw two outlines of a dropper.
2. Label the first outline *Dropper Before Squeeze*. Label the second outline *Dropper After Squeeze*.
3. Record your observations about the dropper next to your drawings.

Task 3 Procedure
1. Add water to the soda bottle almost up to the bottle's neck.
2. Fill the dropper about halfway with water. Gently place the dropper into the soda bottle.
3. If the dropper sinks, remove it from the bottle. Empty some of the water from the dropper. Repeat steps 1 and 2 until the dropper just floats at the water's surface, as shown in the figure below.

Water level

Dropper

Water-Filled bottle

4. Carefully fill the soda bottle to the top with water.
5. Screw on the cap tightly. Be careful to trap as little air as possible.
6. Squeeze the body of the soda bottle. Observe what happens to the dropper. Release your grip and observe the dropper.
7. Using the drawings created in the Data Record, draw the size of the air bubble in the dropper before you squeezed the bottle.
8. Draw the size of the dropper's air bubble after you squeezed the bottle.
9. Record your observations next to each of the outlines.

Task 4 Analysis
1. What happened to the dropper when you squeezed the bottle?
2. How did the air bubble trapped inside the dropper change when the container was squeezed?
3. What happened to the dropper when you released your grip?

Task 5 Conclusion
Explain how the forces applied to the bottle and the air bubble in the dropper controlled the dropper's buoyancy.

Extension

Repeat this activity. This time screw on the container cap without filling the bottle to the top. How does this affect the behavior of the dropper? Explain your observations.

Everyday Application

Get your parent's permission to carefully remove the lid to the tank behind your toilet. You will see a rubber float about the size of a softball. Push this float under water and observe what happens. What is the float's function?

Themes in Science
Systems and Interactions
Moving fluids result in pressure differences that can be used to support heavier-than-air objects. Ask students to draw an airplane and indicate the forces that act on the plane as it flies. Have them include their drawings in their portfolios.

Integrating the Sciences
Earth Science Wind blows up a mountain slope from a valley below during the day from midmorning until sunset. These air currents are called *valley winds*, or *thermals*. Thermals occur when air is warmed by the valley floor and rises. Birds and glider planes are able to soar in these air currents for a long time.

Section Objectives
For a list of section objectives, see the Student Edition page.

Skills Objectives
Students should be able to:

Observe forces in moving fluids.

Make a Model of a paper airplane.

Infer how an object's shape affects its movement through fluids.

Vocabulary
airfoil, lift, thrust, drag

4.3 Forces in Moving Fluids

Objectives

▶ **Describe** Bernoulli's principle.

▶ **Explain** how airplanes and birds fly.

▶ **Generalize** about things that fly.

▶ **Infer** how an object's shape affects its movement through a fluid.

I magine flying an airplane! As the plane moves through the sky, what holds it up? You know that as you fly the plane, you must make sure that it maintains a certain speed. You know that if the plane slows down or stalls, it can't stay up. Somehow the speed of the plane is connected to the force that keeps the plane in the air.

Your airplane moves through a fluid, air. Its motion through the fluid creates unbalanced forces. As the plane moves, air rushes over and under the wings. The plane's wings create forces that hold it up.

Pressure Differences in Moving Fluids

Look at the student blowing across the top of a sheet of paper in Figure 4.10. Just as the force of moving air keeps a plane in the sky, the paper rises due to the force of the moving air created by the blowing action.

When a fluid moves, its pressure drops. As the student blows across the paper, he creates a low-pressure region above it. The air beneath the paper is not affected by the blowing. Its pressure remains the same. The pressure is greater on the bottom of the paper. The unbalanced pressures produce an upward force on the paper. When the boy stops blowing, the air above the paper returns to its original pressure. The pressure on both sides of the paper is the same, so it sinks.

In the 1700s, Swiss scientist Daniel Bernoulli studied the relationship between moving fluids and pressure. He observed that as the speed of a fluid increases, the pressure in the fluid decreases. This concept is called Bernoulli's principle.

▼ **ACTIVITY**

Observing

Flying Paper
Blow across the top of a sheet of loosely hanging tissue paper, as shown in Figure 4.10. Explain your observations.

SKILLS WARMUP

Figure 4.10
Blowing across the paper creates a low pressure area above it. Why does the paper rise upward? ▼ ①

Low pressure

High pressure

MOTIVATE

Skills WarmUp
To help students understand forces in moving fluids, have them do the Skills WarmUp.
Answer The initial air pressure is equal everywhere. The air moves across the top of the tissue. Because moving air exerts less pressure than still air, the tissue is pushed upward by air pressure from underneath it.

Prior Knowledge
Gauge how much students know about moving fluids by asking the following questions:

▶ How do birds respond to the wind? Why?

▶ How does the area of the leading edge of a wing affect the speed of an airplane? Why?

Answer to In-Text Question
① The blowing creates a pressure imbalance.

**The Living Textbook:
Physical Science Sides 1-4**

Chapter 9   Frame 01713
Wind Flow (1 Frame)
Search:

Directed Inquiry

Have students study Figure 4.11. Ask the following questions:

▶ Describe the air pressure above and below an airplane's wings. (Lower pressure above the wings, higher pressure below the wings)

▶ What force on an airplane opposes the thrust? (Drag)

▶ For an airplane to fly, which force must be greater, the weight or the lift? (Lift)

▶ Would the plane move more slowly or more quickly if it were shaped more square? Explain. (More slowly; streamlining reduces drag; drag slows the plane down.)

Skills Development

Infer Tell students to imagine that an aircraft, such as a helicopter, is hovering over a single location. Ask, What can you infer about the force of gravity and air pressure beneath the helicopter? (The air pressure beneath the helicopter must be equal to the force of gravity pulling down on the helicopter.)

Social Studies Connection

Explain to students that airplane travel has changed the way people all over the world are able to live. Ask students how air travel affects their lives. (Examples include: mail, farming, hospitals, food shipment, photography, news, international travel, and communication.)

Writing Connection

Ask students to research the achievements of an aviation pioneer, such as Orville or Wilbur Wright, Richard E. Byrd, Charles Lindberg, Amelia Earhart, Richard Rutan, or Jeana Yeager. Have students write a news story describing a single, important achievement of one of these people.

Using Pressure Differences for Flight

Notice the special shape of the cross section of an airplane wing in Figure 4.11. This shape is called an **airfoil**. An airfoil has a curved upper surface and a relatively flat-bottom surface.

An airfoil's design uses Bernoulli's principle. As air moves past an airfoil, the airfoil's shape creates a pressure difference. The air that moves over the upper curved surface has farther to travel. So, air moving over the upper surface must move faster than air moving across the lower surface to reach the back edge of the wing at the same time. As a result, a low-pressure area is created on the wing's upper surface.

The difference between the pressure on the airfoil's upper and lower surfaces results in an upward force, called **lift**. When the lift is greater than the plane's weight, the plane rises. When the lift is less than the plane's weight, the plane sinks. When the lift and the plane's weight are equal, the plane levels off.

Both propellers and jet engines produce a force that moves the plane and its airfoil-shaped wings forward. The force that pushes the plane forward is

Figure 4.11
How an Airplane Flies ▼

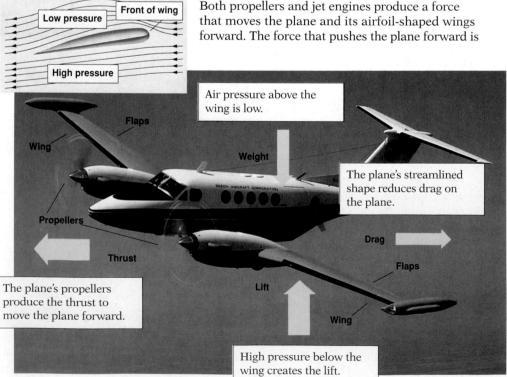

Low pressure

Front of wing

High pressure

Air pressure above the wing is low.

Flaps

Wing

Weight

The plane's streamlined shape reduces drag on the plane.

Propellers

Drag

Flaps

Thrust

The plane's propellers produce the thrust to move the plane forward.

Lift

Wing

High pressure below the wing creates the lift.

called **thrust**. The shape and movement of the propeller blades produce thrust. As the blades spin, they create a low-pressure region in front of the propeller and a high-pressure region behind it. Like the pressure difference that creates lift, this pressure difference produces a directional force. In this case, the force pushes the plane forward. Jet engines take in air, compress it, and then forcefully expel the heated air to produce thrust.

The forward motion of an aircraft is slowed by an opposing force called **drag**. Like friction, drag opposes the movement of objects. Disturbances in the flow of air or other fluids increase drag. By designing streamlined aircraft, drag is reduced.

Before landing, the pilot lowers the aircraft's hinged wing parts called the flaps. As the flaps drop, the shape of the wings changes. The drag and lift of the wings change. By changing the wings' characteristics, the pilot can control the plane's speed and direction.

SkillBuilder *Making a Model*

Paper Airplane Design

Paper airplanes must develop lift to stay aloft. To extend their time aloft, paper airplanes also need a streamlined shape that produces little drag.

Make a paper airplane following the design shown. Copy the table below. To test for lift, launch your airplane. Measure the distance it traveled. Record the distance in your table. Decide how to alter your plane to increase the lift. Make adjustments to your plane. Test for lift and record the distance. Continue to adjust, launch, and record distances for two more trials. Answer the questions below about your airplane.

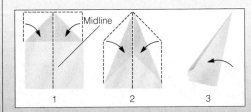

1. Which adjustment most affected the lift of your plane?

2. Discuss how you could adjust your plane to increase drag.

3. Draw your plane and label the forces affecting your plane when it flies.

4. Compare the forces of gravity and lift affecting your plane.

Testing for Lift on a Paper Airplane

Trial	Adjustment	Distance Flown (m)
1		
2		
3		

TEACH ▪ *Continued*

Explore Visually

Have students study the text and photographs on pages 100 and 101. Ask:

▶ What are the forces that act on a bird in flight? (The weight of the bird creates a downward force. Wing flapping creates upward lift, forward thrust, and drag.)

▶ How can a hawk move upward without flapping its wings? (By gliding in an updraft of warm, rising air)

Integrated Learning

Use Integrating Worksheet 4.3.

Answers to In-Text Questions

① A bird creates lift and thrust, like an airplane. Unlike an airplane, birds can monitor and change the shape of their bodies by moving, tucking in wings. They are also able to change the shape and size of their wings during flight.

② Soaring birds can survey an area from great heights and can plunge quickly toward prey.

Portfolio

Ask students to collect photographs and drawings of birds for their portfolios. Tell them to look for a variety of birds that are in different stages of flight. Have students label some of the photographs to show the forces acting on the bird. Have students include some information about the wing size, size of bird, and the climate in which it lives.

Cooperative Learning

Have students work in cooperative groups of three to make and explain a model of the wing of a specific kind of bird, such as a hawk or a gull. One student in the group could assemble the model and the second student could write a description of the types of feathers birds have. The third student could present the model to the class.

Bird Flight

Have you ever held a bird? If so, maybe you discovered how little the bird weighed. Low body weight is an important adaptation for flight. If you examine a bird's skeleton, you will discover that many bones aren't solid! Although they are long and sturdy, bird bones have pockets of air to make them light.

Feathers are another important adaptation for flight. Feathers are lightweight and stiff. Firmly attached to the skin, these structures form a streamlined body covering, which can withstand the stresses of flight.

Like the wing of an airplane, a bird's wing is an airfoil. The wing has a curved upper surface and a flat underside. Air passing over and under the bird's wing creates the lift.

The wings of a bird can also produce thrust. A bird can flap its wings when flying. During each flap, the wing tips twist and push air behind the bird propelling the bird forward. Birds such as hawks, hummingbirds, and gulls use lift and thrust to produce distinctive flying patterns.

Figure 4.12 ▼
How is the way a bird flies similar to the way a plane flies? How is it different? ①

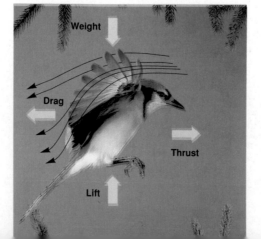

Hawks Hawks are adapted for soaring flight. These birds need to use very little effort to remain aloft. They just extend their large wings and glide on the lift produced by passing air currents.

Hawks often fly in a circular path. As shown in Figure 4.13, they circle within a rising column of warm air, a thermal. By staying in a thermal, the birds rise without flapping their wings. They take advantage of the warm air moving upward. Only when they leave the thermal, do they flap their wings.

Figure 4.13 ▲
How does soaring help hawks and other soaring birds catch their prey? ②

Hawks are adapted for flying in moving air currents. A hawk's broad wing presents a large lift surface to the passing air. Feathers at the end of the hawk's wing tips spread out in a fingerlike pattern. Because this arrangement reduces drag, less effort is needed for staying aloft. To change directions, the hawk twists some of the extended feathers, changing its wing shape.

Themes in Science

Energy Overcoming the force of gravity and moving from one place to another each requires energy. Encourage students to choose a bird and make an outline of the way in which it uses air pressure efficiently.

Multicultural Perspectives

Explain to students that the feathers of different kinds of birds are important in Native American, Maya, and Inca cultures. These groups use feathers in various rituals and to show rank. Have students prepare a report on how feathers are used by one of these groups.

Hummingbirds Look at Figure 4.14. The hummingbird has a unique flying style. With wing movements too rapid to see, this tiny bird can dart in any direction. Like a helicopter, it can remain stationary over a fixed point. The hummingbird can even fly backward!

The hummingbird's wings and body are adapted for flapping flight. Powerful muscles flap the wings back and forth at a rate of nearly 100 times per second. The rapid movement produces the humming sound from which these birds get their name. A hummingbird can easily twist its short, triangular wings to propel itself in any direction.

To maintain such a high flapping rate, a hummingbird's muscles need a large energy supply. To meet this demand, hummingbirds feed on flower nectar, a concentrated sugar solution.

Figure 4.14
The rapid movement of a hummingbird's wings allows it to stay aloft without the lift generated by forward thrust. ▼

Gulls The wings and body of a gull are adapted for flight that is a combination of gliding and flapping. Figure 4.15 shows the gull's flying pattern.

On a windless day, a gull uses its powerful flight muscles to flap its wings. The flapping produces thrust, which propels the bird forward. Air passing over the extended wings produces lift to raise the bird high in the air.

On a windy day, a gull uses updrafts and stays aloft with little effort. The gull simply extends its long, slender, pointed wings. Like the narrow wings of a glider, the gull's outstretched wings generate lift from the passing air. The streamlined wings cut through the air with very little drag. If the wind blows fast enough, the gull can remain motionless over the ground without flapping its wings. Once out of the updraft, however, the gull must flap its wings to stay aloft.

Figure 4.15 ▲
Gulls are known to range over thousands of kilometers. How does their flying style make this possible?

▶ Why is a gull able to stay aloft without flapping its wings? (It has long, narrow wings that allow it to glide on updrafts.)

▶ How does a bird change direction in flight? (By twisting some wing feathers to change the shape of the wing)

Critical Thinking

Reason and Conclude
Ask students to determine why different types of birds have different body or different wing shapes. (Adaptations vary because birds use different flight patterns to survive.)

Enrich

Ask students to think of animals, other than birds, that can fly. Have them use references to research how the animals fly. Ask one student to make a diagram of at least one animal on the chalkboard. Have another student label the forces: *weight, thrust, drag,* and *lift.* (For example: bats use many of the same flying techniques as birds; most insects have more than two pairs of wings, so the flying principles vary. Students may include manta rays, which use the principles of flight to move through water.)

Answer to In-Text Question
③ **Gulls conserve energy whenever possible by using wind for gliding.**

💿 **The Living Textbook:
Physical Science Sides 1-4**

Chapter 9   Frame 01490
Hummingbird (2 Frames)
Search: Step:

101

EVALUATE

WrapUp

Reinforce Ask students to think about what happens when they close a door against the wind. Does the wind blow faster or slower through the door crack? (Faster) Does the air pressure behind the door increase or decrease? Why? (Decrease; when the speed of the fluid through a confined space increases, the pressure drops.)
Use Review Worksheet 4.3.

Check and Explain

1. As the speed of a fluid increases, the pressure in the fluid decreases.

2. The shape of an airplane's wing creates a pressure difference on the top and bottom of the wing as the plane moves through the air. The pressure difference creates a lift. Both planes and birds rely on interactions with fluids (air) to provide lift.

3. All things that fly must create pressure difference or lift great enough to overcome the force of gravity.

4. Its surface shape affects drag, wrong shape affects lift.

Answer to In-Text Question

① **They all rely on wind to produce force.**

The Living Textbook:
Physical Science Sides 1-4

Chapter 9   Frame 01715
Kites (1 Frame)
Search:

102

Multicultural Perspectives

Between 200 B.C. and A.D. 200, the Han Dynasty of China flew kites as defense weapons. Soldiers attached bamboo poles to kites before sending them aloft. As the kites flew, air moved through the poles, making an eerie whistle. Enemy forces often retreated in fear.

Art Connection

Have students work in teams to make working box kites. One or two students could plan and build the kites. The other students could design images and paint on the surface of the kites.

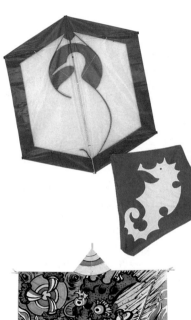

Figure 4.16 ▲
In addition to the kites shown here, the word *kite* also refers to a type of soaring bird and to the highest sails on a ship. How are all these objects similar? ①

Science and Society *Kite Flying*

Ancient people from cultures all around the world built working kites and gliders. In China, kites shaped like birds, butterflies, and dragons were in use 2,500 years ago. Some of these ancient kites had airfoil-shaped wings. In Egypt, working model gliders more than 2,200 years old have been found. In Central America, the ancient Maya built giant, round kites for festivals.

Kite flying is still a popular activity. Every year in the city of Hamamatsu, Japan, hundreds of people fly kites during the annual kite-flying festival. In the United States, children and adults fly kites year round from windy hills, beaches, city parks, and open fields. Even the modern sport of hang gliding is based on kite technology. Participants strap themselves into a harness hanging below a large kite. They use the kite to ride thermals, like soaring birds do.

A kite stays aloft by deflecting wind downward. The deflected wind exerts a force on the underside of the kite, acting to lift it upward. The weight of the kite and its string, and the force exerted by the string act to pull the kite downward. When the upward force from the wind is greater than the downward forces, the kite rises. As the wind grows stronger, the upward force exerted on the kite increases. Thus, kites fly best on windy days.

Some kites are made with two strings attached to their frames to give the people flying the kites greater control. Pulling more on one string than the other changes the shape of the kite's surface. This change affects the forces on the kite, causing it to move. A person can make the kite move to the left or right, or make it dive and then rise again.

Check and Explain

1. What is Bernoulli's principle?

2. How do airplanes fly? What does airplane flight have in common with bird flight?

3. **Generalize** Write a general statement about all things that can fly.

4. **Infer** How does an object's shape affect how it moves through a fluid?

Chapter 4 Review

Concept Summary

4.1 Fluid Pressure

▶ Fluids are any substances that flow, such as water and air.

▶ A force applied over an area is called pressure. Pressure is measured in newtons per square meter (N/m^2) or pascals (Pa).

▶ Since the environment is made of air and water, fluid pressure exists everywhere.

4.2 Buoyancy

▶ The downward force on an object in a fluid is the force of gravity. The force of gravity on an object is equal to the object's weight.

▶ The force that pushes up on an object in a fluid is the buoyant force.

▶ The buoyant force on an object is equal to the weight of the fluid that is displaced by the object. This relationship is called Archimedes' principle.

▶ Density is the ratio of an object's mass to its volume. The average density of an object affects its buoyancy.

4.3 Forces in Moving Fluids

▶ Bernoulli's principle states that the faster a fluid moves, the lower the fluid's pressure is.

▶ An airfoil's shape creates a low-pressure area above it and a high-pressure area below it. The difference generates lift.

▶ The forces involved in flight are lift, weight, the forward force called thrust, and the rearward force called drag.

▶ Birds and aircraft use pressure differences, low body weight, and streamlined shapes to aid in flight.

Chapter Vocabulary

fluid (p. 85)	buoyant force (p. 91)	lift (p. 98)	drag (p. 99)
pressure (p. 85)	airfoil (p. 98)	thrust (p. 99)	

Check Your Vocabulary

Use the vocabulary words above to complete the following sentences correctly.

1. Planes, birds, and boats are streamlined to reduce _____ .

2. The _____ on an object is equal to the weight of the fluid the object displaces.

3. Force per unit area is _____ .

4. The shape of an airplane wing is a(n) _____ .

5. Any substance that can flow is a(n) _____ .

6. The force that moves a plane forward is _____ .

7. As air moves over an airfoil, _____ is generated.

Pair each numbered word with a vocabulary term. Explain in a sentence how the words are related.

8. Friction
9. Wing
10. Float
11. Pascal
12. Flow
13. Up
14. Forward
15. Area
16. Pressure
17. Sink

Write Your Vocabulary

Write sentences using the vocabulary words above. Show that you know what each word means.

Check Your Vocabulary

1. drag

2. buoyant force

3. pressure

4. airfoil

5. fluid

6. thrust

7. lift

8. drag: Drag is the force caused by friction from the motion of an object through a fluid.

9. airfoil: The shape of a wing is called an airfoil.

10. buoyant force: An object floats in a fluid because of the buoyant force below it.

11. pressure: The pascal is the SI unit of pressure.

12. fluid: A fluid is a gas or liquid that flows.

13. lift: Lift is an upward force.

14. thrust: Thrust is the force that moves a flying object or organism forward.

15. pressure: Pressure is a measure of the force exerted on a particular area.

16. lift: Lift is the upward pressure that is produced during flight.

17. buoyant force: Without a buoyant force equal to or greater than the gravitational force on an object, the object sinks.

Write Your Vocabulary

Students' sentences should show that they know the meaning of each word as well as how to use it in a sentence.

Use Vocabulary Worksheet for Chapter 4.

Check Your Knowledge

1. A fluid is any substance that flows. Liquids and gases are fluids.

2. Pressure is the force exerted on a given unit of area. In the SI system, pressure is the force in newtons divided by the area in m^2.

3. Air pressure varies depending on altitude. The higher the altitude, the lower the atmospheric pressure, and vice versa. Weather conditions affect the air pressure at the earth's surface.

4. The force of gravity pulls down on the object; the buoyant force from the fluid pushes up on the object.

5. The denser the object, the greater the buoyant force needed to make it float.

6. As a fluid moves faster, the pressure in the fluid decreases. As the fluid moves slower, the pressure increases.

7. An airfoil has a curved upper surface and a flat, or less-curved, lower surface. It provides lift when moving through a fluid.

8. Lift pushes upward; weight pulls downward; thrust pushes forward; drag pulls backward.

9. pressure

10. fluids

11. area

12. decreases

13. N/m^2

14. lift

15. moves slower

Check Your Understanding

1. The volume of your body pushes away an equal volume of water. The level rises because there is no place else for the displaced water to go.

2. Ice is less dense than liquid water. Ice will float in water.

3. The atmospheric pressure on your body is balanced by pressure pushing outward from within your body.

4. The popping is the sound of air escaping from your middle ear through an opening in the pharynx to equalize the pressure on each side of your eardrum.

5. Bird wings are like airplane wings in that they are shaped like an airfoil, which provides lift and directional control for flight. In contrast, bird wings are not fixed in relation to the body.

6. Under normal circumstances, the buoyant force is equal to the weight of the fish, so the fish floats at any depth.

7. a. Air and water

   b. Water

   c. A rock in 5 m of water

8. There is more pressure at the bottom of a pitcher of water 35 cm deep, because the height of the column of water is greater.

9. The average density of an air-filled balloon is greater than that of air. Because helium is much less dense than air, a helium-filled balloon has a lower average density than air.

10. Twice as much pressure

Chapter 4 Review

Check Your Knowledge

Answer the following in complete sentences.

1. What is a fluid?

2. Explain what pressure is and how it is measured.

3. Explain how air pressure varies from place to place on the earth's surface.

4. Describe the forces acting on a floating object.

5. How does density affect buoyancy?

6. What happens to the pressure as a fluid moves faster? Slower?

7. Describe an airfoil.

8. What are the forces involved in airplane flight?

Choose the answer that best completes each sentence.

9. The motion of air particles inside a bicycle tire produces (friction, pressure, lift).

10. Air and water are (solids, fluids, mixtures, liquids).

11. To calculate pressure, you divide the force by the (volume, weight, area, length).

12. As you travel upward in the earth's atmosphere, the pressure (increases, stays the same, decreases, inflates).

13. The SI unit of pressure, the pascal, is equal to one (g/cm^3, N/m^3, N/m^2, J).

14. To fly, an airplane must have sufficient (friction, thrust, drag, lift).

15. According to Bernoulli's principle, the pressure in a fluid increases if the fluid (moves faster, moves slower, changes density, flows downward).

Check Your Understanding

1. **Application** When you get into a filled bathtub, the water level changes. Explain what happens and why.

2. Which is less dense? Ice or water? Explain your answer.

3. Why aren't you crushed by the column of air above you?

4. Why do your ears "pop" when you move to a higher or lower altitude?

5. **Critical Thinking** How are a bird's wings like airplane wings? How are they different?

6. How does the buoyant force that acts on a fish compare to the weight of the fish?

7. **Mystery Photo** The photograph on page 84 shows a whirlpool of water.

   a. Name two common fluids on the earth's surface.

   b. Which has the greater density, air or water?

   c. Which has greater pressure acting on it—a rock in 5 m of water or a rock 5 m above sea level?

8. **Application** Is there more pressure at the bottom of a bathtub of water 30 cm deep or at the bottom of a pitcher of water 35 cm deep?

9. **Application** When you let go of an air-filled balloon, it sinks. When you let go of a helium-filled balloon, it rises. Why?

10. **Extension** A diver at 10 m below the water surface goes to twice this depth. How much more water pressure is exerted on her ears?

Develop Your Skills

1. a. Block B will sink because there is a greater downward force acting on it.

b. Block A will float because there is a greater upward force on it.

c. Block C is neutrally buoyant, so it will remain at a fixed depth.

d. B, C, A. This assumes the blocks have the same volume.

2. An egg is more dense than tap water, but less dense than salt water of a particular concentration.

3. a. The bird is faster than the fish, but the fish moves through a denser medium (water is denser than air).

b. A dolphin swims through water faster than a human does. The surface area of the human is much less streamlined than the surface area of the dolphin, so the swimming human has to overcome greater drag.

Make Connections

1.

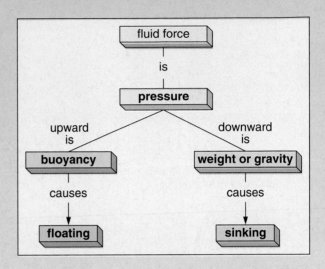

2. The scientific meaning of pressure is force per unit area. Examples of everyday usage include *peer pressure, job pressure,* or *a physical sensation of pressure.*

3. Student reports will vary. Boats must take into account qualities of buoyancy, drag, and thrust. Different boats are designed to take advantage of one or more of these qualities.

4. Like atmospheric pressure, blood pressure is greater at lower heights because of the force exerted by the fluid above. To get an accurate measure of the pressure your heart produces, blood pressure must be measured at the same level as the heart. High blood pressure can lead to heart attacks, atherosclerosis, and strokes.

Develop Your Skills

Use the skills you have developed in this chapter to complete each activity.

1. Interpret Data The drawings below show the forces acting on three different blocks placed in the same fluid.

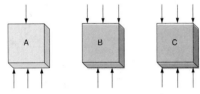

a. Which block(s) will sink? Why?

b. Which block(s) will float? Why?

c. For which block is the buoyant force equal to its weight?

d. Judging from the buoyant force acting on them, rank the blocks from heaviest to lightest. Explain your ranking.

2. Experiment Try to float an egg in water. Then dissolve salt in the water until the egg floats. How does the density of an egg compare to tap water? To salt water?

3. Data Bank Use the information on page 638 to answer the following questions.

a. Compare the speeds of a sailfish and a spine-tailed swift. Which is faster, the fish or the bird? Which must move through a denser fluid?

b. Compare the speed, in water, of a human and a dolphin. Explain the difference using the words *streamlined* and *drag.*

Make Connections

1. Link the Concepts Below is a concept map showing how some of the main concepts in this chapter link together. Only parts of the map are filled in. Copy the map. Using words and ideas from the chapter, complete the map.

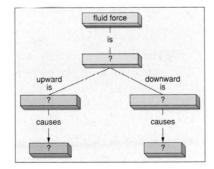

2. Science and Language Arts The word *pressure* is used often in everyday life. Make a list of those situations in which pressure is used. Write a report comparing the everyday meaning of the word to its scientific meaning.

3. Science and Technology Ships and other watercraft have specialized designs suited for their specific uses. Do a research project on ship and boat design. Use models, photographs, or diagrams to compare similarities and differences. Present your findings in an oral report or class display.

4. Science and You Why is your blood pressure measured in your upper arm, on a level with your heart? Is the blood pressure in your legs greater? Research the effects that high blood pressure can have on your body and how the condition can be prevented.

Overview

This chapter addresses work, machines, and energy. Work and power are defined in the first section. The second section explains how to determine the mechanical advantage and the efficiency of a machine. The third section describes six simple machines and defines a compound machine. The final section of the chapter discusses various forms of energy and defines the Law of Conservation of Mass and Energy.

Advance Planner

▶ Supply samples of electric bills for TE page 111.

▶ Provide 2-L plastic soft drink bottles, with caps, for TE page 115.

▶ Obtain a mechanical model of the inner ear for TE page 117.

▶ Collect hot plate, teakettle, toy car or pinwheel, plastic drinking straws, strips of cloth, scissors, and masking tape for SE Activity 5, page 126.

Skills Development Chart

Sections	Calculate	Classify	Communicate	Compare and Contrast	Define Operationally	Infer	Measure	Observe	Predict
5.1 Skills WarmUp			●	●	●				
Skills WorkOut									
Practice Problems	●								●
5.2 Skills WarmUp						●			
Practice Problems	●								
5.3 Skills WarmUp		●							
SkillBuilder		●							
5.4 Skills WarmUp						●			
Activity			●			●	●	●	

Individual Needs

▶ **Limited English Proficiency Students** Photocopy the figures on pages 108 and 116 to 119 with the labels masked. Draw arrows to the important parts of each figure. Have students make labels from strips of index cards and place the labels in the correct place on the photocopies. Have them refer to the text to check the placement of the labels. For each of the machines shown on pages 116 to 119, students can make a label telling the kind of machine and give an example of each. Students should remove and save the labels, then review the chapter by repeating the exercise.

▶ **At-Risk Students** Provide pictures of simple machines for the group. Have students identify all the machines in each picture by name. Have students label each machine on the pictures. Encourage them to use the textbook as a reference. Have students discuss how each machine works.

▶ **Gifted Students** Invite students to do a study of Einstein's famous equation, $E = mc^2$. They should try to answer questions such as the following: How did scientists compare mass and energy before Einstein's theory? What are the processes by which mass can be converted into energy? Encourage students to make a visual display to present their findings.

Resource Bank

▶ **Bulletin Board** Place the title *Energy Conversion* at the top of the bulletin board. Attach several pictures that represent energy being converted from one form to another. Make a number of labels for each of the five forms of energy listed in Section 5.4. Also, make labels that show arrows only. Have volunteers label each picture with energy labels linked by arrow labels to show the energy conversion involved. Encourage them to include as many steps in the conversion as possible. For example, for a picture of a person exercising, the labels should be chemical energy→mechanical energy→heat energy.

CHAPTER 5 PLANNING GUIDE

Section	Core	Standard	Enriched	Section	Core	Standard	Enriched
5.1 Work and Power pp. 106–111				**Blackline Masters** Review Worksheet 5.3	•	•	
Section Features Skills WarmUp, p. 107	•	•	•	Skills Worksheet 5.3a	•	•	
Skills WorkOut, p. 108	•	•	•	Skills Worksheet 5.3b	•	•	
Blackline Masters Review Worksheet 5.1	•	•		Integrating Worksheet 5.3	•	•	•
Reteach Worksheet 5.1	•	•	•	**Ancillary Options** *One-Minute Readings,* pp. 101–102	•	•	•
Laboratory Program Investigation 9	•	•		**Overhead Blackline Transparencies** Overhead Blackline Master 5 and Student Worksheet	•	•	•
Investigation 10	•	•					
5.2 Work and Machines pp. 112–115				**Laboratory Program** Investigation 11		•	•
Section Features Skills WarmUp, p. 112	•	•	•	**5.4 Energy and Its Forms** pp. 122–126			
Career Corner, p. 114	•	•	•	**Section Features** Skills WarmUp, p. 122	•	•	•
Blackline Masters Review Worksheet 5.2	•	•		Activity, p. 126	•	•	•
Integrating Worksheet 5.2	•	•	•	**Blackline Masters** Review Worksheet 5.4	•	•	
5.3 Simple and Compound Machines pp. 116–121				Skills Worksheet 5.4a	•	•	•
Section Features Skills WarmUp, p. 116	•	•	•	Skills Worksheet 5.4b	•	•	•
SkillBuilder, p. 120		•	•	Vocabulary Worksheet 5	•	•	
Color Transparencies Transparencies 9, 10, 11, 12	•	•	•	**Ancillary Options** *Multicultural Perspectives,* pp. 123, 124	•	•	•
				Color Transparencies Transparency 13	•	•	•

Bibliography

The following resources can be used for teaching the chapter. See page T-46 for supplier codes.

Library Resources

The Diagram Group. *Comparisons.* New York: St. Martin's Press, 1980.

Lafferty, Peter. *Energy and Light.* New York: Gloucester Press, 1989.

Macauley, David. *The Way Things Work.* Boston, Houghton Mifflin Company, 1988.

Sherwood, Martin, and Christine Sutton. *The Physical World.* New York: Oxford University Press, 1988.

Technology Resources
Software

The Even More Incredible Machine. Mac, Win. ER.
Learning All About Machines and Mechanics. Mac, Dos. LS.
The Way Things Work. Mac, Win. ER.

CD-ROMs

An Odyssey of Discovery for Science Insights: Have students try the activity *Recycler* on the Earth and Space Disk. *SFAW.*

Laserdiscs

Living Textbook. (See barcodes on pages in this chapter.) Optical Data.

Videos

Simple and Compound Machines: How They Work. AIMS, QE.

Audio-Visual Resources

The Lever. Film. BFA.
Simple Machines. Filmstrip. EB.
Work and Play Made Easier: Using Simple Machines. Film. MF.
Work and Power. Filmstrip. EB.

Writing Connection

Ask students to study the photograph and have them imagine being trapped inside a huge clock. Ask students to write a description of what they would see, hear, and feel.

Social Studies Connection

Societies throughout history have used a variety of devices to keep track of time: sundials, water clocks, hour glasses, and mechanical clocks run by weights, springs, and pendulums. Ask students to research early time-keeping devices. They should find out how they worked, how they were used by different societies, and who in a community controlled or owned them.

Introducing the Chapter

Have students read the description of the photograph. Ask if they agree or disagree with the description.

Directed Inquiry

Have students study the photograph. Ask the following questions:

▶ What do you think this is a picture of? (Students should recognize it as the mechanism inside a clock or watch.)

▶ What is the function of the wheel-like structures? (Students should say that they make the hands on the watch face move.)

▶ How do you think these wheels work? (Students may mention that their "teeth" interlock, so that when one turns, they all turn.)

▶ How do you think this picture relates to the title of the chapter? (The gears of a watch or clock are machines that use energy to do the work of moving hands to record the passing of time.)

Chapter Vocabulary

compound	power
machine	simple
joule	machine
machine	watt
mechanical	work
advantage	
mechanical	
efficiency	

Chapter 5 — Work, Machines, and Energy

Chapter Sections

5.1 Work and Power

5.2 Work and Machines

5.3 Simple and Compound Machines

5.4 Energy and Its Forms

What do you see?

❝ I see gears that could be in a wristwatch or even a factory. They are used to move things by turning and interlocking their little teeth on the circumference. By working together, they use less energy to complete their work. ❞

Marie Fridman
Bair Middle School
Sunrise, Florida

To find out more about the photograph, look on page 128. As you read this chapter, you will learn about work, machines, and energy.

5.1 Work and Power

Objectives

▶ **Describe** the conditions which must be met to do work.

▶ **Distinguish** between work and power.

▶ **Calculate** work and power.

▶ **Interpret data** from a sample electric bill.

▼ **ACTIVITY**

Defining Operationally

Work Is . . .

Make a list of five activities that you consider to be work. Compare the items listed to determine how they are alike. Use these similarities to write a definition of the term *work*.

SKILLS WARMUP

What does the word *work* make you think of? You probably think of tasks that you would rather not do. For example, you might think it is work to rake leaves in your front yard or run laps around a school track.

Your idea of work might be quite different from another person's idea. If you enjoy being outside, you might like to rake leaves. If you are a member of a sports team, you might like to run. In everyday life, the word *work* means different things to different people. But in science, work has a specific meaning. In science, work relates to forces, motion, and energy.

Work

Two conditions must be met in order for **work** to be done on an object:

▶ The object moves.

▶ A force must act on the object in the direction the object moves.

When you rake leaves, as the boy is doing in Figure 5.1, you do work. You apply a force against the leaves and they move. Most people push the rake downward and pull horizontally. The force directed downward doesn't do any work on the leaves because it doesn't make them move. Only the horizontal force that moves the leaves does work on them.

When you run laps around a track you do work. Your legs apply a force against the track to move your body forward. As a result, you move a certain distance around the track. The amount of work you do depends only on force and distance. How much time it takes to do work is not involved.

Figure 5.1
The boy is doing work. How is he meeting the two conditions which are necessary for work to be done? ▼ ①

Skills WorkOut

To help students relate energy to work, have them do the Skills WorkOut.

Answer The amount of work is equal.

Critical Thinking

Classify To help students understand what work means in science, ask, Are you doing work when you're walking? (Yes) Standing? (No) Sitting? (No) Lifting up a book to read? (Yes) Throwing a ball? (Yes) Catching a ball? (No)

Compare and Contrast Have students think about how a joule of energy compares to a joule of work. Ask, how much work is done if you move a 100-N desk 2 m and how much energy was used to move it? (200 J of work and 200 J of energy)

Skills Development

Infer Have students make up their own problems using the mathematical formula $W = Fd$. For example, they could assign values to the horizontal and vertical components of force that do work to push the mower in Figure 5.2 and to the distance the mower is pushed.

Answer to In-Text Question

① **Though reading this page takes effort, it is not work because it does not produce motion.**

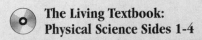
The Living Textbook: Physical Science Sides 1-4

Chapter 10   Frame 01772
Work Formula and Diagram (1 Frame)
Search:

108

Language Arts Connection

Have students research the origin of the technical word for a unit of work, the *joule*, or the technical word for a unit of force, the *newton*. They can find the answers in a dictionary as well as in an encyclopedia. Have them write the explanation in their own words.

Integrating the Sciences

Life Science Remind students that animals were once used to do all the work that internal combustion engines do today. Students have probably seen horses used as draft animals to pull coaches or wagons. Have students name other animals that were used to do work. Then ask why what the animals are doing is called work. (Some examples might be oxen used on farms; elephants used in the lumber industry; sled dogs; reindeer.)

▼ ACTIVITY

Predicting

More or Less Work

Which task is more work: lifting a 2 N box 1 m or lifting a 1 N box 2 m? On what did you base your prediction?

SKILLS WORKOUT

Figure 5.2 ▲
The downward force does not do work. Only the force applied in the same direction the lawn mower moves does work.

Energy is needed to rake leaves or to do any kind of work. In fact, energy is defined as the ability to do work. Are you doing work right now? ①

Can you think of a situation when you use energy but do not do work? When an Olympic weight-lifter presses a barbell over his head, he must hold it there until the judges say he can put it down. If the weight-lifter holds the barbell perfectly still while it is over his head, is he doing work? The answer is no. He is applying force against the barbell, but he is not moving the force through a distance. For work to be done, a force must move an object through a distance.

Measuring Work

Imagine that you earn money by mowing your neighbors' lawns like the girl in Figure 5.2. What factors would you consider when deciding how much to charge? You might vary your fee according to the size of the lawn being mowed. It takes a large amount of work to mow a large lawn. The farther the lawn mower is pushed, the greater is the amount of work done.

To determine the amount of work done, you use a mathematical formula. The formula relates work to force and distance. Two measurements are needed to use this formula. One measurement is the amount of force exerted in the direction of motion. The other measurement is the distance moved. Multiplying the force measurement by the distance measurement gives you the amount of work done.

$$\text{work} = \text{force} \times \text{distance}$$
$$W = Fd$$

The amount of force exerted on an object is measured in newtons. The distance the object moves is measured in meters. As a result, the unit for work is sometimes called the newton meter (Nm). Another word for the Newton meter is the **joule** (JOOL). One joule (J) equals the work done by a force of 1 N that moves an object a distance of 1 m.

The joule is a unit that is also used to measure energy. Lifting a glass of water from a counter top to your mouth, for example, would require you to use about 1 J of energy and to perform about 1 J of work. As you can see, energy and work are related.

Social Studies Connection

James Watt (1736–1819) was a Scottish engineer who invented many improvements to the steam engine, making it a useful source of power. In the 18th century, steam engines were used to run the machines used in the new iron industry. Watt's new steam engines helped to power the Industrial Revolution.

Power

Imagine that you and a friend each mow a lawn of equal size. You both use the same force and push the lawn mowers the same distance. You and your friend do equal amounts of work. However, you finish the job 20 min faster than your friend. To do this you had to use a greater amount of **power**. Power is the rate at which work is done. To calculate power, you divide the amount of work done by the time it took to do the work.

$$\text{power} = \frac{\text{work}}{\text{time}}$$

When the work is in joules and the time in seconds the power is in joules per second (J/s). Another name for a joule per second is the **watt** (W). One watt is equal to one J/s. One watt is about the amount of power it takes for you to lift a glass of water one meter in one second. One hundred joules of work done in one second is equal to one hundred watts of power. Study Figure 5.3 and compare the power involved in each situation.

The SI unit of power was named for James Watt, a Scottish engineer. Watt coined the term "horsepower" (hp), which is used to rate electric motors and gasoline engines. He defined one horsepower as the amount of work a horse could do in one second. One horsepower is equal to 745.56 W.

 Figure 5.3
The backhoe has more power than a person with a shovel. Why? ②

109

Critical Thinking

Compare and Contrast Pose the following situation for students: Suppose that you and another person each mow a different lawn in the same amount of time. However, one lawn is larger. Which person has to use a greater amount of power, you or your friend? Why? (The larger lawn takes more work so the person doing more work in the same amount of time uses the greater amount of power.)

Enrich

Students know that some jobs are done faster with a machine. Have them identify appliances they use to make work easier. (Examples: washing machines, dryers, bicycles, stoves, cars, toasters, mixers) Ask students how each appliance they mention reduces work. Ask how they know these machines use power to make work easier. (Students should relate power to the reduction in time it takes to do the work. Adding power decreases the time work takes.)

Answer to In-Text Question

② The backhoe has more power than a person with a shovel because the backhoe can do more work in less time.

The Living Textbook:
Physical Science Sides 1-4

Chapter 10   Frame 01779
Horsepower (2 Frames)
Search: Step:

TEACH ▪ Continued

Practice Problems

Work through the sample problems with students. Then have them do the practice problems.

Answers

1. Work = force × distance
   = 60 N × 6 m = 360 Nm
   = 360 J

2. Work = force × distance
   = 20 N × 4.2 m = 84 Nm= 84 J

3. Work = 500 N × 2 m
   = 1000 Nm = 1000 J

4. Work = force × distance
   = 50 N × 3 m = 150 Nm
   =150 J

5. Work = force × distance
   = 40 N × 2 m = 80 Nm = 80 J

6. Time = 14 × 60 s = 840 s
   Power = work/time
   = 168 000 J/840 s = 200 J/s =
   200 W

7. Work = force × distance
   = 500 N × 1.5 m = 750 Nm
   = 750 J
   Power = work/time
   = 750 J/10 s = 75 J/s = 75 W
   750 J/5 s = 150 J/s = 150 W

8. Power = work/time
   = 3000 J/30 s
   = 100 J/s
   = 100 W

9. Work = force × distance
   = 250 N × 10 m
   = 2500 Nm = 2500 J
   Power = work/time
   = 2500 J/20 s
   = 125 J/s = 125 W

10. Work = force × distance
    Force = work/distance
    = 800 Nm/5 m = 160 N
    Power = work/time
    = 800 J/6 s = 133 J/s
    = 133 W

Enrich

Assign problems on this concept from Math Appendix page 646.

Integrating the Sciences

Meteorology Lightning may have many thousands of watts, or kilowatts of power. Suppose lightning struck a large oak tree weighing 100 000 newtons and hurled it 10 meters in 1.5 seconds. Calculate how much power was used. (100 000 N × 10 m = 1 000 000 Nm. Power = Nm/time. Therefore, the lightning's power was 1 000 000 Nm/1.5 s, or 666 667 watts, or 666.7 kilowatts.)

Math Connection

James Watt used the English unit of force, the *pound*, to define work in terms of foot-pounds, or *horsepower*. A foot-pound is the work done by moving one pound over a distance of one foot. One horsepower is equal to 745.56 Nm/s. One newton is 0.225 pounds at the earth's surface, and one meter is 3.28 feet. What is one horsepower? (745.56 Nm/s × 0.225 pounds/N × 3.28 ft/m = 550.22 ft-lb/s.)

Sample Problems

1. Rita mows lawns on the weekends. If she uses 15 N of force to move a lawn mower a distance of 10 m, how much work does Rita do?

   Plan To find the amount of work done, multiply the force by the distance.

   Gather data The force is 15 N, the distance is 10 m.

   Solve Work = force × distance
   = 15 N × 10 m
   = 150 Nm =150 J

2. How much work did Joe do when he used 30 N of force to pull a table a distance of 3 m?

   Plan To find the amount of work done, multiply the force by the distance.

   Gather data The force is 30 N. The distance is 3 m.

   Solve Work = force × distance
   = 30 N × 3m
   = 90 Nm = 90 J

3. You run up several flights of stairs in 1.5 min. If the work you do is equal to 9000 J, how much power do you use?

   Plan Divide the amount of work done by the time it took to do it. Since time is given in minutes, it needs to be converted to seconds before you divide by it.

   Gather data The work done was 9000 J. The time was 1.5 min. There are 60 s in 1 min.

   Solve 1.5 min × 60 s = 90 s

   $$power = \frac{work}{time}$$

   $$= \frac{9000 \text{ J}}{90 \text{ s}}$$

   $$= 100 \text{ J/s} = 100 \text{ W}$$

Practice Problems

1. How much work is done by a force of 60 N that moves an object 6 m?

2. In preparing for a classroom activity, two students work together to push a desk a distance of 4.2 m. The combined force they used to complete the task was 20 N. How much work did they do together?

3. Five students exert a combined force of 500 N to lift a heavy crate a distance of 2 m off the ground. How much work did the students exert together in lifting the crate?

4. Nancy stores her holiday decorations in the garage rafters. She uses a ladder to lift a 50 N box 3 m off the ground. How much work does she do?

5. A cat weighing 40 N jumps 2 m onto a fence. How much work does the cat do?

6. Two students decide to go rowing on the weekend. They row the boat for 14 min and together do 168 000 J of work. How much power did they exert?

7. How much power would a forklift need to raise a 500 N load 1.5 m high in 10 s? How much power would be needed to do the same work in 5 s?

8. You do 3000 J of work to slide a box across the floor in 30 s. Calculate your power.

9. You apply a 250-N force for 20 s to slide a box 10 m across the floor. Calculate your power.

10. You do 800 J of work to slide a box 5 m across the floor. How much force did you use? If it took 6 s to slide the box, what was the power used?

Math Connection

Suppose the electric company supplies 1000 watts of electricity for one hour for $0.08. If you were paid this rate for your work mowing the lawn, how much would you make for providing one-half horsepower for one hour? (Since 1 horsepower = 746 watts, 1/2 horsepower = 373 watts. At $0.08 per kilowatt-hour, you would be paid about 3 cents ($.08 × [373 W ÷ 1000 W].)

Language Arts Connection

Electric power in watts is the electrical current in amperes multiplied by the voltage in volts. Have students find out the origin of the words *watt, volt,* and *ampere* and give their definitions.

Science and You *Your Electric Bill*

Your electric meter is read each month. The bill you receive may contain information about gas usage, as the bill does in Figure 5.4. To check the accuracy of the electric part of the bill, study the following items:

A. The amount of electricity you used that month.

B. Baseline, or Lifeline Allowance. This is the amount of electricity you can buy at the cheapest rate.

C. Lifeline usage. The amount of your Lifeline Allowance you actually used.

D. The cheapest electricity rate. This rate applies only for your Lifeline Allowance.

E. The rate you pay for electricity that is over your Lifeline Allowance.

Calculate your own bill using items A-E.

1. If A is smaller than B, multiply A and D. The product is the cost of the electricity. Then, you can skip steps 2-4 below.

2. If A is larger than B, multiply C and D.

3. Subtract C from A. Multiply the difference by E.

4. Add the products from steps 2 and 3. This sum, along with any taxes and service charge, is the amount you owe for electricity.

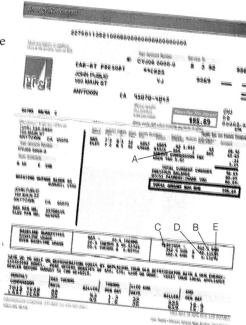

Figure 5.4 ▲

It is a good idea to check the accuracy of your electric bill each month.

Check and Explain

1. Suppose you tried to move a large boulder by pushing it, but it didn't move. Did you do work? Explain.

2. How are work and power similar? How are they different?

3. **Calculate** How much work is done in lifting a 500-N crate to a height of 1.5 m? If it takes 2 s to lift the crate, how much power is required?

4. **Interpret Data** Use Figure 5.4 to determine the charge for electricity (not counting tax and the service charge).

WrapUp

Reteach Most sports involve work in the scientific sense. Athletes exert force to move their bodies and other objects across distances. Ask students to describe track-and-field events (running, jumping, and throwing) in terms of work and power. Ask them which events have a power component and why. (Running events do because the results actually compare power—work done over time.)

Use Review Worksheet 5.1.

Check and Explain

1. No; even though the push required effort, by definition work is done only if an object moves.

2. Both are measurements that relate force and distance. Power is the rate at which work is done, so it includes a measurement of time.

3. Work = 500 N × 1.5 m = 750 J; Power = 750 J/2 s = 375 W

4. The charge for electricity usage is $63.43.

Reteach

Use Reteach Worksheet 5.1.

 The Living Textbook: Physical Science Sides 1-4

Chapter 15   Frame 02629
Kilowatt Hours (2 Frames)
Search: Step:

111

Section Objectives
For a list of section objectives, see the Student Edition page.

Skills Objectives
Students should be able to:

Infer the relationship between energy and work efficiency.

Communicate the cost efficiency of an appliance through analysis.

Vocabulary
machine, mechanical advantage, mechanical efficiency

MOTIVATE

Skills WarmUp

To help students understand work and machines, have them do the Skills WarmUp.
Answer Answers may vary. Using a ramp would be the simplest answer. Students may also suggest lifting it by ropes and pulleys.

Misconceptions

Students may think that all machines have moving parts. Introduce them to the definition of a machine as a device that changes the size or direction of a force used to do work.

Answer to Link

Chalk is too brittle to work with and it would break in usage.

Themes in Science

Energy Energy is required to do work. Machines make work easier, but they do not change the amount of work done, or the amount of energy used. When you use a lever to lift an object, the force at the effort end changes but the amount of work done is the same.

Integrating the Sciences

Earth Science Paleontologists searching for dinosaurs often uncover fossilized bones that weigh thousands of newtons. Machines remove them from the earth. Jacks, inclined planes, cranes, and sometimes helicopters lift the fossil onto trucks. Museums use pulleys to lift the bones.

▼ **ACTIVITY**

Inferring

Lifting a Lawn Mower

You have been asked to load a lawn mower onto the bed of a pickup truck. The lawn mower is too heavy to lift directly. How will you move the lawn mower onto the truck?

SKILLS WARMUP

Geology
L I N K

Early humans made and used stone tools. Many of these tools were simple machines. Although working with stone takes great force, you can model the making of a stone tool. Collect the following items: scissors, pieces of chalk.

1. Break a few pieces of chalk in half.

2. Use your scissors to carve the pieces into wedge shapes.

Would chalk be a good material for real stone tools? Explain.

A C T I V I T Y

5.2 Work and Machines

Objectives

▶ **Explain** how machines make work easier.

▶ **Calculate** mechanical advantage.

▶ **Infer** the relationship between energy use and mechanical efficiency.

Suppose your music teacher is preparing for a concert. He needs to move a piano from the third floor music room to the first floor gym. The piano fits easily through the classroom door. From there, the instrument would have to be carried down three flights of stairs. The piano is very heavy. Another way to move the piano is out the music room's large window. For the second method to work, a device is needed to gently lower the instrument down to the ground. The teacher asks the class for suggestions on how to accomplish the task. How would you plan to move the piano?

Machines

You and your classmates probably have many different ideas about how to move a piano. More than likely your plans are similar in one way. They probably involve using a **machine**. A machine is a device that makes work easier. Machines make work easier by changing the direction or the size of the force needed to do work.

Two forces are involved when you use a machine. The force applied *to* the machine is called the *effort force*. For example, when you push down on a screwdriver to remove the lid from a can of paint, you apply effort force to the screwdriver. The force opposing the effort force is the *resistance force*. The lid on the paint can is the resistance, or opposing, force. Often, resistance is the weight of the object.

Ropes and pulleys, boards with wheels, and ramps are examples of machines that might make moving the piano easier. A rope and pulley can reduce the amount of force needed to raise or lower the piano. A flat board with wheels reduces the amount of force needed to push the piano across the floor. A ramp reduces the

Cooperative Learning

Have students work in cooperative groups of three or four to identify machines that they use at home or in school to gain a mechanical advantage, M.A. Have them estimate the M.A. and classify the machines according to whether the M.A. is greater than 1 or less than 1. Have them explain their choices.

Students may identify the claw on a hammer used to take out nails, pressing the keys on a piano or using a flyswatter. These machines may or may not increase the user's force. Some of these machines would have an M.A. close to 1, or even less.

---

amount of force needed to move the piano down three flights of stairs.

Machines can't save work. A machine lets you apply less force to overcome a resistance. However, you must apply the force over a greater distance. A bicycle and a doorknob are other examples of machines.

Mechanical Advantage

Most machines multiply the force of your efforts. The number of times a machine multiplies an effort force is its **mechanical advantage** (M.A.). A machine with an M.A. of 2 doubles your effort force. As a result, you only have to use half of the effort force needed to do the same amount of work without a machine.

Machines can also change the direction of a force. A machine that only changes the direction of a force has an M.A of 1. An M.A. of 1, however, does not change the force you have to apply. Machines with an M.A. less than 1 increase the force you have to apply.

To find out a machine's mechanical advantage, divide the resistance force by the effort force.

$$\text{M.A.} = \frac{\text{resistance force}}{\text{effort force}}$$

For example, if you can lift a 300 N object by applying only 20 N of force to a lever, the M.A. of the lever is 15.

Figure 5.5 ▲
A screwdriver can be used as a lever to open a can of paint. Identify the forces being applied. ①

Discuss

Have students consider the two forces that are involved in doing work. Have them explain in their own words what these forces are. For example, effort force is the force applied to the object to do the work. Resistance force is the force that resists the doing of work. A piano would provide a great deal of resistance force when lifted because it has a great deal of mass.

Discuss

Write the formula for finding mechanical advantage on the chalkboard. Have students suggest why there are no units for mechanical advantage. (Mechanical advantage is simply a ratio of two forces, and each has the same unit.)

Practice Problems

Work through the sample problems with students. Then have them do the practice problems.

Answers
1. M.A. = resistance force/effort force; M.A. = 500 N/50 N = 10
2. Effort force = resistance force/M.A.; effort force = 500 N/5 = 100 N. **3.** M.A. = resistance force/effort force; M.A. = 200 N/50 N = 4

Enrich

Assign additional problems on mechanical advantage from the Math Appendix page 646.

Answer to In-Text Question

① Effort force is applied to the screwdriver. The lid on the paint can is the resistance force.

Sample Problem

Jill likes to work on old automobiles. She has constructed a pulley system to help her lift the engine out of the car. She can lift a 600-N engine by applying only 150 N of force. What is the M.A. of her pulley system?

Plan Divide the resistance force by the effort force to find M.A.

Gather data The resistance force is 600 N. The effort force is 150 N.

Solve M.A. = $\frac{600 \text{ N}}{150 \text{ N}}$ = 4

Practice Problems

1. John works at a construction site. The foreman told him that with a particular crowbar he needs 50 N of force to lift 500 N. What is the M.A. of the crowbar?

2. A smaller crowbar is available to John. It has an M.A. of 5. How much force will John need to apply to the smaller crowbar to lift the same concrete block?

3. You use 50 N of force to push a 200-N crate up a ramp. What's the M.A. of the ramp?

TEACH ▪ Continued

Skills Development

Communicate Ask students to explain mechanical efficiency in their own words for each of the following:

▶ A typical automobile engine has a mechanical efficiency of about 30 percent. (The engine converts only about 30 percent of the energy released by the fuel into turning the drive shaft.)

▶ Roller skates can lose 10 percent of their mechanical efficiency in a year. (It takes 10 percent more effort to use the roller skates after a year because the worn parts cause more friction in the wheel bearings.)

Career Corner

Reason and Conclude Have students think about the following: When a mechanical product is advertised to be new and improved, what do you think can probably be stated about the mechanical efficiency? (That the mechanical efficiency is improved) How might the mechanical efficiency of a car be improved by its design? (Answers will vary, but students might mention reducing the weight of the car, streamlining the body design, or improving the combustion of the fuel with engine design.)

 **The Living Textbook:
Physical Science Sides 1-4**

Chapter 17　　　Frame 02956
Efficiency (2 Frames)
Search:　　　　　Step:

114

Themes in Science

Energy Energy may change from one form to another, but it is not destroyed or created. This is the law of conservation of energy. Ask students to explain why a ball finally stops moving after you throw it. Where does the energy go? (The friction of the air and ground converts the ball's motion to heat energy.)

Social Studies Connection

Many inventors have dreamed of designing a machine that has more work output than work input. One example would be a perpetual motion machine that, once it is started, would continue in motion forever. These inventors have always ignored the fact that small amounts of friction always convert some mechanical energy into sound and heat energy.

Mechanical Efficiency

Machines make it easier to do work. However, the amount of work put into a machine, or *work input*, is always greater than the amount of work done by the machine, or *work output*. Work input is always greater than work output because some of the work put into the machine is used to overcome friction.

The **mechanical efficiency** of a machine compares its work output with the work input. In general:

$$\text{mechanical efficiency} = \frac{\text{work output}}{\text{work input}} \times 100\%$$

Because the work output is always less than the work input, the mechanical efficiency of a machine is always less than 100%. The efficiency of a machine, such as a bicycle or automobile, can be increased by keeping its parts clean and well lubricated. Such measures help reduce friction and result in higher efficiency.

Career Corner　*Mechanical Engineer*

Who Designs Machines?

Suppose you visited a bike store, and noticed a moped display. A sign read that the moped was "new and improved." You wondered how this moped was different from previous models. The moped's improvements were probably made by a mechanical engineer.

Mechanical engineers explore ways to produce and use mechanical power. They design and test all types of machines. Some mechanical engineers do research and design new types of machines. Other mechanical engineers work to improve existing machines, like the moped.

Mechanical engineers work on a wide variety of machines. Automobiles, air conditioners, heating systems, and industrial equipment are examples of machines developed and improved by mechanical engineers.

To be a mechanical engineer, you should be curious about how things work. You also should be able to find creative ways of solving problems. Mechanical engineers need a strong background in math and science. Most mechanical engineers have at least a four-year college degree. You can learn more about this profession by writing to the American Society of Mechanical Engineers, 345 E. 47th Street, New York, NY 10017.

Language Arts Connection

The word *efficient* can be applied to people as well as to machines. The writer and historian Arthur Schlesinger wrote of Washington, DC, that "Washington is a city of southern efficiency and northern charm." Have students compare the meaning of the word *efficiency* in this context to its scientific meaning. Explain that the quote is meant to be witty.

Integrating the Sciences

Biology Some biologists study the efficiency with which different animals move their bodies as they hunt for food. The energy animals gain from their food divided by the energy required to find and eat the food is a measure of hunting efficiency.

Use Integrating Worksheet 5.2.

Science and Society
Energy Efficiency

Have you ever seen a commercial for a new, more energy-efficient model of a refrigerator or other household appliance? Such machines use less energy and therefore cost less to operate. Automobiles and household appliances often have labels that tell the buyer how energy-efficient the product is. An example of these labels is shown in Figure 5.6. Consumers who use this information to choose energy-efficient products can save money. They also help conserve energy resources.

Design improvements and advanced technology help to make many appliances more energy efficient. But in spite of the improvements, no machine is 100% efficient. Some of the work put into any machine is used to overcome friction between the machine's moving parts. Since friction produces heat, the work used to overcome friction is lost as waste heat energy.

In general, the more moving parts a machine has, the lower its mechanical efficiency is. A machine with only a few moving parts can be up to 98% efficient. Such a machine uses 98% of the energy it takes in to do useful work. It loses only 2% as waste heat.

Only about 30% of the energy produced by burning gasoline in an auto engine does useful work. About 35% of the energy is lost as heat to the cooling system. The remaining 35% is lost as heat in the exhaust gases. The amount of gas the car uses depends on the efficiency of the engine. How might car engines become more energy efficient? ①

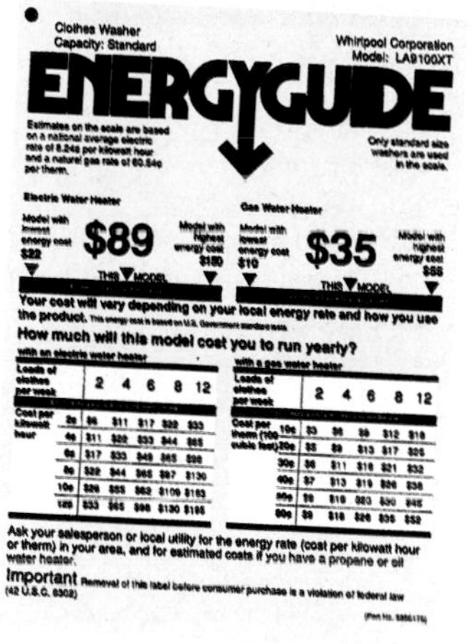

Figure 5.6 ▲
This label is an estimation of the yearly energy cost of using a particular model washing machine.

Check and Explain

1. How do machines make work easier?
2. You apply 20 N of force to a machine consisting of pulleys that can lift 80 N of bricks. What is the M.A. of the machine?
3. **Analyze** A refrigerator that is 78% efficient costs more than a similar appliance that is only 46% efficient. The salesperson tells the consumer that the more expensive appliance will save money. Explain.
4. **Infer** How does properly maintaining your bicycle increase its mechanical efficiency?

Skills Development

Infer Have students consider how a gasket on a refrigerator may improve the refrigerator's mechanical efficiency. (It seals the door when it is closed so that the refrigerator will not have to run as often to keep the refrigerator cool inside.)

EVALUATE

WrapUp

Reinforce Ask students to work in pairs. Furnish each pair with an empty, tightly capped, 2-liter beverage bottle. Ask the first student to hold the body of the bottle still while the second twists the cap off. Then have them reverse the bottle so the first student holds the cap firmly while the second twists the bottle. Have them repeat the experiment. Ask, Which was the easier way to remove the cap? Explain. (Twisting the bottle should have seemed easier. Discuss the reasons for this. Twisting the bottle reduces the force by letting you apply it over a greater distance.) Ask them to discuss the design of a machine for removing a cap that works in a similar way.

Use Review Worksheet 5.2.

Check and Explain

1. Machines change the size or direction of the force needed to do work, but not the amount of work done.
2. The M.A. is 4.
3. The more efficient refrigerator uses less energy and will cost less to operate over time.
4. Worn parts cause greater friction, which reduces efficiency. Maintenance includes lubrication, which reduces friction and wear.

Answer to In-Text Question

① Car engines might become more energy efficient if less heat were lost to the atmosphere.

Multicultural Perspectives

Of all the pyramids built by various cultures throughout the world, the pyramids of Egypt are the best known. Did the Egyptians use machines? Archaeologists think that inclined planes were built, and stone blocks were pushed up to great heights using rollers to reduce friction. The ramps were gradually lengthened to reach higher.

Art Connection

The Guggenheim Museum in New York City was designed by the architect Frank Lloyd Wright (1867–1959) in 1959 to display modern art. Inside, the building resembles a giant screw. A circular inclined plane allows visitors to walk up and down five floors on one long, spiraling ramp as they view twentieth-century paintings. The ramp is an example of a machine that has a functional design.

Section Objectives
For a list of section objectives, see the Student Edition page.

Skills Objectives
Students should be able to:

Classify some ways that the work involved in getting to school is reduced.

Predict the M.A. of a pulley system.

Vocabulary
simple machine, compound machine

► MOTIVATE

Skills WarmUp

To help students understand machines, have them do the Skills WarmUp.
Answer Answers will vary, but should include such things as bikes, cars, and buses, all of which do the work of moving students between home and school. Students may include things that get them into the classroom inside the building, like stairs and ramps.

Prior Knowledge

Gauge how much students know about simple and compound machines by asking the following questions:

► If you had to lift a heavy crate, what are some machines you could use?

► Do those machines use more than one movement to do their work?

► Do you think those machines are simple or compound?

► How do compound machines differ from simple machines?

▼ **ACTIVITY**

Classifying

Working Toward School
List some ways you can reduce the amount of work you do to get to school. Classify each one according to how work is made easier.

SKILLS WARMUP

5.3 Simple and Compound Machines

Objectives

► **Explain** how six simple machines make work easier.

► **Classify** the simple machines in a compound machine you are familiar with.

► **Predict** the mechanical advantages of simple machines.

Machines are almost everywhere you look. How many can you see around you? Below are two groups of devices.
Group 1: Ramp, bottle opener, pulley, wheelbarrow
Group 2: Car, escalator, lawn mower, hair dryer
Which group of items contains machines? All devices in both groups make work easier. Each changes the size or direction of a force applied to it. Therefore, every device in both groups is a machine. The devices in Group 1 are examples of **simple machines**. Simple machines do work with one movement. There are six types of simple machines: the inclined plane, wedge, screw, lever, wheel and axle, and pulley.

Inclined Plane

A simple machine that has a sloping surface is an *inclined plane*. The ramp shown in Figure 5.7 is an inclined plane. You use less force to pull the crate up a ramp than if you lifted it vertically. In exchange for using less force, you must pull the crate a greater distance. An inclined plane will not change the amount of work. It reduces the effort force.

A *wedge* is an inclined plane that can move. An ax is a wedge. The resistance force required to split a log is great. The effort force driving the ax into the log is less, but it must be applied over a greater distance.

A *screw* is also an inclined plane. Many car jacks are screws. A great many turns are needed to move a car jack a short distance. However, the car jack produces a far greater force than the force needed to turn it.

Figure 5.7
A ramp makes moving a heavy crate easier. ▼

Effort force

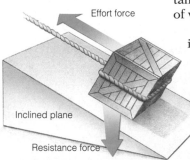
Inclined plane

Resistance force

Levers

A balance, a wheelbarrow, and a shovel are all machines. They all have a straight part that moves when a force is applied. And they all have one point that does not move. The fixed point is called the *fulcrum*. Machines that do work by moving around a fixed point are called levers. The three classes of levers are shown below. Levers are classified according to the location of the fulcrum, the effort force, and the resistance force.

First Class Lever A balance like the one shown is an example of a first class lever. The fulcrum is always between the effort force and the resistance force. First class levers multiply the effort force and also change its direction.

A crowbar is a first class lever. A large resistance force is required to pull nails from boards. This force can be achieved when a small effort force is applied to a long crowbar. However, no work is saved. The effort force applied to the crowbar moves farther than the resistance force. Other examples of first class levers include a pair of shears and a teeter-totter or seesaw.

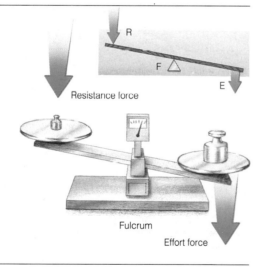

Resistance force

Fulcrum

Effort force

Second Class Lever A wheelbarrow is an example of a second class lever. The resistance force is between the fulcrum and the effort force. Notice in the picture to the right that in second class levers, the distance from the fulcrum to the resistance force is less than the distance from the fulcrum to the effort force. When you lift the handles of the wheelbarrow, you apply less force than the weight of the load. In return, you have to move the handles a greater distance than the load is raised. Second class levers multiply the effort force without changing its direction. Examples of second class levers include bottle openers, doors, and some nutcrackers.

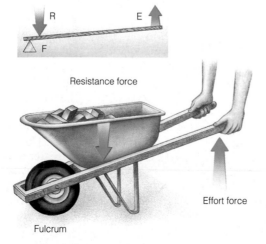

Resistance force

Effort force

Fulcrum

TEACH • Continued

Critical Thinking

Reason by Analogy Have students consider the following questions:

▶ Why are a rake and a fishing pole both examples of third class levers? (The effort force is between the fulcrum and the resistance. In fact, the fulcrum is close to the end where the effort force is applied.)

▶ How is a wheel like a lever? (The radius of the wheel, or the distance between the effort force or the resistance and the center of the wheel, is like a lever. The fulcrum is at the center of the wheel.)

Discuss

Have students practice determining the mechanical advantage of the three kinds of levers:

▶ In a first class lever, if the effort distance is 2 m and the resistance distance is 2 m, what is the M.A.? (1)

▶ In a second class lever, if the effort distance to the fulcrum is 5 m and the resistance distance is 2.5 m, what is the M.A.? (2)

▶ In a third class lever, if the effort distance is 2 m and the resistance distance is 5 m, what is the M.A.? (0.4)

 **The Living Textbook: Physical Science Sides 1-4**

Chapter 10   Frame 01853
Wheel and Axle (3 Frames)
Search: Step:

118

Art Connection

Some painters of the 20th century were fascinated by machines and their capacity to both help and hurt the individual and society. French painters Francis Picabia and Fernand Léger depicted people as machines and machines as people. It has been suggested that their paintings mean that machines have replaced people as the basis for myths in the twentieth century.

Use Integrating Worksheet 5.3.

Math Connection

Make a first class lever with a meter stick. Place the fulcrum at 10 cm and a 1 kg weight at the short end. Construct a graph showing mechanical advantage on the y-axis, and distance of the effort force to the fulcrum (1 to 100 cm) on the x-axis. Have students change the effort force distance several times and calculate the M.A. Have them plot the M.A. on the graph. How can the graph be used to predict M.A.? What is the control?

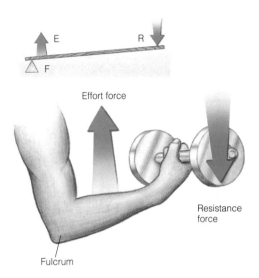

Effort force

Resistance force

Fulcrum

Third Class Lever Your forearm is an example of a third class lever. The effort force is between the fulcrum and the resistance force. When a weight lifter curls a dumbbell upward, his forearm pivots at the elbow. His elbow is the fulcrum. The biceps muscle is attached to the forearm just below the elbow. When the biceps muscle contracts, the effort force is applied to the attachment point on the forearm. When you use a third class lever, the effort force is greater than the resistance force. The mechanical advantage is less than one. The reason for using a third class lever is to increase the distance moved, not to reduce the force. Examples include a rake and a fishing pole.

M.A. of Levers

The mechanical advantage of a lever is calculated by dividing the effort distance by the resistance distance.

$$\text{M.A.} = \frac{\text{distance of the effort force from the fulcrum}}{\text{distance of the resistance force from the fulcrum}}$$

The M.A. of first and second class levers is usually greater than 1, while the M.A. of third class levers is less than 1.

Wheel and Axle

Effort force

Resistance force

Axle

Wheel

Figure 5.8 ▲
The effort force applied to the wheel overcomes the resistance force of the axle.

The steering mechanism on a car, like the one shown in Figure 5.8, is an example of a wheel and axle. This type of simple machine consists of two circular objects called a wheel and an axle. The wheel has a larger radius than the axle does. The radius is the distance from the center of the wheel to the edge. An effort force applied at the wheel is multiplied at the axle to overcome a resistance force. The effort force applied to the wheel moves over a greater distance than the resistance force does. The mechanical advantage of a wheel and axle is equal to the radius of the wheel divided by the radius of the axle. The M.A. of a wheel and axle is always greater than 1. Examples include a door knob, a Ferris wheel, and a wheelchair.

Pulleys

Window blinds are raised and lowered using pulleys. A *pulley* is a rope wrapped around a grooved wheel. The two main types of pulleys are called fixed pulleys, and movable pulleys.

Look at Figure 5.9. A fixed pulley is attached to a stationary structure. The mechanical advantage of a fixed pulley is 1 because it does not multiply the effort force. A fixed pulley can make lifting an object easier by changing the direction of the effort force. Why is it easier for you to pull down than it is for you to lift? ①

A movable pulley is hung on a rope and hooked to a resistance. The movable pulley in Figure 5.10 is hung from a fixed pulley. As you pull on one end of the rope, the resistance and the movable

pulley move together. Movable pulleys can multiply your effort force. They have a M.A. of 2. Notice that this pulley system also changes the direction of force.

When two or more pulleys are used together, a pulley system is formed. Compare the pulley systems in Figures 5.10 and 5.11. Each consists of a fixed and movable pulley. Notice, however, that the two pulley systems differ in the number of rope segments that support the resistance force. As a result, they do not have the same mechanical advantage.

The pulley system in Figure 5.11 has a M.A. of 3. The system in Figure 5.10 has a M.A. of 2. The mechanical advantage of a pulley or pulley system is equal to the number of rope segments pulling up on the resistance force. What is the direction of force in Figure 5.11? ②

Effort force

Resistance force

Figure 5.9 ▲
This fixed pulley has one rope segment supporting the resistance force. It has a M.A. of 1.

Effort force

Resistance force

Figure 5.10 ▲
This 2-pulley system has 2 rope segments supporting the resistance force. It has a M.A. of 2.

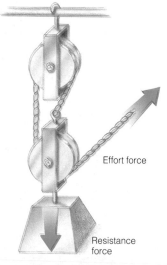

Effort force

Resistance force

Figure 5.11 ▲
This 2-pulley system has 3 rope segments supporting the resistance force. It has a M.A. of 3.

TEACH ▪ *Continued*

Discuss

Have students explain how a compound machine differs from a simple machine in mechanical advantage and why. (A compound machine has a much greater mechanical advantage than a simple machine because the combination of simple machines multiplies the total mechanical advantage.)

Skills Development

Classify Ask students to identify some common compound machines and to list the simple machines they contain. (Faucet, hinged door, door latch, window locks, adjustable office chair)

SkillBuilder

Answers

1. **a.** inclined plane—the ramp on which the ball rolls down to the basket; **b.** wheel and axle—the car wheels; **c.** pulley—the two fixed pulleys that will remove the hat; **d.** lever—the board on which the car falls to raise the ball

2. Drawings will vary, but they should contain more than one simple machine. An option would be to suggest that students use a Tinkertoy® set.

Answers to In-Text Questions

① Scissors are a first class lever and a wedge; a tape dispenser is a wheel and axle and a wedge.

② At least 3: handle—lever; turning blades—wheel and axles and inclined planes.

Cooperative Learning

Have students work in cooperative groups of three or four to design and sketch their own compound machine for performing a simple task. Use the hat removal machine as an example. Have them identify each simple machine used in their device. Have each group describe their machine to the class.

Figure 5.12 ▲
How many simple machines are there in this pencil sharpener? ②

Compound Machines

Some household appliances, some bicycles, and many mechanical devices that you use every day are compound machines. A **compound machine** is a system of two or more simple machines. The mechanical advantage of a compound machine is much greater than that of a simple machine. The combination of simple machines in the compound machine multiplies the total mechanical advantage.

Look at the compound machine in Figure 5.12. What simple machines do you see? If you look carefully, you can find wheels and axles and inclined planes.

Take a close look at other mechanical devices that you use every day. Identify the simple machines that they contain. All of the simple machines in a compound machine work together as a system to accomplish a task. What types of machines are in a pair of scissors and a tape dispenser? ①

SkillBuilder *Classifying*

The Hat-Removal Machine

The Hat-Removal Machine below is similar to all compound machines. Compound machines are made up of a number of simple machines working together as a system. Identify the various simple machines that make up the Hat-Removal Machine.

1. Describe how the Hat-Removal Machine contains each of the following simple machines:

   a. inclined plane

   b. wheel and axle

   c. pulley

   d. lever

2. Design and draw a compound machine. Give your machine a name, and label each simple machine in it.

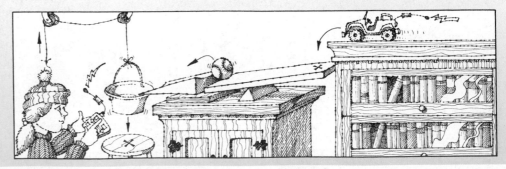

Science and Technology *Travel by Bicycle*

In the late 1800s, a bicycle called the "ordinary" was the most efficient and inexpensive way to travel. The rider sat above a huge front wheel. Each time the pedals completed a turn, so did the big wheel. The ordinary was dangerous because riders often fell off. Designers found that by adding simple machines to the bicycle they could reduce the size of the front wheel and increase its performance.

Each pedal on a modern ten-speed bicycle moves in a circle like a wheel, and is part of a wheel and axle. The axle is a front sprocket. The bicycle chain transfers the force to a rear sprocket attached to the rear wheel. The rear sprocket is the effort wheel of the rear wheel and axle system. As the rear sprocket turns, it causes the rear wheel to turn. The turning rear wheel overcomes the force of friction between the tires and the road. What other simple machines does a bicycle contain? ③

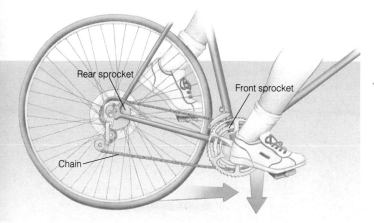

Rear sprocket

Front sprocket

Chain

◀ **Figure 5.13**
The simple machines on a well-maintained bicycle form a compound machine with a very high mechanical efficiency.

Check and Explain

1. Name six simple machines. Explain how each works.

2. What simple machines make up a crank-type pencil sharpener?

3. **Classify** Choose a compound machine you are familiar with. What simple machines does it contain?

4. **Predict** What is the M.A. of a pulley system that uses four rope segments to support the resistance force?

5.4

Section Objectives
For a list of section objectives, see the Student Edition page.

Skills Objectives
Students should be able to:

Infer how energy changes form in everyday things.

Themes in Science
Systems and Interactions
Energy in the environment is detected through the senses. Ears detect the mechanical energy of sound, eyes detect the electromagnetic energy of light, and the tongue and nose detect chemical energy. Some fishes have receptors that detect electric energy. Ask students, Which organ detects heat and pressure? (Skin has receptors for heat and pressure.)

STS Connection
Windmills are used worldwide to provide energy to pump water, grind grain, and generate electricity. The first windmills were built around A.D. 600. By A.D. 1100, windmills were being used in Spain, the Netherlands, and other countries. In the 1920s, French inventor Georges Darrieus improved the design with a wind turbine that uses wind from all directions. Review with students how windmills use wind energy.

MOTIVATE

Skills WarmUp

To help students understand energy conversions, have them do the Skills WarmUp.
Answer Electric energy changes into light, sound, and heat energy.

Prior Knowledge

Gauge how much students know about energy and its forms by asking the following questions:

▶ What are some examples of different kinds of energy?

▶ What happens to the electricity that is used in appliances? Where does it go?

▶ What does it mean to say someone is "full of energy"?

 **The Living Textbook:
Physical Science Sides 1-4**

Chapter 17   Frame 03138
Mechanical Energy (2 Frames)
Search: Step:

 **The Living Textbook:
Physical Science Sides 1-4**

Chapter 16   Frame 02754
Windmills and Wind Machines (5 Frames)
Search: Step:

▼ **ACTIVITY**

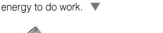
Inferring

Energy on TV

   Explain how a television set changes energy from one form to other forms. Compare your explanation with that of a classmate.

SKILLS WARMUP

Figure 5.14
A windmill is a compound machine that uses mechanical energy to do work. ▼

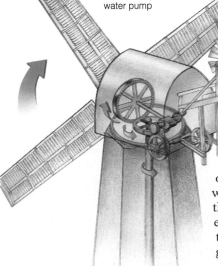

Drive shaft powers water pump

5.4 Energy and Its Forms

Objectives

▶ **Name** and **describe** five forms of energy.

▶ **Give examples** of energy conversions.

▶ **Describe** the Law of Conservation of Mass and Energy.

▶ **Infer** the role of energy conversions in an everyday situation.

As you learned in the previous section, machines can make your work easier. You would not try to pull a nail out of a board without a crowbar or cut a lawn without a lawn mower.

Despite their usefulness, machines have limitations. Machines can't save work or energy. The amount of work you get out of a machine can never be greater than the amount of work or energy put into it. The work a lawn mower engine does is less than the energy in the gasoline that is burned. Most of the energy is converted to heat, due to friction between moving parts in the motor.

Work and energy are related. Energy is the ability to do work. Both work and energy are measured in joules. Energy has many forms. In some way, all of these forms are related to each other. Energy can be converted from one form to another.

Mechanical Energy

Mechanical energy is the energy of the movement or the position of an object. The mechanical energy of a moving object is also called its kinetic energy. The mechanical energy of an object due to its position is also called *potential energy*.

Wind and moving water have mechanical energy. Not only do they move, they also can move objects. For thousands of years people have used the wind's mechanical energy to do work. Windmills like the one in Figure 5.14 use the wind's mechanical energy to operate a water pump or to generate electricity. Wheels turned by moving water were used to grind grain into flour.

Integrating the Sciences

Biology The brain controls behavior, such as moving the body, perceiving the world, and thinking. Nerve cells of the brain carry information over long distances using electrical energy. Nerve cells use electric energy to transmit signals. A sensitive voltmeter will record a difference in electric charge between the inside and the outside of a nerve cell.

Nuclear Energy

All matter is made up of particles called atoms. A great amount of energy is stored in an atom's core, or nucleus. This energy, called nuclear energy, is released when an atomic nucleus breaks apart, or when a new nucleus forms. Look at Figure 5.15. The sun's energy is a result of nuclear reactions like these. Nuclear power plants use energy from nuclear reactions to generate electricity.

Chemical Energy

Chemical bonds between atoms hold substances together. Look at Figure 5.16. In a car engine, chemical bonds between atoms in gasoline are broken. Breaking these bonds releases large amounts of energy. In a car engine, the chemical reaction is controlled so that the energy can be used to do useful work. Chemical energy is the energy stored in the bonds between atoms.

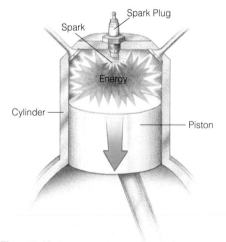

Figure 5.16 ▲
Energy released from gasoline drives the piston that moves the car wheels.

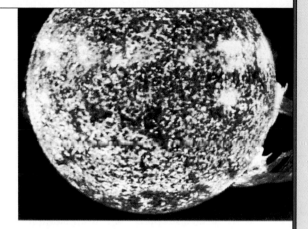

Figure 5.15 ▲
The sun has great amounts of nuclear, heat, and electromagnetic energy.

Electromagnetic Energy

Atoms are made of even smaller particles. One of these smaller particles is the electron. In an atom, electrons carry an electric charge. Have you ever gotten a mild shock after walking across a carpet and touching a metal doorknob? The shock you felt was caused by this charge. When electrons flow through conducting material, a moving charge is formed. This moving charge is electricity, a form of electromagnetic energy. Light is another form of electromagnetic energy.

Heat Energy

When something is colder than its surroundings, it will warm up. When a substance becomes warmer, its particles move faster. The kinetic energy of the particles increases. Contact between different substances, such as cold water and warmer air, will transfer this kinetic energy. The fast-moving particles of air collide with the slower moving water particles, increasing their motion. Energy flows from the warm air to the cool water. Heat is the energy that flows from a warm substance to a cooler one.

Enrich

After students read about energy conversions involved in striking a match, help them to understand the energy conversions in a car. To start a car, chemical energy in the battery is converted to electric energy. Some of the electric energy is converted to heat, as an electric spark ignites the fuel, releasing chemical energy as heat inside the engine's cylinders. Gases expand in the cylinders, which push the pistons and give them mechanical energy. It is this mechanical energy that is transferred to the wheels of the car to make it move.

Discuss

In actual energy conversions, one form is never completely converted into another, and none of the original energy is lost. Give some examples of incomplete energy conversions, then ask students to suggest more. Examples include a light bulb, in which some electricity becomes light, and some becomes heat; or a toaster, in which electricity becomes heat, but also produces the light from the glowing coils.

Research

Some food for livestock is grown in water and nutrients and without dirt. This process is called *hydroponics*. The entire plant is fed to the animal. Have students research this process in terms of energy gained by using the whole plant. Have them prepare data on the energy in and out of the hydroponics process.

 The Living Textbook: Physical Science Side 2

Chapter 31   Frame 25179
Energy Conversions (Movie)
Search: Play:

Integrating the Sciences

Chemistry Discuss the chemical process that occurs when you strike a match. The friction produces heat, which ignites the phosphorus in the match head. Potassium chlorate ($KClO_4$) decomposes, releasing oxygen, which causes the flame to get hotter, igniting the sulfur. Wax in the head melts and ignites the match stick. Ask students to think of other examples of light energy from chemical reactions.

Social Studies Connection

Albert Einstein (1879–1955) was a German physicist who revolutionized our thinking about energy, matter, and the origin of the universe. While working in the Swiss patent office at the age of 26, he wrote a paper called "Does the Inertia of a Body Depend Upon Its Energy Content?" that led to his most famous equation, $E = mc^2$. He became an American citizen in 1940 and helped to develop uses for nuclear energy.

Figure 5.17 ▲
Striking a match involves mechanical, chemical, heat, and light energy.

Energy Conversions

What happens when you strike a match? You hear the match head scratch against the striking strip. A puff of smoke rises. The match head changes color and a small yellow and blue flame appears. The burning match gives off light that you can see and heat that you can feel.

Look at Figure 5.17. Think about this series of events in terms of energy. How does energy change from one form to another as you light the match? When you move the match head against the striking strip, particles in the match head begin to move faster. As this happens, mechanical energy changes to heat energy. The heat energy causes a chemical change to begin. The match head begins to change color and release stored chemical energy. The chemical energy changes into heat energy and light energy.

In the world around you, energy is constantly changing from one form to another. A toaster changes electrical energy to heat energy. Power plants use generators to change mechanical, chemical, or nuclear energy into electric energy. Your body changes the chemical energy in food to kinetic energy and heat. By changing from one form to another, energy is recycled throughout the world.

The Law of Conservation of Mass and Energy

In each of the energy conversions you have just read about, the total amount of energy remained the same. As energy changes from one form to another, it is never created or destroyed. This fact has been observed to be true in so many different situations that it has become a scientific law. According to the *Law of Conservation of Mass and Energy*, the amount of mass and energy in the universe is always the same.

This scientific law was once thought of as two separate laws, one for energy and one for mass. Scientists combined the two laws into one after observing nuclear reactions in which matter was transformed directly into energy, and energy into matter. Albert Einstein predicted the relationship between matter and energy. He expressed it in mathematical form as:

$$E = mc^2$$
Energy = mass × (the speed of light)^2

Themes in Science

Patterns of Change/Cycles

Devices that change energy from one form to another are transducers. A microphone is a transducer that changes sound energy to electric energy, and transducer cells in the skin convert heat into chemical and electric energy that signals warmth to the brain. Without transducers, we would be unable to communicate.

Integrating the Sciences

Health If your body loses too much heat, you may suffer from a serious condition called *hypothermia*. This can be life-threatening, but there are times when hypothermia can save a life. People drowned in cold water can sometimes be revived after many minutes. Body tissues require less oxygen just to stay alive when cooled. For reasons not fully understood, this is especially true with young children.

Science and You
Energy Conversions in Your Body

As you read the words on this page, energy is changing from one form to another right in your own body! At this minute, your digestive system is hard at work breaking down the food you ate for breakfast or lunch. As digestion takes place, a new supply of chemical energy is released that can do work in your body.

Chemical energy in your body changes to mechanical energy every time you move a muscle to do work. You use mechanical energy for all your daily activities such as walking, talking, and writing. Chemical energy from your food is used also to build or repair body tissues. In this case, the chemical energy from your food is stored again as chemical energy in new body tissues.

Some of the chemical energy from your food is changed into heat energy. This heat energy helps to keep your body temperature at about 37°C. When the surrounding air is less than 37°C, your body must generate heat energy to maintain your body temperature.

The thermogram in the margin shows how heat is distributed over your body's surface. When your body temperature is more than 37°C, your body must release heat energy so that your body temperature doesn't get too high. Your body transports water to the surface of your skin where it can evaporate, releasing heat energy and cooling your body.

Figure 5.18 ▲
This thermogram of a person shows the warmest areas in red. Compare the warmest and coolest areas.

Check and Explain

1. What are five forms of energy? Give an example of each form.

2. Describe the energy conversions that occur in each of the following situations:

   a. an automobile driving down a road

   b. an athlete running around a track

3. **Communicate** State the *Law of Conservation of Mass and Energy*. Explain its meaning in your own words.

4. **Infer** Usually, a person will perspire when they exercise. How might this be triggered by energy changing form?

Discuss

Point out that in some situations the body is kept from getting too hot by the evaporation of perspiration from the skin. Evaporation requires heat and cools the body as the liquid evaporates into the air. Some liquids, such as alcohol, are very volatile and evaporate quickly. Rubbing alcohol applied to your skin evaporates quickly, creating a noticeable cooling effect. This technique is sometimes used by physicians to cool patients with very high fevers.

EVALUATE

WrapUp

Reinforce Have students discuss why people are concerned about using up energy resources when it is a scientific law that energy can't be destroyed.

Use Review Worksheet 5.4.

Check and Explain

1. Mechanical energy—mixer; nuclear energy—reactors in a nuclear power plant; chemical energy—combustion of gasoline; electromagnetic energy—electricity; heat—energy used in cooking

2. **a.** Chemical energy stored in the gasoline is converted to heat and mechanical energy in the engine. **b.** Chemical energy released from food by the body is converted into heat and mechanical energy used in running.

3. Students' explanations will vary. Energy changes from one form to another, it is never created or destroyed.

4. Heat energy is released during exercise, because when you move, your body changes stored energy from the food you eat into heat energy and mechanical energy.

Time 40 minutes   **Group** four

Materials

8 hot plates

8 tea kettles

8 toy cars

16 plastic straws

8 strips of cloth

8 scissors

8 rolls of masking tape

Analysis

1. Trial 2

2. The amount of force used to start the car moving varied.

3. Trial 2; Acceleration varies with force, so the force of the steam's energy must have been greater at the beginning of Trial 2.

4. Yes; The force produced by the energy of the steam was applied to an object (the toy car) to move it over a distance.

Conclusion

By increasing the kinetic energy of water with heat, steam was produced by the kettle. The car's sail used the kinetic energy of the steam as mechanical energy to do the work of moving the car.

The steam's kinetic energy became the car's mechanical energy in both trials. The car had the most acceleration in Trial 2, when mechanical energy was being produced at a faster rate.

Prelab Discussion

Have students read the entire activity. As an alternative to the toy car setup, you may wish to give each group a pinwheel. Students can compare the rate at which the pinwheel turns in the steam. Tag one of the pinwheel blades with colored tape so that revolutions can be counted over a period of seconds. Control the distance from the steam source to the pinwheel to make counting possible.

Activity 5   *How does the rate of energy change affect work?*

Skills   Observe; Measure; Infer

Task 1   Prelab Prep

Collect the following items: 1 hot plate, 1 tea kettle, water, 1 toy car, 2 plastic straws, small piece of cloth, scissors, and tape. You will need to set up the activity near an electrical outlet.

Task 2   Data Record

1. Copy the data table below on a separate sheet of paper.

Table 5.1   Trial Measurements

Trial Run	Distance Car Traveled
1	
2	

Task 3   Procedure

1. Place the hot plate where the cord will be able to reach an electric outlet. Do not plug it in, yet.

2. Fill the tea kettle with water. Place it on top of the hot plate.

3. Cut the cloth so its width is approximately equal to the width of the toy car.

4. Tape each edge of the cloth to the straws. The cloth should look like a volleyball net.

5. Place the car in front of the tea kettle. Hold the bottom of the straws on either side of the car. Position the straws so that the cloth lies directly in front of the spout of the tea kettle. To do this, you may have to cut a section off the bottom of each straw. When the cloth is at spout level, tape the straws to the sides of the car.

6. Plug in the hot plate. Wait and observe.

7. When the car has stopped moving, unplug the hot plate. Use the meter stick to measure the distance the car moved. Record the data under Trial Run 1 in the data table.

8. Refill the tea kettle to the same volume of water as you used in Trial Run 1. Plug in the hot plate.

9. Once you hear the kettle start to whistle or when you see steam, *carefully* place the car in front of the spout. Be sure that the cloth "sail" is directly in front of the spout, exactly as it was at the beginning of Trial Run 1!
CAUTION! Be careful not to put your hand or arm in front of the spout. Steam can burn your skin.

10. When the car has stopped moving, unplug the hot plate. Use the meter stick to measure the distance the car moved.

11. Record the data under Trial Run 2 in the data table.

Task 4   Analysis

1. In which trial did the car move the greatest distance?

2. What variable was different between the two trial runs?

3. In which trial run was the car's "sail" hit with the greatest force?

4. Was work done in this activity? Explain your answer.

Task 5   Conclusion

Identify the various ways energy changed form in this activity. In this activity, you observed energy change forms. Explain how the rate at which the change occurred affected the amount of work done?

Chapter 5 Review

Concept Summary

5.1 Work and Power
▶ Work is done on an object when the object moves in the direction of a force acting on it. No work is done when the object does not move. Work is equal to force times distance.
▶ Power is the rate at which work is done. Power is equal to work divided by time required to do work.

5.2 Work and Machines
▶ A machine is a device that helps do work. Machines change the size or direction of the force used to do work.
▶ The mechanical advantage of a machine equals the resistance force divided by the effort force.
▶ The mechanical efficiency of a machine is a comparison of work output to work input. Because of friction, no machine can be 100 percent efficient.

5.3 Simple and Compound Machines
▶ The six kinds of simple machines are inclined planes, wedges, screws, levers, wheels and axles, and pulleys.
▶ A compound machine is a combination of two or more simple machines working together as a system.

5.4 Energy and Its Forms
▶ Mechanical energy is due to the position of something (potential energy) or the movement of something (kinetic energy).
▶ Forms of energy are mechanical, nuclear, heat, chemical, and electromagnetic.
▶ Energy can change from one form to another.
▶ The *Law of Conservation of Mass and Energy* states that the total amount of mass and energy in the universe is constant. Energy and mass can't be created or destroyed.

Chapter Vocabulary

work (p. 107)   watt (p. 109)   mechanical efficiency (p. 114)
joule (p. 108)   machine (p. 112)   simple machine (p. 116)
power (p. 109)   mechanical advantage (p. 113)   compound machine (p. 120)

Check Your Vocabulary

Use the vocabulary words above to complete the following sentences

1. The ____ is a unit used to measure work.
2. A lever is an example of a(n) ____ .
3. The ____ is a unit used to measure power.
4. A device that helps do work is a(n) ____ .
5. To calculate ____ , you divide the amount of work done by the time it took to do the work.
6. The ____ of a machine compares its work output with the work input.
7. A machine with a(n) ____ of two doubles the force applied to the machine.
8. The product of force and distance is called ____ .
9. A system using simple machines, such as levers and pulleys working together, makes up a(n) ____ .

Write Your Vocabulary

Write sentences using each vocabulary word above. Show that you know what each word means.

Check Your Vocabulary
1. joule
2. simple machine
3. watt
4. machine
5. power
6. mechanical efficiency
7. mechanical advantage
8. work
9. compound machine

Write Your Vocabulary
Students' sentences should show that they know the meaning of each word as well as how to use it in a sentence.
    Use Vocabulary Worksheet for Chapter 5.

Check Your Knowledge

1. The object must move and a force must act in the direction of the motion.

2. Work is measured in joules; power in J/s, or watts.

3. Machines make work easier by reducing the amount of effort force that must be used for a given resistance force or by changing the direction of the effort force.

4. A simple machine does work in one movement. A compound machine is made up of several simple machines.

5. $E = mc^2$; Energy is equal to mass times the speed of light squared.

6. Answers may vary. Possible answers include: In a nuclear power plant, nuclear energy is converted into heat energy that causes water to turn to steam. The kinetic energy of the moving steam turns turbines connected to generators which convert mechanical energy into electricity.

7. False; distance

8. True

9. False; mechanical advantage

10. True

11. True

12. False; simple

13. True

14. True

Check Your Understanding

1. Work has not been done because, although a force was exerted, there was no movement.

2. Three times as much work is needed to lift the barbell three times as high.

3. When pushing a door far from the hinges, it is acting like a second class lever. When pushing from close to the hinges, the door is a third class lever (in which the M.A. is less than 1).

4. Answers may vary, but may include: chemical energy to heat in the combustion of gasoline; heat to kinetic energy in the pistons; kinetic energy to electrical energy in the generator; electrical energy to kinetic energy in the starter motor, windshield wiper motors, fan.

5. Power (W) = work (J) ÷ time (s); if work = 1000 J done over 10 s, then the power output is 1000 ÷ 10 = 100 W.

6. Gears are an example of a wheel and axle simple machine. A small force turning a gear through a large distance can produce a larger output force by turning a smaller gear. Since the watch has many gears, it is a compound machine.

7. The 10-m ramp provides a greater mechanical advantage.

8. a, b; student diagram

   c. W = F x d = 40 N x 10 m = 400 Nm = 400 J

Chapter 5 Review

Check Your Knowledge

Answer the following in complete sentences.

1. What two conditions must be met for work to be done on an object?

2. What units are used to measure work and power?

3. How do machines make work easier?

4. What is the difference between a simple machine and a compound machine?

5. What is the equation that relates matter and energy? Use words to describe the meaning of this equation.

6. Describe a series of energy conversions involving at least three forms of energy.

Determine whether each statement is true or false. Write *true* if it is true. If it is false, change the underlined term to make the statement true.

7. Work relates force and <u>simple machines</u>.

8. Power is the rate at which <u>work</u> is done.

9. The number of times a machine multiplies a force is the machine's <u>mechanical efficiency</u>.

10. The mechanical efficiency of a machine is always <u>less</u> than 100 percent.

11. A machine that works with one movement is a <u>simple machine</u>.

12. A combination of <u>complex</u> machines is a compound machine.

13. <u>Energy</u> can be converted from one form to another.

14. A <u>wedge</u> is a type of inclined plane.

Check Your Understanding

Apply the concepts you have learned to answer each question.

1. **Application** You push against a car, but the car doesn't move. Has work been done? Explain.

2. Work is needed to lift a barbell. How many times more work is needed to lift the barbell three times as high?

3. **Critical Thinking** To open a swinging door, you usually push on the part of the door farthest from the hinges. Use you knowledge of levers to explain why it would be harder to open the door if you pushed on the the center of the door.

4. **Application** Describe at least three energy conversions that take place in a moving automobile.

5. If it takes 10 s for you to do 1000 J of work, what is your power output?

6. **Mystery Photo** The photograph on page 106 shows the gears of a watch. Explain how these gears help do work. Use the terms *force* and *distance* in your answer. Is this a simple machine or a compound machine? Explain.

7. Which has the greater mechanical advantage, a ramp that is 10 m long and 2 m high or a ramp that is 5 m long and 2 m high?

8. **Application** A person slides a box 10 m across a floor. The floor exerts a friction force on the box of 40 N.

   a. Draw a picture of this situation.

   b. Label the effort force, resistance force, and distance.

   c. How much work was done?

Develop Your Skills

1. a. Several answers are possible. Examples include: differing amounts of force exerted on each crate as it was pushed, the roughness of the crates' surfaces.

   b. The least power was used in moving crate C.

2. 10 N x 10 m = 100 J

3. a. A simple lever has the highest mechanical efficiency; a gasoline engine has the lowest mechanical efficiency. The human body has the lowest mechanical efficiency on the graph.

   b. Machines with a mechanical efficiency of less than 50 percent include electrical generating plants, diesel engines, gasoline engines, and (if considered as a machine) the human body.

Make Connections

1. Concept maps will vary. You may wish to have students do the map below. First draw the map on the board, then add a few key terms. Have students draw and complete the map.

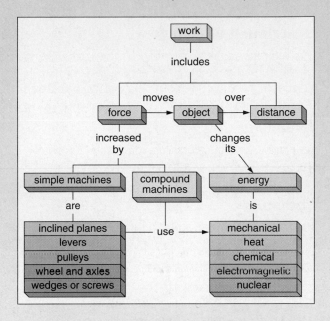

2. Newton (1642–1727): invented calculus, discovered law of gravitation; he was a professor of mathematics for most of his career. Joule (1818–1889): owned a brewery; first to recognize a relationship between heat and energy

3. Student reports will vary. Make sure simple machines are properly identified.

4. When more energy is taken in than is used by the body, the added calories must be stored, so the person gains weight. If more energy is used by the body than is taken in, the extra energy must come from the body's reserves, so the person will lose weight. An undernourished person will not have a large energy reserve, and so would be unable to do much extra work without extra food.

Develop Your Skills

Use the skills you have developed in this chapter to complete each activity.

1. Interpret Data Three crates, each weighing 200 N, are pushed down a hallway. The amount of work done on each crate is shown on the bar graph below.

   a. What factor(s) could account for the differences in the amount of work done on each crate?

   b. Suppose each crate was pushed for 2 min. To which crate was the least power applied?

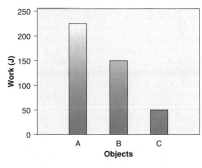

2. Calculate How many joules of work are done on an object when a force of 10 N pushes it a distance of 10 m?

3. Data Bank Use the information on page 638 to answer the following questions.

   a. What machine has the highest mechanical efficiency? The lowest?

   b. What machine(s) have a mechanical efficiency less than 50 percent?

Make Connections

1. Link the Concepts Make a concept map to show how the following concepts from this chapter link together: work, force, distance, energy, object, simple machines, and compound machines.

2. Science and Social Studies James Watt was a Scottish engineer. He built a fast, efficient steam engine in the 1760s. The SI unit for power is named for him. The Joule and the newton are also named for scientists from the past. Find out as much as you can about James Prescott Joule and Isaac Newton. When did they live? What were their occupations? What did they invent or discover?

3. Science and Technology The earliest bicycles were very different in design from modern ones. They had no gears or steering systems. Pedals were not added until 1861. Research the development of the modern bicycle. Draw diagrams of bicycles from the past that show its evolution. Label your drawings with the names of simple machines that are part of each machine.

4. Science and You The energy required for maintaining life comes from the chemically-stored potential energy in food. During digestion this is changed into other forms of energy. What happens to a person whose work output is less than the energy taken in? What happens when the person's work output is greater than the energy taken in? Can an undernourished person perform extra work without extra food? Explain your answers.

About the Literary Work

"The Boy Who Reversed Himself" was adapted from the novel *The Boy Who Reversed Himself* by William Sleator, copyright 1986 by E. P. Dutton. Reprinted by permission of E. P. Dutton.

Description of Change

The reference to the effect of the fourth dimension on the human anatomy has been edited from the selection to reduce the complexity of the passage.

Rationale

As it appears, the selection explores the notion of frames of reference—a concept covered in Unit 1.

Vocabulary

fourth dimension, pulsated, octagon, 3-D, 4-D

Teaching Strategies

Directed Inquiry

After students finish reading, discuss the story. Be sure to relate the story to the science lesson in this unit. Ask the following questions:

▶ How do the two characters described in the selection differ? (Omar has the ability to enter the fourth dimension while Laura on her own has the ability to perceive two-dimensional space.)

▶ Which character are you more like? Why? (Laura, because all humans can perceive two-dimensional space)

Critical Thinking

Compare and Contrast Discuss the term *frames of reference* with the class. Ask students to compare the frames of reference of a person riding on a bus, other students on the same bus, and the trees that line the road upon which the bus is traveling. Then ask, How might the frames of reference differ in 2-, 3-, and 4-D space? (The stationary objects will appear more defined in the second and third dimensions; the moving objects will appear more confusing in the fourth dimension.)

Science and Literature Connection

The Boy Who Reversed Himself

The following excerpts are from the novel The Boy Who Reversed Himself *by William Sleator*

Omar took the end of the coil of rope, squatted down and tied it firmly around one of the legs of my desk.

"Why are you doing that?"

"So we can find our way back, in case we get lost [in the fourth dimension]." He stood up and hooked a strap from his harness around one of my belt loops. "Take my hand, Laura." He reached out his left hand, and I took it with my right. His hand was unpleasantly moist. "We won't go far. We'll just look around your room. But still, no matter what happens, you must *not* let go of my hand. You got that, Laura? Do *not* let go."

"Why not? What about this strap?"

"Straps can get unhooked. And if we ever got separated, you could easily get lost. And you might never find your way back. And I might never be able to find you. It's big out there, and it's complicated. If I lost you . . . It's too terrible to even think about. Do you promise not to let go?"

"Yes, yes, I promise."

He squeezed my hand. "Here we go."

Omar bent his knees and lifted his arms like a plump little Superman preparing to take off. I did the same. His face reddened and a vein stood out on his forehead. He tilted over in a sideways direction. Then his body was stretching out at an impossible angle. He rippled and pulsated like a reflection in a distorting mirror. He grunted.

The floor lurched and tilted away. I closed my eyes. It was like falling down an unexpected stairway in the darkness. Dizziness slammed through me. My stomach jumped. My fingers loosened and began to slip away from Omar's.

He gripped my hand harder. We weren't falling. The dizziness stopped.

"Open your eyes, Laura," Omar said.

I opened them. Instantly I squeezed them shut, moaning, dizzier than before.

"Take it slow, Laura. Try not to move your head. You'll get used to it."

Cautiously, my heart pounding, I opened my eyes again.

My bedroom floor hung directly above me. I saw the woven pattern of the rag rug, the grain of the floorboards. There was a dark, dusty area to one side that didn't look familiar, until I noticed the dim cover of an old romance comic that had fallen under my desk. Next to the comic book, a black column about three inches stretched off to the left and the right. On the other side of the column I could see a bright pattern of blue-and-white octagons. It took me a moment to realize it was the bathroom floor.

"Keep your eyes fixed in one place, Laura," Omar said, invisible beside me. "You okay?"

"But nothing makes sense! I can hardly tell what I'm looking at."

Skills in Science

Reading Skills in Science

1. The characters are Omar, who can enter the fourth dimension, and Laura, who deals only with two dimensions.

2. The selection explores differences that exist in a 2-D, 3-D, and 4-D world.

Writing Skills in Science

1. Likely responses might be that Laura is able to see objects from the inside and outside at the same time.

2. Answers may vary. The picture might be the inside of Laura's desk drawer, as described in the lines "a confusing jumble of objects in separate compartments" and "pencils and rubber bands and keys."

Activities

Communicate Before students create their models, you may wish to discuss the idea that a two-dimensional model will have length and height while a three-dimensional model will have length, height, and depth.

Collect Data You may wish to invite a holographer to speak with the class about the 3-D images made with holograms.

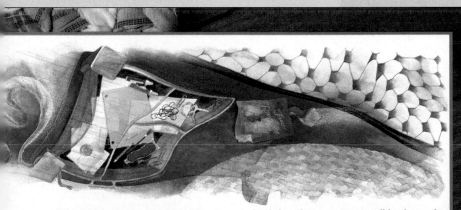

"That's because you don't have 4-D eyes, so you can only see a 3-D cross section of 4-D space. When you move your eyes, you'll see a different section. You have to learn how to put them all together. Now, move your head just a little bit."

I turned my head about an inch. There was a confusing moment of things rushing past. Then another picture stabilized. . . .

I saw a confusing jumble of objects in separate compartments, heavily outlined by shadows. I began to recognize pencils and rubber bands and keys, an old school work-book from last year, a pyramidlike shape of many layers that seemed to be a pile of paper viewed from some peculiar angle. And what was that wrinkled red oval thing with a thin black edge? A tube of red paint, seen from the inside and the outside at the same time.

I lifted my hand to take the tube of paint out of the desk. In the flashlight beam, I saw white bones enclosed in layered strips of pink, thin branching wires with blue liquid coursing through them.

"My hand!" I whispered. "I can see the inside of my hand!"

Skills in Science

Reading Skills in Science

1. **Find Context Clues** Identify the two main characters in the selection.

2. **Find the Main Idea** What is the main idea of the selection?

Writing Skills in Science

1. **Compare and Contrast** Describe how Laura's perspective of her room is different in four dimensions than it is in three.

2. **Predict** What do you think the picture being stabilized at the end of the reading might be? Identify the lines on which you based your prediction.

Activities

Communicate Illustrate the difference between the second and third dimensions by creating a model of each dimension.

Collect Data Use reference materials to learn about techniques artists use to create a three-dimensional effect on a two-dimensional medium.

Where to Read More

A Wrinkle in Time by Madeline L'Engle. New York: Farrar, 1962. Meg and her brother travel through time and space to the planet of Camazotz in search of their scientist father.

U nit 2 discusses particles of matter and introduces some properties of matter. Chapter 6 addresses some observable properties of matter and relates them to particle motion. The chapter also distinguishes between physical and chemical changes in matter. Chapter 7 presents characteristics of atoms, elements, compounds, and mixtures. The chapter explains how compounds are classified. It also introduces chemical symbols and explains how to write a chemical formula. Chapter 8 presents the periodic table of elements and describes the systematic arrangement of elements within the table. The chapter discusses the properties and classifications of metals, nonmetals, and metalloids and describes properties unique to each. Chapter 8 also provides examples of various families and groups of elements, highlighting their placement within the table.

Introducing the Unit

Directed Inquiry

Have students examine the photograph. Ask:

▶ Is most of the matter shown in the photograph solid, liquid, or gas? (Most of the matter is solid or gas. Accept all reasonable answers.)

▶ What kinds of matter are shown in this photograph? (Metal, glass, water, and air; accept all reasonable answers.)

▶ How can buildings be made stable at great heights? (Architects and builders combine materials to make the structures both strong and flexible. Accept all reasonable answers.)

Writing About the Photograph

Ask students to imagine they are walking among the buildings shown in the photograph. Have them write a journal entry about the different kinds of matter they might observe during their walk and describe their properties. (Students might note properties such as wet streets, hard metal buildings, or cold or warm air.)

Unit 2
Particles of Matter

Chapters

6 Properties of Matter

7 Atoms, Elements, Compounds, and Mixtures

8 Introduction to the Periodic Table

Data Bank

Use the information on pages 634 to 643 to answer the questions about topics explored in this unit.

Observing

List three patterns in the placement of the elements in the modern periodic table.

Comparing

Which element has the highest density: helium, iron, oxygen, or uranium?

Generalizing

Make a general statement about the relationship between atomic mass and atomic number.

Interpreting Data

How does the amount of iron in the earth's crust compare to the amount of silicon?

The photograph to the left shows downtown Chicago at night. What are some kinds of matter used in these buildings?

Data Bank Answers

Have students search the Data Bank on pages 634 to 643 for the answers to the questions on this page.

Observing Elements are placed in a pattern of increasing atomic number, metals are placed on the left side, and nonmetals are placed on the right side of the periodic table; elements are also grouped in vertical columns according to how they react with other elements. The answer is found in the Periodic Table of Elements, on pages 634 and 635.

Comparing Uranium has the greatest density. The answer is found in the table, Properties of Common Elements, on page 641.

Generalizing The atomic mass of an element is more than double the atomic number of the element. The answer is found in the table, Properties of Common Elements, on page 641.

Extension Ask students if they think there is a relationship between the boiling point and the melting point of common elements. (There is no direct relationship between the two properties. The answer is found in the table, Properties of Common Elements, on page 641.)

Interpreting Data There is 5.5 times more silicon than iron in the earth's surface. The answer is found in the circle graph, Elements in the Earth's Crust, on page 643.

Answer to In-Text Question

Metal, glass, steel, concrete, and bricks are some of the materials used in these buildings.

Overview

The properties of matter are described in this chapter. The first section discusses some observable properties of matter and relates these properties to particle motion. The second section defines the three phases of matter in terms of shape and volume, as well as the energy of the particles of the substance. The chapter also presents Boyle's and Charles' laws. Physical and chemical changes in matter are described in the last section.

Advance Planner

▶ Provide a hand lens for TE page 135.

▶ Prepare a selection of items for TE page 137.

▶ Obtain a container of vinegar for TE page 142.

▶ Prepare Y-tube, balloons, one-hole stopper, and plastic soft-drink bottle for TE demonstration, page 143.

▶ Provide bricks and self-lock plastic bags for TE page 148.

▶ Collect hot plates, vials with lids, 1-L self-lock plastic bags, phenol red solution, baking soda, and calcium chloride for SE Activity 6, page 152.

Skills Development Chart

Sections	Classify	Communicate	Compare and Contrast	Define Operationally	Hypothesize	Interpret Data	Model	Observe	Predict
6.1 Skills WarmUp								●	
Skills WorkOut							●		
6.2 Skills WarmUp			●						
Skills WorkOut	●								
SkillBuilder		●							●
6.3 Skills WarmUp					●				
Skills WorkOut				●					
Activity					●	●	●		

Individual Needs

▶ **Limited English Proficiency Students** Have students identify each object on pages 136 to 139. Have them list the properties of each object in terms of color, texture, odor, luster, and transparency. For each object they list, have them identify a common object that has the same properties. Next, have them use Figures 6.8 and 6.9 to compare Charles' and Boyle's laws in 25 words or less. Finally, have students write a description of the physical and chemical changes that occur during an explosion. All work should be kept in the students' portfolios.

▶ **At-Risk Students** Have students work in pairs to create "property cards." On one side of each card have students list the senses: touch, taste, hearing, sight, smell. Then ask each pair to think of four items commonly found at home or in the classroom. Ask them to write a description of each item using only one word under each of the senses. On the back of the card have them write the name of the object. Allow groups to exchange cards. For two of the items, have the groups see if they can identify the object using the descriptions listed. For the remaining two items, have groups give one word descriptions and compare their descriptions with those already on the cards.

▶ **Gifted Students** Invite students to choose three different substances, each in a different phase at room temperature, such as gold, corn oil, and oxygen. Ask them to imagine that they can shrink themselves so that they can stand among the particles of matter. Have them write descriptions of the particles of the substance from their new point of view. Encourage students to include a description of how the particles are linked, how they move, and what happens if the substance is heated or cooled. Students may want to do some research to find out more about the characteristics of the particles in the kind of matter they chose.

Resource Bank

▶ **Bulletin Board** Title one side of a bulletin board *Physical Changes* and the other *Chemical Changes*. Ask students to find pictures from newspapers or magazines that represent these changes and place them under the correct heading. Ask students to write a short description of the pictures on large index cards. Remind them to include information about the changes the pictures represent. Place the descriptions in an envelope attached to the bulletin board. Invite students to come to the board, select a description card, and place it next to the appropriate picture.

Section	Core	Standard	Enriched
6.1 Matter pp. 135–139			
Section Features Skills WarmUp, p. 135 / Skills WorkOut, p. 138	• •	• •	• •
Blackline Masters Review Worksheet 6.1	•	•	
Ancillary Options *One-Minute Readings,* pp. 46–47	•	•	•
Color Transparencies Transparencies 14, 15, 16	•	•	•
6.2 Phases of Matter pp. 140–146			
Section Features Skills WarmUp, p. 140 / Skills WorkOut, p. 142 / SkillBuilder, p. 145	• • •	• • •	• • •
Blackline Masters Review Worksheet 6.2 / Reteach Worksheet 6.2 / Skills Worksheet 6.2 / Integrating Worksheet 6.2	• • •	• • • •	• •
Overhead Blackline Transparencies Overhead Blackline Master 6 and Student Worksheet	•	•	•

Section	Core	Standard	Enriched
Laboratory Program Investigation 12 / Investigation 13 / Investigation 14	• • •	•	•
6.3 Changes in Matter pp. 147–152			
Section Features Skills WarmUp, p. 147 / Skills WorkOut, p. 149 / Career Corner, p. 150 / Activity, p. 152	• • • •	• • • •	• • • •
Blackline Masters Review Worksheet 6.3 / Skills Worksheet 6.3 / Integrating Worksheet 6.3 / Vocabulary Worksheet 6	• • • •	• • • •	•
Color Transparencies Transparency 17	•	•	•
Ancillary Options *CEPUP,* Activities 1–3 in Chemical Survey	•	•	•
Laboratory Program Investigation 15			

Bibliography

The following resources can be used for teaching the chapter. See page T-46 for supplier codes.

Library Resources

Berger, Melvin. Solids, Liquids, Gases. New York: G. P. Putnam's Sons, 1989.

Cobb, Vicki, and Kathy Darling. Bet You Can! Science Possibilities to Fool You. New York: Avon Books, 1980.

Cobb, Vicki, and Kathy Darling. Bet You Can't! Science Impossibilities to Fool You. New York: Avon Books, 1980.

The Diagram Group. Comparisons. New York: St. Martin's Press, 1980.

Lafferty, Peter. Energy and Light. New York: Gloucester Press, 1989.

Sherwood, Martin, and Christine Sutton. The Physical World. New York: Oxford University Press, 1988.

Technology Resources

Software

Learning All About Matter. Mac, Dos. LS.
Matter. Mac, Dos. ESI.
Superstar Science. Mac, Win. LS.

CD-ROMs

An Odyssey of Discovery for Science Insights: Have students try the activity *Recycler* on the Earth and Space Disk. *SFAW.*

Laserdiscs

Living Textbook. (See barcodes on pages in this chapter.) Optical Data.

Mass and Density: Investigating Matter. AIMS.

Videos

All About Matter. FM.

Writing Connection

The crystals in the photograph look like flowers, ferns, or other natural structures. Point out that all natural objects have patterns at some level of observation, whether close or distant. Have students write a descriptive paragraph about a pattern that they observed in an unexpected place, such as in a close-up study of a favorite object, or in a crowd of people at a stadium.

Introducing the Chapter

Have students read the description of the photograph. Ask if they agree or disagree with the description.

Directed Inquiry

Have students study the photograph. Ask:

▶ What three words would you use to describe the picture? (Students may mention some of the same things noted in the quote.)

▶ Do you think the photograph shows something you could see with the unaided eye? Explain. (No. It is greatly magnified. The shapes and colors don't match anything in the students' experience.)

▶ How do you think the picture shows properties of matter? (Answers will vary but students should suggest that the photograph shows the structure or the small particles of matter. Some might identify crystals.)

Chapter Vocabulary

chemical change	particle model
gas	physical change
liquid	plasma
matter	solid

Chapter **6** Properties of Matter

Chapter Sections

6.1 Matter

6.2 Phases of Matter

6.3 Changes in Matter

What do you see?

"As I look at the picture, I see many different designs. One design is an overhead view of different colored palm trees. The trees are very close together. I also see flowers in full bloom with soft crevices deep in their petals. The flowers are blowing in the wind. Or, I see many shapes of windmills spinning rapidly. Turning the picture causes the shapes to look like rocks or shells artistically arranged."

LaToya Cobbins
Sullivan High School
Chicago, Illinois

To find out more about the photograph, look on page 154. As you read this chapter, you will learn about matter, phases of matter, and changes in matter.

Themes in Science

Scale and Structure From the moon, you could see swirls and different colors on the earth's surface, but it still looks like a single piece of matter. From an airplane, however, you can observe more detail, such as water and land. Similarly, an organism looks like just a single animal until a part of it is viewed without a microscope. Under a microscope, however, individual living cells can be seen. With an electron microscope, scientists can see that living and nonliving matter is composed of very tiny particles. Have students describe a blueberry muffin from across the classroom, from two meters away, and using a hand lens.

6.1 Matter

Objectives

▶ **Define** matter and describe its major properties.

▶ **Explain** how the arrangement of particles in a substance may determine its properties.

▶ **Classify** kinds of matter based on their properties.

▶ **Make a model** illustrating the particle model of matter.

I magine you are an astronaut approaching the earth from space. At first the earth appears as a distant blue and white sphere. As you get closer, you see the shapes of continents. Then rivers, mountains, highways, and cities come into view. When you near the surface, you see cars on the highways, houses in the cities, and beaches by the ocean. If you land on a beach, you see sand and waves. Looking closer, you see even the individual grains of sand that make up the beach. Do you think the grains of sand are made of things that are still smaller?

Particle Model of Matter

Grains of sand and everything else you see, hear, smell, touch, and taste are made of **matter**. Matter is anything that has mass and takes up space. Matter exists in many shapes, colors, textures, and forms. Water, rocks, living things, and stars are all made of matter.

To understand matter, you need to take a closer look at it. As an astronaut approaches the earth from outer space, the features of the planet's surface become more visible. Similarly, as you examine matter more closely, more of its parts are revealed.

All forms of matter are made up of tiny particles that are in constant motion. This idea is known as the **particle model** of matter. The particles that make up matter are much too small to see. Even the tiniest speck of matter contains huge numbers of particles. Particles vary in their size, shape, arrangement, motion, and individual properties. These factors help explain the properties of matter.

Figure 6.1 ▲
The closer you get to something, the more you can observe about the parts that make it up. What can you observe about the earth when standing on its surface that you can't observe from outer space? ①

Section Objectives
For a list of section objectives, see the Student Edition page.

Skills Objectives
Students should be able to:

Observe similarities among objects.

Make a Model demonstrating a property of matter.

Classify objects by grouping them according to physical properties.

Vocabulary
matter, particle model

Skills WarmUp

To help students understand some of the properties of matter, have them do the Skills WarmUp.
Answer Students' lists will vary, but should indicate that all substances have mass and take up space.

Misconceptions

Students may identify matter as only things that they can see. Stress that there are two ways to identify matter: Does it take up space and have mass? Demonstrate that air is matter by squeezing a sealed plastic bag to show how it moves when displaced.

Answer to In-Text Question

① **Answers will vary; example: people, insects, buildings, plants, slight variations in elevation.**

 The Living Textbook: Physical Science Side 1

Chapter 21   Frame 12941
Atomic Molecular Theory (Movie)
Search: Play:

Explore Visually

Have students study the material on pages 136 and 137. Discuss the following:

▶ Color is a property of matter. Make a list of the colors that appear on these two pages. (Answers will vary. Students should identify the colors of the objects on these pages.)

▶ Luster is a property of matter. Describe the luster of the metal shield and face mask. (Answers will vary. Students should identify aluminum foil, mask, shield, and metal objects as having luster.)

▶ Which of the wires has the greatest amount of insulation? How can you tell? (The wire with the thickest plastic coating—plastic is an insulator.)

▶ What do the paper clips and nails have in common? (They contain iron, a metal that is affected by a magnetic field.)

Decision Making

If you have classroom sets of *One-Minute Readings*, have students read Issue 27 "Law of Conservation of Matter" on pages 46 and 47.

Answer to In-Text Question

① The slate would feel smooth and the granite would feel rough.

**The Living Textbook:
Physical Science Sides 1-4**

Chapter 3   Frame 00893
Physical Properties (11 Frames)
Search: Step:

Art Connection

Have students collect pictures and small objects that show how properties of matter vary among objects. Encourage students to work in cooperative groups. Have each group find pictures or objects that all show how the same property of matter varies. Students can choose a single property, such as color, texture, odor, luster, or transparency. Each group will use their pictures to make a collage. For example, a group that chooses the property of color will make a collage showing how the color of matter varies.

Properties of Matter

Investigating the properties of a sample of matter gives you important clues about its nature and composition, or makeup. Each of the many kinds of matter in the universe has characteristics that help to identify it. These characteristics are known as properties. Knowing the properties of a sample of matter can help you to classify it with other substances.

Some properties such as mass, volume, and density are common to all matter. These properties can be measured by using the methods described in Chapter 1. You can observe many other properties of matter using your senses. Some properties that are easily observed include color, texture, odor, luster, and transparency.

These common rocks are similar, but they have different textures. The dark-colored slate has a smooth, fine-grained texture. The speckled granite has a coarse, large-grained texture. How do you think each rock would feel if you could touch it? ▼ ①

▲ These leaves appear green because they reflect green light back to your eyes. All objects that appear green, whether living or nonliving, reflect green light.

Most metals, such as copper, silver, and gold, have a shiny appearance, or luster. ▼

Integrating the Sciences

Geology Have students work in cooperative learning groups. Ask each group to test the hardness of several common objects, such as chalk, a nickel, and a plastic bottle. Explain that geologists identify hardness by the ability of one mineral to scratch another. For example, if mineral A scratches mineral B, then mineral A is harder than mineral B. Have students scratch the objects with different materials, such as a fingernail, a penny, and a piece of glass. Students should rank the objects from hardest to softest. Have a class discussion to compare results.

Many other properties of matter can be observed by using simple tests and measurements. These properties include hardness, resistance to breakage, and the ability to dissolve in water. Various kinds of matter also differ in how they interact with other substances, and how they are affected by temperature changes.

Baking soda reacts strongly with vinegar, and less strongly with water. Baking soda is used in cooking to make quick breads rise. ▼

▲ Some types of matter, including iron, nickel, and cobalt, are affected by magnetic fields. This lodestone contains permanently magnetized iron.

Electricity flows easily through the copper in the center of these wires. Copper is a conductor. In contrast, the plastic covering the wires does not conduct electricity at all. Plastic is an insulator. ▼

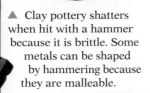

▲ Clay pottery shatters when hit with a hammer because it is brittle. Some metals can be shaped by hammering because they are malleable.

Observe Provide a selection of items, such as a leaf, sandpaper, nickel, and a round candy wafer, each in a small paper bag. Have students reach inside each bag and describe the properties of the object they feel. Ask students to identify the items in each bag.

Class Activity

Ask each student to write the name of a classroom object on a sheet of paper. Then have them list as many properties of the object as possible. Have volunteers read their lists one property at a time. The class should then try to identify the chosen object. Point out the different ways students have chosen to describe the same properties.

 The Living Textbook: Physical Science Sides 1-4

Chapter 15   Frame 02363
Copper Wire: Conductor and Insulator
(1 Frame)
Search:

 **The Living Textbook: Physical Science Sides 1-4**

Chapter 2   Frame 00857
Iron, Cobalt, Nickel: Magnetic Properties
(3 Frames)
Search: Step:

TEACH ▪ *Continued*

Skills WorkOut

To help students understand the particle model of matter, have them do the Skills WorkOut.

Answer Even a tiny droplet of water is made of a large number of particles that can be divided in half many times. The smallest particle, if you could see it, would be a combination of two hydrogen atoms and one oxygen atom. Students' descriptions will vary.

Critical Thinking

Generalize Ask students to make a general statement about the relationship between the hardness of a substance and the strength of the bonds between the particles. (The stronger the bond is among particles, the harder the substance will be.)

The Living Textbook: Physical Science Sides 1-4

Chapter 2   Frame 00835
Carbon: Charcoal (1 Frame)
Search:

The Living Textbook: Physical Science Sides 1-4

Chapter 02   Frame 00890
Carbon: Pencil Graphite and Diamond
(2 Frames)
Search: Step:

Themes in Science

Diversity and Unity All forms of matter in the universe, from invisible gases to solid rocks, are made of atoms. This great diversity of atomic matter springs from the diverse ways in which a relatively small number of different atoms combine with one another to form many different kinds of compounds.

▼ ACTIVITY

Making a Model

Dividing the Water

How many times can the water in a glass be divided in two? Develop a mental model of what would happen if you halved the volume over and over again until you were left with the smallest particle that was still water. How small would it be? What would it look like if you could see it?

SKILLS WORKOUT

Figure 6.2
Diamond, graphite, and soot have different properties because the arrangement of their carbon particles differs. ▼

Explaining Matter's Properties

Why is matter so varied? What gives each kind of matter its special properties? The properties of any kind of matter are determined in part by the way its particles are arranged.

Look at Figure 6.2 below. Diamond, graphite, and soot are made up of identical particles of carbon, even though they are very different substances. These three kinds of matter are different because their carbon particles are arranged differently. Notice that the particles making up the diamond form a rigid, three-dimensional framework. All the particles are held together strongly. Graphite particles, in contrast, form layers. The layers are held together so weakly that they slide past one another, making graphite very soft. The particles in soot are randomly arranged and held together weakly.

Many other properties of matter are determined by the characteristics of the particles themselves. For example, particles that reflect green light give a substance the property of being green in color. The particles in baking soda, not their arrangement, account for how it reacts in vinegar.

The motion of the particles in matter is also important. The speed of particle movement changes with temperature. As the temperature increases, the speed of the particles in matter increases. Particle movement determines whether a substance will be a solid, liquid, or gas.

Diamond

Graphite

Soot

Multicultural Perspectives

Fascinating myths have grown up around gemstones all over the world. The ancient Greeks thought that diamonds could counteract certain poisons; the people of India thought they were formed by lightning. In Europe during the Middle Ages, darkening rubies were thought to forecast misfortune and death. Suggest that students learn about the cultural traditions surrounding a gemstone.

Integrating the Sciences

Earth Science Point out to students that different gems are found in different types of rocks. For example, beryl, topaz, and tourmaline are found in igneous rock. Rubies, sapphires, and jades are found in metamorphic rock, and diamonds, spinel, and moonstone are found in sedimentary rock. Ask students to explain why knowing types of minerals is necessary for people who mine gemstones.

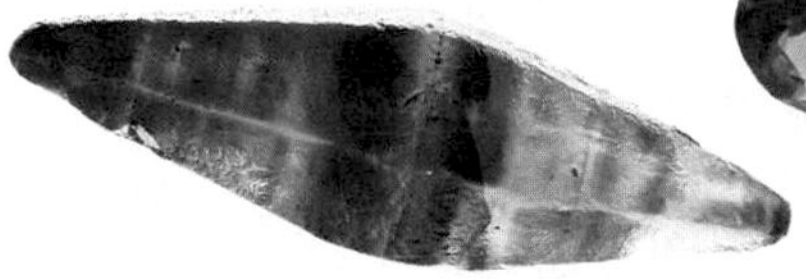

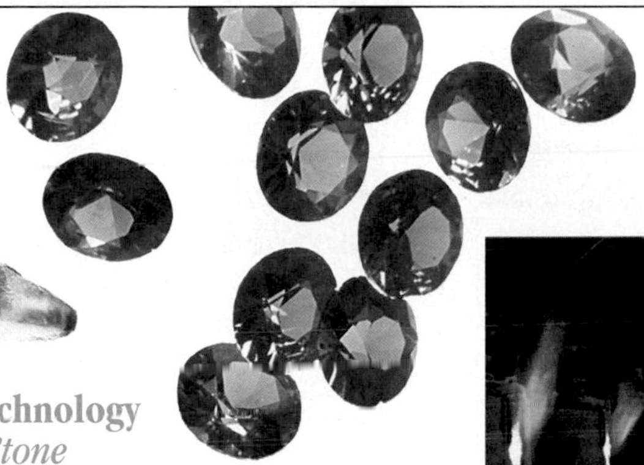

Science and Technology
Enhancing the Stone

Throughout history, gemstones have been heated to make them look clearer and to deepen their color. The ancient Romans heated agate, a variety of quartz, to enhance its color. In Sri Lanka, the current method for heating rubies dates back to about the year 1240.

Clear, deeply colored gems are very valuable. The color of any gemstone depends on the type and amount of particles present in the stone. So, if you can increase the number of certain kinds of particles present in a gem, you may be able to increase its value.

Not only heating, but other specialized techniques can heighten the clarity and color of gems. In one technique, colorless sapphires are packed in metal oxide powders. These precious packages are heated above 2,000°C for 25 days. During this process, the gemstones absorb particles from the metal oxides. The gems that result, shown in Figure 6.3, are polished to a deep, clear blue. Unfortunately, the gems are not completely transformed by this process. If you cut one in half, the inside is still colorless!

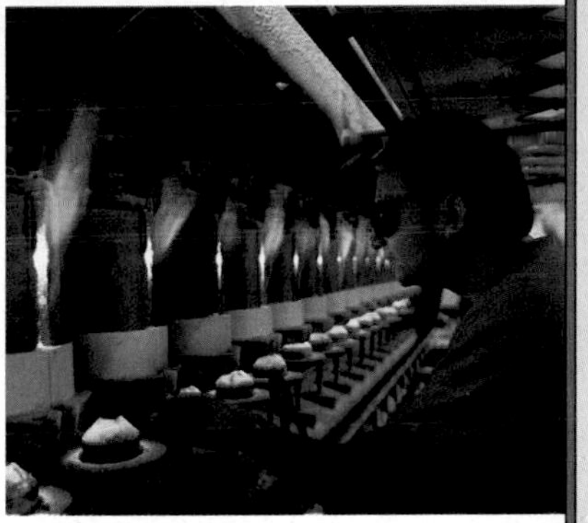

Figure 6.3 ▲
Gems such as sapphires begin as uncut stones (left). Before they become finished gems (center) they may go through a heating process (right).

Check and Explain

1. Define matter and give three examples of matter.
2. Make a list of ten objects in your classroom and name at least one physical property for each object.
3. **Classify** Organize ten different objects by grouping them by physical properties. Describe the properties on which you based your classification.
4. **Make a Model** Choose one property of matter and draw a diagram to show an arrangement of particles that could determine the property.

Research

Have students research gemstones to learn about synthetic, or artificially made gemstones. Have them prepare a bulletin-board display that shows how synthetic gemstones are made and how they compare to natural gemstones.

EVALUATE

WrapUp

Portfolio Have students write a letter asking a friend to identify an unknown object by describing its properties. Encourage them to use their new vocabulary to describe some familiar kinds of matter.

Use Review Worksheet 6.1.

Check and Explain

1. Matter is anything that has mass and takes up space. Answers will vary, sample answers include air, water, and rocks.
2. Students' lists will vary but will probably include easily observed properties such as color, texture, odor, luster, and transparency.
3. Students' objects and classifications will vary.
4. Diagrams will vary, but should indicate that students understand that the properties of matter are determined in part by the way its particles are arranged.

6.2

Section Objectives
For a list of section objectives, see the Student Edition page.

Skills Objectives
Students should be able to:

Classify substances.

Predict the outcome of an experiment.

Make a Model to illustrate Charles' Law.

Vocabulary
solid, liquid, gas, plasma

MOTIVATE

Skills WarmUp
To help students understand the three phases of matter, have them do the Skills WarmUp.
Answer Students' tables and lists may vary. Similarities: Students might record that ice, steam, and water are all forms of water. Differences: Ice holds its shape, water pours, and steam moves readily into the air.

Misconceptions
Students may identify steam as a gas. Remind them that steam is condensed water vapor made of tiny water droplets. Have students view a boiling tea kettle at a safe distance. Ask them what they observe. (Nothing close to the spout because the space is filled with invisible water vapor; a short distance from the spout, they will see steam.)

 The Living Textbook:
Physical Science Sides 1-4

Chapter 4   Frame 00926
Phases of Matter: Properties and Particles
(1 Frame)
Search:

Themes in Science
Energy The three phases of matter, solid, liquid, and gas, are distinguished by the energy of the particles in the matter. Remind students that in solids the particles have a small amount of kinetic energy and remain in a rigid pattern. Particles of a liquid move around one another and have greater kinetic energy. Ask students to describe a gas in terms of the energy of its particles. (Particles of a gas move in random patterns through space; particles in gases have more kinetic energy than particles in solids or liquids.)

▼ ACTIVITY

Comparing

Alike and Different
How are ice, steam, and water alike? How are they different? Make a table and list their similar and different properties. Compare your table with that of a classmate.

SKILLS WARMUP

Figure 6.4
In each phase of matter, the particles move about in a different way. ▼

6.2 Phases of Matter

Objectives

▶ **Give examples** of solids, liquids, and gases.

▶ **Relate** the particle model to solids, liquids, and gases.

▶ **Make models** illustrating the gas laws.

Imagine that you and your classmates represent particles of matter. During class, everyone is seated at desks in neatly arranged rows. This arrangement of students is like the arrangement of particles in a solid. You can move in your seats while at your desks, just as particles in a solid move about a fixed point.

At the end of class, you get up from your desks and move freely toward the door of the classroom. This close, but unorganized, movement resembles the motion of particles in a liquid. Finally, as you and your classmates leave the classroom, you travel in many different directions through the school grounds. This movement is similar to the way particles of a gas spread out to fill a space.

Familiar Phases of Matter

The three most familiar states of matter are solid, liquid, and gas. Each of these states of matter is called a phase. Like the students described above, particles of matter in each phase are arranged differently and have different ranges of motion.

Solid

Liquid
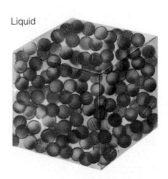

Gas

Integrating the Sciences

Earth Science Explain that liquid, molten rock called *magma* forms deep within the earth. When magma moves to the surface of the earth, it is in the liquid form of lava. When lava cools, it forms a porous rock. Ask students how the motion of particles in molten lava compares to the motion of particles in cooled lava rock. (Particles in molten lava flow past each other freely. Once the lava cools, the particles form solid rock.)

Language Arts Connection

Encourage students to use a dictionary such as the *Oxford English Dictionary* to look up the origin of the word *amorphous* and explain why it is used to describe certain solids. (*Amorphous* comes from the Greek prefix *a*, meaning "without," and *morphos*, meaning "form.")

Solids

The shape and volume of a rock are the same whether you put the rock in a shoe box or on a rock pile. When matter has a definite shape and a definite volume, it is a **solid**. A solid has these characteristics because of its closely packed particles. The particles can move slightly, but they do not change positions.

Most solids occur as crystals. Salt, bones, diamonds, computer chips, and snowflakes are all made up of crystals. Particles in a crystal are arranged in a regular, orderly way.

At some temperature, a solid substance melts to form a liquid. When the temperature of the melted substance is lowered, it becomes a solid again.

Materials such as glass, hard candy, and candle wax appear to be solid, but the arrangement of their particles is less regular. These materials are sometimes called amorphous (uh MOR fuhs) solids.

Figure 6.5 ▲
A quartz crystal is a typical solid. Why do its shape and volume remain the same?

Liquids

Matter with a definite volume, but no definite shape, is a **liquid**. Particles in a liquid behave something like bird seed in a sack. Like the bird seed, the liquid particles easily slide over each other. As a result, a liquid will take the shape of its container.

Look at Figure 6.6. It shows that the particles in a liquid are close together, but move enough so they do not stay in fixed positions. The particles flow freely past one another. Some liquids, like water, flow quickly. Other liquids, such as syrup, molasses, or motor oil, flow more slowly because the particles tend to stick together.

In most liquids at room temperature, some of the particles move fast and can escape into the air. This process, called evaporation, forms a vapor or gas. The opposite of evaporation is condensation (KAHN duhn SAY shuhn). When condensation occurs, a gas forms a liquid.

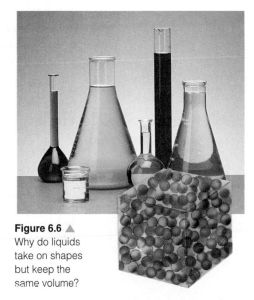

Figure 6.6 ▲
Why do liquids take on shapes but keep the same volume?

TEACH ■ *Continued*

Skills WorkOut

To help students understand the gas phase of matter, have them do the Skills WorkOut.

Answer Students' lists will vary. Many students may include water on one or more lists. Students should not confuse steam and water vapor.

Skills Development

Infer Open a container of vinegar in the front of a classroom in which the doors and windows are closed. Tell students to raise their hands as soon as they smell the vinegar.

▶ Ask students why they were able to smell the vinegar. (Some of the liquid evaporated and formed a gas that spread throughout the room.)

▶ Ask students to explain why some students smelled the vinegar before others did. (The gas reached those close to the vinegar first.)

Answer to In-Text Question

① **The air inside the balloon takes up space.**

Integrated Learning

Use Integrating Worksheet 6.2.

 The Living Textbook: Physical Science Sides 1-4

Chapter 17   Frame 03032
Gas: Definition, Properties, and Particles (2 Frames)
Search: Step:

The Living Textbook: Physical Science Sides 1-4

Chapter 2   Frame 00866
Bromine Gas (1 Frame)
Search:

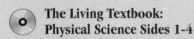

Integrating the Sciences

Botany Explain to students that plants use energy from the sun to combine carbon dioxide and water to produce glucose. During this process, called *photosynthesis*, plants release oxygen into the air. If an aquarium containing live plants is available, show students the bubbles of oxygen forming on the plant leaves. Shake off the bubbles, then have students look at the leaves during the next class.

Answer to Link

As you blow up the balloon the volume of your lungs decreases. This change is related to the increase in pressure as your muscles contract so you can blow out air.

▼ **ACTIVITY**

Classifying

Phasing In

Make a list of the things you used today that were in the gas phase. Then make lists of things you used that were solids and liquids. Did you use the same substance in two different phases? How is this possible?

SKILLS WORKOUT

Figure 6.7 ▶
How do you know that a blown-up balloon contains matter? ①

Gases

Matter that has no definite shape and no definite volume is a **gas**. Like a liquid, a gas will take the shape of any container. Unlike a liquid, a gas expands to fill whatever space is available. The scent of a flower and the odor of a rotten egg come from gases that can fill a room.

The air is made up of several different gases. Although air is invisible, you can feel the effect of gas particles striking you when the wind blows. Gases fill balloons, propel rockets, and enable your cells to release energy from nutrients.

Look at the gas particles shown in Figure 6.7. Notice that the particles do not stick to one another. They move in straight lines, flying all over. They change direction only when they strike the walls of their containers or bump into other particles. The particles move very far apart from one another.

Unlike the particles in a solid or liquid, each gas particle is mostly unaffected by its neighbors. Only temperature and pressure can affect the way the particles move and the volume they occupy. Because each gas particle is independent of other gas particles, the behavior of gases can be described by general laws. These laws, called gas laws, hold true for a wide range of temperatures and pressures. However, at very high or very low temperatures or pressures, gases behave differently than the gas laws predict.

Integrating the Sciences

Life Science Make a simple model of the lungs as follows. Cut the bottom out of a plastic soft drink bottle. Attach a balloon to each arm of a Y-tube. Push the stem of the Y-tube through a stopper so that the stopper seals the Y-tube and balloons inside the bottle. To make a model "diaphragm" cut a piece of rubber from a large balloon. Stretch the rubber over the bottom of the bottle and secure it with a rubber band. Demonstrate the mechanics of breathing by pressing in lightly on the "diaphragm" and watching the balloon "lungs" collapse. Releasing the "diaphragm" refills the lungs. Ask students to describe what's happening.

Boyle's Law A gas sealed in a container exerts a certain pressure. Recall that pressure is the force created by particles striking the walls of a container. You have seen the effect of pressure on the rubber walls of balloons like those in Figure 6.7. The walls of the balloons are pushed out by the constant bumping of the gas particles trapped inside.

What happens to the pressure exerted by a gas when the volume of its container is changed? If you squeeze a gas into a smaller space, its particles will strike the walls of the container more often. The pressure on the walls will increase. If you increase the space, the gas particles strike the container's walls less often and the pressure will decrease. This relationship between pressure and volume is called *Boyle's Law*. It was discovered by Robert Boyle, a British scientist who lived in the 1600s.

Boyle's Law states that if a sample of gas is kept at a constant temperature, decreasing its volume will increase the pressure the gas exerts. Boyle's Law can be tested using a cylinder with a movable piston like the one shown in Figure 6.8. Data on pressure and volume can be used to construct a graph similar to the one you see below. What inferences can you make from the shape of the curve? ②

Life Science
L I N K

Blow up a balloon. What happened to your lungs while you were blowing up the balloon? Write about how your lungs work in terms of Boyle's Law.

A C T I V I T Y

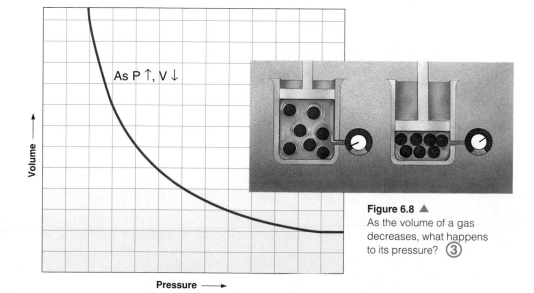

As P ↑, V ↓

Volume →

Pressure →

Figure 6.8 ▲
As the volume of a gas decreases, what happens to its pressure? ③

Skills Development

Interpret Data Ask students to examine Figure 6.8. Have a student translate "As P↑, V↓" into a sentence, and write it on the chalkboard. (As the pressure of a gas increases in a closed container, its volume decreases.) Have another student translate the following sentence into symbols and write it on the chalkboard: As volume of a closed container increases, pressure decreases. (As V↑, P↓)

Enrich

Explain to students that Figure 6.8 is a graph of an *inverse relationship*. Explain that in an inverse relationship, as one quantity increases, the second quantity decreases. Challenge students to identify other pairs of objects or events that have an inverse relationship.

Answers to In-Text Questions

② **Students may infer from the flattening of the curve that increased pressure produces smaller changes in volume.**

③ **As the volume of a gas decreases, the pressure increases, if the temperature is constant.**

The Living Textbook: Physical Science Sides 1-4

Chapter 9   Frame 01723
Pressure and Molecules: Volume Relationship (2 Frames)
Search: Step:

The Living Textbook: Physical Science Side 2

Chapter 25   Frame 18302
Pressure Caused by Moving Molecules (Movie)
Search: Play:

143

TEACH ▪ *Continued*

Discuss

Have students study the page. To help them understand Charles' Law discuss the following:

▶ What part does the motion of gas particles play in Charles' Law? (As the temperature increases, the gas particles move faster and the volume increases.)

▶ How does Charles' Law explain why gasoline cans should not be left in the sun? (The temperature of the vapor in the can will increase. The vapor particles will move faster and increase in kinetic energy. The can will explode from the increased pressure.)

Enrich

Explain to students that Figure 6.9 is a graph of a *direct relationship*. Explain that in a direct relationship, as one quantity increases or decreases, the second quantity also increases or decreases, respectively. Ask students to give examples of direct relationships.

Answers to In-Text Questions

① The volume of air decreases.

② The volume increases.

The Living Textbook:
Physical Science Side 2

Chapter 26   Frame 21268
Charles' Law: Pressure and Temperature
(Movie)
Search: Play:

Themes in Science

Systems and Interactions

According to Charles' Law, as one quantity in a system, such as temperature, changes, other quantities in the system, such as volume, change in response. Have students give an example of this kind of interaction from their own experiences.

Charles' Law The relationship between the temperature of a gas and its volume was first described in the late 1700s by a French scientist named Jacques Charles. According to *Charles' Law*, if a sample of gas is kept at constant pressure, its volume increases as the temperature increases. The graph in Figure 6.9 shows this relationship. Many products in spray cans, such as whipped cream and paint, contain gas at a fairly high pressure. Their labels warn you to keep them away from heat or fire. Why?

Adding heat energy to a gas causes the gas particles to move faster. When the particles move faster, they strike the walls of their container harder and more often. If the container walls aren't flexible, as in a can of whipped cream, the pressure of the gas will increase. Since the can will withstand only so much pressure, the result could be explosive and dangerous!

However, if a gas in a container with flexible walls is heated, the volume of the gas will increase. You can see the volume increase in the balloons in Figure 6.9. Cooling a gas causes the reverse to happen. The volume of the gas decreases. Have you noticed what happens to the air in sealed bags of food you put in the refrigerator? ①

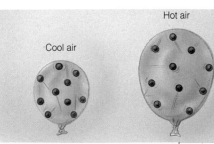

Cool air

Hot air

Figure 6.9 ▲
What happens to the volume of a gas as its temperature increases? ②

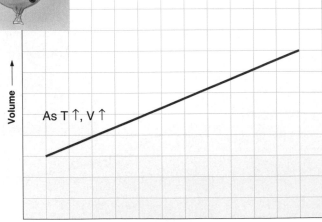

As T ↑, V ↑

Volume

Temperature ⟶

The super-hot natural plasmas that form the interior of stars are similar to the much cooler artificial plasmas created inside neon and fluorescent lamps. In artificial plasmas, the atoms of a gas are ionized by an electric current. Ask students how a fluorescent light is different from an incandescent light bulb. (It does not have a filament and is shaped differently.) The reason that super-heated artificial plasmas are found only in laboratories is that they are so difficult to contain. Scientists are especially interested in harnessing super-heated plasmas at temperatures higher than 100 000 000°C, which is the temperature at which controlled thermonuclear reactions can be produced.

Plasmas

At very high temperatures, over 1 000 000°C, gas particles break down, forming a **plasma** (PLAZ muh) phase. Temperatures high enough to form plasmas exist naturally only in stars. Plasma, called the fourth phase of matter, is the most common phase of matter in the universe. The sun and other active stars are made up mostly of plasmas. These plasmas are formed from the gases hydrogen and helium.

Plasmas have unusual properties that gases do not have. For example, plasmas conduct electricity. Also, they are affected by magnetic fields. On earth, plasmas can be manufactured and studied only in special laboratories. These laboratories must be able to handle the extreme temperatures at which plasmas exist. No solid substance can contain plasma. Therefore, super-heated plasma is created and confined within a strong magnetic field, called a "magnetic bottle."

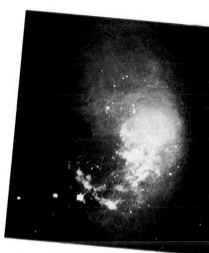

Figure 6.10 ▲
Matter in the plasma phase makes up much of the universe.

SkillBuilder Predicting

Going Through a Phase

When you make ice cubes in an ice cube tray, the ice cubes take up more space than the water you poured into the tray. Based on this observation, predict what will happen in the following situation.

Two identical cups are filled with the same mass of water. One cup is placed in the freezer. The water in the other cup is kept at room temperature. After the water freezes, its mass is measured again. The masses of the cup of water and the cup of ice are compared. Are they the same or different? Try the experiment yourself:

1. Fill two plastic cups with 100 mL of water each. Using a balance, adjust the amount of water in the cups (a dropper can be used) until the two cups are the same in mass. Record this mass in a data table like the one shown.

2. Place one of the cups in the freezer overnight. Predict what will happen to the mass of the water when ice forms.

3. The next day, measure the mass of the cup of water and the cup of ice. Record your observations.

4. How did your prediction match your observations?

Write a paragraph describing the differences you observed when water changed from the liquid phase to the solid phase.

	Starting mass	Treatment	Ending mass
Cup A		None	
Cup B		Frozen	

Skills Development

Infer   Plasma is found in lightning bolts and neon signs. What property of plasma is found in both? (Plasma conducts electricity.)

SkillBuilder

Apply   Explain to students that one solid or liquid will float on another if the density of the first solid or liquid is less than the density of the second. Ask students to use their knowledge of ice and water to determine which has the greater density. (Ice floats on water; it is less dense.) Explain that water is an exception to the rule that the volume of matter decreases as it is cooled. Water expands between 4°C and 0°C.

Answers
1. Starting masses may vary.
2. Students may predict incorrectly that the mass will increase.
3. Ending masses are the same.
4. Answers depend on students' predictions. Student paragraphs will vary, but should indicate that the mass of the ice cube stayed the same; the volume increased.

Reteach
Use Reteach Worksheet 6.2.

**The Living Textbook:
Physical Science Sides 1-4**

Chapter 13   Frame 02187
Plasma on Sun (1 Frame)
Search:

**The Living Textbook:
Physical Science Sides 1-4**

Chapter 4   Frame 01055
Plasma Research at Los Alamos Laboratory (1 Frame)
Search:

EVALUATE

WrapUp

Reteach Describe the following events to students and ask them to describe the events by using the terms *solid, liquid,* and *gas.*

▶ A pat of butter on your breakfast pancakes melts.

▶ A small air freshener fills the whole house with a pine scent.

▶ You put a bottled soft drink in the freezer to cool it quickly. The bottle breaks.

▶ A car in subzero temperatures develops low tires.

Use Review Worksheet 6.2.

Check and Explain

1. Answers will vary. Solids: salt, ice; liquids: water, gasoline; gases: air, carbon dioxide

2. Check student drawings.

3. Higher at the end. As the tire rolled along the road it would get warmer. The volume in the tire is a constant, so the pressure will increase.

4. The balloon's volume should be less when submerged in ice water, greater when placed in very warm water.

ice water	smallest
room temperature	mid-size
very warm water	largest

As the temperature increased, the volume of the gas increased.

Answers to In-Text Questions

① It is difficult to tell because of the shapes of the containers.

② No; they are the same.

**The Living Textbook:
Physical Science Sides 1-4**

Chapter 8   Frame 01418
Liquids in Various Containers (1 Frame)
Search:

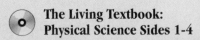

146

Math Connection

Have students imagine that they need to buy a bottle of juice. They have a choice of three varieties. The first contains 1 liter and costs $1.90. The second holds 2 liters and costs $2.90. The third, called the "budget buy," holds 3 liters and costs $4.75. Which bottle is the most economical? (The second; the juice costs, respectively, $1.90 per liter, $1.45 per liter, and $1.58 per liter.)

Figure 6.11 ▲
Can you tell which of these containers holds the most liquid?
①

Science and You *Packaging Liquids*

When you shop for a liquid product, such as a mouthwash, how do you decide which product gives you the most mouthwash for your money? One way is to compare the shape and size of bottles. If you have tried this comparison, however, you may have discovered that appearances can fool you.

Bottles can be designed to fool your eye and make you think that containers hold more liquid than they actually do. Sometimes, unusual shapes with indentations are used to make bottles appear larger. You know that a liquid takes the shape of its container. But shape and volume have a complex relationship that is difficult to determine just by observation. As a result, it is hard to tell how much liquid is present by comparing the containers.

A better way to tell how much of a product is in a container is to read the label. The law requires that labels tell you the volume of liquid you are purchasing. Usually this measurement is given in liters or milliliters. By determining the cost per unit volume of several different brands, you can decide which product is the most economical. You divide the price by the volume. For example, a 0.5-liter bottle of mouthwash costing $2.50 is $5.00 per liter. Is this a better buy than mouthwash costing $3.00 for 0.6 liters? ②

Check and Explain

1. List two examples each of a solid, a liquid, and a gas.

2. Draw a diagram to show the spacing of particles in a solid, a liquid, and a gas.

3. **Find Causes** If you take a bicycle trip on a hot summer day, would you expect your tire pressure to be higher at the beginning or at the end of the trip? Explain.

4. **Make a Model** Place a balloon filled with air in a container of ice water and observe its volume. Then place the balloon into a container of very warm water. Make a table to record your observations of the volume of the balloon at room temperature, in the ice water, and in the very warm water. Explain how this illustrates Charles' Law.

Themes in Science

Patterns of Change/Cycles

When matter gains or loses energy, it may change phase. A phase change is a physical change that alters the size, shape, texture, or appearance of the matter, but does not alter the particles that make up the matter. Ask students to identify which of the following are physical changes: tearing paper, burning wood, mixing baking soda and vinegar, mixing oil and water. (Tearing paper, mixing oil and water)

6.3 Changes in Matter

Objectives

▶ **Give examples** of physical and chemical changes.

▶ **Compare** and **contrast** physical and chemical changes.

▶ **Interpret data** about a phase change.

I f you hang your wet washcloth in the bathroom, it will dry. If you forget to clean your paintbrush and the paint dries, the paintbrush becomes hard and useless. The drying washcloth and the hardening paint are examples of changes in matter. The water in the washcloth and also in the paint changed to water vapor in the air. As the water in the paint changed to water vapor, the paint hardened. The small particles in the paint joined together to form long chainlike particles. This change made the paint form a hard, shiny film on the brush.

Physical Changes in Matter

If you break a piece of glass, the shape of the glass changes. However, the fragments of glass contain the same particles and have the same properties as the original piece of glass. If you cut and sand a piece of wood to make a model, only the size and shape of the wood changes. When you freeze water into an ice cube and then let it melt, the liquid that remains is still water.

When matter undergoes a change in size, shape, or phase, it is a **physical change**. Physical changes do not change the particles that make up matter. The arrangement of the particles, however, may be moved around during a physical change.

Are you causing a physical change when you mix salt and water? A mixture of salt and water can be compared to a mixture of nails and screws. You can separate a mixture of nails and screws by hand. In a similar way, a mixture of pebbles and sand can be separated with a strainer. If you make a mixture of salt and water, the particles are too small for you to separate by hand or strainer. However, the water can be boiled away, leaving the salt behind.

▼ **ACTIVITY**

Hypothesizing

It's in the Bag

If you place a pencil, a piece of bread, and a piece of apple in separate, sealed, plastic bags, what will happen? State your hypothesis about which items will change and which items will not change.

SKILLS WARMUP

Figure 6.12 ▲
What physical change will occur as the warm sun strikes these icicles?

TEACH

Class Activity

Students can demonstrate ice wedging and weathering of rock using a brick. Soak each brick in water, then put it in a sealed plastic bag and place it in a freezer. Have students work in two groups. Each group should inspect the brick every few days and record any changes. After making its observations, one group should return the brick to the freezer. The second group should dip the brick in water again, smoothing the water into any cracks that may exist before refreezing.

Explore Visually

Have students study Figure 6.13. Ask:

▶ What happens when water in a crack freezes? (The water expands, making the crack bigger.)

▶ What happens to the crack when the ice in it melts? (It fills with more water.)

▶ How does the process of freezing and thawing affect the rock? (It breaks it into smaller and smaller pieces.)

Integrated Learning

Use Integrating Worksheet 6.3.

The Living Textbook: Physical Science Sides 1-4

Chapter 6   Frame 01158
Mixture of Trail Mix (2 Frames)
Search: Step:

The Living Textbook: Physical Science Sides 1-4

Chapter 6   Frame 01162
Mixture of Sand Particles (1 Frame)
Search:

148

INTEGRATED LEARNING

Integrating the Sciences

Geology Explain to students that if they have seen a boulder cracked by tree roots they have seen an example of a physical change caused by a plant. Encourage students to imagine other ways in which plants or animals might cause physical changes in rocks. They may draw pictures of examples in their portfolios. (Drawings should include examples of erosion, abrasion, and organic activity.)

Because the particles in a mixture do not change and can be easily separated, making a mixture is also an example of a physical change.

Physical changes help shape the earth's surface. The weathering and erosion of rocks involves many kinds of physical changes. For example, rocks are broken apart by the repeated freezing and thawing of water in the cracks, as shown in Figure 6.13. Heat from the sun also breaks rocks into smaller pieces. The outer layer of rock expands as it gets hot in the sun. As the rock cools quickly at night, its outer layer shrinks and cracks.

The pieces of rock produced by these weathering processes are then carried away by gravity, water, and wind. These forms of erosion grind and break the rock pieces into even smaller bits. The sand grains that result have the same kinds of particles as the rocks they came from.

Figure 6.13
Rocks are physically changed by processes such as ice wedging.

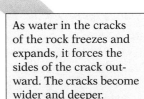

As water in the cracks of the rock freezes and expands, it forces the sides of the crack outward. The cracks become wider and deeper.

When the water freezes again, the cracks get larger. This process breaks large rocks into smaller pieces.

The ice thaws when the rock is warmed by the sun. More water fills the larger cracks.

148   Chapter 6   Properties of Matter

Chemical Changes in Matter

Have you seen matter undergo a change that was not just a physical change? If you leave an iron nail outside, it will rust. When you compare the rust with the iron nail, you will find that both the nail and the rust have different properties. The color and hardness of rust and iron are different. Rust is a new substance, resulting from a **chemical change** in the iron nail. In a chemical change, particles of one substance are changed in some way to form particles of a new substance that has new and different properties.

Evidence of Chemical Changes How do you know when a chemical change has occurred? Look at the photographs below to see different kinds of evidence for chemical changes. The production of heat or light, the appearance of gas bubbles, and the formation of a solid all indicate that a chemical change has taken place.

▼ **ACTIVITY**

Defining Operationally

Kinds of Changes

Think about what happens to a newspaper when it burns. Identify any physical changes or chemical changes that take place in the newspaper. Explain how you would know whether each change is a physical change or chemical one.

SKILLS WORKOUT

▲ What evidence of chemical change do you see on the surface of this plant? What kind of substance is being given off by the chemical change? ①

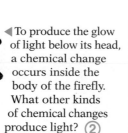
◄ To produce the glow of light below its head, a chemical change occurs inside the body of the firefly. What other kinds of chemical changes produce light? ②

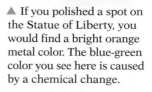
▲ If you polished a spot on the Statue of Liberty, you would find a bright orange metal color. The blue-green color you see here is caused by a chemical change.

◄ **TEACH** ▪ *Continued*

Discuss

Students may be familiar with chemical weathering of stone buildings or statues. Ask them to give specific examples of chemical weathering in your area. You may also want to discuss the effects of acid rain on historically important ancient structures in Greece, Italy, Egypt, Mexico, and Southeast Asia.

Career Corner

Students may wonder why a chef must acquire institutional training. Explain that the United States Food and Drug Administration has strict regulations about food preparation procedures. Observing these regulations requires the chef to be an expert in the areas of sanitation and quality control.

Discuss Suggest that chefs occasionally make discoveries while they are at work. Ask students to share any interesting discoveries in the kitchen that they have made.

The Living Textbook: Physical Science Sides 1-4

Chapter 8   Frame 01413
Chemical Change: Fireworks (2 Frames)
Search: Step:

The Living Textbook: Physical Science Sides 1-4

Chapter 8   Frame 01363
Chemical Change: Limestone-Acid Reaction (1 Frame)
Search:

Integrating the Sciences

Life Science Remind students that chemical changes take place in organisms every day. For example, when a person eats a cracker, the ingredients in the cracker undergo a chemical change, the starches in the cracker are changed to sugar. Have students draw a concept map of the physical and chemical changes they think food goes through when it is eaten.

Earth Science Explain to students that water plays an important part in chemical weathering. Water often combines with pollutants in the air to form acid rain. The primary forms of acid rain contain sulfurous acid (H_2SO_3) and sulfuric acid (H_2SO_4). Have students use litmus paper to test the acidity of the local rainwater.

How can you tell a chemical change from a physical change? One way is to observe whether the matter that has changed can be changed back to the original form by physical means. Any change in phase, for example, can be reversed. Ice can melt to form water, and water can freeze to form ice. Physical changes are often more readily reversed than chemical changes.

Chemical Changes in Rocks The earth's surface is shaped by chemical changes as well as physical changes. Gases in the atmosphere and water combine with minerals in rocks to create new substances. These chemical changes weaken rocks so that they chip, crack, and break apart more easily. Chemical weathering happens to rocks all over the earth's surface. Chemical changes work together with physical changes to weather and erode the earth's surface. These changes in matter help to shape mountains and plains, and to form soil.

Career Corner   Chef

Who Causes Physical and Chemical Changes in Food?

A chef is responsible for the preparation of food in the kitchen of a restaurant or institution. In a large kitchen, the chef supervises the work of cooks who may each be in charge of one type of food preparation. In small restaurants, one or two chefs, often the owners, prepare all the food themselves.

Think of a kitchen as a laboratory. A chef, like a chemist, separates, mixes, measures, and heats various substances. A chef must know how to cause the right kinds of chemical and physical changes in food.

The preparation of many dishes involves changing food products physically. For example, when a chef chops onions or chiles, only the size and shape of the vegetables change.

When a chef cooks food, it is often changed chemically. Heat breaks down large food particles into smaller ones. The cooked dish usually has very different properties from the properties of the starting ingredients. For example, when the chef cooks an egg, chemical changes occur. The color of the egg yolk and the egg white change. The texture of the egg changes as well.

If you want to be a chef, you can learn the required skills at a culinary school or in some community colleges. You may also be able to train on the job. For more information, write to the National Institute for the Food Service Industry.

Multicultural Perspectives

Tell students that people throughout history have used both physical and chemical means to change their hairstyles. Men and women in ancient Egypt shaved their heads to feel cool and clean (physical change). The ancient Romans curled their hair with heated irons and lightened the color with bleach (chemical). Japanese women coated their hairdos with lacquer to hold them in place (physical). Have students cut out pictures of hairstyles and label the change (physical or chemical) involved.

Science and You *Haircuts and Permanents*

When you change your hairstyle, you may be making use of physical or chemical changes. Cutting your hair is a physical change. The hair itself has not been changed, only the length of the hair shafts. However, permanent waves and hair relaxers cause chemical changes in your hair.

Each hair shaft is made of ropelike bundles of protein fibers produced by your hair follicles. These bundles are held together by chemical bonds. The bonds hold the shape of each shaft of hair by preventing the bundles from moving.

A substance called thioglycolic (THY oh gly KAH lihk) acid can break the bonds holding the bundles together. It is the active ingredient of most permanent wave solutions. After thioglycolic acid has been applied, the fiber bundles can slide past one another. The hair becomes soft and stretchable. At this point, straight hair can be made curly, by wrapping it around rollers. Curly hair can be made straight by stretching and combing. After styling, the fiber bundles are bonded back together in their new positions using a hardening solution of hydrogen peroxide.

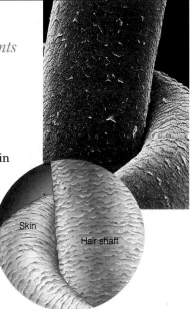

Skin

Hair shaft

Figure 6.14 ▲
Making straight hair curly or curly hair straight requires chemical changes affecting the hair's structure.

Check and Explain

1. Give three examples of physical changes and three examples of chemical changes.

2. Explain how to distinguish between a chemical change and a physical change.

3. **Classify** Identify each of the following as a chemical or a physical change.

   a. Oxygen gas is liquefied.

   b. Liquid oxygen is burned to power a space shuttle.

   c. Liquid oxygen evaporates.

   d. Space shuttle passengers breathe oxygen gas.

4. **Interpret Data** A student measured the temperature of a recently melted ice cube at 0°C. After freezing the water back into an ice cube, she found that its temperature was the same. Explain why the temperature remained the same.

Critical Thinking

Classify Discuss various techniques for changing the appearance of hair. Have students classify each change as physical (braiding or cutting) or chemical (dyeing or relaxing).

EVALUATE

WrapUp

Portfolio Have students collect magazine pictures showing changes in matter. Have them attach the pictures on notebook paper, identify each change as physical or chemical, and explain their choices.

Use Review Worksheet 6.3.

Ancillary Options

If you are using CEPUP modules in your classroom for additional hands-on activities have students do Activities one, two, and three in Chemical Survey of *Chemical Survey & Solutions and Pollution.*

Check and Explain

1. Possible answers: Physical—rocks breaking, paper tearing, clothes shrinking; chemical—iron rusting, paper burning, making steel from iron and carbon.

2. A chemical change is indicated by the production of heat or light, the appearance of gas bubbles, or the formation of a solid. A physical change is a change in size, shape, or phase. The matter is the same before and after a physical change and different after a chemical change.

3. **a.** physical; **b.** chemical; **c.** physical; **d.** chemical

4. The freezing point of a substance is the same as the melting point of that same substance.

Time 40 minutes   Group pairs

Materials

15 vials with lids

15 1 L-sized self-locking plastic bags

300 mL phenol red solution

30 g baking soda

30 g calcium chloride

Analysis

1. Accept any reasonable observations.

2. The release of heat, color change (to yellow), gas produced (bag expands)

3. Students may note the change in consistency of the mixture.

Conclusion

Students' paragraphs should include their observations of the evidence of chemical change: the color change, the production of gas, and the release of heat.

Everyday Application

Accept any reasonable description that includes the necessary ingredients and a way to keep them from mixing unintentionally.

Extension

The exothermic reaction was caused by CaCl$_2$ and water. Baking soda dissolving in water is an endothermic reaction. All reagents combined to cause the color change.

Prelab Discussion

Have students read the entire activity before beginning the discussion. Show students the materials you will be mixing in this activity. Review the various physical properties of matter. Review the signs of chemical change and ask for examples.

Activity 6 *What is the evidence for a chemical change?*

Skills Observe; Measure; Infer; Interpret Data

Task 1 Prelab Prep

Gather the following materials: 1 teaspoon baking soda, 1 teaspoon calcium chloride, 10 mL phenol red solution, a vial with a lid, and 1 liter-sized self-locking plastic bag.

Task 2 Data Record

1. On a separate sheet of paper, draw the data table shown.

2. Record your observations about the properties of each of the substances in the data table.

Task 3 Procedure

1. Put 1 teaspoon of baking soda (NaHCO$_3$) into the self-locking plastic bag. **CAUTION! Wear gloves, a laboratory apron, and goggles when using these chemicals.**

2. Put 1 teaspoon of calcium chloride (CaCl$_2$) into the bag with the baking soda and mix the two substances.

3. Measure 10 mL of phenol red solution and pour it into the vial.

4. Place the vial into the self-locking plastic bag so that it is standing upright in the dry powder.

5. Carefully seal the self-locking plastic bag, taking care not to spill the contents of the vial.

6. From the outside, work with the bag and its contents so that you spill the phenol red solution in the vial into the baking soda and calcium chloride. Be careful not to unseal the bag.

7. Hold the bag in your hands and observe any changes. **CAUTION! Wash your hands after the activity.**

Task 4 Analysis

1. Describe any changes in the properties of the substances in the bag.

2. What is the evidence that a chemical change has taken place?

3. What is the evidence that a physical change has taken place?

Task 5 Conclusion

Have the substances in the bag gone through a physical change or a chemical change? Write a paragraph explaining your answer.

Everyday Application

Describe how you could make an emergency hand-warmer.

Extension

Hypothesize which of the substances in this activity caused heat energy to be released. Write out the procedures that you would use to test your hypothesis.

Table 6.1 Observations

| | Before mixing | | After mixing |
Substance	Properties		Properties of mixture
Baking powder			
Calcium chloride			
Phenol red			

Chapter 6 Review

Concept Summary

6.1 Matter
▶ Matter is anything that has mass and takes up space.
▶ All forms of matter are made up of tiny, constantly moving particles.
▶ Matter has properties that can be observed and measured.
▶ The properties of matter are determined in part by the arrangement of the particles that make it up, and in part by the properties of the particles themselves.

6.2 Phases of Matter
▶ A solid has a definite shape and a definite volume.
▶ A liquid has a definite volume but no definite shape.

▶ A gas has neither a definite shape nor a definite volume.
▶ According to Boyle's Law, a decrease in the volume of a certain amount of gas will result in an increase in its pressure.
▶ According to Charles' Law, an increase in the temperature of a certain amount of gas will result in an increase in its volume.

6.3 Changes in Matter
▶ A physical change is a change in the size, shape, or phase of matter.
▶ A chemical change occurs when new kinds of particles are created.
▶ Chemical changes may produce heat or light, create bubbles of gas, or form a new solid.

Chapter Vocabulary

matter (p. 135)	liquid (p. 141)	physical change (p. 147)
particle model (p. 135)	gas (p. 142)	chemical change (p. 149)
solid (p. 141)	plasma (p. 145)	

Check Your Vocabulary

Use the vocabulary words above to complete the following sentences correctly.

1. Matter with a definite volume but no definite shape is a _____ .
2. The evaporation of a liquid into a gas is an example of a _____ .
3. Everything you can see or touch is made up of _____ .
4. Matter in the _____ phase fills whatever space is available to it.
5. The _____ of matter describes matter as made up of tiny, constantly moving particles.
6. Matter in the _____ phase can be held in your hand.
7. Stars are made up mainly of _____ .

8. If you combine two kinds of matter and heat is produced, you know a _____ has taken place.

Explain the difference between the terms in each pair.

9. Gas, plasma.
10. Physical change, chemical change.
11. Phase change, weathering.
12. Gas, air.
13. Particle model, phase change.

Write Your Vocabulary

Write sentences for each of the vocabulary words in the list. Show that you know what each word means.

Check Your Vocabulary

1. liquid
2. physical change
3. matter
4. gas
5. particle model
6. solid
7. plasma
8. chemical change
9. Gas and plasma are different phases of matter. A plasma is a superheated gas.
10. A physical change is a change in size, shape, or phase, without rearranging the atoms in the matter. A chemical change involves rearranging atoms to form a new substance.
11. In a phase change, particles gain or lose energy, and change between solid, liquid, and gas. Weathering simply breaks down a solid into smaller bits.
12. Gas is a phase of matter. Air is the mixture of specific types of gas that makes up the atmosphere.
13. According to the particle model, all matter is made up of tiny particles. In a phase change, the particles that make up a substance gain or lose energy.

Write Your Vocabulary

Students' sentences should show that they know the meaning of each vocabulary word as well as how it is used.

Use Vocabulary Worksheet for Chapter 6.

Check Your Knowledge

1. solid, liquid, gas, plasma

2. Examples may include rusting metal and combustion. The production of heat, light, gas bubbles, or solids are all evidence for a chemical change.

3. Answers will vary, although students are likely to describe a solid or a liquid.

4. Diamonds and graphite have different properties because each has a different arrangement of carbon atoms.

5. Evaporation is the opposite of condensation.

6. Ice wedging breaks apart large rocks as water trapped in cracks freezes and expands.

7. The particles in a solid move around slightly, staying in the same general position.

8. melting

9. density

10. volume

11. physical change

12. chemically changed

13. solid

Check Your Understanding

1. Particles in a solid move slightly but do not change positions. In a liquid, the particles slide over each other, but tend to stick together. The particles of a gas move in straight lines, only changing directions after striking something.

2. The volume of a gas can never reach zero because the particles of the gas have mass and take up space.

3. There are conditions under which any *element* could be made to exist in any phase, but there may be *compounds* that cannot exist in all three phases.

4. The regular, repeating structure is evidence of crystals. Also, the concentric rings indicate growth outward from central points.

5. a. chemical
   b. physical
   c. chemical and physical
   d. physical
   e. physical
   f. physical

6. To change from one phase to another, particles must gain enough energy to overcome the forces holding them to each other. Normally, energy is gained gradually—solids change to liquids; liquids change to gases. The particles of a solid can gain enough energy to escape the solid phase and enter the gas phase directly. Dry ice goes from the solid to the gas phase without becoming a liquid. This process is called *sublimation*.

7. The air will be cold because, according to Charles' Law, as volume decreases, temperature decreases.

Chapter 6 Review

Check Your Knowledge

Answer the following in complete sentences.

1. What are the four phases of matter?

2. Give an example of a chemical change. What is one way of knowing that a chemical change has occurred?

3. Choose a kind of matter you can see right now. List five of its properties.

4. Why do diamonds and graphite have different properties?

5. What is the opposite of condensation?

6. What is ice wedging?

7. Describe the movement of the particles in a solid.

Choose the answer that best completes each sentence.

8. The phase change from solid to liquid is called (melting, boiling, freezing, evaporation).

9. One of the properties common to all matter is (luster, electrical conductivity, density, transparency).

10. If the temperature of a gas is increased, its (mass, density, volume, weight) will increase also.

11. Breaking a balloon is an example of a (phase change, physical change, chemical change, temperature change).

12. Chemical weathering occurs when the minerals in rocks are (heated, broken apart, frozen, chemically changed).

13. The particles of matter move slowest in a (solid, liquid, gas, plasma).

Check Your Understanding

Apply the concepts you have learned to answer each question.

1. Contrast the movement of particles in solids, liquids, and gases.

2. **Critical Thinking** According to Charles' Law, the volume of a gas decreases as its temperature is decreased. Is there a temperature at which the volume of a sample of gas will reach zero? Explain.

3. Do all kinds of matter exist in all three phases? Give reasons for your answer.

4. **Mystery Photo** The photograph on page 134 shows the crystalline structure of aspirin. Look closely at the photograph. What evidence do you see that the aspirin has particles arranged as crystals?

5. **Classify** For each of the following, tell whether it involves a physical change or a chemical change.

   a. Burning wood
   b. Shaking up a soft drink
   c. Digesting food
   d. Boiling water
   e. Writing with a pencil
   f. Putting mousse on your hair

6. **Extension** Some kinds of matter change directly from a solid to a gas at a certain temperature. Solid carbon dioxide, or "dry ice," is an example of matter that does not go through a liquid phase. Using the particle model, develop an explanation for this behavior.

7. **Application** When you inflate a bicycle tire, you force a large volume of air into a small space. If you release some air from a fully inflated tire, will it be warm or cold? Explain how Charles' Law helps you make this prediction.

Develop Your Skills

1. a. 50 cm³, 31 cm³, 21 cm³, and 15 cm³

b. Increased by 41,000 Pa

c. The pressure would be about 134,000 Pa. This could be predicted by making a line graph of volume versus pressure.

2. Students' graphs should show a diagonal line extending from approximately 63 on the *x*-axis through approximately 270,000 on the *y*-axis.

3. a. The melting point of gold is 1064°C.

b. Bromine is a liquid at 25°C.

4. 50 × 67,000 = 3,350,000
31 × 108,000 = 3,348,000
21 × 159,000 = 3,339,000
15 × 222,000 = 3,330,000
The product of pressure × volume is essentially constant.

Make Connections

1.

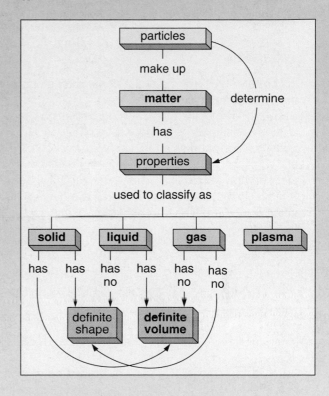

2. Reports will vary. Democritus used reasoning, rather than the scientific method, to explain his ideas.

3. The seven different crystal systems are cubic, tetragonal, orthorhombic, monoclinic, triclinic, hexagonal, and rhombohedral. Drawings will vary.

Develop Your Skills

Use the skills you have developed in this chapter to complete each activity.

1. Interpret Data The table below contains data from an experiment in which the pressure of a sample of gas was measured at various volumes.

a. For which volumes are pressure measurements given?

b. When the volume was reduced from 50 cm³ to 31 cm³, by how much did the pressure increase?

c. Estimate the pressure at 25 cm³. How could you make a reasonably accurate prediction without doing any calculations?

Volume (cm³)	Pressure (Pa)
50	67,000
31	108,000
21	159,000
15	222,000

2. Graph Use the data in the table above to draw a line graph. If you were not sure how to answer question 1b above, read it again after you have completed the graph.

3. Data Bank Use the information on page 641 to answer the following questions.

a. What is the melting point of gold?

b. At room temperature (25°C) is bromine a solid, liquid, or gas?

4. Calculate Look again at the table in question 1 above. Multiply each volume by its corresponding pressure measurement. What do you notice?

Make Connections

1. Link the Concepts Below is a concept map showing how some of the main concepts in this chapter link together. Only parts of the map are filled in. Copy the map. Using words and ideas from the chapter, complete the map.

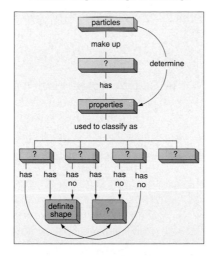

2. Science and History The idea that matter is made up of tiny particles is very old. An ancient Greek scientist named Democritus was one of the first to propose a particle theory. Research Democritus and his ideas about matter. How did the method he used to reach his conclusions differ from modern scientific method?

3. Science and Geometry Crystals exist in seven different basic shapes, called systems. Research these seven crystal systems. Discover the name of each one and make a drawing of it.

Overview

This chapter presents the characteristics of atoms, elements, compounds, and mixtures. The first section introduces the successive models of the atom, and describes how the number of subatomic particles determines an atom's identity. A discussion of elemental properties and chemical symbols follows in the second section. The third section describes compounds, including how to classify compounds and how to write chemical formulas. In the last section, mixtures are defined and the similarities and differences between compounds and mixtures are discussed.

Advance Planner

▶ Supply modeling clay, raisins, and marbles of various sizes for TE page 160.

▶ Provide several colors of chalk for TE pages 163 and 171.

▶ Collect jars, measuring cups or graduated cylinders, liquid detergent, glycerin, coat hangers, labels, and watches with second hands for SE Activity 7, page 178.

Skills Development Chart

Sections	Classify	Communicate	Compare and Contrast	Graph	Infer	Interpret Data	Measure	Model	Observe	Research
7.1 Skills WarmUp	●									
Skills WorkOut										●
SkillBuilder		●						●		
7.2 Skills WarmUp		●								
Skills WorkOut					●					
Skills WorkOut				●						
7.3 Skills WarmUp		●								
Skills WorkOut								●		
Consider This		●								
7.4 Skills WarmUp			●							
Skills WorkOut	●									
Activity		●			●	●	●		●	

Individual Needs

▶ **Limited English Proficiency Students** On a left-hand page in their science portfolios, have students make a concept map of the vocabulary terms that apply to the structure of atoms. On the facing page, ask students to make a concept map using the terms that apply to elements, compounds, and mixtures. Have them leave about a half page of space beneath each map. Encourage them to draw illustrations that show the relationships between the terms in the map. Finally, have them write sentences beneath each concept map that use words from both maps. For example, students might draw an illustration for the sentence "An ion is an atom that has gained or lost an electron."

▶ **At-Risk Students** Give students a brief biographical account of John Dalton's idea of the atom, and review the Dalton model. Divide students into groups. Ask them to imagine that John Dalton has returned to life and is eager to learn what people know about atoms today. Ask each group to write and produce for their classmates a dramatization in which John Dalton is introduced to the different atomic models, as well as to the modern concepts of elements, compounds, and mixtures. Students can make drawings or models of each concept to present in their skit.

▶ **Gifted Students** Invite students to do research and make scrapbooks of subatomic particles, such as quarks, leptons, and mesons. For each particle, they should make a diagram and then write a description of the particle that includes what the particle does; what, if any, charge it has; and how it was discovered and named.

Resource Bank

▶ **Bulletin Board** Place the title *Elements in the Earth's Crust* at the top of the bulletin board. Divide the class into nine small groups and assign each of the most common elements found in the earth's crust to a group (silicon, oxygen, aluminum, calcium, sodium, potassium, and magnesium). Ask the ninth group to find a few of the less common elements in the earth's crust. Ask groups to learn the percentage of their elements found in the crust. Hang a large circle in the center of the board and have the groups use it to make a circle graph showing percentages of elements in the crust. Invite them to arrange pictures of compounds made up of those elements around the graph.

Section	Core	Standard	Enriched	Section	Core	Standard	Enriched
7.1 Structure of the Atom pp. 157–163				**7.3 Compounds** pp. 168–173			
Section Features Skills WarmUp, p. 157 Skills WorkOut, p. 161 SkillBuilder, p. 162	● ●	● ● ●	● ● ●	**Section Features** Skills WarmUp, p. 168 Skills WorkOut, p. 170 Consider This, p. 172	● ●	● ● ●	● ● ●
Blackline Masters Review Worksheet 7.1 Enrich Worksheet 7.1 Skills Worksheet 7.1a Skills Worksheet 7.1b Integrating Worksheet 7.1	● ● ● ●	● ● ● ● ●	● ● ●	**Blackline Masters** Review Worksheet 7.3 Integrating Worksheet 7.3	●	● ●	●
Color Transparencies Transparency 20	●	●	●	**Color Transparencies** Transparency 21	●	●	●
7.2 Elements pp. 164–167				**Overhead Blackline Transparencies** Overhead Blackline Master 7 and Student Worksheet	●	●	●
Section Features Skills WarmUp, p. 164 Skills WorkOut, p. 166 Skills WorkOut, p. 167	● ● ●	● ● ●	● ● ●	**7.4 Mixtures** pp. 174–178			
Blackline Masters Review Worksheet 7.2 Integrating Worksheet 7.2	● ●	● ●	●	**Section Features** Skills WarmUp, p. 174 Skills WorkOut, p. 177 Activity, p. 178	● ● ●	● ● ●	● ● ●
Ancillary Options *One-Minute Readings,* pp. 54–55	●	●	●	**Blackline Masters** Review Worksheet 7.4 Skills Worksheet 7.4 Vocabulary Worksheet 7	● ● ●	● ● ●	
Laboratory Program Investigation 16		●	●	**Ancillary Options** *CEPUP,* Activities 1–2 in Solutions and Pollution	●	●	●

Bibliography

The following resources can be used for teaching the chapter. See page T-46 for supplier codes.

Library Resources

Apfel, Necia H. *It's All Elementary: From Atoms to the Quantum World of Quarks, Leptons, and Gluons.* New York: Lothrop, Lee & Shepard Books, 1985.

Ardley, Neil. *The World of the Atom.* New York: Gloucester Press, 1990.

Berger, Melvin. *Atoms, Molecules and Quarks.* New York: G.P. Putnam's Sons, 1986.

Technology Resources

Software

Learning All About Matter. Mac, Dos. LS.
Science Elements. Win. ER.
Superstar Science. Mac, Win. LS.

Laserdiscs

Living Textbook. (See barcodes on pages in this chapter.) Optical Data.
Atoms and Molecules. AIMS.

Audio-Visual Resources

An Introduction to the Atom. Filmstrip. NGSES.
Learning About Chemicals. Two Filmstrips. NGSES.

✧ *Writing Connection*

Tell students that miners, smelters, and other workers process rocks such as the ones shown in the photograph in order to extract as much gold as possible. Have students prepare a written description of how to extract something valuable from a place or from a substance.

◆ Introducing the Chapter

Have students read the description of the photograph. Ask if they agree or disagree with the description. Make sure students know that iron pyrite (fool's gold) is *not* shown.

Directed Inquiry

Have students study the photograph. Ask:

▶ What are the different things you see in the photograph? (Answers will vary.)

▶ Do you think that these things are made of only one kind of atom or several? Why? (Several. The gold is made of a single kind of atom, but the rock at the lower right is made of several.)

▶ How do you think the photograph is related to the chapter title? (The photograph shows examples of an element, gold, while the rock at the lower right is probably a mixture of elements and compounds.)

◆ Chapter Vocabulary

atom	ion
compound	isotope
electron	molecule
element	neutron
heterogeneous	nucleus
mixture	proton
homogeneous	
mixture	

Chapter **7** **Atoms, Elements, Compounds, and Mixtures**

Chapter Sections

7.1 Structure of the Atom

7.2 Elements

7.3 Compounds

7.4 Mixtures

What do you see?

❝This photograph contains many different substances. They appear to be different minerals, perhaps gold or iron pyrite (commonly referred to as 'fool's gold'). The conglomerate in the center contains other substances. There is also a large rock, perhaps the rim of a basin, as suggested by the dampness of the specimens. These are all made of basic elements and compounds.❞

Chad Henderson
Woodford County School
Versailles, Kentucky

To find out more about the photograph, look on page 180. As you read this chapter, you will learn about atoms, elements, compounds, and mixtures.

7.1 Structure of the Atom

Objectives

▶ **Summarize** how models of the atom have changed.

▶ **Name** and **describe** the parts of the atom.

▶ **Calculate** the numbers of protons, neutrons, and electrons in an atom given its mass number.

Y
ou have learned that all matter in the universe is made up of tiny particles. A glass of water, for example, has many water particles, each too small to see. If you could see them, what would they look like? What makes them different from the particles of other kinds of matter?

Atoms and Elements

Water particles can actually be divided into even smaller units. The pieces of matter that result from dividing a water particle are no longer water. They are examples of the most basic units of matter called **atoms**. Atoms can't be broken down into smaller pieces by any common methods of separating matter.

Atoms are the building blocks of the universe. As with other sets of building blocks, there are different kinds of atoms. Scientists have identified nearly 100 different kinds of naturally-occurring atoms. Each kind has unique properties and is called an **element**. An atom of an element can't be broken down and retain its properties.

Look at Figure 7.1. The particles of matter can be made of single atoms, two or more atoms of the same element, or two or more atoms of different elements. You can see that a water particle is made up of three atoms, two of hydrogen and one of oxygen.

Models of the Atom

All atoms share the same basic structure. During the past 200 years, scientists have proposed different models for this structure. Each model was the best one for its time. With new observations or experiments, however, the model had to be changed.

Particle of helium
1 atom of 1 element

Particle of oxygen
2 atoms of 1 element

Particle of water
3 atoms of 2 elements

Figure 7.1
Some atoms exist alone as separate particles. Other atoms form particles by joining together in groups of two or more.

TEACH

Discuss

Help students understand Thomson's model by discussing the following:

▶ Propose the following to students: If an electron is part of an atom and an atom is electrically neutral, what must be present in the atom besides a negative charge? Why? (A positive charge; atoms are electrically neutral, but because each electron has a negative charge there must be a positive charge in the atom to balance each negative charge.)

▶ Write the following on the chalkboard:

> – 6 electrons
> <u>+ 6 positive charges</u>
>   0 charge

▶ Describe plum pudding and tell students that Thomson's model is also called the "plum pudding" model. Have students explain the analogy.

**The Living Textbook:
Physical Science Sides 1-4**

Chapter 4   Frame 00925
Composition of Matter Diagram (1 Frame)
Search:

**The Living Textbook:
Physical Science Sides 1-4**

Chapter 15   Frame 02505
Thomson's Experiment (1 Frame)
Search:

158

Multicultural Perspectives

The idea of the smallest individual piece of matter and the word *atom* were proposed by the Greek philosopher Democritus about the 5th century B.C. Twelve hundred years later the Arab alchemist Jabir ibn Hayyan speculated that the chemical nature of elements and compounds depended on proportions of the quantities hot, cold, moist, and dry. Have students make a concept map showing the work of Democritus, Jabir, and Dalton.

STS Connection

Tell students that they are familiar with variations of the equipment Thomson used to explore the atom. A glass vacuum tube with metal electrodes is the basis of several modern conveniences such as neon lights, fluorescent lights, and television. Have students discuss any other inventions they think might have been a by-product of scientific research.

Dalton's Model   In the early 1800s, John Dalton performed experiments with gases. His results convinced him that matter was made up of tiny, indivisible particles.

Dalton observed, for example, that the same amounts of hydrogen and oxygen always combined to form a given amount of water. He reasoned that each element must be made of its own unique kind of particle and that these particles combine in simple ways. Dalton called these basic particles atoms and pictured them as tiny, solid spheres.

Based on his experiments, Dalton developed a theory of the structure of matter. His theory contained four main concepts.

▶ All matter is composed of tiny, indivisible particles called atoms.

▶ Atoms of each element are exactly alike.

▶ Atoms of different elements have different masses.

▶ Atoms of different elements can join to form compounds.

In the early 1800s, John Dalton proposed the first scientific theory about atoms. In this model, atoms were solid spheres.

Thomson's Model   At the end of the 1800s, J. J. Thomson discovered that atoms were not just simple, solid spheres. They contained even smaller, *sub*atomic particles. The subatomic particles Thomson discovered were very small and negatively charged. Thomson called them **electrons**.

Thomson discovered electrons while experimenting with a glass vacuum tube containing metal electrodes. When he connected the tube to a source of high-voltage electricity, glowing green "rays" appeared inside. Thomson discovered that electric charges bent the rays. The rays, he inferred, had to be made of charged particles.

Thomson knew that atoms are electrically neutral. Therefore, he reasoned, an atom must contain enough positive charge to balance the negative charge of the electrons. Thomson developed an atomic model in which electrons were stuck into a positively charged sphere, like chocolate chips in cookie dough. A positive charge in the substance of the sphere balanced the electrons' charge.

Electrons

J. J. Thomson discovered the first subatomic particle, the electron. He imagined electrons to be stuck in the atom's surface.

Social Studies Connection

The atomic models of Rutherford and Bohr, in which electrons encircle a central nucleus, were influenced by both scientists' knowledge of the structure of the solar system. One reason such models made sense at the time was the persisting Renaissance philosophy that small structures are often models of very large structures. The small structure (also called the *microcosm*) of the atom therefore replicated the larger structure (*macrocosm*) of the solar system.

Use Integrating Worksheet 7.1.

Rutherford's Model By the early 1900s, scientists knew that the positive charge of an atom comes from subatomic particles called **protons**. A proton is a positive particle with a mass much greater than that of an electron. At that time, scientists hypothesized that electrons and protons were evenly scattered throughout an atom.

In 1911, Ernest Rutherford set out to test this theory. He aimed a beam of positively charged particles at a sheet of gold foil only a few atoms thick. Most of the particles passed straight through the foil. To Rutherford's surprise, however, some particles bounced back. The only explanation for this result was that the particles had struck objects larger than single protons.

Rutherford reasoned that the protons are concentrated in a small area at the center of the atom. He called this region the **nucleus** (NOO klee uhs). According to this model, an atom is mostly empty space. The nucleus is tiny compared to the whole atom, but it contains nearly all the atom's mass.

Bohr's Model Niels Bohr modified Rutherford's model in 1913. He proposed that each electron in an atom has a fixed amount of energy. This energy keeps an electron moving around the nucleus within a specific region called an *energy level*. In Bohr's model, energy levels surround the nucleus in rings or shells, like the layers of an onion.

The energy levels in Bohr's model can be compared to the rungs of a ladder. Moving out from the nucleus, each energy level is like a higher rung on the ladder. By absorbing or releasing a specific amount of energy, an electron can move from one energy level to another just as you can climb up or down a ladder. And just as you can't be between rungs on a ladder, an electron can't be between energy levels.

Bohr's model has been called the planetary model. It compares electrons to planets and the nucleus to the sun. The energy levels occupied by electrons are like the orbits of planets at different distances from the sun.

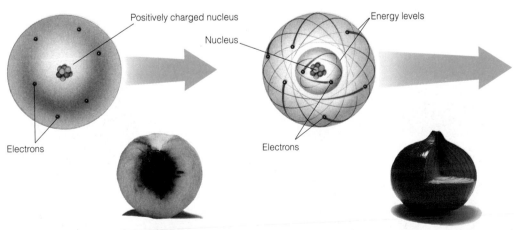

Positively charged nucleus

Nucleus

Electrons

Energy levels

Electrons

Ernest Rutherford's experiments showed that an atom's mass is concentrated in the nucleus.

Niels Bohr discovered that electrons surround the nucleus in specific regions called energy levels.

Skills Development

Infer State the following about Rutherford's experiment to students: Only 1 out of every 8,000 particles bounced back from the gold foil. Ask, What might this tell you about the structure of the atom? How does the diagram of Rutherford's model show this? (Most of an atom is empty space. The center of the atom is very small; the model shows a tiny solid center of the atom.)

Critical Thinking

Reason by Analogy To help students think of analogies for the atom, you may wish to ask, How are the atomic models of Rutherford and Bohr like the planets in the solar system? (The energy levels of the electrons circling the nucleus are like the orbits of planets as they travel around the sun.)

Misconceptions

Students may think of Bohr's model when they visualize atoms, since many symbols used to represent atoms are based on it. Make sure they understand the differences between Bohr's model and the electron cloud atom.

 **The Living Textbook:
Physical Science Sides 1-4**

Chapter 4   Frame 00929
Rutherford's Experiment (1 Frame)
Search:

 **The Living Textbook:
Physical Science Sides 1-4**

Chapter 4   Frame 00935
Bohr's Model (2 Frames)
Search: Step:

TEACH ▪ *Continued*

Class Activity

Have students work in small groups to make models of the atoms such as those shown on pages 158 through 160. You may wish to supply a variety of materials such as clay, raisins, and marbles of various sizes. Ask students, How does your model atom compare to what we know about a real atom? (Answers will vary, but students should indicate that their model, like an atom, has a nucleus that is surrounded by electrons.)

Discuss

Have students explain how the models of the atom changed from Dalton's model to the modern model of the nucleus and electron cloud. Ask students to draw a timeline showing the dates various atomic discoveries were made. Review each of the atomic models with students and help them understand how and why the models changed over time.

 The Living Textbook: Physical Science Sides 1-4

Chapter 4　　　Frame 00937
Electron Movement Between Energy Levels (1 Frame)
Search:

 The Living Textbook: Physical Science Sides 1-4

Chapter 4　　　Frame 00949
Behavior of Electrical Forces in Atom (1 Frame)
Search:

Cooperative Learning

Have students work in cooperative learning groups of three to develop a presentation about the atom. One student in each group could research the theories behind either Thomson's, Rutherford's or Bohr's model. Another student could build a three-dimensional model associated with the theory. The third student could present the theory and its model to the class.

Electron Cloud Model Each atomic model offered new ideas and information about the nature of matter. Today scientists know that electrons do not actually orbit the nucleus as in Bohr's planetary model. The electron cloud model is now used to describe atoms. In this model, electrons dart about within an energy level in an ever-changing path. Most of this path falls into a region called an electron cloud. At any given time, there is a high probability that the electron exists in the electron cloud.

The idea of an electron cloud is not so strange. You have probably seen the blur of a fan when it spins at high speed. The fast-moving blades appear to fill the space between them, just as fast-moving electrons seem to fill the space around the nucleus. The paths of an atom's electrons account for nearly all of its volume. If the nucleus of an atom was the size of a marble on the 50-yard line of a football field, the electron cloud would extend to the end zones!

Inside the Nucleus

As scientists learned more about atomic structure, they found that the nucleus is more complicated than they had thought. In 1932, James Chadwick showed that most atomic nuclei contain a third kind of subatomic particle, called a **neutron** (NOO trahn). A neutron has about the same mass as a proton but has no electrical charge.

An atomic nucleus is a positively charged, tightly-packed cluster of protons and neutrons. If you remember that like electric charges repel each other, you may wonder how protons can be packed so tightly into the nucleus. The answer is that the electric force repelling the protons is overwhelmed by a much stronger force that holds the neutrons and protons together. It is called the strong force, one of the four universal forces that operate in nature. The strong force is a short-range force that is significant only when particles are close together.

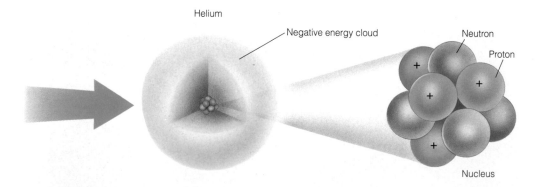

Helium — Negative energy cloud — Neutron — Proton — Nucleus

In the atomic model accepted today, the rapid and random motion of electrons creates an electron cloud around the nucleus.

The nucleus is known to be made up of both protons and neutrons, held together by the strong force.

Integrating the Sciences

Biochemistry An isotope of hydrogen that is twice as heavy as regular hydrogen is used to study chemical reactions. Water containing this isotope of hydrogen is given to a green plant. By analyzing the compounds taken from the plant, researchers could tell how the water was used during photosynthesis. Ask students to find out other uses for isotopes.

Literature Connection

Explain the term *subatomic* particles by using other words with the prefix *sub-*: subtitles (titles within titles) and subcategories (categories within categories). Ask students to give more examples using the prefix *sub-*.

Atomic Numbers and Isotopes

All atoms of an element contain the same number of protons. This number, called the *atomic number*, identifies an element. Sodium, for example, has an atomic number of 11. If all iron atoms contain 26 protons, what is the atomic number of iron? ①

The atomic number also represents the number of electrons in an atom. Remember that an atom is electrically neutral. Thus the number of negative particles must equal the number of positive particles.

As you may recall, Dalton hypothesized that all atoms of an element are exactly alike. Today scientists know that he was not completely correct. Atoms of the same element do have the same number of protons and electrons, but they may differ in the number of neutrons they contain. Atoms of the same element with different numbers of neutrons are called **isotopes** (EYE suh TOHPS).

For each element, only a limited number of different isotopes are possible. Figure 7.2 shows two of several possible isotopes of carbon. Some elements have isotopes that exist in nature but are unstable. These unstable isotopes are called radioactive isotopes. The structures of their nuclei may change suddenly. Carbon-14 is such an isotope.

▼ ACTIVITY

Researching

Radioactivity

Find out about the medical uses of radioactive isotopes. What properties do they have that make them useful in medicine?

SKILLS WORKOUT

Directed Inquiry

Have students study the diagrams and text on this page. Lead a discussion using the following questions:

▶ How many protons would there be in the isotope carbon-13? How many neutrons? How many electrons? (6; 7; 6)

▶ A bromine atom has 35 protons. What is its atomic number? How can you be sure? (35; the number of protons identifies the element and all bromine atoms have 35 protons.)

▶ What is a radioactive isotope? (An isotope that is unstable; the structure of its nucleus may change suddenly.)

Answers to In-Text Questions

① Iron has an atomic number of 26.

② Carbon-12 and carbon-14 are both carbon because they both have 6 protons. They differ in the number of neutrons they have.

Enrich

Use Enrich Worksheet 7.1.

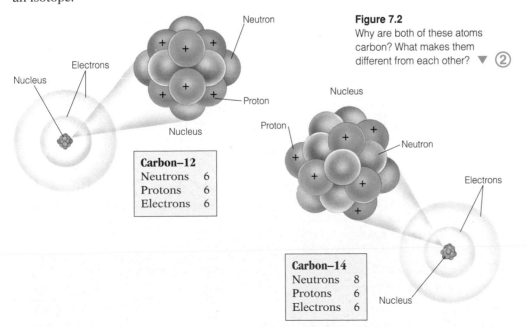

Figure 7.2
Why are both of these atoms carbon? What makes them different from each other? ▼ ②

Neutron

Electrons

Nucleus

Nucleus

Proton

Carbon–12
Neutrons   6
Protons   6
Electrons   6

Nucleus

Proton

Neutron

Electrons

Nucleus

Carbon–14
Neutrons   8
Protons   6
Electrons   6

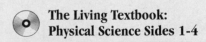

**The Living Textbook:
Physical Science Sides 1-4**

Chapter 2   Frame 00747
Iron: Atomic Number on Periodic Table
(1 Frame)
Search:

161

TEACH ▪ *Continued*

Discuss

Use the following discussion starters to help students understand atomic number, mass number, and amu:

▶ The mass number of an element is 40. What is its mass in amu? (About 40 amu)

▶ Both hydrogen and helium have isotopes with a mass of 3 amu. Explain the differences and similarities between the two atoms. (Each atom has an atomic mass of 3, each has 3 particles in the nucleus. The hydrogen atom has 1 proton and 2 neutrons; the helium atom has 2 protons and 1 neutron.)

SkillBuilder

Answers

1. No

2. No
Paragraphs will vary, but students might compare the spinning pinwheel to an electron cloud and the X on the spinning pinwheel to a single electron traveling in a complex path. Like the X on the pinwheel, the electron, because it is constantly moving, can be anywhere in its path around the atom's nucleus.

Answer to In-Text Question

① **Carbon-12 has 6 neutrons and carbon-14 has 8 neutrons. They have mass numbers of 12 and 14, respectively.**

The Living Textbook: Physical Science Sides 1-4

Chapter 2   Frame 00729
Elements: Mass Numbers on Periodic Table (6 Frames)
Search:

Themes in Science

Diversity and Unity Different atoms of the same element can vary in the number of neutrons they carry. All isotopes of the same element, however, have the same number of protons in their nuclei.

Mass Number and Atomic Mass

Almost every atom contains one or more neutrons in its nucleus. The number of neutrons does not affect the charge of an atom, but it does affect its mass. The total number of protons and neutrons in an atom is called its *mass number*. This number is usually written with a hyphen after the element's name. For example, a helium atom with 2 protons and 1 neutron is called helium-3. The mass number helps to distinguish one isotope from another. What is the difference between carbon-12 and carbon-14? ①

Scientists also have a way of describing the actual mass of an atom. Since the mass of a single atom is so small, a special unit of measurement, called the *atomic mass unit*, is used to describe its mass. Atomic mass units are abbreviated as *amu*. An atomic mass unit is defined as ½ the mass of a carbon-12 atom. An atom of hydrogen-1 has a mass of approximately 1 amu.

SkillBuilder *Making Models*

Model of an Atom

You can use a simple pinwheel as a model of an atom. To construct a pinwheel, follow the steps below.

1. Draw an 8 cm square on a piece of construction paper. Cut out the square.

2. Make four diagonal cuts to within 1 cm of the center of the square. Draw a bold **X** on one point of the pinwheel.

3. Bend the paper to form a pinwheel as shown. Use a straight pin to fasten the pinwheel to one end of a plastic soda straw.

Blow on the pinwheel and observe its motion. Watch the **X** as the pinwheel moves. Then answer the following questions:

1. Can you see the blades of the pinwheel when it spins rapidly?

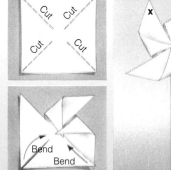

2. Can you describe the location of the **X** at any point in time when the pinwheel is spinning rapidly?

Based on your observations, write a short paragraph explaining the relationship between the spinning pinwheel, the **X**, and the electron cloud model of the atom.

Recall that most elements have more than one naturally occurring isotope. A sample of one of these elements, therefore, will contain atoms with different atomic masses! How can scientists describe an element's mass? This measurement is given as an average. When the relative amounts of each isotope in a sample of an element are known, an average atomic mass for that element can be calculated. For example, copper is 69.1 percent copper-63 and 30.9 percent copper-65, giving it an average atomic mass of 63.6 amu.

Science and Technology
Tracking Subatomic Particles

How can you study particles too small for you to see? Scientists at Fermi National Accelerator Laboratory near Chicago, Illinois use a machine, called an accelerator, to smash atoms and release atomic particles. Devices attached to the accelerator detect these particles.

The simplest particle detector is a bubble chamber. It is a large, sealed metal cylinder with a glass window containing supercold liquid hydrogen. When subatomic particles from the accelerator pass through the bubble chamber, they cause the cold liquid to boil. A line of bubbles, called a track, marks each particle's path. The tracks are recorded on photographs.

A track tells a lot about a particle. For example, the direction a track curves in a magnetic field tells what kind of charge it has, and the amount of curve indicates its mass and energy. Learning about these particles allows scientists to understand more about matter.

Figure 7.3 ▲
Photographs of the tracks left by subatomic particles in a bubble chamber are magnified for study by scientists.

Check and Explain

1. What does an atomic number tell you about an element?

2. Describe one way each atomic model after Dalton's improved on earlier models.

3. **Compare and Contrast** How are an atom's nucleus and its electron cloud different? Alike?

4. **Calculate** The atomic number of oxygen is 8. How many protons, neutrons, and electrons are in oxygen-16? Oxygen-17? Oxygen-18?

WrapUp

Reteach Provide colored chalk and have five volunteers draw models of a neon atom on the chalkboard. Provide them with the number of protons (10), neutrons, and electrons (10). One student should draw Dalton's model; one, Thomson's; one, Rutherford's; one, Bohr's; and one student should draw the electron cloud model. Have other students label the protons, neutrons, and electrons on the models. Then have one student use the model to estimate the atomic weight of neon. (About 20)
Use Review Worksheet 7.1.

Check and Explain

1. An atomic number tells the number of protons and electrons of an element.

2. Thomson's model includes electrons. Rutherford's model includes the nucleus. Bohr's model includes levels of energy around the nucleus.

3. Both the atom's nucleus and electron cloud contain charged particles. The atomic nucleus is positively charged; the electron cloud is negatively charged. Particles in the electron cloud move around the nucleus.

4. Oxygen-16 has 8 protons, 8 neutrons, and 8 electrons. Oxygen-17 has 8 protons, 9 neutrons, and 8 electrons. Oxygen-18 has 8 protons, 10 neutrons, and 8 electrons.

 The Living Textbook: Physical Science Sides 1-4

Chapter 4   Frame 01032
Tracks in Bubble Chamber (3 Frames)
Search: Step:

SECTION

7.2

Themes in Science

Diversity and Unity Atoms of the 100 or so different kinds of elements in the universe are made of the same subatomic particles. The atoms differ from one another because of the different number and arrangement of the subatomic particles.

Multicultural Perspectives

Many of the elements discovered in the 20th century were named for their discoverers or the country where they were discovered. Encourage students to work in pairs and use the periodic table to make a chart showing the name, symbol, and discoverers of the rare earth elements.

Section Objectives
For a list of section objectives, see the Student Edition page.

Skills Objectives
Students should be able to:

Communicate the uses for five familiar elements.

Infer how the chemical symbols are abbreviated.

Graph the number of atoms of iron, copper, fluorine and iodine in the human body.

Make a Model by drawing iron atoms in solid iron.

MOTIVATE

Skills WarmUp

To help students understand elements, have them do the Skills WarmUp.

Answer Answers will vary. Some students may need help in choosing substances that are elements. Have students save their work so they can refer to it in the section WrapUp.

Misconceptions

Students are likely to consider substances such as water and steel as elements. Have them list some substances and use sources, such as a dictionary or an encyclopedia, to find out which ones are elements.

The Living Textbook:
Physical Science Sides 1-4

Chapter 2   Frame 00886
Element: Pure Gold (1 Frame)
Search:

▼ **ACTIVITY**

Communicating

It's Elemental

Choose five elements you are familiar with. For each, describe as many uses as you can.

SKILLS WARMUP

Table 7.1

Elements in the Earth's Atmosphere	
Element	**Percent**
Nitrogen	78
Oxygen	21
Argon	0.9
Other	0.1

7.2 Elements

Objectives

▶ **Describe** what elements are.

▶ **Give examples** of common elements.

▶ **Make a model** that relates the particle model to a familiar property of matter.

High in the Rocky Mountains or on the streets of New York City, the oxygen in the air you breathe is the same. The air is different, but the oxygen atoms in both places have the same properties. All oxygen atoms have eight protons and eight electrons.

Oxygen is an element. As you have learned, elements are the basic kinds of matter in the universe. If you compare atoms to the bricks used to construct a building, then learning about the elements is like finding out what kinds of bricks are available.

Elements and Matter

An element is a substance made of just one kind of atom. You may recall that many kinds of matter can be broken down or changed into other kinds of matter by chemical changes. An element, however, cannot be broken down or changed by chemical means.

Even though all matter is made up of elements, only a few elements exist in nature in their pure form. You may remember that the oxygen and nitrogen in air are elements. Diamond is a natural form of the element carbon. Occasionally pure deposits of silver, gold, or copper are found. However, most elements in nature are combined with other elements.

You would probably not recognize many elements in their pure form because you rarely see them this way. Take sodium, for example. Although many common substances contain sodium, the only place you are likely to see pure sodium is in a chemistry laboratory.

Of the more than 100 known chemical elements, only about 30 play an important role in your daily life. About 18 elements do not occur in nature. They are created in laboratories and known as synthetic elements.

164

Integrating the Sciences

Life Science Ask students to consult a reference source to find out which elements are most common in the human body. Have students list these elements and explain their importance. (The main elements are carbon, hydrogen, nitrogen, and oxygen. Hydrogen and oxygen are the components of water, which makes up about 65% of the body. Nearly every other molecule contains carbon. Nitrogen is an important part of protein molecules.)

Properties of Elements

The same properties used to describe matter in general can be used to describe the elements in their pure forms. These properties include luster, texture, color, density, and the ability to conduct electricity. Elements differ in how they react with other elements. Most elements are solids, but some are gases and others are liquids.

Helium

At room temperature, helium is a colorless, odorless gas. The only element less dense than helium is hydrogen. Because helium has a very low density, it is used to inflate balloons and blimps. ▼

Iron ▲

Pure iron is a silvery-white metal. Like copper, it can be drawn into wires or rolled into sheets. Iron is one of the few metals that can be magnetized. In a moist environment, iron atoms combine easily with oxygen atoms to form the substance called rust. You can see rust on these iron bolts.

Copper

Copper is a useful metal because it conducts heat and electricity well. It can also be shaped in many different ways. Copper can be drawn into wires, rolled into sheets, or hammered into different shapes. When polished, this reddish metal has a shiny luster. ▶

Mercury

Mercury is the only metal that is a liquid at room temperature. Because the metal and its vapor are poisonous, mercury must be handled carefully. It is used in some thermometers because it expands and contracts with heat changes. ▼

Sulfur

Pure sulfur is a yellow solid. It is one of the few elements that exists free in nature. Pure sulfur is often deposited around volcanic vents. When it burns, sulfur combines with oxygen to form a toxic gas called sulfur dioxide. ▼

Chapter 7   Atoms, Elements, Compounds, and Mixtures   **165**

Directed Inquiry

Have students study the material on this page. Ask:

▶ What are some properties of elements? (Luster, texture, color, density, and the ability to conduct electricity)

▶ What are some properties of helium? (Colorless, odorless gas; low density)

▶ How would you describe copper? (A reddish metal that conducts heat and electricity; easily shaped; has a shiny luster when polished)

▶ How is mercury different from all other metals? (It is liquid at room temperature.)

▶ What are some properties of sulfur? (Yellow solid when pure; exists free in nature; forms a toxic gas when burned)

▶ Why would iron be a poor choice for foil and copper a poor choice as a coffee mug? (Iron rusts easily, foil made from iron would soon have holes; copper is a good conductor, not an insulator. The mug would be too hot to handle.)

The Living Textbook:
Physical Science Sides 1-4

Chapter 1   Frame 00624
Mercury (1 Frame)
Search:

The Living Textbook:
Physical Science Sides 1-4

Chapter 2   Frame 00860
Copper (1 Frame)
Search:

165

TEACH ▪ *Continued*

Skills WorkOut

Help students infer how chemical symbols are abbreviated by having them do the Skills WorkOut.
Answer Some examples are AL, Alabama; AZ, Arizona.

Directed Inquiry

Have students study the table. Ask:

▶ What symbols stand for sodium, strontium, magnesium, and iodine? (Na, Sr, Mg, I)

▶ Where is iodine found and what are its uses? (In nitrate deposits in Chile and Bolivia; as a mild antiseptic, for iodizing salt, and in photographic film)

▶ Halite is the source of what element? What are the element's uses? (Sodium; sodium vapor lamps and compounds used in synthetic fibers, petroleum products, and paper pulp)

▶ What is magnesium used for? (Photoflash bulbs, alloys, and compounds used in dyeing cloth and making medicines)

▶ What are several uses for strontium? (Red color in fireworks and flares, used in paint driers, used to extract sugar from molasses)

Skills Development

Infer Have students use a list of elements from the dictionary to infer why K, rather than P or a two-letter abbreviation, is a useful symbol for potassium. (P, Po, Pt, and Pm are abbreviations for other elements; there are four more abbreviations beginning with P.)

The Living Textbook: Physical Science Sides 1-4

Chapter 2   Frame 00722
Symbols of Several Elements on Periodic Table (11 Frames)
Search: Step:

Language Arts Connection

Ask students to use a dictionary such as the *Oxford English Dictionary*, to determine the source word for the symbols used for copper, silver, iron, and lead. Have students record the meaning of the source word and make a chart showing source word, meaning, and symbol for several elements. (Copper comes from *cuprum,* silver comes from *argentum,* iron comes from *ferrum,* and lead comes from *plumbum.*)

▼ ACTIVITY

Inferring

State Symbols

Chemical symbols are similar to the two-letter abbreviations for each of the 50 states. Make a list of as many state abbreviations as you can, writing the full name of the state next to each one. Study the list and decide what rules were followed to create the abbreviations. Use the same set of rules to create two-letter abbreviations for all of your classmates' first names.

SKILLS WORKOUT

Chemical Symbols

Instead of labeling your papers with the complete date, you may use symbols to abbreviate it. For instance, you may write 7/10/96 to indicate July 10, 1996. To simplify their work, chemists use symbols to represent the names of elements. The symbol of an element also represents the atom of that element.

A chemical symbol is one or two letters taken from the name of the element. In some cases, the symbol is derived from the element's name in a language other than English. For example, the symbol for gold, Au, comes from *aurum,* the Latin word for gold. Latin words are also the basis for the symbols of such common elements as copper, silver, iron, lead, and tin.

Chemical symbols are useful for two reasons. First, they are shorter to write and to work with than the names of elements. Second, the symbols form a kind of universal chemical shorthand. Ca means calcium to chemists in Japan, Mexico, Kenya, India, and everywhere else.

Table 7.2   Some Elements: Their Sources and Uses

	Element Name, Symbol	Source	Common Uses
	Sodium, Na	Mineral: halite	▶ Sodium vapor lamps ▶ Compounds used in synthetic fibers, petroleum products, and paper pulp
	Strontium, Sr	Minerals: celestite, strontianite	▶ Compounds used to make red color in fireworks and flares, to extract sugar from molasses, and in paint driers
	Magnesium, Mg	Minerals: magnesite, brucite, dolomite	▶ Photoflash bulbs ▶ Alloys used for spacecraft, auto parts, aircraft, tools ▶ Compounds used in dyeing cloth and making medicines
	Iodine, I	Nitrate deposits in Chile, Bolivia (occurs as sodium iodate or periodate)	▶ Mild antiseptic (tincture of iodine) ▶ Compounds used in iodized salt and photographic film

Integrating the Sciences

Health Compared to elements such as carbon, hydrogen, nitrogen, and oxygen, that are abundant in the body, elements such as iron, calcium, phosphorus, sulfur, potassium, sodium, and magnesium are present in small quantities. Ask students to make a table listing the functions of these elements in the human body. (Calcium, magnesium, and phosphorus are essential to bones and teeth; potassium helps enzymes to function effectively; sodium helps to regulate the flow of water in the body.) Other elements are needed in even smaller quantities. Have students make another table and list the functions of the trace elements discussed in the text. (Iron is part of blood hemoglobin; iodine makes up thyroid hormones; flourine is important to healthy bones and teeth; copper, zinc, and chromium aid in enzyme function; cobalt is part of B12.)
Use Integrating Worksheet 7.2.

 ### Science and You
Trace Elements in Your Body

Iron is just one of many elements that are found in your body. Your body needs iron to make hemoglobin, the part of your blood that carries oxygen throughout the body. Because your body contains only a small amount of iron, it is called a trace element. Other trace elements in your body include zinc, copper, iodine, fluorine, cobalt, and chromium.

How scarce are these elements in your body? One way to picture this is to think in terms of individual atoms. It is estimated that the human body contains some 10 trillion cells. A single cell has room for about 90 trillion atoms. Thus the number of atoms in the body is about 9×10^{26}, or 9 followed by 26 zeros! Of every billion atoms in your body, only 38,000 atoms are iron and 1,500 atoms are zinc. And the numbers get smaller! Out of each billion atoms, there are just 170 copper atoms, 125 fluorine atoms, 20 iodine atoms, and 5 cobalt atoms.

To look at it another way, a human body contains about 3 to 5 grams of iron. This is about the mass of one nickel coin. There are just a few hundred micrograms of chromium in your body. One microgram is one-millionth of 1 gram. The dot of ink at the end of this sentence has a mass of about 4 micrograms.

You get supplies of these elements naturally in the food you eat. Even though they make up only a small part of your body, trace elements are important for your body's proper functioning. Lack of iodine, for example, can cause a serious condition called goiter.

Check and Explain

1. Tell what an element is in your own words.

2. Name at least three properties that can be used to describe an element.

3. **Reason and Conclude** Write several statements that support the conclusion that the properties of a sample of an element are the properties of its atoms.

4. **Make a Model** On paper, draw a diagram of iron atoms in solid iron.

▼ **ACTIVITY**

Graphing

Atoms in the Body

Make a bar graph comparing the numbers of iron, copper, fluorine, and iodine atoms for every billion atoms in the body.

SKILLS WORKOUT

Skills WorkOut

To help students gain an understanding of the elements in the human body, have them do the Skills WorkOut.
Answer The graph would show copper (170), fluorine (125), and iodine (20). Student graphs should indicate that iron extends beyond the graph.

Critical Thinking

Reason and Conclude Have students discuss the relationship between health and diet. Ask if they get all the elements they need from their diets. (Answers will vary. A balanced diet includes foods that provide all of the elements needed for good health.)

Decision Making

If you have classroom sets of *One-Minute Readings*, have students read Issue 31 "Hazardous Chemicals, Dioxin, and Molecular Formulas" on pages 54 and 55. Discuss the questions.

EVALUATE

WrapUp

Portfolio Allow time for students to study their work from this section's Skills WarmUp. Have them revise and expand their lists of elements.
Use Review Worksheet 7.2.

Check and Explain

1. Answers may vary. An element is made up of only one kind of atom.

2. Answers may vary. Luster, color, density.

3. Answers may vary. An element is made up of only one kind of atom, which has an equal number of protons and electrons. A single atom has the same chemical properties as a large sample of the element.

4. Check students' diagrams for accuracy.

Section Objectives

Section Objectives
For a list of section objectives, see the Student Edition page.

Skills Objectives
Students should be able to:

Communicate what compounds they are familiar with.

Make a Model by drawing an ionic solid with a cubic crystal structure.

Define Operationally by writing the chemical formula for a compound.

Vocabulary
compound, molecule, ion

MOTIVATE

Skills WarmUp

To help students understand compounds, have them do the Skills WarmUp.
Answer Answers will vary. Possible answers include water (H_2O), sugar ($C_6H_{12}O_6$), salt (NaCl), carbon dioxide (CO_2).

Prior Knowledge

Gauge how much students know about compounds by asking the following questions:

▶ If only 92 elements exist in nature, why are there thousands of different substances in nature?

▶ How are elements related to compounds?

The Living Textbook: Physical Science Sides 1-4

Chapter 17   Frame 02878
Compound: Definition and Example
(2 Frames)
Search: Step:

Integrating the Sciences

Biochemistry Organic compounds found in the body always contain carbon atoms in addition to atoms of other elements. Organic compounds contain carbon and form the proteins, fats, carbohydrates, and nucleic acids in the body. Have students read food labels to find out what foods contain proteins, fats, and carbohydrates.

Themes in Science

Patterns of Change/Cycles
When atoms of elements combine chemically, compounds result. The compounds have unique chemical characteristics.

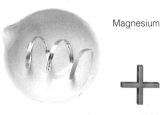

▼ ACTIVITY

Communicating

Compound Familiarity

On a piece of paper, write the names of all the compounds you are familiar with. Share your list with a classmate and discuss your reasons for thinking each item is a compound.

SKILLS WARMUP

Magnesium

+

Chlorine

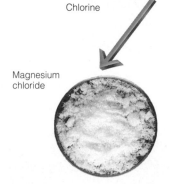

Magnesium chloride

Figure 7.4 ▲
Two different elements can combine to form a compound.

7.3 Compounds

Objectives

▶ **Describe** the properties of a compound.

▶ **Give examples** of common compounds.

▶ **Define operationally** the composition of a compound by writing its chemical formula.

Nearly all the products you use are made of more than one element. The clothes you wear, the food you eat for breakfast, and the toothpaste you use to brush your teeth are all combinations of elements. You can add any number of items to this list, such as the paper and ink used to print this book and the sports equipment you use in physical education class. Almost everything you can think of is made up of some combination of elements.

Defining Compounds

The atoms of most elements are reactive. They do not exist alone in nature. They tend to combine with the atoms of other reactive elements to form **compounds**. A compound is a substance made of two or more elements, chemically combined.

There are millions of compounds in, on, and around the earth. Many compounds are found in living things. Compounds also make up most of the nonliving world. You may know that water is a compound. Rocks and soil are made up of many different compounds.

How are compounds formed? Many are created by geologic processes deep in the earth. Some compounds are formed when an element combines with one of the gaseous elements in the air. Also living things create many compounds. An organism must manufacture compounds to stay alive. Plants, for example, are always making the compound glucose.

Many products you buy are made of compounds that aren't found in the natural world. For example, if you look at the list of ingredients on food packages you will probably see some compounds you don't recognize. People create these compounds in factories and chemical plants.

Integrating the Sciences

Earth Science Calcium carbonate is the primary component of chalk and of limestone, a common building material. Calcium carbonate is subject to chemical weathering whenever it is exposed to acid rain. Encourage students to offer examples of ways in which acid rain might change the appearance of landscape features, structures, and sculptures. (Students may discuss changes in cliffs and caves, as well as in buildings and sculptures.)

Properties of Compounds

The properties of a compound are different from those of the elements that make it up. Hydrogen and oxygen are both gases, but they combine to form water. A compound also has a definite composition. The elements that make it up always combine in a specific proportion. Carbon *di*oxide is two parts oxygen and one part carbon. Carbon *mon*oxide is made of equal amounts of the two elements. The properties of the compounds described below are the result of unique combinations of elements.

Sodium Chloride

This compound of sodium and chlorine is a white solid with a salty taste. By contrast, the element sodium is a soft, silvery metal that reacts explosively with water. Chlorine is a greenish yellow poisonous gas. ▼

Silicon Dioxide ▲

This compound makes up a large part of many rocks and minerals. It is made of one silicon atom and two oxygen atoms. Because silicon dioxide resists chemical breakdown better than other compounds in rocks, most grains of sand are almost 100 percent silicon dioxide.

Calcium Carbonate

Three elements—calcium, carbon, and oxygen—make up calcium carbonate. Limestone is one of its many natural forms. Calcium carbonate dissolves when it comes in contact with an acid. Caves can be formed when parts of limestone bedrock are slowly dissolved through this process. ▼

Propane ▶

This compound is a gas at room temperature. You may have used liquid propane as fuel. Propane molecules are made of three atoms of carbon and eight atoms of hydrogen.

TEACH ▪ Continued

TEACH ▪ Continued

Skills WorkOut

To help students make a model of an ionic compound, have them do the Skills WorkOut.
Answer Check students' models for accuracy.

Skills Development

Predict Salt is a crystal. What type of compound is salt? (Ionic; salt is a solid, most ionic compounds are solids, and crystals occur in solid, ionic compounds.)

Reteach

After students have studied ionic compounds, have them answer the following questions:

▶ If an element gains or loses one or more electrons, what is it? (An ion)

▶ What is the difference between an atom and an ion? (An atom's electrons are equal in number to its protons, but an ion has more or fewer electrons than the number of protons in its nucleus. As a result, an ion has an electric charge.)

▶ If an atom gains an electron, what charge does the ion have? (Negative)

▶ What is an ionic compound? (A combination of positive and negative ions)

▶ What does the crystal shape in Figure 7.6 tell you about copper sulfate? (It's an ionic compound.)

The Living Textbook: Physical Science Side 1

Chapter 19   Frame 03443
Bonding: Ionic and Molecular
Compounds (Movie)
Search: Play:

170

Math Connection

A crystal has a regular geometric shape. Some examples of simple crystal shapes include the isometric, tetragonal, hexagonal, and rhombohedral. Ask students to use a geometry book to research and draw each of these four crystal shapes. Challenge them to describe what the crystals have in common. (They are all symmetrical.)

Oxygen   Oxygen
        Carbon

Figure 7.5 ▲
The molecular compound carbon dioxide normally exists as a gas. At a very low temperature, however, it freezes, forming the solid called dry ice.

▼ ACTIVITY
Making a Model

Ions and Oranges

Ionic compounds form crystals in a variety of shapes. One of the most common shapes is a cube. Imagine you have several grapefruits representing negative ions and several oranges representing positive ions. How can you pack your "ions" together to form a cubic structure? On a sheet of paper, draw a model of an ionic solid with a cubic crystal structure.

SKILLS WORKOUT

Types of Compounds

Compounds differ in the kinds of atoms that make them up. Compounds also differ in the way the atoms are joined. Compounds can be classified into two groups based on how their atoms are bonded, or joined to each other.

Molecular Compounds What do you call a single particle of water? It is a **molecule** (MAHL ih KYOOL). A molecule is a particle of matter made up of two or more atoms held together by the sharing of electrons. A compound made up of molecules is a molecular compound.

Most liquids and gases are molecular compounds. Examples include carbon dioxide and ammonia. Although many compounds are molecules, some molecules are not compounds. Oxygen gas, for example, exists as molecules formed by two oxygen atoms.

Ionic Compounds In many compounds, the elements exist not as atoms but as **ions** (EYE ahnz). An ion is a charged particle formed when an atom or a group of atoms gains or loses one or more electrons. A positive ion has lost one or more electrons, and a negative ion has gained one or more electrons.

An ionic compound is a combination of positive and negative ions. The ions are held together by electrical attraction. Most ionic compounds are solids. In ionic compounds that are solids, the ions are arranged in a regular three-dimensional crystal structure. A good example is copper sulfate, shown in Figure 7.6. Ionic compounds are usually soluble in water. When melted or dissolved in water, they conduct electricity.

Figure 7.6 ▲
Ionic compounds such as copper sulfate exist as solid crystals. Ions in these crystals form a characteristic three-dimensional shape.

Formulas of Compounds

What you see in Figure 7.7 may look like an unfamiliar language. They are chemical formulas. A chemical formula is a combination of symbols and numbers that represent the composition of a compound. The symbols show the kinds of atoms in the compound. The numbers, called subscripts, show the number of each kind of atom. When more than one atom of an element is present in a compound, a subscript is written to the right and below the element's symbol. If there is only one atom of the element, no subscript is used.

How do you write a formula for a compound? First you need to know what it is made of. A molecule of carbon dioxide, for example, has one atom of carbon and two atoms of oxygen. To write the formula for this compound, begin by writing the symbol for carbon: C. Because the molecule has only one carbon atom, you do not need to write a subscript after the C. Now write the symbol for oxygen: O. Because there are two atoms of oxygen, write a small 2 below and to the right of the oxygen symbol. The formula is CO_2.

Here are the formulas for several of the compounds described on page 169.

Calcium carbonate	$CaCO_3$
Sodium chloride	NaCl
Propane	C_3H_8
Silicon dioxide	SiO_2

Figure 7.7
Writing Formulas for Compounds
▼

H is the symbol for hydrogen.

O is the symbol for oxygen.

N is the symbol for nitrogen.

H is the symbol for hydrogen.

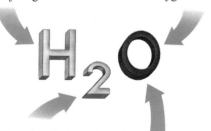

The subscript means each molecule of water has two atoms of hydrogen.

No subscript after oxygen means each molecule of water has only one atom of oxygen.

No subscript after nitrogen means each molecule of ammonia has only one atom of nitrogen.

The subscript means each molecule of ammonia has three hydrogen atoms.

The Living Textbook:
Physical Science Sides 1-4

Chapter 4   Frame 00946
Formulas of Different Compounds
(1 Frame)
Search:

The Living Textbook:
Physical Science Sides 1-4

Chapter 4   Frame 00993
Models of Ammonia and Methane: Write Formulas (2 Frames)
Search: Step:

TEACH ▪ Continued

Consider This

Research Have students use periodicals and other references to find out about one food-fortifying additive of their choosing, such as iodine added to salt or iron added to cereals. Have them write a paper that describes why the additive is used and what its benefits and risks are.

Discuss

You may want to ask students to think about their views of conservation as they study plants and drugs. Point out that native groups living within tropical rain forests rely on forest plants to provide medicines for illness and injury. However, the economy of the tropical forest nations depends on cutting and selling tropical rain forest timber. Ask students what may be gained and what may be lost as the timber in rain forest regions is sold for profit. (Students' answers will vary. Possible answer: The developing countries may be able to improve living conditions for their people with the profits from timber sales. However, plants that may benefit people's health worldwide may be lost forever.)

Multicultural Perspectives

For thousands of years people have used medicines made from plants. Native North Americans made a drug from willow bark to alleviate joint pain. It was an early form of aspirin. Native South Americans passed on their knowledge of cinchona bark as a treatment for malaria to European settlers, who made quinine from it. Ancient Chinese physicians gave patients with respiratory diseases a tea made from the herb *Ephedra sinica*. It contained ephedrine, which is used today to relieve allergy symptoms. Have students find out about modern medicines that were originally herbal remedies used by earlier cultures. They can display their information in a chart that shows each medicine, the plant it came from, and the culture that first used it.

Consider This

Should Fluoride Be Added to Public Water Supplies?

In the 1930s, U.S. health officials noticed a link between tooth decay in children and the amount of fluorine in drinking water. To lower the amount of tooth decay, sodium fluoride was added to public water supplies starting in 1945. Today more than 60 percent of the people in the United States drink fluoridated water.

Studies have shown that water fluoridation does prevent tooth decay. Also, fluoridated water poses no risk to human health.

Adding fluoride to public water, however, takes away a person's freedom of choice. People who want fluoride can get it in other ways. Fluoride is available in products such as toothpaste and in treatments at the dentist. Some people, however, cannot afford fluoride products or treatments.

Large amounts of fluoride may cause cancer. In one study, a few rats given large amounts of fluoride in drinking water got bone cancer. However, no human studies have linked fluoride with cancer.

Think About It Do you think fluoridation of water is necessary to prevent tooth decay? How do the benefits compare with the risks?

Write About It Write a paper stating your position for or against adding fluoride to public water supplies. Include the reasons for choosing your position.

Science and Society
The Origins of Pharmacy

For thousands of years, humans have treated sick people with natural compounds from plants and animals. Every culture has a heritage of using natural medicines, and in many places, they are still used. To treat snakebite, for example, some tribes in Africa use plants containing ouabain (WAH bayn), a heart stimulant, and strychnine (STRIHK nin), a nerve tonic. Other cultures use the bark of willow trees to treat rheumatism. The bark contains salicylic acid, the active ingredient in aspirin.

People have specialized in making drugs and medicines for a long time. As long ago as 3600 B.C., Egyptian physicians wrote prescriptions on stone tablets. These records show they used about 1,000 different animal, plant, and mineral products in treating illness.

Integrating the Sciences

Health Encourage students to research a common nonprescription drug, such as aspirin, antacids, analgesics, or antihistamines. Have students use the information on and inside the package to make a chart showing the name of the drug, its uses, any warnings, and any possible side effects. Suggest that students take their charts home and post them near the cabinet where medicines are kept.

Use Integrating Worksheet 7.3.

◀ **Figure 7.8**
What is the job of a pharmacist today? ①

In Europe, early physicians and other healers made their own medicines, using a process called compounding. True pharmacists, called apothecaries, sold medicine in Europe at least as far back as the twelfth century. The walls of an apothecary shop were lined with jars of herbs. The apothecaries measured out the herbs and then ground them into powder with a mortar and pestle. To temper the medicinal taste, they added honey and spices.

During the Industrial Revolution, machines began to replace the hand tools used by apothecaries. New technology allowed the large-scale manufacture of drugs. In industrialized countries today, most prescriptions are for manufactured drugs. Filling these prescriptions involves just counting and labeling. Pharmacists still learn methods of compounding, but their main job is to advise patients about how and when to take medication. They also warn patients about common side effects and substances to avoid while taking the medication.

Check and Explain

1. Explain why compounds are more common than pure elements.
2. Name three compounds and describe their properties.
3. **Compare and Contrast** List ways in which ionic and molecular compounds are alike and ways in which they are different.
4. **Define Operationally** Write the chemical formula for a molecule that has 12 carbon atoms, 22 hydrogen atoms, and 11 oxygen atoms.

WrapUp

Reinforce Have students choose a compound that is an ingredient in a common product, such as water, sulfates, or nitrates, which are present in prepared foods. Each student may choose a different compound. Have them use reference sources to find out what elements make up the compound. Have them compare and contrast the properties of the elements and the compound.

Use Review Worksheet 7.3.

Check and Explain

1. Currently there are only 112 elements. Compounds are combinations of these elements. There are more compounds than elements because there are many more than 112 different ways elements can combine.

2. Answers may vary.

3. Both ionic and molecular compounds are combinations of atoms. Ionic compounds are made up of positive and negative ions. Molecular compounds are made up of atoms that share electrons.

4. $C_{12}H_{22}O_{11}$

Answer to In-Text Question

① **The job of a pharmacist today is to fill prescriptions and to advise patients about how and when to take medications.**

7.4

Skills Objectives
Students should be able to:

Classify mixtures as either homogeneous or heterogeneous.

Define Operationally a procedure for separating a mixture.

Vocabulary
homogeneous mixture, heterogeneous mixture

MOTIVATE

Skills WarmUp

To help students understand mixtures, have them do the Skills WarmUp.
Answer Students should mention the mingling of textures, temperatures, and even aromas, as well as that of flavors as compared to the texture and flavor of each individual substance.

Misconceptions

If the mixture is a solution, students may consider the mixture to be a compound. Encourage them to ask questions like: Does the combination have the same properties as the individual components? Can it be separated into the individual components? Tell them that a *yes* answer may mean that the combination is a mixture.

Ancillary Options

If you are using CEPUP modules in your classroom, for additional hands-on activities, experiments, and exercises have students do Activities one and two in Solutions and Pollution of *Chemical Survey & Solutions and Pollution.*

Themes in Science

Scale and Structure To the unaided eye, mixtures, such as air and soil, may appear uniform. With the use of techniques such as filtering and tools such as microscopes, the individual elements of a mixture can be distinguished.

▼ ACTIVITY

Comparing

Banana Split

Describe how eating a mixture of ice cream, bananas, and hot fudge is different from eating all of these ingredients separately. What does this tell you about mixtures?

SKILLS WARMUP

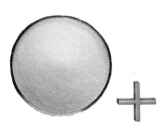

Figure 7.9 ▲
When two substances are mixed without chemically combining, they form a mixture.

7.4 Mixtures

Objectives

▶ **Compare** and **contrast** mixtures and compounds.

▶ **Distinguish** between homogeneous and heterogeneous mixtures.

▶ **Define operationally** a method for separating a mixture.

I f you look closely at a sample of garden soil, you will see that the soil particles are not all alike. They may be different sizes and colors. You may also find plant roots and bits of decaying plant and animal matter.

In a similar way, the air you breathe contains many different substances. Air is made up of several elements, including nitrogen and oxygen, and compounds such as carbon dioxide. City air may also contain soot particles. Both soil and air are classified as mixtures.

Comparing Mixtures and Compounds

How is a mixture different from a compound? The different parts of a compound—either atoms or ions—are combined chemically. The different parts of a mixture, in contrast, are simply mixed together. Also, mixtures and compounds differ in other ways:

▶ The makeup, or composition, of a mixture can vary. The composition of a compound, on the other hand, is constant.

▶ The components of a mixture keep their original properties. You can still taste the sodium chloride dissolved in sea water, for example. A compound, however, has properties different from the elements that make it up.

▶ Because the components of a mixture are not combined chemically, they can usually be separated by physical means. Distillation and filtering are examples of physical means used to separate mixtures. In contrast, the elements in a compound must usually be separated by chemical means, such as the addition of heat energy.

Cooperative Learning

The kitchen can be a rich source of mixtures. Have students work in cooperative groups of three to make an unusual mixture of food ingredients. (Make sure that students choose reasonable food combinations.) Encourage students to make mixtures in which three or more ingredients can be distinguished by look, smell, or touch. Have each group exchange their mixture with another group and challenge each other to identify the ingredients in each mixture.

Properties of Mixtures

Mixtures can be made up of any number of different compounds or elements. The substances that make up a mixture determine the mixture's properties. Ketchup, for example, is made of tomatoes, sugar, salt, vinegar, and other ingredients. Its taste is a combination of the flavors of these ingredients. The sweetness comes from the sugar and the tanginess from the vinegar. The tomatoes also add flavor to the ketchup. Ingredients also determine a mixture's texture, shape, and form.

Seasoning Mix ▲

At home, you may use seasoning mixes. The product shown here is a mixture of 14 herbs and spices. This particular blend of ingredients was chosen because someone liked its flavor. If you tasted the mix, could you identify some of the ingredients?

◀ **Iodized Table Salt**

Iodized table salt is a mixture of sodium chloride and potassium iodide. Like sodium chloride, potassium iodide is safe to eat and tastes salty. It supplies you with iodine, which your thyroid gland needs to function properly.

Iron and Aluminum Nails

Suppose you have a mixture of iron and aluminum nails. How could you easily separate the two kinds of nails? If you remember that iron is magnetic, you probably know the answer. ▼

Chocolate Milk ▲

Chocolate milk is more than just a mixture of milk and chocolate. Milk and chocolate are each themselves mixtures of many compounds. Milk contains more than 60 compounds. The chocolate flavor is a blend of about 300 flavor compounds!

Critical Thinking

Classify Ask students, Is fruit salad a compound or a mixture? Have students provide three points to support their answers. (Fruit salad is a mixture because its composition can vary depending on who prepares it; the fruits retain their individual flavors; and individual fruits can be separated from the salad.)

Directed Inquiry

Have students study the material on this page. You may wish to bring to class iron and aluminum nails, and labels from packages of the foods shown. Ask:

▶ Why is ketchup classified as a mixture? (It is made of tomatoes, sugar, salt, and vinegar. Its taste is a combination of flavors. The various compounds in ketchup can be physically separated.)

▶ How do you know a blend of herbs and spices is a mixture? (You can taste the individual ingredients.)

▶ How can you separate a mixture of iron and aluminum nails? (A magnet held near the mixture will attract the iron nails.)

▶ Why is there no formula for iodized salt? (Iodized salt is a mixture, not a compound.)

 The Living Textbook: Physical Science Sides 1-4

Chapter 6   Frame 01160
Properties of Mixtures: Dry Chicken Soup (1 Frame)
Search:

175

TEACH ▪ Continued

Discuss

To help students distinguish between homogeneous and heterogeneous mixtures, ask:

▶ Is lemonade a homogeneous or heterogeneous mixture? Explain. (Homogeneous; the lemonade tastes the same throughout.)

▶ Steel is an alloy of carbon and iron. Is steel a mixture? If so, what kind? (Yes, steel is a mixture; homogeneous)

Reteach

Have students put two or three spoonfuls of soil in a glass of warm water. Ask them what they observe. (Some of it dissolves, some floats, some sinks.) Have students identify soil as a homogeneous or heterogeneous mixture and explain their choices. (Heterogeneous; different parts of the soil mixture act differently in the water.)

Answers to In-Text Questions

① **Students might say that peanut brittle is a heterogeneous mixture.**

② **A homogeneous mixture**

The Living Textbook: Physical Science Sides 1-4

Chapter 6   Frame 01170
Homogeneous Mixture: Ice Tea (1 Frame)
Search:

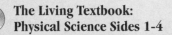

The Living Textbook: Physical Science Sides 1-4

Chapter 6   Frame 01158
Heterogeneous Mixtures: Trail Mix/Dry Soup (3 Frames)
Search: Step:

Language Arts Connection

Ask students to look up the roots of the words *heterogeneous* and *homogeneous*. Ask students to explain how the meaning of each term fits its scientific use. (Heterogeneous and homogeneous come from the Greek words *heteros*, meaning "other," *homos*, meaning "same," and *genos*, meaning "kind.")

Answer to Link

Mixtures that can be separated are heterogeneous mixtures with definite phase boundaries. Whole grain foods will fall into this category. Homogeneous mixtures don't have obvious phase boundaries. Liquids typically fall into this group.

The body has such complex nutritional needs that getting our nutrients from substances would be very inefficient. Most of the foods we get from nature come to us as mixtures that are not easily separated.

Health LINK

Almost all of the foods you eat are mixtures. Identify two foods in your daily diet that are heterogeneous mixtures. Collect samples of each food.

1. Observe each sample. Can you see the components of the mixture?

2. Try separating the components of each mixture by hand. Which mixtures can you separate? Which can't be separated?

Write about why mixtures are important foods in your diet.

ACTIVITY

Types of Mixtures

To make grape juice from concentrate, you stir the concentrate into water. If the water and the concentrate are completely mixed, every sip tastes exactly like every other sip. The drink is a **homogeneous** (HOH moh JEE nee uhs) **mixture**. All parts of a homogeneous mixture contain the same amount of each component. Most mixtures formed by dissolving a compound in a liquid are homogeneous mixtures. Perfume is a homogeneous mixture of dozens of fragrance compounds dissolved in alcohol.

As you can see, the ingredients of the seasoning mix on page 175 are not evenly mixed. One part of the mixture has more of certain kinds of spices than another part. This is a **heterogeneous** (HEHT ur oh JEE nee uhs) **mixture**. Not every part of a heterogeneous mixture has the same composition. Can you think of another example of a heterogeneous mixture?

Different metals can be combined to form a special kind of mixture, called an alloy. An alloy is made by heating two or more metals until they melt together, and then cooling the mixture. All coins are made of alloys. Pennies made before 1982 are a mixture of copper and zinc, an alloy you can see in Figure 7.12. Is an alloy a homogeneous or a heterogeneous mixture?

Figure 7.10 ▲
When you make fruit juice from concentrate, you create a homogeneous mixture.

Figure 7.11 ▲
Shells mixed with sand on a beach form a heterogeneous mixture.

Figure 7.12 ▲
An alloy is a homogeneous mixture of a metal and another metal or nonmetal.

Science and You *Hard Water or Soft Water*

When you turn on a faucet, the water that comes out is not pure H_2O. Tap water usually contains many dissolved substances. Water that contains a high concentration of dissolved calcium and magnesium compounds is called hard water.

Well water, or ground water, is usually harder than surface water from a lake or reservoir. This is because water dissolves substances as it moves down through soil and bedrock. Rainwater is the best example of naturally soft water because it has few opportunities to dissolve other substances.

Hard water can cause several problems. Sometimes it has an unpleasant taste. Hard water also hinders the cleaning action of soaps. The compounds in hard water react with soap, forming a scum that sticks to bathtubs, dishes, clothes, and skin. Suds will not form until all of these compounds have been used up to make the scum. This means that cleaning in hard water uses up more soap. Synthetic detergents help solve the scum problem, but you still have to use more detergent to clean effectively with hard water than you do with soft water.

Another problem with hard water is that it can leave scaly deposits that build up in hot water heaters and plumbing systems. The buildups can eventually block the flow of water. Many people in areas with hard water use an ion-exchange water softener to remove the calcium and magnesium compounds. The water softener replaces the unwanted compounds with sodium chloride. A water softener creates softer water, but the water tastes saltier.

Check and Explain

1. Name and describe both a homogeneous mixture and a heterogeneous mixture. How do they differ?
2. Is lemonade an element, a compound, or a mixture? Explain your answer.
3. **Compare and Contrast** How are mixtures and compounds alike? How are they different?
4. **Define Operationally** Write down a numbered set of instructions for separating a mixture of table salt and sand.

▼ **ACTIVITY**

Classifying

Mixtures

At the top of a piece of paper, write the words *homogeneous* and *heterogeneous*. Then put each of the following mixtures under the correct heading: fruit salad, ink, cement, pancake syrup, toothpaste, and blood. Add to the appropriate column any other mixtures you can think of.

SKILLS WORKOUT

Time 40 minutes   **Group** pairs

Materials

60 jars

15 measuring cups or graduated cylinders

1 L liquid dishwashing detergent

1 L glycerin

15 coat hangers

60 labels

15 watches with second hands

Analysis

1. The experimental variable is the amount of glycerin added to the soapy water.

2. Students' results will vary. Check to make sure they have calculated correctly.

3. By taking an average of several trials, you reduce the possibility that a single extreme value will skew the results.

4. Students' answers should agree with their data.

5. Students' answers should agree with their data.

Conclusion

Hypotheses in the students' conclusions should follow logically from the data. The hypothesis might involve some "sticky" property of the glycerin molecules, for example.

Everyday Application

Students' answers may include cost, amount, and whether mixtures are nontoxic or nonstaining.

Extension

Students' answers may include adding more soap or more glycerin.

Prelab Discussion

Have students read the entire activity. Discuss the following points before beginning the activity:

▶ Discuss with the class the reasons for taking an average of three time measurements.

▶ Ask students to speculate about the function of the glycerin in making bubbles.

Activity 7 *What makes a soap bubble last?*

Skills   Measure; Observe; Infer; Interpret Data

Task 1 Prelab Prep

1. Collect the following items: 4 jars, measuring cup, liquid dishwashing detergent, glycerin, warm water, labels, coat hanger, watch to measure seconds.
2. Bend a wire coat hanger into a loop about an inch in diameter. Leave a handle about 6-inches long.
3. Prepare the following labels: No glycerin; 7.5 mL glycerin; 15 mL glycerin; 22.5 mL glycerin.

Task 2 Data Record

On a separate sheet of paper, draw the data table shown below. Use the table to record your observations.

Task 3 Procedure

1. To each jar, add 15 mL liquid dishwashing detergent and 120 mL warm water. Then add glycerin to each jar as indicated on the labels. Gently stir the mixture in each jar to mix it well.
2. Dip the loop into the jar containing no glycerin and gently wave it through the air to make a bubble. Use the watch to time how long the bubble lasts before bursting. Make two more bubbles with this mixture and time each one.
3. Repeat step 2 for the other three mixtures.

Task 4 Analysis

1. What is the variable in this activity?
2. For each mixture, calculate the average time a bubble lasted. Add all the times for that mixture and then divide by three.
3. Why is it better to average three different time measurements than to test each mixture only once?
4. Which mixture produced the longest-lasting bubbles?
5. List the mixtures you tested in order of performance, starting with the one that produced the longest-lasting bubbles.

Task 5 Conclusion

Write a short paragraph comparing the performance of the bubble mixtures you tested. Make a hypothesis to explain the differences you observed.

Everyday Application

Try to find out how commercial bubble mixtures are made. What characteristics other than long-lasting bubbles would influence your choice of a mixture?

Extension

How might you use your data to create a mixture that makes even longer-lasting bubbles?

Table 7.3   Bubble Data from Various Mixtures

	Length of Time Bubble Lasted			
Mixture	**1**	**2**	**3**	**Average**
No glycerin				
7.5 mL glycerin				
15 mL glycerin				
22.5 mL glycerin				

Check Your Vocabulary

1. molecule
2. homogeneous mixture
3. atom
4. isotopes
5. ion
6. nucleus
7. electrons
8. proton
9. element
10. compound
11. heterogeneous mixture
12. neutron

Write Your Vocabulary

Students' sentences should show
that they know the meaning of
each word as well as how to use it
in a sentence.
   Use Vocabulary Worksheet for
Chapter 7.

Chapter 7 Review

Concept Summary

7.1 Structure of the Atom

▶ Atoms are the basic units of matter.
There are nearly 100 different kinds of
atoms in nature; each is called an element.

▶ Atoms are made up of a nucleus surrounded by a cloud of electrons at
different energy levels. The nucleus
contains protons and neutrons.

▶ Atoms of the same element have the
same number of protons, but different
isotopes of the element have different
numbers of neutrons.

▶ The total number of protons and neutrons in an atom is its mass number.

7.2 Elements

▶ An element is a substance made of just
one kind of atom.

▶ Elements differ in their properties.

▶ Each element can be represented with
a one- or two-letter chemical symbol.

7.3 Compounds

▶ A compound is a substance made
of two or more elements chemically
combined.

▶ The properties of a compound differ
from the properties of the elements
that make it up.

▶ Some compounds exist as molecules;
others are ionic compounds.

▶ The makeup of a compound can be
described by a chemical formula.

7.4 Mixtures

▶ A mixture is formed when two or
more different substances are mixed
but not chemically combined.

▶ Each part of a mixture keeps its original properties and can be separated
from the others by physical means.

▶ Mixtures can be homogeneous or
heterogeneous.

Chapter Vocabulary

atom (p. 157)	proton (p. 159)	isotope (p. 161)	ion (p. 170)
element (p. 157)	nucleus (p. 159)	compound (p. 168)	homogeneous mixture (p. 176)
electron (p. 158)	neutron (p. 160)	molecule (p. 170)	heterogeneous mixture (p. 176)

Check Your Vocabulary

Use the vocabulary words above to complete
the following sentences correctly.

1. When the atoms of a compound share
electrons, it is a _____ .

2. All of a _____ has the same composition.

3. Every _____ contains a nucleus.

4. Atoms with the same number of protons but different numbers of neutrons
are _____ .

5. When an atom loses an electron, it
becomes a positive _____ .

6. Protons and neutrons make up the _____ .

7. An atom's _____ have different energy
levels.

8. The subatomic particle called a(n) _____
has a positive charge.

9. Oxygen is an example of a(n) _____ .

10. A substance made up of two or more
elements is a _____ .

11. If you add black beads to a box of
white beads, you create a _____ .

12. A subatomic particle with no charge
is a _____ .

Write Your Vocabulary

Write sentences using each of the vocabulary terms above. Show that you know
what each word means.

Check Your Knowledge

1. The electron has a negative charge and the smallest mass of the three subatomic particles. Protons have a much larger mass than electrons, and have a positive charge. Neutrons have about the same mass as protons and have no charge.

2. An element is a substance made up of one kind of atom. A compound is a substance made up of two or more kinds of atoms.

3. Homogeneous: cola, air; heterogeneous: tea with ice cubes, sand in water

4. C_6H_6

5. Answers will vary. Make sure students accurately describe the elements they choose.

6. One atomic mass unit is defined as 1/12 of the mass of an atom of carbon-12.

7. The atomic mass of an element is an average, because isotopes of an element vary in mass.

8. False; atom

9. False; isotopes

10. True

11. False; neutrons

12. False; 92

13. False; homogeneous mixture

14. False; Bohr

Check Your Understanding

1. Answers may vary. Possible answers include: cola with ice becomes a homogeneous mixture when the ice melts; a mixture of salt crystals and sugar crystals becomes homogeneous when dissolved in water.

2. *Oxide* means that the compound contains oxygen.

3. Gold is an element, so pure gold contains only one type of atom. The rock is most likely to be a mixture, judging by the patchy colors and textures.

4. Dalton was correct that all matter is composed of atoms, though we know now that they are not indivisible. He thought that the atoms of all elements were alike; this is not true. He was correct in realizing that atoms of different elements have different masses, and that atoms of different elements could join to form compounds.

5. Molecular compounds are made of atoms while ionic compounds are made of ions.

6. The car would take up a microscopic amount of space.

7. It is most likely an ionic compound. When an ionic solid is dissolved, the ions are free to conduct electricity.

Chapter 7 Review

Check Your Knowledge

Answer the following in complete sentences.

1. What are the subatomic particles that make up an atom? Compare the charge and mass of each.

2. What is the difference between an element and a compound?

3. Give examples of four different mixtures and classify each as homogeneous or heterogeneous.

4. Write the chemical formula for a compound containing six carbon atoms and six hydrogen atoms.

5. Name three elements and list one property of each.

6. What is an atomic mass unit?

7. Why is the atomic mass of an element an average?

Determine whether each statement is true or false. Write *true* if it is true. If it is false, change the underlined word(s) to make the statement true.

8. An ion is a <u>subatomic particle</u> that has gained or lost an electron.

9. Zinc-64 and zinc-66 are different <u>elements</u>.

10. The compound written as KNO_3 has <u>three</u> atoms of oxygen.

11. Protons and <u>electrons</u> make up the nucleus.

12. There are about <u>100</u> naturally-occurring elements.

13. When you dissolve sugar in water, you create a <u>compound</u>.

14. <u>Dalton</u> proposed the planetary model of the atom.

Check Your Understanding

Apply the concepts you have learned to answer each question.

1. Give an example of a heterogeneous mixture that could be turned into a homogeneous mixture. Describe how the change could be carried out.

2. **Infer** Several of the compounds you learned about in this chapter have names that end in the word *oxide*. Based on what you know about the makeup of these compounds, infer what *oxide* means.

3. **Mystery Photo** The photograph on page 156 shows gold nuggets and rocks. Is the gold an element, a compound, or a mixture? How can you tell? Is the rock in the lower right an element, a compound, or a mixture? What visual evidence do you have to support your answer?

4. **Summarize** Review the four concepts that make up Dalton's theory of matter. Compare them to what is known today about atomic structure. What was correct about Dalton's ideas? What was incorrect?

5. **Compare and Contrast** How do molecular and ionic compounds differ?

6. **Predict** Describe what would happen if all the atoms making up a car were packed together so that the nuclei touched each other.

7. **Application** A certain compound is a solid at room temperature and conducts electricity when dissolved in water. Is it most likely an ionic compound or a molecular compound? Why?

Develop Your Skills

1. a. tritium

   b. They have the same atomic number.

2. Students' circle graphs should contain "slices" in proportion to the quantities listed in the table.

3. a. 55.847

   b. lead, gold, mercury, or any other element with a density greater than 7.87 g/mL

Make Connections

1.

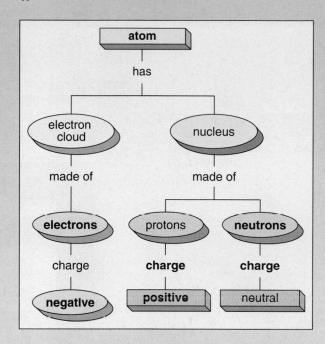

2. Photons, gluons, gravitons, mesons, muons, leptons, quarks, tachyons, hadrons, bosons, antineutrons, and antiprotons are some other subatomic particles.

3. The meanings given to the elements of Chinese alchemy were related in many ways to religious beliefs, as were the "elements" of western alchemists.

Develop Your Skills

Use the skills you have developed in this chapter to complete each activity.

1. **Interpret Data** The table below shows the atomic number, number of neutrons, and mass number for three isotopes of hydrogen.

   a. Which hydrogen isotope has the most neutrons?

   b. What information tells you that protium, deuterium, and tritium are isotopes rather than three different elements?

Isotope	Atomic Number	Neutrons	Mass Number
Protium	1	0	1
Deuterium	1	1	2
Tritium	1	2	3

2. **Graph** Construct a circle graph showing the data in the table below.

Isotope	Percent of All Zinc
Zinc–64	50
Zinc–66	27
Zinc–67	4
Zinc–68	19

3. **Data Bank** Use the information on page 641 to answer the following questions.

   a. What is the atomic mass of iron?

   b. What is one element with a density higher than that of iron?

Make Connections

1. **Link the Concepts** Below is a concept map showing how some of the main concepts in this chapter link together. Only parts of the map are filled in. Copy the map. Using words and ideas from the chapter, complete the map.

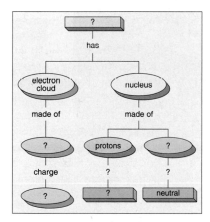

2. **Science and Technology** Scientists have discovered many subatomic particles in addition to protons, neutrons, and electrons. Read about the branch of science called particle physics and find out what these other subatomic particles are.

3. **Science and Social Studies** Throughout history, people in different cultures have thought of matter as being made of a few kinds of basic substances or energies. The ancient Chinese, for example, considered everything to be some combination of wood, fire, earth, metal, and water. Research this philosophy and find out more about the meaning given to these five "elements."

Overview

This chapter provides an introduction to the periodic table of elements. The systematic arrangement of information in the periodic table is described in the first section. The properties and classifications of metals are explained in the second section, followed by a description of the properties of nonmetals and metalloids in the third section. Examples of the various families and groups, and their placement within the periodic table, are provided.

Advance Planner

▶ Provide a wall chart of the periodic table for the entire chapter.

▶ Provide chemistry books for TE page 186.

▶ Supply old magazines for TE pages 189, 191, and 196.

▶ Provide outline maps for TE page 190.

▶ Provide index cards for TE page 192.

▶ Provide dictionaries for SE Activity 8, page 200.

Skills Development Chart

Sections	Classify	Collect Data	Communicate	Graph	Infer	Interpret Data	Predict
8.1 Skills WarmUp		●					
8.2 Skills WarmUp Skills WorkOut	●						●
8.3 Skills WarmUp SkillBuilder Activity	● ●	●	● ●	●	●	●	

Individual Needs

▶ **Limited English Proficiency Students** Photocopy the periodic table on pages 186 to 187, masking everything except the table's outline and its vertical divisions. Also photocopy a square for hydrogen and the portions of the periodic table illustrated on pages 191,192, and 195 to 197. Give students the table outline and a set of pieces, and ask them to place the pieces in the correct positions on the outline. Remind them to leave space for the groups not discussed in the text. Have them use colored pencils to indicate the metals, metalloids, and nonmetals, and then label each group. They may refer to the text as they complete this exercise.

▶ **At-Risk Students** Make a copy of the periodic table. Block out the symbols and the numbers. Leave only the names. Make a very large copy and cut the elements apart. Mix up the pieces and divide them among the students. Have them put the correct symbols and numbers on the pieces, and then work together to reassemble the periodic table. Students should check each other for accuracy as they work.

▶ **Gifted Students** Ask the students to make an "element card" for each element listed in the chapter. The card should include the name of the element, a description of its atomic structure, and a list of the physical properties of its atoms. Ask students to try to find a way to classify and group the elements that is different from the periodic table. Invite them to draw charts of their classification system and explain the system to the class.

Resource Bank

▶ **Bulletin Board** Attach strips of paper to the bulletin board to form the outline of the periodic table. Make the outline large so each element can have its own square. Invite students to choose an element and design a square for it. The square must include the element name, symbol, and atomic number. The rest of the square may be used to show something about the element. Encourage students to be creative. For example, they may include drawings or pictures of objects made of the element.

Section	Core	Standard	Enriched	Section	Core	Standard	Enriched
8.1 The Modern Periodic Table pp. 183–188				**Blackline Masters** Review Worksheet 8.2 Skills Worksheet 8.2 Integrating Worksheet 8.2	● ●	● ● ●	●
Section Features Skills WarmUp, p. 183	●	●	●	**8.3 Nonmetals and Metalloids** pp. 194–200			
Blackline Masters Review Worksheet 8.1 Skills Worksheet 8.1 Integrating Worksheet 8.1	● ●	● ● ●	●	**Section Features** Skills WarmUp, p. 194 SkillBuilder, p. 198 Activity, p. 200	● ● ●	● ● ●	● ● ●
Ancillary Options *One-Minute Readings,* p. 56	●	●	●	**Blackline Masters** Review Worksheet 8.3 Skills Worksheet 8.3 Integrating Worksheet 8.3 Vocabulary Worksheet 8	● ● ● ●	● ● ● ●	
Laboratory Program Investigation 17	●	●	●	**Laboratory Program** Investigation 18	●	●	●
8.2 Metals pp. 189–193							
Section Features Skills WarmUp, p. 189 Career Corner, p. 190 Skills WorkOut, p. 193	● ● ●	● ●	● ●				

Bibliography

The following resources can be used for teaching the chapter. See page T-46 for supplier codes.

Library Resources

Ardley, Neil. *The World of the Atom.* New York: Gloucester Press, 1990.

Gardner, Robert. *Famous Experiments You Can Do.* New York: Franklin Watts, 1990.

Sherwood, Martin, and Christine Sutton. *The Physical World.* New York: Oxford University Press, 1988.

Technology Resources

Internet

PLANETDIARY at *http://www.planetdiary.com*
• Discover more about radioactivity in *Radioactivity* by clicking on *Phenomena Backgrounders.*

Software

Interactive Periodic Table. Win. ESI.
Learning All About Matter. Mac, Dos. LS.
Science Elements. Win. ER.
Superstar Science. Mac, Win. LS.

CD-ROMs

An Odyssey of Discovery for Science Insights. Have students explore the activity "Dig It" on the Earth and Space Disk.

Laserdiscs

Living Textbook. (See barcodes on pages in this chapter.) Optical Data.

Audio-Visual Resources

Element Probe: An A/V Game for Teaching the Chemical Elements. Slides. UL.
Periodic Table. Film. EME.

Introducing the Chapter

Have students read the description of the photograph. Ask if they agree or disagree with the description.

Directed Inquiry

Have students study the photograph. Ask the following questions:

▶ What do you think this photograph shows? (Students will probably say a neon sign.)

▶ Why does a neon sign light up when you turn on the electricity? (Students may say that the electricity travels through tubes that contain gas.)

▶ Do you think that the gases in the tubes of a neon sign are permanently changed by electricity? Why? (No; because the sign can be turned on and off)

▶ What causes the different colors? (The color depends on the type of gas. Neon gives off red light, for example. Mercury vapor light is greenish-blue, and krypton produces purple light.)

Chapter Vocabulary

halogen	metalloid
luster	ore
malleability	periodic

Writing Connection

Have students imagine a scene that includes the neon sign pictured in the photograph. The scene might be a crowded street in a big city or a rainy, country road. Ask students to write a vivid description of the scene. Encourage them to be creative.

Chapter 8 **Introduction to the Periodic Table**

Chapter Sections

8.1 The Modern Periodic Table

8.2 Metals

8.3 Nonmetals and Metalloids

What do you see?

❝ I see a 'neon' sign. The tubes have noble gases in them. They have different colors because they contain different gases. The signs work by passing electricity through the noble gases. This produces colored light.❞

Ben Barrett-Nisbet
Tuckahoe Middle School
Richmond, Virginia

To find out more about the photograph, look on page 202. As you read this chapter, you will learn about the noble gases and the other elements in the periodic table.

Themes in Science

Diversity and Unity All elements are alike in that they are made up of protons, neutrons, and electrons. Yet each element has a different number of protons and electrons and different chemical properties.

Music Connection

Discuss the periodic nature of the days of the month, then ask, How is music periodic? Explain that most music, from simple songs to symphonies, has repeating, or periodic, patterns. Play or sing a short piece of music that has an obvious pattern. Have students identify the basic melody and point out when the melody is repeated.

8.1 The Modern Periodic Table

Objectives

- **Describe** the kinds of information provided by the periodic table.
- **Explain** the structure of the periodic table in terms of the periods and groups.
- **Generalize** about the properties of metals, nonmetals, and metalloids on the periodic table.
- **Organize** data to develop a table of atomic masses.

ACTIVITY

Collecting Data

Metals and Their Uses

List ten metals and at least one use for each one. Compile a class list from each person's list.

SKILLS WARMUP

Imagine looking for the answer to a homework question in a book with no table of contents! You would have to thumb through the book—page by page. Why is it easier to find information in a book with a table of contents? Data that have been organized are easier to find, compare, and interpret. What other tables have you used? How did each of these tables help you find or use information?

Developing the Modern Periodic Table

One kind of table you use often is a calendar. Look at the calendar in Figure 8.1. Think of the calendar as a grid made up of horizontal rows and vertical columns. Each column represents a different day of the week. Each day is repeated in every row through the whole month. In the calendar in Figure 8.1, for example, Monday is repeated five times. This arrangement of the days in the month is **periodic**. Things that are periodic have a regular, repeating pattern.

June

S	M	T	W	Th	F	S
	1	2	3	4	5	6
7	8	9	10	11	12	13
14	15	16	17	18	19	20
21	22	23	24	25	26	27
28	29	30				

Figure 8.1 ▲
How are the days of a month organized in a calendar? ②

Like the days of the month, the chemical elements can be arranged in a way that shows a repeating, or periodic, pattern. The chemical properties of the elements repeat as the elements increase in atomic number. A table that shows these patterns in the elements' properties is called a periodic table. Look at the modern periodic table of the elements on pages 186–187. How does it resemble a calendar? What do you think the vertical columns represent? ①

In 1869, a Russian chemist named Dmitri Mendeleev (MEN duh LAY uhf) created the first periodic table of the elements. At that time, chemists had identified about 70

SECTION

8.1

Section Objectives
For a list of section objectives, see the Student Edition page.

Skills Objectives
Students should be able to:

Collect Data about metals.

Organize Data using the atomic masses of elements in Group 2.

Vocabulary
periodic, metalloid

MOTIVATE

Skills WarmUp

To help students understand the classification of elements in the periodic table, have them do the Skills WarmUp.

Answer Student lists will vary, but may include aluminum (soft-drink cans), copper (pennies and other coins), iron (frames of buildings).

Prior Knowledge

Gauge how much students know about the periodic table by asking the following questions:

- What does *periodic* mean?
- What are some events that occur periodically?
- All the elements are grouped in a table called the periodic table. Why do you think it is called the periodic table?

Answers to In-Text Questions

①–② The calendar and periodic table are organized into vertical columns and horizontal rows. In a calendar, days with the same name are organized into columns. In the periodic table, elements with similar properties are organized into columns. As you read across rows of the calendar, the days repeat. Across the periodic table, properties repeat.

Critical Thinking

Reason and Conclude Remind students that during Mendeleev's time, about 70 elements were known. To use the growing number of elements, scientists needed to know each one's properties. Ask students why scientists felt the need to classify the elements. (They needed a quick way to find the element that would suit their purposes.)

Discuss

Refer students to Figure 8.2. Discuss how Mendeleev organized the table of elements by asking:

▶ Why do you think Mendeleev put information about the elements on cards? (He could see the element's properties at a glance and see how each element related to the others.)

▶ How did Mendeleev try to organize the elements? (In order of increasing atomic mass while keeping elements with similar properties together)

▶ What problem did Mendeleev have with this system? (When he kept elements in order by atomic mass, he couldn't always group elements with similar properties.)

 **The Living Textbook:
Physical Science Sides 1-4**

Chapter 1   Frame 00698
Mendeleev (1 Frame)
Search:

 **The Living Textbook:
Physical Science Sides 1-4**

Chapter 1   Frame 00720
Periodic Table (1 Frame)
Search:

184

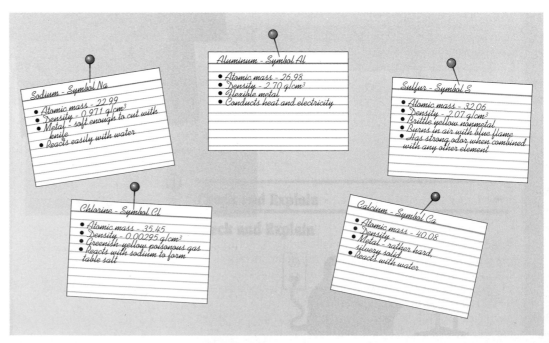

Portfolio

Write the number sequence 1, 2, 3, 4, 3, 2, 1 on the chalkboard and ask students to describe the pattern in words. (It begins at 1, increases to 4, then decreases to 1.) Have students draw visual representations of the pattern on the chalkboard. Then have students develop an original pattern and express it visually on the board. Have students at their seats work to decipher the patterns. Then ask students to describe how they deciphered the patterns. Have them compare their work to the process Mendeleev must have used to develop the periodic table. Students may wish to keep their notes and patterns in their portfolios.

elements. Mendeleev spent years collecting information about the properties of these elements.

Mendeleev wrote each element's name, atomic mass, and properties on a card. He ordered the cards from lowest to highest atomic mass and pinned them to his laboratory wall. He grouped elements that had similar properties and put these cards in rows along the wall. Mendeleev's project took up so much time and thought, his friends called it the "game of patience."

Arranging the elements in this way, Mendeleev ran into several problems. Certain elements could not be put into groups with similar properties and at the same time stay in order of increasing atomic mass. Mendeleev had to ignore the atomic masses of the elements. Also, there were spaces where no element seemed to fit, so Mendeleev put question marks in these spaces.

Look at Mendeleev's table in Figure 8.3. It shows how he arranged the cards. Mendeleev predicted the properties of

Figure 8.2 ▲
Mendeleev discovered how to organize the elements in his periodic table by making an information card for each element.

 **Themes in Science**

Scale and Structure The position an element occupies in the periodic table gives information about its atomic structure. Elements are grouped because they share similar properties. An element's properties are determined by the arrangement of electrons in its atoms.

Multicultural Perspectives

Have students prepare a bulletin-board display about Dmitri Mendeleev and Henry Moseley. Have students work in two groups, and ask each group to research the lives and discoveries of one of the two scientists. After the students finish their displays, ask members of each group to share what they've learned with the class.

Critical Thinking

Find Causes Have students explain why the order of the elements is slightly different when arranged according to atomic number rather than by atomic mass. (Elements do not increase in atomic number in the same order as they do in atomic mass because of the presence of neutrons in the nucleus.)

Class Activity

If Mendeleev made his predictions of unknown elements in modern times, how would the media cover the event? Have the class work in groups to act as reporters for a news reporting medium such as TV, radio, magazine, newspaper, or computer bulletin board. Each group can report the predictions made by Mendeleev in the media format they represent.

Discuss

In a class discussion, relate the periodicity of elements to their properties. Use Mendeleev's periodic table in Figure 8.3. Have students turn the periodic table so that the left side is the top. Review Mendeleev's discoveries, then ask, If the first element, lithium, is very reactive, which element in the next period would you also expect to be very reactive? (Sodium) Chlorine is a reactive, nonmetallic gas. Can you name another one like it? (Fluorine is the most reasonable answer.)

Answer to In-Text Question

① **It resembles today's periodic table. Mendeleev's question marks represent 45, scandium; 68, gallium; 70, germanium; and 180, hafnium.**

 The Living Textbook: Physical Science Sides 1-4

Chapter 4   Frame 00936
Energy Levels of Electrons (1 Frame)
Search:

	Ti=50	Zr=90	?=180.
	V=51	Nb=94	Ta=182.
	Cr=52	Mo=96	W=186.
	Mn=55	Rh=104,4	Pt=197,4
	Fe=56	Ru=104,4	Ir=198.
Ni=Co=59		Pl=106,6,	Os=199.
H=1	Cu=63,4	Ag=108	Hg=200.

Be=9,4   Mg=24   Zn=65,2   Cd=112
B=11   Al=27,4   ?=68   Ur=116   Au=197?
C=12   Si=28   ?=70   Sn=118
N=14   P=31   As=75   Sb=122   Bi=210
O=16   S=32   Se=79,4   Te=128?
F=19   Cl=35,5   Br=80   I=127
Li=7   Na=23   K=39   Rb=85,4   Cs=133   Tl=204
Ca=40   Sr=57,6   Ba=137   Pb=207.
?=45   Ce=92
?Er=56   La=94
?Yt=60   Di=95
?In=75,6   Th=118?

Figure 8.3 ▲
Turn Mendeleev's periodic table so the left side is the top. How does it compare to the modern periodic table on the next two pages? Can you guess which elements go where Mendeleev left question marks? ①

elements that would be discovered to fill in the blank spaces. One element he left space for, gallium, was discovered in 1875. The discovery of the elements whose properties were predicted by the blank spaces in the table established the value of Mendeleev's periodic table.

After Mendeleev's death, a British physicist named Henry Moseley carried on Mendeleev's work. Moseley arranged the elements in order of increasing atomic number instead of atomic mass. He discovered that the pattern had no irregularities. The position of an element in the modern periodic table is related to its atomic number and the arrangement of electrons in its energy levels.

TEACH ▪ Continued

Explore Visually

Have students study these two pages. Then ask some or all of the following questions:

▶ How many vertical columns, or groups, are in the table? (18) What group does iron belong to? (Group 8)

▶ How many rows, or periods, are there? (Seven) What element begins Period 4? (Potassium) What period do elements 57 to 71 fall into? (Period 6) What are elements 57 to 71 called? (Lanthanide series)

▶ Within a period, what is the relationship between the numbers above the atomic symbols? What are these numbers called? (The numbers increase from left to right; they are called atomic numbers.)

▶ What do the different colors in the table tell you? (Elements of the same color belong to the same group; the groups are listed by name below the table.)

▶ Where are metals on the periodic table? (Left of the zigzag line)

Enrich

Use Enrich Worksheet 8.1.

**The Living Textbook:
Physical Science Side 1**

Chapter 20   Frame 11549
Arrangement of Periodic Table (Movie)
Search: Play:

**The Living Textbook:
Physical Science Sides 1-4**

Chapter 2   Frame 00715
Periodic Table: Groups and Periods
(1 Frame)
Search:

Cooperative Learning

Have students work in cooperative groups to name each group of elements. Assign each student group one or more element groups. Provide some high school chemistry textbooks so that students can research the chemical properties of their assigned elements. Explain that their task is to find a descriptive name for the group or groups of elements they have been assigned to work on. This exercise will seem difficult; encourage students to be creative in how they word their names. They should also consider the uses for their elements in industry.

The Modern Periodic Table

On these pages, you will tour the modern periodic table. During this tour, you will learn more about the structure of the table and the patterns that make it useful. As you will see, the periodic table is an important tool in the study of chemistry.

**Figure 8.4
Periodic Table of the Elements** ▶

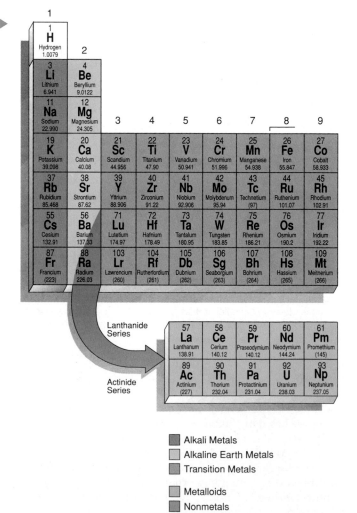

Group

Vertical columns are called groups. Elements within a group may have many similar properties. Their properties are similar because they have a similar arrangement of electrons.

Group number

Groups of elements are identified by numbers from 1 to 18, beginning at the left side of the table.

Period

The seven horizontal rows are called periods. Elements 57–71 and 89–103 fit into periods 6 and 7. The elements in a period are not alike. As you move from left to right in a period, elements range from metals to nonmetals.

Integrating the Sciences

Earth Science Tell students that different elements make up the earth's atmosphere, oceans, and land. The atmosphere is made up mainly of nitrogen, oxygen, and argon. Carbon dioxide, nitrous oxide, methane, hydrogen, and the noble gases make up the rest. The oceans are composed mainly of hydrogen and oxygen. However, many ionic compounds are dissolved in ocean water. These compounds consist mostly of sodium, magnesium, sulfur, chlorine, potassium, and calcium. By weight, oxygen, silicon, aluminum, iron, calcium, magnesium, sodium, and potassium make up nearly 99 percent of the earth's crust.

Use Integrating Worksheet 8.1.

▶ What are metalloids? (Metalloids have properties of metals and nonmetals.) Where are metalloids found on the periodic table? (They border both sides of the zigzag line that separates metals and nonmetals.)

▶ If the rare earth metals were not separated from the rest of the table, how would the appearance and usefulness of the table change? (The table would be very wide.)

▶ **Infer** Why do you think an element's symbol is sometimes different from the first letter of the element's name? (Because the symbols are often taken from the Latin and Greek names for the elements.)

Discuss

Remind students that the electrons in the outermost energy level of an atom are important to how an element reacts with other elements. Ask how atoms of elements with similar properties probably compare in structure. (They would have the same number of electrons in their outer shells.) How does this influence an element's position on the periodic table? (It puts them in the same group.)

Decision Making

If you have classroom sets of *One-Minute Readings*, have students read Issue 32 "Manganese, Platinum, Chromium, and Foreign Policy" on page 56. Discuss the questions.

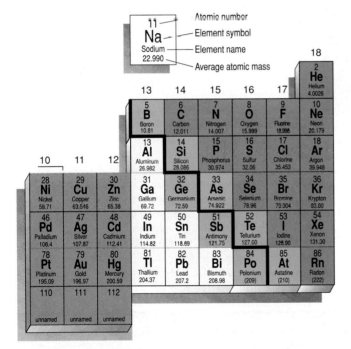

Nonmetals

Nonmetals occupy the upper right hand corner of the periodic table. All of these elements, except hydrogen, are to the right of the zigzag line.

Metals

About 80 percent of the known elements are metals. They occupy the large area to the left of the zigzag line in the periodic table.

Metalloids

Elements that have properties of both metals and nonmetals are **metalloids**. In the periodic table, metalloids border both sides of the zigzag line that separates the metals from the nonmetals.

Rare Earth Metals

These two rows of elements are separated from the rest of the table to make it a more convenient size.

The Living Textbook: Physical Science Sides 1-4

Chapter 2   Frame 00717
Periodic Table:
Metals/Metalloids/Nonmetals (3 Frames)
Search: Step:

TEACH ▪ *Continued*

Research

Ask students to research the benefits and dangers of plutonium. What is done with excess plutonium? Why is plutonium difficult to dispose of?

EVALUATE

WrapUp

Reinforce Obtain a recording of "The Elements" by Tom Lehrer and play it for the class. Point out that Lehrer organized the elements to fit the music. Then discuss different ways of organizing the elements.

Use Review Worksheet 8.1.

Check and Explain

1. Both the periodic table and calendar have repeating, periodic patterns. Columns represent groups with similar properties and similar arrangements of electrons. Rows represent elements in order of increasing atomic number.

2. Moseley arranged the elements by increasing atomic number and found that he could maintain grouping of properties.

3. From metals to nonmetals

4. Student tables should reflect this data: beryllium, 9.0128; magnesium, 24.305; calcium, 40.08; strontium, 87.62; barium, 137.33; radium, 226.025.

Answer to In-Text Question

① **Mendelevium was named for Dmitri Mendeleev.**

 The Living Textbook: Physical Science Sides 1-4

Chapter 2   Frame 00814
Periodic Table: Transuranium Elements
(15 Frames)
Search: Step:

188

STS Connection

Students may be interested in knowing more about pacemakers. Tell them the heart has two locations that generate electric signals. These signals cause the heart to beat rhythmically. The locations are called the sinoatrial (SA) node and the atrioventricular (AV) node. Sometimes these nodes stop sending regular signals to the heart. In such cases, doctors may implant a lightweight metal pacemaker in the chest near the heart. This device does the work of the defective nodes. The pacemaker must be able to send a steady electric signal for years. For this reason, radioactive elements that have a long life, such as plutonium, are needed as energy sources for artificial pacemakers.

Figure 8.5 ▲
This device, called a pacemaker, helps people with irregular heartbeats. It is powered by the synthetic element plutonium.

Science and Technology *Synthetic Elements*

What do the elements neptunium, plutonium, einsteinium, and mendelevium have in common? None of them are found in nature. How, then, can they exist?

All of these elements, and many others, are synthetic. Synthetic elements must be manufactured in laboratories.

Most synthetic elements are "transuranium elements," meaning "beyond uranium." They are "beyond uranium" because they have an atomic number greater than 92, the atomic number of uranium. The first transuranium elements were made in the 1940s, when scientists bombarded uranium with neutrons. The bombardment changed the atomic number of uranium. Since no two elements have the same atomic number, a new element was formed!

The first transuranium element had an atomic number of 93 and was named neptunium. In the solar system, the planet Neptune is next to Uranus. Uranium was named after Uranus, so neptunium was named after Neptune. Some of the other names of the synthetic elements may sound familiar to you. Einsteinium, for example, was named after the physicist Albert Einstein. Who do you think mendelevium was named after? ①

Transuranium elements have many uses. For example, plutonium, like all transuranium elements, is radioactive. Its radioactivity makes it useful as an electric power source for artificial hearts and pacemakers. Americium is used in smoke detectors. It has properties that help make an electric connection when smoke is present.

Check and Explain

1. How is the periodic table like a calendar? What do the columns and rows on the periodic table represent?

2. What did Moseley discover that influenced the organization of the modern periodic table?

3. **Generalize** What change occurs in the properties of elements as you move across a period from left to right?

4. **Organize Data** Find the atomic masses of the elements in Group 2. Use this data to make a table.

Multicultural Perspectives

The ancient cultures of the world developed the ability to refine and work metals. Metals such as gold, silver, iron, copper, bronze, and steel were used in a variety of ways by early civilizations. Have students choose one of these metals and research how it was used by several early civilizations. Ask them to find out how the metal was refined and any special beliefs the various cultures held about it. Have them make posters that display their findings about the metal. They can illustrate them with their own drawings or pictures from magazines.

Section Objectives
For a list of section objectives, see the Student Edition page.

Skills Objectives
Students should be able to:

Predict whether an element is a metal using knowledge of properties.

Classify elements using the periodic table.

Vocabulary
luster, malleability, ore

8.2 Metals

Objectives

▶ **Describe** common properties of metals.

▶ **Generalize** about the trend in Groups 13 through 16.

▶ **Classify** metals using the periodic table

Try to imagine a world without metals. What products would disappear from your home or school? Many items, such as pipes, file cabinets, and wire, are made mostly of metal. Products, such as thermostats and telephones, contain important metal parts that are hidden. Transportation would be different, too, since cars, bikes, and airplanes are mostly metal. The properties of metals make them very useful substances.

Properties of Metals

Metals share many of the same properties. Observe the metals in Figure 8.6. What visible properties do they have in common? Most metals are silvery or gray in color. When polished, they usually have a surface that reflects light, a quality called **luster**. Luster is one of the properties of metals.

Metals also have properties that you *can't* see. For example, metals conduct heat and electricity. These properties make metals useful materials to use in making cooking utensils and wire.

Most metals are hard and have high melting points, but there are many exceptions. For example, pure gold and pure silver are relatively soft, so they are not often used alone in jewelry and coins. Gold and silver are combined with other metals to make them more durable. A few metals, such as gallium, have melting points that aren't much higher than room temperature. One metal, mercury, is actually a liquid at room temperature.

One of the most useful properties of metals is **malleability** (MAL ee uh BIHL uh tee). Materials that are malleable can be flattened, bent, and shaped without breaking. Aluminum, for example, can be flattened into foil by heavy rollers. Most metals are also *ductile*— they can be pulled into wire. To make wire, a metal is pulled, or drawn, through a tiny hole called a die.

▼ **ACTIVITY**

Predicting

Testing Your Metals

Predict whether elements with the following properties are metals. Element A is a black, brittle solid. Element B conducts an electric current. Element C has a silvery, shiny surface. Element D is a gas. Element E can be stretched into wire.

SKILLS WARMUP

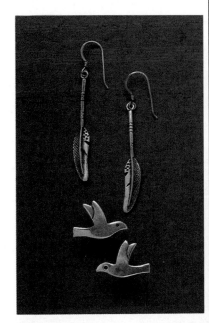

Figure 8.6 ▲
What are some of the properties of metals that make them useful for jewelry? ②

MOTIVATE

Skills WarmUp
To help students understand the properties of metals, have them do the Skills WarmUp.
Answer Elements B, C, and E are probably metals.

Portfolio
Have students collect pictures that show the properties of metals, specifically luster, malleability, and ductility. Tell students to label each picture with the name of the metal or metals. Students should keep their collections in their portfolios.

Misconceptions
Students may think that all metals are solids. Explain that a few metals melt at temperatures very close to room temperature. Point out that mercury, which is used in many thermometers, is liquid at room temperature.

Answer to In-Text Question
② **Luster, malleability, and ductility**

189

Career Corner

Communicate Suggest that students talk to a machinist. Have them find out what machines and tools the machinist uses, how they are used, and how much training is needed to operate them. Have students write a report and present it to the class.

Answer to Link

The grains of cereal moved as though attracted to the magnet. Some of them must have a high elemental iron content. Many cereals are iron-fortified because the body needs iron.

**The Living Textbook:
Physical Science Sides 1-4**

Chapter 17   Frame 02954
Ductile: Definition and Example
(2 Frames)
Search: Step:

   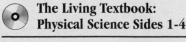

**The Living Textbook:
Physical Science Sides 1-4**

Chapter 4   Frame 00938
Electrons of Metals (2 Frames)
Search: Step:

Geography Connection

Photocopy an outline map of the United States. Assign one of the following metals to each student: iron, copper, aluminum, zinc, gold, silver, platinum, cobalt, molybdenum, and uranium. Students should label their maps, showing where their metals are mined. Compile the maps in a book for class use.

Art Connection

Encourage students to collect discarded or lost metal objects, such as cans, wire, aluminum foil, washers, and paper clips. Students can use these found objects to create metal sculptures. Caution students to recycle or throw out objects with sharp or jagged edges. After students finish their sculptures, have them give their works a title and list all the metals they used.

Life Science
LINK

Iron in the blood carries oxygen throughout the human body. What foods in your diet contain iron? Collect the following items: a magnet, a small box of breakfast cereal, and a bowl.

1. Pour breakfast cereal into the bowl. Separate out some crumbs onto a piece of white paper.

2. Hold the paper above the magnet. and move the paper around.

What happened to the cereal? Explain.

ACTIVITY

Why do metals share all these properties? Recall that atoms have their electrons arranged in different energy levels. The electrons in the highest energy level are most important, because they determine an element's properties. Although metals have very different total numbers of electrons, most have from one to three electrons in the highest energy level. This low number of outer electrons is what gives metals their properties.

A metal atom gives up its outer electrons very easily. They are not held tightly by the nucleus. When many metal atoms are combined, they all share their outer electrons. These electrons move in a "cloud" around the metal atoms. As a result, a metal can change shape without breaking. The metal atoms slide past each other. They are held together, but not locked into a particular structure. This behavior makes metals ductile and malleable. And they conduct electricity because the outermost electrons are free to move.

Career Corner *Machinist*

Who Makes Machines and Tools?

Machinists are highly skilled workers who operate machine tools such as drill presses and lathes. Machinists work with metals such as steel, aluminum,

and brass. To form these metals into precise shapes, a machinist must understand their properties. Metals vary in their melting point, strength, malleability, and hardness.

Many of the metal parts and tools machinists make are used to build engines and other machinery. Machinists cut precision gears. They make tools and dies for cutting and shaping metal.

Machinists may work in small machine shops where parts and tools are made to order for customers. Many machinists work in large industrial machine shops.

To be a machinist, you should enjoy working with your hands. You must also have the patience it takes to do highly accurate work. High school courses in math, mechanical drawing, and shop are useful background classes for becoming a machinist.

A high school graduate can become a machinist by completing a four-year apprenticeship program. These programs often include both on-the-job and classroom training. You can also qualify as a machinist by attending a technical college that offers programs in advanced machining skills.

Integrating the Sciences

Oceanography The shells of clams and other mollusks contain large amounts of the alkaline earth metal calcium. Ask students to determine which shells, called "tests" by oceanographers, have silica and which are calcium carbonate. Students can research how mollusks make their shells and diagram the animals' anatomical structure. Students can also bring in photographs or collections of shells to display.

Health Tell students that the body uses calcium to build bones, control muscles, and send messages through the nerves. As people age, their bodies are less able to take calcium from food and start using calcium in the bones. Older people can develop a serious condition called *osteoporosis* which can cause their bones to develop tiny holes. The bones weaken and break easily.

Use Integrating Worksheet 8.2.

Critical Thinking

Compare and Contrast Use the periodic table to point out that atoms get bigger as you move down a group. Tell students that the larger an atom, the more loosely the outermost electrons are held by the nucleus. Ask, How do you think the reactivity of alkali metals compares from the top of the group to the bottom? (It tends to increase. The largest atom of the alkali metals, francium, is the most reactive.)

Enrich

Tell students that an oxide of calcium is used to make steel and heat-resistant bricks. Calcium oxide is also used to reduce acidity in lakes polluted by acid rain. Another calcium compound, calcium chloride, is used to deice roads in winter.

Discuss

Even though hydrogen is a gas, it is still grouped with the alkali metals because it has one electron in its outer shell. Students may be interested to know that some scientists think that in the centers of Jupiter and Saturn, where the temperature and pressure are very high, hydrogen may form a metallic solid with properties similar to the other alkali metals.

Alkali Metals

Group 1 in the periodic table on pages 186–187 contains six elements known as the alkali (AL kuh LY) metals. The alkali metals are very reactive, which means they combine easily with other elements, as you can see in Figure 8.7. They all have just one electron in the highest energy level of their atoms. Because this electron is so easily lost, alkali metals are found in nature only as positively-charged ions. They combine with negatively-charged ions to form salts. Table salt is made of sodium ions and ions of the element chlorine.

In pure form, all of the alkali metals have similar properties. For example, they are so soft that they can be cut easily with a knife. They have low densities and melt at low temperatures. Cesium, in fact, will melt on a hot day.

Alkaline Earth Metals

Look to the right of the alkali metals in the periodic table. The six elements in Group 2 are called the alkaline earth metals. Alkaline earth metals are reactive, but they are not as reactive as the alkali metals. Alkaline earth metal atoms have two electrons in the highest energy level. Like the alkali metals, they occur in nature as ions combined with other elements.

Magnesium and calcium are common alkaline earth metals. Calcium compounds make up much of your bones and teeth. These elements are also used to make building materials, such as cement. The shells of sea animals also contain calcium. You may be familiar with the compound magnesium hydroxide. It's also called milk of magnesia, and is used to soothe upset stomachs.

**The Living Textbook:
Physical Science Sides 1-4**

Chapter 4   Frame 00938
Electrons of Alkali Group (2 Frames)
Search: Step:

**The Living Textbook:
Physical Science Sides 1-4**

Chapter 12   Frame 01955
Alkali Earth Metal: Calcium in Bones
(1 Frame)
Search:

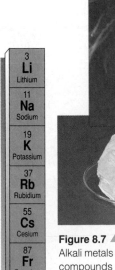

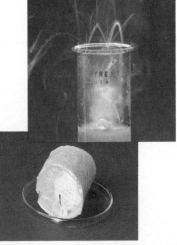

Figure 8.7 ▲
Alkali metals are always found in compounds because they are so reactive.

Figure 8.8 ▲
Alkaline earth metals are a major part of objects such as sea shells and magnesium wheels.

TEACH ▪ *Continued*

Enrich

Tell students that the compound called neodymium oxide is used in some lasers. Neodymium is a lanthanide. Students may also be interested in learning that curium, an actinide, does not occur in nature. It is produced by the slow bombardment of plutonium by neutrons. Curium is used as the energy source in nuclear generators in satellites.

Class Activity

Have the class make three mobiles of the transition metals. Pass out 3 × 5 index cards, one for each student. Assign each student one transition metal. On one side of the index card, students should write the symbol and atomic number of their metal. On the other side they should write some of its uses and properties. Provide students with reference materials. Have students work in groups to finish constructing the mobiles of the transition elements.

**The Living Textbook:
Physical Science Sides 1-4**

Chapter 2   Frame 00714
Periodic Table: Transition Metals
(1 Frame)
Search:

**The Living Textbook:
Physical Science Sides 1-4**

Chapter 2   Frame 00714
Periodic Table: Rare-Earth Metals
(1 Frame)
Search:

192

Students may be interested to know that rare earth elements are used in lenses, television screens, and artificial gems. Tell students that rare earth elements are found in ores called rare earth minerals. Have students find out how rare earth minerals are mined and purified and what they are used for.

Transition Metals

Locate the transition metals in the periodic table using the color key. Most transition metals are shiny. They have high melting points and are good conductors of heat and electricity. Because of the arrangement of their outer electrons, transition metals are much less reactive than the alkali or alkaline earth metals. They can, however, combine with other elements.

Groups of transition metals share similar properties. Neighboring elements in the same period may also have like properties. For example, iron, cobalt, and nickel are the only metals with magnetic properties.

Transition metals are often found in **ores**. Ores are minerals containing relatively large amounts of metal compounds. Zinc comes from an ore called sphalerite (SFAL uh RYT). Hematite and magnetite ores are very rich in iron.

Figure 8.9 ▲
Transition metals make up most metal objects. Some form colorful compounds.

Rare-Earth Metals

The elements located in the two separate rows at the bottom of the periodic table are the rare-earth metals. The lanthanide series, elements 58–71, follows lanthanum in Period 6. The actinide series, elements 90–103, follows actinium in Period 7. Except for element 61, all of the lanthanides occur in nature. Most of the actinides, however, are synthetic, or made in laboratories.

Lanthanides are found in certain special ores. They are called "rare-earths" because they occur only in small amounts in the earth's crust. Pure lanthanides look like steel and have steel-like properties. Tiny amounts of pure lanthanides are used in lasers. Certain lanthanide compounds create the red color in color televisions.

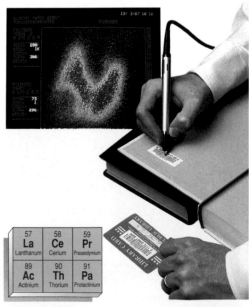

Figure 8.10 ▲
Rare earth metals have properties that make them useful in certain special devices.

Science and Technology *Making Alloys*

Almost every metal product you use is made of some kind of alloy. An *alloy* is a material formed by mixing a metal with other metals or nonmetals. Brass is an alloy of two metals, copper and zinc. Steel is an alloy made with a metal, iron, and a nonmetal, carbon. Adding different amounts of these elements or others can change the properties of steel. For example, more carbon makes a harder steel.

Steel-making is not a new process. In the second century B.C., the Chinese developed a process for making steel from cast iron. When iron is melted and reformed, it contains carbon. To make steel, the Chinese removed just enough of the carbon to create the right proportion of carbon and iron.

Alloyed metals create materials with just the right combination of properties for a particular use. For example, airplane bodies need a material that is both light and strong. Aluminum is lightweight, but it is also soft, and bends easily. Steel is hard, but it is very heavy. An alloy of aluminum with copper, magnesium, and other metals, however, has the right mixture of properties for an airplane body. The alloy is both strong and lightweight.

You may know that silver and gold jewelry is often made of alloys, because alloys are less expensive than the pure metals. Cost is not the only reason. Other metals, such as copper, are added to make these soft metals more durable. The percentage of gold in a piece of jewelry varies. Twenty-four-karat gold is pure gold, while fourteen-karat gold contains $^{14}/_{24}$ gold and $^{10}/_{24}$ other metals.

Figure 8.11 ▲
The alloy bronze has been used for making metal objects for thousands of years.

Check and Explain

1. What properties do most metals have in common? What gives metals these properties?

2. Why do the alkali metals and alkaline earth metals exist in nature as ions?

3. **Infer** Where might you find calcium in your school?

4. **Classify** Use the periodic table to determine the groups of the following elements: barium, cesium, chromium, lithium, mercury, and uranium.

Section Objectives
For a list of section objectives, see the Student Edition page.

Skills Objectives
Students should be able to:

Infer properties of nonmetals based on the properties of metals.

Graph Data to understand the relationship between atomic mass and atomic number.

Communicate the difference between metal, nonmetal, and metalloid objects.

Vocabulary
halogen

MOTIVATE

Skills WarmUp

To help students understand the properties of nonmetals, have them do the Skills WarmUp.

Answer The properties of metal include luster, malleability, ductility, and the ability to conduct heat and electricity. Most metals have few atoms in their highest energy levels. They are often hard solids with high melting points. None are gases at normal temperatures. Students will probably infer that the opposites of these things are properties of nonmetals.

Prior Knowledge

Gauge how much students know about nonmetals and metalloids by asking these questions:

▶ How do you think nonmetals differ from metals in the structure of their atoms.

▶ Name and describe some nonmetals.

▶ What are metalloids?

Portfolio

Tell students that much of the body is made of nonmetals. Write on the chalkboard these percentages (by weight) of nonmetals in the body: oxygen, 65 percent; carbon, 18 percent; nitrogen, 3 percent; phosphorus, 1 percent; sulfur, 0.25 percent; other, 12.75 percent. Ask students to organize this data in a circle graph and keep their graphs in their portfolios.
Use Integrating Worksheet 8.3.

▼ **ACTIVITY**

Inferring

Nonmetals

Nonmetals have properties that are different from those of metals. List some of the properties of metals. Use your list to infer what the properties of nonmetals might be.

SKILLS WARMUP

Figure 8.12 ▲
Computer chips are made from wafers of the metalloid silicon, a semiconductor.

8.3 Nonmetals and Metalloids

Objectives

▶ **Identify** the groups containing nonmetals and metalloids.

▶ **Explain** why nonmetals have different properties than metals.

▶ **List** the nonmetals essential to life.

▶ **Communicate** in a chart the different properties of metals, nonmetals, and metalloids.

D id you know your life depends on nonmetals? Look to the right of the zigzag line in the periodic table. In Periods 2 and 3, locate carbon, nitrogen, oxygen, sulfur, and phosphorus. These five nonmetals make up much of your body. Together with hydrogen, they form fats, carbohydrates, proteins, and nucleic acids—the building blocks of living things.

Metalloids also play an important role in daily life. For example, silicon is used to make computer chips. These chips are used in computers, watches, calculators, and even cars.

Properties of Nonmetals and Metalloids

Unlike metals, nonmetals do not have luster and are poor conductors of heat and electricity. Solid nonmetals are usually dull and brittle. They are neither malleable nor ductile. Many nonmetals are gases at room temperature.

Compared to metals, most nonmetals have many electrons in their highest energy levels. These electrons are held tightly by the nucleus. As a result, the electrons are not free to move around. The atoms of many nonmetals tend to accept electrons from other elements to form negatively-charged ions.

Metalloids have properties of both metals and nonmetals. All the metalloids are shiny solids, but they do not have as much luster as the metals. Most metalloids conduct heat and electricity, but not as well as metals do. Some metalloids, such as silicon, are semiconductors. A semiconductor conducts electricity when small amounts of certain substances are added.

Integrating the Sciences

Environmental Science Tell students that aluminum is used in many products, including billions of beverage cans. Then point out the importance of recycling cans and other aluminum products. Explain that producing aluminum takes a lot of energy and that a discarded aluminum can will still be around 500 years from now.

Have students make a poster about local aluminum recycling facilities. The poster should include the location, hours, and phone number. It should also explain what materials can be recycled and how to prepare them.

Apply

Have students look at the periodic table. Metalloids are those elements touching the zigzag line. Which elements on the nonmetals side are metalloids? (Boron, silicon, arsenic, tellurium, astatine) Which elements on the metals side are metalloids? (Germanium, antimony, and polonium)

Enrich

Students will be interested in knowing that more than one million carbon compounds are known to exist. The tissues of all living things are made of carbon compounds, so all life is carbon based.

Boron Group

The only element in Group 13 that is not a metal is boron. Boron is a brittle, black metalloid. It is used to make boric acid, a mild antiseptic. Boron is also part of borax, a compound used in laundry products as a water softener.

Below boron in the periodic table is aluminum. Aluminum has many uses because it is light, soft, and easy to cut. It also conducts heat and electricity very well. Aluminum is used to make soft drink cans, bicycles, aircraft parts, and cooking utensils. The properties of aluminum also make it very useful in many kinds of building materials.

Aluminum is the most abundant metal in the earth's crust. However, extracting aluminum from bauxite, its major ore, requires great amounts of energy. The other elements in the boron group are the uncommon metals gallium, indium, and thallium.

Carbon Group

How is the lead in your pencil like a diamond? Both are made of carbon. Carbon is the only nonmetal in Group 14. It has two common forms: graphite and diamond. Graphite makes up much of the "lead" in your pencil. Carbon is unique because it can form an unlimited number of different compounds. Most of the compounds found in living things contain carbon.

Silicon and germanium are metalloids. The silicon compounds in rocks and soil make up 60 percent of the earth's crust. Many minerals, like the agate in Figure 8.14 are made of natural silicon components.

Tin and lead are both metals. Tin is obtained from cassiterite ore, and lead from galena. "Tin" cans are steel food containers lined with tin. Lead and its compounds are poisonous.

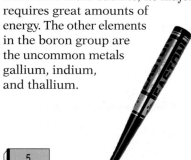

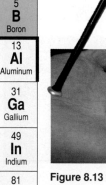

| 5
B
Boron |
| 13
Al
Aluminum |
| 31
Ga
Gallium |
| 49
In
Indium |
| 81
Tl
Thallium |

Figure 8.13 ▲
Aluminum is used to make baseball bats. Your body heat will melt the metal gallium.

| 6
C
Carbon |
| 14
Si
Silicon |
| 32
Ge
Germanium |
| 50
Sn
Tin |
| 82
Pb
Lead |

Figure 8.14 ▲
Carbon makes up graphite, an excellent lubricant. Silicon is a major part of many minerals.

The Living Textbook:
Physical Science Sides 1-4

Chapter 2   Frame 00718
Periodic Table: Nonmetals/Nobel Gases/Metalloids (2 Frames)
Search: Step:

The Living Textbook:
Physical Science Sides 1-4

Chapter 2   Frame 00843
Silicon (1 Frame)
Search:

Skills Development

Interpret Data Tell students to look at Group 15 of the periodic table. Ask students which of the elements in the nitrogen group is a metal. (Bismuth)

Critical Thinking

Compare and Contrast Have students consider how oxygen and sulfur are alike and how they are different. (Alike—arrangement of electrons in outer level, nonmetals; different—oxygen is a colorless gas in the free state and sulfur is a yellow solid)

Integrating the Sciences

Life Science The carbon dioxide–oxygen cycle sustains life on earth. In photosynthesis, plants use light to produce glucose and oxygen from carbon dioxide and water. In the process they give off some oxygen that animals and people take in. During respiration, oxygen helps release energy from glucose, and in the process carbon dioxide is released. Have students cut photographs from magazines to show plants, animals, and people involved in the carbon dioxide–oxygen cycle.

Nitrogen Group

About 80 percent of the air is nitrogen, a nonmetal in Group 15. You breathe in nitrogen molecules with every breath. Pure nitrogen is a gas that does not combine easily with other elements. Nitrogen is one of the elements essential to life. Living things need nitrogen compounds to make proteins. If its temperature is lowered to -210°C, nitrogen gas becomes a liquid.

Phosphorus is another nonmetal element in Group 15 that living things need. It is in bones, teeth, and DNA. Phosphorus reacts very easily with other elements. Even the friction from cutting it can make white phosphorus ignite. You may be familiar with the red phosphorus you see in Figure 8.15.

Arsenic and antimony are metalloids. Arsenic compounds are used as a pesticide. One use of antimony is to harden and strengthen lead.

Oxygen Group

Oxygen, one of the most important elements on the earth, is also the most abundant. In combination with other elements, it makes up about 20 percent of air, 60 percent of the mass of the human body, and 50 percent of the mass of the earth's crust. Most oxygen is combined with silicon in silicate rocks in the earth's crust. Oxygen is also produced by plants during photosynthesis.

Sulfur is a nonmetal. Texas and Louisiana have large underground deposits of nearly pure sulfur. Major uses of sulfur include making rubber and sulfuric acid.

Selenium is a nonmetal that conducts electricity in the presence of sunlight. Because of this property, selenium is used in light meters, solar cells, and photocopiers.

The Living Textbook: Physical Science Sides 1-4

Chapter 2   Frame 00845
Red Phosphorus (1 Frame)
Search:

The Living Textbook: Physical Science Sides 1-4

Chapter 2   Frame 00864
Arsenic (1 Frame)
Search:

Figure 8.15 ▲
Phosphorus is used to make matches. Liquid nitrogen will instantly freeze a rose.

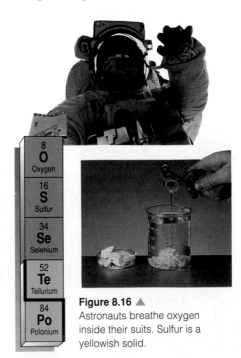

Figure 8.16 ▲
Astronauts breathe oxygen inside their suits. Sulfur is a yellowish solid.

196

Halogens

The elements in Group 17 are called **halogens**. Most of the food you eat contains a halogen compound. You call it table salt. Halogen means "salt-former." Halogens combine with metals to form salts. Sodium chloride, or table salt, is a halogen compound with many uses. Your body needs sodium chloride to conduct nerve impulses.

Fluorine is the most reactive of all nonmetals. It comes from a mineral called fluorspar. Fluoride toothpaste is made with fluorine. You are probably familiar with another use of fluorine: it is combined with other nonmetals to make the nonstick coatings on pans.

Chlorine, bromine, iodine, and astatine are the other halogens. Chlorine is a green gas. Bromine is the only nonmetal that is liquid at room temperature.

Noble Gases and Hydrogen

Group 18 contains six colorless gases. They are called noble gases, because they don't readily combine with other elements. All the noble gases exist in the earth's atmosphere.

Neon, argon, krypton, and xenon can be removed from air. You have probably seen neon and other noble gases in advertising signs. Helium is the second lightest gas. Since it is less dense than air, helium is used to fill balloons and blimps.

Hydrogen is set apart from other elements in the periodic table because its properties do not fit any single group. Although its physical properties resemble those of helium, hydrogen reacts easily with other elements. In some chemical reactions hydrogen acts like a metal; in others it acts like a nonmetal.

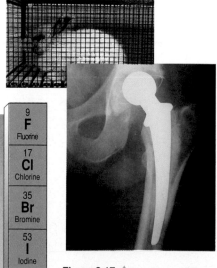

| 9 F Fluorine |
| 17 Cl Chlorine |
| 35 Br Bromine |
| 53 I Iodine |
| 85 At Astatine |

Figure 8.17 ▲
The rabbit's salt lick contains a halogen compound, as does the plastic hip replacement.

Figure 8.18 ▲
Helium makes blimps float, and other noble gases are responsible for the colors of neon lighting.

| 2 He Helium |
| 10 Ne Neon |
| 18 Ar Argon |
| 36 Kr Krypton |
| 54 Xe Xenon |
| 86 Rn Radon |

TEACH ▪ Continued

Research

Have students discover other industrial uses of helium. Ask them to prepare reports of their findings.

SkillBuilder

Answers

1. The line is not straight, showing a steady increase. It shows that the atomic mass is never less than double the atomic number but may be more than double the atomic number.

2. Yes, the atomic mass of element 18, or argon, is more than the atomic mass of element 19, or potassium. The curve goes up to the plotted point for argon, then down to the plotted point for potassium.

3. The graph would have other elements that would seem to be out of place.

   Answers will vary, but students should write that the graph shows that the periodic table is arranged by atomic number, in some cases, because arranging elements according to atomic mass would result in elements with unlike properties being grouped together.

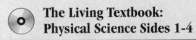

The Living Textbook: Physical Science Sides 1-4

Chapter 2   Frame 00717
Periodic Table: Gases Noble (2 Frames)
Search: Step:

The Living Textbook: Physical Science Sides 1-4

Chapter 2   Frame 00839
Neon Gas in Signs (2 Frames)
Search: Step:

Integrating the Sciences

Astronomy Tell students that stars are composed largely of hydrogen and helium. Hydrogen provides energy for a star when hydrogen atoms combine, or fuse, to produce helium atoms. Because the mass of two hydrogen atoms is slightly greater than one helium atom, some matter is leftover after fusion. This leftover matter is converted to a tremendous amount of energy.

Writing Connection

Both hydrogen and helium have been used for decades in lighter-than-air craft. Most students have probably seen flying blimps and observed their slow, stately motion. Have students write a short story about taking a ride in a blimp.

Science and Technology *Uses of Noble Gases*

The most important property of a noble gas is that it doesn't readily combine with other elements. It is chemically inactive. This property is useful in manufacturing processes that use reactive elements. Forming the microscopic patterns in an integrated circuit, for example, requires a carefully controlled series of chemical reactions. A protective layer of helium or argon gas prevents reactions with oxygen that would interfere with the procedure.

Each noble gas has special properties that make it useful for certain purposes. Helium, for example, has a very low density. Many times a day, hundreds of helium-filled weather balloons rise into the air. They carry instruments that record temperature, humidity, and pressure readings from various levels of the atmosphere. This information is sent back to weather stations. These measurements help meteorologists prepare long-range weather forecasts.

SkillBuilder Making a Graph

Atomic Mass

How is atomic mass related to atomic number? The best way to understand this relationship is to plot the atomic mass and atomic number of each element on a graph.

First, set up a graph like the one to the right. Look in the periodic table in the Data Bank to find out the range of numbers you will need to use for the atomic mass of elements 1 to 20, hydrogen to calcium. Write this scale of numbers on the y-axis of the graph.

Plot each element from hydrogen to calcium as a point, using the data in the periodic table. Connect the points with straight lines.

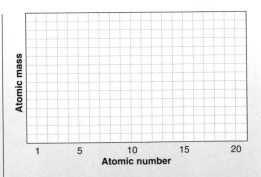

1. What does your curve look like? What does it tell you about the relationship between atomic number and atomic mass?

2. Are there any points on your graph that seem out of place compared to the others? Explain.

3. What do you think your graph would look like if you plotted all the elements up to uranium?

   Use your graph to explain in a short paragraph why the periodic table is arranged by increasing atomic number instead of increasing atomic mass. How does your graph support your explanation?

Integrating the Sciences

Health Tell students that asthma is an allergic response. It causes spasms of the muscles that line tiny air tubes in the lungs. In the past, people with asthma were encouraged not to exercise. However, treatment has improved, and people with asthma now compete in the Olympics and other athletic events. Students may be interested in doing a biographical sketch of Jackie Joyner-Kersee, an athlete who has asthma.

◀ **Figure 8.19**
Krypton gas is used in the lights marking airport runways.

People with asthma or other breathing problems may be treated with a mixture of helium and oxygen. Helium atoms are small and light. The helium-oxygen mixture can be pumped in and out of the lungs more easily than air can. A helium-oxygen mixture is also used in the breathing tanks of deep-sea divers.

Krypton and xenon gases are used in high intensity light bulbs because they conduct very little heat away from the filament. The filament gets hotter and glows brighter than ordinary bulbs do. Airport landing strips are lined with powerful krypton bulbs. Bulbs made with these denser noble gases also last longer because they slow down evaporation of the metal filament. A longer-lasting filament means a longer-lasting bulb.

Electronic photoflash units also contain krypton, xenon, or both. Passing an electric current through the gas produces a brilliant flash of light. One electric photoflash unit can produce thousands of flashes.

Check and Explain

1. List the groups containing nonmetals and metalloids.

2. What nonmetals are essential to life? What is the importance of each?

3. **Generalize** What trend do you notice in the elements as you move down Groups 13, 14, 15, and 16?

4. **Communicate** Identify ten objects in your school. List each item on a chart under metals, nonmetals, and metalloids. Share your chart with the class.

Time 2 days   **Group** individuals

Materials

dictionaries

Analysis

1. Students are likely to find carbon and oxygen most often, because carbon can form an unlimited number of compounds and oxygen is a gas and one of the most abundant elements.

2. Students are unlikely to have found any pure metals. The mercury in a thermometer is a pure metal.

3. Answer will depend on compounds found.

4. Two compounds with the same chemical formula may have very different physical and chemical properties. In fact, isomers of the same compound can have such different properties that they may be thought of as different compounds.

5. You are unlikely to find noble gases because they do not react to form compounds with other elements, and gases are difficult to contain.

Conclusion

Check students' conclusions for accuracy.

Extension

See the Prelab Discussion for chemical formulas of household substances. The chlorine in bleach (sodium hypochlorite, NaOCl) is a gas at "normal" temperatures and pressures.

Prelab Discussion

Have students read the entire activity. You may want to give students the chemical names and formulas for some common household substances:

▶ baking soda (sodium bicarbonate—$NaHCO_3$)

▶ vinegar (acetic acid—$C_2H_4O_2$)

▶ salt (NaCl)

▶ sugar (sucrose—$C_{12}H_{22}O_{11}$)

▶ vanilla extract (vanillin—$C_8H_8O_3$)

▶ ammonia, NH_3

▶ rubbing alcohol (isopropyl—C_3H_8O)

Activity 8 *What elements can you find in your kitchen?*

Skills Classify; Collect Data; Interpret Data

Task 1 Data Record

On a separate sheet of paper, copy the table shown on this page. You will use it to record the data you discover in your search for elements.

Task 2 Procedure

1. Find at least five common cooking or baking products that are made up of one or a few simple chemical compounds. You may include the following: sugar, baking soda, baking powder, vinegar, and vanilla extract (vanillin).

2. Use the dictionary to determine the elements that make up the compounds in these products. To do this, you may have to practice your detective skills. For example, if you look up *sugar* in the dictionary, it will tell you that sucrose is one kind of sugar. Then if you look up *sucrose*, you will find its chemical formula.

3. In your data table, write down all the chemical formulas that you find in your dictionary search.

4. Use the periodic table to determine the full name of each element listed in the chemical formulas. Write down the names of the elements in your table.

Task 3 Analysis

1. What element occurred most often in the products you examined? What are the properties of this element? Why do you think the element is a part of so many different compounds?

2. Did you find any elements that are metals in their pure form? What products contain them?

3. Did you find two or more compounds that were made up of the same elements? If so, how do the products that contain them differ from one another?

4. Can two compounds have the same chemical formula but be different substances? Why or why not?

5. What elements are you *not* likely to find in cooking and baking products? Why?

Task 4 Conclusion

Write a paragraph summarizing what you have discovered about the chemical elements in your kitchen. Use the periodic table to identify the family and group of each element.

Extension

Discover which elements make up other kinds of common household products, such as ammonia, rubbing alcohol, and chlorine bleach. Make another table to record your findings.

Table 8.1 Elements in Your Kitchen

Product	Compound	Chemical Formula	Elements

Chapter 8 Review

Concept Summary

8.1 The Modern Periodic Table

▶ The Russian scientist Dmitri Mendeleev developed the first periodic table in 1869.

▶ The periodic table is a systematic arrangement of the elements. The elements are arranged by atomic number and properties.

▶ The modern periodic table has numbered groups in vertical columns and periods in horizontal rows.

▶ Elements in the table are divided into metals, nonmetals, and metalloids.

8.2 Metals

▶ Common properties of metals include luster, ability to conduct heat and electricity, malleability, and ductility.

▶ Metals vary in their hardness, melting point, and reactivity.

▶ When metal atoms are grouped together, their electrons are free to move. This structure accounts for the properties of metals.

▶ The groups of metals include the alkali metals, alkaline earth metals, transition metals, and rare-earth metals.

8.3 Nonmetals and Metalloids

▶ Nonmetals have properties that are opposite those of metals.

▶ Metalloids are elements that have properties of both metals and nonmetals.

▶ The nonmetals and metalloids are found in the boron group, carbon group, nitrogen group, oxygen group, halogens, and noble gases.

▶ The nonmetal hydrogen is in a group of its own.

Chapter Vocabulary

periodic (p. 183)	luster (p. 189)	ore (p. 192)
metalloid (p. 187)	malleability (p. 189)	halogen (p. 197)

Check Your Vocabulary

Use the vocabulary words above to complete the following sentences correctly.

1. The elements that combine with metals to form salts are called _____ .

2. A pattern that repeats is called _____ .

3. The shininess of a metal's surface is a property called _____ .

4. A mineral that contains relatively large amounts of one or more metal compounds is called a(n) _____ .

5. Elements that have properties of both metals and nonmetals are _____ .

6. Some metals have _____ , a property that allows them to be shaped without breaking.

Explain the difference between the words in each pair.

7. Metalloid, nonmetal
8. Ore, metal
9. Halogen, noble gas
10. Malleability, ductility

Write Your Vocabulary

Write sentences for each vocabulary word from the list. Show that you know what each word means.

Check Your Vocabulary

1. halogens

2. periodic

3. luster

4. ore

5. metalloids

6. malleability

7. Metalloids have properties of both metals and nonmetals, while nonmetals have no luster and are poor electrical conductors.

8. Metals are elements that share a certain set of characteristics, such as luster and ductility. Ores are minerals from which metals are taken.

9. Noble gases are nonmetals that don't combine readily with other elements, while halogens are nonmetals that do readily combine with metals to form salts.

10. Malleability is the ability of a metal to be shaped without breaking, while ductility is the ability of a metal to be pulled into a wire.

Write Your Vocabulary

Students' sentences should show that they know the meaning of each word as well as how to use it in a sentence.

Use Vocabulary Worksheet for Chapter 8.

Check Your Knowledge

1. Groups are identified by numbers from 1 to 18.

2. Luster is the ability to reflect light. Malleability is the ability to be flattened, bent, or shaped without breaking. Ductility is the ability to be pulled into a wire. Conductivity is the ability to conduct heat and/or electricity.

3. Alkali metals (Li, Na, K, Rb, Cs, Fr); alkaline earth metals (Be, Mg, Ca, Sr, Ba, Ra); transition metals (groups 3 to 12); rare earth metals (lanthanide series, actinide series)

4. Some characteristics of nonmetals: poor conductors of heat and electricity, dull and brittle as solids, gases at room temperature, have many electrons in their highest energy levels, many form negative ions.

5. Carbon is unique because it can form an unlimited number of different compounds. Graphite and diamond are two common forms.

6. Oxygen is the most abundant element on the earth.

7. Moseley's discovery led to the arrangement of the elements of the periodic table by increasing atomic number, instead of by increasing atomic mass.

8. metals

9. malleable

10. metals and nonmetals

11. reactive

12. essential to life

13. alkali

Check Your Understanding

1. The ductility of metals makes wire-making possible. To make wire, metal is pulled through a tiny hole called a die.

2. Pure alkali metals react readily, often violently, in air and water.

3. In order to be used as building materials, calcium must be mixed with other materials to counteract the brittleness. Compounds have properties that are different than their component elements.

4. a. The noble gases are colorless in their natural state.

   b. The noble gases exist in the earth's atmosphere.

5. The word *halogen* means "salt maker" and halogens react with metals to form salts.

6. Each period is a horizontal row of elements. There are seven periods. The number of elements in each period ranges from 2 to 32 (including the lanthanide and actinide series).

7. The properties of these metals (heat conduction, high melting point, durability, nonreactivity) make good utensils.

8. They are called rare earth metals because they are found in small quantities in the earth's crust. They are found in the two rows of the periodic table separated from the rest. Rare earth metals are used in lasers and to create the color red on television screens.

Chapter 8 Review

Check Your Knowledge
Answer the following in complete sentences.

1. How are the groups on the periodic table identified?

2. Describe three properties of metals.

3. What are the four groups of metals? Name one example from each group.

4. What are the properties of nonmetals? Give two examples of each property.

5. What makes carbon unique? Identify the two common forms of carbon.

6. What is the most abundant element on Earth?

7. How did Henry Moseley's discovery influence the arrangement of the atoms in the modern periodic table?

Choose the answer that best completes each sentence.

8. About 80 percent of the known elements are (nonmetals, metalloids, metals, transuranium elements).

9. Materials that are (malleable, ductile, soft, ores) can be bent and shaped without breaking.

10. Metalloids have properties of (nonmetals, metals, metals and nonmetals, gases).

11. Pure alkaline earth metals are (negatively charged, stable, radioactive, reactive).

12. The elements carbon, nitrogen, oxygen, sulfur, and phosphorus are (poisonous, essential to life, metals, alloys).

13. The most reactive of all the metals are the (alkali, alkaline earth, transition, rare-earth) metals.

Check Your Understanding
Apply the concepts you have learned to answer each question.

1. **Application** What important property of metals makes wire-making possible? How are wires made?

2. Why are pure alkali metals usually kept away from air or water?

3. **Critical Thinking** Pure calcium is brittle. How can calcium compounds be used as building materials?

4. **Mystery Photo** The photograph on page 182 shows tubes filled with different noble gases. The tubes are often called "neon lights" and are used for signs or lighting. The tubes give off light when electricity is passed through them. The color of the light depends upon the gases filling the tube. When energized, helium produces a yellowish light, argon a lavender light, krypton a whitish light, xenon a blue light, and neon an orange-red light.

   a. What are the colors of the noble gases in their natural state?

   b. Where are the noble gases on Earth?

5. Why are the elements in Group 17 called halogens?

6. How is a period identified in the periodic table of the elements? How many elements are in each period?

7. Why are cooking utensils often made of metals such as iron, stainless steel, aluminum, and copper?

8. Why are lanthanides and actinides called rare-earth metals? Where are they located in the modern periodic table? Give one example of how rare-earth metals are used.

Develop Your Skills

1. a. 1851–1900

   b. Mendeleev's work occurred during the time of greatest discovery of elements. It is unlikely that a periodic table could have been developed before 1800 because so few elements had been discovered. It would have been difficult to identify any periodic properties.

2. a. oxygen, silicon, aluminum

   b. 2.6 percent

3. Several elements would be moved: potassium before argon, nickel before cobalt, iodine before tellurium, protactinium before thorium, neptunium before uranium, and americium before plutonium.

Make Connections

1. Concept maps will vary. You may wish to have students do the map below. First draw the map on the board, then add a few key terms. Have students draw and complete the map.

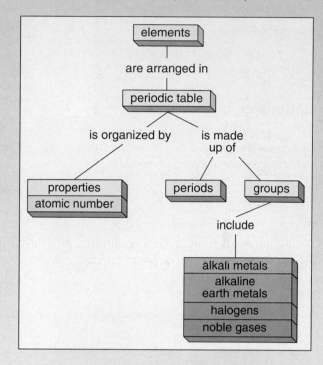

2. In the early theater, stage lighting consisted of lamps in which calcium was heated until it glowed brightly.

3. Student reports will vary.

4. Aluminum, carbon, and titanium are some of the materials used in jet airplanes. They are used for their combined strength and lightness.

5. Many alchemists worked with the notion that all common metals could be somehow turned into gold. In their efforts, they discovered new elements and reactions. Comparisons should note similarities between alchemists and modern scientists—such as both made use of experimentation and other methods of science—and differences—such as the application of the alchemists' work to finding gold, versus the modern scientists' work on improving materials for industry or analyzing the nature of matter.

Develop Your Skills

Use the skills you have developed in this chapter to complete each activity.

1. **Interpret Data** The chart below shows the number of elements discovered during different historical periods.

   a. During which period were the most elements discovered?

   b. How did Mendeleev's work fit into the pattern of element discovery? Could a periodic table have been constructed before 1800? Explain.

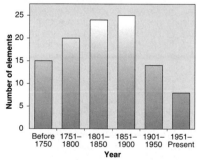

Discovery of Elements

2. **Data Bank** Use the information on page 643 to answer the following questions.

   a. What are the first, second, and third most common elements in the earth's crust?

   b. What percentage of the earth's crust is potassium?

3. **Hypothesize** How would the placement of the elements in the periodic table change if they were arranged by increasing atomic mass instead of increasing atomic number?

Make Connections

1. **Link the Concepts** Construct a concept map that shows how the following concepts in this chapter link together: element, periodic table, chemical property, atomic number, period, group, alkali metal, alkaline earth metal, halogen, noble gas.

2. **Science and Language Arts** The expression "in the limelight" is directly related to an alkaline earth metal: calcium. Research the relationship of calcium to the expression, and write a brief report. Hint: calcium oxide is also known as "quicklime." Investigate properties of calcium and how calcium oxide is formed.

3. **Science and Social Studies** Large areas of the ocean floor are covered with nodules, or lumps, of the metal manganese. No particular country owns the oceans. Should manganese nodules be harvested? If so, who should harvest them? Research the issue and write a report on how manganese nodules could be harvested, who might benefit, and how to decide which countries should get to harvest them.

4. **Science and Technology** Research the elements and alloys used in making jet planes and jet engines. What special properties make each kind of metal just the right one for the job?

5. **Science and History** People called alchemists built a foundation for modern chemistry many hundreds of years ago. Find out more about the alchemists, what they believed, and what they did. Compare them to modern scientists.

About the Literary Work

"Invitation to the Game" was adapted from the novel *Invitation to the Game* by Monica Hughes, copyright 1990 by Simon & Schuster, Inc. Reprinted by permission of Simon & Schuster, Inc.

Description of Change

The excerpt is taken from a short section of the novel and reflects the original text.

Rationale

In keeping with the concepts presented in the unit, emphasis was placed on passages that explore various forms of matter.

Vocabulary

molten, garish, tantalizing, obnoxious, smelted

Teaching Strategies

Directed Inquiry

After students finish reading, discuss the story. Be sure to relate the story to the science lesson in this unit. Ask the following questions:

▶ What is the focus of this story? (Exploration of a new land)

▶ Why don't the explorers swim in the lake? (They have been told that it is full of chemicals that could be harmful.)

▶ What metal do the explorers observe on their journey? (Copper)

▶ How are the explorers able to identify this substance? (By observing the physical traits of the metal)

Skills Development

Infer Tell students that copper is easy to shape and therefore relatively valuable. Then ask, What do the lumps of copper on the surface of the land indicate about whether or not people live there? (Since the copper is lying on the surface, it is unlikely that people reside at this location. It is likely that local inhabitants would use the mineral to make tools and other instruments.)

Make a Model Imagine you are one of the explorers in the passage. Your supply of pure water has run out and the only body of water you can locate is the one described in the passage. How could you change this "chemical soup" into a form suitable for drinking? (Answers may vary but may include a device that boils the "chemical soup" and catches the steam or water vapor. The water vapor could then be condensed. The distilled water would not contain harmful chemicals.)

Science and Literature Connection

I t was an extraordinary place. The surface of the water was very still, reflecting the sky in blinding blue-white, like a sheet of molten metal. What we had thought was a froth of wavelets along the shore had no movement. Like a frozen foam. It wasn't until we got close that we could see the waves were really a thick deposit of salty crystals. From a distance they reflected the sun as dazzling white, although as we got closer we could see that the white was streaked with garish shades of yellow, orange, and green.

"Let's swim," I suggested. "I've always wanted to swim in a real lake, haven't you?"

"Great idea!" Scylla began to unlace her boots.

"No, don't!" Alden's voice was sharp. "It's salt. Like the Dead Sea. So full of minerals that nothing can live in it."

"People swim in the sea, don't they? That's salty."

"Not like this. This is a chemical soup. It'll itch and burn. And we don't have enough fresh water to wash it off."

Invitation to the Game

The following excerpts are from the novel Invitation to the Game *by Monica Hughes*

It was so tantalizing. I bent down, not quite believing Alden, touched the water and licked my fingers. My tongue burned and my mouth watered. I spat and spat. The obnoxious taste reminded me of the salts they used to give us at school for upset stomachs. . . .

We walked steadily, in a rhythm that we could keep up for hours if we needed to. The air was clean and spicy, and we strode along, arms swinging, breathing deeply, not talking very much, just enjoying the sense of space and incredible, unaccustomed freedom. Until Paul stumbled and sprawled headlong.

"Are you all right? What happened?"

"I tripped over something. Something heavy and hard, too. I can feel it through my boot." He hopped on one foot.

We knelt and scuffed back grass and sand. Just beneath the surface was an extraordinary, bubbly mass of metal, greenish above the surface, pinky-gold beneath. Together we tugged at it and finally pulled it free.

"Copper!" exclaimed Katie, after spitting

Skills in Science

Reading Skills in Science

1. Copper; smelling salts; the "chemical soup" or sea

2. The streaks are mineral deposits possibly containing sand, salt, copper, and other minerals.

Writing Skills in Science

1. The narrator and Scylla thought they saw wavelets in the water and that the lake was safe for swimming. Alden knew the waves were streaks of harmful minerals.

2. Answers may vary. Students may list the use of copper to conduct heat in cooking or for providing warmth. Copper can also be shaped for use as a tool or weapon.

Activities

Collect Data The Dead Sea and the Great Salt Lake contain limited saltwater vegetation and large amounts of magnesium, potassium, chlorine, and bromine. People use the lakes to extract these minerals and other chemical products.

Communicate Answers may vary. Students may write or draw a copper knife or drill.

---

on the lump and rubbing it clean. "Native copper!"

"Then there are people here? Do you suppose they're friendly?" I looked anxiously around. The grass that fringed the dry riverbed was at least a yard high. It would be possible for a person to hide in it and creep closer and closer. . . .

Katie laughed. "Native copper just means copper occurring naturally on the surface, not having to be mined and smelted. If there are many big lumps around, it's really a sign that the country's uninhabited. Copper's so valuable, so easy to shape, that it would have all been picked up and used by now if there were people here."

I stopped looking over my shoulder every few minutes. I'd read so many adventures about Africa—and this place *felt* like Africa—that I was expecting anything to happen. . . .

Skills in Science

Reading Skills in Science

1. **Classify** Identify one element, one compound, and one mixture referred to, either directly or indirectly.

2. **Infer** What are the yellow, orange, and green streaks in the crystals along the shore of the lake?

Writing Skills in Science

1. **Compare and Contrast** The narrator and Scylla react differently than Alden does when they see the lake. Explain how and why their initial perspective is different from Alden's.

2. **Communicate** Imagine you are one of the explorers in the wilderness. What are three ways you could use the native copper? Be specific.

Activities

Collect Data Research the Dead Sea and the Great Salt Lake. Identify life forms and minerals present in each one. How are these lakes used by people?

Communicate Research early Native-American, Chinese, or Egyptian uses of copper. Describe a common usage in writing, or draw a picture of an ancient copper tool.

Where to Read More

The Meteorite Craters by Willy Ley. New York: Weybright and Talley, Inc., 1964. An in-depth study of impact craters.

Rocks and Minerals by Herbert Zim and Paul Shaffer. New York: Golden Press, 1957. This field guide identifies substances in your own backyard!

Introducing the Unit

Directed Inquiry

Have students examine the photograph. Ask:

▶ Infer what the source of heat is in the photograph. (The heat source is magma near the earth's surface. Groundwater heated by the magma enters the lake. Accept all reasonable answers.)

▶ Why is water condensing above the lake even though it is surrounded by snow? (The water is heated, increasing its rate of evaporation. As the water vapor comes into contact with the cold surrounding air, it condenses, forming clouds above the lake. Accept all reasonable answers.)

▶ How does heat from the surface of the lake affect the surrounding land? (Heat from the lake surface warms the air and land surface close to it. It's possible for water vapor from the lake to condense on the trees and the surrounding area and freeze in cold weather, coating the trees and the environment with a thin coat of ice. Accept all reasonable answers.)

Writing About the Photograph

Have students imagine they are on a camping trip in a snowy wilderness. Ask them to think about sources of heat hidden in an environment similar to the one shown in the photograph. Ask them to write a true or fictional story about using the lake to keep warm.

Unit 3 presents a scientific view of heat energy and the technology for using heat energy. Chapter 9 examines the nature of heat and explains how it's measured. The chapter describes the methods of heat transfer: conduction, convection, and radiation. It also describes the changes that occur in matter as a result of the transfer of heat energy. Chapter 10 explains conventional and solar heating systems. The role of evaporation in cooling and the function and parts of a refrigerator are explained. The chapter also describes internal- and external-combustion engines, showing how they convert heat energy into mechanical energy.

Unit 3
Heat

Chapters

9 Heat

10 Using Heat

Data Bank

Use the information on pages 634 to 643 to answer the questions about topics explored in this unit.

Classifying

What air pollutants are produced by transportation?

Inferring

Which animal would be most likely to survive in a cold environment: an ascaphus frog, a domestic rabbit, or a lungless salamander?

Calculating

What percent of the normal body temperature of a Canada jay is the normal body temperature of a human?

The photograph to the left shows steam given off by a lake heated from beneath the earth's surface. How do you think the deposits around the lake were formed?

CHAPTER 9

Overview

The chapter presents a scientific view of heat energy and heat transfer. The first section examines the nature of heat and explains the measurement of heat energy. The transfer of heat by conduction, convection, and radiation is described in the next section, which also defines specific heat and explains how heat transfer is measured. How matter is affected by heat transfer is described in the final section.

Advance Planner

▶ Provide cups, ice, and Celsius thermometers for TE pages 211 and 224.

▶ Collect metal and plastic-handled spoons for SE page 213.

▶ Provide colored paper for TE page 217.

▶ Provide foam cups, Celsius thermometers, tongs, bolts, nuts, large paper clips, Bunsen burners, and clocks with a second hand for SE Activity 9, page 221.

▶ Obtain a potato for SE page 226.

Skills Development Chart

Sections	Calculate	Hypothesize	Infer	Interpret Data	Measure	Model	Observe	Research
9.1 Skills WarmUp Historical Notebook							●	●
9.2 Skills WarmUp Practice Problems Activity	● ●	●	●		●			
9.3 Skills WarmUp SkillBuilder Skills WorkOut				●		●	●	

Individual Needs

▶ **Limited English Proficiency Students** Have students copy the vocabulary list on page 227. They should group the words by section. Have them explore the photographs and art in each section of the chapter. Students should write a new caption for each picture in the chapter, using the appropriate words from the vocabulary list. On those pieces of art that have labels rather than captions, students should write a caption for the concept explained by the art.

▶ **At-Risk Students** Photocopy the concept summary on page 227. Have students form groups of four, and distribute a photocopy to each group. They can search through magazines for a photograph that relates to each item in the concept summary. Students should use the text and figures as a reference. Have each group make a "concept" collage that includes a short written description. Photocopy each group's collage and distribute one to each student. Encourage them to use the "concept" collage when they review the chapter by relating it to the summary.

▶ **Gifted Students** Ask each student to use an atlas to identify wind or ocean currents associated with the transfer of heat energy from the sun. Encourage them to choose one wind or ocean current and to make a model of the current showing how heat is transferred as the current moves, and how the climate of the region is affected by the current. Have each make a presentation to the class, explaining the relationship of the sun's heat to wind or ocean current, and to the climate in the region.

Resource Bank

▶ **Field Trip** Take students to a local food processing plant, such as a candy maker, meat processor, cannery, or other factory where heat control is important. Ask the guide to show how the heat is generated, controlled, used, and disposed of in the factory.

Section	Core	Standard	Enriched	Section	Core	Standard	Enriched
9.1 Heat Energy pp. 209–212				**Color Transparencies** Transparencies 23, 24	●	●	●
Section Features Skills WarmUp, p. 209 Historical Notebook, p. 210	● ●	● ●	 ●	**Laboratory Program** Investigation 19 Investigation 20	● ●	● ●	
Blackline Masters Review Worksheet 9.1 Skills Worksheet 9.1	● ●	● ●	 ●	**9.3 Heat and Matter** pp. 222–226			
Color Transparencies Transparency 22	●	●	●	**Section Features** Skills WarmUp, p. 222 SkillBuilder, p. 224 Skills WorkOut, p. 226	● ● ●	● ● ●	● ● ●
9.2 Transfer of Heat pp. 213–221				**Blackline Masters** Review Worksheet 9.3 Enrich Worksheet 9.3 Integrating Worksheet 9.3 Vocabulary Worksheet 9	● ● ●	● ● ● ●	 ● ●
Section Features Skills WarmUp, p. 213 Activity, p. 221	● ●	● ●	● ●	**Overhead Blackline Transparencies** Overhead Blackline Master 8 and Student Worksheet		 ●	 ●
Blackline Masters Review Worksheet 9.2 Skills Worksheet 9.2 Integrating Worksheet 9.2	● ●	● ● ●	 ●	**Color Transparencies** Transparency 25	●	●	●
Ancillary Options *One-Minute Readings,* pp. 85–86	●	●	●				

Bibliography

The following resources can be used for teaching the chapter. See page T-46 for supplier codes.

Library Resources

The Diagram Group. Comparisons. New York: St. Martin's Press, 1980.

Lafferty, Peter. Energy and Light. New York: Gloucester Press, 1989.

Sherwood, Martin, and Christine Sutton. The Physical World. New York: Oxford University Press, 1988.

Technology Resources

Internet

PLANETDIARY at *http://www.planetdiary.com*
• Learn more about the atmosphere and hurricanes by clicking on *Phenomena Backgrounders.*
• Find meteorological news by exploring *Current Phenomena.*

Software

All About Science I. Mac, Dos. ESI.
Heat. Mac, Dos. ESI.
Learning All About Heat and Sound. Mac, Win. LS.

CD-ROMs

An Odyssey of Discovery for Science Insights: Have students explore the activity *Recycler* on the Earth and Space Disk. *SFAW.*

Laserdiscs

Living Textbook. (See barcodes on pages in this chapter.) Optical Data.

Videos

The Flow of Heat Energy. FM.
Heat and How We Use It. EB.

Introducing the Chapter

Have students read the description of the photograph. Ask if they agree or disagree with the description.

Directed Inquiry

Have students study the photograph. Ask:

▶ What does this photograph show? (Students will recognize a hand and a keyboard.)

▶ What do you think the different colors represent? (They represent different temperatures, with blue being the coldest and magenta the warmest.)

▶ How do you think this photograph was made? (By heat-sensitive thermographic imaging)

▶ How could you use such an image? (To find tissues that are warmer than their surroundings or regions of warm water in a lake; engineers might use them to show the areas of machines that heat up during use.)

▶ How does this photograph show energy? (The heat energy forms the colored image.)

▶ Why is this photograph a good way to begin a chapter on heat? (Heat is a form of energy that can be transferred from one place or object to another.)

Chapter Vocabulary

absolute zero	Kelvin
boiling point	melting point
calorie	radiation
conduction	specific heat
convection	temperature
heat energy	thermal expansion
internal energy	

Writing Connection

Ask students to imagine a hot, summer day. How does it feel? What evidence of the heat do they see, hear, taste, touch, and smell? Have students write a short story in which they use vivid, sensory details to describe the hot day. Suggest one of the following situations: going for a swim, running in a sprinkler, going into an air-conditioned building, or drinking a very cold drink.

Integrating the Sciences

Life Science Remind students that animals have developed ways to keep their bodies warm. Point out that body heat can be generated by metabolism, a process called *endothermy*. Heat can also be absorbed from the environment in *ectothermy*. Ask for examples of animals that use these strategies. (Endothermy: mammals, birds; ectothermy: reptiles. Students may also give specific examples: cats, dogs, rabbits; lizards, frogs.)

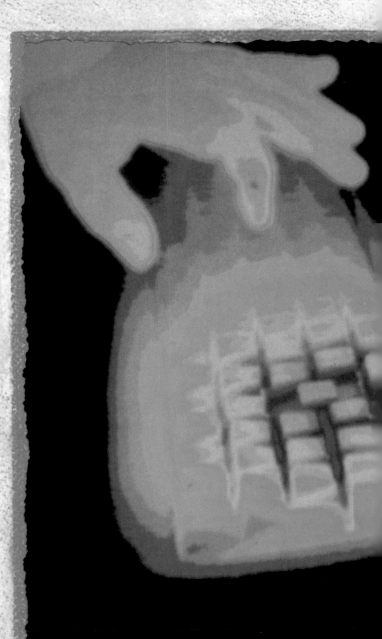

Chapter 9   Heat

Chapter Sections

9.1 Heat Energy

9.2 Transfer of Heat

9.3 Heat and Matter

What do you see?

❝ I see a hand coming down to type on a keyboard. I think this waffle-looking thing is a keyboard. The colors indicate the heat of the hand and keyboard and the differences in heat given off by them. There are hot areas (in red) and cold areas (in blue) and other areas in between.❞

Stephanie Donihoo
North Garland High School
Garland, Texas

To find out more about the photograph, look on page 228. As you read this chapter, you will learn about heat energy.

SECTION
9.1

Themes in Science

Energy Point out to students that heat energy is related to the motion of molecules. Ask, What happens to the molecules of a substance when it is heated? What happens to the molecules when the substance cools? (Molecules gain energy and move faster when heated; they lose energy and move slower when cooled.)

Patterns of Change/Cycles Emphasize that heat energy always flows from an object or area with a higher temperature to an object or area with a lower temperature. Ask students to use heat energy to explain what happens to a dish of ice cream in a warm room. (Heat energy from the room flows to the ice cream and melts it.)

Skills Objectives
Students should be able to:

Observe temperature changes caused by friction.

Define Operationally the process by which a substance loses heat.

Vocabulary
temperature, heat energy, internal energy, Kelvin, absolute zero

9.1 Heat Energy

Objectives

▶ **Relate** heat energy to moving molecules.

▶ **Distinguish** between the Celsius and Kelvin temperature scales.

▶ **Compare** temperature, internal energy, and heat energy.

▶ **Define operationally** a temperature change.

Y ou meet your friends for a game of basketball on a cool autumn day. While playing, you feel hot and take off your sweatshirt. During a break, you go for a drink. The ice in your soft drink is partially melted. You take a drink. It is still cold. If this were summer, the heat would have made the drink warm by now. You feel chilly and put your sweatshirt on again. You experience heat all the time, and you use words such as *hot*, *cold*, and *heat* often. In science, heat has a different and very specific meaning.

Molecules in Motion

Recall that all matter is made of molecules that are in constant motion. The gas molecules that make up air move freely all around you. Molecules of water move about in a container. The molecules in your chair constantly move back and forth, or vibrate. Matter that moves has kinetic energy. The measurement of the *average* kinetic energy of the molecules in a substance is called **temperature**.

If two objects with different temperatures come into contact, energy flows from the object with the higher temperature to the one with the lower temperature. Energy that is transferred from one substance to another is called **heat energy**. Heat is energy that flows between objects that have different temperatures. The official SI unit of heat is the joule.

When heat energy transfers to a substance, it adds to the **internal energy** of the substance. Internal energy is the total amount of energy a substance contains. Most of the internal energy of a substance is kinetic energy.

▼ **ACTIVITY**

Observing

Cold Hands, Warm Face?

1. Press the palms of your hands to your face. Which is warmer, your hands or your face?

2. Now rapidly rub your hands together for 30 seconds and then put them against your face again. Has the temperature of your hands changed? Explain.

SKILLS WARMUP

Figure 9.1 ▲
What happens to the temperature of the water that cools the runner? ①

MOTIVATE

Skills WarmUp
To help students understand heat energy, have them do the Skills WarmUp.
Answer After rubbing their hands together for 30 seconds, students should find that their hands are warmer. Friction gives the skin molecules more kinetic energy.

Misconceptions
Students may think that cold moves just as heat does. In fact, only heat energy moves. The hotter molecules transfer some of their energy to molecules moving more slowly. When students perceive that cold is moving, they are usually referring to cold, dense air displacing warm air.

Answer to In-Text Question
① The temperature increases.

🔘 **The Living Textbook: Physical Science Side 1**

Chapter 21   Frame 12941
Molecules in Motion (Movie)
Search: Play:

TEACH

Skills Development

Observe Have students recall the last time they used a thermometer or saw someone use one. Ask, What was the thermometer being used for? Why was the measurement important? (Answers will vary, but students may indicate that a person's temperature was taken. This would have been done to determine if the person had a fever, which is an indication of illness. Other common uses include checking the outdoor temperature before going out, checking an indoor thermostat, or checking the temperature of something in the oven.)

Reteach

You may wish to remind students what a *joule* is. It was defined in Chapter 5 as a unit of work, or one newton meter. It has also been defined as a unit of energy and related to the amount of energy needed to do work. One joule of energy performs about one joule of work. In this chapter, the unit for heat energy is the joule.

Historical Notebook

Research Have students use references to find out more about Benjamin Thompson, or Count Rumford as he came to be known. Ask them to find out how Rumford's ideas influenced Sir Humphrey Davy and James Prescott Joule. Student volunteers may make reports to the class or develop a skit to show how these scientists' ideas built on one another.

 The Living Textbook: Physical Science Sides 1-4

Chapter 4   Frame 00944
Molecular Motion (1 Frame)
Search:

Themes in Science

Scale and Structure Be sure students understand the difference between the terms *temperature* and *internal energy*. Ask, Which has more internal energy, a cup of boiling water or an iceberg? (An iceberg has a greater total amount of energy because its mass is much greater.)

STS Connection

Tell the class that mercury and ethanol (alcohol) are used in liquid thermometers because they have low freezing and high boiling points. Mercury freezes at –38.87°C and boils at 356.58°C. Ethanol freezes at –114°C and boils at 78°C. However, constant-volume gas thermometers are more accurate for scientific use and can measure temperatures from –270°C to 1477°C. Have students find out how these thermometers work.

Measuring Temperature

You probably think about how hot or cold something is in terms of its temperature. When the temperature of a substance is high, its molecules are moving rapidly. Imagine that you fill a bucket and a teacup with water from a bathtub. The temperature of the water is the same in each container, because temperature is a measure of the *average* movement of the molecules in a substance. Volume doesn't affect temperature.

You measure temperature with a thermometer. Most thermometers are thin glass tubes connected to a reservoir of liquid mercury or colored alcohol. A numbered scale is marked on the outside of the tube. As a thermometer heats up, the molecules in its liquid begin to move faster and farther apart. The liquid expands and rises in the tube. The scale indicates the temperature reading. In science, two scales are often used for temperature; the Celsius scale and the Kelvin scale.

Historical Notebook

Understanding Heat

Two hundred years ago, most scientists thought that heat was an invisible, weightless substance. They called the substance caloric. People believed the hotter an object was, the more caloric it contained. It was thought that a piece of matter contained a specific amount of heat.

In 1798, the American-born scientist Benjamin Thompson, better known as Count Rumford, questioned the caloric theory of heat. Count Rumford observed the hole-drilling process in cannon barrels in Munich, Germany. He saw that heat was produced as long as the cutting tool moved through the cannon.

Water was used to cool the cutting tool and the cannon as the hole was drilled. The water got boiling hot! As you can see in the picture above, water is still sometimes used to cool cutting tools. Rumford noticed that no heat or matter was added during the drilling. Since matter cannot be

created out of nothing, he reasoned that heat could not be a material substance. Rumford hypothesized that the energy used to turn the drill was being transformed into heat. He concluded that heat, therefore, must be a form of energy. Rumford's theory was confirmed forty years later by the British scientist James Prescott Joule.

Celsius Temperature Scale The **Celsius** scale, sometimes called the centigrade scale, is the standard scale for measuring temperature in countries that use the metric system. On this scale the normal freezing point of water is 0°C and the normal boiling point of water is 100°C.

To convert from Celsius to Fahrenheit, multiply by nine, divide by five, and then add 32. To convert from Fahrenheit to Celsius, subtract 32, multiply by five, and then divide by nine.

Kelvin Temperature Scale Another temperature scale used by scientists is the **Kelvin** scale. The Kelvin scale, also called the absolute scale, is used primarily in the physical sciences.

The Kelvin scale begins at 0 K (–273.15°C or –459.67°F), where an object has no kinetic energy. This point, called **absolute zero**, is the lowest possible temperature. Because it begins with absolute zero, the Kelvin scale has no negative numbers and is convenient to use when dealing with low temperatures.

Compare the Celsius and Kelvin thermometers in Figure 9.2. Notice that 0 K equals –273°C. You can convert the Celsius temperature of an object to the Kelvin temperature by adding 273. Since the boiling point of water is 100°C, the boiling point of water on the Kelvin scale is 100 plus 273, or 373 K. What is the freezing point of water on the Kelvin scale? ①

The Kelvin temperature scale is used in science because it relates directly to energy. For example, 1 cm³ of a substance at 200 K has twice the kinetic energy of 1 cm³ of the same substance at 100 K.

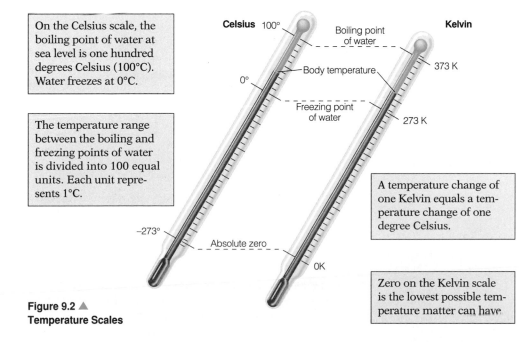

On the Celsius scale, the boiling point of water at sea level is one hundred degrees Celsius (100°C). Water freezes at 0°C.

The temperature range between the boiling and freezing points of water is divided into 100 equal units. Each unit represents 1°C.

A temperature change of one Kelvin equals a temperature change of one degree Celsius.

Zero on the Kelvin scale is the lowest possible temperature matter can have.

Figure 9.2 ▲
Temperature Scales

TEACH ▪ *Continued*

Skills Development

Infer Have students study Figure 9.3. Have them notice the fan blades attached to the pulley next to the radiator. Ask, What does the fan do? (It helps to cool the metal fins on the radiator.)

EVALUATE

WrapUp

Reinforce Have students draw pictures on the chalkboard of water in each of its three phases. They should label each phase with its temperature in degrees Celsius and in Kelvins. Have them classify and label the phases according to which has the most or least internal energy. They should also give a temperature for the air surrounding each phase and show whether heat energy is moving into or out of the water. Ask students to explain briefly whether heat energy is added to or removed from the water as it freezes and as it boils.

Use Review Worksheet 9.1.

Check and Explain

1. As heat energy increases, molecules move faster.

2. The zero on the Kelvin scale is absolute; it is the lowest possible temperature matter can have.

3. The temperature will decrease, and its internal energy will decrease as heat energy flows out to the cooler air.

4. The molecules move more slowly as heat energy flows from the hot water to the cool air. They lose kinetic energy.

Answer to In-Text Question

① The engine can't be cooled, so it overheats.

Portfolio

Have students think about how heat energy is transferred from the engine to the air through a car's cooling system. Have them draw a picture that shows how this cooling system illustrates the second law of thermodynamics: Heat flows naturally from a hot object to a cold object. Students can include their drawings in their portfolios.

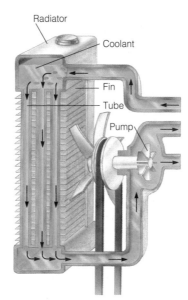

Figure 9.3 ▲
A radiator is part of a car's cooling system. What happens when a car's radiator is broken? ①

Science and Technology *A Cool Engine*

What liquid does a car need to run properly? Most people answer "gasoline." However, another liquid—water—is just as vital to a car's performance.

Large amounts of heat are given off when gasoline is burned in the cylinders of an engine. Also, an engine contains many moving parts that rub against each other. Even though oil lubricates engine parts, enough friction still exists to produce heat. Because excessive heat can seriously damage the engine, cars have a cooling system that controls engine temperature.

A car's cooling system consists of a radiator, hoses, and channels that are filled with a mixture of water and antifreeze, called a coolant. The channels carry the coolant through the engine block. The engine block contains the cylinders and other moving parts that get hot when the engine is running.

A pump circulates the coolant through the engine. Heat is transferred to the coolant as it flows over hot engine parts. The heated coolant then moves away from the engine and through the hoses to the car's radiator.

Look at the radiator in Figure 9.3. Follow the path of the coolant as it moves through the radiator. Inside the radiator, the heated coolant passes through metal tubes. Heat transfers from the coolant to the metal tubes by conduction. Metal fins surrounding the tubes absorb the heat and transfer it into air circulating around the fins. In this way, the coolant mixture loses the heat it receives from the engine. The coolant is no longer as hot and is pumped back to the engine where the cycle starts over again!

Check and Explain

1. How are heat and moving molecules related?

2. Negative temperature readings are common on the Celsius scale. Explain why you don't get a negative reading on the Kelvin scale.

3. **Compare** How do the temperature, internal energy, and heat energy in a cup of hot tea change overnight?

4. **Define Operationally** Suppose you put some hot water in the refrigerator for two hours. Explain what happens to the molecules of water.

Themes in Science
Systems and Interactions
Explain that not all substances conduct heat at the same rate. Substances that transfer heat quickly are good conductors. Poor conductors are often used as insulators to reduce the transfer of energy. Ask students why many pots and pans have copper bottoms and wood or plastic handles. (Copper is a good conductor, while wood and plastic are not.)

STS Connection
Present the following scenario to students: Doors are being selected for the south side of a school building in northern Minnesota. Have students discuss the materials and color they would select for the doors. They should explain their choices in terms of heat conduction and conservation, both internally and externally.

9.2 Transfer of Heat

Objectives

▶ **Identify** three ways heat is transferred.

▶ **Explain** how heat transfer is measured.

▶ **Calculate** the amount of heat transferred between two substances.

▶ **Infer** how heat transfer affects climate.

H ave you ever cooked food in a cast-iron skillet? You probably used a pot holder to insulate your hand from the heat of the skillet's handle. Did you wonder why the handle was hot even though it didn't come in direct contact with the burner? Heat energy is transferred from the bottom of the skillet, up through the sides, and into the handle by the process of conduction. Heat is also transferred by convection and radiation.

Conduction

Heat energy flows from a warm substance to a cool substance. When solid substances are in contact, heat energy transfers by **conduction**. Conduction is the transfer of heat energy throughout a substance, or when one substance comes in contact with another.

When you put the lower part of a spoon in boiling water, heat transfers from the boiling water to the cool spoon. The spoon's molecules that are in contact with the water move more rapidly and collide with the molecules in the upper portion of the spoon. Through a continuous series of collisions, heat energy transfers throughout the entire spoon. The hot spoon handle is evidence that heat energy has been transferred.

Some materials conduct heat better than others. For example, a cloth pot holder conducts heat poorly. It is an insulator. Wood, plastic, and glass are also insulators. Look at Figure 9.4. The sun heats the wood door and the metal doorknob on the outside. Soon, the inside doorknob gets hot also. Why doesn't the inside of the door get hot? ③

▼ ACTIVITY

| Hypothesizing |

Spooning

Collect the following items: an all-metal spoon, a metal spoon with a plastic handle, and a mug of boiling water.

1. Place the two spoons in the mug of boiling water.

2. Gently touch the handles of the spoons after two minutes. Touch the handles again after five minutes.

Write a hypothesis to explain what you observe. How could you test your hypothesis further?

SKILLS WARMUP

Knob heated by radiation   Knob heated by conduction

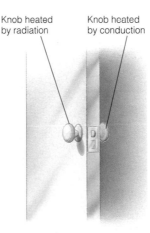

Figure 9.4 ▲
Which methods of heat transfer contribute to heating the inside doorknob? ②

SECTION

9.2

Section Objectives
For a list of section objectives, see the Student Edition page.

Skills Objectives
Students should be able to:

Hypothesize about the conduction of heat energy.

Infer how weather patterns would change if the earth tilted 90 degrees.

Calculate the specific heat of metal.

Predict what materials are the best insulators.

Vocabulary
conduction, convection, radiation, specific heat, calorie

MOTIVATE

Skills WarmUp
To help students understand transfer of heat, have them do the Skills WarmUp.
Answer Hypothesis: The handle of an all-metal spoon will heat and cool more rapidly than the plastic-handled spoon. Students could test their hypotheses by trying spoons made of different metals and a variety of other substances.

Answers to In-Text Questions
② Conduction and radiation
③ The inside of the door doesn't get hot because wood is an insulator.

 The Living Textbook: Physical Science Sides 1-4

Chapter 17   Frame 02898
Conduction (2 Frames)
Search: Step:

Misconceptions

Some students may think that the term *fluid* only refers to liquids. Stress that a fluid is either a liquid or a gas and that moving currents flow in both kinds of fluids.

Explore Visually

Have students study this page. Then ask:

▶ Where do air molecules go when you heat an oven? (They move faster, spread apart, become less dense, and rise. Some excess heat escapes into the room from the oven vents.)

▶ Why do convection currents keep forming in the oven? (As long as there is a heat source, the air near it will warm up and rise, forcing cooler air down toward the heat source.)

▶ What happens to the currents as you turn up the heat? (They move faster and faster.)

▶ Why will the bottom of the bread brown faster than the top? (It is subject to a higher temperature.)

The Living Textbook: Physical Science Sides 1-4

Chapter 17   Frame 02906
Convection (2 Frames)
Search: Step:

The Living Textbook: Physical Science Sides 1-4

Chapter 17   Frame 02908
Convection Current (2 Frames)
Search: Step:

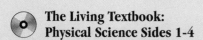

214

Themes in Science
Patterns of Change/Cycles

Explain that the pattern of convection currents is always the same: hot air rises, cold air sinks. This is because cool air is denser, or has more mass per volume. You may wish to help students understand that warm gases are less dense than cool gases by reviewing phase changes.

Convection

Air in contact with a wood-burning stove spreads out to warm an entire room. Water boils when heated in a pan. These are examples of heat transfer by a process called **convection**. Convection is the transfer of heat energy by the movement of a fluid, such as a liquid or a gas.

Heat energy flows through a fluid in a pattern called a convection current. Convection currents form because heated fluid expands and is less dense than surrounding fluid, which is cooler. The difference in the density causes warm fluid to rise and cooler fluid to sink. The result is a convection current that moves heat energy through the fluid.

If you have ever boiled water, then you have observed convection currents in a liquid. Convection currents cause the rolling motion of gently boiling water. The water at the bottom of the pan heats up. The heated water molecules move faster, spread apart, and become less dense. They rise to the surface. Cooler, denser water at the top moves downward toward the bottom of the pan. This water then heats up and rises. Convection currents continue to form as long as there is a heat source.

To understand how convection currents form in a gas, think about how heat moves in an oven. Look at the convection currents that circulate hot air in the oven in Figure 9.5. Trace the movement of the convection currents with your finger.

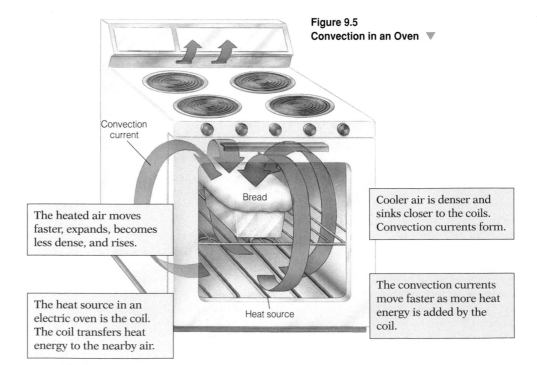

**Figure 9.5
Convection in an Oven** ▼

Convection current

The heated air moves faster, expands, becomes less dense, and rises.

Bread

The heat source in an electric oven is the coil. The coil transfers heat energy to the nearby air.

Heat source

Cooler air is denser and sinks closer to the coils. Convection currents form.

The convection currents move faster as more heat energy is added by the coil.

Integrating the Sciences

Astronomy Tell students that the sun's energy comes from a chain of reactions that convert mass directly into tremendous amounts of energy. The temperature at the sun's core, where most of these reactions take place, is estimated to be 15 million degrees Celsius.

Radiation

Every time you feel the sun or a fire warm your skin, you experience **radiation.** Both the sun and fire give off radiation. Radiation is the transfer of energy primarily by infrared waves. When infrared waves strike your skin, the molecules in your skin vibrate faster and become warmer. Radiation can move energy over long distances.

Radiation differs from conduction and convection because matter isn't needed to transfer energy by radiation. Recall that conduction depends on the collision between the molecules of a substance. Convection depends on the expansion of a fluid when molecules collide. However, radiation can occur in a vacuum, where no molecules of matter are present.

Any form of energy that is transferred by radiation is called radiant energy. Radiant energy and radiation shouldn't be confused with harmful radioactivity, or nuclear radiation. All rays from the sun are forms of radiant energy that transfer by radiation. When any object gets hot, it gives off radiant energy. For example, if you move your hand close to a fire or hot electric coil, you can feel radiant energy.

Matter can reflect or absorb radiant energy. Look at Figure 9.6. Most of the sun's radiant energy that reaches the earth is in the form of light. Observe that the earth and its atmosphere reflect and absorb radiant energy from the sun. When radiant energy is absorbed, it is later re-radiated as heat. The heat increases the temperature of the atmosphere.

Figure 9.6   Solar Radiation ▼

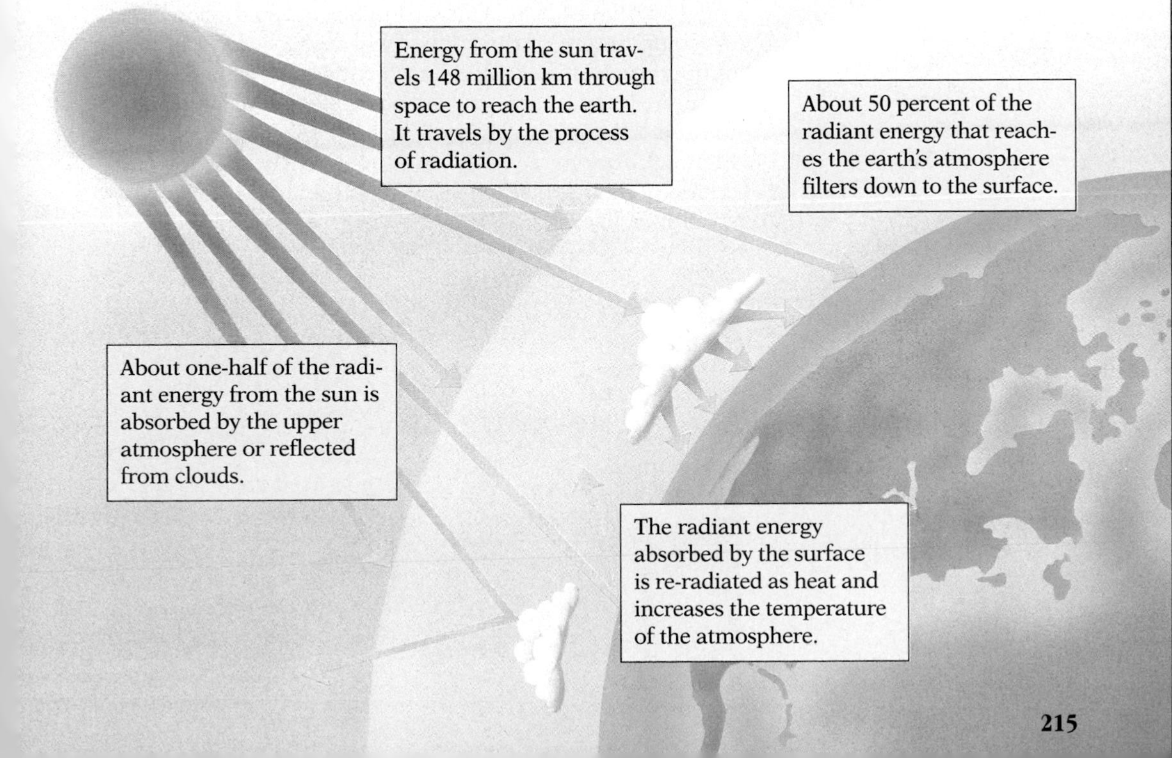

Energy from the sun travels 148 million km through space to reach the earth. It travels by the process of radiation.

About 50 percent of the radiant energy that reaches the earth's atmosphere filters down to the surface.

About one-half of the radiant energy from the sun is absorbed by the upper atmosphere or reflected from clouds.

The radiant energy absorbed by the surface is re-radiated as heat and increases the temperature of the atmosphere.

Directed Inquiry

Have students study the text and Figure 9.6 on this page. Then discuss the following questions:

▶ Why can radiation occur in a vacuum? (It can move heat energy without conduction or convection, so it is independent of matter.)

▶ What is radiant energy? (It is energy transferred by infrared waves.)

▶ What percent of the sun's radiant energy reaches the earth's surface? (50 percent)

▶ Why does sunlight cause the temperature to go up? (Sunlight is absorbed by the earth, and then re-radiated as heat, which warms the air.)

▶ **Infer** When radiant energy is absorbed by the earth's solid surface, what kind of heat transfer takes place as it moves through the earth? (Conduction)

▶ **Infer** What kind of heat transfer occurs as warm air currents move through the earth's atmosphere? (Convection)

 **The Living Textbook:
Physical Science Sides 1-4**

Chapter 9   Frame 01603
Sun's Radiant Energy to Earth (1 Frame)
Search:

 **The Living Textbook:
Physical Science Sides 1-4**

Chapter 13   Frame 02186
Sun Radiating Energy (1 Frame)
Search:

TEACH ▪ *Continued*

Directed Inquiry

After students read this page, ask the following questions:

▶ How can specific heat be used to identify a substance? (Every substance has a different specific heat)

▶ Of the substances listed in Table 9.1, which substance has the highest specific heat? Which has the lowest? (Water; gold)

▶ Why do you think gold has a lower specific heat than air? (It is a solid and can conduct heat more rapidly.)

▶ **Infer** If you have 1 kg of two substances and apply the same amount of heat to each, which will get warm first? (The one with the lowest specific heat)

Answers to In-Text Questions

① The specific heat of tin is lower than that of aluminum and copper.

② Aluminum, 899; copper, 385; tin, 213

③ Divide the number of joules by 4.186 to get calories.

**The Living Textbook:
Physical Science Sides 1-4**

Chapter 17   Frame 03350
Specific Heat (2 Frames)
Search: Step:

Math Connection

Remind students that the joule is a unit of energy. Ask them how much heat is needed to raise the temperature of a kilogram of water from 20°C to 100°C. Help them work the problem by showing them how to cancel the units involved.
(4186 J/kg°C × 1 kg × 80°C = 334 900 J)

Integrating the Sciences

Meteorology Explain that water can absorb and store a lot of heat energy. Large bodies of water, such as lakes and oceans, absorb heat during the day and release it slowly at night, thus moderating nearby temperatures. Have students check national weather reports and compare coastal regions to inland areas to find evidence of this phenomenon.

Table 9.1   Specific Heats

Substance	Specific Heat (J/kg°C)
Water	4186
Wood	1750
Air	1000
Aluminum	899
Carbon (graphite)	711
Sand	664
Iron	443
Copper	385
Tin	213
Gold	130

Measuring Heat Transfer

Wooden spoons are often used in cooking to stir hot liquids and sauces. As you know, wood is a poor conductor, so the handle of the spoon stays cool while the hot liquid is stirred. There is another reason wooden spoons are used in cooking. Not only is wood a poor conductor, its temperature increases less than many other substances when it absorbs heat energy. For example, when metal and wooden spoons of equal mass absorb the same amount of heat energy, the wooden spoon's temperature increases less.

Specific Heat The effect of heat energy on a substance's temperature is a physical property of that substance. Each substance requires a different amount of heat to raise its temperature 1°C. The amount of heat 1 g of a substance must absorb to raise its temperature 1°C is called the **specific heat** of the substance. Specific heat can be used to identify a substance.

Look at Table 9.1 to compare the specific heat of some common substances. For example, the specific heat of copper is lower than the specific heat of water. When an equal amount of heat is applied to both copper and water, the temperature of the copper will be higher than the temperature of the water. Less heat energy is needed to raise the temperature of 1 kg of copper than is needed to raise the temperature of 1 kg of water. The items in Figure 9.7 are made of different metals. Use Table 9.1 to compare their specific heat. Which metal has the lowest specific heat? ①

Figure 9.7 ▶
These items are made of aluminum, copper, and tin. What is the specific heat of each metal? ②

Integrating the Sciences

Oceanography Tell students that the temperature of ocean water is higher at the surface due to the energy absorbed from sunlight. The temperature of water at the ocean bottom seldom goes below 4°C. Ask students to discuss and explain how the circulation of ocean water at the surface compares with the circulation at the ocean bottom. Ask students to compare the specific heat of seawater to distilled water.

Calories You know that the official SI unit of heat is the joule. Another unit still commonly used to measure heat is the **calorie**. One calorie equals 4.186 J. One calorie is the amount of heat needed to raise the temperature of 1 g of water 1°C. Five calories of heat are needed to raise the temperature of 1 g of water 5°C.

Scientists in the 1700s thought that heat was an invisible substance they called *caloric* (kuh LOR ihk). Today's word *calorie* comes from the word caloric. A device called the calorimeter was invented to measure the amount of heat given off when a substance is burned. The calorimeter is still used today.

Look at the calorimeter in Figure 9.8. A thick layer of insulation surrounds the

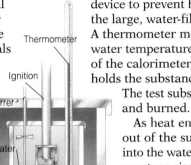

Figure 9.8 ▲
A Calorimeter

device to prevent heat loss from the large, water-filled chamber. A thermometer measures the water temperature. In the center of the calorimeter, a chamber holds the substance being tested. The test substance is ignited and burned.

As heat energy flows out of the substance and into the water, the water temperature rises. The amount of heat gained by the water equals the amount of heat lost by the substance being tested. To calculate the joules of heat lost, multiply the mass of the water times the specific heat of the water times the temperature change of the water. How would you convert the result into calories? ③

Sample Problem

How much heat is needed to raise the temperature of 0.5 kg of aluminum from 15°C to 20°C?

Plan Multiply the mass by the specific heat by the change in temperature.

Gather Data
 a. Specific heat = 899 J/kg°C (See Table 9.1)
 b. Mass = 0.5 kg
 c. The temperature difference is
  20°C − 15°C = 5°C

Solve Heat = mass × specific heat × change in temperature

 heat = 0.5 kg × 899 J/kg°C × 5°C
 heat = 2247.5 J

Practice Problems

1. How much heat is needed to raise the temperature of 0.02 kg of iron from 20°C to 30°C?

2. How much heat is needed to raise the temperature of 5 g of gold from 15°C to 25°C?

3. How much heat is given off by 30 g of tin as it cools from 90°C to 20°C?

4. On a hot stove burner, the temperature of a 500 g aluminum pan increases 120°C. How much heat was added?

5. You receive an unknown substance. A note with the substance says that to increase the temperature of 100 g of the substance 1°C, about 21.5 J of heat is needed. What is the unknown substance?

Explore Visually

Have students study Figure 9.9, then discuss the following questions:

▶ What influences the angle of solar radiation that reaches your home? (The positions of the sun and the earth; latitude and longitude)

▶ Where would you go on the earth to receive the most direct waves of radiant energy? (Near the equator)

▶ Why are Alaska and Antarctica cooler than Equador? (Near the North and South poles, the sun's rays strike the earth at an angle. So these regions receive less solar radiation.)

▶ How do convection cells form above the earth? (Heat re-radiated from the ground warms the air. Warm air is less dense, so it rises. Eventually, the air cools and sinks to the ground where it is warmed again.)

Geography Connection

Help students identify the approximate location of your school on a globe. Have them determine the angle of the sun's rays as they fall on your location at this time of year. Relate this to the type of climate you have. (Have students first do the Skills Development on page 219.)
Use Integrating Worksheet 9.2.

Multicultural Perspectives

Have students work in groups of four to find out how people around the world have developed shelters to protect them in different climates. Be sure the class covers most continents of the world. Have each group make a picture or a model to show how its shelter is well suited to a particular climate. Also have students consider what kinds of building materials are available.

Heat Transfer and Climate

Imagine that you win a vacation to any place in the world. Where would you like to go? You'd probably like a location that has a climate quite different from your own. You might pick a warm, tropical climate, where you could swim any day of the year. Perhaps you'd prefer to go to a cold, snowy place, where you could ski in July!

Think about places on the earth that have different climates. For example, you know that if you travel to a region near the equator, the weather will probably be hot and humid. You know if you head to

the far north, it will probably be cold and snowy. Why do different locations on the earth's surface have different types of climates? The differences in weather conditions are due to the transfer of heat energy. The heat-transfer processes of conduction, convection, and radiation all play a role in determining weather and climate.

Solar Radiation Heat energy from the sun reaches the earth by radiation. As the earth moves around the sun, some places receive more solar radiation than others. Solar radiation is the most intense when the sun is directly overhead.

The Living Textbook: Physical Science Sides 1-4

Chapter 10   Frame 01877
Solar Radiation (1 Frame)
Search:

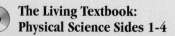

The Living Textbook: Physical Science Sides 1-4

Chapter 9   Frame 01607
Rays in Different Seasons (1 Frame)
Search:

Figure 9.9   Heat and Climate ▼

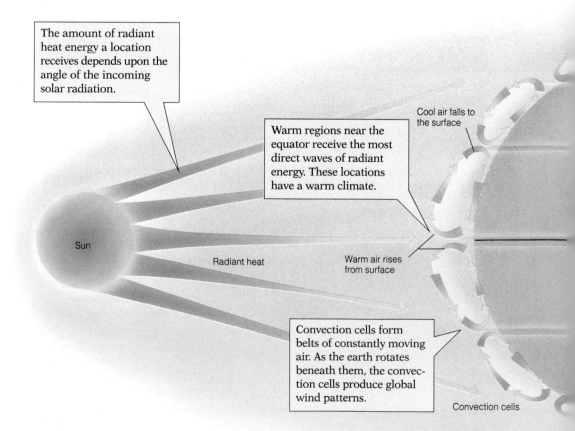

The amount of radiant heat energy a location receives depends upon the angle of the incoming solar radiation.

Warm regions near the equator receive the most direct waves of radiant energy. These locations have a warm climate.

Cool air falls to the surface

Warm air rises from surface

Radiant heat

Sun

Convection cells form belts of constantly moving air. As the earth rotates beneath them, the convection cells produce global wind patterns.

Convection cells

Integrating the Sciences

Earth Science Explain to students that not all equatorial regions have lush rain forests. Have students find out why the equatorial regions of Africa have different and sparser vegetation than those of Asia and South America. Have them give a general description of the different types of vegetation. (Students should compare the jungle to the Serengeti and desert regions. Also, they should mention the monsoon rain patterns.)

STS Connection

Explain that a sailplane, a type of glider, uses the sun's energy indirectly. Point out that some areas on the earth's surface absorb the sun's heat more quickly than other areas. These hot spots, such as dry plains and deserts, produce rising columns of heated air called *thermals*. Sailplanes can ride thermals for great distances. Have students find out how people have designed sailplanes to be energy efficient.

▶ Where do convection cells form? (All around the earth)

▶ Why do you think tundra occurs near the North Pole? (Little solar radiation reaches the North Pole, making it cool, so plant growth is sparse.)

▶ **Infer** Why do lush rain forests grow near the equator but not in the far north? (A great deal of solar radiation reaches the equator, and plants use sunlight to grow. The climate is warm, and there is much rain. The sun and rain cause more lush growth.)

Skills Development

Infer Ask students which areas on the earth have sunlight from directly overhead on the first day of summer and winter. How is climate affected by this occurrence? Why? (Sunlight comes from directly overhead at the Tropic of Cancer on the first day of summer. On the first day of winter, sunlight comes from directly overhead at the Tropic of Capricorn. The temperature increases in summer because the sun's rays travel a shorter distance through the atmosphere. In winter, the temperature is lower because the sun's rays must travel farther through the atmosphere.)

Decision Making

If you have classroom sets of *One-Minute Readings,* have students read Issue 50 "Convection" on pages 85 and 86. Discuss the questions.

At the extreme northern or southern latitudes, solar radiation strikes the earth at a low angle. The sun's rays must travel a long distance through the atmosphere to reach the surface. As a result, northern and southern latitudes receive less solar radiation than the equator does. The climate at these latitudes is cool.

Heat in the Atmosphere Radiant energy from the sun warms the earth's surface. The earth's surface transfers heat to the air by conduction. Actually, the air around you is warmed by the earth, which is heated by the sun.

Convection currents form as air is heated by the earth's surface. Warm air expands and rises. It displaces the cool, dense air at higher elevations. The dense air sinks.

The warm rising air carries moisture to higher elevations. As the air cools, the moisture condenses and falls to the earth as rain or snow. Convection currents in the atmosphere are called convection cells. Convection cells are responsible for the wind and rain patterns over the earth's surface. Look at Figure 9.9 to see how radiation, conduction, and convection affect climate.

Areas of sparse growth, called tundra, are located in the region near the North Pole.

Equator

Lush rain forests grow in the sunny, wet climate near the equator.

Convection cells

The Living Textbook:
Physical Science Sides 1-4

Chapter 9　　　　Frame 01605
Rays at Different Latitudes (2 Frames)
Search:　　　　　　Step:

Skills Development

Infer Explain to students that in aerobic exercise classes, the heart rate is often raised for at least 30 minutes, which burns a lot of Calories. Ask students, Why is it important for people to get aerobic exercise regularly? (Aerobic exercise promotes oxygen use in the body, which increases metabolism and helps control weight. It may also reduce the risk of heart disease.)

EVALUATE

WrapUp

Reinforce Remind students that heat is lost through windows, especially in the winter. Have a class discussion about the ways heat could leave a house through conduction, convection, and radiation. Make a class display showing these things. Discuss and add to the display a list of ways to reduce heat loss through windows.

Use Review Worksheet 9.2.

Check and Explain

1. Conduction: by transferring heat energy from molecule to molecule; convection: by the movement of a fluid; radiation: by infrared rays

2. Temperature changes, measured with thermometers or a calorimeter

3. 115.5 J

4. Countries at the poles would warm up. Weather in countries on the equator would be warm or cold depending on their new latitude.

Integrating the Sciences

Biology Explain that the human body gets energy from the chemical bonds of foods—carbohydrates, lipids, and proteins. Point out that the ultimate source of that energy is the sun. Ask students, What is the link between the sun's energy and the energy found in foods? (Green plants and photosynthesis)

Zoology Tell students that the normal body temperature for most birds is 40°C. Because birds have a higher body temperature than mammals, they need more food in relation to their sizes to maintain that higher temperature. Have students find out the amount of food consumed daily by different birds. (The kinglet, a tiny bird, eats one-third of its weight; the starling eats one-eighth.)

Science and You *Food Calories and Energy*

Diet! Exercise! Calories! You hear these words used together all the time. Radio, television, and magazines carry ads for products that will help you to consume fewer calories or to burn them off. But what does the calorie, a unit of heat, have to do with diet and exercise?

To determine the amount of heat energy available in food, it is burned in a calorimeter. Do you know what unit is used to measure the heat energy released? If you said the *calorie*, you wouldn't be quite right. A calorie is too small a quantity to conveniently measure the energy in food. A chocolate chip cookie has 75 000 calories!

Instead of writing 75 000 calories, nutritionists write 75 Calories. Notice that *Calorie* is written with a capital C. When a capital C is used, it refers to a *food* Calorie, which is 1,000 calories, or a kilocalorie. The unit *Calorie* is always used when referring to the energy in food.

Your body uses food energy to perform all your activities, to maintain your body temperature, and to function. Compare the energy requirements for the activities in Table 9.2. Even when you do absolutely nothing, your body gives off heat at a rate of about 1,200 Calories each day!

If you reduce your Calorie intake by dieting, your body still needs energy in order to function properly. It gets some of that energy by breaking down its own tissues. Your body will break down both fat and muscle tissue to use as energy when your food intake is inadequate.

Table 9.2   Calorie Use

Activity	Calories per Minute
Running	13.0
Swimming	8.0
Dancing	6.5
Bicycling	6.0
Walking	3.5
Resting	0.8

Check and Explain

1. What are three ways heat can be transferred? Describe how each occurs.

2. What evidence indicates heat transfers either into or out of a substance? How can it be measured?

3. **Calculate** The specific heat of copper is 385 J/kg°C. How much heat is needed to raise the temperature of 20 g of copper from 25°C to 40°C?

4. **Infer** What would happen to the weather if the earth turned "on its side" so that the equator and poles switched places?

Prelab Discussion

Have students read the entire activity. As an alternative to heating the objects over a flame, you may wish to have students submerge the objects in a beaker of boiling water (100°C). Discuss a few points before beginning:

▶ Why is it important to use foam cups?

▶ What are some possible sources of heat loss? How might they affect the results?

▶ Caution students against handling containers of boiling water.

Time 60 minutes   **Group** pairs

Materials

30 plastic foam cups

15 Celsius thermometers

15 pairs of tongs

15 bolts

15 nuts

15 large paper clips

Bunsen burners

15 marking pens

15 pencils

clock that can measure seconds

Analysis

1. The temperature of the water rose because it gained heat from the hot object.

2. The amount of heat transferred depends on the specific heat of each object and its mass. Student answers should agree with their recorded data.

Conclusion

You could use the setup from this activity to measure the change in temperature of water caused by the warm keys.

Activity 9 *How do you measure the transfer of heat?*

Skills Measure; Calculate; infer

Task 1 Prelab Prep

1. Collect the following items: 2 plastic foam cups, pen, pencil, graduated cylinder, Celsius thermometer, tongs, Bunsen burner, bolt, nut, large paperclip, clock that can measure seconds.

2. With the pen, number the cups *1* and *2*.

Task 2 Data Record

1. On a separate sheet of paper, draw a data table like the one shown.

2. Notice that the column titled *Mass of water* is shown in grams (g). Recall that 1 mL of water has a mass of 1 g. You will need to measure 75 mL, or 75 g, of water with the graduated cylinder.

3. Record the initial water temperature in column T_i. Record the highest temperature in column T_f. Subtract T_i from T_f.

4. To calculate the heat transferred to the water, use the following formula: heat = mass of the water × temperature change × specific heat. The specific heat of water is 4186 J/kg × °C.

Task 3 Procedure

1. Measure 75 mL of tap water with a graduated cylinder and pour it into the cup labeled *1*.

2. With a sharp pencil, make a small hole in the side of cup *2* near the rim. Gently ease a

thermometer through the hole. Place cup *2* upside down over cup *1* so the rims meet. Adjust the thermometer bulb so it is completely submerged in the water in cup *1*. Hold the thermometer in place.

3. Light the Bunsen burner. **CAUTION! Tie back loose hair and clothing around an open flame.**

4. Record the temperature of the water, T_i, in your data table.

5. With the tongs hold the bolt in the flame for 10 s. **CAUTION! metal objects will become very hot. Use tongs.**

6. Lift cup *2* and gently drop the bolt into the water in cup *1*. Immediately replace cup *2*. Keep the thermometer bulb in the water.

7. Record the highest temperature, T_f, in your data table.

8. Replace the water in cup *1* with fresh tap water. Repeat steps 4–7 using the nut, and again using the paperclip.

Task 4 Analysis

1. Why did the temperature of the water rise?

2. How did the amount of heat transferred from each object differ? Why?

Task 5 Conclusion

A set of keys near a portable heater gets hot. How would you apply the method used in this activity to determine how much heat energy was transferred to the keys?

Table 9.3 Heat Transfer

Heated object	Mass of water (g)	T_i (°C)	T_f (°C)	Temperature change T_f–T_i (°C)	Heat transferred (J)
bolt	75				
nut	75				
paperclip	75				

Themes in Science

Patterns of Change/Cycles Point out that all substances require heat to change from a solid to a liquid or a liquid to a gas. Similarly, all substances give off heat when they change from a gas to a liquid or a liquid to a solid.

Integrating the Sciences

Meteorology Explain that sublimation is the change in phase of any substance directly from solid to vapor. Wet clothes hung outside in sub-zero weather will dry. For sublimation to occur, 680 calories per gram must be given off. Have students find out how much heat is required for the water-to-gas phase (600 calories) and for the ice-to-liquid phase (80 calories). How does this compare to the heat exchange during sublimation? (It's the same.)

Section Objectives
For a list of section objectives, see the Student Edition page.

Skills Objectives
Students should be able to:

Make a Model of temperature changes.

Interpret Data in a graph and in a table and use it to identify unknown substances.

Generalize about the movement of molecules at melting and boiling points.

Interpret Data to identify a substance by its melting point.

Vocabulary
boiling point, melting point, thermal expansion

MOTIVATE

Skills WarmUp
To help students understand heat and matter, have them do the Skills WarmUp.
Answer Students' pictures will vary. Remind students that only heat energy moves.

Prior Knowledge
Gauge how much students know about heat and matter by asking, What are the three phases of matter, and how is heat related to them?

Answers to In-Text Questions
① She expects the beach to be warm.

② She would probably use little or no ice if she could leave her cooler in the snow, or even fill it with snow.

③ Liquid water turns solid as heat leaves it.

▼ **ACTIVITY**

Modeling

Running a Temperature

1. Draw three pictures showing objects undergoing temperature changes.

2. Beneath each picture, write "temperature increasing" or "temperature decreasing."

3. Use arrows to show whether heat is moving into or out of the object.

SKILLS WARMUP

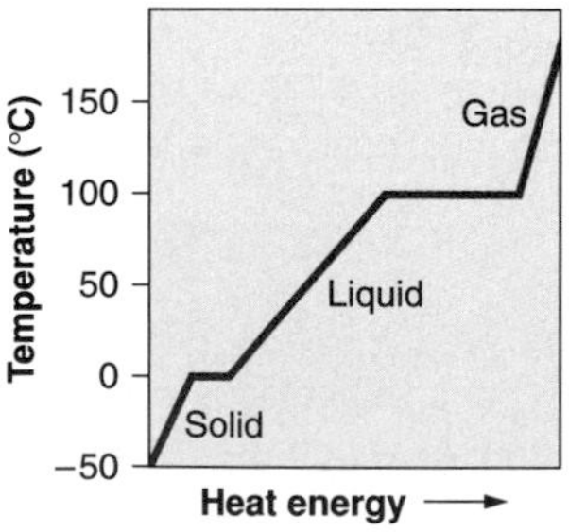

Figure 9.10 ▲
Notice that during phase changes, heat is added without an increase in temperature.

9.3 Heat and Matter

Objectives

▶ **Describe** the role of heat in phase changes.

▶ **Identify** three examples of thermal expansion.

▶ **Generalize** about what occurs at the boiling point or melting point of a substance.

▶ **Interpret data** to identify an unknown substance by its boiling point.

Sandra packed a picnic lunch to take to the beach. She put a container of yogurt, some carrot sticks, an apple, and a bottle of juice in a small cooler. Sandra then placed some ice cubes in the cooler. What do Sandra's actions tell you about the temperature conditions she expected at the beach? Suppose Sandra was ① going to spend the day snow skiing. How would the way she packed her lunch be different? ②

Heat and Phase Changes

Recall that matter can change phases from solid to liquid to gas. When heat sufficiently increases the motion of molecules in a substance, a phase change occurs. Look at Figure 9.10 to see how heat affects the temperature and the phases of water.

When heat is applied to ice, the water molecules in the ice vibrate faster. The ice melts as it changes from a solid to a liquid. The temperature doesn't change until all the ice melts. When all the ice is melted, additional heat causes the temperature of liquid water to rise again until it reaches 100°C. At 100°C, a phase change occurs and the water evaporates, or changes to its gaseous phase.

Phase changes also occur when heat leaves matter. For example, water vapor in the air condenses, or changes from a gas to a liquid, on the outside of a glass of ice water. Condensation occurs because the temperature of the water vapor decreases when it comes in contact with the cold glass. The water vapor undergoes a phase change and becomes a liquid. What kind of phase change occurs when you make ice cubes in your freezer? ③

Integrating the Sciences

Earth Science Explain to students that the phase changes known as *evaporation* and *condensation* play an important role in the water cycle. Have several students draw diagrams on the chalkboard showing how heat affects the water cycle.

Botany When a dramatic drop in air temperature is foreseen, people can take precautions to save crops from freezing. One technique involves sprinkling plants with plenty of water. Ask students how they think this technique protects plants from cold temperatures. (The water freezes around the plant; ice is a good insulator because it must lose a relatively large amount of energy in order to freeze.)

Boiling Point

Think about what happens when you heat a beaker of water. After a time, the liquid water enters the gas phase. This change occurs when the water reaches its **boiling point**. The boiling point is the temperature at which a substance changes from a liquid phase to a gas phase.

In order for a substance to reach its boiling point, it must gain heat energy. Study Figure 9.11. How did the water molecules in the beaker gain heat energy to reach the boiling point? ④

As the molecules in the liquid gain heat energy, their motion increases. The amount of internal energy in the liquid also increases. Eventually, the molecules have so much energy that they break free of the liquid surface and move away as a gas. In Figure 9.11, water molecules rise from the beaker as steam.

Every substance has its own boiling point. You know that water boils at 100°C. The chemical element fluorine boils at about -188°C. Nitrogen boils at about -196°C. The boiling point of copper is 2,595°C. Since air pressure affects boiling, standard boiling-point measurements are made at sea level.

Figure 9.11
Liquid-Gas Phase Change ▼

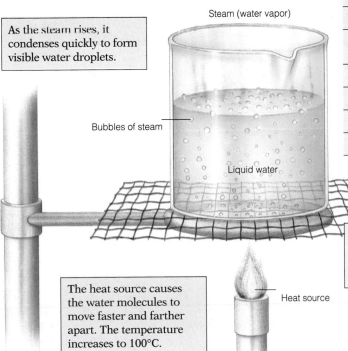

As the steam rises, it condenses quickly to form visible water droplets.

Steam (water vapor)

Bubbles of steam

Liquid water

When water approaches 100°C, molecules escape the surface of the liquid as water vapor, or steam.

The heat source causes the water molecules to move faster and farther apart. The temperature increases to 100°C.

Heat source

Table 9.4 Boiling Point of Common Substances	
Substance	**°C at Sea Level**
Mercury	356.9
Water	100.0
Isopropyl alcohol	82.5
Acetone	56.5
Ether	35.0
Oxygen	−183.0
Nitrogen	−195.8

TEACH

Skills Development
Predict Ask students, What will happen to rain puddles in the sun? (Heat turns the water into a gas, which moves into the air.)

Directed Inquiry
Ask students the following:

► What happens to a liquid when it reaches its boiling point? (It changes from liquid to gas.)

► How does increased energy affect water molecules? (Their motion increases and they move farther apart.)

► **Infer** What causes condensation? (Steam contacts cold air or a cold surface, loses heat, and turns back into a liquid.)

Enrich
Explain that when water reaches its boiling point, the pressure in the bubbles of steam equals the pressure of the surrounding air. At sea level, air pressure is about 101 300 Pa, and water boils at 100°C. At higher altitudes, air pressure is lower, so the pressures equalize at a lower temperature. For example, at 4,301 meters, the height of Pikes Peak in Colorado, water boils at 85°C. Ask students what problems this might cause for cooking. (Since water boils at a lower temperature, it may not be hot enough to cook food.)

Answer to in-Text Question
④ The flame heated the glass. Heat from the glass warmed water molecules and spread by convection.

 The Living Textbook: Physical Science Sides 1-4

Chapter 5   Frame 01076
Ice Melting (8 Frames)
Search: Step:

223

TEACH ▪ Continued

Skills Development

Interpret Data Ask students to interpret Table 9.5 by asking, What is the phase of mercury at 0°C? Why? (It is a liquid, because its melting point is –39°C.)

SkillBuilder

Answers

1. A—iron
   B—silver
   C—aluminum
   D—tin
   E—phosphorus

2. Iron, silver, and aluminum would be solids at 600°C. Tin, possibly polyethylene, and phosphorus would be liquid.

3. Iron, silver, aluminum, and tin would be solids at 200°C. Phosphorus, and possibly polyethylene, would be liquid.

4. They cannot all be liquids at the same time because of their boiling points (see Table 9.4).

5. At –219°C

6. Because the melting point and freezing point are the same

Enrich

Have students draw the graph in the SkillBuilder using the Kelvin scale. Then ask, What are the melting points of these five substances, using the Kelvin scale? (Iron—1808 K, silver—1233 K, aluminum—933 K, tin—505 K, phosphorus—317 K) Have students answer question 5 in the SkillBuilder using Kelvin. (54 K)
Use Enrich Worksheet 9.3.

**The Living Textbook:
Physical Science Sides 1-4**

Chapter 5   Frame 01102
Expansion (4 Frames)
Search: Step:

Cooperative Learning

Have students work in pairs to investigate what happens when they add ice cubes to a glass of water at room temperature. Where does that heat go? What is the temperature of the water at the surface and at the bottom when all the ice has melted? (Heat energy from the water melts the ice. Temperature should be 0°–18°C; coldest at the bottom.)

Portfolio

Have students draw two examples of melting caused by radiant energy. Ask them to write a description of the movement of heat energy in each instance. (Sun can melt snow or hail, tar on a hot day, candy or ice cream, and so on.) Students can add the descriptions to their portfolios.

Table 9.5   Melting Point of Common Substances

Substance	Melting Point °C
Iron	1,535.0
Silver	960.5
Aluminum	660.0
Tin	232.0
Polyethylene plastic	85.0
Phosphorus	44.0
Water (Ice)	0.0
Mercury	–39.0
Oxygen	–218.4

Melting Point

What happens to ice cream on a very hot day? If you don't eat it quickly, the ice cream changes phase—from a solid to a liquid. This occurs when the ice cream reaches its **melting point**. The melting point is the temperature at which a solid becomes a liquid. Heat energy moves from the warm air to the ice cream. The molecules in the ice cream move about more rapidly and the solid ice cream becomes a liquid.

You know the melting point of ice is 0°C. The freezing point of water is also 0°C. For any substance, the melting and freezing points are always at the same temperature. If heat energy is applied to ice at 0°C, the ice will melt. If liquid water at 0°C is cooled further, it will freeze.

Every substance has its own melting point. Melting point is an important physical property of a substance. Look at Table 9.5. Scientists use melting-point tables to help identify unknown substances.

SkillBuilder Interpreting Data

Melting Points

The melting point of a substance is a physical property that can be used to identify the substance. Most substances have a melting point that is different than the melting point of other substances. The bar graph at the right shows the melting point of five unknown substances. Study the graph. Use the graph and Table 9.5 above to answer the following questions.

1. What substance does each bar in the graph represent? Copy the graph on a sheet of paper and label each bar with the correct substance.

2. Which substances would be solid at 600°C? Which would be liquid?

3. Which substances would be solid at 200°C? Which would be liquid?

4. At what temperature would all the substances be liquids?

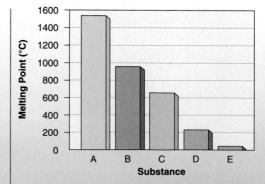

5. At what temperature would all the substances be solids?

6. Explain why the vertical axis of the graph could also have been labeled "Freezing point (°C)"?

Integrating the Sciences

Earth Science Explain to students that water is an exception to the thermal expansion principle. Because water expands as it nears its freezing point, icebergs float. Ask students to explain this. (Because water expands as it freezes, ice is less dense than liquid water, and icebergs float.)

Use Integrating Worksheet 9.3.

STS Connection

Point out that hot-air balloons rely on thermal expansion to stay airborne. Propane burners heat the air inside the balloon. The warmed air expands, becoming less dense than the cooler air outside the balloon, and the balloon rises. Have students find out how hot-air balloons are piloted.

Research

Have students use references to find out what a bimetallic bar is and what it may be used for. Ask, What do bimetallic bars have to do with thermal expansion? (Bimetallic bars are made of two metals that expand at different rates. They are used in bimetallic strip thermometers and thermostats.)

Directed Inquiry

Have students study the photograph on this page. Discuss the following:

▶ Why is it a good idea to have expansion joints in bridges and freeways? (Metal and concrete expand with heat, and expansion joints keep these structures from buckling.)

▶ How can you avoid having a container break when water is frozen in it? How would you prevent a balloon from bursting in a heated room? (Don't overfill them, and allow for thermal expansion.)

Answers to In-Text Questions

① The liquid will expand so that the can will buckle outward and possibly burst.

② Answers will vary, but students may indicate the expansion of gases in volcanoes or mention other things that expand in the heat.

Answer to Link

The water, now turned to ice, expanded and pushed one of the clay pieces away from the end of the straw. This is a model of thermal expansion in nature, ice wedging.

Thermal Expansion

As heat energy flows into a substance, molecules vibrate and move about more rapidly. As the molecules move away from each other, the substance expands. An increase in the volume of a substance due to heat is called **thermal expansion**. Thermal expansion occurs in solids, liquids, and gases.

You have observed thermal expansion in different types of matter. Perhaps you have run hot water over the top of a glass jar to loosen the metal lid. The lid expands and is easy to remove!

Have you ever filled a pot to the brim with water and heated it on a stove? If so, you may have wondered why the water spilled over the top of the pot when it got hot. The water overflowed because of thermal expansion.

When you inflate a bicycle tire, you leave room for the thermal expansion of the air inside the tire. Heat energy caused by friction between the tire and the road causes the gas to expand. After a long ride an over inflated tire may burst.

> **Geology**
> **LINK**
>
> Rainwater in the cracks of rocks can freeze, expand, and crack the rock. Collect the following items: a straw, waterproof clay, and a glass of water.
> **1.** Suck water into the straw. Hold your finger over one end. Plug the other end with a piece of clay.
> **2.** Plug the unplugged end.
> **3.** Place the straw in the freezer for several hours.
> What changes do you notice? Relate the weathering of rocks to thermal expansion.
>
> **ACTIVITY**

Expansion in Solids

The concrete and metal in bridges and freeways expand in the hot sun. To prevent the road from buckling or breaking, engineers build gaps, called expansion joints, between segments of the road. ▼

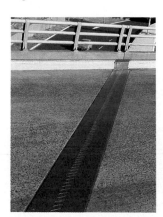

Expansion in Gases

The bladder of the football below expanded and split the seam. The ball was over-inflated and left in the sun on a hot day. Can you think of other examples of thermal expansion in gases? ▼ ②

Expansion in Liquids ▲
Most liquids expand when heated. There is one exception to this rule, however. Between 4°C and 0°C, water expands as it cools. Why should you not put an unopened soft drink can in the freezer? ①

 **The Living Textbook: Physical Science Sides 1-4**

Chapter 23   Frame 09578
Thermal Expansion (Movie)
Search: Play:

TEACH ▪ Continued

Skills WorkOut

To help students observe how radiant energy affects a slice of potato, have them do the Skills WorkOut.

Answer The potato turns a little dark and dries out, because moisture leaves the potato as it heats up in the sunlight.

EVALUATE

WrapUp

Review Discuss heat and phase changes in mercury, water, and oxygen. Ask students to devise a graph that will show the melting and boiling points for each of these substances. Have them discuss the phase changes in terms of molecular activity and volume change. (Graphs can be based on Tables 9.4 and 9.5.)

Use Review Worksheet 9.3.

Check and Explain

1. It causes molecules to move closer together or farther apart. The phase depends on the position, and also on how fast the molecules move.

2. Heat energy causes thermal expansion; concrete increases in volume and buckles unless there are expansion joints between concrete slabs.

3. At its melting point, they slow down and get closer together; at the boiling point, they speed up and spread apart.

4. Substance 1 is phosphorus, Substance 2 is polyethylene plastic.

Answer to In-Text Question

① Answers will vary; fruit may be dried, meats may be smoked or cooked, some foods may be in small cans.

Integrating the Sciences

Health Explain to students that botulism is a type of food poisoning that can occur when people eat foods that were not properly preserved. The bacteria that cause botulism live in the soil. They form heat-resistant spores that give off a toxin, which contaminates food. Food must be sufficiently heated to kill the bacteria.

▼ ACTIVITY

Observing

Potato Under Glass

Collect the following items: a slice of potato, a paper towel, and a glass.

1. Place a slice of potato on a paper towel beneath an upside-down glass on a sunny windowsill.

2. Don't disturb the potato for one hour.

What happens? Explain your observations.

SKILLS WORKOUT

Science and Society   *Food for Tomorrow*

Since ancient times, people all over the world have looked for ways to preserve food for future use. Some methods developed by ancient people are still in use today. To preserve food, it must be changed in some way to prevent spoilage by bacteria and mold.

Methods using heat were probably among the first used in food preservation. For example, one ancient method was to dry foods in the sun. Heat energy from the sun evaporated the water from the food. As the water evaporated, the food became drier. The sugar and protein in the food became more concentrated. Mold and bacteria couldn't grow in the food because these organisms need a moist environment to survive. Another ancient method was to dry meat in hot smoke from a fire. This method of smoking meat is still used.

People who lived in cold climates were able to freeze their food by simply keeping it outdoors. The water in the food turned to solid ice. Most bacteria and molds can't grow at 0°C. When thawed, the food wasn't spoiled. Today, electric refrigerators and freezers slow or prevent the growth of bacteria in food.

In the early 1800s, canning was invented. Canning involves packing and sealing food in sterile containers that are heated in boiling water for 20 to 30 minutes. The heat kills any harmful bacteria present in the food. How was the food in your lunch preserved? ①

Check and Explain

1. How does heat energy cause matter to change phases?

2. Explain how heat can crack concrete driveways and sidewalks. How are driveways and sidewalks constructed to prevent cracking?

3. **Generalize** Explain what happens to the molecules of a liquid at its melting point and at its boiling point.

4. **Interpret Data** You test the melting point of two unknown solids. Substance 1 begins to melt at 44°C. Substance 2 begins to melt at 85°C. Use Table 9.5 to identify each substance.

Check Your Vocabulary

1. radiation
2. boiling point
3. specific heat
4. convection
5. internal energy
6. Kelvin
7. absolute zero
8. conduction
9. calorie
10. heat energy
11. melting point
12. thermal expansion
13. temperature

Write Your Vocabulary

Students' sentences should show that they know the meaning of each word as well as how to use it in a sentence.

Use Vocabulary Worksheet for Chapter 9.

Chapter 9 Review

Concept Summary

9.1 Heat Energy
▶ Energy that is absorbed, given up, or transferred from one substance to another is called heat energy. Heat is measured in joules.
▶ Internal energy is the total amount of energy a substance contains.
▶ Temperature measures the average kinetic energy of the molecules in a substance.
▶ Temperature is measured on the Celsius and Kelvin scales.

9.2 Transfer of Heat
▶ Heat transfer can occur by conduction, convection, or radiation.
▶ Heat transfer is measured as a temperature change in a substance.

▶ Specific heat is the amount of heat needed to raise the temperature of 1 g of a substance 1°C.
▶ The amount of heat transferred to an object equals the object's mass times its specific heat times the temperature change.

9.3 Heat and Matter
▶ Adding heat energy increases the motion of a substance's molecules.
▶ At the boiling point, molecules in a liquid become a gas.
▶ At the melting point, the molecules of a solid become a liquid.
▶ Thermal expansion occurs when heat causes the molecules of a substance to spread out.

Chapter Vocabulary

temperature (p. 209) absolute zero (p. 211) specific heat (p. 216) melting point (p. 224)
heat energy (p. 209) conduction (p. 213) calorie (p. 217) thermal expansion (p. 225)
internal energy (p. 209) convection (p. 214) boiling point (p. 223)
Kelvin (p. 211) radiation (p. 215)

Check Your Vocabulary

Use the vocabulary words above to complete the following sentences correctly.

1. Energy transfers in a vacuum by ____.
2. At its ____, a substance changes from liquid to gas.
3. The amount of heat needed to raise the temperature of 1 kg of a substance 1°C is its ____.
4. Heat transfer caused by density differences in a fluid is called ____.
5. The ____ of a substance includes all the energy it contains.
6. One ____ is equal to 1°C.
7. At ____, the molecules of a substance have no kinetic energy.

8. When a hot object is in contact with a cool one, heat moves by ____.
9. The ____ is a unit used to measure heat.
10. When objects are in contact, ____ flows to the cooler object.
11. A substance changes from solid to liquid at its ____.
12. Cracks in cement are caused by ____.
13. The Celsius scale measures ____.

Write Your Vocabulary

Write sentences using the vocabulary words above. Show that you know what each word means.

Check Your Knowledge

1. Heat is energy that flows between objects that have different temperatures.

2. When a substance gets hotter, its molecules move more rapidly. When it gets colder, the molecules move more slowly.

3. You know that heat has been transferred when the temperature of an object has changed.

4. Absolute zero is the temperature at which the molecules of a substance have no kinetic energy.

5. The SI unit for heat is the joule.

6. Less heat is required to change the temperature of an object with a lower specific heat.

7. Radiation can occur through a vacuum.

8. Thermal expansion is an increase in the volume of a substance due to heat absorption.

9. False; temperature

10. True

11. True

12. True

13. False; colder

14. False; slower

15. True

Check Your Understanding

1. Solar radiation heats the surface of the earth. The earth's surface warms and transfers heat to the air. Heated air rises, forcing cooler air downward. The convection currents formed by this heat exchange in the atmosphere cause wind and precipitation.

2. Conduction is the direct transfer of heat energy between solid objects that are in contact with each other. Radiation is the transfer of heat by way of infrared waves.

3. The Kelvin and Celsius scales both measure temperature. A degree is of equal measure on both scales. Zero K equals –273°C. The Kelvin scale relates directly to kinetic energy.

4. Students' diagrams should show both rising and falling fluid currents. Labels might indicate warmer, less dense, rising fluid and cooler, denser, sinking fluid.

5. Convection does not occur in outer space because where there is no matter, there are no molecules to flow.

6. Substance B requires almost twice as much energy to reach the same temperature, because its specific heat is almost twice as large.

7. a. The desktop is the coolest, because little or no heat has been transferred to it. The keyboard keys are warmer than the desktop because they have absorbed some heat from the person's fingers.

   b. The interior of the keyboard is the warmest because of the heat generated by electricity.

8. 1 g of liquid water

9. Heat from your hand is quickly conducted away into the metal sprinkler (metal is a good conductor), making the metal feel cold to the touch. The rubber garden hose does not conduct away the heat from your hand as quickly (rubber is a poor conductor), so it does not feel as cold to the touch. The sprinkler and the hose are actually at the same temperature.

Chapter 9 Review

Check Your Knowledge

Answer the following in complete sentences.

1. What is heat?

2. What happens to molecules in a substance when it gets hotter? When it gets colder?

3. How do you know when heat has been transferred?

4. What is absolute zero?

5. What is the SI unit for heat?

6. What does it mean when one substance has a lower specific heat than another substance?

7. What energy-transfer process can take place when no matter is present?

8. What is thermal expansion?

Determine whether each statement is true or false. Write *true* if it is true. If it is false, change the underlined term(s) so that it is true.

9. The Celsius scale is used to measure heat.

10. When a substance gets hotter, its molecules move faster.

11. The boiling point of water at sea level is defined as 100°C.

12. The melting point of a substance is the same as its freezing point.

13. A temperature reading of 0 K is warmer than 0°C.

14. When the same amount of heat is applied, a substance with greater specific heat will get hot faster than one with a lower specific heat.

15. A Calorie is equal to one kilocalorie.

Check Your Understanding

Apply the concepts you have learned to answer each question.

1. Summarize how heat-transfer processes affect the earth's climate.

2. What is the difference between conduction and radiation?

3. How are the Celsius and Kelvin temperature scales similar and different?

4. Draw a diagram of a convection current. Label the diagram to explain what is taking place.

5. Explain why convection doesn't occur in outer space.

6. **Critical Thinking** Two substances are heated to the same temperature. Substance A has a specific heat of 380 J/kg°C. Substance B has a specific heat of 664 J/kg°C. Which substance requires more heat energy? Explain.

7. **Mystery Photo** The photograph on page 208 shows a hand and a computer keyboard as seen by heat-sensitive thermography imaging. The different colors show the varying amounts of heat in the different parts of the objects. Blue indicates the least amount of heat. Magenta, a pinkish-red color, indicates the greatest amount of heat.

   a. What parts are the coolest? Give a possible explanation.

   b. What parts are the hottest? Give a possible explanation.

8. Which has more internal energy: 1 g of ice or 1 g of liquid water?

9. On a winter morning why does a metal lawn sprinkler feel colder than the rubber hose to which it is attached?

Develop Your Skills

1. a. hydrogen; iodine

    b. hydrogen; mercury

    c. water—solid; hydrogen—gas; chlorine—solid, liquid; radon—gas, liquid, solid; bromine—solid; iodine—solid; mercury—liquid, solid

2. a. Canada jay; Ascaphus frog

    b. The jay uses the most energy because it keeps a small body very warm—a small body loses heat faster than a larger one. The frog uses the least; it is cold-blooded, meaning that it does not use energy to keep its body temperature above that of its surroundings.

Make Connections

1.

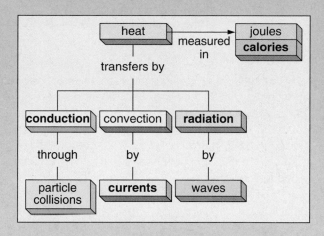

2. Short stories will vary.

3. Student reports will vary. In general, heat is used for melting or softening and welding materials.

4. Students' diagrams should show points at which evaporation and condensation occur, give boiling points of the materials involved, and indicate products.

5. 62.8 J; Answers should include the conversion of grams to kilograms: $5 \cancel{g} \times \dfrac{213\ \text{J}}{\text{k}\cancel{g}°\cancel{C}} \times \dfrac{1\ \cancel{\text{kg}}}{1000\ \cancel{g}} \times 5°\cancel{C} = 5.33\ \text{J}.$

Develop Your Skills

Use the skills you have developed in this chapter to complete each activity.

1. Interpreting Data The graph below compares the temperatures at which phase changes occur for various substances.

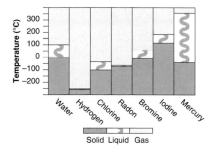

Solid Liquid Gas

a. Which substance has the lowest melting point? The highest melting point?

b. Which substance has the lowest boiling point? The highest boiling point?

c. Two Viking spacecraft have landed on the planet Mars. The highest temperature recorded was –21°C in summer. The lowest temperature recorded, during winter, was –124°C. Describe the phase or phases in which each substance would exist on Mars within this temperature range.

2. Data Bank The illustration on page 640 shows the normal body temperatures of various animals.

a. Which animal has the highest body temperature? Which has the lowest?

b. At rest, which animal probably uses the most calories per gram of body weight? Which animal uses the least? Explain.

Make Connections

1. Link the Concepts Below is a concept map showing how some of the main concepts in this chapter link together. Only part of the map is filled in. Finish the map, using words and ideas you find on the previous pages.

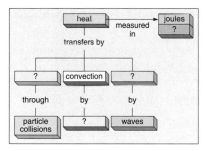

2. Science and Literature The climate in the location where a story takes place often affects the mood of the story. Write a short story where the temperature affects the mood, or the feeling, of the story.

3. Science and Art Artists, such as metal sculptors, jewelry makers, and potters use heat to shape their materials. Do library research on the processes each kind of artist uses. Write a report discussing the role of heat for each artist.

4. Science and Technology The process of distillation takes advantage of a substance's unique boiling point to separate it from other substances. In the library, research the distillation process for water or oil. Prepare a labeled diagram to illustrate the process.

5. Science and Mathematics The temperature of a 5 g tin medal increases 5°C as you hold it inside your fist. How much heat transferred to the medal?

Overview

This chapter describes the practical uses of heat. Common heating systems as well as solar heating systems are described. Next the chapter presents the role of evaporation in cooling. An explanation of how a refrigerator works is also provided. Finally, internal- and external-combustion engines are described, showing how heat engines convert heat energy to mechanical energy.

Advance Planner

▶ Obtain small plants for TE page 235.

▶ Obtain several types of insulation for TE page 236.

▶ Supply coffee cans, identical plastic containers with lids, graduated cylinders, ice cubes, insulating materials such as fabric and newspaper, polystyrene packing materials, and aluminum foil for SE Activity 10, page 238.

▶ Provide rubbing alcohol for SE page 239.

▶ Supply thermometers, cotton, and fans for TE page 240.

▶ Obtain pieces of cardboard and dowling for TE page 246.

Skills Development Chart

Sections	Classify	Communicate	Graph	Infer	Interpret Data	Observe	Predict	Reason and Conclude
10.1 Skills WarmUp	●							
Skills WorkOut						●		
Activity		●	●		●	●	●	
10.2 Skills WarmUp					●			
Skills WorkOut	●							
10.3 Skills WarmUp					●			
Consider This		●						
Skills WorkOut								●

Individual Needs

▶ **Limited English Proficiency Students** Photocopy figures 10.2, 10.3, 10.7, 10.12, and 10.13 with the labels masked. Draw arrows to the important parts of each figure. Have students make labels from strips of index cards and place them in the correct place on the photocopy. Encourage students to refer to the text to check the placement of the labels. Students may wish to save the labels and review this section of the chapter by repeating the activity.

▶ **At-Risk Students** Provide students with photocopies of Figures 10.2, 10.3, 10.4, 10.5, 10.6, and 10.7 with the labels removed. Have students write each of the following words on a separate sheet of paper: conduction, convection, and radiation. Students should match the photocopied figures to the three words by attaching the photocopies to the appropriate sheet of paper.

▶ **Gifted Students** Invite students to build a model of either an external- or internal-combustion engine. The model should show the internal mechanism of the engine and its parts should actually move. Students should use easily obtained materials to make their models. Encourage them to be creative. For example, they might simulate the firing of the spark plug using a flashlight bulb.

Resource Bank

▶ **Bulletin Board** Prepare two headings for the bulletin board: *Problems with Heating* and *Solutions for Heating Problems.* Show a house with heat loss problems, such as fuel inefficiency or environmental damage. Be sure to show the heating system. Have them attach the "problem" pictures beneath the appropriate heading. Have students place drawings or cut out pictures of possible solutions to the problems on the *Solutions* side of the board. When students are finished supplying pictures for the bulletin board, have them use colored yarn or string to connect each problem to its possible solution.

Section	Core	Standard	Enriched	Section	Core	Standard	Enriched
10.1 Heating Technology pp. 231–238				**Blackline Masters** Review Worksheet 10.2	●	●	
Section Features Skills WarmUp, p. 231 Activity, p. 238	●●	●●	●●	Skills Worksheet 10.2a	●	●	●
Blackline Masters Review Worksheet 10.1 Integrating Worksheet 10.1	●●	●●	●	Skills Worksheet 10.2b	●	●	
Overhead Blackline Transparencies Overhead Blackline Master 9 and Student Worksheet	●	●	●	**Ancillary Options** *One-Minute Readings,* p. 82	●	●	●
Color Transparencies Transparencies 26, 27, 28, 29, 30	●	●	●	**Color Transparencies** Transparency 31	●	●	●
Laboratory Program Investigation 21	●	●	●	**10.3 Heat Engines** pp. 244–248			
10.2 Cooling Technology pp. 239–243				**Section Features** Skills WarmUp, p. 244 Consider This, p. 247 Skills WorkOut, p. 248	●●●	●●●	●●●
Section Features Skills WarmUp, p. 239 Skills WorkOut, p. 241	●●	●●	●●	**Blackline Masters** Review Worksheet 10.3 Reteach Worksheet 10.3 Integrating Worksheet 10.3 Vocabulary Worksheet 10	●●●●	●●●●	●●
				Color Transparencies Transparencies 32, 33, 34	●	●	●

Bibliography

The following resources can be used for teaching the chapter. See page T-46 for supplier codes.

Library Resources

Lafferty, Peter. *Burning and Melting.* New York: Gloucester Press, 1990.

Sherwood, Martin, and Christine Sutton. *The Physical World.* New York: Oxford University Press, 1988.

Whyman, Kathryn. *Heat and Energy.* New York: Franklin Watts, 1986.

Technology Resources
Software

Heat. Mac, Dos. ESI.
Learning All About Heat and Sound. Mac, Win. LS.
Superstar Science. Mac, Win. LS.

Laserdiscs

Living Textbook. (See barcodes on pages in this chapter.) Optical Data.
Heat: Molecules in Motion, 2nd Edition. AIMS.

Videos

Sun Power: Harnessing the Sun's Energy. SVE.

10

Introducing the Chapter

Have students read the description of the photograph. Ask if they agree or disagree with the description. Explain to students that the picture shows a closeup of fiberglass, which is an insulating material. The magnified fibers *do* look very much like wires.

Directed Inquiry

Have students study the photograph. Ask:

▶ How would you describe the photograph? (Students will probably mention that it looks like wires, fibers, or hairs.)

▶ How do you think these fibers would feel if you touched them? (Students may respond that individual fibers would feel hard and smooth, but together they might feel soft. The fibers would be pliable.)

▶ How do you think the fibers are made? (Students may respond that they are made of glass that has been spun into threads.)

▶ How do you think the picture is related to using heat? (Students may respond that the fibers could be put around things to keep them warm.)

Chapter Vocabulary

central heating
  system
combustion
insulation

R-value
refrigerant
turbine

Writing Connection

Have students imagine that they live on a planet that has an average daytime temperature of 50°C and an average nighttime temperature of –5°C. Have them write a radio advertisement for school clothes and one for evening clothes for the climate on this planet.

Chapter 10   Using Heat

Chapter Sections

10.1   Heating Technology
10.2   Cooling Technology
10.3   Heat Engines

What do you see?

66 What I think I see in the picture is some sort of electrical wire or wires. People may use this for a light or a television or any kind of electrical appliance. It works well because it is small and convenient. 99

Erin Fargo
Highland Park School
St. Paul, Minnesota

To find out more about the photograph, look on page 250. As you read this chapter, you will learn about how people use heat.

Systems and Interactions Point out that heating and cooling systems transfer heat energy into or out of buildings. Explain that thermostats regulate these systems, so the temperature inside a building stays within a certain range. Ask, What are the advantages of a thermostat over a simple on/off switch? (The thermostat automatically responds to changes in temperature.)

Integrating the Sciences

Biology Explain to students that scientists think body temperature is regulated by a region of the brain called the *hypothalamus*. Have students find out how the human body regulates its temperature. (By adjusting rates of breathing, metabolism, and blood circulation; changing blood sugar levels; panting; sweating)

Section Objectives
For a list of section objectives, see the Student Edition page.

Skills Objectives
Students should be able to:

Classify changes in heat energy in common substances.

Observe how and where heat can escape from a building.

Infer how fabrics are insulators.

Predict the most effective heating system in a given climate.

Vocabulary
central heating system, insulation, R-value

10.1 Heating Technology

Objectives

▶ **Identify** five types of central heating systems.

▶ **Compare** active and passive solar heating systems.

▶ **Infer** why a material makes a good insulator.

▶ **Analyze** central heating systems to determine the best one for a particular geographic location.

▼ **ACTIVITY**

Classifying

Heat Changes

Every day you witness changes in substances because they have gained or lost heat energy. Make a list of five heat-energy changes you observed today. Classify each change as conduction, convection, or radiation.

SKILLS WARMUP

MOTIVATE

Skills WarmUp

To help students identify when heat is gained and lost, have them do the Skills WarmUp.
Answer Answers will vary. Students should include at least one of the three kinds of change.

TEACH

What was the weather like this morning on your way to school? Maybe it was so cold outside that you bundled up in many layers of clothing and a heavy coat. Perhaps it was warm enough for you to go without a jacket.

Once you're inside your school, the weather outside is less important. The temperature inside most buildings is maintained at a comfortable level. Heating and air-conditioning systems control the environment inside a building. These systems keep the indoor temperature within a comfortable range by transferring heat energy into or out of the building.

Central Heating Systems

The temperature inside your school, your home, or a local store stays warm on a cold day because of a central heating system. **A central heating system** generates heat from a central location. A network of wires, pipes, ducts, and vents transfers the heat from the heat source to different locations throughout the building.

Central heating systems use forced-air, hot-water, steam, radiant, or heat-pump networks. Although these systems differ in the way they distribute heat, they share common traits. For example, most central heating systems use some type of fuel to provide heat energy.

In addition, a thermostat is used to control a central heating system. The thermostat turns on the heating system when the air reaches a preselected low temperature. The thermostat also shuts off the system at a preselected high temperature. Look at Figure 10.1 to see how a thermostat works.

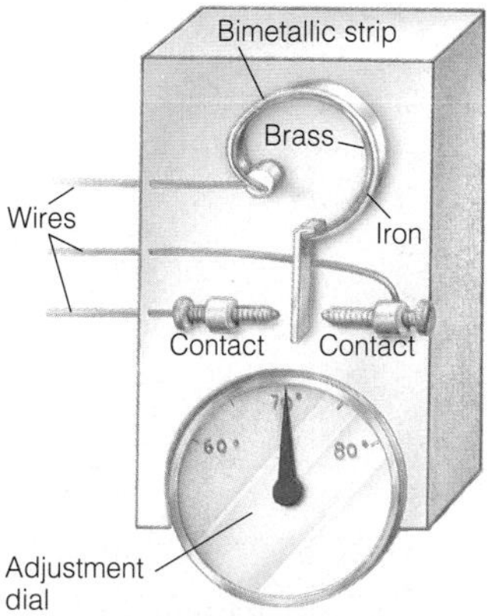

Figure 10.1 ▲
Metals in a bimetallic strip expand at different rates when heated. The strip bends and turns the heat switch off or on.

Directed Inquiry

Have students look at Figure 10.1. Tell them that the brass strip expands faster than the iron strip does as they heat up. Ask:

▶ Which contact will the bimetallic strip touch when the temperature is high? Low? (The right one for high temperature, the left one for low)

▶ What does the contact on the right do? The left contact? (Turns off the heat switch; turns on the switch)

▶ What do you think the adjustment dial does? (Moves the contacts closer to and farther from the bimetallic switch)

TEACH ▪ *Continued*

Prior Knowledge

Gauge how much students know about heating technology by asking the following questions:

▶ What kind of a heating system do you have in your home?

▶ How does the movement of heat from warm areas to cool areas help or hinder in heating buildings?

Discuss

Ask students to discuss which parts in the classroom are the warmest and the coolest. Ask why they think so. (Area near the heater will be warmer than the area near the door.)

Critical Thinking

Find Causes Have students examine Figure 10.3. Ask, What have you learned about heat that explains the need for the expansion tank in this system? (Water expands as it is heated [thermal expansion is covered in Chapter 9] and the tank holds the extra water volume the system creates.)

 The Living Textbook: Physical Science Sides 1-4

Chapter 5   Frame 01107
Bimetallic Strip (2 Frames)
Search: Step:

 The Living Textbook: Physical Science Sides 1-4

Chapter 10   Frame 01890
Thermostat (3 Frames)
Search: Step:

Cooperative Learning

Have students work in four cooperative groups to rate the heating and cooling systems of your school. Have one group make a diagram showing how each system works; a second group could interview the maintenance staff about the advantages and disadvantages of each system; a third group could investigate the energy efficiency of each system; and the fourth group could interview students and teachers to find out how well they think each system works. Have all the groups collaborate on a *Consumer Reports*–style rating of both systems.

Forced-Air Heating A common type of central heating system is forced-air heating, shown in Figure 10.2. In this system, air is heated inside a furnace. The warm air moves from the furnace to the walls of the building. The warm air travels through a network of connected passages called ducts. The ducts connect to outlets, or registers, in individual rooms.

When warm air enters a room, it rises and creates a convection current. As the warm air moves through the room, heat energy is lost. The air cools, sinks, and passes through a cold-air register in the room. The register connects to a duct that carries the cool air toward a blower. The blower draws the air through a filter and back into the furnace. The air is reheated and circulated again through the system.

Hot-Water Heating Like forced-air heating, hot-water heating also creates convection currents. In this type of central heating system, the furnace heats water. The hot water is pumped through a network of pipes. The pipes lead to metal radiators in individual rooms. The heat from the water transfers to the metal in the radiators.

Heat energy moves from the radiator and warms the surrounding air by conduction. The warm air rises, creating convection currents in the room. The water inside the radiator cools as heat energy is lost to the air. Pipes carry the cool water back to the furnace, where it is reheated and recirculated through the pipes. Study the movement of hot water and heat energy in the hot-water heating system shown in Figure 10.3.

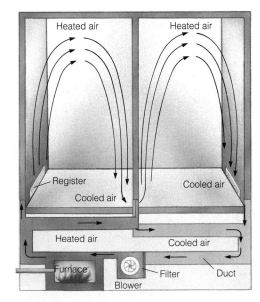

Figure 10.2 ▲
In a forced-air heating system, air is warmed by burning fuel in a furnace. Trace the flow of warm air through the system.

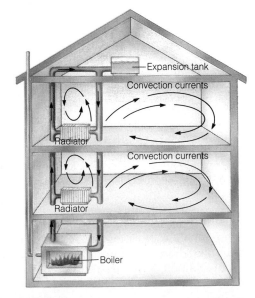

Figure 10.3 ▲
In a hot-water heating system, water is warmed by burning fuel in a furnace. Compare the hot-water system to the forced-air system.

Social Studies Connection

Explain to students that the ancient Romans developed a form of central heating called the *hypocaust system*. Fuel burned in a furnace, producing hot gases that were piped into a space beneath the floor. From there the gases rose through hollow tubes in the walls. Ask, What modern system does the hypocaust system resemble? (Radiant heating system)

Themes in Science

Diversity and Unity Explain that all heating systems rely on the three basic methods of transferring heat energy: conduction, convection, and radiation. Have students analyze each heating system presented in this section to determine how heat is transferred.

Steam Heating At high temperatures, water changes into steam. Steam heat uses water in both the gas and liquid phases. The steam heating system shown in Figure 10.4 is similar to a hot-water heating system. Both of these systems use water. In a steam heating system, water is heated in a tank, or boiler, above the furnace until steam forms. Instead of using the hot water, steam is pumped through the network of pipes. The pipes connect to radiators in each room.

The steam heats the metal in the radiators. Heat energy transfers from the radiator to warm the air in the room. As the steam in the radiator loses heat energy, it condenses to form liquid water. The cooled water returns to the furnace through another pipe. The water is then reheated to form steam, and the process is repeated.

Radiant Heating Hot water and electric wires radiate heat. Both are used in radiant heating systems. A hot-water radiant system is shown in Figure 10.5. In this system, water is heated in a furnace and then pumped through pipes embedded in the concrete floor of a room. Heat energy radiates from the pipes and warms the floor. In an electric radiant system, an electric current moves through wires in the floor, walls, or ceiling of a room. Heat energy radiates from the wires and warms the concrete floor.

Radiant heating systems are generally used to heat individual rooms. Heat radiating from the floor surface warms a room evenly. Usually, there is little temperature difference between the floor and ceiling of a room warmed with a radiant heating system.

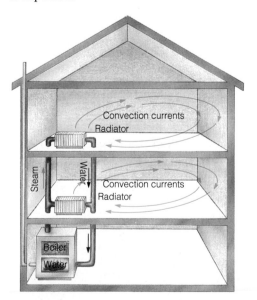

Figure 10.4 ▲
Locate the water in the steam heating system. Follow the flow of steam from the boiler through the system.

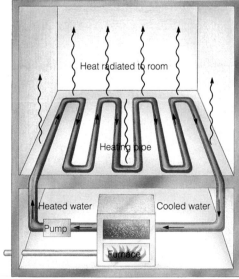

Figure 10.5 ▲
In a radiant heating system, the heat source can be hot water or electricity. Which type is shown in this picture? ①

233

TEACH ▪ *Continued*

Critical Thinking

Compare and Contrast Have students study Figure 10.6. Ask, How does the heat pump differ from the forced-air heating system shown in Figure 10.2 on page 232? (The heat pump uses a pump and a condenser and is connected to an outside unit. The forced-air heating system has a blower and a furnace and is completely indoors.)

Enrich

Ask students for examples of the sun's effects on plants and animals. Ask, Do plants use solar energy? Explain. How does working outdoors on a hot day make you feel? Why? (Yes, in photosynthesis; hot, because the body absorbs solar energy.)

STS Connection

Explain to students that the heat pump absorbs heat from the warm air inside the building. The liquid in the condenser evaporates and the vapor transports stored heat energy to the outside where heat is released as the vapor condenses to a liquid. Ask students whether air flows out of, or into, the evaporator during cooling. Have them explain their answers. (Out; as heat is released, warm air flows out from the evaporator.)

Multicultural Perspectives

Tell students that in some cultures, animals are kept in pens adjacent to the family house so the humans can take advantage of the heat the animals give off. Ask students to find out in what countries and climates this practice is used. (Examples: the Yakuts, Tungis, and Samoyeds, who are Asian people of north-central Siberia; the Lapps of Lapland, which is in exteme northern Europe)

Heat Pumps Even on cold days, the outside environment can supply enough heat energy to warm a building. A heat pump collects the heat energy with a network of coiled pipes on the outside of the building. Heat from the air or ground evaporates the liquid inside the coils. The vapor moves through pipes to a condenser inside the building. The condenser uses pressure to raise the vapor temperature further. A heat exchanger uses the heated vapor to warm the surrounding air. The warm air moves through the building in the same way forced-air heat does. As the vapor in the condenser loses heat, it condenses to a liquid. The liquid returns to the unit outside the building and the process is repeated.

Figure 10.6
During winter, the heat pump collects heat from the outside. In summer, a heat pump is reversed to draw heat from the inside. ▼

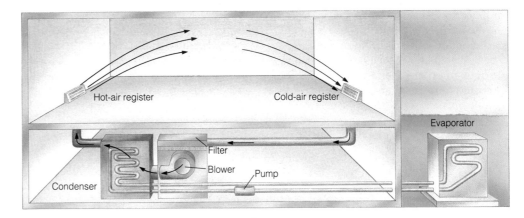

Solar Heating Systems

Solar heating systems differ from most central heating systems in an important way. They use a renewable energy source. Forced-air, hot-water, steam, and radiant heating systems all depend on some nonrenewable fuel to produce heat. Fossil fuels such as oil, natural gas, and coal are the fuels most commonly used to heat buildings. A typical central heating system uses large amounts of one of these fossil fuels every day.

A solar heating system doesn't need to use any fossil fuel. A solar heating system uses heat energy from the sun. As long as the sun shines, solar heating has a free, unlimited energy source. There are two types of solar heating systems in use today: active solar heating and passive solar heating. These systems differ in the way solar energy is captured and used to heat a structure.

Active Solar Heating A solar collector consists of a glass sheet, a black metal panel, and pipes for carrying liquid. In active solar heating, solar collectors are carefully positioned to receive direct sunlight. Sunlight is absorbed by the black panel, and the glass prevents much of the heat from escaping. The energy collected heats a liquid moving through the pipes. The hot liquid warms a tank of water. Hot water from the tank is used to heat the building, as shown in Figure 10.7.

Active solar heating must have energy from the sun. On cloudy days and at night, the sun's energy doesn't reach the solar collectors. Therefore, buildings with active solar heating must have some type of backup heating system.

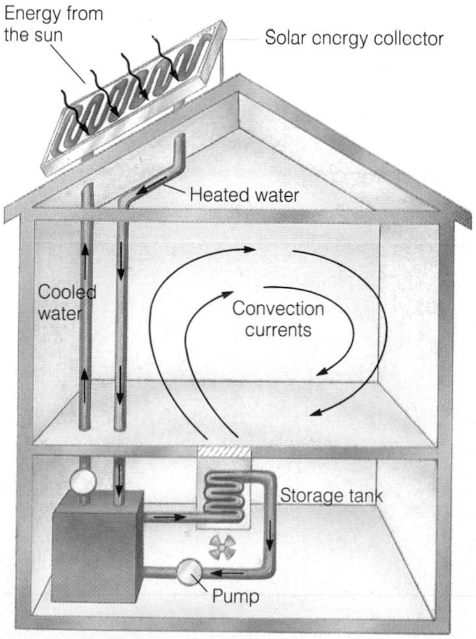

Passive Solar Heating You have probably warmed your home with passive solar heating and never knew it! Every time you raise a shade or open a curtain to let sunlight shine through a window, you start your own passive solar heating system. Solar energy streams through the glass and warms the objects in the room. The warm objects transfer heat into the air by conduction. Some buildings take advantage of passive solar heat by installing large windows and skylights in locations that receive the maximum amount of direct sunlight.

Another passive solar heating method is shown in Figure 10.8. A solar greenhouse is attached to a building. The sun's rays pass through the glass to heat the walls and floor of the greenhouse. This heat warms the room connected to the greenhouse.

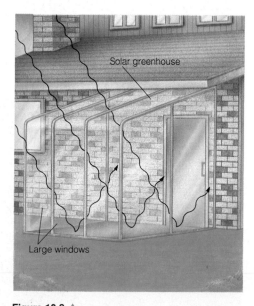

Figure 10.7 ▲
Follow the path of heat energy as it moves through this solar heating system.

Figure 10.8 ▲
Heat energy from the sun builds up inside a solar greenhouse, warming the wall and the room.

 The Living Textbook: Physical Science Sides 1-4

Chapter 16   Frame 02718
Solar Collectors (11 Frames)
Search: Step:

Critical Thinking

Generalize Ask students, Why would insulation help keep a building cool on very hot days? (Since insulation slows the movement of heat, it would keep heat energy from entering the building.)

Class Activity

Bring samples of various types of insulation to school for students to see. Pass them around the classroom. Ask, How would you describe these materials? Do they have any common properties? (Students should note that all are lightweight and make use of small air pockets.) Ask a student to place a thermometer on one arm and cover it over with each of several of the insulating materials. Have the class observe and discuss the differences in temperature. Caution: Do not place fiberglass insulation against the skin.

Answer to In-Text Question

① **Insulation should be placed inside all the walls, in the ceilings, and under the roof.**

The Living Textbook: Physical Science Sides 1-4

Chapter 10   Frame 01888
Thermos (1 Frame)
Search:

The Living Textbook: Physical Science Sides 1-4

Chapter 10   Frame 01900
Reflective Insulation (1 Frame)
Search:

Multicultural Perspectives

Adobe houses, used for centuries in the southwestern United States and elsewhere, are very energy efficient. Have students find out which cultures have used adobe and why traditional adobe houses are well insulated. Students may make models of adobe houses to include in their portfolios.

Integrating the Sciences

Life Science Explain to students that animals need insulation from the cold. Ask, What kinds of insulation do animals have? (Skin, fur, fat, feathers) Point out that fur and feathers trap air, which serves as insulation. What animals use each kind of insulation? (Examples: People use both skin and fat, beavers rely on fur and fat, and ducks use feathers.)

Use Integrating Worksheet 10.1.

Insulation

Figure 10.9 ▲
Fiberglass insulation has many tiny spaces to trap heat within a building's walls or ceilings.

Figure 10.10
Insulation is placed in areas where heat might escape. Where would you put insulation in this house? ▼ ①

All heating systems use heat transfer to move heat where it's needed. Heat moves from an area of higher temperature to an area of lower temperature. However, heat transfer can be a problem. The heat tends to flow out of a heated building. To keep the inside of a building warm, people need a way to stop the flow of heat to the outside. The best way to do this is to use **insulation** (IHN suh LAY shuhn). Insulation is a substance that slows the movement of heat. Materials commonly used for insulation include fiberglass, cellulose, metal foil, and some types of plastic foam.

Insulation materials vary in the amount of heat transfer that occurs through them. Every insulation material is assigned an **R-value**. An R-value is a measurement of a material's ability to stop heat flow. The higher a material's R-value, the greater is its ability to trap heat energy. For example, a layer of fiberglass insulation like the one shown in Figure 10.9 has a higher R-value than a single pane of glass.

When a building is constructed, insulation is placed in the areas where heat is most likely to escape. Usually, these areas are the ceilings, attic floor, and the outside walls. Insulation around doors and windows, called weather stripping, prevents heat loss through air leaks. A well-insulated building conserves heat energy.

STS Connection

Explain to students that infrared photography can reveal areas of high heat loss in buildings. Usually, the images show areas of heat loss in "hot" colors, such as yellow, orange, and red. Areas that are well insulated show up as "cool" colors, such as blue and green. Ask students to draw "infrared photos" of the classroom showing areas of heat loss.

Themes in Science

Systems and Interactions

Explain that heat loss is directly proportional to the difference between the indoor and outdoor temperatures: the greater the difference in temperatures, the greater the flow of heat energy. Ask, How would you equalize the temperature between the inside and outside of your home? (Turn down the heat at night and when the house is empty to reduce the temperature difference.)

Science and You *Weatherize Your Home*

Many homes waste heat energy. Heat leaks through small openings, such as cracks around windows and under doors. Drafts are a sure sign of escaping heat.

You can test the energy efficiency of your home by going on a "heat-escape hunt." Begin by examining your doors for heat loss. Hold a thin sheet of paper in front of the place where the door meets the floor. Observe the paper to see if it moves. If the paper moves toward you, air is blowing in. The draft is probably created by a space underneath the door. You may also be able to see light coming in. If light and air enter your home through this opening, then heat energy also leaves your home through this space.

You can minimize energy loss by insulating the opening beneath the door. You could use newspaper for insulation by rolling the newspaper, wrapping it in a towel, and placing it against the doorsill. You could also try using other materials for insulation. What materials do you think might make good insulation?

Next examine the windows of your home. Look carefully for any cracks or openings along the window frames. Some people cover their windows with sheets of plastic during winter to reduce heat loss. Storm doors and storm windows used during winter prevent some heat loss. If you find any openings around the windows, design ways to block the flow of heat to the outside. The result of your work will be a home that is more energy efficient and less costly to heat!

Check and Explain

1. List five kinds of central heating systems. Briefly describe how each system works.

2. What are two types of solar heating systems? How are they different? How are they alike?

3. **Infer** Why is winter clothing often made of wool? What criteria do fabrics need to meet to keep you warm in winter?

4. **Analyze** Which one of the heating systems discussed in this section is best suited to a warm, sunny climate? Explain your answer.

▼ ACTIVITY

Observing

Hot Pursuit

Conduct a "heat-escape hunt" in your home or classroom. Record the places where you find heat escaping. Design a device that could prevent heat loss from these openings.

SKILLS WORKOUT

Skills WorkOut

To help students observe locations of heat loss, have them do the Skills WorkOut.
Answer Sites of heat loss will vary. Preventive devices should have insulating properties.

EVALUATE

WrapUp

Reinforce Have the class work in small groups and ask each to design a house that will use heat energy in the most efficient, least wasteful way. Houses should be appropriate for your part of the country. Have groups describe and draw the direction the house will face, how it will be insulated, what kind of heating system it will have, and so on. Ask each group to present its design to the rest of the class.

Use Review Worksheet 10.1.

Check and Explain

1. Forced-air, hot-water, steam, radiant heating, heat pumps

2. Active solar heating uses collectors and pumps, while passive solar heating occurs through glass windows. Both systems use radiant energy to increase the temperature of either water (active) or air (passive).

3. Wool has many fibers that trap air and slow heat flow. A winter fabric should have many dead air spaces and overlapping fibers for insulation.

4. The heat pump because it can also be used to cool a building

Answer to In-Text Question

② A strip of rubber or plastic attached to the bottom of the door, or a rug pushed against the door would also work.

Time 70 minutes   **Group** 3

Materials

20 coffee cans

20 identical plastic containers with lids

20 graduated cylinders

20 ice cubes

insulating materials—choose from newspaper, sponges, sawdust, polystyrene packing materials, and aluminum foil

Analysis

1. Answers will vary depending on insulating material, but should agree with recorded observations.

2. Answers will depend on each group's choice of materials.

3. Answers will depend on each group's results.

Conclusion

Students' conclusions will vary. In general, the best insulators are those materials that conduct the least amount of heat. In most cases, the best insulator is the material that has the greatest number of air pockets per unit volume.

Everyday Application

Students' devices should make use of what they have learned about insulation material.

Extension

Graphs will depend on individual results. A poor insulator will produce a steep curve, indicating that a given amount of ice took less time to melt in a container insulated with that material.

Prelab Discussion

Have students read the entire activity before beginning. Discuss the following points:

▶ Review the properties of materials that make good insulators.

▶ Have students make predictions about the insulating abilities of the materials used in this activity.

▶ Have students suggest ways to make better insulators by using combinations of available materials.

Activity 10 *What materials make the best heat insulators?*

Skills Observe; Predict; Interpret Data

Task 1 Prelab Prep

1. Collect the following items: marking pen, 2 identical plastic containers with lids, 2 coffee cans, 2 ice cubes, and 2 graduated cylinders. *NOTE: Each coffee can should be large enough to hold 1 plastic container.*

2. Choose two insulating materials. Possible insulating materials include newspaper, sponges, sawdust, packaging materials, and aluminum foil.

3. Label one container *A* and the other container *B*. Label one coffee can *A* and the other coffee can *B*.

Task 2 Data Record

1. On a separate sheet of paper, draw the data table shown.

2. Predict which material will be the best insulator. Record your prediction in the table.

Task 3 Procedure

1. Place an ice cube in each plastic container.

2. Place each plastic container in the coffee can with the same letter.

3. Pack a different insulating material in the coffee can around each plastic container. As you finish packing each coffee can, record the time in your data table.

4. Record in the data table the type of material placed in each coffee can.

5. After ten minutes, remove the plastic container from each can.

6. Pour any water present from container *A* into a graduated cylinder. Measure the amount of water from the melted ice and record it in the data table. Repeat the process for container *B*.

7. Return the containers to their appropriate cans. Repack the cans with the same insulating materials.

8. Repeat steps 5, 6, and 7 for each time span noted in the data table.

Task 4 Analysis

1. Which ice cube turned to liquid water first?

2. What packing material surrounded the container holding this ice cube?

3. Which of the packing materials you tested is the better insulator?

Task 5 Conclusion

Write a short paragraph identifying the type of materials that make good insulation. In what situation do you think the insulation you used would be most effective?

Everyday Application

Use your findings to invent a device you could use to keep soup hot on a cold winter day. Make a diagram of your device to show how it slows down the transfer of heat energy.

Extension

Construct a line graph of your data for each insulating material. Place the time in minutes on the *x*-axis, and the amount of water in mL on the *y*-axis. Which set of data produces a curve? Explain.

Table 10.1 Insulation Materials

	Insulation Material	Time Began	Amount of Water (mL) after:				
			10 min	20 min	30 min	40 min	50 min
Can A							
Can B							

Themes in Science

Patterns of Change/Cycles A cooling system demonstrates the principle that heat flows naturally from a hot object to a cold one. Heat flows from a hot, enclosed space to the coolant. Ask, What phase change absorbs energy in the coolant? (The change from liquid coolant to vapor)

Social Studies Connection

Tell students that ice houses that sold ice existed in every city in the country before mechanical refrigeration became widespread in the 1920s. Ice was delivered to peoples' homes by an "iceman" and stored in iceboxes. The iceman was well known throughout the neighborhood, and is a part of our country's heritage. Have students find out about the ice business, ice wagons, and even songs that existed in the days of the icebox.

Section Objectives
For a list of section objectives, see the Student Edition page.

Skills Objectives
Students should be able to:

Infer how a cooling system works.

Classify traits of heating systems that resemble traits of cooling systems.

Vocabulary
refrigerant

10.2 Cooling Technology

Objectives

▶ **Explain** how a cooling system works.

▶ **Discuss** the role of evaporation in refrigeration.

▶ **Compare** and **contrast** heating systems and cooling systems.

▶ **Infer** how your body is similar to other cooling systems.

I n the early 1900s, people used iceboxes to keep food cold. An icebox was a large insulated wood box with two compartments. A large block of ice was placed in the top compartment and food items were put in the bottom compartment.

The early icebox worked on a simple principle. As warm air rose from the bottom compartment, the air lost heat energy to the block of ice. The cool, dense air sank from the ice to the bottom compartment. The cool air absorbed heat energy from the food. Until the ice melted, the food items remained chilled through a continuous pattern of heat-energy transfer.

Since the invention of the early icebox, refrigeration technology has advanced a great deal. Refrigerators, freezers, and air conditioners now cool enclosed areas. The structure of these modern cooling devices is quite different from that of the icebox.

Principles of Cooling Systems

All cooling systems remove heat energy from an enclosed space. A substance with a low boiling point, called a coolant, is used to absorb heat energy. Depending upon where it is located in the system, the coolant may be either a liquid or a gas. As the liquid coolant absorbs heat, its molecules move more rapidly. When the liquid reaches its boiling point, it evaporates. Recall that when a liquid evaporates, it becomes a gas. For the liquid coolant to evaporate, its molecules must gain energy. The heat source for evaporating the coolant comes from the enclosed space. As heat flows out of the enclosed space, the space and any objects inside it lose heat energy.

▼ **ACTIVITY**

Inferring

Cooling Systems

Collect the following items: a paper towel and rubbing alcohol.

1. Use a paper towel to wipe a small amount of water onto your arm.

2. Blow on the water. How does it feel?

3. Now wipe a small amount of rubbing alcohol onto your arm. Blow on it. How does it feel?

Infer how cooling systems work based on your observations.

SKILLS WARMUP

MOTIVATE

Skills WarmUp

To help students understand the cooling process, have them do the Skills WarmUp.

Answer Students should find that the water makes their arms feel cool, but the rubbing alcohol makes them feel even cooler. They should infer that cooling systems use substances to absorb heat energy from the object being cooled.

Misconceptions

Students may think that leaving the refrigerator door open will cool a hot room, but it will actually become hotter. With its door open, the refrigerator takes in heat from the room. Its cooling system then must work harder to cool the space, which now includes the room. As the vapor condenses into a liquid, which absorbs heat energy, the vapor releases heat into the room.

 The Living Textbook:
Physical Science Sides 1-4

Chapter 4   Frame 00960
Phase Changes of Water (1 Frame)
Search:

TEACH

Class Activity

Have students work in groups of four or five. Each group should have two thermometers, cotton, water, and the use of a fan. Have them wrap the bulbs of both thermometers in cotton, then dip the cotton of one thermometer in water. Allow the fan to blow on both thermometers. Groups should record the temperature of each thermometer every 15 seconds for two minutes. Students should find that the thermometer with the wet cotton shows a rapid decrease in temperature. Ask students how this activity relates to the cooling system of the body. (The activity is a model of perspiration.)

Explore Visually

Have students study the text and Figure 10.11. Then ask:

▶ Where does sweat come from? (It comes from sweat glands, moves through narrow sweat ducts, and emerges from pores in the skin.)

▶ What is sweat made of? (Water, salt, and other body waste.)

▶ How does perspiration cool you off? (It absorbs heat from the skin and then evaporates, carrying away heat energy.)

▶ **Infer** Why doesn't the sweat cool the skin while it is still in the sweat glands? (The water in the sweat needs to come in contact with the air in order to lose energy through evaporation.)

Decision Making

If you have classroom sets of *One-Minute Readings*, have students read Issue 48 "Air Conditioning" on page 82. Discuss the questions.

Themes in Science

Stability and Equilibrium Explain to students that the human body maintains a relatively constant body temperature. Point out that perspiration helps cool the body. Then ask, How does the human body generate heat? (By burning food in metabolism and through activity)

Integrating the Sciences

Zoology The skin of pigs does not have sweat glands. Pigs will die if their internal temperature gets too high. In order to keep cool in summer, pigs will "root" into the soil and dig a hole in which to lay, since the soil is cooler than the air. Modern pig farmers raise pigs in air conditioned buildings. Ask students what other measures pig farmers might take to keep their pigs cool. (Keep pigs in the shade)

Your Body's Cooling System

You get hot when you're involved in strenuous physical activity, or when the weather is hot. Whenever your internal temperature gets too high, your body's cooling system goes into action. You perspire. Your body's cooling system works on the same principle that a refrigerator or air conditioner does. Your body transfers heat energy through evaporation.

Your brain controls your body temperature much as a thermostat controls room temperature. When your body temperature rises, your brain sends a message to your skin's sweat glands. The message triggers the sweat glands to produce sweat. Sweat is secreted through tiny holes in the skin, called pores, onto your skin surface. Heat is transferred from your skin to the watery sweat and the water evaporates into the air around you.

Evaporation needs energy to occur. The energy is supplied by the heat from your body. As the excess heat is removed from your body, you begin to feel cooler. After the water in the sweat evaporates, salts and other substances are left behind on the surface of your skin. Your skin may feel sticky and taste salty when you are no longer sweating.

**Figure 10.11
The Cooling System of the Human Body** ▼

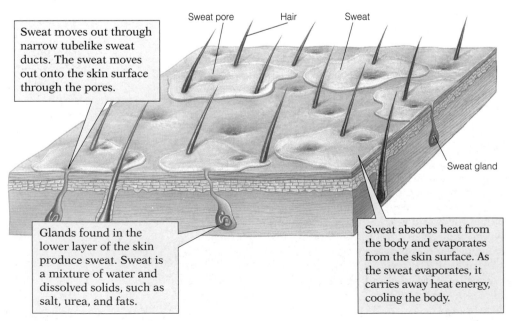

Sweat moves out through narrow tubelike sweat ducts. The sweat moves out onto the skin surface through the pores.

Sweat pore   Hair   Sweat

Sweat gland

Glands found in the lower layer of the skin produce sweat. Sweat is a mixture of water and dissolved solids, such as salt, urea, and fats.

Sweat absorbs heat from the body and evaporates from the skin surface. As the sweat evaporates, it carries away heat energy, cooling the body.

Use of Refrigerants

You know that a cooling system works by evaporation. Cooling systems are most efficient if they use a chemical that evaporates easily at low temperatures. These chemicals, called **refrigerants**, are used in air-conditioners for automobiles, homes, and office buildings. They are also used in freezers and refrigerators. Refrigerants are pumped throughout a cooling system. As they change phase from liquid to gas, they remove heat from the enclosed space to the outside air.

Air, water, ammonia, and carbon dioxide are examples of natural refrigerants. However, most cooling systems use manufactured chemicals called chlorofluorocarbons. Chlorofluorocarbons are good refrigerants because they evaporate at a low temperature and are nonflammable, nontoxic, noncorrosive, and odorless. However, chlorofluorocarbons are harmful to the ozone in the upper atmosphere if not handled properly.

TEACH ▪ *Continued*

Explore Visually

Have students study Figure 10.12, then ask:

▶ What phase is the refrigerant in as it travels through the freezer unit? What happens to it? (Liquid; it evaporates.)

▶ How does the condenser change the refrigerant vapor back into a liquid? (It removes heat from the vapor in a network of condenser coils.)

▶ Where does the heat from the refrigerant vapor go? (From the condenser coils into the room)

▶ **Infer** A dial in most refrigerators allows the temperature to be adjusted. What would the dial control to make the refrigerator cooler or warmer? (The speed at which the refrigerant is pumped; the faster it flows, the more heat is removed.)

Themes in Science

Energy Remind students that the energy of the particles in the matter determines whether a material is a solid, liquid, or gas. Have students identify which part of the refrigeration cycle requires the most energy and which releases the most energy. (The phase change from liquid to vapor requires the most energy; phase change from vapor to liquid releases the most energy.) Students may ask why the outside energy from electricity is required. (Electricity powers the compressor and the pump that moves the refrigerant.)

Cooling Systems at Work

Study the refrigerator shown in Figure 10.12. The basic parts of a refrigerator are the compressor, condenser coils, freezer unit, storage tank, refrigerant, and pump. How do these parts work to cool the inside of the refrigerator? A refrigerator repeatedly evaporates and condenses a refrigerant. The refrigerant moves through the system and transfers heat from inside the refrigerator to the room outside. Although a refrigerator cools the food inside, it actually heats the room.

**Figure 10.12
The Cooling System of a Refrigerator ▼**

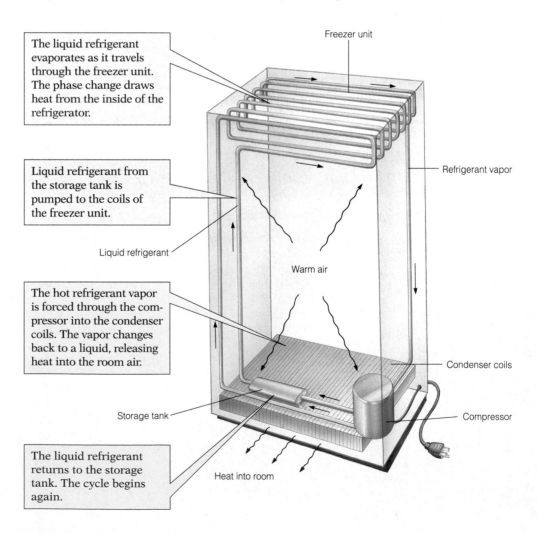

The liquid refrigerant evaporates as it travels through the freezer unit. The phase change draws heat from the inside of the refrigerator.

Liquid refrigerant from the storage tank is pumped to the coils of the freezer unit.

The hot refrigerant vapor is forced through the compressor into the condenser coils. The vapor changes back to a liquid, releasing heat into the room air.

The liquid refrigerant returns to the storage tank. The cycle begins again.

Freezer unit · Refrigerant vapor · Liquid refrigerant · Warm air · Condenser coils · Compressor · Storage tank · Heat into room

Science and Society
CFCs and the Ozone Layer

Many cooling systems use special chemicals called chlorofluorocarbons, or CFCs. Chlorofluorocarbons contain the elements carbon, chlorine, and fluorine. One property of these chemicals is their ability to rapidly absorb large amounts of heat energy. Another property is their ability to change phase easily. These properties make CFCs good refrigerants.

During the early 1970s, scientists began to express concern about the effect CFCs have on the atmosphere. Investigations indicated that soon after CFCs enter the atmosphere, they are broken down by radiation from the sun. The free chlorine that is released reacts with ozone molecules in the upper atmosphere. This reaction reduces the amount of ozone.

Ozone protects life on the earth from harmful radiation from the sun. Overexposure to this harmful radiation causes sunburn, skin cancer, and cataracts. People are concerned because this protective layer of ozone is disappearing.

In 1990, an international treaty signed by many countries limited the use of products that use CFCs. This limitation includes the chemicals used in cooling systems and in aerosol cans. The treaty reflects a global effort to protect the environment. Is it enough?

Table 10.2 Commonly Used CFCs

Generic Name	Use	Chemical Name	Chemical Formula
Freon-11	Aerosol propellants	Trichlorofluoromethane	CCl_3F
Freon-12	Refrigerators, air conditioners, freezers	Dichlorodifluoromethane	CCl_2F_2

Check and Explain

1. Draw and label a diagram of a refrigerator to explain how a cooling system works.

2. What is the role of evaporation in a refrigeration system?

3. **Compare and Contrast** How are heating and cooling systems alike? How are they different?

4. **Infer** How is your body's cooling system similar to the cooling system in a refrigerator?

Section Objectives
For a list of section objectives, see the Student Edition page.

Skills Objectives
Students should be able to:

Infer what transportation would be like without engines.

Reason and Conclude how to reduce air pollution.

Classify motorized vehicles by the types of engines they have.

Vocabulary
combustion, turbine

MOTIVATE

Skill WarmUp
To help students understand heat engines, have them do the Skills WarmUp.
Answer Answers will vary. Students should remember to list ways of transporting goods and people that are still used in developing countries.

Prior Knowledge
Gauge how much students know about heat engines by asking the following questions:

▶ Why would people call car engines "heat engines"?

▶ How would you describe what an internal combustion engine does?

▶ What other uses for heat engines other than in motor vehicles can you think of?

Themes in Science
Energy Explain to students that no heat engine is 100 percent efficient; that is, able to convert all available heat energy into mechanical energy. Most engines are considered adequate if they are 40 percent efficient. Ask, Where does the remaining energy go? (Much is transferred into the surrounding air and engine parts as heat.)

Social Studies Connection
Have students research areas of the world where automobiles are not common. Ask them to identify the methods of transportation used in those areas, such as buses, bicycles, boats, animals, or walking, and estimate how energy efficient these methods are.

▼ ACTIVITY

Inferring

Transportation

List as many methods of transporting goods and people as possible. Identify those that use some type of engine. Think about what transportation would be like if the engine hadn't ever been invented. How might your daily life be different?

SKILLS WARMUP

10.3 Heat Engines

Objectives

▶ **Explain** how two kinds of heat engines work.

▶ **Identify** the parts of an internal-combustion engine.

▶ **Compare** and **contrast** internal- and external-combustion engines.

▶ **Classify** motors according to their types of heat engines.

Insert a key into the ignition of a car, turn the key, and the car starts. Shift into gear, press on the gas pedal, and the car moves. Whether you drive or not, you've probably experienced this sequence of activities many times. But do you know what occurs under the hood to make the car move? Inside the car's engine, chemical energy changes to heat energy. The heat energy is then changed into mechanical energy that moves the car down the road.

How Heat Engines Work

Heat energy is changed into mechanical energy by a heat engine. Most motor vehicles, such as cars, buses, and trucks, are powered by heat engines. Heat engines also power some airplanes.

Many heat engines use fuel. The most commonly used fuels are gasoline and diesel fuel. Heat engines that use fuel have enclosed tubes called cylinders. A mixture of fuel and air enters the cylinder. A spark or temperature change causes the fuel to ignite. When the fuel is ignited, the explosion causes the piston in the cylinder to move. The piston moves a rod that transfers mechanical energy to the wheels or propeller.

There are two main types of heat engine. The difference between the two types is where the fuel burns, or where **combustion** occurs. Combustion is any type of chemical reaction with oxygen that can give off heat or light. In an internal-combustion engine, such as an automobile engine, gasoline or diesel fuel burns directly inside the cylinders. In an external-combustion engine, such as a steam engine, fuel burns outside the cylinders.

STS Connection

Nikolaus August Otto demonstrated the first four-stroke internal-combustion engine in 1867. It used coal gas and was very noisy. In 1876, he demonstrated a much quieter engine. Have students research the changes Otto made between 1867 and 1876.

Writing Connection

Ask students to imagine themselves as gasoline molecules going through the four-stroke engine in Figure 10.13. Have them write stories about their journey through the engine.

Internal-Combustion Engine Some cars, motor scooters, and snowmobiles have gasoline engines. Most tractors, large trucks, buses, and construction equipment have diesel engines. Although the engine structure and type of fuel may differ, all of these machines are powered by internal-combustion engines. All internal-combustion engines burn fuel inside the engine to change heat energy into mechanical energy. A four-stroke gasoline engine is shown in Figure 10.13.

**Figure 10.13
How a Gasoline Engine Works**

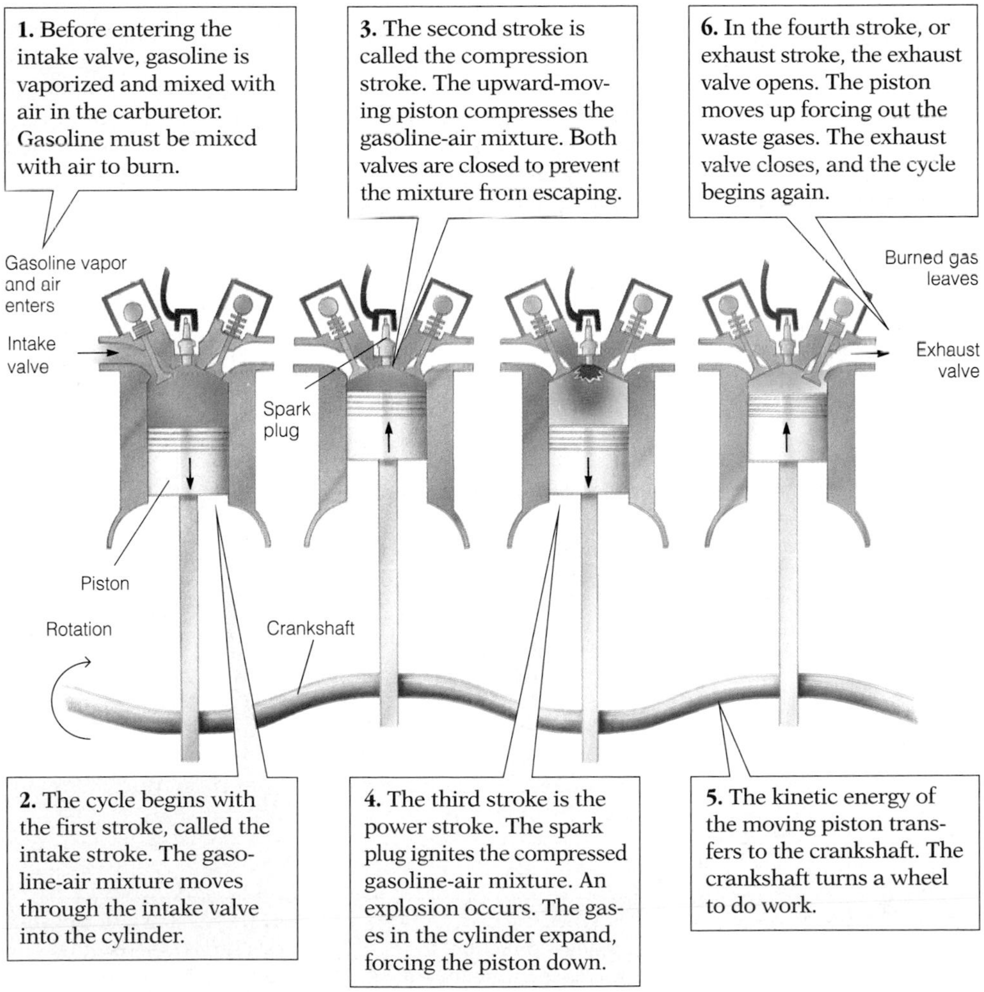

1. Before entering the intake valve, gasoline is vaporized and mixed with air in the carburetor. Gasoline must be mixed with air to burn.

3. The second stroke is called the compression stroke. The upward-moving piston compresses the gasoline-air mixture. Both valves are closed to prevent the mixture from escaping.

6. In the fourth stroke, or exhaust stroke, the exhaust valve opens. The piston moves up forcing out the waste gases. The exhaust valve closes, and the cycle begins again.

Gasoline vapor and air enters
Intake valve
Spark plug
Burned gas leaves
Exhaust valve
Piston
Rotation
Crankshaft

2. The cycle begins with the first stroke, called the intake stroke. The gasoline-air mixture moves through the intake valve into the cylinder.

4. The third stroke is the power stroke. The spark plug ignites the compressed gasoline-air mixture. An explosion occurs. The gases in the cylinder expand, forcing the piston down.

5. The kinetic energy of the moving piston transfers to the crankshaft. The crankshaft turns a wheel to do work.

TEACH

Skills Development
Observe Ask students, Which kinds of engines do you see most often? Why? (Internal-combustion engines are seen most often because cars and buses are more common than steam engines.)

Explore Visually
Have students study Figure 10.13, then ask:
▶ Why does air move into the cylinder with the gasoline? (Combustion requires oxygen.)
▶ What do the first and second strokes accomplish? (The gasoline-air mixture enters the cylinder and is compressed.)
▶ How does the spark plug start the power stroke? (It ignites the gasoline-air mixture, forcing the piston down.)
▶ Explain why combustion makes the fourth stroke necessary. (Combustion burns the gasoline and oxygen, releasing energy and leaving waste gases.)
▶ How does the engine move a vehicle? (Its energy moves the driveshaft and the wheels.)

The Living Textbook: Physical Science Side 2
Chapter 33   Frame 27871
Internal Combustion Engine (Animation)
Search: Play:

The Living Textbook: Physical Science Sides 1-4
Chapter 10   Frame 01903
Internal Combustion Engine (2 Frames)
Search: Step:

TEACH ▪ Continued

Explore Visually

Have students study Figure 10.15. Ask the following questions:

▶ How many ducts lead steam into the cylinder? How do they affect the piston? (Two; they direct steam against the piston to move it in alternate directions.)

▶ How does moving the piston in different directions help the engine work? (The moving piston alternately pushes and pulls levers that turn a wheel. The wheel does work.)

Critical Thinking

Generalize Both internal-combustion and external-combustion engines use heat energy to push pistons. How is the mechanical result the same? (The pistons of each engine are connected to devices that use mechanical energy to do work.)

Enrich

Explain that a flywheel is a wheel with an off-center fulcrum. Make a flywheel with a piece of stiff cardboard and a piece of dowling to demonstrate how it works.

The Living Textbook:
Physical Science Side 2

Chapter 32   Frame 27299
Steam Engine (Animation)
Search: Play:

STS Connection

Research Explain to students that because diesel engines use heat from the compression of air, not an electric spark, to ignite the fuel-air mixture, they tend to be larger and slower than gasoline-powered engines. However, they use diesel fuel, which is cheaper than gasoline. Ask students to find out why many trucks and buses are designed to use diesel engines and report their findings to the class.

Social Studies Connection

Explain to students that the first successful heat engine was a steam engine. Have students research and report on where the Industrial Revolution began, who instigated it, and what role the steam engine played in it.
Use Integrating Worksheet 10.3.

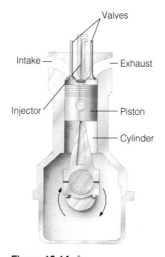

Valves

Intake —

Exhaust

Injector —

Piston

Cylinder

Figure 10.14 ▲
A diesel engine has no spark plug or carburetor. Compare the fuel flow through a diesel engine and a gasoline engine.

Figure 10.15
How a Steam Engine Works ▼

Diesel and gasoline engines are both internal-combustion engines. Look at the cylinder of a diesel engine in Figure 10.14. In a diesel engine, air alone is drawn into the cylinder. The air is compressed, increasing its temperature to over 700°C. Diesel fuel is then sprayed into the cylinder, where the high temperature causes it to ignite. The gases expand and produce mechanical energy.

External-Combustion Engine Unlike diesel and gasoline engines, the fuel in an external-combustion engine burns outside the engine. A steam engine is an example of an external-combustion engine. In a steam engine, water heated in a boiler changes to steam. The steam piped into the engine forces the piston to move back and forth inside the cylinder. The moving piston is connected to a flywheel that does work. Look at Figure 10.15.

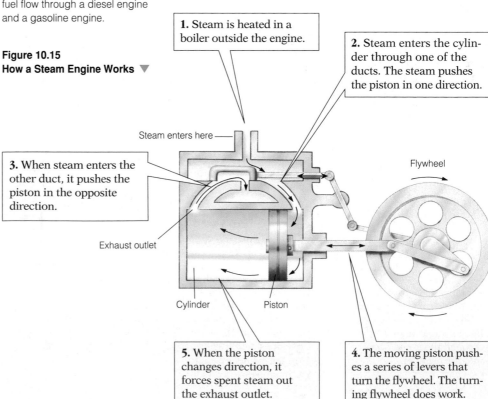

1. Steam is heated in a boiler outside the engine.

2. Steam enters the cylinder through one of the ducts. The steam pushes the piston in one direction.

Steam enters here —

3. When steam enters the other duct, it pushes the piston in the opposite direction.

Flywheel

Exhaust outlet

Cylinder   Piston

5. When the piston changes direction, it forces spent steam out the exhaust outlet.

4. The moving piston pushes a series of levers that turn the flywheel. The turning flywheel does work.

A steam engine like the one shown was improved by James Watt in the 1700s. Watt's steam engine was responsible for starting the Industrial Revolution. The engine powered trains and factory machines.

Use of Turbines

Years ago, most steam engines contained pistons that moved up and down in cylinders. Steam piped into the cylinders caused the motion of the pistons. The mechanical energy of the pistons moved parts on the machine, enabling it to do work. However, modern steam engines have a different design. The pistons on modern steam engines have been replaced with turbines.

A **turbine** is a set of curved blades mounted on a long shaft. When steam strikes the turbine blades, the shaft rotates. The mechanical energy of the rotating shaft is used to turn objects, such as ship propellers or electric generators.

Geology LINK

Eruptions of steam from the ground (called geysers) and hot water in the ground are a useful energy source. Make a model of a geyser. Collect the following items: funnel, large can, plastic tubing.

1. Fill the can with water.
2. Place the funnel in the can upside down.
3. Place an end of the tubing under the funnel in the can.
4. Blow on the other end of the tubing.

What happened? Are geysers good sources of energy?

ACTIVITY

Consider This

Should Cars Use Solar-Powered Engines?

Waste gases from automobile engines are major contributors to air pollution. To reduce air pollution and conserve fossil fuels, engineers are studying the use of sunlight to "fuel" automobiles. Solar cells on the automobile convert sunlight to electricity. As sunlight strikes a solar cell, it triggers the movement of electrons within the cell to produce an electric current. This electric current is used to power the car's engine.

The sun is a good source of unlimited, free energy. Solar-powered engines don't release harmful pollutants into the atmosphere.

However, sunlight isn't always available. A backup system is needed to power the automobile on cloudy days and at night. In addition, currently the cost of producing a solar-powered car is quite high.

Solar-powered engines aren't as powerful as gasoline engines. Therefore, solar cars are slower and smaller than cars with gasoline engines.

Think About It Would you be willing to buy a solar-powered automobile that may not be large or powerful but that doesn't pollute the air? Would the extra cost be worth it? Why or why not?

Write About It Write a paper stating your position for or against using solar-powered cars. Include your reasons for choosing your position.

Skills WorkOut

To help students use reason when solving a problem about reducing air pollution, have them do the Skills WorkOut.

Answer Answers will vary. Be sure that students give logical explanations.

EVALUATE

WrapUp

Reinforce Henry Ford was told that the internal combustion engine would never work in an automobile. Use what you learned in this chapter to explain why it does.

Use Review Worksheet 10.3.

Check and Explain

1. Both convert heat energy into mechanical energy.

2. Parts include intake and exhaust valves, pistons and cylinders, and a spark plug. Students may also describe the carburetor and drive shaft. Make sure students correctly describe the function of each part.

3. Both run on heat energy, which is generated inside the internal-combustion and outside the external-combustion engine. The internal-combustion engine turns a crank shaft, the external-combustion engine turns a flywheel.

4. Lawnmower: gasoline (internal-combustion); locomotive: steam (external-combustion) or diesel; heavy road equipment: diesel (internal); motor scooter: gasoline; submarine: diesel or nuclear power; automobile: gasoline or diesel.

STS Connection

Explain that jet engines, called *turbofan* engines, rely on huge turbines driven by high-pressure gases. Have students do research and make diagrams showing how these engines help keep the jet in the air.

Writing Connection

Have students imagine that they design engines for new cars. Ask each student to write a short report for the company president explaining why people will buy cars with a new, nonpolluting engine.

A turbine needs a continuous flow of fluid to turn the shaft. Often this fluid is steam. However, falling water also moves turbines, such as those in hydroelectric power plants. High-pressure gases are also used to drive turbines. Gas turbines are used in jet engines.

Science and Society *Combustion Waste*

All heat engines burn some kind of fuel. These burning fuels produce waste products in the form of gases and small particles. A major source of air pollution is the exhaust from automobiles. Exhaust fumes carry waste gases, such as carbon monoxide, hydrocarbons, and nitrogen oxides. During this century, the levels of these air pollutants have increased drastically from automobile use.

Central heating systems used in most homes and offices release pollutants into the atmosphere. Heat engines used in electric power plants and in industrial plants also contribute to the air-pollution problem. As more heat engines are used, air-pollution problems continue to get worse.

Each year in the United States, air-pollution costs are about $16 billion for health care, building maintenance, and damage to the environment. Air pollution causes eye irritations and respiratory problems. People with asthma, young children, and elderly people suffer the most from health problems related to air pollution.

▼ **ACTIVITY**

Reasoning

Clean Air Actions

Make a list of the ways that air pollution could be reduced. Explain how each of the ideas on your list would help to solve the air-pollution problem.

SKILLS WORKOUT

Check and Explain

1. Why are internal- and external-combustion engines called "heat" engines?

2. List the major parts of an internal-combustion engine. Explain the function of each part.

3. **Compare and Contrast** Describe the similarities and the differences between internal- and external-combustion engines.

4. **Classify** Classify each of the following according to the type of engine it has: lawn mower, locomotive, heavy road equipment, motor scooter, submarine, and automobile.

Chapter 10 Review

Concept Summary

10.1 Heating Technology
▶ Central heating systems generate heat from a central location and are controlled by a thermostat.
▶ Some common types of central heating systems include forced air, hot water, steam, radiant, and heat pumps.
▶ Active and passive solar heating use energy supplied by the sun.
▶ Insulation in a building stops the flow of heat to the outside.

10.2 Cooling Technology
▶ Cooling systems use evaporation and condensation to transfer heat.
▶ Your body is cooled by sweat, which absorbs heat as it evaporates from your skin.

▶ The basic parts of a refrigerator are the compressor, condenser coils, storage tank, refrigerant, and pump.
▶ Refrigerants evaporate at low temperatures to remove heat from an enclosed space.

10.3 Heat Engines
▶ Heat engines burn fuel to convert heat energy into mechanical energy.
▶ A heat engine can be an internal-combustion or an external-combustion engine.
▶ Internal-combustion engines are either gasoline or diesel engines.
▶ The most common external-combustion engine is the steam engine.

Chapter Vocabulary

central heating system (p. 231)   R-value (p. 236)   combustion (p. 244)
insulation (p. 236)   refrigerant (p. 241)   turbine (p. 247)

Check Your Vocabulary

Use the vocabulary words above to complete the following sentences correctly.

1. The greater the ability to trap heat energy, the higher the material's _____.
2. A chemical reaction with oxygen that produces heat or light is called _____.
3. Heat that is generated in one location and distributed by a network of wires, pipes, ducts and vents is a(n) _____.
4. A chemical that changes phase from liquid to gas at a low temperature is used as a(n) _____.
5. Substances, such as fiberglass, that slow the flow of heat are called _____.
6. A set of blades on a shaft used to produce mechanical energy is a(n) _____.

Identify the word or term in each group that doesn't belong. Explain why it doesn't belong with the group.

7. plastics, fiberglass, aluminum
8. combustion, evaporation, condensation
9. forced-air heating, steam heating, passive solar heating
10. ammonia, carbon dioxide, metal foil
11. gasoline engine, steam engine, diesel engine

Write Your Vocabulary

Write sentences using the vocabulary words above. Show that you know what each word means.

Check Your Vocabulary
1. R-value
2. combustion
3. central heating system
4. refrigerant
5. insulation
6. turbine
7. Aluminum: Plastics and fiberglass are insulating materials; aluminum is not.
8. Combustion: Evaporation and condensation are physical processes. Combustion is a chemical process.
9. Passive solar heating: Both forced-air and steam heating use convection to heat a room or building, and are active methods of heating. Passive solar uses radiation, and is not active.
10. Metal foil: Ammonia and carbon dioxide are examples of natural refrigerants.
11. Steam engine: The gasoline engine and diesel engine are both internal combustion heat engines.

Write Your Vocabulary
Students' sentences should show that they know the meaning of each word as well as how to use it in a sentence.
Use Vocabulary Worksheet for Chapter 10.

Check Your Knowledge

1. The two types of solar heating systems are passive and active.

2. A diesel engine and a gasoline engine are two examples of internal combustion engines.

3. The parts of a refrigerator are the compressor, condenser coils, pump, storage tank, and refrigerant.

4. The first stroke (intake) brings the fuel-air mixture into the cylinder. During the second stroke (compression), the piston compresses the gases in the cylinder. During the third stroke (power), the spark plug ignites the fuel-air mixture. The resulting explosion pushes down on the piston. During the fourth stroke (exhaust), the piston moves up, forcing waste gases out of the cylinder.

5. Any fluid can be used to power turbines.

6. The parts of a steam engine are the boiler, valves, cylinder, piston, and flywheel.

7. Insulation is commonly used in ceilings, attic floors, outside walls, windows, and doors.

8. thermostat

9. convection

10. lower

11. piston

12. turbines

13. chlorofluorocarbons

Check Your Understanding

1. A refrigerator is like a heat pump in that it uses a liquid refrigerant to extract heat from a cooler region and move it to a warmer region.

2. A cooling system works by using a liquid with a low boiling point (refrigerant) to remove heat from an enclosed space. The refrigerant is then pumped to the outside where it gives up the heat it gained.

3. Northern Alaska: Any but solar or heat pump systems, because of the extreme cold temperatures and long periods of little or no sunlight. Southern Texas: Any type of heating system would be feasible, because the climate is mild. The choice would have to depend on the relative advantages/disadvantages of each type.

4. In an icebox, the food is cooled as the melting ice cools the air that absorbs heat from the food. In the electric refrigerator, the heat from the food is used to evaporate the liquid refrigerant, which carries the heat to the coils.

5. Perspiration excreted onto the skin evaporates. As the water evaporates, it absorbs heat from the body and carries it into the environment.

6. A diesel engine uses compression to ignite the fuel, while a gasoline engine uses the energy from a spark plug.

7. All heat engines use fuel, have enclosed cylinders, and convert the kinetic energy of expanding gases into the rotation of a wheel.

8. Students' answers will vary. Polystyrene foam, sawdust, and shredded paper are examples of materials used as insulators. Safety issues include toxicity and flammability.

9. A compressor circulates a refrigerant from an evaporator through a condenser and back to the evaporator. A fan blows hot, humid air over the evaporator, which takes heat from the air, leaving cooler air to blow back into the room.

Chapter 10 Review

Check Your Knowledge

Answer the following in complete sentences.

1. What are two types of solar heating systems?

2. What are two examples of internal-combustion engines?

3. What are the parts of a refrigerator?

4. Describe the cycle of a four-stroke internal-combustion engine.

5. What fluids are used to power turbines?

6. List the parts of a steam engine.

7. Where is insulation most commonly located in buildings?

Choose the answer that best completes each sentence.

8. When the air reaches a preselected low temperature the (thermostat, heat pump, compressor, condenser) turns on the central heating system.

9. Warm air spreads throughout a room by (conduction, radiation, convection, evaporation) currents.

10. Heat always flows from an area of high concentration to an area of (equal, high, low, deep) concentration.

11. In some heat engines, mechanical energy is transferred to the crankshaft by the movement of the (cylinder, spark plug, piston, carburetor).

12. Modern steam engines replaced pistons with (turbines, propellers, generators, cylinders).

13. The refrigerant most commonly used in cooling systems is (water, air, carbon dioxide, chlorofluorocarbons).

Check Your Understanding

Apply the concepts you have learned to answer each question.

1. How is a refrigerator like a heat pump?

2. **Critical Thinking** Heat always moves from a warm body to a cool body. How does this fact explain how a cooling system works?

3. **Application** What type of heating system would you choose for a building located in northern Alaska? In southern Texas? Explain your choice for each location.

4. **Extension** How does the way an icebox cools food differ from the way an electric refrigerator cools food?

5. Explain how your body's cooling system works.

6. How is a diesel engine different from a gasoline engine?

7. List two features that are common to all heat engines.

8. **Mystery Photo** The photograph on page 230 is a closeup view of fiberglass. The magnified fiberglass threads look very similar to small wires. The space between the threads traps air. Trapped air conducts heat extremely slowly. This makes fiberglass a good insulator. Make a list of other materials that could trap air to make good insulators. Evaluate the materials on your list for safety and cost as potential building insulators.

9. **Critical Thinking** Based on the principles of cooling systems, explain how an air-conditioning system works. You may use drawings or diagrams to explain your answer.

Develop Your Skills

1. a. Concrete wall

b. Hardwood floor

c. One with double windows

2. a. Sulfur oxides from power plants/heating

b. Carbon monoxide from transportation

c. Nitrogen oxides and hydrocarbons are produced mainly by transportation; internal-combustion-engine vehicles used for transportation are concentrated in cities.

3. Students' models will vary. Largest windows and solar collectors will face south. Walls facing in other directions will have only a few small windows. Interior walls might be constructed with vent systems to encourage convection currents.

Make Connections

1. Concept maps will vary. You may wish to have students do the map below. First draw the map on the board, then add a few key terms. Have students draw and complete the map.

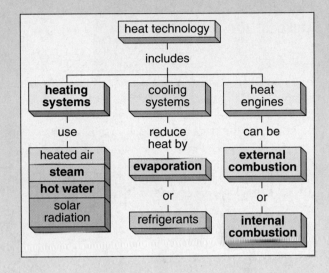

2. Results of students' surveys will vary depending on location.

3. Students' reports will vary. The steam engine made it possible to build many machines that worked faster and more efficiently than human laborers and draft animals, increasing productivity.

4. In a two-stroke engine, there is a compression stroke and a power stroke. Fuel is injected at the end of the compression stroke, and exhaust gases are forced out of the cylinder by a blower when the piston is at the bottom after the power stroke. Some motorcycles use two-cycle engines. They are noisier than four-stroke engines.

Develop Your Skills

Use the skills you have developed in this chapter to complete each activity.

1. Interpret Data The table below shows data about the R-value for four selected building materials.

a. Which building material has the greatest R-value?

b. Which building material is the poorest insulator?

c. Which house is better insulated: one with double windows or one with single windows?

R-value for Building Materials

Material	R-value
Concrete wall	8.00
Hardwood floor	0.71
Single window	1.00
Double window	2.00

2. Data Bank Use the table on page 640 to answer the following questions.

a. What is the major source of air pollution in the United States?

b. What is the second major source of air pollution?

c. Nitrogen oxides and hydrocarbons are the major causes of smog. What is the major source of these two pollutants? Where is this source of pollution likely to be the most concentrated?

3. Make a Model Design a model of a building that uses passive solar heating to its full potential. Label the direction that the front of the building faces.

Make Connections

1. Link the Concepts Below is a concept map showing how some of the main concepts in this chapter link together. Only part of the map is filled in. Finish the map, using words and ideas from the chapter.

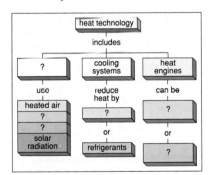

2. Science and Society Conduct a survey to find out the type of heating system used for homes in your area. Survey at least ten homes in different locations.

3. Science and Social Studies The invention of the steam engine helped start the Industrial Revolution. Use the library to research the Industrial Revolution. Find out what role the steam engine played during this time. Do you think the Industrial Revolution would have occurred without the invention of the steam engine? Why?

4. Science and Technology Most gasoline engines are four-stroke engines. However, there are also two-stroke engines. Find out how a two-stroke engine works. Compare the flow of fuel in a two-stroke engine to a four-stroke engine. You may use drawings for your comparison.

About the Literary Work

"Child of the Owl" was adapted from the text *Child of the Owl* by Lawrence Yep, copyright 1977 by Harper and Row Publishers. Reprinted by permission of Harper and Row Publishers.

Description of Change

Paw-Paw is the female narrator's maternal grandmother. The girl's natural mother is deceased. In its original form, this text makes references to the girl's often frustrating attempts to be like her deceased mother. These references were edited from the selection for the sake of space.

Rationale

This excerpt focuses on heat and chemical reactions.

Vocabulary

dinky, cruddy, acrid

Teaching Strategies

Directed Inquiry

After students finish reading, discuss the story. Be sure to relate the story to the science lesson in this unit. Ask the following questions:

▶ While the rice was being washed, what happened to the rice and water? (The water turned milky as it absorbed starch from the rice.)

▶ What happened while the narrator slept? (The fire was too hot. The water in the pot that wasn't absorbed by the rice evaporated. The rice burned.)

Skills Development

Predict Be sure that students understand that rice takes in water as it cooks. After a while, all the water in the cast-iron pot was either absorbed by the rice grains or it evaporated. You may wish to have student volunteers describe their own experiences when cooking rice. Then ask:

▶ What might have occurred if Paw-Paw had not come home when she did? (The rice grains would have continued to burn in the heated pot. It is possible that this might have started a fire.)

▶ How does this passage demonstrate the importance of smoke detectors in a home? (If the kitchen had contained a smoke detector, smoke from the burning rice would have activated the detector and wakened the girl.)

Critical Thinking

Reason and Conclude Given the scene she walked into, why did Paw-Paw think she had "lost" the narrator? (She thought that the gas from the oven had filled the apartment and killed the narrator, who was slumped over in her chair.)

Science and Literature Connection

Child of the Owl

The following excerpts are from the novel Child of the Owl *by Lawrence Yep*

I started to wash the rice like Paw-Paw had told me, though it took half an hour. Once I'd bought the wrong kind, getting short-grain rice when Paw-Paw liked Texas long, which she said was the closest to good Chinese rice. I had to wash it carefully, pouring it into a pot and then adding water and swirling it around with my hand, then pouring off the excess water which would turn milky from the washing. Then repeat the whole thing about a dozen times till the water I poured out was almost clear—which wasn't all that easy to see since we only had a dinky forty-watt bulb dangling from the kitchen ceiling. That way the rice never stuck. . . .

Anyway, so there I was in the kitchen in practically all the clothes I had, and I still didn't feel any warmer. The water in the pots hadn't boiled yet. I had hot water coming out of the tap to warm my hands but you couldn't wash the rice for too long in hot water or it would start to cook and by the time it came off the stove it would be as mushy as that cruddy [instant] rice. Though I started out using lukewarm water, it got cold fast in the frigid air and my hands got as cold as the water.

To [heck] with it, I thought. I could turn off the oven before she got back. So I got a book of Paw-Paw's matches and opened the oven. Then I lit a match and turned the gas on, putting the match near the little hole and hearing the soft explosion of gas igniting. Finally I twisted the gas up to three hundred fifty and went back humming to the kitchen sink to finish washing the rice.

I did that for the next few days without getting caught. Now five will get you two

that I normally stay awake during the daytime. I usually never nap, but there was something that Friday about how the rainwater dripped from the fire escapes and the heat filled the place. After I had put the rice on, I started to do my homework but somehow all the little numbers began to run around on the page and I was asleep.

The next thing I knew, there was an acrid smell in the air and the banging of pots. A cloud of steam came from the kitchen. I ran to the door and saw Paw-Paw there, still in her scarf and coat, holding our cast-iron pot under the faucet. The pot was so hot that it made the water turn into steam.

I glanced at the stove. Paw-Paw had turned off both the burners and the oven. "It's . . . it's a good thing that

Skills in Science

Reading Skills in Science

1. The narrator lit the oven to heat the apartment.

2. The acrid smell was caused by the burning of rice grains in the cast-iron pot.

Writing Skills in Science

1. Clothes are insulators. They prevent heat from escaping (or transferring) from the body.

2. Speeches should identify evaporation as a physical change in which liquid changes to a gas when it is heated. Condensation is a physical change in which vapor changes to liquid when it comes in contact with a cold surface.

3. The rice is rinsed with water. The milky water is discarded. This process is repeated until the water is almost clear.

Activities

Communicate Posters should illustrate the transfer of heat from the stove, to the pot, to the water, to the rice.

Reason and Conclude Students' research should rank the fabrics as follows: wool (warmest), cotton, linen, and polyester. Wool has the coarsest fibers. The fibers have spaces that trap warm air and prevent heat transfer. Coarser fibers have more air spaces per unit of material.

Predicting Answers may vary. Students should note that starch is the substance rinsed from rice. Boiling the milky water will demonstrate how the starch congeals. With less starch, the rice will stick together less.

---

the pot wasn't aluminum. It would have warped like crazy."

"Yes?" Paw-Paw said absently. With a big spoon she scraped the burnt rice out onto a newspaper and wrapped it up into a neat bundle. Then she set the cooling pot on the sink and reached for [a scouring] pad. In the same tight-lipped silence, she began to scrub out the burn marks from the pot, only she wasn't having too much luck.

"Did I ruin the pot, Paw-Paw?". . .

Paw-Paw glanced at me. Then she turned her eyes back to the pot and went on scrubbing. I went back into the other room and sat down on the bed and tried to read my arithmetic book, only the numbers kept on blurring. Paw-Paw came out

a moment later, wiping her hands on a dish towel. She sat down on the bed beside me. "When I came in and saw you with your head lying on the table and the stove door open, I thought you were dead. I thought I'd lost you."

I kept my eyes on the page of the book. "Really?" I mumbled. I felt ashamed.

"Yes, really." Paw-Paw hesitated at saying any more. Like me, she didn't like to talk about her own feelings. Even so she decided to go on. "Respect differences, cherish the things you share in common." She took my hands and felt them. "But you are cold." Looking worried, she rubbed them between her warm palms. "Well, if you're sure you won't kill us or explode the stove, I guess we could light it."

Skills in Science

Reading Skills in Science

1. **Find the Main Idea** Why did the narrator light the oven?

2. **Find Context Clues** What caused the acrid smell in the air?

Writing Skills in Science

1. **Reason by Analogy** The narrator says she had on "practically all" of her clothes trying to keep warm. How are clothes like insulation in a house? Use your knowledge of heat transfer to explain how clothes keep you warm.

2. **Communicate** A number of events were due to the evaporation or condensation of water. These concepts are difficult for young children to understand. Write a speech explaining one of these concepts to a kindergarten class. Be sure to include a demonstration!

3. **Define operationally** The narrator described how the rice should be prepared before boiling it. Describe the procedure she used.

Activities

Communicate Make a poster showing how turning on the stove resulted in burning the rice. Illustrate the transfer of heat throughout the process.

Reason and Conclude Research information on cotton, wool, linen, and polyester fabrics. Rank these fabrics according to how warm they keep you. Give reasons for your ranking.

Predicting What do you think the substance rinsed from the rice is? To find out, rinse some rice thoroughly only once, catching the milky water in a pan. Boil the milky water. Describe what happens. Let the water mixture cool. Describe the cool mixture. Use a cookbook or other source to find out why rice that is not rinsed sticks together.

Where to Read More

Chemistry for Every Kid by Janice Van Cleave. New York: John Wiley and Sons, 1989. This book contains 101 chemistry experiments that use household materials.

This unit presents electricity, magnetism, and electromagnetism and discusses their applications in electronic devices. Chapter 11 explains the nature of electric charge and static electricity. It also compares electric conductors and insulators. The chapter identifies sources and types of electric current, and explains Ohm's law. It also identifies and explains the parts of a circuit showing how current flows through series and parallel circuits. Chapter 12 describes the properties of magnets and the behavior of magnetized materials. The relationship between magnetism and electricity is explored. The chapter illustrates applications of electromagnetism in devices, such as electric motors and meters. It closes with an explanation of electromagnetic induction and its function in operat-

Introducing the Unit

Directed Inquiry

Have students examine the photograph. Ask:

▶ What materials in this photograph do you think conduct electricity? (The metals and the materials inside the transistors and semiconductors conduct electricity. Accept all reasonable answers.)

▶ What materials shown probably do not conduct electricity? (The plastic board, the ceramic, plastics, or rubber coatings, and the paint probably do not conduct electricity. Accept all reasonable answers.)

▶ What do you think the metal pathways are for? (They direct the flow of electric signals through the circuit board. Accept all reasonable answers.)

Writing About the Photograph

Have students study the photograph and pretend that the circuit board is a miniature electronic city. Have them write a short story describing what life is like there. Students should explain how the inhabitants get around in the city and what various structures are used for. Ask volunteers to read their stories to the class.

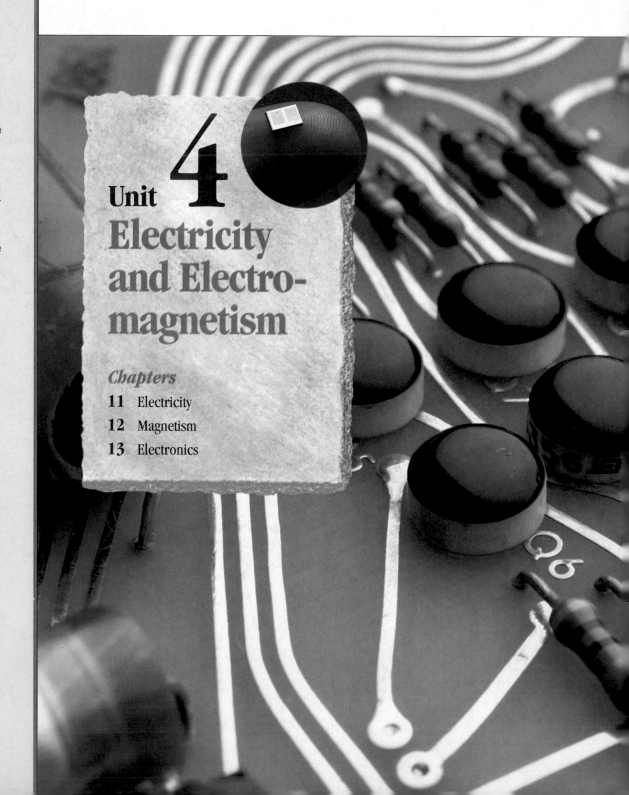

Unit 4
Electricity and Electro-magnetism

Chapters

11 Electricity
12 Magnetism
13 Electronics

ing electric generators and transformers. Chapter 13 introduces various electronic devices used to transmit electric signals. The chapter explains analog and digital signals and their use in audio and video electronics. Finally, the chapter describes the parts of a computer, and compares computer hardware and software.

Data Bank

Use the information on pages 634 to 643 to answer the questions about topics explored in this unit.

Calculating

How many years ago was the first general-purpose computer developed?

Classifying

List in order, five metals that are the best conductors of electricity.

Inferring

If the compass needle is always attracted to 0°, in what direction must you turn your compass to find geographic north?

Interpreting Data

What is the magnetic declination of the compass in your state?

The photograph to the left is a circuit board. Tiny silicon chips, resistors, and transistors are connected in the circuit. What electronic devices use circuit boards?

Data Bank Answers

Have students search the Data Bank on pages 634 to 643 for the answers to the questions on this page.

Calculating The first general-purpose computer, Mark I, was developed in 1944. The answer is found in the timeline, Development of the Computer, on page 636.

Extension Ask students to find out the size and capabilities of ENIAC, the first electronic digital computer. (ENIAC took up more than 135 square meters of space and could perform 5,000 additions and 1,000 multiplications per second.)

Classifying Silver, copper, gold, aluminum, magnesium, and zinc are the six best conductors of electricity. The answer is found in the chart, Electric Conductivity of Metals, on page 639.

Inferring Answer depends on the magnetic declination for your location. Use the map, Magnetic Declination in the United States, on page 639.

Interpreting Data Answers will vary depending on students' location. Necessary information is found in the map, Magnetic Declination in the United States, on page 639.

Answer to In-Text Question

Computers, microwave ovens, and televisions are a few electronic devices that use circuit boards.

Overview

Electricity is discussed in this chapter. The first section explains the nature of electric charges. The second section describes static electricity, charging by conduction and induction, and conductors and insulators. Electric current and Ohm's law are discussed in the third section. The final section identifies the parts of a circuit and series and parallel circuits.

Advance Planner

▶ Provide rice and split peas for TE page 258.

▶ Supply tissue paper, glass, silk, balloons, cotton balls, and flannel, polyester, and wool cloth for SE pages 259 and 260.

▶ Obtain different brands of plastic wrap for TE page 266.

▶ Collect copies of circuit diagrams for SE page 274.

▶ Supply dry cells, bulbs, sockets, and switches for page 277.

Skills Development Chart

Sections	Calculate	Collect Data	Compare and Contrast	Generalize	Hypothesize	Interpret Data	Model	Observe	Predict
11.1 Skills WarmUp			●						
Skills WorkOut								●	
Activity								●	●
11.2 Skills WarmUp									●
Skills WorkOut					●				
11.3 Skills WarmUp			●						
Skills WorkOut						●			
Practice Problems	●								
Skills WorkOut		●							
11.4 Skills WarmUp								●	
Skills WorkOut							●		
Skills WorkOut				●					
11.5 Skills WarmUp						●			
Practice Problems	●								
SkillBuilder								●	
Skills WorkOut									●

Individual Needs

▶ **Limited English Proficiency Students** Have students use the boldface heads to make up "What are/is . . ." questions for each section in the chapter. For example, "What is static buildup?" Have them write each question on a separate page of their science portfolios. As they read each section, have them write a two- or three-sentence answer to the questions. They should use their own words as well as the boldface terms in their answers. Have students use diagrams to illustrate their answers. Allow students to meet in groups of four or five to discuss what they have written. Allow them to make changes or additions to their answers. Encourage students to use the questions and answers during their review of the chapter.

▶ **At-Risk Students** Make enlarged photocopies of Figures 11.21 and 11.22. Distribute a copy to each student along with one meter of string. Have them cut out the dry cells and the lights and paste them onto a sheet of paper. Next have them "wire" the lights in parallel and in series by pasting the string in place. Have students use Figure 11.19 as a model and make a circuit diagram for each. Students can keep these in their portfolios.

▶ **Gifted Students** Encourage students to find out more about electricity in the human body. Have them find the answers to questions such as: What role does electricity play in the nervous system or the circulatory system? What can go wrong with electricity in the body? How does medicine make use of the body's electricity in diagnosis and treatment? Have students make an oral report to the class presenting their findings.

Resource Bank

▶ **Bulletin Board** Draw the face of a blank electric meter on notebook paper and make 25 photocopies. Post these on the board and label each row of five with a different date. On each of the dates posted, get the school's meter reading from the school engineer or custodian. Have students fill in the meter faces. Use the readings to track the school's electricity usage.

CHAPTER 11 PLANNING GUIDE

Section	Core	Standard	Enriched
11.1 Electric Charges pp. 257–260			
Section Features Skills WarmUp, p. 257 Skills WorkOut, p. 259 Activity, p. 260	● ● ●	● ● ●	● ● ●
Blackline Masters Review Worksheet 11.1	●	●	
11.2 Static Electricity pp. 261–266			
Section Features Skills WarmUp, p. 261 Skills WorkOut, p. 266	●	● ●	● ●
Blackline Masters Review Worksheet 11.2 Skills Worksheet 11.2	● ●	● ●	
Ancillary Options *Multiculturalism in Mathematics, Science, and Technology,* pp. 155–160	●	●	●
Color Transparencies Transparencies 35, 36a, 36b	●	●	●
Laboratory Program Investigation 22		●	●
11.3 Electric Current pp. 267–273			
Section Features Skills WarmUp, p. 267 Skills WorkOut, p. 269 Career Corner, p. 272 Skills WorkOut, p. 273	● ● ● ●	● ● ● ●	● ●
Blackline Masters Review Worksheet 11.3 Enrich Worksheet 11.3	● ●	● ●	●

Section	Core	Standard	Enriched
Skills Worksheet 11.3a Skills Worksheet 11.3b Integrating Worksheet 11.3	● ● ●	● ● ●	●
Color Transparencies Transparencies 37, 38	●	●	●
11.4 Electric Circuits pp. 274–278			
Section Features Skills WarmUp, p. 274 Skills WorkOut, p. 277	● ●	● ●	● ●
Blackline Masters Review Worksheet 11.4 Skills Worksheet 11.4	● ●	● ●	●
Ancillary Options *Multiculturalism in Mathematics, Science, and Technology,* pp. 103–106	●	●	●
Color Transparencies Transparencies 39, 40	●	●	●
Laboratory Program Investigation 23		●	●
11.5 Electric Power and Safety pp. 279–282			
Section Features Skills WarmUp, p. 279 SkillBuilder, p. 280 Skills WorkOut, p. 282	● ● ●	● ● ●	● ● ●
Blackline Masters Review Worksheet 11.5 Integrating Worksheet 11.5 Vocabulary Worksheet 11	● ● ●	● ● ●	●
Overhead Blackline Transparencies Overhead Blackline Master 10 and Student Worksheet	●	●	●

Bibliography

The following resources can be used for teaching the chapter. See page T-46 for supplier codes.

Technology Resources

Internet

PLANETDIARY at *http://www.planetdiary.com*
- Discover more about the atmosphere in *Atmosphere* by clicking on *Phenomena Backgrounders.*
- Find meteorological news in *Current Phenomena.*

Software

Learning All About Electricity and Magnetism. Mac, Dos. LS.

CD-ROMs

hip Physics. Mac. ESI.

Laserdiscs

Living Textbook. (See barcodes on pages in this chapter.) Optical Data.

Audio-Visual Resources

Experimenting with Electricity. Filmstrip. EB.

Writing Connection

Have students think about what their lives would be like if the light bulb had never been invented. Have them describe how it would affect their activities at home, at school, and at play.

Multicultural Perspectives

Discuss places in the world where there is no electricity, such as villages in the New Guinea highlands. Ask students to write about what their lives might be like if they lived in one of those places. Have students research a modern culture that does not have access to electricity. Ask students to compare two activities in their own lives that involve electricity to three similar activities in the lives of members of the culture they choose.

Introducing the Chapter

Have students read the description of the photograph. Ask if they agree or disagree with the description.

Directed Inquiry

Have students study the photograph. Ask:

▶ What is this a photograph of? (Students will identify it as a light bulb.)

▶ What makes the wires inside the bulb glow? (Electricity or energy moving through the wires)

▶ How does the electric energy change as it passes through the wires? (Lead students to observe that it is changing to light and heat energy.)

▶ Why do the wires inside a light bulb glow and get hot when other electric wires don't? (Students may respond that the wires are made out of special material. Some may mention resistance to the current is very high; the wires get very hot and glow.)

▶ Why is the bulb made of glass? (The vacuum inside the glass bulb prevents the filament from oxidizing and breaking; it also protects the filament; it lets the light shine through.)

Chapter Vocabulary

charge	induction
circuit	insulator
conduction	resistance
conductor	voltage
electric current	

Electricity

Chapter 11

Chapter Sections

What do you see?

❝I see a light bulb with many winding wires and electricity creating light. The part in the middle that's glass is there to hold the wires together. The electricity can't go through the glass.❞

Dawn Schoffelman
Axtell Park Middle School
Sioux Falls, South Dakota

To find out more about the photograph, look on page 284. As you read this chapter, you will learn about electricity.

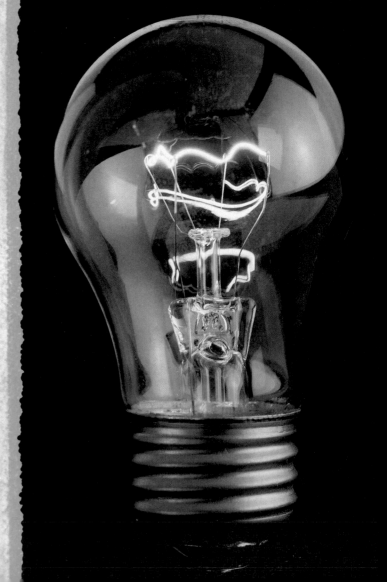

11.1 Electric Charges

Objectives

▶ **Identify** two forces that result from electric charges.

▶ **Explain** why objects attract and repel each other.

▶ **Communicate** how a positively charged object can be used to determine the charge on another object.

▶ **Infer** how electric charges behave in everyday situations.

▼ **ACTIVITY**

Comparing

Simply Shocking

List several situations when you received an electric shock. Describe the circumstances in each situation. How are the circumstances in each situation alike or different?

SKILLS WARMUP

Perhaps you have noticed that occasionally, when you comb your hair with a plastic comb, your hair becomes attracted to the comb, as in Figure 11.1. Sometimes you get a shock if you walk across a rug and then touch a metal doorknob. Each of these reactions occurs because of electric charge.

Charge and Force

You learned that all matter is made of atoms that contain electrons, neutrons, and protons. Recall that protons and electrons in atoms have an electric **charge**. Electrons have a negative charge, and protons have a positive charge. Neutrons have no electric charge.

When the atoms in an object have more electrons than protons, the total charge of the object is negative. When the atoms in an object have more protons than electrons, the total charge of the object is positive. When an object has an equal number of protons and electrons, the object has no charge. It is neutral. Neutrons have no effect on the total charge of an object because neutrons have no charge.

The positive and negative electric charges in objects can produce a force between the objects. Objects are forced together, or attracted, when their charges are different. An object with a positive charge is attracted to an object with a negative charge. When objects have the same electric charge, they are pushed apart, or repelled. For example, two negatively charged objects repel each other. You can predict whether objects will attract or repel each other by remembering that unlike charges attract and like charges repel.

Figure 11.1
Do the comb and the girl's hair have like or unlike charges? How do you know? ▼ ①

Explore Visually

Have students study the text, the pictures, and the captions. Ask:

▶ How do the charges on the balloon and the cloth change after rubbing? (The balloon's charge is negative and the cloth's charge is positive.)

▶ Do the cloth and balloon repel each other or attract each other? Why? (Attract each other; because they have unlike charges.)

▶ What happens when two charged balloons are brought near each other? Why? (They repel each other because both have negative charges, and like charges repel.)

Skills Development

Make a Model Have students make two drawings of a comb and a balloon side-by-side. Tell them that both the comb and the balloon are neutral in the first drawing. In the second drawing the balloon has been rubbed by a cloth and the comb has been used to comb hair. Have students draw the correct charges on the objects in each drawing. Also have them draw arrows to show whether the objects are attracted or repelled.

Answer to In-Text Question

① **The hairs on your head stand away from each other because they have like charges. When you comb your hair the hairs lose electrons so that the hairs are positively charged and repel each other. The charge on the comb is negative; it picks up the electrons.**

 The Living Textbook: Physical Science Sides 1-4

Chapter 15   Frame 02501
Opposite/ Like Charges (2 Frames)
Search: Step:

Art Connection

Have students make models representing charge and force on posterboard. They can begin by choosing a situation in which electric charges are created, as in a balloon rubbed on carpeting, running a comb through hair, or a lightning storm. To build their models, students can use glue, beans (for protons), and rice (for electrons). They can draw the sequence of electrical events with crayons and then glue the proton beans to their drawings. Students can simulate how electrons are added or subtracted by adding or removing the rice.

Figure 11.2 ▲
The cloth and the balloon are both neutral objects. They are neither attracted nor repelled.

Figure 11.3 ▲
Vigorous rubbing by the cloth changes the charge of both objects.

Figure 11.4 ▲
Notice the change in the position of the string holding the balloon. The balloon moved from its original position toward the cloth.

Electrical Attraction The cloth and the balloon in Figure 11.2 are both neutral objects. The atoms in each object have an equal number of protons and electrons. When two neutral objects are rubbed together, electrons may leave one object and move onto the other. The objects will then no longer be neutral. The total, or net, charge of each object will become either positive or negative.

When the cloth rubs against the balloon as in Figure 11.3, some electrons in the cloth move to the balloon. Since the balloon now has more electrons, its net charge is negative. Since the cloth loses electrons, its net charge is now positive. Because unlike charges attract, the positively-charged cloth attracts the negatively-charged balloon, as you can see in Figure 11.4.

Electrical Repulsion Imagine a second balloon is rubbed with the cloth. How will this balloon react to the negatively-charged balloon shown in Figure 11.4 when they are brought near each other? As the second balloon is rubbed with the cloth, more electrons leave the cloth and move onto the balloon. The second balloon now has more electrons than it has protons. Like the first balloon, its net charge is negative. When the balloons are brought near each other, they will repel, or push apart. This force of repulsion occurs because the objects have like charges. Why do you think the hairs on your head stand away from each other when you comb your hair? What is the charge of the comb? ①

Integrating the Sciences

Life Science All living things, including people, give off small amounts of electricity in water. Some fish, such as "electric" eels, have an organ in their bodies that can produce a strong electric current. In fact, a six-foot-long eel can produce a shock of up to 600 volts of electricity, which can kill frogs and small fishes. Some fishes, such as sharks and catfish, have electric receptors. They can detect electricity. Ask students to suggest how the fish might use these abilities. (An electric field helps the fish in defense, capturing prey, and communicating. Some fish navigate with the help of receptors that sense tiny changes in an electric field. Sharks can locate a fish buried in the sand by sensing the tiny electric field it gives off. Eels can locate prey by sensing changes in their own electric field.)

Electric Field

An electric field surrounds all charged objects. The electric field is stronger close to the charged object and grows weaker with distance. The electric field of a positively charged object is positive. A negatively charged object is surrounded by a negative electric field. An electric field applies an electric force on other charged objects that come into contact with it. A positive electric field attracts negative electric charges and pushes positive ones away. A negative field does the opposite. It attracts positive charges and repels negative charges.

 Science and You *Your Electric Nerves*

How do you know to let go of a hot object? Your body uses electric signals to communicate with your brain. Even though the net charge of your body is neutral, some parts have positive or negative charges. For example, the outside of a nerve cell has a positive charge, and the inside of the nerve cell has a negative charge. These charges are separated by a membrane that covers the nerve cell.

If you touch a hot pan, negative charges on the inside of the nerve cells pass through the membrane. The net electric charge on each side of the membrane changes. A continuous change of electric charge moves along the length of the nerve, producing an electric signal, or impulse. This impulse travels to your spinal cord. A reflex from your spinal cord sends another impulse to your hand. Your muscles respond, and you drop the hot pan.

Check and Explain

1. What are two types of electrical forces that can result from electric charges?

2. You bring two balloons together and they repel. Explain what happens in terms of charges.

3. **Communicate** How can a negatively charged comb be used to determine the charge of an object?

4. **Infer** Why does the television screen attract dust after the screen has been wiped clean?

▼ **ACTIVITY**

Observing

Electric Bits

Collect the following items: two textbooks, pieces of glass, a piece of silk, tissues.

1. Set the text books several centimeters apart.

2. Place small bits of tissue between them.

3. Lay two pieces of glass across the books. Then rub the glass hard with a piece of silk.

What happens to the tissue bits? Explain what you see.

SKILLS WORKOUT

Skills WorkOut

To help students observe electric charges, have them do the Skills WorkOut.

Answer The bits of tissue are attracted to the glass.

Critical Thinking

Reason and Conclude Ask students why tiny pieces of paper will be attracted to a charged object. (The paper moves toward the object because it is negatively charged and the paper is positively charged.)

EVALUATE

WrapUp

Reinforce Present the following: Raissa takes her younger sisters to the park. As the girls slide down the slide, Raissa stands underneath it. Suddenly, she feels her hair stand up on end. Ask students, What caused Raissa's hair to do this? Have them show what happened with a simple diagram.

Use Review Worksheet 11.1.

Check and Explain

1. Attraction and repulsion

2. The balloons both have the same charge, positive or negative, and like charges repel.

3. If an object is attracted to the comb, the object has an unlike, or positive, charge. If the object is repelled, it has a like, or negative, charge.

4. An electric field exists around the TV set. The screen will attract particles having an unlike charge.

 **The Living Textbook: Physical Science Sides 1-4**

Chapter 15   Frame 02498
Static Charges (2 Frames)
Search: Step:

259

Time 40 minutes   **Group** pairs

Materials

30 balloons

15 pieces each of flannel, polyester, and wool cloth

15 cotton balls

string

Prelab Discussion

Have students read the entire activity. Discuss a few points before beginning:

► Ask students to compare and contrast charge, attraction and repulsion.

► Have students describe what they think is happening when the objects are rubbed together.

Analysis

1. Cloth and balloon

2. Two balloons

3. The force of attraction is greater between two charged objects than between a charged object and a neutral object.

4. The negative charge of both balloons caused them to repel each other.

Conclusion

Conclusions depend on students' actual observations. Different materials give up electrons more or less easily. Wool gives up electrons more easily than cotton when rubbed. The greater the amount of electrons given up, the greater the force of attraction or repulsion.

Activity 11 *Which material has the greatest force of attraction?*

Skills Observe; Infer; Predict

Task 1 Prelab Prep

Collect the following items: 2 balloons; two 6-cm pieces of string; a piece of flannel cloth; a cotton ball; a piece of polyester cloth; and a piece of wool cloth.

Task 2 Data Record

1. Make a data table like the one shown.

2. As you carry out the procedure, fill in your data table. Indicate whether you did or did not rub the objects together, the force you observe between the objects, and the strength of this force (weak, medium or strong).

Task 3 Procedure

1. Blow up the balloons and tie the end in a knot. Attach a string to each balloon. Gently rub the two balloons against each other for about 30 s. Hold each balloon by its string and bring the two balloons together. Record your observations.

2. Rub one of the balloons with the flannel cloth for about 30 s. Move the flannel cloth near the balloon. Record your observations.

3. Place a cotton ball next to the balloon you rubbed with the flannel cloth. Record your observations.

4. Place the polyester cloth next to the same balloon. Record your observations.

5. Rub the second balloon with the wool cloth for 30 s. Move the wool cloth near the balloon. Record your observations.

6. Place the cotton ball near the balloon you rubbed with the wool cloth. Record your observations.

7. Place the polyester cloth near the balloon you rubbed with the wool cloth. Record your observations.

8. Bring the two balloons near each other. Record your observations.

Task 4 Analysis

1. What objects were the most attracted to each other?

2. What objects were the most repelled by each other?

3. Hypothesize why the force of attraction to the balloon was greater for some materials than it was for others.

4. Explain why the two balloons interacted in the way they did.

Task 5 Conclusion

Cotton and wool are natural materials. Based on your observations, which of these natural materials gives up electrons more easily? Give reasons why this might occur. Explain how the amount of electrons given up affects the force of attraction or repulsion between objects. Discuss the amount and direction of force you observed between objects.

Table 11.1   Force between Objects

Objects	Rubbed/Not rubbed	Force observed	Strength of force
1			
2			
3			
4			
5			
6			

INTEGRATED LEARNING

Themes in Science

Energy One form of energy is electrical energy. Static electricity is a buildup of charges. Electrical energy stored in an electric field changes to mechanical energy as motion occurs. An example is the movement of the metal foil leaves in an electroscope. Ask students to think of other examples of electricity changing to another form of energy. (A spark gives off light. Lightning generates heat.)

Language Arts Connection

The word *static* has several different meanings. Students might be familiar with the word as it applies to a noisy radio signal. Have them use a dictionary to find the meaning of the word *static* as it applies to static electricity. Ask them to discuss how these two meanings are related.

Section Objectives
For a list of section objectives, see the Student Edition page.

Skills Objectives
Students should be able to:

Predict which substances will act as conductors and insulators.

Hypothesize about interactions of electric charges.

Infer whether being exposed to electricity will be dangerous.

Vocabulary
conduction, induction, conductor, insulator

11.2 Static Electricity

Objectives

▶ **Identify** three ways static charge can build up.

▶ **Explain** what causes lightning.

▶ **Compare** electric conductors and insulators.

▶ **Infer** why lightning can be dangerous.

H ave you ever wondered what causes lightning? How about the shock you sometimes get from touching a metal doorknob? Actually, these two events are quite alike. Both are caused by static electricity.

Electric current results from the movement of electrons. The current used by the lights in your classroom consists of charges that continuously flow through a wire. Static electricity, however, consists of electric charges at rest. The electrons that cause static electricity can move from one object to another, and then remain at rest. The word *static* means not moving, or stationary. When electrons gather in one location, a build-up of static electricity results.

Static Build-up

A neutral object builds up an electric charge by gaining or losing electrons. An electroscope, like the one shown in Figure 11.5, is used to observe static electric charges. The electroscope is made with a glass flask and a metal rod with a knob at the top. A rubber stopper holds the metal rod in place and keeps it from touching the glass. The metal rod has a pair of thin, metal leaves at the bottom. A charged object placed on or near the knob causes the metal leaves at the bottom of the metal rod to repel each other.

Movement of charge depends on the forces of attraction and repulsion and the way charges act in different materials. To understand static electricity, you must understand how electric charges build up on an object. The build-up of static charge can be caused by friction, conduction, or induction.

▼ ACTIVITY

Predicting

Keeping Current

List five different kinds of matter in your classroom. Predict which materials would conduct electric current. What do these materials have in common?

SKILLS WARMUP

Figure 11.5
Why do you think it is important that the metal rod does not touch the glass flask? ▼ ①

Knob

Rod

Leaves

MOTIVATE

Skills WarmUp

To help students understand static electricity, have them do the Skills WarmUp.
Answer Answers will vary. Students will probably predict that materials, such as metals, water, solutions, and acids, will conduct electric current. All conductors allow electric energy to pass through them.

Misconceptions

Students may think that electrons move only between objects that are touching. To prepare them for the concept of induction, have them move a negatively charged object close to the knob of an electroscope without touching it. Or have them experiment by bringing a negatively charged balloon close to a partner's hair without actually making contact. Ask if the movement of the objects could be related to their electric fields.

Answer to In-Text Question

① The glass does not conduct electricity, so it would interrupt the flow of electricity in the metal rod.

Portfolio

Have students run a comb through their hair, then bring the comb near a few small pieces of newspaper. The paper is attracted to the comb, but after a short time, is repelled. Ask students to explain their observations by making a series of diagrams in their portfolios. They should use plus and minus signs to show charges, and arrows to show movement.

Discuss

Have students study this page. Then ask:

► If you charge an electroscope by touching it with a negatively charged object, what happens? What is this called? (The leaves spread apart. This is called charging by conduction.)

► If you charge an electroscope by bringing a negatively charged object near it without making contact, what happens? What is this called? (The leaves spread apart. This is called charging by induction.)

Class Activity

Let students experiment with electroscopes to discover how induction differs from conduction. Ask students to describe what happens in an electroscope charged by conduction compared to an electroscope charged by induction. Students should be able to explain the difference. (If you take the charging object away, the electroscope charged by conduction will remain charged, because electrons were transferred. The electroscope charged by induction does not remain charged, because no electrons were transferred.)

Language Arts Connection

Conduction contains the ending *-duction*, which comes from the Latin word *ducere*, meaning "to lead." Have students use the dictionary to list other words with the prefix *con-*. Write the other *con-* words on the chalkboard. Help them to discover that *con-* generally refers to things being brought together. Have students suggest how the meanings of *con-* and *-duction* describe the conduction of electricity.

Friction   Charging by friction occurs when objects rub together and electrons move from the surface of one object to the surface of the other. Friction separates electrons from the surface of an object whose atoms hold electrons loosely. Once separated, the electrons move onto another object. The movement of electrons from the cloth to the balloon shown in Figure 11.3 resulted from charging by friction. The balloon receives and holds electrons from the cloth.

Conduction   Charging by **conduction** occurs when electrons are transferred from one material to another by direct contact. An electroscope can be charged by conduction, as shown in Figure 11.7. When the knob of the electroscope is touched with a negatively-charged ruler, electrons move from the ruler to the knob. The electrons then move down the

rod to the leaves. Each leaf becomes negative and repels the other. Conduction causes the small electric shock you feel when you rub your shoes on a carpet and touch metal. The shock you feel occurs when electrons move from you to the metal.

Induction   When charges on an object are rearranged without physical contact, charging by **induction** occurs. Look at Figure 11.8. A negatively-charged object is near, but not touching, the knob of the electroscope. The electrons inside the electroscope are repelled by the negative charge of the object. Electrons move from the knob and move down the rod to the leaves. The leaves become negatively charged and the knob is positively charged. Because the object didn't touch the knob of the electroscope or give up any electrons, it remains neutral.

Figure 11.6 ▲
The leaves of this electroscope are neutral. The leaves do not repel, or spread apart.

Figure 11.7 ▲
This electroscope has been charged by conduction, which involves direct contact.

Figure 11.8 ▲
Charging by induction doesn't involve direct contact between the negative object and the knob.

Conductors A material through which electric charges move easily is called a **conductor**. Most metals are good conductors. Recall that metals have a crystalline structure. Electrons in metal atoms are free to move through the crystalline structure. Good conductors have a large number of freely-moving electrons. Gold, silver, copper, aluminum, and mercury are the best conductors of electricity.

Metals that are good conductors can be useful. For example, copper and aluminum are used in electric wiring and telephone lines. Besides electrons, heat also moves easily through conductors. For this reason, some metals used for wires are also used to make cooking pots and pans.

Other materials are also good conductors. For example, the acid used in a car battery conducts electric charges. Water is also a good conductor. To prevent an electric shock, you should handle electrical appliances carefully around water.

Insulators A material through which electric charges can't move easily is called an **insulator**. Electrons move extremely slowly through good insulators. Electrons are tightly bound to the atoms in good insulating materials. The electrons are not free to move around. If substances were arranged according to how well they conduct electricity, the conductors would be at the top of the list and the insulators would be at the bottom.

Materials such as wood, ceramic, rubber, glass, and plastic are electric insulators. You are probably aware that wires used in electric wiring, such as lamp cords, are covered with rubber or plastic. Rubber and plastic are insulators and prevent electric charges inside the wire from flowing to the outside of the wire.

Charges don't flow easily through insulators. But charges do collect on their surfaces. The electrons that build up on the surface of an insulator tend to remain there as static charge.

Figure 11.9 ▲
Why is it an advantage that these objects are good conductors? Explain. ①

Figure 11.10 ▲
Identify three insulators in this photograph. How is an insulator important to each object? ②

Integrating the Sciences

Earth Science At any moment, about 2,000 thunderstorms may exist around the world, producing as many as 100 lightning flashes per second. Lightning most commonly occurs during thunderstorms, but may also occur during snowstorms or sandstorms. Even erupting volcanoes may cause lightning. Have students briefly describe their most memorable experiences with lightning.

Environmental Science Lightning causes an estimated 7,500 forest fires in the United States each year. While people once thought all fires should be put out immediately, it's now known that fire is essential in recycling nutrients. Have students research arguments about controlling forest fires in national forests or parks, such as Yellowstone National Park. You may wish to engage students in a debate on the subject.

TEACH ▪ *Continued*

◆ *Explore Visually*

Have students study the text and Figure 11.11 carefully. Ask the following questions:

▶ How do the particles of matter and water molecules in clouds become charged? (The wind rubs them together and they become charged by friction.)

▶ How can currents of air in the thundercloud affect charges within the cloud? (Negative charges will become concentrated at the lower part of the cloud, and the upper part of the cloud will then have mostly positive charges.)

▶ Do the negative charges at the bottom of a thundercloud have any effect? If so, what is it? (Yes, they induce positive charges on the ground below the cloud.)

▶ What can happen when a difference in charge exists between clouds and the ground? (A giant spark, called lightning, can result from rapid static discharge.)

▶ Why is the top of the cloud on page 265 positively charged? (Convection currents move the negative charges to the bottom of the cloud.)

Answer to Link

An electrical spark will jump the gap between the hand and the doorknob as they are brought close together. Devices using electric sparks (arcs) include spark plugs, arc welders, and stun guns.

The Living Textbook: Physical Science Sides 1-4

Chapter 15   Frame 02495
Lightning (1 Frame)
Search:

Physical Science
LINK

Electric sparks similar to lightning are used to ignite gasoline in automobile engines. You can generate your own small electric spark. You need a carpeted area near a metal door knob.

1. Rub your shoes back and forth on the carpet.

2. Slowly bring your hand close to the door knob until you touch it.

What happens? List other devices that use sparks.

ACTIVITY

Figure 11.11
Lightning Formation and Discharge
▼

Lightning

Electrons that build up as static charge on the surface of an object don't remain on the object forever. Eventually, the electrons leave the object. The electrons may move to the surface of another object, or they may move onto molecules in the air. The loss of static electricity by an object that occurs when electrons move is called a static discharge.

A static discharge may occur slowly and quietly. However, static discharge may also occur rapidly, converting electric energy into sound, light, and heat energy. The lightning you see during a thunderstorm is caused by the discharge of static electricity.

During a storm, water molecules and particles of matter in clouds are rubbed together by the wind. As they move, the water molecules and particles become charged by friction. As a result, areas of positive and negative charges form in the clouds.

The lightning you see during a thunderstorm is a giant electric spark. Lightning is caused by the separation and build-up of negative and positive charges between the cloud and the ground.

Social Studies Connection

Ask if any students have seen pictures of Benjamin Franklin (1706–1790) standing out in a thunderstorm holding a kite string with a key tied to it. Explain that Franklin knew the string and key would conduct electricity when wet. The kite was made of silk. Franklin stood in a sheltered area; he didn't actually hold the string. In this way, he insulated himself. Franklin also suggested the terms *positive* and *negative* to describe electricity. He believed that electricity was a fluid. When an object had more fluid than normal, it had a *plus* amount of fluid. Less fluid gave it a *minus* quantity. Have students discuss how this idea compares with the present knowledge about lightning.

▶ **Predict** On a flat landscape, what objects are most likely to be struck by lightning? Why? (The highest objects; the positive charges in those objects are closer to the negative charges of the cloud.)

▶ **Infer** Can lightning travel horizontally from one cloud to another? Why? (Yes; if the clouds are close together, different charges within them can produce lightning.)

▶ **Communicate** Have students find statistics on the number of people struck by lightning annually in the United States. How does this compare to the number of people killed in automobile accidents? (The number of people killed each year by lightning in the United States is over 100. Automobile-related deaths number in the tens of thousands.)

Powerful convective currents in the thundercloud concentrate negative charges at the lower part of the cloud. The upper part of the cloud has mostly positive charges.

Lightning occurs within the thundercloud when a large charge difference exists between the positive charge at the top of cloud and the negative charge at the bottom of the cloud.

The negative charge in the bottom of the cloud will induce a positive charge in the objects on the ground below it.

Lightning rods protect buildings by conducting an electric charge from the cloud directly to the ground.

 The Living Textbook: Physical Science Sides 1-4

Chapter 15   Frame 02496
Static Discharge (2 Frames)
Search: Step:

TEACH ▪ *Continued*

Skills WorkOut

To help students hypothesize how water moves in relation to a statically charged comb, have them do the Skills WorkOut.

Answer Hypotheses: The water would move away from the comb because the comb is negatively charged and the water is also negatively charged. (Be sure students understand the repulsion of like charges.)

EVALUATE

WrapUp

Reinforce Hold a discussion about the following situation. A golfer is standing on a golf course during a thunderstorm, holding an open umbrella with a metal shaft. Why is this dangerous? What might happen and why? (The umbrella provides a path for lightning to follow, both because it is a conductor and because it is closer to the clouds than the ground is.)

Use Review Worksheet 11.2.

Check and Explain

1. Friction, conduction, and induction

2. Both are static discharges.

3. Conductors allow electricity to pass through them, and insulators stop electricity. Conductors: metals, acids, and water; insulators: glass, rubber, plastic, wood, and ceramics.

4. If the water is struck by lightning, the water would conduct the electricity to you. Also, you are the only object in a flat area to draw the lightning.

266

Cooperative Learning

To determine how a common household product makes use of static electricity, have students work in cooperative groups of three. Give each group several different brands of plastic wrap and glass, metal, and plastic refrigerator bowls. Have them try to cover their bowls with the different kinds of wrap. Ask them to make a chart that shows the results. Then encourage them to try to change the way the wrap sticks by rubbing it, by wetting it and the bowl, or by any other means they can think of. Ask: Does it matter if the container or wrap is wet or dry? Does rubbing the plastic help? What can you do to make the plastic stick more firmly? Less firmly? Have groups make another chart showing the arrangement of positive and negative charges that might account for the different possibilities.

▼ ACTIVITY

Hypothesizing

Electric Comb

Obtain a comb and a piece of cloth.

1. Turn on a water faucet to allow a thin stream of water to flow.
2. Rub the comb with the piece of cloth many times.
3. Hold the comb close to the stream.

What happens? Form two hypotheses to explain what you observe.

SKILLS WORKOUT

Science and You
Fabric Softeners and Hair Conditioners

Do your clothes stick together when you take them out of the dryer? Does your hair follow the comb or brush instead of lying flat? Both of these problems are caused by static electricity.

As clothes tumble in the dryer, they build up negative charges on the surfaces of the cloth. Clothes made of synthetic materials, wool, or silk tend to pick up large amounts of negative charge. Some fabrics lose electrons and become positively charged. Some fabrics remain neutral and don't pick up a charge.

Clothes that have a positive charge attract clothes that have an opposite charge. This force of attraction causes the clothes to stick together, even after they are removed from the dryer. The electrically charged fabric will cling to other objects as well.

Perhaps you brush your hair as you dry it with an electric dryer. Friction causes electrons from the brush to build up on your hair, and it becomes negatively charged. The negative charges on your hair repel, and your hair won't stay flat. It flies everywhere.

Fortunately, modern science is able to help. Fabric softeners and hair conditioners were developed to deal with these problems. These products lubricate surfaces with a waxy or soapy substance. A thin coating of these products reduces the friction between the cloth or hair surfaces during the drying process. The reduced electron buildup controls the amount of static electricity.

Check and Explain

1. Name three different ways static charges can build up on an object.

2. Explain how lightning and a shock from static electricity are related to each other.

3. **Compare and Contrast** How do conductors and insulators of electricity differ? Identify three materials that are good conductors and three materials that are good insulators.

4. **Infer** Why is it dangerous to swim or to be out in a boat during a thunderstorm?

Themes in Science

Energy The energy in an electric charge may change to other forms, but the amount of energy remains constant. Ask students to describe ways that electrical energy is converted to other kinds of energy. (Students will think of appliances that produce light, heat, or movement. You might mention that electricity can also cause chemical changes, as in charging a battery.)

Section Objectives
For a list of section objectives, see the Student Edition page.

Skills Objectives
Students should be able to:

Generalize about household objects that use electricity.

Interpret Data from an electric bill.

Collect Data about the number of amperes used by six electric devices.

Predict resistance in copper wire, depending on the wire's thickness and temperature.

Vocabulary
clootrio ourront, voltago, resistance

11.3 Electric Current

Objectives

▶ **Identify** three sources of electric current.

▶ **Distinguish** between current, voltage, and resistance.

▶ **Calculate** resistance using Ohm's law.

▶ **Predict** how the resistance of a wire changes with wire temperature, length, thickness, and type of material.

▼ **ACTIVITY**

Generalizing

All Electric Household

Make a list of ten objects in your home that require electric current to operate. What features do they have in common?

SKILLS WARMUP

MOTIVATE

Skills WarmUp
To help students understand electric current, have them do the Skills WarmUp.
Answer Answers will vary. Common answers include: hair dryer, TV, washing machine, electric stove, electric clock. Students may be less likely to mention appliances with batteries as sources of power; they may also miss newer gas stoves that start with an electric spark.

Prior Knowledge
Gauge how much students know about electric current by asking the following questions:

▶ What do electrical wires do?

▶ What does the word *current* mean?

▶ Why is electric current important to us?

▶ What are some sources of electric current?

Answer to In-Text Question
① Answers will vary.

W hat would your life be like without electricity? Electricity supplies the energy needed to operate your household appliances, calculator, and radio. You know that electrons at rest produce static electricity. However, electrons in a wire move, or flow. These moving electrons make up **electric current**.

Sources of Electric Current

Electric current flows through a closed, continuous path, called a **circuit**. A source of electrons is needed to produce electric current in the circuit. To keep electric current moving, the electron source must also provide a continuous potential difference, or **voltage**, to the circuit. The voltage provides a sort of "electrical pressure" that moves the electrons between the terminals in a circuit, producing a current.

The potential difference gives electrons energy to move from the negative end of the wire toward the positive end. A device that produces the potential difference needed to move electrons through a circuit is an energy source. Electrochemical cells and thermocouples are two types of energy sources that produce electric current.

Electrochemical Cells Electricity can be generated by a chemical reaction. An electrochemical cell changes chemical energy into electric energy. The two kinds of electrochemical cells are wet cells and dry cells, often referred to as batteries. Actually, a battery is several electrochemical cells working together as a source of electric current.

Figure 11.11 ▲
Which of these electrical devices would be most difficult for you to live without? Explain. ①

TEACH

Research

Have students use references to find out more about how wet cells differ from dry cells. Also have them find out if wet cells are used in machines other than cars.

Discuss

Have students review the material on thermocouples, then begin a class discussion by asking the following:

▶ What is the advantage of having a thermocouple in a gas water heater if the pilot light goes out? (This safety device shuts off the switch to the gas when the electric current stops.)

▶ Why does the gas stop flowing when the pilot light goes out? (When the wire junctions reach the same temperature, the switch closes. As long as there is a flame at the pilot light, the switch stays open.)

Answer to In-Text Question

① **The dry cell has a dry electrolyte; the wet cell has a fluid electrolyte.**

**The Living Textbook:
Physical Science Sides 1-3**

Chapter 17   Frame 02942
Direct Current (2 Frames)
Search: Step:

**The Living Textbook:
Physical Science Sides 1-4**

Chapter 15   Frame 02340
Circuit: Flow of Electrons (1 Frame)
Search:

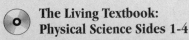

268

Cooperative Learning

Have students work cooperatively to reproduce the first battery built by Italian inventor Alessandro Volta (1745–1827). Have them polish five pennies and five dimes. They can cut blotting paper into nine 1-inch circles, then soak the paper in strong salt water. Tell them to build an alternating stack: penny, paper, dime, paper, penny . . . ending with the fifth dime. They can make terminals for the battery by holding wires against each end of the stack and winding electrical tape around it lengthwise. They can test the battery by touching the leads of a voltmeter to each terminal. The battery should be able to power a small DC lamp.
Use Integrating Worksheet 11.3.

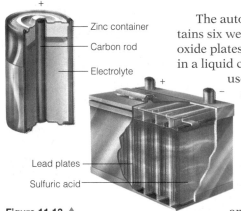

Figure 11.13 ▲
How is the dry cell (top) different from the wet cell battery (bottom)?

Zinc container
Carbon rod
Electrolyte
Lead plates
Sulfuric acid

①

Figure 11.14
Thermocouples are used to control temperature in car engines and as safety devices in gas furnaces and ovens. ▼

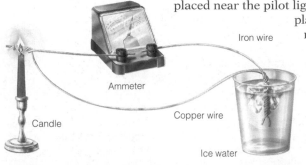

Iron wire
Ammeter
Copper wire
Candle
Ice water

The automobile battery, shown in Figure 11.13, contains six wet cells. A wet cell contains lead and lead oxide plates called electrodes. The plates are immersed in a liquid conductor, called an electrolyte. Car batteries use sulfuric acid as an electrolyte. As the lead and lead oxide react with the acid, electrons are released. Electrons move from the negative lead electrode to the positive lead oxide electrode. When wires are connected to the electrodes, electrons flow through the wires. Dry cells work in much the same way as wet cells. Look at the top left side of Figure 11.13. The electrodes in a dry cell are made of zinc and carbon. The electrolyte is usually a dry base, such as ammonium chloride. It is the dry base that gives the dry cell its name.

Thermocouples Differences in temperature are also used to generate electric current with a device called a *thermocouple*. It consists of a copper wire and an iron wire with the ends of the wires joined together to form a loop. Look at Figure 11.14. An electric current is produced when one iron-copper junction is heated and the other one is cooled. As the temperature difference between the two junctions increases, more electricity is generated. Thermocouples are used in the temperature gauge of an automobile. One end of the thermocouple is inside the engine and the other end is outside. As the temperature inside the engine changes, the current flowing through the gauge changes. The gauge shows the change in engine temperature.

Thermocouples are also used as a safety device in furnaces and ovens to control the gas flow to the pilot light. One iron-copper junction of the thermocouple is placed near the pilot light and gets hot. The other is placed some distance away and remains cool. The temperature difference between the two junctions produces a current that operates a switch to the gas. If the pilot light flame blows out, the wire junctions reach the same temperature. The electric current stops, and the gas shuts off.

STS Connection

An electrocardiograph, or EKG, measures the electric current going through a person's heart muscle. By coupling an EKG with a computer, technicians can plot a model of the heart, showing areas of weakness. Ask students to think about situations in which a computer model of a patient's heart would be useful. (Heart attacks, surgery, stress tests)

Important Note The direction of conventional current is defined as the direction of the flow of positive charges, which is opposite the flow of electrons. However, stressing this difference unnecessarily complicates the study of electricity at this level. To avoid confusion, this text always shows the flow of electrons through a circuit and does not refer to the direction of "current flow." Remind students that electrons flow from the negative terminal through the circuit to the positive terminal.

Types of Current

When an electrochemical cell is connected to a circuit, it causes a steady flow of electric current. Current that flows from an electrochemical cell source moves in one direction. Electrons that flow in the same direction in a wire produce direct current, or DC.

Electrons don't have to move in only one direction to provide electric energy. Current can change direction. The electrons in a wire are made to move first in one direction and then in the other. Electrons that flow in different directions in a wire produce an alternating current, or AC. The electricity in your home is alternating current. For alternating current in the U.S., electrons change direction about 120 times each second.

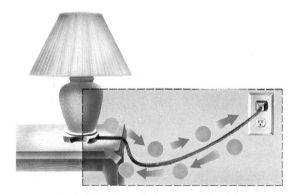

▼ ACTIVITY

Interpreting Data

Usage of Electricity

Obtain a copy of the last electric bill that came to your home. Find the following information on the bill: kilowatt-hours of energy used and the charge per kWh. How does the rate change as you use more electricity?

SKILLS WORKOUT

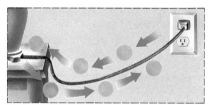

Figure 11.15
The electricity supplied to your home reverses direction as it moves through the wire. ▼

Electric Current Measurement

Accurate measurement and control of electric current are important. Electric wires and appliances are built to handle only a certain amount of electric current. When too much current is present, wires get hot and can cause a fire. If an appliance does not receive enough electricity, it will operate too slowly or not at all. Often the appliance is damaged if it receives too much or too little current.

Each month your family receives an electric bill. It shows how much electricity your family used during a certain period. The electric bill also shows the unit cost of the electricity and the total cost to your family. During what months does your family use the most electricity? Why? ②

Skills WorkOut

To help students interpret data on an electric bill, have them do the Skills WorkOut.
Answer The rate increases after a certain number of kilowatt-hours of electricity is used.

Research

Have students use references to find out the advantages and disadvantages of alternating current and direct current.

Class Activity

Have students copy the labels from electric appliances they have at home. Suggest that they choose from a hair dryer, washing machine, radio, and so on. Discuss in class what the numbers and units mean. Ask, Why do appliance makers make such information available? (To protect consumers who might otherwise overload outlets or accessory appliances; also to indicate how effective a tool or appliance is.)

Answer to In-Text Question

② In the South, electricity would be used most (for air conditioning) in the summer. In the North, the greatest use might be in the winter (for heating). Students should make the connection between outside temperature and electricity usage.

 The Living Textbook:
Physical Science Sides 1-4

Chapter 17   Frame 02796
Alternating Current (2 Frames)
Search: Step:

269

Discuss

Have students think about the flow rate in a circuit. Ask:

▶ What is flowing in a circuit? (Electrons)

▶ How would you define the flow rate of electric current? (The number of electrons that pass a specific point in a circuit in one second)

▶ If a circuit's flow rate is like water flowing through a hose, what determines how fast electrons flow? (How much electricity is being drawn)

▶ What instrument is used to measure current? (An ammeter)

Skills Development

Infer Ask students, What furnishes the voltage that comes into your home? (The source is a power plant.)

Answers to In-Text Questions

① **To measure the strength of electric current in wiring for purposes of safety or efficiency.**

② **They need more voltage than one dry cell provides.**

**The Living Textbook:
Physical Science Sides 1-4**

Chapter 15   Frame 02396
Ammeters in Circuit (1 Frame)
Search:

**The Living Textbook:
Physical Science Sides 1-4**

Chapter 15   Frame 02399
Voltmeter (2 Frames)
Search: Step:

270

Social Studies Connection

The discovery of moving electric currents began with the Italian anatomist Luigi Galvani (1737–1798). In 1791, he noticed that the muscles in a frog's leg jumped when touched by two different metals. Galvani assumed that the muscles contained "animal electricity." Have some students do research to find out about Galvani's experiments.

Language Arts Connection

Units of measure are sometimes named after scientists. Have students find out the origin of the units *volt* and *ampere*. (Volt comes from Alessandro Volta; ampere comes from André Marie Ampère, 1775–1836, a French physicist.)

Current   The rate at which electric charge flows through a wire can be compared to water flowing through a hose. The flow rate of water depends on how much water is coming out of the end of the hose. The amount of electric charge flow, or current, is determined in much the same way. The number of electrons that pass a specific point in a circuit in one second indicates the amount of electric current. Current increases as the number of electrons passing a point each second increases. If fewer electrons pass a specific point each second, the current decreases.

The symbol for current is the capital letter I. In the SI system, current is measured in amperes (AM peerz). Amperes are written as "amps," or as the letter "A."

An instrument called an ammeter can be connected to an electric circuit to measure the amount of electric current. You can see how an ammeter is connected to a circuit. Look at Figure 11.16.

Voltage   Electrons need an energy source to force them through a wire. The dry cell is one such energy source. The energy to move electrons depends on the potential difference between the positive and negative terminals of a dry cell. The positive terminal of a dry cell has high potential. The negative terminal has low potential. The difference between high and low potential is the voltage of the dry cell.

Voltage is the amount of electric energy available to move charges. The higher the voltage, the more work the electrons can do. High-voltage dry cells are required for electric devices that use large amounts of energy. Some electric devices require more than one dry cell to operate. Why? ②

Voltage is measured in the SI system in volts. The symbol for volt is the capital letter "V." Voltage is measured with an instrument called a voltmeter. Notice how the voltmeter is connected to the circuit in Figure 11.17.

Figure 11.16 ▲
An ammeter measures the amount of current in a circuit. The ammeter will also indicate if there is a break in the circuit. How would an electrician use an ammeter? ①

Figure 11.17 ▲
The same device used in Figure 11.16 to measure current can also measure voltage, after some adjustments are made. A device that measures the voltage in a circuit is called a voltmeter.

Resistance   Electrons flow easily through a copper wire to the filament in a light bulb. However, when electrons reach the filament, its resistance is so great that the electric energy is converted into heat and light energy. The force opposing the flow of electrons through the filament is called **resistance**. Good conductors have low resistance. Poor conductors, called resistors, have a high resistance.

A wire's resistance depends on the material from which it is made and its length, thickness, and temperature. Metals, such as copper and aluminum, have relatively low resistance. Long wires have more resistance than do short wires. Thin wires have greater resistance than do thick wires. An increase in temperature also increases the resistance of a material. A long, thin, hot, wire would have more resistance than a short, thick, cold one.

The symbol for resistance is the capital letter R. The SI unit of resistance is the ohm (OHM), and its symbol is Ω, the Greek capital letter "omega." Resistance can be measured by connecting an ohm meter to a circuit, as shown below in Figure 11.18.

Ohm's Law

A German schoolteacher named Georg Ohm related electric current to voltage and resistance. Ohm experimented by keeping the type of material in a wire the same length, thickness, and temperature and changing only the voltage of the circuit. He discovered that when he divided the voltage (V) of the circuit by the current (*I*) he always got the same number. Ohm identified this number as resistance. The relationship among current, voltage, and resistance is known as Ohm's law. Ohm's law states that the current in a circuit is equal to the voltage divided by the resistance. Ohm's law is written:

$$I = \frac{V}{R}$$

If you know the voltage and the resistance of a circuit, you can find current by using this formula: $I = V/R$. If you know the current and the resistance of a circuit, you can find the voltage by solving this form of Ohm's law: $V = IR$. To find the resistance, use the formula $R = V/I$.

 Figure 11.18
An ohm meter has its own power source. This ohm meter is measuring the amount of resistance in the light bulb.

TEACH ▪ Continued

Practice Problems

Work through the sample problem with students. Then have them do the practice problems.

Answers

1. V = *I* R (10 amps × 12 ohms = 120 volts)

2. R = V/*I* (3 volts ÷ 0.5 amps = 6 ohms)

3. V = *I* R (0.067 amps × 1800 ohms = 120 volts)

4. R = V/*I* (12 volts ÷ 0.6 amps = 20 ohms)

Enrich

Assign additional problems on this concept from Math Appendix page 647.

Career Corner

Infer Have students consider what electricians do. Ask, What might an electrician do in a person's home? (Replace old wiring, install wiring to accommodate new appliances and electric devices, and install circuit breakers to replace fuse boxes)

Math Connection

An automobile headlight with a resistance of 30 ohms is attached to a 12-V battery. Ask, What is the current through the circuit? (To find current, divide voltage by resistance. 12 V/30 ohms = 0.4 amps) A lamp draws a current of 0.5 amps when connected to a 120-V power supply. Ask, What is the lamp's resistance? (Resistance = volts/current; 120 V/0.5 amps = 240 ohms)

Sample Problem

The current in a closed circuit measures 6.0 amps. The resistance through the circuit is 20 ohms. What is the voltage in the circuit?

Plan To find the voltage, multiply the current by the resistance.

Gather data The current is 6.0 A, the resistance is 20 ohms.

Solve Voltage = current × resistance
= 6.0 A × 20 ohms
= 120 V

Practice Problems

1. The electric current in a hair dryer measures 10 amps. The resistance of the dryer is 12 ohms. What is the voltage?

2. Two dry cells in a flashlight produce 3 V. The dry cells carry a current of 0.5 amps. What is the resistance of the flashlight?

3. The resistance in a radio is 1800 ohms. The electric current passing through the radio is 0.067 amps. What is the voltage?

4. The dry cells in a portable radio produce 12 V. The dry cells carry a current of 0.6 amps. How much resistance does the radio produce?

Career Corner *Electrician*

Who Installs and Repairs Electrical Systems?

A person who installs, repairs, or maintains electric devices and systems is an electrician. Electricians can work in construction, building maintenance, or repair work. Some electricians work outdoors, and others work indoors. Most electricians work in both environments.

Electricians working in construction follow blueprints. A blueprint is a plan that shows the size and type of wiring. It also shows where to install wiring, circuit breakers, and other electric parts.

Maintenance electricians repair and maintain electric systems in factories, homes, and office buildings. Some have their own shops. Others work for large companies, cities, utility companies or commercial buildings.

All electricians must understand electric circuits, wiring, motors, generators, and transformers. They also need to know about building codes and safety. To start, most electricians serve an apprenticeship under an experienced electrician. Some electricians learn the trade through correspondence or special training courses.

Mathematics, wood shop, mechanical drawing, and physics are some courses you need to take in high school to become an electrician. Most jobs require electricians to be licensed.

Integrating the Sciences

Chemistry Plastics are made up of chains of *monomers,* or simple molecules that have mainly carbon and hydrogen atoms. These chains of molecules are called *polymers.* Usually, neither natural nor synthetic polymers have the free electrons that enable them to conduct electricity. Combining them with compounds, such as salts, can provide the electrons necessary to make them conductors.

STS Connection

Ask students if they have ever lost coins in a vending machine. Electric coin testers in vending machines and highway toll booths can rapidly identify coins and reject fakes. They pass an electric current through the coin. The size of the coin and the type of metal it's made of affect the amount of electricity it conducts. Coins that conduct unusual amounts of electricity are rejected.

Skills WorkOut

To help students collect data about electric devices, have them do the Skills WorkOut.

Answer Answers will vary, but students may say that air conditioners use the most current and that lamps use the least. If students need help converting units from different appliance labels, remember that amps × 120 volts = watts, and 1000 watts = 1 kilowatt (kw).

EVALUATE

WrapUp

Review Return to the analogy on page 270 that compared the flow rate of water and electricity. Ask, What part of the flowing water is like voltage? (Water pressure) What part is like current? (The amount of water) What part is like resistance? (The nozzle on the hose, or the diameter of the hose) Review the terms in Ohm's law.
Use Review Worksheet 11.3.

Enrich
Use Enrich Worksheet 11.3.

Check and Explain

1. Wet cells, used in car batteries; dry cells, used in flashlight batteries; thermocouples, used in automobile temperature gauges

2. Current (*I*) is equal to the voltage (V) divided by the resistance (R). This is Ohm's law.

3. R = 3 ohms

4. The long, thin, hot wire has the greater resistance. Resistance increases with length, temperature, and decreased cross-sectional area (thinness).

Science and Technology *Electric Plastics*

You may know that plastics are used as electric insulators. However, scientists today are developing plastics that can conduct electricity. The research that led to this new use of plastics occurred by accident during the early 1970s. While working on polymers, a student at the Tokyo Institute of Technology discovered a way to change plastics that are nonconductors into electrical conductors.

Recall that some materials conduct electricity because their electrons are free to move. The electrons in plastics don't move easily. However, by adding a few extra atoms to some plastics, the activity of the electrons can be increased. The process of adding atoms to a material to increase electron activity is called *doping.*

Think of the uses for plastics that conduct electricity! A thin plastic film in window glass could screen out heat or keep it in at the flip of a switch. Conducting plastic could be woven into cloth and used to make covers that would act as lightning rods for large structures that do not have lightning rods. Electric cars that require large batteries would be much lighter and more efficient if their batteries were made of plastic.

Unfortunately, the conducting plastics developed so far don't carry electricity as well as metals do. However, scientists continue to experiment with plastics. They are learning more about the relationship between the chemical structure of plastic and its electric properties.

▼ **ACTIVITY**

Collecting Data

Devices and Current

Look at the information on six electric devices you own. Write down how many amperes each device uses. Compare the items on your list with those of a classmate. Which devices use the most current? Which ones use the least?

SKILLS WORKOUT

Check and Explain

1. Name three common sources of electric current. Name a use for each source.

2. Explain how current, voltage, and resistance relate to one another. Identify the symbol for each term.

3. **Calculate** Use Ohm's law to find the resistance of a radio that uses a 9-V battery and carries a current of 3 amps.

4. **Predict** Will a long, thin copper wire at a high temperature have a lower or greater resistance than a short, thick copper wire at a low temperature? Explain.

Section Objectives
For a list of section objectives, see the Student Edition page.

Skills Objectives
Students should be able to:

Observe the effects of completing and breaking an electric circuit.

Make Models to show how electric circuits work.

Hypothesize based on observing circuits.

Predict how the circuit in a room is laid out.

MOTIVATE

Skills WarmUp
To help students understand electric circuits, have them do the Skills WarmUp.

Answer Answers will vary. It is unlikely that all the outlets in the room will be controlled by a single switch.

TEACH

Skills Development

Observe Have students study Figure 11.19. Ask, What three items appear as symbols in the circuit diagram? (Cell, resistor, and switch)

 The Living Textbook: Physical Science Sides 1-4

Chapter 15   Frame 02381
Circuits: Open/Closed (4 Frames)
Search: Step:

TEACHING OPTIONS

Portfolio
To gain practice in using circuit symbols, have each student first draw a model car, showing the headlights, the taillights, the domelight switch, and the battery. Then ask students to draw the circuit for the car, using the symbols in Figure 11.19. Have students think about what would happen to the flow of electricity if one of the bulbs burned out, and write their ideas on their diagrams. Students can add drawings to their portfolios.

Cooperative Learning
Provide copies of a circuit diagram from an automobile or appliance owner's manual. Have students work in cooperative groups to label the diagrams according to how they think the electricity flows, and what it does at each resistance. Have the groups share their diagrams with the class.

▼ ACTIVITY

Observing

Switch Back

Locate a wall switch in your home. Use a lamp to determine which outlets in the room are controlled by the switch. How many outlets does the switch control?

SKILLS WARMUP

Figure 11.19
Beneath this circuit diagram is a key which tells you what each symbol means. ▼

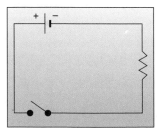

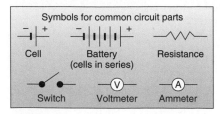

Symbols for common circuit parts

Cell   Battery   Resistance
        (cells in series)

Switch   Voltmeter   Ammeter

11.4 Electric Circuits

Objectives

▶ **Identify** the parts of a circuit.

▶ **Trace** the path of electrons through two types of circuits.

▶ **Compare** series and parallel circuits.

▶ **Predict** how circuits are wired in your home.

What happens when the connection in a water hose comes apart? Normally a hose is connected to a water source, and pressure forces water through the hose. A break in the hose will keep water from moving through the hose. An electric circuit is similar to a hose in several ways. An electric circuit requires a source of electrons and voltage to force the electrons along the circuit. If there is a break in an electric circuit, the electrons stop moving.

Parts of a Circuit

Suppose you rode your bike along a path around a lake, beginning and ending at the same spot. You would complete a circuit. An electric circuit is similar to the bike path. It is a complete, closed path through which electrons travel. In a circuit that uses a dry cell as its energy source, the path of electrons begins in a wire attached to the negative terminal.

For work to be done by the flowing electrons, there must be a resistance in the circuit. Resistance is often supplied by a resistor. A resistor is a device that uses electric energy to do work. Machines, computers, lights, appliances, and motors are examples of resistors. A wire connected from the resistor to the positive terminal completes the circuit. A circuit may have a switch to open and close the circuit. When the switch is open, or off, the path is broken and electrons can't flow through the circuit. In order to picture what a circuit looks like, electrical engineers draw circuit diagrams. A circuit diagram is shown in Figure 11.19. Notice that symbols represent each part of the circuit.

Music Connection

Point out that an electric guitar makes very little sound without an amplifier. As the player plays, the movement of the metal string causes a current to flow in a pickup beneath the string. Strings of different diameters and lengths vibrate at different rates. In turn, the electric current changes. The current carries signals to an amplifier and a speaker.

STS Connection

Challenge teams of students to list as many different kinds of switches as they can. Examples might include switches that open doors when someone approaches, switches that turn a furnace off and on, or switches that turn the light on inside the refrigerator when the door opens. Have them describe the paths of the circuits that are controlled by their switches.

Explore Visually

Have students study Figures 11.19 and 11.20. Ask the following questions:

▶ If the circuit represented by the diagram had a series of cells, or a battery, as its source of electricity, what would the diagram look like?

▶ How does the circuit diagram shown in Figure 11.19 represent the circuit shown in Figure 11.20? (The diagram includes symbols for 1 battery, 1 resistance [the bell], and 1 switch, wired in series.)

▶ From what position on the dry cell do the electrons move? (From the negative terminal)

▶ In what position does the switch have to be for the bell to ring? (It has to be closed.)

Reteach

As students study circuits, you may wish to have them review Ohm's law. Ask, If the voltage from the dry cell shown in the circuit on this page is 1.5 volts and the resistance is 10 ohms, what is the current? ($I = V/R = 1.5$ volts/10 ohms = 0.15 amp)

Ancillary Options

If you are using the blackline masters from *Multiculturalism in Mathematics, Science, and Technology,* have students read about Lewis Howard Latimer on pages 103 and 104. Complete pages 104 to 106.

Answer to In-Text Question

① **The flow of electrons is interrupted. Work is no longer done on the clapper of the bell.**

Path of a Circuit

A simple circuit containing the basic parts of a circuit is shown in Figure 11.20. Locate the negative, or minus, terminal of the dry cell and place your finger on it. Trace the path of electrons by moving your finger along the wire and over each object in the circuit until you reach the positive terminal of the dry cell. By tracing this path, you can see that electrons from the dry cell flows through the wires, the switch, the bell, and back to the dry cell. What happens to the flow of electrons when the switch is opened? On what object is work done? ①

Figure 11.20
The Path of a Current in a Circuit ▼

The dry cell is the energy source for the circuit. That is, the dry cell provides the potential difference, or voltage, needed to move electrons through the circuit.

The bell in the circuit is a resistor. The electric current moving through the bell causes the bell's clapper to move back and forth, and the bell rings.

The wires provide the path through which electrons flow from the negative terminal of the dry cell, through the resistor, and to the positive terminal of the dry cell.

When the switch is closed, the metal strip attached to the insulated handle makes contact with the metal strips on the switch. The circuit is complete and electrons can flow.

When the switch is open, the metal strip connected to the insulated handle doesn't make contact with the metal strips on the switch. The circuit is broken.

TEACH ▪ *Continued*

Skills WorkOut

To help students make models of circuits, have them do the Skills WorkOut.

Answer Diagrams will vary, but be sure students use the correct symbols.

Skills Development

Predict Have students consider the following scenario: Suppose you have two series circuits, each with the same kind of dry cell, but one containing four bulbs and the other containing just one bulb. What would you predict to be the difference in the current between the two circuits? (The current in the circuit having four bulbs would be one fourth as much as the current in the circuit having one bulb. Help students see that the total resistance in a series circuit is equal to the sum of the resistors.)

Answers to In-Text Questions

① All the bulbs will go out because the circuit has been broken.

② You would have to remove and replace one bulb at a time until you found the burned-out bulb.

The Living Textbook: Physical Science Sides 1-4

Chapter 15   Frame 02340
Circuit: Path of Electrons (1 Frame)
Search:

The Living Textbook: Physical Science Sides 1-4

Chapter 17   Frame 03318
Series Circuit (2 Frames)
Search: Step:

🔀 *Math Connection*

Ask students to use Ohm's law to predict what would happen to the brightness of the bulbs in a string of lights wired in series as more bulbs are added. (Each bulb adds resistance. If voltage stays the same and resistance increases, current would decrease. The bulbs would be less bright.)

🔀 *Art Connection*

Some modern art museums display works that incorporate electricity. Some electric advertising signs might also be considered art. Ask students to find and display pictures of such works, research different types of neon (gas-filled) lights and how they are made, or create a work of art of their own using electric lights.

▼ ACTIVITY

Making Models

Circuit Town

Design a circuit and draw a circuit diagram for it. Show all the parts of the circuit in your diagram and use the appropriate symbols. Include at least two appliances in your diagram.

SKILLS WORKOUT

Figure 11.21
Use this photo to explain why lights in a series circuit all go out when one goes out. ▼ ①

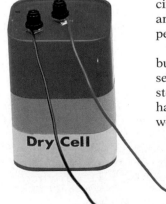

Dry Cell

Types of Circuits

How many lights turn on in your classroom when you flip the switch? You know that each light is a resistor in the circuit. Most electric circuits contain more than one resistor that uses electric energy. The resistors in a circuit can be connected in two ways. They can be connected in series or in parallel. How the parts of the circuit are connected affects the voltage and the current in the circuit.

Series Circuits Suppose you want to connect two resistors, a light, and a bell in a circuit. One way to connect these resistors is to make sure that all of the current that flows through the light also flows through the bell. A circuit in which the current must pass through all the resistors is a series circuit.

All the resistors in a series circuit lie along a single path. Look at the light bulbs connected in series in Figure 11.21. Notice that the dry cell is connected by wires to all of the bulbs. The path of the electrons begins at the negative terminal, passes through each light bulb, and continues back to the positive terminal.

The amount of current in a series circuit is the same at all parts of the circuit. The total resistance in the circuit changes if resistors are added or taken away. Because the same amount of current passes through each of the light bulbs in a series circuit, one bulb will be as bright as any other. If another bulb is added to the circuit, all the lights will be dimmer because the same amount of current has to do more work. What will happen if one of the bulbs is removed from the circuit?

What happens to the current if one of the bulbs burns out? If current can't pass through one bulb in a series, the path of the current is broken and the current stops. If one light goes out, all the lights go out. If you had a long string of lights connected in series, how would you find out which bulb was burned out? ②

Cooperative Learning

Have students work in cooperative groups to make models of circuits by taping string to the floor. The string represents wire. They can add construction paper appliances (resistors), an energy source, and a switch to each circuit. Each group can invite others to walk through the circuit as if they are an electric charge. Have each group demonstrate one of the following: series circuit with three appliances; parallel circuit with two appliances; series circuit with a string of lights that has one burned-out bulb; parallel circuit with a string of lights and one burned-out bulb; and series circuit with the switch closed, then open, then closed. Each group might elect a member to act as a maintenance technician, on hand to make repairs with string, tape, and construction paper.

Parallel Circuits One way to prevent all the lights in a circuit from going out at the same time is to connect them in a parallel circuit. The electrons in a parallel circuit can travel through more than one path. Each path is separate. If there's a break in one path in the circuit, electrons can still flow through the other paths and maintain a complete circuit.

Look at the light bulbs in the parallel circuit in Figure 11.22. Notice that each bulb in the diagram is on a separate path. Part of the current available from the voltage source flows along each path and through each light bulb. How does this differ from the way in which light bulbs connected in a series receive current?

Each bulb in the circuit draws only the amount of current it needs to overcome the resistance in the bulb. As a result, each bulb will light to its full brightness. The total resistance in a parallel circuit depends on the resistances in the paths of the circuit.

What happens if one of the bulbs in Figure 11.22 burns out? Each bulb is located along its own path. Electrons will stop flowing through one bulb and continue to pass through to the others. If one bulb goes out, the others remain lit. Switches can be placed along each path in the circuit. Then, the bulb in each path can be turned on or off without affecting the others.

The electric circuits in buildings are connected in parallel. Circuits in a building carry different amounts of current. For example, a circuit used for a clothes dryer will carry more current than a circuit used for small appliances.

Parallel circuits in your home allow each light or appliance to use the amount of current it needs to work. A parallel circuit also prevents all the lights or appliances from shutting off when one of them stops working. Wall switches make it possible to use only one light or appliance at a time. Electric devices that require different amounts of currents can be used at the same time. Each device uses only the amount of current it needs.

▼ ACTIVITY

Hypothesizing

Flashlight

Obtain a flashlight that takes two dry cells. Take one dry cell out and replace it in a reverse direction. Explain why the flashlight does or does not work.

SKILLS WORKOUT

Figure 11.22
The circuits in your home are connected in parallel. What is the advantage of parallel wiring? ▼ ③

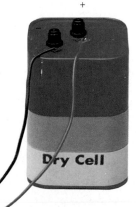

Skills WorkOut

To help students hypothesize why a flashlight does not work, have them do the Skills WorkOut.
Answer The flashlight does not work because the reversed dry cell breaks the flow of electrons.

Class Activity

Have students work in groups of four or five to construct series and parallel circuits. Each group should have a dry cell and two or more bulbs and sockets. Switches are optional. Have them make a series circuit (as on page 276) and then remove one bulb. Then have them make a parallel circuit (as on page 277) and remove one bulb. Discuss the difference between series and parallel circuits again with the class.

Skills Development

Classify Have students compare and contrast series and parallel circuits by asking, Which is the best kind of circuit to use at home? Why? (Parallel circuit; it allows bulbs and appliances to work independently of one another.)

Answer to In-Text Question

③ **The advantage of parallel wiring is that lights or appliances are prevented from shutting off when one of them stops working.**

 **The Living Textbook: Physical Science Sides 1-4**

Chapter 17   Frame 03208
Parallel Circuit (2 Frames)
Search: Step:

 **The Living Textbook: Physical Science Sides 1-4**

Chapter 15   Frame 02389
Bulbs in Parallel Circuit (5 Frames)
Search: Step:

TEACH ▪ *Continued*

Skills Development

Infer Ask students, How does conserving electricity save coal? (Power plants often use coal to produce electricity. If less electricity is used, some coal will be saved.)

EVALUATE

WrapUp

Portfolio Explain to students that strings of holiday lights were once wired as series circuits. Now they are wired in parallel. Have students draw a circuit diagram for 12 lights arranged in series and another for 12 lights in parallel. Ask them to explain in writing why the new lights are better than the old ones. Students can put the diagrams and explanations in their portfolios.

Use Review Worksheet 11.4.

Check and Explain

1. Answers will vary but could include an energy source, a switch, conducting wires, and resistors.

2. Drawings will vary but should include the basic parts of a circuit.

3. In a series circuit, electrons must pass through all the resistors, which lie along a single path. In a parallel circuit, electrons travel in more than one path.

4. Circuit drawings should have at least two switch symbols for lamps, radios, clocks, and so on, each on its own circuit path.

**The Living Textbook:
Physical Science Sides 1-4**

Chapter 15   Frame 02351
Batteries Wired in Series (2 Frames)
Search: Step:

278

Integrating the Sciences

Environmental Science Many appliances now come with a label describing the "energy efficiency rating" of the appliance. This may be stated in terms of what it costs to run the appliance compared to other models. The more efficient and better insulated models cost less to run and use less energy. Have students try to locate the energy efficiency ratings on appliances, such as refrigerators, water heaters, washers, dryers, furnaces, and air conditioners in their homes. If families are considering a new appliance, suggest that students encourage them to purchase one with a high energy efficiency.

Science and Society   *Efficient Energy Use*

Are you aware that some things are being done to improve the energy efficiency of the products you use? For example, guidelines set by the federal government limit the amount of energy new appliances can use. These limits are much smaller than the amount of electricity permitted in older appliances. How does using energy efficiently help to save money and the environment?

Replacing old appliances with the new energy-efficient models reduces household electricity use. Each time you use less electricity, more electricity is available for someone else. When less energy is needed to make electricity, nonrenewable resources like coal and oil are conserved. The whole environment benefits.

Many electric companies have time-of-day and peak-load pricing programs. In these programs, energy used during heavy-usage time periods costs more money. Many people save money by using less energy during peak-load periods.

There are many ways you can conserve energy at home. For example, planting trees around your home provides shade and reduces the energy needed to cool your home in summer. Trees also reduce the chilling effect cold winter winds have on buildings. Doubling the insulation in your home, installing double-pane windows, and adding weather stripping around doors can further reduce cooling and heating costs.

Check and Explain

1. Name and describe three parts of a circuit.

2. Draw a simple circuit. Label your drawing with arrows to trace the path of electrons through the circuit.

3. **Compare and Contrast** How does the path of electrons differ between a circuit connected in series and one connected in parallel?

4. **Predict** The outlets in the circuits in homes are connected in parallel. Draw a picture of a room in a home. Predict how the circuit in the room is laid out so that some of the switches in the circuit are on, while others are not. Draw the path of the circuit.

11.5 Electric Power and Safety

Objectives

▶ **Calculate** electric power and energy.

▶ **Apply** safety guidelines for household use of electricity.

▶ **Calculate** the amount of electricity used by an appliance.

▶ **Infer** about the proper use of safety devices.

Electricity is useful because it changes easily into other forms of energy. For example, a toaster changes electricity into heat energy. An electric typewriter changes electric energy into mechanical energy. Each of these devices makes work easier.

Electric Power and Energy

The rate at which electricity does work or provides energy is called electric power. The amount of electric power a device uses to do work is determined by its resistance. The amount of power used by different appliances is shown in Table 11.2.

You can calculate power (P) if you know the voltage (V) an appliance uses and the current (*I*) in the circuit. Use the formula

$$P = V \times I$$

In SI, the unit for power is joules per second (J/s), or watts (W). Recall that voltage is measured in volts (V), and that current is measured in amperes, (amps or A).

The energy (E) an appliance uses is equal to power (P) multiplied by time (t). The formula for energy is written

$$E = P \times t$$

Power is measured in watts (W). Time is in hours (h).

The SI unit for energy is the joule. However, sometimes energy is measured with a unit called a watt-hour. Because a watt-hour is a very small unit of energy, electric companies measure electric energy in 1,000 watt-hours, or kilowatt-hours (kWh). Kilowatt-hour meters measure the electricity used in your home.

Table 11.2
Power Used by Common Appliances

Appliance	Power (watts)
Refrigerator with freezer	600
Dishwasher	2,300
Clock	3
Microwave oven	1,450
Color television	200
Toaster	1,100
Lamp	100
Hair dryer	1,000
Range/oven	2,600
Radio	100

TEACH

Practice Problems

Work through the sample problem with the class. Then have students do the practice problems.

Answers

1. $P = V \times I = 12\ V \times 30$ amps = 360 W

2. $E = P \times t = 360\ W \times 3\ hr =$ 1080 Wh or 1.08 kWh

3. $E = P \times t = 360\ W \times 6\ hr =$ 2160 Wh or 2.16 kWh

4. $P = V \times I = 120\ V \times 3$ amps = 360 W

5. $E = P \times t = 360\ W \times 5\ hr =$ 1800 Wh or 1.8 kWh

Enrich

Assign additional problems on this concept from Math Appendix page 647.

SkillBuilder

Answers

4. Meter B reads 0548 kWh.
   Meter C reads 9512 kWh.

**The Living Textbook:
Physical Science Sides 1-4**

Chapter 17   Frame 03238
Power (2 Frames)
Search: Step:

**The Living Textbook:
Physical Science Sides 1-4**

Chapter 15   Frame 02629
Electric Meters (2 Frames)
Search: Step:

Integrating the Sciences

Earth Science A piece of the sun's surface the size of a postage stamp constantly emits more energy than 500 sixty-watt bulbs and could light up all the rooms in 48 average-sized American homes. Ask students to imagine that the sun runs on electricity and an electric meter is hooked up to that same stamp-sized spot. What would the meter read after one day? One year? (720 kWh; 262 800 kWh)

Sample Problem

A light bulb has a current of 0.5 amps and is connected to a 120-V source. What is the power of the light bulb? How much energy does it use in 1 hr?

Plan To find power, multiply the voltage by the current. To find energy use, multiply power by time.

Gather data The voltage is 120 V. The current is 0.5 amps.

Solve $P = V \times I$
$= 120\ V \times 0.5$ amps
$= 60\ W$
$E = 60\ W \times 1\ h = 60\ Wh$

Practice Problems

1. An automobile headlight draws 30 amps from a 12-V battery. How much power is used?

2. How much energy is required to operate the headlight from question 1 for 3 h?

3. How much electric energy would the headlight from question 1 need in order to operate for 6 h?

4. Calculate the power used by a fan operating at 120 V and 3 amps.

5. How much electric energy would the fan from question 4 need to operate for 5 h?

SkillBuilder Observing

Reading Electric Meters

An electric meter registers the number of kilowatt-hours of electricity used in your home. You can determine the amount of electricity used during a time period by taking two readings, and subtracting the numbers. The amount of electricity (measured in kWh), used during the time period is the difference between the two meter readings. To take each reading, follow the steps below. Look at one of the three kilowatt-hour meters shown to the right.

1. Notice that the numbers on the dials are marked in opposite directions. On one dial the hand rotates clockwise. On the next dial the hand rotates counterclockwise.

2. The dials are read from right to left as follows: The first dial on the right reads from 0 to 10, the next dial reads from 0 to 100 by tens, the third reads from 0 to 1,000 by

Meter A
KILOWATT HOURS

Meter B
KILOWATT HOURS

Meter C
KILOWATT HOURS

hundreds, and the dial at the left reads from 0 to 10,000 by thousands.

3. Any pointer that is between two numbers on a dial is read as the lower number. For practice, read meter A. The dial on the right reads 2. The next dial reads 40. The next dial reads 600. The dial to the left reads 3,000. Add these 4 dial readings. Meter A reads 3,642 kWh.

4. Read meters B and C.

Electric Safety

Electricity is useful, but it can also be dangerous. Each year, many people are seriously injured or killed from shocks or fire caused by electricity. Most appliances and buildings have safety features built into them.

Many appliances are equipped with a "ground" wire on the plug. The ground wire prevents electric shocks from the surface of the appliance. Look at Figure 11.23. The rounded third prong of a three-way electric plug is attached to the ground wire. It constantly moves static electricity from the appliance to the ground.

Broken wires or water can cause electric appliances to short-circuit. A short circuit occurs when electricity takes a short path and bypasses the resistors in the circuit. As a result, the resistance in the circuit is less, and the current in the wire increases. The increased current can produce enough heat to melt wires and start a fire, or cause a serious electric shock.

Overloading a circuit also may cause a fire. A circuit can become overloaded if too many electric devices are plugged into it. Each added electric device increases the electric current flowing through the wire. When the electric current load is greater than the capacity of the wire, the wire is overloaded.

Circuit Protectors

Fuses and circuit breakers, like those shown in Figure 11.24, protect against overloaded circuits. A number on the fuse indicates the maximum current that will flow through it. When the current goes above the maximum, the metal in the fuse melts. The circuit is broken, and the flow of electrons stops. Resistors must be removed from the circuit, and the fuse must be replaced. A special type of fuse, called a ground-fault interrupter is used with electrical appliances located near water.

Circuit breakers are often used instead of fuses. A circuit breaker is a switch that opens automatically when electric current in a circuit reaches its maximum. When the switch opens, it breaks the flow of electrons in the circuit. Circuit breakers can be reset when the switch is closed again.

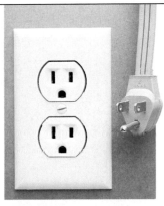

Figure 11.23 ▲

How does the large prong at the bottom of the plug protect the appliance? ①

Figure 11.24 ▲

The top photo shows fuses and the bottom photo shows circuit breakers. Which kind of circuit protector is used in your home? ②

TEACH ▪ Continued

Skills WorkOut

To help students predict why automobile fuses are needed, have them do the Skills WorkOut.

Answer Answers will vary. Every electric device on a car is protected by a fuse. Examples include headlights, ignition, dashboard instruments, blinkers, and safety belt alarm.

EVALUATE

WrapUp

Reinforce Have the class work in groups of four or five. Give each group a 120 V/100 W light bulb. Ask the groups to study it and answer these questions:

▶ How much current would it use? (0.83 amp)

▶ How many kilowatts of energy would it use in 12 weeks if it was on 5 nights a week for 3 hours? (18 kWh)

▶ What would happen to the electricity flowing through it that wasn't changed to light? (It would be lost as heat.)

Use Review Worksheet 11.5

Check and Explain

1. 120 watts

2. Use ground wires, replace broken wires, avoid overloading circuits, use circuit protectors, keep electric wires and appliances away from water.

3. 72 watts, 0.0012 kWh

4. The correct fuse will let the maximum current needed in the circuit flow. An incorrect fuse will either melt at too low a current or allow the circuit to be overloaded.

Answer to In-Text Question
① You could be electrocuted.

Writing Connection

Have each student select one key word from the chapter and write a poem about it using a cinquain—five lines of 2, 4, 6, 8, and 2 syllables, respectively.

Integrating the Sciences

Biology Due to electricity, the human heart can beat continuously for a lifetime. Special cardiac cells called *nodal tissue* transmit electrical impulses throughout the heart. These impulses cause the heart muscle to contract. The impulse starts in a clump of nodal tissue called the *sinoatrial (S-A) node* in the wall of the right atrium. Because the S-A node sets the pace of the heartbeat, it is referred to as the *pacemaker*.

▼ **ACTIVITY**

Predicting

Auto Fuse

Most automobiles have fuses. What electric devices on an automobile might be protected with a fuse?

SKILLS WORKOUT

Science and You
Electric Safety and Your Body

Your body can conduct electricity. Electricity from an appliance can pass through you. If your hand comes in contact with the current in a circuit, a potential difference might exist between the charges in your hand and the ground. As a result, current flows from your hand, through your body, and into the ground. You can be seriously injured from the current that passes through your body.

If you are holding an object that is conducting electricity, the current is redirected through your body due to the potential difference between the object and the ground. Electric energy causes your muscles to contract and you may not be able to release the object. As long as there is a difference in the amount of charge between you and the ground, current will continue. When the current stops, so will the muscle contraction.

Water often contains dissolved substances that make it an excellent conductor of electricity. If your body is wet, the overall resistance of your body is lower. As a result, your body will conduct current more easily. Why do you think appliances have warnings against using them in a tub or shower? ①

You can take safety measures to avoid receiving electric shocks. For example, safety devices, such as ground-fault interrupters, are placed in pool areas and bathrooms where water might be present. A ground-fault interrupter is a fast-acting fuse. This device carries current to the ground if it senses that current is bypassing an appliance.

Check and Explain

1. A radio has a current of 1.0 amp from a 120-V source. What is the power of the radio?

2. What can you do to minimize the risk of an electric shock or fire in your home caused by electricity?

3. **Calculate** A tape player operates on 120 V and 0.6 amp. How much power does it use? How much energy does it use if you operate it for 60 s?

4. **Infer** Why it is important to use the correct fuse in a circuit?

Check Your Vocabulary

1. electric current
2. conductor
3. circuit
4. resistance
5. insulator
6. voltage
7. conduction
8. induction
9. charge

Write Your Vocabulary

Students' sentences should show that they know the meaning of each word as well as how to use it in a sentence.

Use Vocabulary Worksheet for Chapter 11.

Chapter 11 Review

Concept Summary

11.1 Electric Charges
▶ Protons and electrons have electric charges that can produce forces of attraction or repulsion between matter.
▶ Like charges repel. Unlike charges attract.
▶ An electric field is the region around charged particles.

11.2 Static Electricity
▶ The buildup of charges is called static electricity.
▶ Electric charge can be caused by friction, conduction, or induction.
▶ Electrons flow easily through conductors. Electrons don't flow easily through insulators.

11.3 Electric Current
▶ Current flows through a closed continuous path called a circuit.

▶ Voltage is the amount of energy available to move charges.
▶ Resistance is the force opposing the flow of electrons.
▶ Ohm's law states that current equals voltage divided by resistance.

11.4 Electric Circuits
▶ A device that uses electric energy to do work is a resistor.
▶ A series circuit has only one path for current.
▶ A parallel circuit has more than one path for current.

11.5 Electric Power and Safety
▶ Electric power equals voltage multiplied by current.
▶ Fuses and circuit breakers protect circuits from overloading.

Chapter Vocabulary

charge (p. 257)	conductor (p. 263)	circuit (p. 267)
conduction (p. 262)	insulator (p. 263)	voltage (p. 267)
induction (p. 262)	electric current (p. 267)	resistance (p. 271)

Check Your Vocabulary

Use the vocabulary words above to complete the following sentences correctly.

1. The movement of charges, or electrons, through a circuit is _____ .

2. A material that allows electrons to move through it easily is a(n) _____ .

3. A complete, closed path through which electrons can travel is a(n) _____ .

4. The force opposing the flow of electrons through a material is _____ .

5. Plastics, glass, and wood are examples of an electric _____ .

6. The difference in the charges at each end of a circuit is _____ .

7. Charge caused by _____ occurs when charges move from one object to another through direct contact.

8. An object is charged by _____ when no contact is made with the charging object.

9. A proton has a positive electric _____ .

Write Your Vocabulary

Write sentences using the vocabulary words above. Show that you know what each word means.

Check Your Knowledge

1. positive charge
2. electroscope
3. copper
4. static charges
5. circuit
6. False; resistance
7. True
8. False; base
9. False; overloading
10. True
11. False; nearest
12. True

Check Your Understanding

1. By bringing the second object close to the first, and observing the behavior of the second, you could determine the charge on the second. If the second object has the same charge as the first, the objects will repel each other. If they have opposite charges, they will be attracted to each other.

2. Lightning is caused when static charges have been separated in thunderclouds. The part of clouds closest to the ground becomes negatively charged and induces a positive charge on the ground. Lightning results when the difference in charge between the cloud and the ground, or within a cloud, becomes large enough to cause discharge.

3. Dividing voltage by resistance will give the current through the circuit.

4. 5.5 kWh

5. An appliance is a resistor because it resists the flow of electrons as it uses some of the electrical energy in the circuit to operate.

6. The negatively charged object repels electrons in the knob of the electroscope. The repelled electrons move as far away from the object as possible, causing the leaves of the electroscope to become negatively charged. Because both leaves have the same charge, they repel each other. After the leaves separate, the object is still negatively charged, while the knob will have a positive charge.

7. The filament resists the flow of electrons. The electrical energy of the electrons is converted into heat and light energy.

8. P = 120 V x 0.3 amp = 36 W

Chapter 11 Review

Check Your Knowledge

Choose the answer that best completes each sentence.

1. A positive charge will repel a (positive charge, negative charge).

2. An instrument that is used to detect charges is a(n) (voltmeter, ammeter, electroscope).

3. An example of a good conductor is (copper, glass, wood).

4. Lightning occurs as a result of a discharge of (resistance, static charges, amperes).

5. The closed, continuous path through which electrons can flow is a(n) (circuit, resistor, charge).

Determine whether each statement is true or false. Write *true* if it is true. If it is false, change the underlined word(s) to make the statement true.

6. Ohm's law states that current in a circuit is equal to voltage divided by <u>charge</u>.

7. The Greek letter omega, Ω, is the symbol for the unit of <u>resistance</u>.

8. A dry cell uses a(n) <u>acid</u> as its electrolyte.

9. Fuses and circuit breakers protect a circuit from <u>short-circuiting</u>.

10. A material that resists the flow of electrons well is a(n) <u>insulator</u>.

11. The strongest part of an electric field is the area <u>farthest</u> from the charge.

12. A thermocouple uses differences in <u>temperature</u> to generate electricity.

Check Your Understanding

Apply the concepts you have learned to answer each question.

1. If you know the charge of one object, how could you use it to determine the charge of a second object?

2. **Explain** What causes lightning?

3. How can you determine the current if you know the voltage and resistance of a circuit?

4. A home used 5,500 watt-hours of electricity. How many kilowatt-hours is this?

5. Why is an appliance considered a resistor?

6. **Critical Thinking** The knob of an electroscope is neutral. An object with a negative charge is brought near the knob without touching it. The leaves of the electroscope separate. Explain why. After the leaves separate, what is the charge of the object that was brought near the electroscope? What is the charge of the knob?

7. **Mystery Photo** The photograph on page 256 shows the filament in a light bulb. When electric current flows through the filament, it heats up and gives off light. Does the filament conduct or resist the flow of electrons? Explain your answer.

8. What is the power of a light bulb that has a current of 0.3 amps and is connected to a 120-V source?

Develop Your Skills

1. a. circuit diagram

   b. parallel circuit

   c. 3

2. a. arsenic

   b. silver

   c. arsenic, lead, platinum, iron, nickel, zinc, magnesium, aluminum, gold, copper, silver

3. Student designs will vary, but will probably include two wires separated from each other in lemon juice. The other ends of the two wires should be connected to opposite terminals of a battery. One of the wires should also contain a resistor, such as a light bulb or an ammeter. Students' reports should reflect their designs.

Make Connections

1.

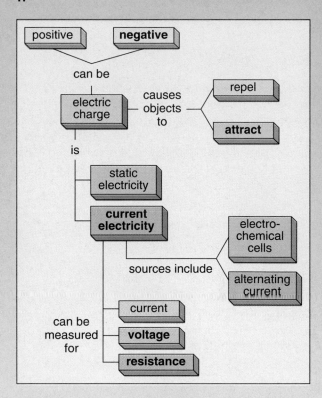

2. Answers will vary. Some other energy sources include: geothermal energy (Japan and Iceland); wind energy (Netherlands); tide energy (France).

3. Answers will vary.

Develop Your Skills

Use the skills you have learned in this chapter to complete each activity.

1. Interpret Data The diagram below shows electric devices connected in a circuit and the location of each one in the circuit.

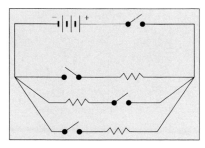

a. What is this diagram called?

b. What kind of circuit is shown in the diagram?

c. How many resistors are shown in this circuit?

2. Data Bank Use the information on page 639 to answer the following questions.

a. Which metal has the most resistance?

b. Which metal has the least resistance?

c. Arrange the metals in the table from most to least resistance.

3. Design an Experiment Lemon juice can be used as an electrolyte to conduct a current. Design an experiment to show this fact. Describe the problem, materials, procedure, expected results, and conclusion.

Make Connections

1. Link the Concepts Below is a concept map showing how some of the main concepts of this chapter link together. Only part of the map is filled in. Finish the map, using words and ideas you find on the previous pages.

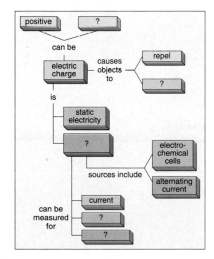

2. Science and Social Studies Petroleum is the most commonly used fuel for generating electricity. Research how electricity is generated in other countries. Identify the energy source for the electricity and the country in which the source is used.

3. Science and Math Locate the electric meter for your home. Read the meter every Monday for one month. Identify how much electricity your family used during each one-week period. How did the energy use change from week to week?

Overview

This chapter discusses magnets and magnetism. First, the properties of magnets and the behavior of magnetized materials are described. Electromagnetism and its applications in electric motors and meters are discussed in the next section. Finally, electromagnetic induction is explained, followed by a description of how it is used to operate electric generators and transformers.

Advance Planner

▶ Supply materials to make hanging bar magnets for TE page 288.

▶ Provide pastels of colored chalk and black or dark blue paper for TE page 291.

▶ Obtain compasses for TE page 292.

▶ Supply dry cells, wire, and nails or iron rods for SE page 294, adding insulated copper wire to the items for use with TE page 295.

▶ Provide toys with DC motors for TE page 296.

▶ Collect old magazines for TE page 298.

▶ Supply insulated electric wire, large iron nails, boxes of paper clips, and 6-V dry cells for SE Activity 12, page 299.

Skills Development Chart

Sections	Classify	Communicate	Graph	Infer	Interpret Data	Model	Observe	Organize Data	Research
12.1 Skills WarmUp Historical Notebook Skills WorkOut	●					●			●
12.2 Skills WarmUp Consider This Activity	●	● ●	●	●	●		●		
12.3 Skills WarmUp Skills WorkOut				●				●	

Individual Needs

▶ **Limited English Proficiency Students** Have students divide a page from their science portfolios into three columns. As they study, students can list boldface terms and other unfamiliar words in the first column. Have students use the glossary or dictionary to find the definition for each term. Ask them to write these definitions in the second column. As students read each section, have them draw a picture or diagram in the third column that represents the words. Encourage students to use the information and figures from the chapter as a resource. Then ask them to write a few sentences explaining why electromagnetism and electromagnetic induction could be thought of as opposites.

▶ **At-Risk Students** Invite students to work in groups to make a working model of a simple electric motor or generator. Give them materials such as magnets, rings, wires, brushes and rods. Provide simple instructions on how to assemble the motor or generator. Students should demonstrate their devices for the class. As they work, ask questions that help students to build an awareness of the concepts of electromagnets, permanent magnets, magnetic poles, current direction, and electromagnetic induction.

▶ **Gifted Students** Ask students to design a small electric generator that converts an unusual source of mechanical energy, such as a hamster running in an exercise wheel, to electric energy. Have them draw detailed diagrams of their generators. Their generators do not necessarily have to be a practical source of electricity, but they should work. If possible, encourage them to actually build and demonstrate the generator.

Resource Bank

▶ **Bulletin Board** Display a safety symbol, such as the skull-and-crossbones *poison* symbol. Have students design and display their own electric safety symbols.

CHAPTER 12 PLANNING GUIDE

Section	Core	Standard	Enriched	Section	Core	Standard	Enriched
12.1 Magnets and Magnetism pp. 287–292				**Blackline Masters** Review Worksheet 12.2	●	●	
Section Features Skills WarmUp, p. 287 Historical Notebook, p. 289 Skills WorkOut, p. 291	● ● ●	● ● ●	● ● ●	**Ancillary Options** *One-Minute Readings,* p. 90	●	●	●
Blackline Masters Review Worksheet 12.1 Reteach Worksheet 12.1 Skills Worksheet 12.1 Integrating Worksheet 12.1a Integrating Worksheet 12.1b	● ● ● ●	● ● ● ● ●	● ● ● ●	**Overhead Blackline Transparencies** Overhead Blackline Master 11 and Student Worksheet	●	●	●
Color Transparencies Transparencies 41, 42	●	●	●	**Color Transparencies** Transparencies 43, 44, 45, 46	●	●	●
Laboratory Program Investigation 24 Investigation 25 Investigation 26	● ● ●	● ● ●	● ● ●	**12.3 Magnetism to Electricity** pp. 300–304			
12.2 Electricity to Magnetism pp. 293–299				**Section Features** Skills WarmUp, p. 300	●	●	●
Section Features Skills WarmUp, p. 293 Consider This, p. 295 Activity, p. 299	● ● ●	● ● ●	● ● ●	**Blackline Masters** Review Worksheet 12.3 Skills Worksheet 12.3 Vocabulary Worksheet 12	● ● ●	● ●	
				Color Transparencies Transparency 47	●	●	●

Bibliography

The following resources can be used for teaching the chapter. See page T-46 for supplier codes.

Library Resources

The Diagram Group. Comparisons. New York: St. Martin's Press, 1980.

Lafferty, Peter. Energy and Light. New York: Gloucester Press, 1989.

Sherwood, Martin, and Christine Sutton. The Physical World. New York: Oxford University Press, 1988.

White, Jack R. The Hidden World of Forces. New York: Dodd, Mead and Company, 1987.

Technology Resources

Internet

PLANETDIARY at *http://www.planetdiary.com*

- Learn more about astronomy and space in *Astronomy/Space* by clicking on *Phenomena Backgrounders* and *Current Phenomena.*

Software

Magnets. Mac. ESI.

CD-ROMs

An Odyssey of Discovery for Science Insights: Have students explore the activity *Aquarium* on the Living Science Disk, and the activity *Recycler* on the Earth and Space Disk. SFAW. hip Physics. Mac. ESI.

Laserdiscs

Living Textbook. (See barcodes on pages in this chapter.) Optical Data.

Audio-Visual Resources

Electromagnets and Their Uses. Film. C/MTI.
Learning About Magnets, 2nd Edition. Film. EB.

Introducing the Chapter

Have students read the description of the photograph. Ask if they agree or disagree with the description. Explain to students that the eyes actually appear at the bottom of the photograph.

Directed Inquiry

Have students study the photograph. Ask:

▶ What does this photograph show? (Students will probably identify it as a view through the middle of the human head, from either above or below.)

▶ What process was used to make this picture? (Students may mention X-ray, ultrasound, CAT scan, or MRI.)

▶ Can you think of how a picture like this is used? (It gives an accurate image of the brain for doctors to use in diagnosing and treating disease.)

▶ What do you think the picture has to do with the subject of this chapter? (Students will say that the process used to make the image must involve magnets or magnetism.)

Chapter Vocabulary

compass	magnetic domain
electromagnet	magnetic field
electromagnetic	magnetic pole
induction	permanent magnet

Themes in Science
Stability and Equilibrium
Magnetic forces work in ways we can predict, such as pulling things together or pushing them apart. Ask students for examples of how magnets work.

Writing Connection
Have students write a short story in which the main character uses a magnet to solve a problem. Suggest that the problem could relate to moving something, opening or closing a door, or holding things together.

Chapter 12 Magnetism

Chapter Sections

12.1 Magnets and Magnetism

12.2 Electricity to Magnetism

12.3 Magnetism to Electricity

What do you see?

❝I see a circle with a lot of different blobs of color and two round dark balls at the side. I think it is an ultrasound of a brain with the dark balls at the side as eyes. I think it is a brain because of the shape and the eyes. They made this image by ultrasound or a radar or something of that sort. This method is helpful because they don't have to cut a person open to view certain parts like the brain.❞

Tim Carey
Stivers Middle School
Dayton, Ohio

To find out more about the photograph, look on page 306. As you read this chapter, you will learn about magnets and magnetism.

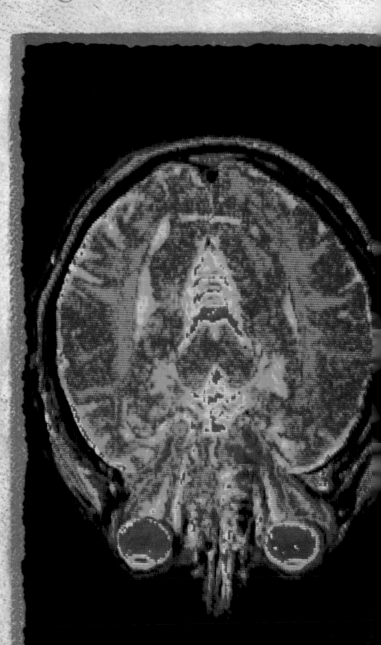

12.1 Magnets and Magnetism

Objectives

▶ **Describe** two properties of magnets.

▶ **Explain** how a material can become magnetized.

▶ **Infer** how the earth is like a magnet.

▶ **Predict** how a material might become magnetic.

What do doorbells, telephones, electric motors, radios, and televisions have in common? All of these everyday devices use magnets in order to operate. Magnets create a force called magnetism. You may use the force of magnetism to hold notes on a refrigerator door. The cluster of metal pieces in Figure 12.1 is held together magnetically. The force of magnetism can lift something as small as a paper clip or as large as an automobile!

Many everyday items use magnetism in ways that you may not suspect. For example, magnetism is used to record and play back audio cassettes and videotapes. Credit cards and subway tickets have magnetic strips that carry information. Computers store information on disks coated with magnetic material.

Magnetism is a universal force like gravity or the strong and weak forces inside the nucleus of an atom. But what causes magnetic force? The properties of magnets can help you to understand what magnetism is and how it works.

Properties of Magnets

To investigate the properties of magnets, you can experiment with two bar magnets by hanging each one from a string. When you bring the hanging magnets together, you can observe magnetic force operating in one of two ways.

▶ The ends of the magnets attract each other and the magnets stick together.

▶ The ends of the magnets repel each other and the magnets move apart.

Figure 12.1 ▲
What universal force is holding together the pieces of this metal sculpture? ①

287

TEACH

Class Activity

Have students work in groups of four or five. Provide each group with materials to set up a hanging bar magnet like Figure 12.2. Pass around another magnet so each group can bring the like poles together to see what happens. Then have groups bring the unlike poles together to see what happens. Have groups report on what happens in each case. (Like poles repel and unlike poles attract.)

Critical Thinking

If...Then Arguments Have students study Figure 12.3. What would happen to a handful of iron filings dropped at the magnet's north pole? In the middle? At the south pole? Have students write if...then arguments for their answers. (Most filings will gather at the poles.)

Answers to In-Text Questions

① **They attract.**

② **All the filings will cling to the magnet or the filings that are clinging to the magnet. There will be more filings on each end than in the center.**

**The Living Textbook:
Physical Science Sides 1-4**

Chapter 15   Frame 02476
Doorbell (1 Frame)
Search:

**The Living Textbook:
Physical Science Sides 1-4**

Chapter 15   Frame 02450
Magnetized Needle (1 Frame)
Search:

288

Language Arts Connection

In 1269, Peter Peregrinus of France wrote a famous treatise on magnets. He was the first to use the word *pole* to describe each end of a magnet. Ask students to find the Greek origins of the word *pole*. Have students use references to find out why Peregrinus used this word. (Latin *polus* is from the Greek *polos* for "pivot," or "pole"; Latin and Greek were the languages of science in the thirteenth century.)

STS Connection

A magnetometer is a device that measures the strength of a magnetic field. Ask students how magnetometers would be useful to prospectors trying to locate deposits of iron ore and other metallic resources with magnetic properties.

Magnetic Poles If you allow a simple bar magnet to hang freely, it will act as a compass. This is due to its **magnetic poles.** The end of the magnet that points north is called the north pole, and the end that points south is called the south pole. All magnets have both a north and a south pole.

Notice the position of the hanging magnet in Figure 12.2. When two north poles or two south poles are brought near each other, they repel. However, if the north and south magnetic poles are brought near each other, they will attract.

The force between magnetic poles is similar to the force between electric charges. Recall that unlike charges attract, and like charges repel. However, magnetic poles can't be separated from each other like electric charges can. If you break a magnet in half, each piece is still a complete magnet with its own north pole and south pole. You can think of north and south poles like the two sides of a coin—one doesn't exist without the other.

Magnetic Field All magnets are surrounded by a magnetic region called the **magnetic field.** The magnetic field is strongest at the poles of a magnet, but exists around the entire magnet.

The lines around the magnet in Figure 12.3 show its magnetic field. These lines, called magnetic field lines, extend from one pole to the other. The arrows indicate the direction of the magnetic field. The number of field lines in any given region indicates the relative strength of the field. Note that the field lines are most concentrated at the poles, but appear everywhere outside the magnet.

Although the magnetic field is invisible, you can see its effect around a magnet by placing a piece of paper on top of a magnet and then sprinkling iron filings over the paper. The iron filings form a pattern similar to the magnetic field lines shown in Figure 12.3

If you were to place a magnetic material, such as iron, near the magnet, it would be most attracted to either the north or south pole. However, iron would also be attracted by the magnetic field around the magnet. What do you think happens if you place the entire magnet in a dish of iron filings? ②

Figure 12.2 ▲
Two north poles will repel. What happens when poles with unlike charges are brought together? ①

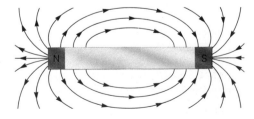

Figure 12.3 ▲
All magnetic material has a magnetic field around it. Identify the magnetic field in the drawing.

Magnetic Materials

Why are some materials magnetic and others not magnetic? The electrons of all atoms spin as they move about the nucleus. A spinning electron produces a magnetic field with both a north and a south pole. Each atom acts like a tiny magnet. In most materials, the magnetic fields of individual atoms cancel each other, so the materials aren't magnetic.

In materials like iron, cobalt, and nickel, the magnetic field of each individual atom is so strong that the atoms group together. The poles line up in the same direction in microscopic magnetic regions, called **magnetic domains**. When all the domains are arranged with their poles in the same direction, the iron bar becomes a **permanent magnet**. When the domains are arranged randomly, the iron bar is not magnetized. Look at Figure 12.4. Notice how the arrangement of the magnetic domains differs in the two iron bars.

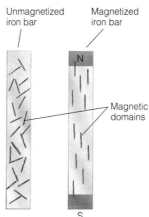

Unmagnetized iron bar   Magnetized iron bar

N

Magnetic domains

S

Figure 12.4 ▲
How can you tell which iron bar is magnetized? ③

Historical Notebook

Magnetism in Ancient Times

More than 2,000 years ago, people in Asia discovered that certain black metallic rocks attracted iron. In medieval times these rocks were called *lodestones*, meaning "leading stone." When hung, these stones always pointed in the same direction. These stones are now known as *magnetite*, named for the district of Magnesia which is located in present-day Turkey.

People in China also knew about the properties of magnetite. They discovered that when a small, flat piece of iron was rubbed over magnetite, it became magnetized. The magnetized iron pointed in a north-south direction when it hung by a silken thread. These pieces of magnetized iron were the first compasses.

The early Chinese used compasses for a variety of scientific and nonscientific purposes. By the tenth century, the Chinese were using compasses to navigate ships. European and Arabic navigators

probably acquired the compass from the Chinese around the twelfth century.

1. Use your library to find out why the compass was important to twelfth century navigators.

2. Could a piece of magnetite be used as a compass? Explain.

TEACH ▪ Continued

Explore Visually

Have students read the page and study Figure 12.5, then ask the following questions:

▶ How does a compass determine direction? (Its needle aligns with the earth's magnetic field.)

▶ Are the magnetic north and south poles the same as the geographic North and South poles? Explain. (No. The North and South poles of the earth's axis are the geographic poles. The magnetic poles are aligned with the earth's magnetic field.)

▶ What is the angle between magnetic north and true north called? (Magnetic declination)

▶ **Infer** Ask students why the domains in the metals in molten rock would line up with the earth's poles. (They are free to move and their poles would be attracted to opposing poles of the earth.)

Critical Thinking

Reason and Conclude Ask students, If you were standing right on the North Pole and wanted to walk to the north magnetic pole, would you head east, west, or south? (South is the only direction possible from right on top of the North Pole.)

The Living Textbook: Physical Science Sides 1-4

Chapter 15   Frame 02443
Magnetic Declination (1 Frame)
Search:

Social Studies Connection

In 1600, William Gilbert, personal physician to Queen Elizabeth I of England, was the first to show that the earth is a giant magnet. Have students research how Gilbert reached this conclusion.

Integrating the Sciences

Geology Have students research seafloor spreading and plate tectonics. Ask how magnetic evidence is used to support the theory of plate tectonics. (Paleomagnetism, showing alternating north-south poles in rocks on both sides of ocean ridges, proves that the earth's magnetic field has switched many times. It also shows that the ocean floor is spreading apart, moving the continents apart.)

Earth as a Magnet

If you hang a magnet by a string, the north-seeking pole will always point north because the earth itself is a huge magnet. The magnetic field around a bar magnet is a good model for the earth's magnetic field. Imagine that a giant bar magnet extends from the North Pole to the South Pole. Magnetic field lines around the earth are like the magnetic field lines around a bar magnet.

An instrument that takes advantage of the earth's magnetic field is the **compass**. A compass has a magnetized needle in it that turns freely. Because the magnetized needle always aligns with the earth's magnetic field, a compass is used to determine direction.

Recall that the earth turns on its axis.

The North Pole and South Pole of the earth's axis are referred to as geographic poles. The geographic North Pole, sometimes called *true north*, is located in a different place from the magnetic north pole.

Notice in Figure 12.5 that the magnetic north pole is in Canada, about 1,400 km from the geographic North Pole. The magnetic south pole is in Antartica, about 2,750 km from the geographic South Pole. The angle between magnetic north and true north is called the *magnetic declination*.

Evidence suggests that the earth's magnetic field is caused by the movement of molten metals near the earth's core. Measurements show that the earth's magnetic poles change position over time. Changes in the flow of the molten metals inside the earth may cause the magnetic poles to move.

Figure 12.5
The Earth's Magnetic Field ▼

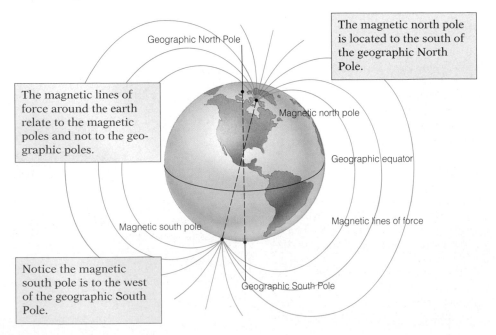

The magnetic north pole is located to the south of the geographic North Pole.

The magnetic lines of force around the earth relate to the magnetic poles and not to the geographic poles.

Notice the magnetic south pole is to the west of the geographic South Pole.

Geographic North Pole

Magnetic north pole

Geographic equator

Magnetic south pole

Magnetic lines of force

Geographic South Pole

Magnetic Effects

The most visible effect of the earth's magnetic field is a colorful light display, called an aurora, like the one shown in Figure 12.6. An aurora hangs like a curtain of light stretching over the polar regions of the earth. Since the earth's magnetic field is strongest near the poles, charged particles given off by the sun collect there. Collisions between the charged particles and other particles in the upper atmosphere create glowing lights. The lights are called the *aurora borealis* (the northern lights) or the *aurora australis* (the southern lights). The color of an aurora depends on the kind of atoms in the atmosphere.

Another effect is disturbances in the earth's magnetic field, called magnetic storms, which interfere with compass needles and radio and television waves. Magnetic storms occur when solar flares produce charged particles that become trapped in the earth's magnetic field. The trapped particles follow corkscrew paths around the earth's magnetic field lines, causing temporary changes in the magnetic field.

The earth's magnetic field also affects living things. Scientists have discovered tiny particles of the magnetic mineral magnetite in the body tissues of pigeons, bees, bacteria, and other organisms. Such particles may help these organisms use the earth's magnetic field to find their way.

▼ **ACTIVITY**

Making a Model

Compass

Construct a model compass to see the earth's magnetic field in action. Collect the following items: a steel sewing needle, a bar magnet, and a piece of thread.

1. Stroke the needle in one direction with a bar magnet for ten minutes.

2. Tie a thread at the midpoint of the needle and suspend the needle from the thread.

Where is north and south?

SKILLS WORKOUT

◀ **Figure 12.6**
This photo shows the aurora borealis, or northern lights. What causes the aurora? ①

TEACH ▪ *Continued*

Skills Development

Infer A magnet that is dropped repeatedly onto a hard surface will lose some or most of its magnetism. Ask students to explain why. (The magnetic domains are no longer aligned so the magnet loses strength.)

EVALUATE

WrapUp

Reteach Hold up two identical-looking pieces of metal and ask: If one is a magnet and one is not, how could you determine which piece was the magnet? (The magnet would attract magnetic materials. It would also cause a compass to move.)
Use Review Worksheet 12.1.

Check and Explain

1. Opposite poles/charges attract; like poles/charges repel.

2. Magnetized iron has aligned magnetic domains. Iron will not act as a magnet if its domains are arranged randomly.

3. The earth's magnetic field causes the bar magnet to align north and south. This implies that the earth has a magnetic field.

4. Atoms in nickel act like small magnets because of electron spin. Atoms with the same north-south orientations combine in magnetic domains. When domains line up in the same north-south direction, the metal is magnetized. If nickel is melted, domains are free to fall out of alignment.

Answer to In-Text Question

① The compass would help you to keep going in one direction so you wouldn't walk in circles.

Cooperative Learning

Have students work in cooperative pairs. Provide each pair with a compass. Have them create a series of directions for finding an object in the classroom that requires the use of a compass. Have the students exchange directions and then find the objects. (For example: From the door, walk three steps 20° northeast.)

Portfolio

Have students write a newspaper article about the rescue of three Boy Scouts lost in a heavily wooded area. The article should include a map used by the scouts. It should also discuss the use of a compass. Have students keep their articles in their portfolios.

Figure 12.7 ▲
How would a compass be useful if you hiked through a very dense wooded area like the one shown above? ①

Science and You *The Helpful Compass*

Imagine you're lost in the woods. Because the sun isn't visible, you don't know which direction is north. How can you find your way out? A compass can help.

Since a compass needle always points north and south, you align the needle with the *North* marking on the compass case. You can read the compass markings to locate the direction you want to go. As you walk in that direction, you check the compass now and then to be sure that you're still going the right way. Soon you're out of the woods!

Sometimes people give directions to a place by telling you to turn north on one street and east on another instead of telling you to turn left or right. If you aren't familiar with the area, you may have trouble following these directions. If you have a compass, it's much easier to reach your destination.

Although compasses may look different, they all work the same way. A pointer, or needle, inside the compass is a magnet that aligns with the earth's magnetic field. This small magnet balances on a sharp point or floats in a liquid.

Look at Figure 12.7. The large markings on every compass indicate north, south, east, and west. The smaller markings around the edge are the 360 degrees of a circle with the needle at the center. The degree markings precisely identify direction and are important to navigators on ships and aircraft.

Check and Explain

1. How are magnetic poles similar to electrical charges?

2. Explain why some pieces of iron act as magnets and other pieces of iron don't.

3. **Infer** You know that on the earth, the north pole of a hanging magnet always points north. What does this tell you about the earth as a magnet? Explain.

4. **Predict** Explain how the atoms in nickel create the magnetic domains in a magnetized material. Based on your answer, predict what would happen if nickel were melted and all its atoms were able to float freely.

292

Themes in Science
Patterns of Change/Cycles
Moving electric charges produce magnetic effects. The direction of the electric current affects the alignment of the north and south poles in a material.

Social Studies Connection
Although Hans Christian Oersted observed an electric current's effect on a compass in 1820, it was first observed by Gian Domenico Romagnosi of Italy in 1802, but his announcement was ignored. Romagnosi was a jurist, while Oersted was a physicist and chemist and a professor at the University of Copenhagen since 1806. Ask students why they think Romagnosi's observations were ignored.

Section Objectives
For a list of section objectives, see the Student Edition page.

Skills Objectives
Students should be able to:

Classify appliances into those with and without motors.

Predict the behavior of an electric motor based on changes in the electromagnet.

Infer how changes in an electric current will affect a magnetic field.

Vocabulary
electromagnet

12.2 Electricity to Magnetism

Objectives

▶ **Relate** electricity to magnetism.

▶ **Explain** how an electric motor works.

▶ **Compare** and **contrast** electric motors and galvanometers.

▶ **Predict** how the direction of the current affects a motor.

▼ **ACTIVITY**

Classifying

Motoring

Make a list of electric devices you use each day. Divide the list into two groups: Appliances with Motors and Appliances without Motors. On what did you base your classification? Explain.

SKILLS WARMUP

Y ou can dry your hair with an electric dryer and wash your clothes in a washing machine because electricity and magnetism are related! The relationship between electricity and magnetism is called *electromagnetism* (ee LEK troh MAG nuh TIHZ uhm). How are these two forces related?

Recall that iron makes a good permanent magnet because its spinning electrons group together. Moving electric charges produce a magnetic field. Therefore, electric currents also produce magnetic fields. Whenever charges move, they produce magnetic effects. The electric motors in electric clothes dryers and washing machines rely on electromagnetism to work.

Electromagnetism

For centuries, people thought electricity and magnetism were completely unrelated. However, in 1820, Hans Christian Oersted, a Danish physicist, made an interesting observation. He noticed that when a compass was brought near electric current, the compass needle no longer pointed north! It turned 90 degrees.

Oersted discovered that the compass needle turned in the opposite direction when he reversed the current. When the wire was disconnected, as in Figure 12.8, it no longer affected the compass. The compass needle turned to the north. Oersted knew the point of a compass needle would follow a magnet. He hypothesized that when an electric current flowed through it, the wire acted like a magnet. Somehow electricity could produce magnetism.

Figure 12.8
What happens to the compasses when the wires are connected to the battery? ▼ ②

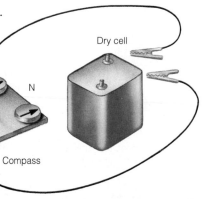

Dry cell

N

Compass

Skills WarmUp
To help students understand the relationship of electricity to mechanical energy, have them do the Skills WarmUp.
Answer Students will probably base their classifications on whether motion is used in the appliance. For example, a washing machine is under Appliances with Motors, and an iron under Appliances Without Motors.

Prior Knowledge
To gauge how much students know about electricity and magnetism, ask the following questions:

▶ What produces the electricity you use at home?

▶ How can electrical energy be changed into mechanical energy?

Answer to In-Text Question
② **The compass needles will all be deflected by the electric current.**

Research

Have students use library sources to find out about tools based on Oersted's discovery. Who invented them? What were they used for? Are any still used today?

Class Activity

Have students experiment with the magnetic effects of electricity in cooperative groups. Give each group a dry cell, two compasses, and a single wire. Each group should produce five diagrams or more showing the effect of an electric current on a compass placed nearby. Diagrams should show positive and negative terminal connections, the path of the electrons, the direction of the compass needles, and the distance of the compasses from the wire. Summarize the groups' observations in a class discussion.

Decision Making

If you have classroom sets of *One-Minute Readings*, have students read Issue 53 "High-Voltage Power Lines" on page 90. Discuss the questions.

Answers to In-Text Questions

① **Reversing the direction of the current reverses the direction of the magnetic field. The compass needle follows the direction of the magnetic field.**

② **Increasing the number of coils increases the strength of the electromagnet.**

The Living Textbook: Physical Science Side 3

Chapter 45   Frame 36309
Electromagnet (Movie)
Search: Play:

294

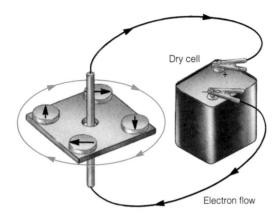

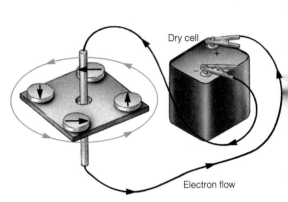

Language Arts Connection

The coil of current-carrying wire that behaves like a bar magnet is called a *solenoid.* Ask students to use the dictionary to discover the origins of the term. (From the Greek *solen,* meaning "pipe")

STS Connection

Explain to students that ultrasonic vibrators use electromagnets to create vibrations that are so rapid that they cannot be heard. These vibrators are used to do delicate work such as removing dirt from watches and cutting hard substances such as silicon. Ask students to research the use of electromagnets in various industries and share their findings in brief oral reports.

Figure 12.9 ▲
The compasses above detect the magnetic field produced by the moving electrons. Why do the compass directions reverse when the wires are reversed? ①

To see how the magnetic force produced by an electric current behaves, look at the compasses in Figure 12.9. The circular pattern of the compass needles shows the magnetic field around the current-carrying wire. When the electrons flow *up* the wire, the magnetic field exerts a force in a clockwise direction. When the electrons flow *down* the wire, the magnetic field exerts a force in a counterclockwise direction.

Electromagnets

Oersted's discovery was responsible for the invention of new tools based on the principles of electromagnetism. For example, soon after Oersted's experiments, scientists learned to build powerful magnets that could be turned on and off. The first such magnet consisted of a coil of current-carrying wire. When a bar of soft iron is placed inside the wire coil, the magnetic force increases. A simple example of this device, called an **electromagnet**, is shown in Figure 12.10.

The strength of an electromagnet depends on the number of turns in the coil and the size of the iron core. The greater the number of turns the coil has, the stronger is the magnetic field it can produce. The greater the size of the soft-iron core, the stronger the magnet is. How could you change the magnetic strength of an electromagnet?

When the magnet is turned on, an electric current flows through the wire coil, creating a magnetic field around the coil. The magnetic domains in the soft-iron core align with the magnetic field of the coil. The soft-

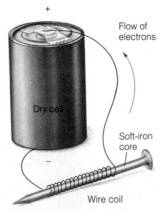

Figure 12.10 ▲
What effect does the number of coils have on the strength of the electromagnet? ②

iron core becomes magnetized. The shape of the magnetic field around an electromagnet is similar to the shape of the magnetic field around a bar magnet.

One end of the soft-iron core is a north pole, and the other end is a south pole. The magnetic field of the magnetized soft-iron core combines with the magnetic field of the wire coil. The combined magnetic fields create a very strong magnet.

The soft iron used for the core of an electromagnet isn't really "soft." Pure iron is referred to as soft iron. It is easy to magnetize, but soft iron loses its magnetism quickly when the electric current stops. In contrast, "hard" iron, or steel, remains magnetized for a long time. Why do you think steel might be unsuitable for making an electromagnet? Recall that material is magnetized when all of its domains line up in the same direction. The domains in steel are more resistant to change than the domains in soft iron.

Health Science
L I N K

Electromagnetic fields may be harmful to your health. Using a TV and a compass, you will determine if an electromagnetic field is present.

1. Place the compass on the television. Turn the television on and observe.

2. Place the compass 1 m away from the television. Observe the result.

What happened? Explain why some health officials advise keeping a distance from electromagnetic fields.

A C T I V I T Y

Consider This

Should People Avoid Low-level Magnetic Fields?

Appliances, such as electric blankets, dishwashers, and televisions, all have an electric field around them. The electric field is created by the electric current running through the appliance. These fields are called extremely low frequency (ELF) electromagnetic fields.

Groups concerned about the safety of ELF fields recommend that people stay at least 1 m away from computer and television screens. However, all electric devices produce ELF fields. People are surrounded by electric wiring and electric devices at home, school, and work. The effects

of long-term exposure to ELF fields are still unknown.

People studying disease patterns in human populations have noticed that there may be a relationship between ELF fields and an increase in cancer rates.

Groups of people exposed daily to ELF fields have a higher-than-normal rate of brain cancer and leukemia. The groups studied include electricians, telephone-line workers, and people who live near high-voltage power lines. The higher cancer rates don't prove that ELF fields cause cancer. Many other unknown

factors could be involved.

Some physicists think that ELF fields are too weak to affect the human body. They feel the studies don't prove that ELF fields cause cancer and more research is needed.

Think About It How might a possible health risk from ELF fields affect the use of electric appliances? How might ELF fields affect where people live?

Write About It Write a short paper arguing for or against avoiding ELF fields. Explain your reasons.

Skills Development

Predict Use an overhead projector to show students the magnetic field around a wire-carrying current by using iron filings. Run the wire under a piece of clear plastic and sprinkle the filings on the clear plastic around the wire. Ask students, What kind of pattern will an electric current produce in the iron filings? (Concentric circles around the wire) Hook the wire to the terminals of a dry cell and lightly tap the plastic. The filings will form a pattern of concentric rings.

Consider This

Think About It If it is found that ELF fields pose a health risk, the use of electric appliances will probably decrease. People will also move away from high-voltage power lines if they can.

Write About It Student opinions will vary, but papers should include reasons to support their opinions.

Answer to Link

The compass on the TV deflects when the TV is switched on. The compass 1 m away is not affected. The strength of an electromagnetic field decreases quickly as you move away from it.

The Living Textbook:
Physical Science Sides 1-4

Chapter 15   Frame 02468
Electromagnet Parts (1 Frame)
Search:

The Living Textbook:
Physical Science Sides 1-4

Chapter 15   Frame 02659
ELF Effects on Bees (1 Frame)
Search:

TEACH ▪ Continued

Explore Visually

Have students study the text and Figure 12.11. Point out each part of the motor and, if possible, show these parts using an electric motor in the classroom. Then ask:

▶ What are the three main parts of the DC electric motor? (An electromagnet called an armature, a permanent magnet, and a commutator)

▶ How do the armature and the permanent magnet affect each other? (Poles of the armature rotate away from the like poles of the permanent magnet.)

▶ Why is it important for the current to change direction every time the commutator, or split ring, makes a half turn? (The reversed current direction makes the poles of the armature reverse, so the armature keeps rotating.)

▶ How is the rotating armature used to do work? (The armature turns the drive shaft of a motor.)

▶ What will happen if the commutator turns and moves rapidly? (The poles of the armature will reverse more rapidly and the drive shaft will turn more rapidly.)

Discuss

Explain to students that most home appliances use alternating current. Direct current is used in a device that has a dry cell (clock) or a transformer box (calculator, answering machine). The telephone also uses direct current.

 The Living Textbook: Physical Science Sides 1-4

Chapter 15   Frame 02482
Electric Motor (5 Frames)
Search: Step:

296

Cooperative Learning

Many small electric toys are battery-operated. Have pairs of students work cooperatively to take apart a toy run by a DC motor and label the parts of the motor according to Figure 12.11. The toys you choose should have a motor that is easy to remove and replace.

Portfolio

Ask students to list the types of electric appliances in their homes that require direct current and those that require alternating current. Have students compare and contrast the lists in a class discussion. They can include the two lists and notes on the class discussion in their portfolios. See Discuss on this page before assigning the Portfolio.

Uses for Electromagnetism

You probably use items every day that contain electromagnets. Any appliance with an electric motor uses an electromagnet to convert electric energy to energy of motion. An electromagnet exerts a magnetic force that can make things move. Vacuum cleaners, tape recorders, and hair dryers all contain electromagnets.

Figure 12.11
Simple Electric Motor ▼

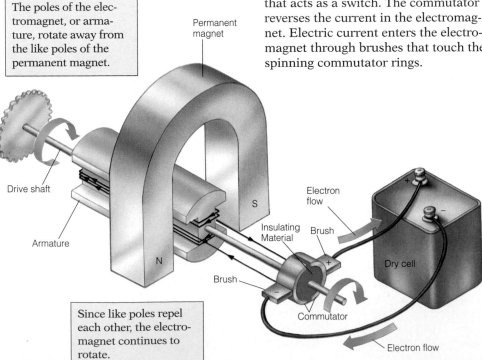

The poles of the electromagnet, or armature, rotate away from the like poles of the permanent magnet.

Permanent magnet

Drive shaft

Armature

S

Electron flow

Insulating Material

Brush

Brush

N

+

Dry cell

Commutator

Electron flow

Since like poles repel each other, the electromagnet continues to rotate.

Every time the commutator makes a half turn, current direction changes.

Electric Motors A simple direct current, or DC, electric motor like the one in Figure 12.11, contains an electromagnet, a permanent magnet, and a commutator. An electromagnet, called an armature, is placed in the magnetic field of the permanent magnet.

When current flows through the electromagnet, its poles repel the like poles of the permanent magnet. When the direction of the current changes, the poles on the electromagnet reverse, and the electromagnet spins. The armature turns a drive shaft that does work.

The commutator is a split metal ring that acts as a switch. The commutator reverses the current in the electromagnet. Electric current enters the electromagnet through brushes that touch the spinning commutator rings.

Themes in Science

Scale and Structure Explain to students that galvanometers are designed to measure very small amounts of electric current. To expand their usefulness they are often attached to voltmeters or ammeters, so they can show small increments of current usage.

Figure 12.12
How a Meter Measures Current ▼

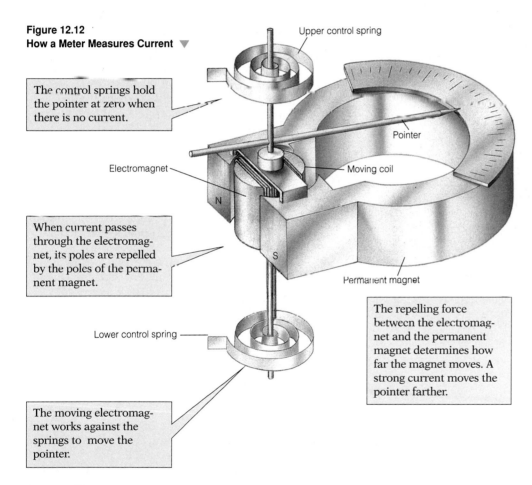

Upper control spring

The control springs hold the pointer at zero when there is no current.

Pointer

Electromagnet

Moving coil

N

When current passes through the electromagnet, its poles are repelled by the poles of the permanent magnet.

S

Permanent magnet

The repelling force between the electromagnet and the permanent magnet determines how far the magnet moves. A strong current moves the pointer farther.

Lower control spring

The moving electromagnet works against the springs to move the pointer.

Current Meters The response of magnetic forces between an electromagnet and a permanent magnet is used in various kinds of meters, such as voltmeters, ammeters, and galvanometers (GAL vuh NAH muh turs). All these devices, called current meters, measure electric current.

A galvanometer, like the one shown in Figure 12.12, measures small amounts of electric current passing through a resistor. The two springs connected to the rod through the electromagnet control the pointer of the galvanometer. When an electric current passes through the electromagnet, the poles of the electromagnet respond to the poles of the permanent magnet. If the poles are alike, they repel and force the pointer in one direction or the other.

The galvanometer's scale has equally spaced markings on either side of the zero. The direction of the current through the electromagnet determines whether the pointer moves to the right or to the left of center. The pointer's position away from zero indicates how much current is traveling through the wire coil. How are current meters used? ①

Reteach

Before students study how a meter measures current, review what a current is. Remind students that a current is the negative charges, or electrons, that move in a wire. In direct current, negative charges will move from the negative terminal to the positive terminal of a dry cell.

Explore Visually

Have students study Figure 12.12. Ask:

▶ What parts of the galvanometer are like those of a DC motor? (Both have a permanent magnet and an electromagnet.)

▶ What controls the pointer of the galvanometer? (Two springs attached to the shaft of the electromagnet)

▶ How do the poles of the electromagnet respond when current passes through it? How does the pointer respond? (The poles of the electromagnet are repelled by the poles of the permanent magnet; the pointer is forced in one direction or the other.)

▶ Explain how galvanometers measure current. (The pointer indicates how much current is traveling through the wire coil of the electromagnet. A strong current moves the pointer farther.)

Answer to In-Text Question

① Current meters are used to find out how much electric current has been used. These are used to determine an electric bill.

**The Living Textbook:
Physical Science Sides 1-4**

Chapter 15   Frame 02358
Galvanometer (1 Frame)
Search:

TEACH ▪ *Continued*

Critical Thinking

Compare and Contrast Ask, What are the advantages of an electric car over a gasoline-powered car? (Electric cars cost less and cause less air pollution.)

EVALUATE

WrapUp

Reinforce Refer students to the lists of appliances with motors that they made for the Skills WarmUp. Have the class choose several of these appliances and discuss the kind of energy converted to by each electric motor. Ask students to explain how the energy conversion takes place.

Use Review Worksheet 12.2.

Check and Explain

1. An electric current affects the magnetic poles; reversing the current reverses the magnetic poles; electricity can produce magnetism.

2. Electric current causes an electromagnet to spin when its poles are repelled by those of a permanent magnet. The spinning electromagnet turns a drive shaft.

3. Both contain an electromagnet and a permanent magnet.

4. The armature would not spin.

Answer to In-Text Question

① **The weight of the batteries slows down an electric car by increasing the force required to produce a given acceleration.**

 The Living Textbook: Physical Science Sides 1-4

Chapter 15   Frame 02663
Electric Car (2 Frames)
Search: Step:

Art Connection

Ask students to bring in newspaper or magazine pictures of high-speed trains. Use their clippings to discuss magnetic levitation trains, or maglev trains, which use magnetic force to travel. These high-speed trains can travel at 300 miles per hour. Have students research the two types of maglev trains—superconducting and electromagnetic—and make a poster of how electricity and magnetism make the trains move.

Figure 12.13 ▲
What effect does the weight of the batteries have on the efficiency of an electric car? ①

Science and Technology *Electric Cars*

Someday you might go to an electric recharging station instead of a gasoline station to refuel your automobile! Instead of kilometers per liter, you would measure your fuel consumption in kilometers per kilowatt. Your electric car of the future could look like the one in Figure 12.13.

Electric cars aren't a new idea. Some of the earliest cars were electric. However, cars with gasoline engines replaced electric cars because gasoline engines provide more power per unit weight than electric motors. Also, at that time, gasoline was both abundant and cheap. Today the reduction of fossil-fuel reserves, the cost of gasoline, and air pollution make electric cars a good idea.

People want an electric car that travels as fast and as far as a gasoline-powered car. Older electric cars required heavy DC batteries to power inefficient DC motors. Also, because the windshield wipers, starter, radio, and lights all use direct current, older test models of electric cars needed more DC batteries. To solve the problem, engineers are working to develop an efficient, lightweight electric car.

The new electric cars could use newly-developed alternating-current, or AC, motors with lightweight moving parts. Since batteries produce direct current, a "power inverter" will change the DC power to AC power. A newly designed electronic power inverter has a mass of only 27 kg instead of the 136 kg of older power inverters. Many other ideas are being developed and tested to make the electric car the car of your future.

Check and Explain

1. Name three things Oersted discovered about the relationship between electricity and magnetism.

2. Explain how an electric motor works.

3. **Compare and Contrast** How is the operation of a galvanometer similar to that of an electric motor?

4. **Predict** What would happen if the current in the electro-magnet of an electric motor didn't change direction?

Prelab Discussion

Have students read the entire activity. Have rods made of other materials on hand for students to test as electromagnets. Discuss the following:

▶ Ask students to describe what is happening inside the nail when the battery is connected.

▶ Have students make predictions about the strength of each electromagnet.

Time 40 minutes   **Group** pairs

Materials

30 m insulated electrical wire

15 boxes of paper clips

15 large iron nails

15 6-V dry cells

tape

Analysis

1. The nail with 25 coils should have picked up the largest number of nails; 10 coils should have picked up the fewest.

2. Increasing the number of coils increases the magnetic force.

3. Students' answers should agree with the graph. It should show a fairly straight diagonal curve—a linear positive relationship between number of coils and number of paper clips.

Conclusion

Students should observe that a greater number of coils creates a stronger magnetic field, so the electromagnet is stronger.

Extension

Students should find that the size of the nail also has an effect on the strength of the electromagnet. Some students may try removing the nail altogether after making the coils. This will reduce but not eliminate the electromagnetic attraction. Adding a second dry cell will increase the current through the coil, increasing the strength of the magnet.

Activity 12 *Does the number of coils affect magnetic force?*

Skills Predict; Infer; Observe; Graph; Interpret Data

Task 1 Prelab Prep

Collect the following items: 2 m insulated electric wire, 1 box of paper clips, 1 large iron nail, one 6-V dry cell, and tape.

Task 2 Data Record

1. Prepare a table like the one shown.
2. Record the number of paper clips the electromagnet attracted for each number of coils.

Table 12.1

Number of Coils	Number of Paper Clips
10	
15	
20	
25	

3. Prepare a graph to show how magnetic force changes as the number of coils in the electromagnet increases. Put the number of coils on the x-axis and the number of paper clips on the y-axis.

Task 3 Procedure

1. Remove about 2 cm of insulation from the ends of the electric wire.
2. Place a pile of paper clips on the table.
3. Wind the electric wire around the iron nail 10 times. The coils should be close together. You can use the diagram in Figure 12.10 as an example.
4. Connect the ends of the electric wire to the dry cell with tape. Pick up as many paper clips as possible with the electromagnet.
5. Count and record the number of paper clips picked up. Disconnect the dry cell.

6. Wind 5 more loops of wire around the nail to make 15 loops. Repeat steps 4 and 5.
7. Repeat steps 4 and 5 with 20 and 25 loops of wire around the nail.

Task 4 Analysis

1. How many coils around the nail picked up the largest number of paper clips? The smallest number of paper clips?

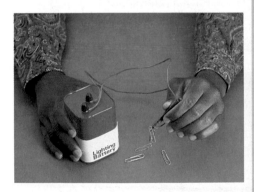

2. How does changing the number of coils affect the magnetic force of the electromagnet?
3. What does the graph tell you about the relationship between the number of coils and the strength of the electromagnet?

Task 5 Conclusion

Write a short paragraph describing how the strength of the electromagnet depends on the number of coils wound around the nail. Explain what effect the number of coils would have on the magnetic field around the electromagnet also.

Extension

To find out more about how to change the electromagnet's strength, use a bigger or smaller nail and observe what happens. Add a second dry cell and test the strength of the electromagnet.

12.3

Section Objectives
For a list of section objectives, see the Student Edition page.

Skills Objectives
Students should be able to:

Infer how the world would function with only direct current

Collect Data to use in making a flowchart on energy conversion.

Compare the energy conversion in a motor and generator.

Predict how a transformer works based on the number of coils involved.

Vocabulary
electromagnetic induction

MOTIVATE

Skills WarmUp
To help students understand the relationship of magnetism to electricity, have them do the Skills WarmUp.

Answer Answers will vary. Students will probably say that large batteries would be required. Homes might be lit by current from batteries, but industries that needed large amounts of electricity would probably not exist.

Answer to In-Text Question
① Answers will vary. Encourage students to describe power poles and lines in their neighborhoods.

 **The Living Textbook:
Physical Science Sides 1-4**

Chapter 15   Frame 02628
Power Lines (1 Frame)
Search:

Themes in Science
Energy Magnetic force can be changed into electric energy. The electric energy can be converted into mechanical, light, heat, or sound energy, or back into magnetic force.

Writing Connection
Explain to students that nearly ten years before Michael Faraday (1791–1867) was able to prove electromagnetic induction, he wrote a goal in his notebook: "Convert magnetism into electricity." Ask students to write a goal for discovering something that could be of great importance to society. Have them state the goal, then list several benefits to society and several possible ways of achieving the goal.

▼ ACTIVITY

Inferring

Minimal Electricity

Before scientists learned that magnetism could be used to produce electricity, the only sources of electricity were electrochemical cells and batteries. How might the world around you be different if that were the case today?

SKILLS WARMUP

Figure 12.14 ▲
This tower is part of a network that supplies power to many homes and buildings. How does this tower compare to the power poles near your home? ①

12.3 Magnetism to Electricity

Objectives

▶ **Describe** how magnetism is used to produce electricity.

▶ **Identify** two uses of electromagnetic induction.

▶ **Compare** and **contrast** the energy conversions in a generator with those in an electric motor.

▶ **Predict** the conditions under which a transformer will operate.

Think about what happens when you turn on an electric light. You simply flick a switch, and a room is filled with light. You know that light uses electricity, but do you know how the electricity it uses is produced?

You learned that electric current can produce a magnetic field. Did you know that a magnetic field can produce electricity? The electric power that operates your lights comes from a generator that changes magnetic force into electricity. Electricity moves through wires like those shown in Figure 12.14 to supply energy to electric clocks, motors, and appliances. Actually, most electric devices in today's world depend on the electricity produced by magnetism.

Induction of Electric Current

After Oersted showed that an electric current can produce magnetic fields, scientists began to wonder if they could reverse the process. They hypothesized that magnetic fields could somehow produce electric currents. Two scientists, Joseph Henry of the United States and Michael Faraday of England, worked independently to test this hypothesis.

Henry and Faraday both learned that when they placed a strong magnet next to a wire coil, a brief surge of current existed in the coil. However, if they moved the magnet in and out of the coil, current flowed through the coil. As long as the magnet was moving, the current would continue to flow. This process of inducing a current by moving a magnetic field through a wire coil without touching it is known as **electromagnetic induction**.

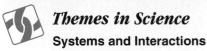
Themes in Science
Systems and Interactions

Electromagnetic induction occurs whenever there is motion between a wire and a magnetic field. The direction and speed of the motion affect the direction and strength of the electric current produced.

Electromagnetic Induction

To observe the process of electromagnetic induction, look at Figure 12.15. As the magnet moves through the wire coil, it induces an electric current. The direction of the magnet's motion affects the direction of the electric current.

Electromagnetic induction occurs any time motion takes place between the wire and the magnetic field. The results are the same when the wire moves, when the magnetic field moves, or when both move. The speed of the motion affects the strength of the electric current. A weak current is produced when the movement of the wire or the magnetic field is slow. A strong current is produced when the movement is fast. The number of loops in the wire coil also affects the strength of the current. If two wire coils with different numbers of loops are moved through the same magnetic field, the current will be stronger in the coil with the larger number of loops.

Any changing magnetic field will induce a current. For example, changing current in an electric circuit induces current to flow in a nearby circuit that isn't connected to it. A steady current won't do this. Why do you think the current must be changing? ②

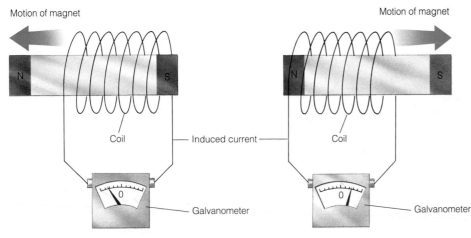

Figure 12.15 ▲

Look at the needle and direction of the magnet in the art above. How do the galvanometer needles in each figure relate to the direction of the magnets? ③

TEACH ▪ *Continued*

Explore Visually

Have students study Figure 12.16. Ask the following questions:

▶ What turns the drive shaft of the generator? (Mechanical energy applied to a gear system or a crank; mechanical energy may be created by steam turning a turbine.)

▶ When the drive shaft turns, what happens to the armature? (It rotates through the magnetic field of the permanent magnet, inducing a current.)

▶ How does electric current leave the generator? (It flows from the wire coil to the slip rings. Brushes touching the slip rings are attached to wires that transfer the electric current.)

▶ If the current coming to the slip rings is reversed every time the armature makes one-half of a turn, what kind of current is it? (Alternating current)

▶ What is a generator? (Any device that creates an electric current by turning a coil of wire through a magnetic field.)

▶ **Infer** If you turn the drive shaft more rapidly, what will happen to the voltage? (It will increase.)

The Living Textbook: Physical Science Sides 1-4

Chapter 15   Frame 02469
Generator Parts (1 Frame)
Search:

The Living Textbook: Physical Science Sides 1-4

Chapter 15   Frame 02615
Hydroelectric Plant (1 Frame)
Search:

Themes in Science

Systems and Interactions The mechanical energy that drives the generator in an automobile is part of a system of belts and pulleys. Ask students to use what they learned in previous chapters to explain how the system works.

Uses of Electromagnetic Induction

Because a moving magnetic field induces current in a wire coil, it is possible to build many useful devices. For example, generators use electromagnetic induction to make electric power that you use in your home and school. Transformers use electromagnetic induction to change the voltage and current between different locations.

Generators One of the most common devices that uses electromagnetic induction is an electric generator. Any device that creates an electric current by turning a coil of wire through a magnetic field is a *generator*. A generator changes mechanical energy into electric energy. A simple AC generator has an armature, permanent magnet, and slip rings. Study the generator in Figure 12.16.

Figure 12.16
Simple AC Generator ▼

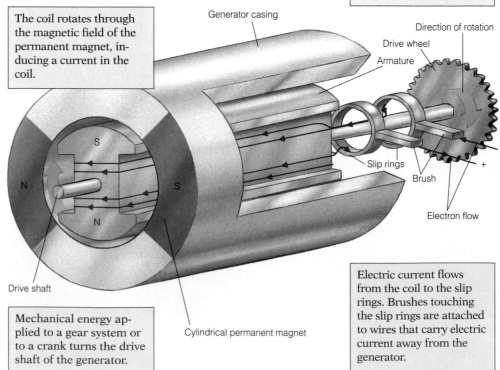

The coil rotates through the magnetic field of the permanent magnet, inducing a current in the coil.

The armature contains an electromagnet and is free to spin on a drive shaft. A permanent magnet surrounds the armature.

Generator casing

Direction of rotation

Drive wheel

Armature

Slip rings

Brush

Electron flow

Drive shaft

Mechanical energy applied to a gear system or to a crank turns the drive shaft of the generator.

Cylindrical permanent magnet

Electric current flows from the coil to the slip rings. Brushes touching the slip rings are attached to wires that carry electric current away from the generator.

Transformers Transformers use electromagnetic induction to change the voltage and current in a circuit. Look at Figures 12.17 and 12.18. Step-up transformers increase the voltage and decrease the current. Step-down transformers reduce the voltage and increase the current.

Transformers adjust the voltage for appliances that use voltages greater or smaller than the 120/240 volts supplied by electric companies in the United States. Transformers also make it possible to send power over long distances through power lines.

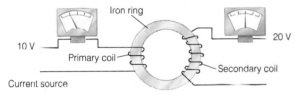

As current moves through a wire, the wire gets hot. When heat is lost, energy is lost. Less energy is lost as heat when voltage is high and current is low. Power companies avoid the loss of power by sending high-voltage electricity along power lines. However, the voltage needed in your home is less than the voltage in the power line. Step-down transformers reduce the voltage in the lines connected to your home.

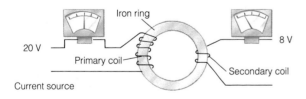

A transformer has a primary coil wound around one portion of a soft iron core. The primary coil is connected to the power source. A secondary coil winds around an opposite portion of the soft iron core. The wire from the secondary coil connects to the wiring in your home.

As current in the primary coil alternates and changes, it induces a magnetic field in the soft-iron core. The changing magnetic field induces a current in the secondary coil. When the current in the circuit changes, the voltage also changes.

Figure 12.17
This is called a step-up transformer. How is the amount of current in the primary coil different from the amount of current in the secondary coil?

Figure 12.18
This is called a step-down transformer. How is the amount of current in the primary coil different from the amount of current in the secondary coil? ②

TEACH ▪ Continued

Skills WorkOut

To help students organize data in a flowchart, have them do the Skills WorkOut.

Answer Chart boxes should include mechanical to mechanical (pedals to wheels to drive shaft), mechanical to electrical (magnet on drive shaft), and electrical to light energy (light bulb).

EVALUATE

WrapUp

Portfolio Ask students to make and label a diagram showing how a power-company generator produces electricity from mechanical energy. Show the power source and any transformers.

Use Review Worksheet 12.3.

Check and Explain

1. Putting a magnet next to a wire causes a brief surge of current. Moving a magnet in a wire coil causes a continuous current.

2. Students should describe generators and transformers.

3. In a motor, an electromagnet produces mechanical energy. In a generator turning a wire mechanically in a magnetic field produces electric energy.

4. Amount of current going out equals amount coming in.

Answer to In-Text Question

① **Mechanical energy from your legs turns the bike wheel, which turns the drive shaft in the generator, which creates electric current to light the bulb.**

The Living Textbook: Physical Science Side 2

Chapter 31   Frame 25179
Energy Conversion (Movie)
Search: Play:

Language Arts Connection

Dynamics is the name of a branch of physics. The name shares its root with the word *dynamo,* short for *dynamoelectric machine,* an early name for generators. Have students research the words *dynamics* and *dynamo* and explain how their definitions relate. Ask, How is a dynamo dynamic? (A generator, or dynamo, produces energy or change.) Students can also research the word *dyne* and the prefix *dyna-.*

Social Studies Connection

Students know that mechanical energy from turning wheels can be converted into electrical energy through electromagnetic induction. Explain that before farms and rural towns received electricity through power lines, many had generators powered by the turning wheels of windmills. Have students research the kinds of energy used by farmers before they had electricity.

▼ ACTIVITY

Organizing Data

Charting the Course

A flowchart is like a map of the steps involved in a process. Boxes, each with one step, are connected by lines to show the process. Create a flowchart of the energy conversions that take place as you pedal a bicycle to operate a generator light.

SKILLS WORKOUT

Figure 12.19 ▲
How does a small bike generator convert your energy into light? ①

Science and Technology
Generators for Bikes

When you ride a bike, you can generate enough energy to light your path! A small generator attached to a bicycle wheel can use the wheel's rotation to produce enough electricity to light a lamp. Where do you think this mechanical energy comes from?

The light bulb's energy source is the food you eat. Food contains stored energy. Your body converts the food to chemical energy that moves your leg muscles. Your muscles move your legs, transferring mechanical energy to the pedals of the bicycle. Mechanical energy transfers from the pedals to the gears that turn the bike's rear wheel. Mechanical energy from the turning wheels transfers to the generator's drive shaft. A permanent magnet on the drive shaft induces an electric current in the coil. This electric current supplies the energy that lights the bulb in the lamp.

In the evening, when you ride a bicycle with the generator against the wheel, you probably notice that the bicycle is more difficult to pedal. Your observation agrees with the principles of energy conservation. The work you do to supply current to the light bulb increases the amount of energy you need to pedal the bicycle.

You might also notice that the faster you pedal, the brighter the generator light becomes. The light gets brighter because the increase in energy that you supply by pedaling increases the amount of current the generator produces. The faster you pedal, the faster the electromagnet spins. When more current is generated, the bulb is brighter.

Check and Explain

1. Name two ways a magnet can induce current in a wire.

2. Describe two uses of electromagnetic induction.

3. **Compare and Contrast** Describe how energy conversion in an electric motor differs from the energy conversion in a generator.

4. **Predict** What would happen if the number of coils on both sides of a transformer were the same?

Chapter 12 Review

Concept Summary

12.1 Magnets and Magnetism

▶ A magnet has two magnetic poles and is surrounded by a magnetic field. Like poles repel and unlike poles attract.

▶ Magnetic materials contain magnetic regions called domains. When the domains align, the material is magnetized.

▶ The earth has a magnetic field that resembles a giant bar magnet.

12.2 Electricity to Magnetism

▶ An electric current in a wire produces a magnetic field around the wire. The magnetic poles change when the direction of the current changes.

▶ An electric motor converts electric energy to mechanical energy. A spinning electromagnet turns a drive shaft that does work.

▶ In a galvanometer, an electromagnet works against springs to move a pointer along a numbered scale.

12.3 Magnetism to Electricity

▶ When a magnetic field moves through a wire coil, it induces an electric current.

▶ Electromagnetic induction is used to operate electric generators, transformers, and many other devices.

▶ A generator converts mechanical energy to electric energy. An outside energy source turns a drive shaft that rotates a coil in a magnetic field.

Chapter Vocabulary

magnetic pole (p. 288)   permanent magnet (p. 289)   electromagnet (p. 294)
magnetic field (p. 288)   compass (p. 290)   electromagnetic induction (p. 300)
magnetic domain (p. 289)

Check Your Vocabulary

Use the vocabulary words above to complete the following sentences correctly.

1. A current-carrying wire wrapped around an iron core is (a)n _____ .

2. A magnetized steel needle that aligns with the magnetic field of the earth is a(n) _____ .

3. Every magnet has a north and a south _____ .

4. During the process of _____ , a magnetic field moves across a wire coil.

5. Every magnet is surrounded by a(n) _____ .

6. Iron atoms respond to a microscopic magnetic region called a(n) _____ .

7. Unlike a(n) _____ , an electromagnet can be turned on and off.

Pair each numbered word with a vocabulary term. Explain in a complete sentence how the words are related.

1. Alignment   6. Coil
2. Nickel   7. Generator
3. Pattern   8. Aurora
4. Two   9. Galvanometer
5. Direction

Write Your Vocabulary

Write sentences using the vocabulary words above. Show that you know what each word means.

Check Your Vocabulary

1. electromagnet
2. compass
3. magnetic pole
4. electromagnetic induction
5. magnetic field
6. magnetic domain
7. permanent magnet

1. Compass: A compass indicates the presence of a magnetic field by alignment with the field.

2. Magnetic domain: Nickel is a magnetic material that contains magnetic domains.

3. Magnetic field: Magnetic force around an object is called the magnetic field, which makes a pattern.

4. Magnetic pole: All magnets have two magnetic poles.

5. Compass: A compass shows the direction of a magnetic field at a particular location.

6. Magnetic field: The magnetic field of a current-carrying wire is strengthened by winding the wire in coils.

7. Electromagnetic induction: A generator moves a conducting wire through a magnetic field, generating current.

8. Magnetic pole: An aurora is charged particles near the earth's magnetic poles.

9. Electromagnetic induction: The needle of a galvanometer moves due to induction as current through a wire in a magnetic field creates a force.

Write Your Vocabulary

Students' sentences should show that they know the meaning of each word as well as how to use it in a sentence.

Use Vocabulary Worksheet for Chapter 12.

Check Your Knowledge

1. Magnetism is a universal force between magnetic materials.

2. A permanent magnet is made from a material whose magnetic domains have been made to align. An electromagnet is created when a magnetic field is created by current flowing through a wire coiled around a solid core.

3. A magnetic field is the area affected by the magnetic force around an object. The field is strongest near the poles of the magnet.

4. The earth has magnetic poles and is surrounded by a magnetic field like a magnet is.

5. A compass is a tiny bar magnet that turns freely and aligns with the earth's magnetic lines of force.

6. An electromagnet can be turned off because the magnetic domains in the core need an external magnetic field, which is created by the current in the coil, to remain aligned.

7. When current flows through the motor, a magnetic field is created in the armature. The field interacts with the field of the permanent magnet, causing the armature to spin. The commutator causes the current to change directions every half-turn, which switches the direction of the magnetic field of the armature, so the armature "gets a push" every half turn.

8. When the wires in the armature are moved through the field of the permanent magnet, an electric current is induced.

9. A transformer increases or decreases the voltage in a circuit.

10. Answers may vary, but may include: any device containing an electric motor, an audio speaker, telephone, computer screen, television screen.

11. north magnetic pole

12. two magnets

13. an outside force turns it

Check Your Understanding

1. Magnetic poles are like electric charges in that like poles repel, while unlike poles attract. They are different in that magnetic poles cannot move or be transferred from one object to another as electric charges can.

2. The magnetic field of the earth is strongest near the poles.

3. a. skull, brain hemispheres, eyes, nose

   b. MRI is useful because it does not require surgery and produces images of soft tissue, unlike X-ray images which cannot image soft tissue.

4. An electric motor and a generator are opposites of each other. A generator converts mechanical (kinetic) energy into electrical energy; a motor converts electrical energy into kinetic energy. Both employ a rotating armature inside the magnetic field of a permanent magnet.

5. The box is a step-down transformer, which reduces the voltage of the outlet to a level safe for the device.

Chapter 12 Review

Check Your Knowledge

Answer the following in complete sentences.

1. What is magnetism?

2. What are the two kinds of magnets? Describe each type.

3. What is a magnetic field? Where is a magnetic field strongest?

4. How is the earth like a magnet?

5. Explain how a compass works.

6. Why can an electromagnet be turned on and off?

7. List the steps involved in the operation of an electric motor.

8. Describe how an electric generator produces electricity.

9. What does a transformer do?

10. Name five everyday devices that contain electromagnets.

Choose the answer that best completes each sentence.

11. A compass needle always points to the earth's (north geographic pole, south geographic pole, north magnetic pole, sun).

12. When you cut a magnet in half you get (a north pole and a south pole, one north pole, two magnets, one south pole).

13. The armature of a generator rotates because (like poles repel, unlike poles attract, current flows out, an outside force turns it).

Check Your Understanding

Apply the concepts you have learned to answer each question.

1. How are magnetic poles like electric charges? How are they different?

2. Auroras are seen most often in the regions near the earth's north and south magnetic poles. Suggest a possible reason for this.

3. **Mystery Photo** The photograph on page 286 is an artificially colored magnetic resonance image, or MRI, of a section of a human head. To create the image, the patient is placed inside a machine with a huge magnet. The magnetic field causes the nuclei of certain atoms within the body to line up. The machine then sends out a radio signal that causes the nuclei to change direction. These changes create weak radio signals that a computer shows as an image.

   a. What parts of the head can you identify?

   b. Why do you think that MRI is a useful tool for doctors?

4. **Critical Thinking** How is an electric motor like a generator? How is it different?

5. **Application** Many small, electric devices require low voltage and can't be plugged directly into a wall socket. A small box plugs into the wall socket. A wire connects the device to the box. Explain what is happening in the box.

Develop Your Skills

1. Students' models should show a bar magnet with magnetic field lines between the poles.

2. a. B, because there are more turns in the coil
   b. D, because it has a larger nail (core)
   c. B, because there are more turns in the coil

3. a. The lines get closer together near the pole.
   b. Wisconsin, Illinois, Kentucky, Tennessee, Alabama, Florida panhandle
   c. 20° west of true north
   d. to the right

Make Connections

1.

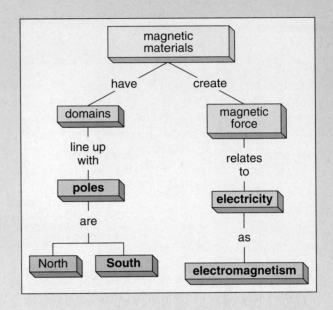

2. Different cultures have navigated with the help of the stars, ocean currents, prevailing winds, and the earth's magnetic field. Today, navigation often uses electronic beacons and orbiting satellites.

3. Students' reports will vary.

Develop Your Skills

Use the skills you have developed in this chapter to complete each activity.

1. **Make a Model** Make a model of the magnetic field of a bar magnet.

2. **Interpret Data** The drawing below shows four electromagnets. Each is made from a coil of current-carrying wire wrapped around a nail. Using what you have learned about electromagnets, answer the following questions.

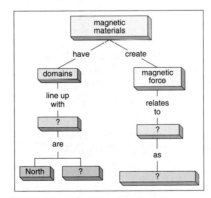

   a. Which electromagnet produces a stronger magnetic field? *A* or *B*? Why?

   b. Which electromagnet produces a stronger magnetic field? *C* or *D*? Why?

   c. Which electromagnet produces a stronger magnetic field? *B* or *C*? Why?

3. **Data Bank** The map on page 639 shows lines of magnetic declination in the continental United States.

   a. Why are the lines closer together at the top of the map than at the bottom?

   b. In what state does a compass point to true north?

   c. If you read a compass in Maine, how many degrees and in what direction does your compass needle vary from true north?

   d. In Los Angeles, is true north to the left or to the right of magnetic north?

Make Connections

1. **Link the Concepts** Below is a concept map showing how some of the main concepts in this chapter link together. Only part of the map is filled in. Finish the map, using words and ideas you find on the previous pages.

2. **Science and Social Studies** Navigation has been an important task for people all over the world since ancient times. Research the methods used by different cultures for navigation. Compare and contrast methods that involve the earth's magnetic field with other methods of navigation.

3. **Science and Literature** During the 1800s, different explorers led expeditions in an effort to be the first humans to reach the earth's north or south poles. The real-life adventure stories of these expeditions are available at the library. Locate a book about one of these expeditions and write a report on it.

Overview

The development and uses of electronics are covered in this chapter. The first section describes various electronic devices used to transmit signals. The second section explains analog and digital signals in audio and video electronics equipment. The last section describes computer systems.

Advance Planner

▶ If possible, provide a vacuum tube for SE page 310.

▶ Supply an adaptable portable radio for TE page 310.

▶ Provide a speakerless radio with earphone jack, permanent magnet, and insulated wire for TE page 311.

▶ Supply tape player and tapes, CD player and CDs, magnifying glasses, and if possible, actual or tape recordings of wax cylinder or vinyl disk recordings for page 317.

▶ Supply magazines, tracing graph paper, tape, and colored pencils or pens for SE Activity 13, page 321.

▶ Obtain a floppy disk and, if possible, an 80-column punch card for TE page 323.

Skills Development Chart

Sections	Classify	Collect Data	Communicate	Compare and Contrast	Estimate	Hypothesize	Infer	Model	Observe	Relate Concepts
13.1 Skills WarmUp	●									
Skills WorkOut			●							
13.2 Skills WarmUp					●					
Skills WorkOut			●						●	
Consider This			●							
Activity				●			●	●	●	
13.3 Skills WarmUp										●
SkillBuilder								●		
Skills WorkOut		●								

Individual Needs

▶ **Limited English Proficiency Students** Tape record the definitions and pronunciations of the chapter's boldface terms. Tell students which figures and definitions in the text illustrate the term. Have them use the tape recorder to listen to the information about each term. Next have students define the terms using their own words. Have them make their own tape recordings of the words and their definitions. They can use this tape to review important chapter concepts.

▶ **At-Risk Students** Ask groups of three or four students to choose an audio or video device described in the chapter. Encourage them to use the information in the text to find out how their device works. They may wish to take apart an old, unrepairable device to examine the parts. Have them label any items they recognize. Have them make diagrams showing how the device works. Finally, ask them to make a list of the jobs connected with manufacturing, selling, and repairing the device.

▶ **Gifted Students** Ask students to find out more about how a computer processes information. They should consider questions such as the following: What is meant by an electronic signal? How are signals carried by electric currents? What is meant by binary code? How are information, signals, and codes related in the world of computers? What functions do computers perform on the information that they receive? Interested students may wish to build a model binary computer and share it with the class.

Resource Bank

▶ **Bulletin Board** Have the class select an electronic device, tool, or instrument. Have students work in cooperative groups to share the task of creating a detailed display of the device. One group could be responsible for finding out how it works; another for finding out about its history; a third group might design the display; a fourth could provide pictures and diagrams; and a fifth group of students could write explanations and captions for the bulletin board.

▶ **Field Trip** Visit a company that makes electronic components or assembles them into electronic devices. Students should be prepared to ask questions about the components in the devices, as well as about the skills and training needed by employees.

Section	Core	Standard	Enriched	Section	Core	Standard	Enriched
13.1 Electronic Devices pp. 309–314				**Overhead Blackline Transparencies** Overhead Blackline Master 12 and Student Worksheet		●	●
Section Features Skills WarmUp, p. 309 Skills WorkOut, p. 312	●	● ●	● ●	**Color Transparencies** Transparencies 48, 49, 50	●	●	●
Blackline Masters Review Worksheet 13.1 Integrating Worksheet 13.1	● ●	● ●	●	**13.3 Computers** pp. 322–326			
13.2 Audio and Video Electronics pp. 315–321				**Section Features** Skills WarmUp, p. 322 SkillBuilder, p. 325 Skills WorkOut, p. 326	● ●	● ● ●	● ● ●
Section Features Skills WarmUp, p. 315 Skills WorkOut, p. 317 Consider This, p. 319 Activity, p. 321	● ● ●	● ● ● ●	● ● ● ●	**Blackline Masters** Review Worksheet 13.3 Skills Worksheet 13.3a Skills Worksheet 13.3b Vocabulary Worksheet 13	● ● ● ●	● ● ● ●	●
Blackline Masters Review Worksheet 13.2 Integrating Worksheet 13.2	●	● ●	●	**Color Transparencies** Transparency 51	●	●	●
Ancillary Options *One-Minute Readings,* p. 91	●	●	●	**Laboratory Program** Investigation 27	●	●	●

Bibliography

The following resources can be used for teaching the chapter. See page T-46 for supplier codes.

Library Resources

Bortz, Fred. *Superstuff.* New York: Franklin Watts, 1990.

Lafferty, Peter. *Energy and Light.* New York: Gloucester Press, 1989.

Lampton, Christopher. *Telecommunications: From Telegraphs to Modems.* New York: Franklin Watts, 1991.

Leon, George deLucenay. *Electronics Projects for Young Scientists.* New York: Franklin Watts, 1991.

Nardo, Don. *Computers: Mechanical Minds.* San Diego, CA: Lucent Books, 1990.

Patent, Dorothy Hinshaw. *The Quest for Artificial Intelligence.* San Diego, CA: Harcourt Brace Jovanovich, 1986.

Technology Resources

Software

Cybercrafts: Digital Technology. Mac, Win, Win 95. ER.
Cybercrafts: Fun with Electronics. Mac, Win. ER.
Inventions of Mention. Mac, Win. ER.

CD-ROMs

An Odyssey of Discovery for Science Insights: Have students explore the activity *Data From Space* on the Earth and Space Disk. SFAW.

Laserdiscs

Living Textbook. (See barcodes on pages in this chapter.) Optical Data.
The Age of Intelligent Machines. AIMS.

Audio-Visual Resources

An Introduction to Computers. Two sound filmstrips. NGSES.
An Introduction to Physical Science, Part II. Two sound filmstrips. NGSES.
Uses of the Personal Computer. Filmstrip. CM.

Introducing the Chapter

Have students read the description of the photograph. Ask if they agree or disagree with the description. Explain to students that the picture shows two computer chips, which are separated by a green band.

Directed Inquiry

Have students study the photograph. Ask:

▶ How would you describe the image in the photograph? (Students will probably say it resembles a map or highway complex.)

▶ What is this a picture of? (Students may be able to identify the image as that of a computer chip or electric circuit on a chip.)

▶ What do you think the function of the lines and squares might be? (The lines carry electric current, and the squares use the current to do work, or compute.)

▶ What do you think is the actual size of a computer chip? (An actual chip is extremely small.)

▶ Why is the small size important? (The chip can perform a large number of operations in a small space.)

Chapter Vocabulary

diode	rectifier
electronics	semiconductor
hardware	software
integrated circuit	transistor
microprocessor	vacuum tube

Writing Connection

Have students write a poem or short story that describes a visit to a world without electronic devices. Before they begin, have students list machines that use computer chips, digital read-outs, or electronic scanners. (Lists may include televisions, stereos, video games, and grocery store checkouts.) Collect students' writing to make a class anthology.

Chapter 13 Electronics

Chapter Sections

13.1 Electronic Devices

13.2 Audio and Video Electronics

13.3 Computers

What do you see?

"The picture in question appears to be a close-up of a microchip used in computers and appliances. Computer chips are often used for calculating large and complicated problems and for processing and storing information. You would find them in computers and appliances such as televisions for changing colors and volume."

Li Ping Chu
Sage Park Middle School
Windsor, Connecticut

To find out more about the photograph, look on page 328. As you read this chapter, you will learn about electronic devices and how they work.

Literature Connection

Provide students with a passage from a diary of an early American family such as *Diary of an Early American Boy* by Eric Sloane. Have students list the activities mentioned in the passage. Across from each activity, they should note how people accomplish the same task today. Have students highlight the tasks that are accomplished with the help of electronic devices.

Use Integrating Worksheet 13.1.

Themes in Science

Systems and Interactions In vacuum tubes, electrons move in response to a difference in potential energy across a gap. In transistors and semiconductors, electrons move in response to differences in atomic energy levels. Have students discuss how the knowledge of electron motion contributes to an understanding of electronics. (All electronic devices control electron flow in some specific way.)

Section Objectives
For a list of section objectives, see the Student Edition page.

Skills Objectives
Students should be able to:

Classify tasks accomplished with electronic devices.

Communicate the events surrounding the development of and uses for semiconductors.

Vocabulary
electronics, vacuum tube, diode, rectifier, semiconductor, transistor, integrated circuit

13.1 Electronic Devices

Objectives

▶ **Relate** electric currents to signals.

▶ **Explain** how a vacuum-tube amplifier works.

▶ **Generalize** about the advantages of semiconductors over vacuum tubes.

▶ **Compare** and **contrast** various types of vacuum-tube and semiconductor devices.

▼ ACTIVITY

Classifying

Elevator Operator

At one time, elevators were operated by a person. Make a list of some other tasks now done electronically that were once done by a person. Compare your list with others in your class.

SKILLS WARMUP

Ⓗow has the world changed over the past 50 years? Your grandparents would probably mention advances in electronics. A radio used to be so big you needed two strong arms to lift it. Today you can wear a radio on your head and forget it's even there! The electronic pen shown in Figure 13.1 was not commonly used until recent years. Computers once filled several rooms. Today, business people can carry computers in their briefcases.

Types of Electronic Devices

The specialized field of **electronics** deals with the behavior and control of electric currents. You know that electric current is moving electrons. Electronics uses electric current to carry information in the form of a signal. Signals represent sounds, pictures, numbers, or other information. Electric current is controlled using electronic devices. Computers, radar scanners, or other kinds of electronic equipment may contain hundreds to millions of electronic devices.

Electronic devices can be divided into two main groups: those that use vacuum tubes and those that use semiconductors. Older electronic devices used vacuum tubes. Televisions still use a special type of vacuum tube to produce a picture. Most newer devices use semiconductors. Radios, calculators, computers, and many other kinds of electronic equipment use semiconductors. An important function of vacuum tubes and semiconductors in electronic devices is to strengthen, or amplify, weak electric signals.

Figure 13.1 ▲
This laser pen is really an electronic scanner. The laser reads information coded in a bar code, such as the item's name and price.

MOTIVATE

Skills WarmUp
To help students understand electronic devices, have them do the Skills WarmUp.
Answer Answers may vary. Students may mention manufacturing operations performed by robotic devices; banking transactions recorded by ATMs; and timing and scoring competitive sports.

Prior Knowledge
Gauge how much students know about electronic devices by asking the following questions:

▶ What are electronic signals?

▶ What is a computer chip?

▶ What are computer chips made of?

▶ How do you think a cordless phone works?

◉ **The Living Textbook:**
Physical Science Sides 1-4

Chapter 15   Frame 02586
Microchip (1 Frame)
Search:

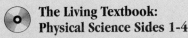

Explore Visually

Have students study the text and the diagram of the vacuum tube. If possible, have several vacuum tubes available for students to inspect. Ask:

▶ How would you describe the structure of a vacuum tube? (It is a glass tube from which air has been removed.)

▶ In a vacuum tube, how are the electron source and the filament related? What name is given to the electron source in a vacuum tube? What charge does it have? (The filament is the electron source; it's called the cathode; negative)

▶ What part of the vacuum tube acts as an electron collector? What charge does it have? What is it called? (The metal plate; positive; anode)

▶ How do electrons move in the vacuum tube? (They move across the gap from the filament to the metal plate.)

Apply

Bring an adaptable portable radio to class. Remind students that batteries supply direct current to the radio. Ask students what kind of electronic device they think is in the radio's AC adapter. (A rectifier) Ask students what other devices use rectifiers. (Answering machines and calculators)

**The Living Textbook:
Physical Science Sides 1-4**

Chapter 7   Frame 03408
Vacuum Tube (2 Frames)
Search: Step:

Language Arts Connection

Ask volunteers to use a dictionary to find the meanings of the words *anode* and *cathode*. (*Anode* comes from a Greek word meaning "way up"; *cathode* comes from a Greek word meaning "way down.") Have students use the information to compose a rhyme or other mnemonic device to help them remember that cathodes are negatively charged and anodes are positively charged.

Integrating the Sciences

Chemistry An anode and a cathode are also identified in the apparatus that separates water into its elements. Ask students to find out which gas collects at the anode, and which collects at the cathode. (Oxygen; hydrogen)

Vacuum Tubes

The careful control of electrons began with the **vacuum tube**. The first vacuum tube was developed for commercial use in 1904. It had two terminals, or electrodes, and was called a **diode**. Electrons flow through a diode in only one direction. Diodes strongly resist the flow of electric current in the opposite direction. Look at Figure 13.2 to see how a simple vacuum-tube diode works.

Figure 13.2   A Vacuum Tube ▼

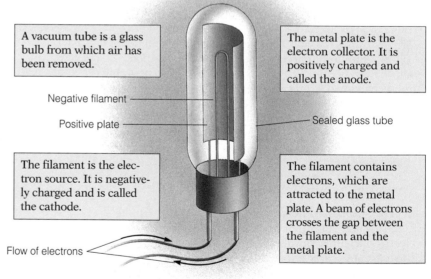

A vacuum tube is a glass bulb from which air has been removed.

The metal plate is the electron collector. It is positively charged and called the anode.

Negative filament

Positive plate

Sealed glass tube

The filament is the electron source. It is negatively charged and is called the cathode.

The filament contains electrons, which are attracted to the metal plate. A beam of electrons crosses the gap between the filament and the metal plate.

Flow of electrons

Rectifiers   Some vacuum-tube diodes are **rectifiers**. A rectifier changes alternating current into direct current. The electricity supplied to your home by an electric power company is alternating current. Recall that in each alternating current cycle the electrons move first in one direction and then in the other.

Alternating current passes easily through rectifiers in one direction, but not in the opposite direction. Current will only pass through the rectifier during half of each AC cycle. The resulting current is direct and pulses in only one direction. Some electronic equipment has parts that require direct current. This equipment contains rectifiers so that it can operate on the alternating current in your home. Televisions, computers, and microwave ovens are a few examples of electronic equipment that contain rectifiers.

Music Connection

Ask students to bring in examples of electronic and acoustic music or musical instruments. Discuss the differences in how electronic and acoustic music are produced. Have students discuss which type of music they like better and why. (Electronic: made with an electronic device that modifies electric signals to produce sound; acoustic: made if a part of an instrument, such as a guitar string, piano wire, or saxophone reed vibrates)

Amplifiers Small, unsteady electric currents, or signals, carry information that is strengthened by amplifiers. For example, a signal is set up in your radio antenna as it receives a broadcast from your favorite radio station. Amplifiers in your radio strengthen the signal, and you hear the music. Amplifiers also increase the strength of weak signals produced by playing a phonograph record. As it makes contact with the grooves in a vinyl record, a phonograph needle creates signals. The amplifier makes the signal powerful enough to operate a loudspeaker. In modern electronic equipment, amplifiers have been replaced by semiconductors. Figure 13.3 shows how a vacuum-tube amplifier works with a loudspeaker.

Astronomy LINK

Radio telescopes use amplifiers to increase the strength of incoming radio waves. You can investigate amplified signals. Obtain a microphone, speakers, and an amplifier.

1. Set up the system. Turn the volume up high.

2. Sitting quietly, listen to the amplified signals. Tap on the microphone and describe the result.

What problems do you notice when listening to highly amplified signals?

ACTIVITY

Figure 13.3   A Vacuum-Tube Amplifier ▼

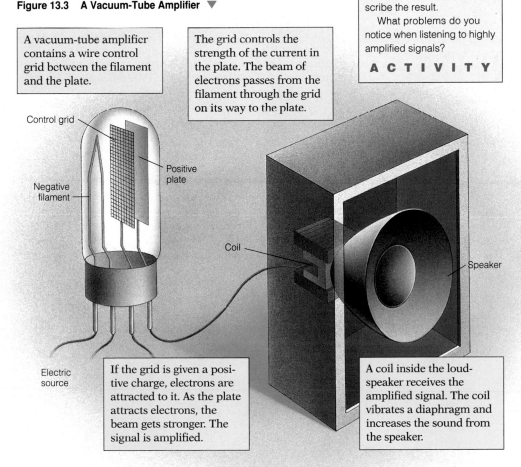

A vacuum-tube amplifier contains a wire control grid between the filament and the plate.

The grid controls the strength of the current in the plate. The beam of electrons passes from the filament through the grid on its way to the plate.

Control grid

Positive plate

Negative filament

Coil

Speaker

Electric source

If the grid is given a positive charge, electrons are attracted to it. As the plate attracts electrons, the beam gets stronger. The signal is amplified.

A coil inside the loudspeaker receives the amplified signal. The coil vibrates a diaphragm and increases the sound from the speaker.

Skills Development

Communicate Have students study Figure 13.13. Have them make a diagram showing the parts of an amplifier and a loudspeaker. Ask them to use their diagrams to explain in their own words how an amplifier in a loudspeaker works.

Class Activity

To make a loudspeaker, you can use a speakerless radio, its earphone jack, a small strong permanent magnet, a paper drinking cup, and 50 cm of insulated wire. Have students assist in constructing the radio. Have several students assist in constructing the loudspeaker. Have a student make a diagram of the loudspeaker on the board.

► Make ten pencil-width turns in the wire and glue the coil to the outside bottom of the cup. Open the radio and attach the free ends of the wire to the leads for the earphone jack.

► Have students describe what happens as you move the magnet close to, then away from the wire coil. (Sound from the radio will be amplified by the paper cup.)

► Discuss the intensity and the quality of the sound.

Answer to Link

Unwanted signals are also amplified. Also, the amplifying equipment can distort the original signal.

 The Living Textbook:
Physical Science Sides 1-4

Chapter 14   Frame 02305
Electric Guitar (1 Frame)
Search:

TEACH ▪ *Continued*

Skills WorkOut

To help students learn about the development of semiconductors, have them do the Skills WorkOut. **Answer** Semiconductors were developed in the early part of the century, but they were not used extensively until the 1950s.

Reteach

Have students turn to the Periodic Table of the Elements on pages 634 and 635 of the Data Bank. Ask, How do the positions of arsenic and gallium compare? (Gallium is a metal that tends to lose electrons, and arsenic is a nonmetal that tends to gain electrons.)

Directed Inquiry

Have students study the text and Figure 13.4. Ask:

▶ How are the crystal structures of germanium and silicon like a rectifier? (They allow current to pass through in only one direction.)

▶ What kind of semiconductor gains electrons? (An n-type)

▶ What kind of semiconductor is a p-type semiconductor? (A semiconductor that loses electrons)

**The Living Textbook:
Physical Science Sides 1-4**

Chapter 17   Frame 03316
Semiconductor (2 Frames)
Search: Step:

**The Living Textbook:
Physical Science Sides 1-4**

Chapter 15   Frame 02562
Semiconductor Wafer (1 Frame)
Search:

Themes in Science

Scale and Structure Vacuum tubes vary in size from large television screens to tiny halogen light bulbs. Transistors range in size from about 0.5 cm to 2 cm. Semiconductor devices tend to be microscopic—hundreds of circuits can fit on a surface smaller than the eye of a sewing needle.

Integrating the Sciences

Life Science Advise students that many life-saving devices, such as the heart pacemaker, depend on electronics. Ask students to find out what simple electronic device is included in an implantable pacemaker. (Pacemakers include amplifiers to strengthen signals.)

▼ ACTIVITY

Communicating

Dopey Devices

Research the development of semiconductors. When were they developed and how were they used?

SKILLS WORKOUT

Semiconductors

Today most electronic devices use semiconducting materials to control electrons. A **semiconductor** is a substance that has a conductivity range between that of a conductor and that of an insulator. Like vacuum tubes, semiconductors are used to amplify currents. Semiconductors have several advantages over vacuum tubes. They are much smaller and give off less heat than vacuum tubes do. Semiconductors also last longer, cost less, use less electricity, and are very durable.

You know that the difference between a conductor and an insulator depends on how electrons move through them. The elements germanium and silicon have crystal structures that cause them to act like diodes. Current passes easily through these elements in one direction only. The conductivity of germanium and silicon increases when a small number of their atoms are replaced with a different kind of atom, called an impurity. Small amounts of these impurities add or remove electrons from the crystal structure of a substance.

Two different types of semiconductors being manufactured are shown in Figure 13.4. The difference between them is the type of impurity used. If the impurity is arsenic, which adds electrons, the semiconductor is called a negative-type, or n-type, semiconductor. If the impurity is gallium, which leaves a lack of electrons in the semiconductor, it becomes slightly positively charged. This is called a positive-type, or p-type, semiconductor. Thin layers of n-type and p-type semiconducting materials sandwiched together make up transistors. Transistors and integrated circuits use semiconducting material.

Figure 13.4
Adding impurities to semiconductors to increase their conductivity is called doping. ▼

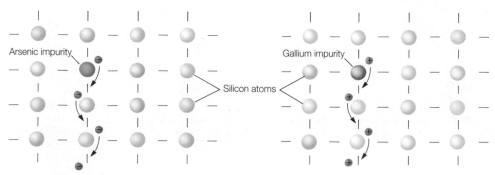

N-type semiconductor

P-type semiconductor

Cooperative Learning

Have students work in cooperative groups of three to find out more about the manufacture of integrated circuits. Groups may choose topics such as, How pure must semiconductors be? Or, How is the complex circuitry applied to a chip? (Impurities in a semiconductor must be less than one part per billion; drawings of circuitry are reduced using the equivalent of a photocopier, and then they are chemically etched onto a treated silicon chip.)

Transistors A semiconducting device that contains layered n-type and p-type semiconducting materials is called a **transistor**. A transistor has three semiconducting sections. Each section is treated with a different impurity. Small wires attached to the layers conduct electricity in and out. The middle portion, called the base, is usually about 0.001 cm thick. The semiconductors on either side of the base are called the emitter and the collector. Weak signals pass through the transistor and are amplified. Today engineers can put more than 100,000 transistors on a silicon chip. A typical chip is about the size of a fingernail!

The commercial use of transistors began in the early 1950s. They were used as amplifiers in hearing aids and pocket radios. By the 1960s, diodes and semiconducting amplifiers had replaced vacuum tubes in many kinds of electronic equipment. In the 1990s, you have transistors in your radio, stereo, and pocket calculator. Some different kinds of transistors are shown in Figure 13.5.

Integrated Circuits A recent breakthrough in electronics is the development of miniaturized circuits. These tiny circuits are called **integrated circuits**. An integrated circuit consists of a tiny semiconductor crystal, or silicon chip, which is razor thin. This single silicon chip contains extremely small amounts of impurities placed at specific locations. Transistors, diodes, resistors, and other circuit elements are constructed at these locations.

Connections between these circuit elements are made by painting "wires" on the chip. It is possible to create a complicated electronic network within a very small area. Wires also connect the integrated circuit to other devices. A small portion of an integrated circuit, or chip, is shown in Figure 13.6.

Integrated circuits have greatly reduced the size of electronic instruments and have revolutionized our way of life. Integrated circuits are much smaller and lighter than wired circuits and are often substituted for them. Home computers, digital watches, spacecraft, and calculators all use integrated circuits.

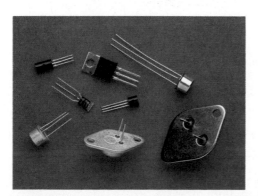

Figure 13.5 ▲
Transistors come in a variety of shapes and sizes. How are these transistors alike? How are they different?

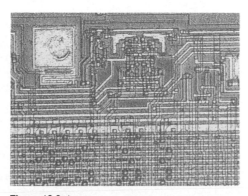

Figure 13.6 ▲
This small portion of an integrated circuit contains 1,000 electronic devices. It is about the size of a baby's fingernail.

Discuss

Have students discuss the following questions:

▶ What kinds of plastic cards could one smart card replace? (All the other identification, ATM, phone-calling, and credit cards people usually have)

▶ When a purchase is made with a smart card, where is a record of the transaction stored? (In the smart card's chip)

EVALUATE

WrapUp

Review Have students make diagrams of the current-controlling or signal-producing devices discussed in this section. Then ask them to list items they use every day that rely on these devices. Have them match the "parts" with the "whole."

Use Review Worksheet 13.1.

Check and Explain

1. Electronic devices use electric current to carry information in the form of signals.

2. A grid placed between the filament and the plate is positively charged. As the plate attracts electrons, the beam gets stronger and the signal is amplified.

3. Semiconductors are a great deal smaller and lighter in weight. Semiconductors give off less heat, cost less, use less electricity, and are more durable than earlier vacuum tubes.

4. In vacuum tubes, electrons move from the negative filament to a positive plate. In semiconductors, electrons move from one atom to an adjacent atom.

314

Cooperative Learning

Have a debate on the topic of smart cards. Students may work in cooperative groups to present different views of smart cards: One team might represent consumers and their concerns about cards and privacy. Another team might describe what companies should do to increase the security of the cards they issue.

Figure 13.7 ▲
A smart card is like an ATM card and a credit card, but can do more.

Microchip

Science and Society *Smart Cards*

An automatic teller machine, or ATM, card and credit cards make it convenient to get cash and to make large purchases. Some people carry a dozen or more plastic cards in their wallets. The cards are easy to carry, but it can be time consuming to deal with the monthly bills for each card. Wouldn't it be more convenient to have just one card? What if it could do more than all the other cards combined?

Credit cards would be more useful if they were "smarter." "Smart cards" look like traditional credit cards but are actually miniature computers. They are composed of tiny electronic circuits, chips, and digital memories sandwiched together.

Smart cards and ATM cards are similar. When inserted into card-reader terminals, a personal identification number, or PIN, is requested. Once the PIN is approved, you tell the terminal the type of transaction you want to make.

Instead of accessing information from a central source like the ATM card does, a smart card stores the information on its own chip. When a purchase is made with a smart card, a record of the transaction is stored in the card's chip. The amount of the purchase can be automatically deducted from the holder's bank account.

In Japan and in many European countries, smart cards are already being used. Banks, transportation systems, telephones, and pay TV use smart cards. In fact, within 15 years, you will probably use a smart card almost daily to make all sorts of transactions.

Check and Explain

1. How do electronic devices use electric current?

2. How does a vacuum-tube amplifier work?

3. **Generalize** What are the advantages semiconductors have over vacuum tubes?

4. **Compare and Contrast** Describe the similarities and differences between vacuum tubes and semiconducting devices.

Multicultural Perspectives

Have students research "talking" drums used by various West African groups such as the Yoruba. Students can find the information they need in encyclopedia articles on "talking" drums or percussion instruments. Ask volunteers to demonstrate how differences in pitch are important in the "talking" drums. Ask them to compare the sounds to Morse code. (Morse code relies on frequency alone, not pitch, to transfer messages.)

13.2 Audio and Video Electronics

Objectives

▶ **Describe** how a telephone works.

▶ **Distinguish** between analog and digital signals.

▶ **Communicate** how a TV works.

▶ **Compare** sound recording techniques.

▼ **ACTIVITY**

Estimating

Audio/Video

Estimate the number of audio or video devices you use in one day. As you go through the day, make a list of the audio or video equipment you use. How close was your estimate?

SKILLS WARMUP

Whenever you watch TV, talk on the telephone, or listen to compact disks (CDs) or tapes, you are using audio and video communication. You know that audio refers to sound and video refers to pictures. Often audio and video are used together to create a sound-and-sight combination. TV combines audio and video communication.

During the past 20 years, cable TV, video cassette recorders, or VCRs, cellular phones, and video games have become commonplace. Advances in audio and video electronics are being made so rapidly that it's difficult to know what kinds of electronics people will use 20 years from now. What kind of electronic equipment do you predict will become commonplace in the next 20 years?

Audio

People have always found ways to communicate with each other over some distance. They have used drums, written letters, and even used mirrors to send messages. The development of electricity made communication rapid and reliable. In the United States, one of the first ways that people communicated over electric wires was with the telegraph. The telegraph was patented in 1844 by Samuel F. B. Morse.

Vacuum tubes improved early radios and made TV possible. Transistors made radios and TVs smaller and more sensitive. Today one of the most important audio communication devices is still the telephone. People around the world are able to communicate instantly by telephone.

Figure 13.8 ▲
The telegraph was one of the first electrical ways of sending messages. What are two ways to send electronic messages today? ①

Section Objectives
For a list of section objectives, see the Student Edition page.

Skills Objectives
Students should be able to:

Estimate the number of audio and video devices they use in a day.

Observe and describe the differences among phonograph records, sound tapes, and CDs.

Hypothesize how changing the size of graph paper squares will affect the clarity of a graph-paper picture.

MOTIVATE

Skills WarmUp

To help students understand audio and video electronics, have them do the Skills WarmUp.
Answer Answers may vary. Students will probably underestimate their use of audio and video equipment.

Misconceptions

Students may think that radio and television stations broadcast sound waves. They actually send radio waves, a form of electromagnetic energy, which travels close to the speed of light.

TEACH

Skills Development

Observe Ask: What kinds of telephones may be used in cars? How does the transmission of information differ between the phones in cars and those in most homes? (Cellular phones; they use radio waves instead of wires.)

Answer to In-Text Question
① Telephone and radio

TEACH ▪ *Continued*

Skills Development

Communicate Have students read the paragraph about the radio. Ask a volunteer to make a diagram or flowchart on the chalkboard showing how signals leave the source, travel to the receiver, are separated and amplified, and leave the radio's loudspeaker. Ask a second volunteer to use the diagram and explain the process in his or her own words.

Explore Visually

Make sure students understand that they talk into the transmitter and listen with the receiver.

▶ What are the diaphragms in the telephone? Where are they located? (They are thin, flexible steel disks that vibrate. There is one in the receiver and one in the transmitter.)

▶ What causes the diaphragm in the receiver to vibrate? (An electromagnet)

▶ What does the vibrating diaphragm in the receiver do? (It sets the air into motion and creates sound.)

▶ What happens to the signal made in the transmitter? (It is carried over wires to the receiver in another person's telephone.)

Decision Making

If you have classroom sets of *One-Minute Readings,* have students read Issue 54 "Current Electricity and the Telephone" on page 91. Discuss the questions.

The Living Textbook:
Physical Science Sides 1-4

Chapter 15   Frame 02520
Morse Code (1 Frame)
Search:

316

STS Connection

On February 14, 1876, the second patent for a telephone receiver was submitted by inventor Elisha Gray, just hours after Alexander Graham Bell applied for his patent. If not for those few hours, Western Union might be running the telephone business today. Have students write a report on how to obtain a patent, a government-issued document that gives a person or company rights over the manufacture and sale of an invention.

Multicultural Perspectives

Remind students that although Edison patented the light bulb and Bell patented the telephone, inventions and patents are often the result of several individuals' work. Have students investigate how the work of African Americans Lewis Howard Latimer and Granville T. Woods influenced each of these inventions. (Latimer improved the light bulb and Woods' designs improved sound transmission of the telephone.)

Radio When your favorite radio station broadcasts, it sends out radio waves from a transmitting antenna. The waves become a small, unsteady current, or signal, in the antenna of your radio. A receiver inside your radio picks up the signal. An amplifier in your radio strengthens the signal to separate it from the broadcasts sent by other radio stations. Another amplifier in the radio strengthens the separated signal so that it is strong enough to operate the loudspeakers in your radio.

Telephone The telephone in your home has a transmitter and a receiver. The transmitter changes sounds from your voice into a signal. The signal travels over wires to your friend's telephone. The receiver in your friend's telephone changes the signal back into sound. To see how your telephone works, look at Figure 13.9.

Figure 13.9 The Telephone ▼

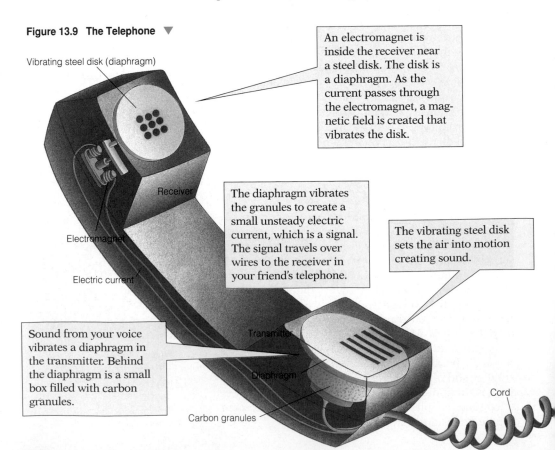

Vibrating steel disk (diaphragm)

An electromagnet is inside the receiver near a steel disk. The disk is a diaphragm. As the current passes through the electromagnet, a magnetic field is created that vibrates the disk.

Receiver

Electromagnet

The diaphragm vibrates the granules to create a small unsteady electric current, which is a signal. The signal travels over wires to the receiver in your friend's telephone.

Electric current

The vibrating steel disk sets the air into motion creating sound.

Transmitter

Sound from your voice vibrates a diaphragm in the transmitter. Behind the diaphragm is a small box filled with carbon granules.

Diaphragm

Carbon granules

Cord

Music Connection

Bring in a phonograph and records, a tape player and tapes, and a CD player and CDs to demonstrate how the quality of sound recordings has improved in the past 35 years. Actual or tape recordings of wax cylinder records will demonstrate the improvements in the past 50 to 100 years. Have students compare and discuss the sound quality and convenience of each medium.

Sound Recording Sound can be recorded in two ways, as analog or digital sound. Records and tapes are analog sound recordings. CDs are digital sound recordings.

Analog sound recording is a process of engraving a tape or record with waves that represent the structure of the sound. To make a record, the sound is first recorded on a stereo master tape. A metal stereo master disk is made from the tape. To make the master disk, electric signals representing sounds are sent from the tape to a sharp recording cutter. The cutter engraves a wavy groove in a plastic-coated metal disk. The pattern of the groove determines the sounds recorded on the record. Plastic copies are made from the master disk.

Digital sound recording is a process of etching microscopic pits on the underside of an aluminum and plastic disk. Pitted regions represent 0s. Regions without pits represent 1s. A laser beam scans the disk. The 0s and 1s form a digital signal. A resistor in the CD player converts the digital recording into an analog signal. The analog signal is amplified and played back through loudspeakers.

The quality of the music produced by digital sound recording is much better than the quality of music on records or cassette tapes. Unlike a record or tape that uses a needle or magnetic head to pick up signals, light is the only thing that touches the CD. Therefore, the

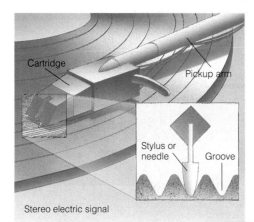

Figure 13.10 ▲
When the stylus rides in the record's groove an analog signal is produced.

Cartridge / Pickup arm / Stylus or needle / Groove / Stereo electric signal

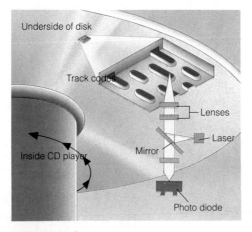

Figure 13.11 ▲
When the laser scans the underside of the CD, a digital signal is produced.

Underside of disk / Track codes / Lenses / Laser / Inside CD player / Mirror / Photo diode

TEACH ▪ *Continued*

Skills Development

Estimate Have students estimate how many hours a day they sit in front of a CRT. Remind them that computers as well as televisions have CRTs. Then have students keep a CRT diary for a week that shows how many hours they actually spend in front of a CRT. Have them indicate how much time is for homework, television, and video games. (Most students will spend over three hours a day looking at a CRT.)

Research

Have students check recent periodicals to learn about some of the potential health risks associated with CRTs and video display terminals (VDTs). Ask them what they can do to protect themselves from the risks associated with CRTs. (Answers will vary, but students should mention decreasing the time they spend in front of CRTs.)

Answer to In-Text Question

① Signal from a TV antenna passes through a tuner and decoder and instructs three electron guns in the CRT to shoot electron beams at the fluorescent screen. The beams sweep across the screen's inner surface and produce the picture.

The Living Textbook: Physical Science Sides 1-4

Chapter 15　　　Frame 02504
Cathode Ray Tubes (14 Frames)
Search:　　　　Step:

The Living Textbook: Physical Science Sides 1-4

Chapter 15　　　Frame 02522
Picture Tube Diagram (1 Frame)
Search:

Portfolio

Have students use a variety of sources to make a timeline of television technology. Ask them to include dates for events, such as the invention of television, television's first broadcast in the United States, the first commercial television broadcast, the first commercial color transmission, and the invention of video players. Have students illustrate their timelines with the names or pictures of famous TV shows or personalities.

Answer to Link

Answers will vary. Generally, the reception on the nice day should have been much better than the reception on the stormy day. Bad weather disturbs transmitted signals as they travel through the air making reception more difficult. The transmitted signals are distorted and scattered more during bad weather.

Meteorology LINK

Weather conditions greatly affect how well audio and video signals can be received. To explore how weather affects transmitted signals, you need either a television that is hooked up to an antenna, or a radio.

1. On a clear, calm day see how many channels or stations your device receives. Describe the quality of each channel or station.

2. Repeat the above step on a stormy, rainy day.

Compare your observations on the two different days. Explain the effect of weather on transmitted signals.

ACTIVITY

Figure 13.12
How does the CRT create a picture from an electric signal? ▼
①

surface of a CD doesn't scratch or wear down. The two-hundredth play of the CD is as good as the first play. The music played from a CD is free of the pops, crackles, and hisses you might hear on a record or tape.

CDs can be played in cars just like audio tapes. Automobile CD players have an extra track on each side of the main track. This extra track helps to keep the laser light focused when the car hits a bump.

Video

Video communication technology began with the type of vacuum tube called the **c**athode-**r**ay **t**ube, or CRT. A CRT is a large vacuum tube that contains an electron source at one end and a fluorescent screen at the other end. The picture tube used in TVs, in computer display terminals, and in oscilloscopes is a CRT.

Television When you watch TV, you are looking at a CRT. The diagram in Figure 13.12 shows how a TV picture is created. A video signal is received from a TV antenna. The signal passes through a tuner and decoder and instructs three electron guns in the CRT to shoot electron beams at the screen. The beams sweep across the screen's inner surface the same way your eyes sweep across each line on this page.

The inside of the screen has tiny circles of fluorescent

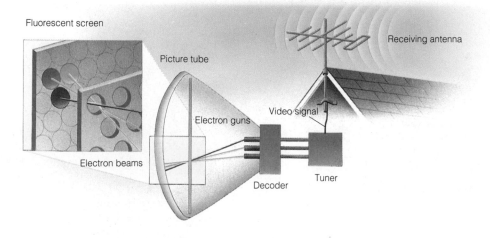

Fluorescent screen
Picture tube
Receiving antenna
Electron guns
Video signal
Electron beams
Decoder
Tuner

Cooperative Learning

Ask students to work cooperatively to create a taped video performance about one or more inventors, such as John Ambrose Fleming, Lee De Forest, and Vladimir Zworykin, whose work influenced television. Students may form four groups as they work on the assignment. One group might research the inventors and their inventions; the second group could use the research to write an outline or script for the videotape; the third group could be the actors in the presentation; and the fourth group could direct and tape the presentation. Allow time for the class to watch the taped video performance.

material that give off red, green, and blue lights. Three electron beams, one for each primary color, scan across the shadow mask behind the screen. The mask contains holes. The beams pass through the holes and strike the stripes of fluorescent material. Each beam strikes only circles of the correct color. The circles light up as each beam passes. The brightness of the circles depends on the strength of the beam. The information for controlling and directing the beams is coded within the color picture signal.

Video Recording VCRs can record TV programs on a video cassette so you can watch them at any time. Audio and video signals that represent the TV show are transferred to videotape. The audio and video signals from a TV station go to audio and video heads inside your VCR. The signals create changing magnetic fields in the heads. The video tape contains magnetic particles on its surface. As the video tape passes over the heads, the mag-

Consider This

Do Computer Networks Invade Your Privacy?

Computers offer you many advantages. They can store enormous amounts of information for you and about you. They will play an even larger role in your life in the future.

Computers from banks, stores, medical facilities, and insurance and government agencies store information about you. These computers are linked together. Computers that are linked together form computer networks. These networks make it easy to identify you in an emergency or when you use your credit card.

Computer networks also have disadvantages. The biggest concern is privacy. By storing your personal information on computer networks, many people have access to information that could be used against you. Advertisers, insurance agents, politicians, and many other groups of people would be interested in knowing what you buy, the state of your health, who you call on the telephone, and other information about you. How might personal information be used against you?

Do you think that the increased convenience provided by computer networks is worth the risk of having your personal privacy invaded?

Think About It An insurance company finds out through a computer network that you have a family history of heart disease. Should the company be allowed to deny you medical insurance even though you seem perfectly healthy?

Write About It Pretend you are a U.S. senator. Write a report in which you: (a) Identify the issue of having personal information stored on computer networks. (b) Write a law that would minimize the problem.

Skills Development

Infer If a TV has a color fluorescent screen, it has circles or clusters of fluorescent material that give off red, green, and blue light. Ask, Why are three beams of electrons needed; why not just one? Why not more than three? (One beam is needed for each primary color to scan the shadow mask for holes and strike the circles of the correct color. The primary colors are used in combinations to make up all the other colors.)

Consider This

Answer You could be denied a job, credit, or benefits due to you.
Consider Some Issues Answers will vary. Some people would not mind having their privacy invaded in this way, but others would strongly object.
Think About It Answers will vary, but most people would say that the company should not deny you medical insurance.
Write About It Answers will vary, but students should identify the issue and write a simple law that restricts the information available on a person.

Enrich

Use Enrich Worksheet 13.2.

 **The Living Textbook:
Physical Science Sides 1-4**

Chapter 15   Frame 02518
Mini Television (1 Frame)
Search:

EVALUATE

WrapUp

Reteach Have the class form teams of four. Ask one member of each group to pick a name out of a grab bag containing the names of the audio and video devices discussed in this chapter. Tell each group to make a diagram with captions to show how their device works. Have them research magazines for illustrations that show some uses of the device. Have the teams combine their work to stage an audio-visual convention for other grades or prepare a bulletin board display for the school.

Use Review Worksheet 13.2.

Check and Explain

1. Sound vibrates a diaphragm making an electric signal that travels to the diaphragm in the receiving telephone, which converts the signal back into sound.

2. Analog signals are formed by the engraving or grooves on a tape or record. Digital signals are formed by the pitted or unpitted regions on a disk.

3. A signal from the TV antenna passes through a tuner and instructs electron guns to shoot electron beams at the screen.

4. Analog: an engraved surface represents the structure of sound; digital: pitted and unpitted regions represent digital information.

 The Living Textbook: Physical Science Sides 1-4

Chapter 13   Frame 02242
Laser Player Diagram (1 Frame)
Search:

STS Connection

If possible, use a CD-ROM player connected to a personal computer to show a multimedia application of the technology. After students have seen how CD-ROM works, suggest that they design their own multimedia application for CD-ROM. Their application should include video, film or animation, sound, graphics, photos, and writing. Have students share their ideas with the class.

netic fields change the patterns of the magnetic particles on the tape. The pattern of the magnetic particles recorded on the video tape corresponds to the TV signals. The audio and video signals are magnetically recorded in diagonal tracks on the videotape.

To replay the video tape, it is reversed through the heads of a VCR. The heads convert the magnetic recordings on the video tape to audio and video signals. These signals are sent to a TV and changed back into sounds and pictures.

Science and Technology *CD-ROM*

Compact Disc-Read-Only Memory systems, or CD-ROM, is a technology that you may use at home or in your classroom. A CD-ROM system is a product that uses the visuals of a TV, the control of a computer, and the sound capability of a CD player. The system includes a disc, a player, and a computer or television.

CD-ROM is a multi-media technology. Each medium is digitized so a computer can understand and control it. A program can jump back and forth between video, film, CD-quality sound, graphics, animation, photos, and text.

Perhaps the most exciting thing about CD-ROM is that it is interactive. The user controls the action, or information. The interactive feature makes it an easy way to learn about or to do almost anything. By touching the screen with your finger, or moving a "mouse," you can interrupt the program, go instantly back to any previous spot, or explore a concept in more detail. You can manipulate the information in many ways to match your learning style. CD-ROM is already used in industry, entertainment, and education.

Check and Explain

1. Describe how a telephone works.

2. How are analog and digital signals different?

3. **Communicate** How does a color television form a picture?

4. **Compare and Contrast** How do sound recording techniques differ for records and CDs?

Prelab Discussion

As part of a homework assignment, have students bring in a color picture from a magazine showing a simple image. Have students read the entire activity before discussing the following:

▶ Ask students if they have ever examined a television picture or a magazine picture with a hand lens or microscope. Have them describe what it looks like.

▶ Have students predict how the image in their drawings might look when seen from a distance.

Time 60 minutes   **Group** 1–2

Materials

magazines

tracing graph paper

tape

colored pencils or pens

Analysis

1. It is likely that the pictures will look most similar at the farthest distance, because the human eye has a limited ability to resolve small details at a distance.

2. Decreasing the size of the squares would increase the clarity of the picture.

Conclusion

Conclusions should follow from students' actual observations. In general, the closer you are, the smaller the dots need to be for the picture to be clear. Larger dots are sufficient if the picture is to be viewed from far away. A stadium scoreboard is an example of this phenomenon.

Extension

Newspaper and TV pictures are both made up of individual dots of varying size and color. However, magazines use much smaller dots and can vary the size of the dots. (Examples can be seen in most newspapers. Students should notice that the magazine picture has smaller dots and is better for detail. It is clearer when viewed at close range.)

Activity 13 *How are dots used to make pictures?*

Skills Hypothesize; Infer; Observe; Compare and Contrast

Task 1 Prelab Prep

Collect the following items: a large, simple color picture from a magazine, a piece of "tracing" graph paper, tape, and colored pencils or pens.

Task 2 Data Record

Construct a table like Table 13.1.

Table 13.1 Dot picture observation

Distance	Observation
1 m	
3 m	
5 m	
7 m	
9 m	

Task 3 Procedure

1. Discuss with a classmate how you think newspaper and television pictures are made. Give reasons why you think so.
2. Write down your hypothesis.
3. Tape a piece of graph paper over the magazine picture.

4. Color each small square on the graph paper entirely with the one color that best matches the color of the picture underneath the square.
5. Repeat this process until each square is colored.
6. You now have two 8 1/2″ × 11″ pictures: the original magazine picture and your copy of it made with colored squares. Hang both pictures next to each other on a wall or bulletin board.
7. Compare the graph-paper picture to the original picture at the following distances. Briefly describe your observations in your table.
   a) 1 m
   b) 3 m
   c) 5 m
   d) 7 m
   e) 9 m

Task 4 Analysis

1. At what distance do the two pictures look most similar? Why?
2. How would increasing or decreasing the size of the graph-paper squares affect the clarity of the graph-paper picture?

Task 5 Conclusion

Explain how pictures are made from tiny dots or squares. Discuss how your distance from the dot picture and the size of the dots affect how clear the picture appears.

Extension

Use a magnifying glass to look closely at a newspaper picture. If a TV is available in your classroom, use a magnifying glass to look at the screen. How are newspaper and TV pictures similar to your graph picture? How are they different? How do TV and newspaper pictures compare to the magazine picture?

13.3

Section Objectives
For a list of section objectives, see the Student Edition page.

Skills Objectives
Students should be able to:

Relate Concepts by giving the advantages and disadvantages of calculators.

Make a Model of a flowchart used in a software program.

Collect Data about software programs.

Classify a list of items as being hardware or software.

Vocabulary
microprocessor, hardware, software

MOTIVATE

Skills WarmUp
To help students understand the advantages of computers, have them do the Skills WarmUp.
Answer Students' times will vary but using a calculator should be faster. Advantages listed by students might include accuracy and speed, while disadvantages might include possibility of error when entering numbers, and dependence on calculators.

Prior Knowledge
Gauge how much students know about computers by asking the following questions:

▶ How does a computer differ from a calculator?

▶ Name some things computers are used for.

▶ How is computer hardware different from software?

Answer to In-Text Question
① **Vacuum tubes were replaced with microprocessors, which are integrated circuits.**

INTEGRATED LEARNING

Social Studies Connection
Census-taking is an activity that dates back to Roman times. Have students do research to find out when the first U.S. census took place, how the information was first recorded, and how long it took to process the information. Some students might prepare graphs that show how the process of collecting, analyzing, and storing information has been improved over the years, and how the needs of the Census Bureau affected the development of computers. Have students present some of the uses for the information gathered during a census. Students can find information in encyclopedia articles, specialized books, or from the United States Census Bureau publications in the local library.

▼ ACTIVITY

Relating Concepts

Long Multiplication

Time how long it takes to multiply 4,562 by 9,483 without using a calculator. How long does it take to multiply the same numbers with a calculator? What are some advantages and disadvantages of calculators?

SKILLS WARMUP

Figure 13.13
The ENIAC computer was made using vacuum tubes. What kind of material replaced vacuum ① tubes in modern computers? ▼

13.3 Computers

Objectives

▶ **Identify** the parts of a computer.

▶ **Compare** the advantages and disadvantages of computer networks.

▶ **Classify** parts of a computer as hardware or software.

Many business transactions involve computers. When you buy groceries or check a book out of your library, the transaction is recorded in a computer. Business, government, medicine, science, and most industries rely heavily on computers. Computers are used to diagnose diseases, guide spaceships, forecast weather, and make music. They make robots move and even design new computers. Recent advances in microelectronics allow smaller and more powerful computers to be built.

Development of Computers

In the 1890s, American inventor Dr. Herman Hollerith developed the "census machine." This device was the first computer to use electricity. The 1890 U.S. census was completed in a record time of three years. In 1946 the United States Army built the Electronic Numerical Integrator and Computer, or ENIAC. Not much more than a gigantic calculator, ENIAC contained thousands of vacuum tubes and used punched tape or cards that carried information. In 1951, the stored-program computer called the Universal Automatic Computer, or UNIVAC, was completed. UNIVAC was the first computer to use magnetic tape instead of punched tape or cards for information input.

As technology developed, computers became smaller, more compact, more versatile, and less expensive. Today computers are made with **microprocessors**. A microprocessor is an integrated circuit that can hold all of a computer's problem-solving capabilities on one small silicon chip.

Computer Hardware

Computer **hardware** is the equipment and components that make up the computer. Hardware, as shown in Figure 13.14, includes a central processing unit, main storage, input devices, and output devices.

CPU The actual computing is done in the central processing unit, or CPU. An important part of the CPU is a microprocessor. The microprocessor is a chip, which stores permanent and short-term memory.

Main Storage Main storage hardware holds the information that you input, and saves it for future use. Main storage includes both hard disks and floppy disks. Both hard and floppy disks store information magnetically.

The hard disk contains very large amounts of information and is permanently sealed inside the computer's casing. On the hard disk, information is stored magnetically.

Information can also be stored magnetically on a floppy disk, which is a smaller round tape encased in a small, plastic cassette. A floppy disk can be carried in a pocket and used in any compatible computer. A floppy disk stores less information than a hard disk.

Input devices Hardware that is used to load information into the computer is called an input device. The most common input device is the keyboard. A "mouse" is an input device that rolls over a pad. The mouse moves a cursor around the screen, open files, and chooses commands. You can input information into some computers with an electronic pen, also. Some computers even respond to a human voice.

Output device An output device receives information from the CPU. Examples include the computer screen and printer. A voice synthesizer and a robot that receives instructions from a computer are also output devices.

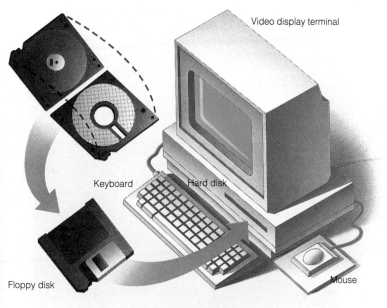

Video display terminal

Keyboard Hard disk

Floppy disk

Mouse

◀ **Figure 13.14**
A hard disk is built into many personal computers. How is a hard disk different from a floppy disk? ②

TEACH ▪ *Continued*

Enrich

Explain to students that spreadsheet programs are often used for financial accounting and inventory control. For example, a bookstore may use a program that identifies a book, records its selling and purchase price, and keeps track of its sales. The spreadsheet program keeps this information current for all of the books in the store.

Skills Development

Infer Have students consider the advantages of using virtual reality during medical training. What would be the advantages of allowing medical students to view three-dimensional images of body parts? (Students could study the body parts closely before doing any laboratory work.)

Answer to In-Text Question

① **The software program on page 324 and the flowchart shown in the SkillBuilder on page 325 both deal with the same computer task.**

**The Living Textbook:
Physical Science Sides 1-4**

Chapter 15   Frame 02552
BASIC Program (1 Frame)
Search:

**The Living Textbook:
Physical Science Sides 1-4**

Chapter 15   Frame 02556
Computer Graphics (3 Frames)
Search: Step:

324

Writing Connection

Have students write advertisements for a new computer program that is voice-activated. It will keep track of homework assignments, practice schedules, and sports scores, and will organize any information you want. It is inexpensive to own and operate and runs on any computer. Students may use drawings in their advertisements.

Integrating the Sciences

Meteorology Tell students that computer programs exist that forecast the weather. These programs can take information about high- and low-pressure systems, wind speeds, and precipitation, and create weather models. The models are used in research and forecasting. Have students watch TV weather reports or collect weather data from a newspaper. Ask them if they can tell what information was taken from a computer model.

```
100 REM THIS PROGRAM
    WILL GREET YOU BY
    NAME
110 REM N$ = YOUR NAME
120 PRINT "WHAT IS YOUR
    NAME?"
130 INPUT N$
140 PRINT "HELLO"; N$
150 END
```

Figure 13.15 ▲
The simple numbered statements shown are a program for printing your name. How does this program relate to the flowchart on the next page? ①

Computer Software

In order for a computer to operate, it needs a set of instructions that tells it exactly what to do. Programs that instruct the hardware during operation are called **software**. There are two different types of software: applications software and operating-system software. Neither one can function effectively without the other.

Applications software allows you to perform specific tasks without having to write the programs yourself. It is provided by the computer manufacturer or can be purchased from a computer store. Video games are an example of applications software.

Operating-system software is a set of instructions that command the electronic parts inside the computer. The instructions tell the computer to operate in a specific way and to accept instructions from the applications software. Working together, the two programs provide the specific results you desire when you operate the computer.

Thousands of applications-software programs are available for computers. You can create your own computer programs, or you can buy ready-made ones. Packaged programs available for computers include adventure games, spreadsheets, and word-processing programs. Word-processing programs allow you to write essays and stories on a computer. A program is usually saved on a hard disk or on a floppy disk.

As computer technology increases, more highly specialized computer hardware and software are being developed. Virtual reality shown in Figure 13.16, will soon be used in medicine, industry, and entertainment. Interactive video is another new technology that involves video, CD, and computer technologies.

Figure 13.16 ▶
Virtual reality combines computer software and special hardware to create realistic images. This photo shows what you would see if you were looking through the virtual-reality hardware.

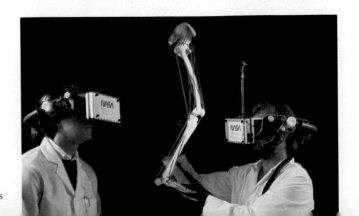

Math Connection

Have students do a computer census. For a two-week period they should list all the situations in which they either directly or indirectly use computers or computer networks. Ask students to organize the information into a bar graph that shows how many times a day they use a computer. They can also organize the information into a circle graph showing where they most frequently use computers.

Integrating the Sciences

Geography Computers used for spacecraft navigation have helped discover that some small landmasses are located incorrectly on maps. Have students use an atlas to locate the Marshall and Gilbert Islands. Ask why islands this size might be incorrectly placed on a map.

Skills Development

Infer Have students consider this question, What are the main advantages of linking computers together by telephone? (People can save time and share information. Information can be transmitted worldwide.)

SkillBuilder

Answers

1. Check students' drawings for accuracy.

2. Students might frame questions such as: How old are you? What year is this? How many people are in your class?

3. Students' charts should show a print command for the answer to question 2.

4. You might suggest questions like: Do you like ice cream? Are you feeling well? Can you finish the flowchart?

Computer Networks

One of the fastest-growing areas in communication involves computers linked together so that people can communicate with each other. You can link two computers together by telephone. To do this, you need a hardware device called a "modem" and special communications software.

When a number of computers are linked together, they form a network. When the computers are linked together in the same room or building, a local-area network, or LAN, is formed. LANs connect computers with cables or wires.

In a LAN, one powerful central computer is connected to many smaller computers. Schools and businesses often use this type of network to save time and share data files and programs. Networks can be expanded into global networks that connect computer users by telephone lines and satellites. Global networks allow information to be sent from city to city, across the nation, and to other countries throughout the world.

SkillBuilder *Making Models*

Flowcharting

Software programs tell your computer what to do with the information you input. Computer programmers use flowcharts to plan their programs. A flowchart is a diagram of a program. The flowchart on the right shows a program to print your name. The table beside the flowchart explains the meaning of each shape that is used in a flowchart. In this *SkillBuilder*, you will practice writing a flowchart.

Draw a flowchart for a program that asks for a number and prints it on the screen. Follow the steps below.

1. Draw an oval with the word *Start* in it. Draw an arrow pointing downward from the oval to the next step.

2. Draw a parallelogram below the arrow. Write a statement in it that asks for a specific number. Draw an arrow pointing downward from the parallelogram.

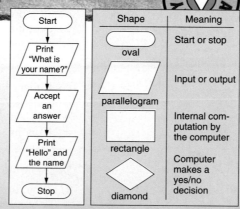

Shape	Meaning
oval	Start or stop
parallelogram	Input or output
rectangle	Internal computation by the computer
diamond	Computer makes a yes/no decision

3. Draw another parallelogram that asks the computer to print the number on the screen. Draw an arrow downward to the next step.

4. Draw an oval with the word *Stop* in it. Look at your flowchart. It should look similar to the one above. Draw a flowchart that asks you to make a yes or no decision.

 The Living Textbook: Physical Science Sides 1-4

Chapter 15   Frame 02553
Network Facility (1 Frame)
Search:

TEACH ▪ *Continued*

Skills WorkOut

To help students collect data about software programs, have them do the Skills WorkOut.

Answers Answers will vary depending on the newspaper or the type of magazine. Students might see that the prime function of most programs in children's magazines is games. In adults' magazines, the prime function of the programs might be forming a database or financial or information programs.

EVALUATE

WrapUp

Portfolio Ask each student to design his or her own ideal computer. Remind them to consider the type of input and output devices the computer would use, how much data it could store, the kinds of information it would access, and the kinds of tasks its software would perform. Have students use drawings as well as written descriptions to illustrate their ideas. Students may add their computer ideas to their portfolios.

Use Review Worksheet 13.3.

Check and Explain

1. CPU, main storage, input and output devices

2. Applications such as operating systems that tell the computer how to operate, and application software, such as spreadsheets

3. Advantages: link computers together and share data; disadvantages: special software is needed and the potential loss of privacy

4. Software: word processing programs, video games; hardware: keyboard, disk, printer, modem

---

Writing Connection

Ask students to write a short story about the life of a laptop, told from the computer's perspective. Their stories should mention who uses the laptop, how it is used, and where it goes. It should include how people react to the laptop, and the dangers it might face in its daily work. Ask students to make the laptop's personality an important element of the story.

▼ ACTIVITY

Collecting Data

Prime Programs

Locate the software ads in a newspaper or magazine. Make a list of the software programs in five ads. Which software programs are advertised the most? What is the prime function of most of the programs in the ads?

SKILLS WORKOUT

Science and You
Laptops: The Book of the Future

Computers are getting smaller and smarter! Imagine yourself in science class five years from now. Your teacher asks you to take out your textbook. Instead of a book, you place a small computer on your lap. The teacher asks you to read page 326. You type in *Science* and *page 326*. The text on page 326 instantly appears on the computer screen.

Next the teacher wants you to take some lecture notes. You press several keys, and a new page appears. The new page has the words *Science Notes* and the date on the top of the page. As your teacher delivers the lecture, you take notes on your computer. This kind of computer, called a laptop computer, is already being used worldwide by many business people and some students.

Laptops are personal computers that operate on rechargeable batteries. Because they can fit into a small briefcase, they are commonly used by traveling business people. Travelers can prepare and even print out reports while flying to a meeting. In their parked cars, sales representatives may use laptops to review information about a prospective client before making the sales call. Can you name some other professions or situations where a laptop computer would be useful?

New advances in computer technology, such as smaller and more powerful microprocessing chips, make laptop computers more convenient and useful. Many laptop computers can print documents. Special built-in hardware called a modem allows laptops to send faxes from a telephone.

Check and Explain

1. What are the main hardware components of a computer?

2. What are the two types of software? Give examples of each.

3. **Compare** What are the advantages and disadvantages of a computer network?

4. **Classify** Identify each of the following as hardware or software: word-processing program, keyboard, hard disk, printer, video game, modem.

Chapter 13 Review

Concept Summary

13.1 Electronic Devices
▶ Electronic devices use electric current to carry information as a signal.
▶ Electronic devices are made of vacuum tubes or semiconductors.
▶ Amplifiers increase the strength of a signal.
▶ Rectifiers change alternating current to direct current.
▶ Semiconductors act like diodes and contain impurities to increase their conductivity.

13.2 Audio and Video Electronics
▶ Sound and visual images are used in audio and video communication.

▶ Phonograph records, as well as audio and video tape recordings, use analog signals.
▶ To make sound, CDs use digital signals, which consist of many different combinations of 0s and 1s.

13.3 Computers
▶ Computer hardware is the equipment used in a computer system.
▶ A computer software program gives instructions to the computer hardware during operation.
▶ A network is formed when computers are linked together.

Chapter Vocabulary

electronics (p. 309)   rectifier (p. 310)   integrated circuit (p. 313)   hardware (p. 323)

vacuum tube (p. 310) semiconductor (p. 312) microprocessor (p. 322)   software (p. 324)

diode (p. 310)   transistor (p. 313)

Check Your Vocabulary

Use the vocabulary words above to complete the following sentences correctly.

1. A CPU, main storage, input devices, and output devices are all ____ .

2. A device that contains thin layers of semiconducting materials sandwiched together is called a(n) ____ .

3. Electronic devices first used ____ to control electrons.

4. A(n) ____ has a conductivity range between that of a conductor and an insulator.

5. Computer programs called ____ instruct hardware during operation.

6. An integrated circuit that holds all a computer's problem-solving capabilities on one silicon chip is called a(n) ____ .

7. The specialized field of ____ deals with the behavior and control of electric currents.

8. The first vacuum tube developed for commercial use was the two-electrode tube called a(n) ____ .

9. To convert alternating current to direct current, an appliance uses an electronic device called a(n) ____

10. A single silicon chip called a(n) ____ contains transistors, diodes, resistors, and other circuit elements.

Write Your Vocabulary

Write sentences using each vocabulary word above. Show that you know what each word means.

Check Your Knowledge

1. A rectifier converts alternating current into direct current.

2. The diaphragm in the transmitter converts sounds into electrical signals that are sent out over the phone lines. The diaphragm in the speaker turns electrical signals coming in over the phone wires into sound.

3. Both audio tapes and video tapes store information on a tape coated with magnetized particles. An audio tape stores only sound information, while a video tape stores both sound and video information.

4. Answers will vary, but may include word processing, calculating, producing graphics, and controlling industrial machinery and robots.

5. Both a floppy disk and a hard disk have a coating that can be magnetized to store information. In a floppy disk, this coating is present on a flexible plastic disk, while in a hard disk, the coating is on a stiff metal disk.

6. Application software and operating-system software

7. Student answers will vary, but may include any input or output devices, storage devices, and the CPU.

8. Semiconductors are smaller, use less electricity, and produce less heat than vacuum tubes.

9. A vacuum-tube amplifier contains a control grid that attracts electrons from the filament when the charge on the grid is positive. The beam from the filament to the plate is continually strengthened, or amplified, as long as the control grid is positive.

10. False; analog

11. True

12. True

13. False; hard disk

14. True

15. False; information carrier

Check Your Understanding

1. A computer network can be used to send mail, to provide access to centrally located resources, to allow communication among people in different parts of the building, or to allow several people to share a limited number of resources.

2. One amplifier helps tune in the signal; another amplifier increases the signal that drives the loudspeaker.

3. a. They look like rows in a farm field.

   b. No, because the green areas do not conduct electricity.

4. The sound from a phonograph record comes from grooves that move the needle back and forth. The sound quality is affected by use and wear. The groove and/or the needle can also wear out over time. A compact disc relies on a laser to read information that has been digitally encoded, so there is no wear and no loss in quality when the player plays the music.

5. b, c, e, and f; all of these devices store information on magnetic tape. A strong external magnetic field can erase the tape.

6. A floppy disk is inexpensive and easily portable, while a hard disk is expensive and is either located inside the computer or must sit near it. A hard disk, though, can store a larger quantity of information than a floppy disk, and can access it more quickly.

7. Electronic components have become smaller, requiring a smaller quantity of raw materials. Also, they are used by more people. Mass producing a product is cheaper. They are designed to be assembled more quickly and easily, decreasing the cost of production.

Chapter 13 Review

Check Your Knowledge

Answer the following in complete sentences.

1. What is the function of a rectifier?

2. Identify the function of each part of a telephone.

3. How is an audio tape like a video tape? How is it different?

4. List three uses of computers.

5. How is a floppy disk similar to a hard disk? How is it different?

6. Name the two main types of computer software.

7. Identify three electronic devices in a computer.

8. Describe three advantages of semiconductors over vacuum tubes.

9. How does a vacuum-tube amplifier increase the strength of an electric current?

Determine whether each statement is true or false. Write *true* if it is true. If it is false, change the underlined word to make the statement true.

10. The process of engraving a tape or record with waves that represent sounds is called a <u>digital</u> sound recording.

11. Today most electronic devices use <u>semiconductors</u> to control electrons.

12. The cathode-ray tube inside a television set is a type of <u>vacuum tube</u>.

13. A <u>floppy disk</u> is permanently attached to the inside of the computer.

14. A keyboard is an example of an <u>input device</u>.

15. Electronics uses current as a <u>power source</u>.

Check Your Understanding

Apply the concepts you have learned to answer each question.

1. **Application** Describe how a computer network could be used in a business or at your school.

2. How many different kinds of amplifiers does a radio contain? Explain why each amplifier is important in a radio.

3. **Mystery Photo** The photograph on page 308 shows two 16K integrated circuits, or chips. The photograph shows the chips magnified about 50 times. The green band is the division between the two chips.

   a. What do the circuit paths on each chip look like?

   b. Will electric current flow over the green areas on the chip? Explain your answer.

4. Explain why the quality of sound on a phonograph record is different from the sound quality of a compact disk.

5. **Infer** Could information on any of the following formats be damaged by a strong magnetic field? Provide a reason for each answer.

   a. CD   d. Phonograph record
   b. Video tape   e. Floppy disk
   c. Audio tape   f. Hard disk

6. **Application** What are the advantages of a floppy disk? What are the advantages of a hard disk? Why would you want your computer to have both?

7. **Critical Thinking** Why do you think the cost of electronic components has decreased over the years?

Develop Your Skills

1. a. "Don't give up"

b. Answers will vary. Have students check the code for accuracy.

c. Answers will vary. Have students check the code for accuracy.

2. Students' flowcharts should make use of the four shapes described on page 325: oval for start and stop; parallelogram for input or output; rectangle for internal computation; diamond for a yes-no decision. Also, the flowchart should make sense.

3. a. 1801: punch cards were first used to automate textile weaving in a process invented by Joseph Marie Jacquard; 1844: telegraph invented by Morse; 1890: census machine invented by Hollerith; 1959: first patent for integrated circuit; 1960s: vacuum tubes replaced by semiconductors; 1984: Apple Macintosh introduced; 1990: four-million-bit computer chips produced.

b. Answers will vary.

Make Connections

1. Concept maps will vary. You may wish to have students do the map below. First draw the map on the board, then add a few key terms. Have students draw and complete the map.

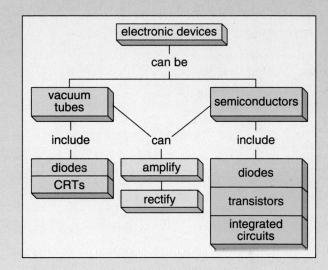

2. Reports will vary. You may wish to ask some students to share their reports with the class.

3. Census information is filled in on forms that can be read by a special scanner directly into a computer. Once in, the computer can carry out many types of analysis on the information very quickly. Census information is available to individuals on CD-ROM.

4. Some topics to suggest might be calculators, watches, radios, pocket video games, and other toys. Student research will vary. Make sure students address each question in their reports.

Develop Your Skills

Use the skills you have developed in this chapter to complete each activity.

1. Interpret Data Morse code is a system of signals that uses a code of dots and dashes to represent numbers, letters, and punctuation.

a. Translate this message:

■●● ■■■ ■● ● ■■● ●● ●●■■ ● ●●■
●■■● ■●■■●

A ●■	B ■●●●	C ■●■●	D ■●●	E ●	F ●●■●
G ■■●	H ●●●●	I ●●	J ●■■■	K ■●■	L ●■●●
M ■■	N ■●	O ■■■	P ●■■●	Q ■■●■	R ●■●
S ●●●	T ■	U ●●■	V ●●●■	W ●■■	X ■●●■
Y ■●■■	Z ■■●●	1 ●■■■■	2 ●●■■■	3 ●●●■■	4 ●●●●■
5 ●●●●●	6 ■●●●●	7 ■■●●●	8 ■■■●●	9 ■■■■●	0 ■■■■■
. ●■●■●■	, ■■●●■■	? ●●■■●●		S.O.S. ●●●■■■●●●	Start ■●■
End of Message ●■●■●		Understand ●■●			Error ●●●●●●●●

b. Write a message to a classmate. Exchange messages and translate the message you receive.

c. Write a short reply in Morse code to the message you translated.

2. Communicate Make a flowchart that shows how you get ready for school in the morning.

3. Data Bank Use the information on page 636 to answer the following questions.

a. Copy the time line onto a piece of paper; then add events you learned about in this chapter that are missing.

b. Extend the time line to show how you think computers will change in the next 5 to 20 years. Illustrate your predictions.

Make Connections

1. Link the Concepts Make a concept map to show how the following concepts from this chapter link together: electronic devices, vacuum tubes, semiconductors, diodes, CRTs, amplify, rectify, transistors, and integrated circuits.

2. Science and Media Science fiction often discusses the future and technology. Find a science fiction book at the library, or watch a science fiction show on TV. While you read or watch, keep a list of predictions that are made about advances in electronic technology. Write a brief report explaining why you think these predictions could or couldn't come true.

3. Science and Social Studies Some of the earliest computers were used in the national census. Research the current role of computers in the national census. How do computers make compiling and sorting information easier, faster, or better? What type of computers does the Census Bureau use? Is census information available to companies or the public on floppy disks?

4. Science and Society Choose one electronic device or piece of electronic equipment that has been invented or has become a common consumer item since you were born. Use the library to do research to provide the following information about the item you choose:

a. Identify the device or equipment.

b. How and when was it developed?

c. What is it used for?

d. How does it work?

e. How has it changed society?

About the Literary Work

"Genie with the Light Blue Hair" was adapted from the novel *Genie with the Light Blue Hair* by Ellen Conford, copyright 1989 by Bantam Books. Reprinted by permission of Bantam Books.

Description of Change

The excerpt was edited from a short section of the text. Deleted material recounted development of the main character, Jeannie, and her relationship with her parents.

Rationale

The excerpt focuses on thunderstorms and electrical power failure, which correlate to unit concepts of electricity, electric power, and electric currents.

Vocabulary

coincidence, rational, atmospheric, harem, turban

Teaching Strategies

Directed Inquiry

After students finish reading, discuss the story. Be sure to relate the story to the science lesson in this unit. Ask the following questions:

▶ How does electricity flow into a home? (Electric current is transmitted through a power line.)

▶ What does the loss of electricity indicate? (There has been a disruption in the electric current coming into the home.)

▶ In addition to taking out flashlights, candles, and matches, what else should Jeannie's family do? (Report the loss of electricity to their local electric utility)

Critical Thinking

Reason by Analogy Develop further the idea that the loss of electricity indicates a disruption in the flow of electric current into Jeannie's home. This break in the current could have occurred either within the home, or in an electric power line leading to Jeannie's neighborhood. Ask: How could Jeannie determine the general location of the disruption? (She could look out her window to see if lights are on in neighbors' homes, or if streetlights are on. If lights are on in her neighborhood, then the disruption occurred at Jeannie's home. If no other neighborhood lights are on, then the failure originates outside her neighborhood.)

Science and Literature Connection

Genie With the Light Blue Hair

The following excerpts are from the novel
Genie With the Light Blue Hair
by Ellen Conford

It wasn't a bad birthday as birthdays go. After dinner Uncle Rocky took me aside and slipped a ten-dollar bill into my hand. "Buy something you really like," he whispered.

Just before they left, Aunt Jean cornered me in the kitchen and tucked a twenty-dollar bill into my skirt pocket.

"I meant to put it inside the lamp, but I forgot," she said.

And then, after they left, we all watched one of my favorite movies on the VCR: *A Night at the Opera.* The Marx Brothers always make me laugh, no matter how down I am.

I had one last piece of birthday cheesecake and went up to my room.

"Close your windows," my mother said. "It's just starting to rain.". . .

Suddenly there was a tremendous clap of thunder and a bolt of lightning so bright that I could see it even through my closed eyelids.

"YIKES!" I opened my eyes. It was completely dark in my room. I blinked a couple of times, trying to see.

"Jeannie?" my father called. "Are you okay?"

"It's dark in here!"

"The lights went out. That was a close one."

Another flash of lightning lit up my room for a moment. I noticed the teapot lamp on my night table.

"Hey!" I yelled. "If someone would bring me a match I could light this stupid lamp Aunt Jean gave me. I don't think it will do any good, but . . ."

"Coming right up." A flashlight beam shone on the stairway, and my mother came into my room. . . .

"Isn't it funny," she said, "that we have a storm the day Aunt Jean gives you the lamp?"

I shrugged. "Just a coincidence."

"But what about losing the electricity? You know how unusual that is."

"It's happened before," I said. "But it will be a good thing to say in a thank-you note."

I took the lid off and struck a match. I had to reach down into the lamp because the candle was so short and stubby. I nearly burned my fingertips before the wick caught the flame. . . .

I saw a little wisp of smoke rise up from the flame. The smoke seemed to be blue. Another puff of smoke followed. They floated toward the ceiling. The second puff joined the first one, and formed what looked like a chubby, upside-down exclamation point.

"There's a rational explanation for this," I told myself. "It must be air currents, or some unusual atmospheric disturbance."

There was nothing to be afraid of. I was on my way to bed anyway. I'd just blow out the candle. . . .

I took a step toward my bed.

The upside-down exclamation point

Skills in Science

Reading Skills in Science

1. The thunderstorm caused a power failure, which caused the lights to go out; Jeannie lit her lamp, which caused the genie to appear.

2. VCR (and television), lights, lamp, flashlight

Writing Skills in Science

1. Students should describe electric lines being struck by lightning, or being knocked down by heavy rain and wind.

2. Answers may vary: Students' stories may include the genie's granting Jeannie three wishes; Jeannie helping the genie become human; or Jeannie discovering that the entire episode was actually a dream.

3. Students' descriptions should note the following: Groucho had a bushy mustache and held a cigar; Harpo had blond curly hair and was silent during their act; Chico wore a bowl-shaped hat and spoke with an Italian accent; Zeppo dressed conservatively.

Activities

Communicate Diagrams should show that electricity is generated at a power plant, flows through a step-up transformer, travels along transmission lines or underground cables to a distribution substation and a step-down transformer, through a circuit-breaker box, and into a place of residence.

Collect Data Answers may vary. Students should note how the electricity flows through their devices.

was growing. Larger. Larger. Until it was the size of an adult human. . . .

As I looked at it, I began to see a body.

I gasped. The body was blue. It had on long, billowy harem pants. And a blue vest. It was entirely blue, from the top of its turban to the tips of its pointy-slippered feet.

Now I began to see a face. It was blue also, except for a thick black moustache that looked as if it had been painted on with shoe polish, and bushy black eyebrows. It wore a pair of black-framed eyeglasses.

I could see arms. And hands, and fingers. It was holding a long, black cigar between its thumb and forefinger.

"Help," I squeaked. "Help."

But the words stuck in my throat. I was weak with fright.

The shadow tapped the cigar with its middle finger.

"Got a light?"

Skills in Science

Reading Skills in Science

1. **Find Causes** Identify the sequence of events leading from the storm to the appearance of the genie.

2. **Classify** Identify events or objects in the excerpt that require electricity.

Writing Skills in Science

1. **Find Causes** Explain how lightning can cause a home to lose its electrical power.

2. **Predict** Imagine you are in the narrator's place at the end of the excerpt. Write a short story explaining what happens next.

3. **Observe** Using pictures of the Marx Brothers, give a written description of each of the four brothers.

Activities

Communicate Research how electricity comes into a home. Make a diagram that illustrates what you learned.

Collect Data Choose a common device that uses electricity. Find out how the device works. Describe the role of electricity in its operation.

Where to Read More

More Power to You by Vicki Cobb. Boston: Little, Brown and Company, 1986. This reader-friendly text uses experiments to explain the nature of electric power.

Simple Electrical Devices by Martin J. Gutnik. New York: Franklin Watts, 1986. The clear, concise directions in this text show you how to build simple electric devices.

Introducing the Unit

Directed Inquiry

Have students examine the photograph. Ask:

▶ What causes the differences in the colors of the paints? (Paints that appear as different colors reflect different wavelengths of light.)

▶ Which paint do you think absorbs the most light? (The black paint absorbs the most light.)

▶ How is the cause of different colors like the cause of different sounds? (Both involve variations in the frequency and wavelength of a wave.)

Writing About the Photograph

Encourage students to look at the photograph and think about how different colors and different sounds affect them. Then have students write a paragraph that relates different colors to different styles of music. Remind students that there is no correct or incorrect way to relate color and sound.

U nit 5 explores the nature of waves, sound, and light. Chapter 14 describes the nature, properties, and interactions of waves, as well as the relationship between energy and waves. Wave characteristics, such as wavelength, amplitude, and frequency, are discussed. Wave reflection, refraction, diffraction, and interference are explained and illustrated. Chapter 15 describes the structure, characteristics, and motion of sound waves as they move through a medium. It also describes the measurement of the energy associated with sound waves and explains reflection, diffraction, refraction, interference, and resonance of sound. Chapter 16 describes the structure and function of the human ear and characteristics of musical sounds and noise. The chapter closes with a discussion of sound technologies, such as sonar, ultrasound, and echolocation. Chapter 17

Unit 5
Waves, Sound, and Light

Chapters

14   Waves
15   Sound
16   Using Sound
17   Light
18   Using Light

explores both the particle and the wave theory of light, in addition to light's intensity and speed. Six types of electromagnetic waves are discussed as is the relationship between light and color. The chapter closes with reflection, refraction, diffraction, and interference of light. Chapter 18 describes illuminated and luminous kinds of light and distinguishes among three kinds of artificial light. The chapter also explains the interactions of light with mirrors and with concave and convex lenses. The chapter closes with descriptions of various light technologies, such as cameras, microscopes, telescopes, lasers, and optical fibers.

Data Bank

Use the information on pages 634 to 643 to answer the questions about topics explored in this unit.

Interpreting Data

Does sound travel faster through gases or through liquids?

Calculating

How much higher is the frequency of VHF waves than the frequency of short wave radio?

Predicting

Why is the central circle in a color wheel black?

Generalizing

What types of sounds are near the pain threshold? What types are barely audible?

The photograph to the left shows pots of different colors of paint. Name some colors you could make by blending the paints.

Data Bank Answers

Have students search the Data Bank on pages 634 to 643 for the answers to the questions on this page.

Interpreting Data Sound travels faster through liquids. The answer is found in the chart, Speed of Sound, on page 640.

Extension Encourage students to find out the speed of light and compare it to the speed of sound. (Light travels at 299 798 km/s, which is close to a million times faster than the speed of sound, which travels at 0.331 km/s through air at 0°C.)

Calculating The frequency of VHF waves is higher than the frequency of short-wave radio waves. The answer is found in the chart, Radio-Band Frequencies, on page 638.

Predicting Black is made of all colors. The answer is found in the Color Wheel on page 640.

Extension Ask students to find out what colors are the primary colors of paint and what colors are the primary colors of light. (Red, yellow, and blue are the primary colors of paint. Red, green, and blue are the primary colors of light.)

Generalizing Infrasonic waves are in or near the pain threshold. Ultrasonic waves are barely audible, or are inaudible. The answer is found in the graph, Sound Spectrum, on page 639.

Answer to In-Text Question

Mixing red and yellow would make orange; mixing yellow and blue would make green; mixing blue and red would make purple.

Overview

This chapter discusses the nature, properties, and interactions of waves. The relationship between energy and waves is described in the first section; the section also explains the different types of waves. The second section identifies the parts of waves and the wave characteristics of wavelength, amplitude, and frequency. The last section explains wave interactions, such as reflection, refraction, diffraction, and interference.

Advance Planner

▶ Collect a large coiled spring toy, paints, markers, magazines, yarn, and glitter for TE page 337.

▶ Supply rods of various materials, table-tennis balls, tubs, and heavy metal washers for SE Activity 14, page 340.

▶ Obtain a copy of Matthew Arnold's poem for TE page 344.

▶ Supply rope for TE page 348.

▶ Provide copies of artwork for TE page 349.

▶ Assemble pans, marbles, and liquids, such as molasses, corn oil, and detergent, for TE page 351.

▶ Collect yarn of different colors for TE page 352.

▶ Provide pans, sand, and a china marker for TE page 353.

Skills Development Chart

Sections	Calculate	Communicate	Compare	Infer	Interpret Data	Model	Observe
14.1 Skills WarmUp						●	
Skills WorkOut			●				
Activity				●			●
14.2 Skills WarmUp			●				
SkillBuilder					●		
Practice Problems	●						
14.3 Skills WarmUp							●
Skills WorkOut							●
Consider This		●					

Individual Needs

▶ **Limited English Proficiency Students** Have students work in cooperative groups of three. Each group should use index cards to make a deck of vocabulary cards, preparing three cards for each vocabulary term: one for the boldface term, one for the definition, and one for a diagram or drawing illustrating the term. Have groups come up with ideas for ways to use the cards—grouping the cards to match the chapter's sections, matching terms with definitions and diagrams, or picking a card and giving the information on the other two cards. Have them use these cards during their chapter review.

▶ **At-Risk Students** Have students work in groups of three or four to design wave-making machines that illustrate the concepts in 14.2 and 14.3. Give them materials such as pans of water, string, springs, pencils, stones, and rulers. If possible, students should build their machines and demonstrate them to the class. As they work, ask questions that will help students build their awareness of concepts such as wavelength, frequency, reflection, diffraction, refraction, and interference.

▶ **Gifted Students** Have students find out about seismic waves. They should explore the different kinds of waves, such as compressional, shear, Love, and Raleigh waves. Have them prepare 3-dimensional models or other displays for the class. The models should compare and contrast the mediums through which the waves travel, their relative speeds, and their effects on earth, rocks, and buildings. Ask them to use their models to identify the wavelength, amplitude, and frequency associated with each type of wave.

Resource Bank

▶ **Bulletin Board** Place four headings on the bulletin board: *Reflection, Diffraction, Refraction,* and *Interference.* Invite students to make drawings, or find and cut out photographs, that illustrate of each of these interactions. Have students make a diagram on an index card that explains a single drawing or photograph. Collect the diagrams, then have the class work together to identify which drawing or photograph is represented by each diagram. Students should attach the diagram card to the bulletin board near the drawing or photograph it explains.

Section	Core	Standard	Enriched	Section	Core	Standard	Enriched
14.1 Nature of Waves pp. 335–340				**Blackline Masters** Review Worksheet 14.2 Skills Worksheet 14.2a Skills Worksheet 14.2b	●	●	
Section Features Skills WarmUp, p. 335 Skills WorkOut, p. 337 Activity, p. 340	● ● ●	● ● ●	● ● ●	**Laboratory Program** Investigation 28	●	●	●
Blackline Masters Review Worksheet 14.1 Integrating Worksheet 14.1	●	●		**Color Transparencies** Transparencies 53a, 53b, 54	●	●	●
Color Transparencies Transparency 52	●	●	●	**14.3 Wave Interactions** pp. 348–354			
14.2 Wave Properties pp. 341–347				**Section Features** Skills WarmUp, p. 348 Skills WorkOut p.350 Consider This, p. 353	● ● ●	● ● ●	● ● ●
Section Features Skills WarmUp, p. 341 SkillBuilder, p. 345	●	● ●	● ●	**Blackline Masters** Review Worksheet 14.3 Enrich Worksheet 14.3 Vocabulary Worksheet 14	● ● ●	● ● ●	●

Bibliography

The following resources can be used for teaching the chapter. See page T-46 for supplier codes.

Library Resources

The Diagram Group. Comparisons. New York: St. Martin's Press, 1980.

Science Universe Series: Sight, Light and Color. New York: Arco Publishing, Inc., 1984.

Sherwood, Martin, and Christine Sutton. The Physical World. New York: Oxford University Press, 1988.

Technology Resources

Internet

PLANETDIARY at *http://www.planetdiary.com*
• Discover more about earthquakes in *Earthquake* by clicking on *Phenomena Backgrounders.*

Software

Experiment City. Mac, Win. ESI.
Waves. Mac, ESI.

CD-ROMs

hip Physics. Mac. ESI.
Interactive Earth. SFAW.

Laserdiscs

Living Textbook. (See barcodes on pages in this chapter.) Optical Data.
The Puzzle of the Tacoma Narrows Bridge Collapse. VID.

Videos

The Mechanical Universe: Resonance and Waves. FI.
Waves and Energy. EB.
What is a Wave? FM.

Audio-Visual Resources

Waves. Four filmstrips. EB.

Introducing the Chapter

Have students read the description of the photograph. Ask if they agree or disagree with the description.

Directed Inquiry

Have students study the photograph. Ask:

▶ What is this a photograph of? (It shows the ripples made by a drop of water that fell into a pool of still water.)

▶ What is happening to the surface of the water? (The drop striking the surface makes waves.)

▶ How would you describe these waves? (The waves spread out in a circle from where the drop hit the water.)

▶ What other kinds of matter do you think waves can move through? (Waves move through air, gases, and solids.)

Chapter Vocabulary

amplitude	reflection
compression	refraction
crest	rarefaction
diffraction	transverse wave
frequency	trough
interference	wave
longitudinal wave	wavelength

Writing Connection

Ask students to imagine that they are at a beach or lakeshore watching waves formed by wind sweeping across the water's surface, raindrops hitting the water, and fish jumping out of the water. Have them write a haiku that describes the appearance and sound of waves.

Chapter 14 Waves

Chapter Sections

14.1 Nature of Waves

14.2 Wave Properties

14.3 Wave Interactions

What do you see?

❝A drop of liquid falls into a calm pool of liquid. The impact of the drop forces it down into the pool and displaces some of the pool's liquid. Notice the rippling wave of liquid, showing the energy radiating in waves.❞

Carmen León
Shattuck Junior High
*   School*
Neenah, Wisconsin

To find out more about the photograph, look on page 356. As you read this chapter, you will learn about the properties and behavior of waves.

SECTION

14.1

Themes in Science

Energy Waves transfer energy. The wave model can be used to predict where the energy will be at a particular time, what happens as the energy moves through different media, and how the energy from two or more sources interacts. Ask students what will happen to a floating dock in the wake of a motor boat. (It will bob up and down.)

Answer to Link

Waves with a relatively short wavelength form on the surface of the water. The harder you blow, the greater the amplitude of the waves.

Section Objectives
For a list of section objectives, see the Student Edition page.

Skills Objectives
Students should be able to:

Make a Model of a wave.

Compare the characteristics of a transverse and longitudinal wave.

Predict the motion of a cork as water waves move past it.

Infer how the number of compressions in a spring relate to the energy in it.

Vocabulary
wave, crest, trough, transverse wave, longitudinal wave, compression, rarefaction

14.1 Nature of Waves

Objectives

▶ **Relate** waves and the transfer of energy.

▶ **Distinguish** between transverse waves and longitudinal waves.

▶ **Predict** the motion of a medium as a wave of energy passes through it.

▶ **Infer** the energy content of a longitudinal wave.

W hen you think of waves, you probably think of waves on water. Actually, waves surround you all the time. Light waves make the world around you visible. Sound waves bring voices and music to your ears. Heat waves warm your skin on a summer day.

Waves and Energy Transfer

Throw a pebble into a pond. Notice how it disturbs the surface of the water. A ripple moves outward from the place where the pebble enters the water.

When the pebble hits the water, kinetic energy transfers to nearby water molecules causing them to collide with other water molecules. Through a series of collisions between molecules, the energy is carried through the water. You see the energy from the pebble move as a small wave or ripple. A **wave** is a disturbance that transfers energy through matter or through space.

Some kinds of waves move through a medium, such as water or air. A medium is matter that is made of molecules and takes up space. A medium may be a solid, liquid, or gas. Other kinds of waves, such as light waves, can move through a vacuum. Light waves are unique in that they don't require a medium.

When energy waves move through a medium, the medium remains at the same location. You can see this occur if you throw a pebble near a leaf floating in water. As the wave of energy passes, the leaf bobs up and down. It doesn't move outward with the wave because the water molecules beneath it remain in the same location. The water molecules simply transfer energy.

▼ **ACTIVITY**

Making a Model

Do the Wave

Demonstrate a human energy wave.

1. Line up in a straight line with eight or ten classmates.

2. Each student in line crouches and then stands up and stretches, in succession.

Describe how the energy wave moves through your line of students.

SKILLS WARMUP

Oceanography
L I N K

Ocean waves are formed as wind blows across the water's surface. Obtain a plate.

1. Place the plate on a level surface and fill it with water until it's almost full.

2. Gently blow across the surface of the water and observe the waves.

3. Repeat step 2, blowing slightly harder this time.

Describe the waves that formed. How did your blowing affect the waves?

A C T I V I T Y

MOTIVATE

Skills WarmUp
To help students understand the nature of waves, have them do the Skills WarmUp.
Answer Students should mention that a wave passes horizontally as the students move vertically.

Misconceptions
Students may think that boats, leaves, or other matter should move along with the wave. Emphasize that waves only carry energy that moves the medium. Except at a shore where waves are cresting, the medium remains at the same location.

 The Living Textbook: Physical Science Sides 1-4

Chapter 9   Frame 01543
Water Waves (2 Frames)
Search: Step:

Discuss

Ask students to identify the medium in which the following waves travel: ocean waves (Water); sound waves (Air); waving flag (Flag); speedboat waves (Water); earthquake waves (Earth).

Reteach

Review right angles with students by drawing a number of straight lines on the chalkboard. Ask students to draw a line or demonstrate a plane that is at a right angle to the drawn line. Have students recall how they moved when doing the Skills WarmUp on page 335.

▶ What was the horizontal surface? (Floor)

▶ At what angle were the students to the floor? (Right angle)

Explore Visually

After students study the text and Figure 14.1, discuss the following:

▶ Describe the direction of a bundle of fibers in the rope. (Up and down)

▶ Why is the wave shown in Figure 14.1 a transverse wave? (The wave is moving at right angles to the rope.)

▶ What is the high point of the wave called? (Crest)

▶ How would you describe the trough of a wave? (The lowest part of the wave)

Answer to In-Text Question

① Rope

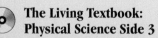
The Living Textbook: Physical Science Side 3

Chapter 19   Frame 03447
Transverse/Longitudinal Waves
(5 Movies)
Search: Play:

Language Arts Connection

Ask students to look up the following words in the dictionary: *crest*, *trough*, and *transverse*. Have volunteers write three different meanings of *crest* and of *trough* on the chalkboard. Guide the class in a discussion of the various meanings of each word and how they are related. (*Crest:* something that sticks out or is above something else; *trough*: something that is lower or is between two higher things) Encourage students to use these meanings to help them identify the crest and the trough of a wave. Ask another volunteer to write the meaning of *transverse* on the chalkboard. (Something that goes across something else) Help students relate the meaning to the motion of transverse waves.

Types of Waves All waves don't have the same effect on a medium. For example, the energy in heat waves and sound waves produces two different types of waves, called transverse waves and longitudinal waves. You can identify the type of wave passing through a medium by the way the medium is disturbed.

Transverse Waves You produce transverse waves when you shake dirt from a blanket or a rug. If you watch closely, you see that the motion of your hand, flipping the edge of the blanket up and down, produces waves in the blanket.

The **crest** is the highest point of a transverse wave. The **trough** is the lowest point of a transverse wave. The waves move through the blanket away from your hand. The threads in the blanket, however, don't move away from you. They only move up and down. Any wave in which the medium moves at right angles to the direction of the wave is a **transverse wave**.

You can see how a transverse wave moves through a rope in Figure 14.1. If you repeatedly move one end of the rope up and down, you produce transverse waves in the rope. The waves move through the rope horizontally from left to right. The fibers that make up the rope, however, only move up and down, or vertically. So, the direction of the moving wave and the direction of the movement of the rope are at right angles to each other.

Figure 14.1
Transverse waves move at right angles to the medium. What is the medium in this photo? ▼

①

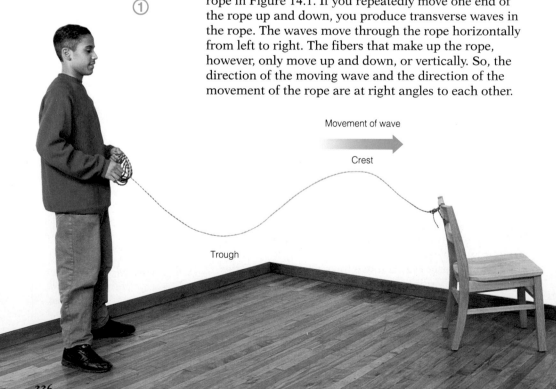

Movement of wave

Crest

Trough

Art Connection

Have students work in cooperative groups of three to make wave murals. Each mural can be a continuous line of different kinds of matter (water, air, gelatin, oil, people), connected or not, that wave energy moves through. Have groups choose whether they will show a transverse or longitudinal wave. One student may sketch the wave. Another may gather the materials, such as paints, markers, magazine pictures, yarn, glue, glitter, and construction paper. The third student can write captions to explain the mural. Remind students that their murals should include a description of the type of wave and show the direction the wave is moving as well as the direction the particles in the medium are moving. When the murals are completed, display them in the classroom or in the hallway.

② You can see transverse waves in flags or tall grass when the wind blows. Can you think of another example of a transverse wave? Does the wave you're thinking of move at a right angle to the movement of the medium?

Longitudinal Waves Energy can also be transferred in the same direction as the medium. You can see longitudinal (lahn juh TOOD uh nuhl) waves in a spring, like the one shown in Figure 14.2. Unlike a transverse wave, a **longitudinal wave** moves in the same direction as the disturbance in the medium.

The energy in the spring comes from compressing coils to produce potential energy. When the compressed coils are released, the potential energy becomes kinetic energy, which moves through the spring like a wave.

The part of a longitudinal wave where the particles of matter are close together is called a **compression**. Compression means "pushed together." The coils in the spring that are pushed together create a compression. Wave motion is in the same direction as the compression of the spring.

If you look closely at Figure 14.2, you'll see that the coils in the part of the spring following the compression are spread out. You can't compress coils in one part of a spring without causing coils to spread apart in another part of the spring. A **rarefaction** (RAIR uh FAK shuhn) is the part of a longitudinal wave where the particles spread apart. All longitudinal waves consist of alternating compressions and rarefactions. Energy transfers from one particle to another in the compressions that move through the medium.

▼ ACTIVITY

Comparing

Spring Waves

Using a large spring, produce both a transverse wave and a longitudinal wave. Compare how each of the waves looks. How is the action you used to create each wave different?

SKILLS WORKOUT

Figure 14.2
Longitudinal waves move in the same direction as the disturbance in the medium.
▼

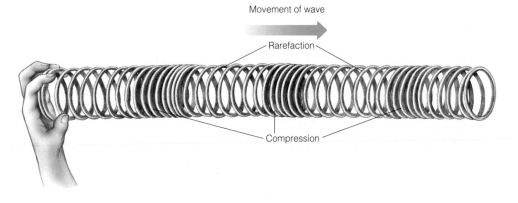

Movement of wave

Rarefaction

Compression

To help students compare waves, have them do the Skills WorkOut.
Answer Compressed coils create the wave in the spring to produce longitudinal waves. An up-and-down motion creates the transverse wave through the spring. Point out the difference to students.

Directed Inquiry

Have students study the text and Figure 14.2. Ask:

▶ How would you describe the direction the energy moves in a longitudinal wave? (It moves in the same direction as the wave.)

▶ What is the difference between a compression and a rarefaction? (Compression: the coils of a spring or particles of a medium push together; rarefaction: the coils of a spring or particles of a medium spread apart)

▶ How is energy transferred in a longitudinal wave? (From one particle to another as the compressions move through the medium)

Answer to In-Text Question

② Answers will vary.
Example: The waves behind a speedboat

 The Living Textbook: Physical Science Side 3

Chapter 21   Frame 05278
Longitudinal Waves in a Coiled Spring (Movie)
Search: Play:

 **The Living Textbook: Physical Science Side 3**

Chapter 23   Frame 06345
Longitudinal Wave: Transfer of Energy (Animation)
Search: Play:

337

TEACH ▪ *Continued*

Explore Visually

Have students study this page and Figure 14.3. Ask:

▶ How are ocean surface waves created? (By the force of friction as the wind moves across the water's surface)

▶ How do individual water molecules in an ocean wave move? (In a circle)

▶ As the waves move into shore, what happens to the way the water molecules near the bottom move? (They move in an ellipse.)

▶ What causes the wave to slow down? (Friction between the bottom of the wave and the sea bottom causes the lower part of the wave to slow down; speed at the wave's top is unchanged.)

Critical Thinking

Reason and Conclude Ask students if they would classify a water wave as transverse or longitudinal. Have them explain. (Transverse: Water particles move at right angles to the wave.)

Integrated Learning

Use Integrating Worksheet 14.1.

The Living Textbook: Physical Science Sides 1-4

Chapter 11   Frame 01933
Breaking Waves (6 Frames)
Search: Step:

The Living Textbook: Physical Science Sides 1-4

Chapter 11   Frame 01924
Movement of Water Particles in Waves
(3 Frames)
Search: Step:

Math Connection

As the height of a wave increases, so does its energy. Measurements have shown that this increase is geometric. In other words, a wave two meters high has four times as much energy as a wave one meter high. A wave three meters high has nine times as much energy as the one-meter wave. Ask them to compare the energy of a two-meter wave with that of a four-meter wave. (The four-meter wave has four times the energy.)

Wave Motion

What do tiny wind ripples in a pond and huge ocean waves have in common? They are both examples of waves that move through the surface of a medium. These waves are called surface waves.

Ocean surface waves are created by the force of friction when the wind moves across the water's surface to make ripples. The ripples expose more surface area for the wind to act upon. The small waves gain energy from the wind and increase in size.

The individual water molecules in an ocean wave move in a circle as shown in Figure 14.3. The size of the circle becomes smaller as the depth of the water increases. The decrease in circle size is due to the decreasing energy of the wave.

Most ocean waves are less than 3 m high. Waves set up by storms may get over 20 m high! These waves travel several thousand kilometers over the open sea. As they move outside the storm area, the height of the wave decreases and the wavelength increases. These waves can do much damage to a shoreline with a sloping beach.

**Figure 14.3
Ocean Waves** ▼

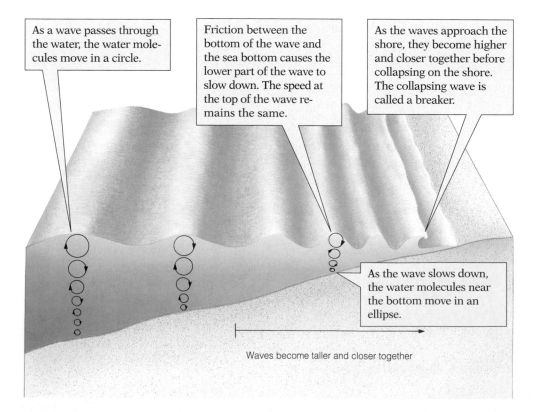

As a wave passes through the water, the water molecules move in a circle.

Friction between the bottom of the wave and the sea bottom causes the lower part of the wave to slow down. The speed at the top of the wave remains the same.

As the waves approach the shore, they become higher and closer together before collapsing on the shore. The collapsing wave is called a breaker.

As the wave slows down, the water molecules near the bottom move in an ellipse.

Waves become taller and closer together

Science and Society *Surfing*

Maybe you've enjoyed the thrill of being carried toward shore by the force of a rolling wave. For many people, this is just fun. For others, it is a sport called surfing.

Surfing, or surfboard riding, started in Hawaii. Surfing is a blend of two sports that were brought to the islands by the Polynesians. Surfing combines *paipai*, "riding waves while lying down on a flat board," with *puku*, "riding waves while standing up in a small canoe."

Modern surfers ride a wave while standing on a flat, tapered board called a surfboard. Most surfboards are made of lightweight plastic resins. They measure about 2 m long, 0.8 m wide, and 3 cm thick.

Successful surfing depends on a person's ability to stay balanced on the surfboard as it slides down the front, or face, of a wave. The surfer in Figure 14.4 started by lying on his board out in the ocean beyond the breakers. As a tall wave approached, the surfer paddled his board just ahead of the wave toward the shore. When the crest of the wave lifted his board, he quickly stood up. As the breaking wave carried him toward the shore, the surfer shifted his weight. He steered the board across the face of the wave, or the smooth water just under the crest. The surfer and the wave moved forward at the same speed.

Figure 14.4 ▲
Surfing requires good balance, sense of timing, and coordination. Surfers can reach speeds of 55 km/h.

Check and Explain

1. What causes the ripple in a pond when a pebble is thrown into the water?

2. Give five examples of waves moving through a medium. List whether each example is produced by a transverse or longitudinal wave. How can you tell?

3. **Predict** What will be the motion of a cork floating in a tub of water as waves pass by it? Give reasons for your prediction.

4. **Infer** In one spring, the compressions consist of four coils. The compressions in a second spring have ten coils. Which spring has more energy? Explain.

Time 40 minutes   **Group** 5

Materials

6 table-tennis balls

6 tubs or basins

12 heavy metal washers

60 cm of string

6 metric rulers

6 rolls of tape

Analysis

1. The ball should bob up and down.

2. The waves got larger when the ruler was pushed with more force.

3. The waves were closer together when the ruler was pushed more frequently.

Conclusion

The frequency of pushing the ruler directly affects the frequency of the water waves created. The force of the pushing directly affects the amplitude of the water waves. Larger waves are caused by a larger force.

Extension

Student accounts will vary. The height of sea waves is directly and positively related to the energy in the wind.

Everyday Application

A buoy must be able to move up and down and slightly back and forth with the passing waves. It will rise and fall with the tides, and rise, fall, and sway back and forth in a storm.

Prelab Discussion

Have students read the entire activity before beginning. Discuss the following points before beginning:

▶ Review with students what happens to the medium through which a wave passes.

▶ Ask students to describe the type of waves being produced in the tub.

▶ Ask students to predict the motion of the ball when waves pass.

Activity 14 *How does the water surface move when waves pass?*

Skills Observe; Infer

Task 1 Prelab Prep

1. Collect the following items: 20 cm of string, table-tennis ball, tape, 2 heavy metal washers, metric ruler, tub or basin about 12 cm deep, and water.

2. Tie the piece of string around a table-tennis ball. Use tape to secure it.

3. Tie 2 metal washers to the opposite end of the string. Leave about 10 cm of string between the washers and the table-tennis ball.

4. Place the washers and the attached table-tennis ball in the center of the tub. Fill the tub with water until the string is almost straight.

Task 2 Data Record

1. On a separate sheet of paper, draw a data table, like the one shown.

2. Use the table to record all your observations about the motion of the table-tennis ball.

Task 3 Procedure

1. When the water is perfectly still, insert the ruler into the water near the edge of the basin. Use the ruler to gently push the surface of the water back and forth in the direction of the table-tennis ball.

2. Observe the motion of the table-tennis ball as each wave passes. Record your observations in the table for trial 1. Allow the water to become perfectly still.

3. Repeat steps 1 and 2. For trial 2, use the same rhythm, but use more force when you move the ruler.

4. Repeat steps 1 and 2 again. For trial 3, use the same gentle force as in trial 1, but push the ruler back and forth more frequently.

Task 4 Analysis

1. Describe the motion of the table tennis ball as the wave passes in trial 1.

2. How were the waves different when you pushed the ruler with more force?

3. How were the waves different when you pushed the ruler more frequently?

Task 5 Conclusion

Explain how frequency and force affect the behavior of surface waves. Explain what gives some waves a larger amplitude than others.

Extension

Hurricanes often cause waves that do a great deal of damage. Research a recent hurricane. Write an account of damage done by sea waves. Explain how wave height relates to wind energy.

Everyday Application

Buoys are floating devices which are anchored to the ocean bottom. They mark channel depth and hazards for ships. Use what you learned in this activity to explain how a buoy is anchored and how it is affected by tides and storms.

Table 14.1   Wave Movement

Trial	Motion of Ruler	Observations
1		
2		
3		

Themes in Science

Diversity and Unity Some waves travel slowly through the earth while other waves move rapidly through space. But all waves carry energy and share the properties of wavelength, frequency, speed, and amplitude. Shake a table on which there are stacks of light and heavy objects. Discuss with students how the energy affects the objects.

Patterns of Change/Cycles A pattern of ocean wave crests indicates the amount of energy used to generate the waves. For example, waves generated by the storms in the Gulf of Alaska create the very high waves that break on the shores of Hawaii. Ask students to look at a globe and find those two locations.

Section Objectives
For a list of section objectives, see the Student Edition page.

Skills Objectives
Students should be able to:

Infer that sound waves can cause a vibration.

Interpret Data to show how triangulation can determine the center of an earthquake.

Predict how a wave's amplitude changes if energy is added to the wave.

Vocabulary
wavelength, amplitude, frequency

14.2 Wave Properties

Objectives

▶ **Identify** the parts of transverse and longitudinal waves.

▶ **Calculate** the wave speed if given the frequency and the wavelength.

▶ **Predict** how energy affects the amplitude of a wave.

▶ **Compare** and **contrast** wave height and amplitude.

▼ **ACTIVITY**

Inferring

Hum Tickler

Moisten your lips and hold them together very loosely. Hum a series of notes until you reach a note that tickles your lips. Explain why your lips tickle.

SKILLS WARMUP

"**H**ere comes a big wave," one surfer yells to another surfer bobbing in the ocean. "It'll be here in four or five seconds."

"The waves are too close together. We won't be able to stand up in time to catch the big wave. Three waves will pass by before we catch one," the second surfer responds.

These surfers are describing the four properties of waves. A "big wave" refers to the height, or amplitude, of the wave. "Four or five seconds" is the time it takes the wave to travel from its present location to the surfers. This is the wave speed. "The waves are too close together" is the distance between two consecutive crests, or two consecutive troughs. This is a wavelength. "Three waves will pass by before we catch one" identifies the frequency of the waves.

Wave Behavior

Many of the characteristics of ocean waves change as they approach the shoreline. What do you notice about the waves shown in Figure 14.5? Are all the waves exactly the same? Actually, the size, speed, and shape of each wave are different.

Even though waves often differ, they all share common characteristics. Waves transfer energy. They have height, speed, length, and frequency. The exact height, speed, length, and frequency of waves, however, will vary from wave to wave. Similarly, all the students in your class have height. However, the height of each student is not the same.

Figure 14.5 ▲
What wave properties are seen as the waves approach the beach? ①

MOTIVATE

Skills WarmUp
To help students understand wave properties, have them do the Skills WarmUp.
Answer The sound waves of the hum transfer their energy to the air between the lips, causing vibration. This in turn causes the moisture and then the skin of the lips to vibrate. These vibrations caused the tickling sensation.

Prior Knowledge
Gauge how much students know about wave properties by asking the following questions:

▶ In what ways can waves in the same medium differ?

▶ What will happen if more energy is added to a wave?

▶ How would you measure the wavelength of transverse waves?

Answer to In-Text Question
① **The crests and troughs are easily seen. The crests become higher and closer together.**

Portfolio

Ask students to draw a transverse wave and a longitudinal wave. Each drawing should show both the motion and the direction of the wave. Have students add their drawings to their portfolios.

Explore Visually

Have students study Figure 14.6. Then ask:

▶ What does the red line on the diagram indicate? (It's the line of origin or the original position of the medium before a transverse wave moves through it.)

▶ What is the crest of a transverse wave? (It's the highest point of the wave above the line of origin.)

▶ What is the trough of a transverse wave? (It's the lowest point of the wave beneath the line of origin.)

▶ What is a wavelength of a transverse wave? (It is the distance between two crests or two troughs.)

▶ How many wavelengths are shown in the diagram of the transverse wave? (Two)

Answers to In-Text Questions

① Transverse waves have crests and troughs; longitudinal waves have compression and rarefactions to show energy in each wave. Transverse wave models have a line of origin; longitudinal wave models don't.

② Two

Themes in Science

Scale and Structure In a transverse wave, wavelength is the distance between two consecutive crests; in a longitudinal wave, wavelength is the distance between two consecutive compressions. In either type of wave, the wavelength, frequency, and speed of a wave are related. If a wave moves at a constant speed and its frequency increases, its wavelength decreases. Have students find out the range of frequencies of electromagnetic waves with wavelengths 10 km to 10^{-10} km. (10 kHz to 10^{15} Hz)

Characteristics of Waves

Just as your body has different identifiable parts, so does a wave. Some of the wave parts you should learn are shown in Figure 14.6. Look at the transverse wave shown on this page and the longitudinal wave shown on page 343.

Each kind of wave behaves differently in a medium. When a transverse wave passes through a medium, it looks like a moving snake. However, when a longitudinal wave passes through a medium, it looks more like a traveling earthworm.

By observing the behavior of a medium, you can see the different parts of transverse and longitudinal waves. Compare the different parts of the transverse and longitudinal waves shown in Figure 14.6. What are the important parts of each wave? ①

**Figure 14.6
Parts of a Wave** ▼

The crest of a transverse wave is the highest point of the wave above the line of origin. Count the number of crests shown in this transverse wave.

The red line shows the original position of the medium before a transverse wave moves through it. This position is called the line of origin for the medium.

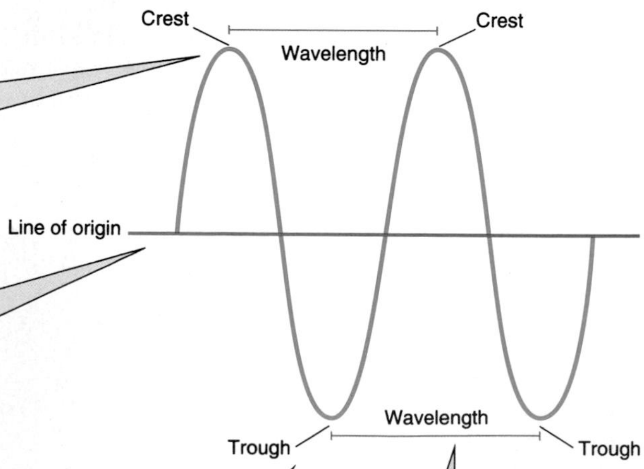

The trough of a transverse wave is the lowest point of the wave beneath the line of origin. How many troughs are shown in this transverse wave? ②

The wavelength of a transverse wave is the distance between two neighboring crests or between two troughs.

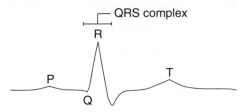
As you compare transverse and longitudinal waves, notice that many parts on each wave are comparable. Longitudinal waves, for example, have compressions, while transverse waves do not. Instead, transverse waves have crests. Even though compressions are not the same as crests, they correspond to one another. Compressions and crests indicate the location of maximum energy in the wave. Rarefactions and troughs indicate locations of lowest energy.

Wavelength The parts of transverse and longitudinal waves are used to describe their characteristics. One characteristic, for example, is wavelength. On a transverse wave, **wavelength** is the distance between two consecutive crests, or two consecutive troughs. The wavelength of a longitudinal wave is the distance between two consecutive compressions, or two consecutive rarefactions.

Life Science LINK

An electrocardiogram (EKG) is a record of electrical changes occurring while your heart beats. A typical EKG has three recognizable deflection waves. Research what an electrocardiogram looks like for a healthy heart. Draw an EKG for a healthy heart. On your drawing, label the P wave, the QRS complex, and the T wave. How are these waves like the wave shown in Figure 14.6?

ACTIVITY

▶ What is a compression in a longitudinal wave? (The area where the medium is pushed together)

▶ What is a rarefaction in a longitudinal wave? (The area where the medium spreads apart)

▶ What is one wavelength in a longitudinal wave? (It is the distance between the centers of two consecutive compressions or between two consecutive rarefactions.)

▶ Which parts of transverse waves and longitudinal waves correspond to one another? (The crests correspond to the compressions, and the troughs correspond to the rarefactions.)

▶ How many wavelengths are shown in the illustration of the longitudinal wave? (Two)

Portfolio

Ask students to take out their drawings of transverse and longitudinal waves. Have them label the crest, trough, rarefaction, compression, and wavelength. Have pairs of students exchange drawings and check each other's work.

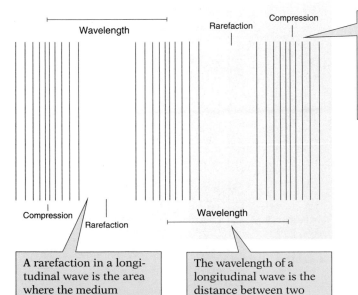

A compression in a longitudinal wave is the area where the medium is pushed together. Compressions in a longitudinal wave compare to the crests of a transverse wave.

A rarefaction in a longitudinal wave is the area where the medium spreads apart. Rarefactions in a longitudinal wave compare to the troughs of a transverse wave.

The wavelength of a longitudinal wave is the distance between two consecutive compressions or rarefactions. Count the number of wavelengths shown in this longitudinal wave.

 The Living Textbook: Physical Science Sides 1-4

Chapter 11 Frame 01913
Parts of a Transverse Wave (3 Frames)
Search: Step:

 The Living Textbook: Physical Science Sides 1-4

Chapter 14 Frame 02261
Parts of a Longitudinal Wave (4 Frames)
Search: Step:

TEACH ▪ Continued

Directed Inquiry

Have students study the text and Figures 14.7 and 14.8. Ask:

▶ What characteristic of a wave describes the amount of energy in the wave? (Amplitude)

▶ Which characteristic of a wave is not affected by a change in frequency? (Amplitude)

▶ How would you describe the distance from the top of a crest to the bottom of a trough? (Wave height, or twice the amplitude)

▶ How are the frequencies of Wave C and Wave D different? (Wave D has twice the frequency of Wave C.)

▶ **Observe** How does the wavelength of Wave C compare with the wavelength of Wave D? (Wave C has a wavelength twice as great as that of Wave D.)

Critical Thinking

Reason by Analogy Have students think about how frequency is measured in transverse waves. Ask, How would frequency be measured in longitudinal waves? (The number of compressions or rarefactions that pass a point in a given amount of time)

Answers to In-Text Questions

① The rope in Wave B

② To increase frequency, move the rope up and down more often. The amplitude is not affected by frequency.

The Living Textbook:
Physical Science Side 3

Chapter 24   Frame 07406
Frequency of a Transverse Wave (Movie)
Search: Play:

344

Literature Connection

Explain to students that waves and their actions have been used in poems or stories. Read several lines from the poem "Dover Beach" by Matthew Arnold. Choose lines rich with wave images, such as the following:

Listen! you hear the grating roar
Of pebbles which the waves draw back,
and fling,

At their return, up the high strand,
Begin, and cease, and then again begin,
With tremulous cadence slow, and bring
The eternal note of sadness in.

Have students discuss the part that waves play in the poem.

Wave Amplitude If you're standing in the surf, you may be knocked over by a wave. Another wave barely nudges you. The two waves differ in some characteristic. What is it? The difference between the ocean waves is the **amplitude** (AM pluh tood) of the waves.

Look at Figure 14.7. The amplitude of a transverse wave is the vertical distance between the line of origin and each crest or trough. The amplitude is related to how much energy the wave transfers through the medium. A wave with a high amplitude has more energy than a wave with a low amplitude.

The height of the ocean wave is a good indication of whether or not it has enough energy to knock you over. How would you avoid being knocked over? Your best move would be to run to the shore when you see a wave with a high amplitude.

Wave Frequency You're in the surf, and a wave knocks you down. No harm done. You get ready for the next wave to arrive. You expect it to arrive 15 or 20 seconds later. You may be caught off guard if the wave arrives in just 5 or 6 seconds. Waves that arrive every 5 or 6 seconds have a greater frequency (FREE kwuhn see) than those arriving every 15 or 20 seconds.

The **frequency** of a wave is the number of wavelengths that pass a point in a given amount of time, such as a second. The unit for frequency is hertz (Hz). One wave per second equals 1 Hz. Hertz was named after Heinrich Hertz, a German physicist who studied waves during the 1800s.

Look at Figure 14.8. The difference between a 1 Hz and 2 Hz wave in a rope is shown. How many complete waves are included in the line indicating 1 second in wave C? How many in wave D?

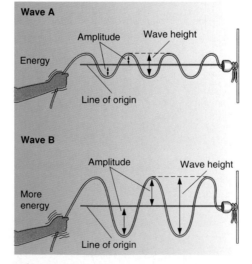

Figure 14.7 ▲
The greater the amount of energy in a wave, the greater is its amplitude. Which rope has the most energy? ①

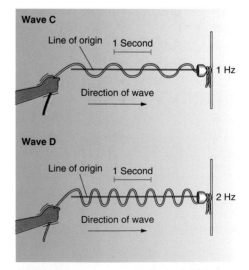

Figure 14.8 ▲
How do you increase the frequency in a rope? How is amplitude affected by a change in frequency? ②

Wave Speed Imagine you are at the beach, waist high in the water. A huge wave approaches. What are your first thoughts? You probably don't care about the wavelength or frequency of the wave. What concerns you is how fast the wave is moving toward you—or its speed.

The frequency and wavelength determine the speed of a wave. If you had time to get to the beach before the wave hit you, you could measure its wavelength and calculate its frequency. One thing you don't have to worry about is that the wave might change its speed. Waves don't change speed as they travel through a medium.

The speed of a wave is equal to the frequency times the wavelength. The speed of the wave is measured in meters per second. Frequency is waves per second, or Hz. Wavelength is measured in meters.

The relationship that exists between the speed, frequency, and wavelength of a wave is expressed in the equation:

$$\text{speed} = \text{frequency} \times \text{wavelength}$$

SkillBuilder *Interpreting Data*

The Center of an Earthquake

Earthquakes are caused by waves moving through the earth. An earthquake produces fast-moving P-waves, which are longitudinal waves, and slower-moving S-waves, which are transverse waves. The exact origin of an earthquake, or the epicenter, is determined by knowing the time difference between the arrival of P- and S-waves at three different locations.

P- and S-waves arrived at station A 3 s apart. From this information, it was determined that the epicenter was 15 km away. In a similar way, it was determined that the epicenter was 45 km from station B and 60 km from station C.

The next step involves a map. Copy the map shown onto a separate piece of paper. Draw a circle around each station on your map with a compass. The size of the circles is important. The radius of each circle is the distance from the station to the origin. Use the scale provided to change

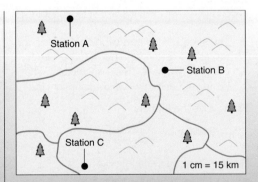

Station A

Station B

Station C

1 cm = 15 km

km to cm. The epicenter is the point where the three circles intersect. Mark the origin with an X.

1. This method is called *triangulation.* Why does the word tell you about the method being used?

2. Describe another situation, real or imaginary, where you could use triangulation.

TEACH ▪ *Continued*

Practice Problems

Work through the sample problems with students. Then have them do the practice problems.

Answers

1. Speed = 3 Hz x 1.2 m
   = 3 wave/s x 1.2 m/wave
   = 3.6 m/s

2. Speed = 680 Hz x 0.5 m
   = 680 wave/s x 0.5 m/wave
   = 340 m/s

3. Frequency = 3 m/s ÷ 1.5 m = 2 Hz

4. Yes. Find the wave velocity:
   speed = 0.2 Hz x 100 m
   = 0.2 wave/s x 100 m/wave
   = 20 m/s. Then find the time it takes for the wave to reach shore:
   t= 200 m ÷ 20 m/s = 10 s.
   Find the time it takes you to reach shore: t = 8 m ÷ 2 m/s = 4 s. You can reach shore
   10 s – 4 s = 6 s before the wave does.

Enrich

Assign additional problems on the concept. See Math Appendix page 648.

Cooperative Learning

Have the class work in three cooperative groups to write two story problems. One group should develop problems to find a wave's speed; the second group to find a wave's frequency; the third group to find the wavelength of a wave. Have groups exchange and solve each other's problems. Be sure students supply answers with their problems.

Sample Problems

1. The frequency of the waves produced by a passing motorboat is 2 Hz. The wavelength is 3 m. How fast are the waves moving toward the beach?

   Plan Use the equation for speed.

   speed = frequency × wavelength

   Gather Data frequency = 2 Hz
   wavelength = 3 m

   Solution Express frequency as the number of waves per second. Express the wavelength as the distance between two wave crests.

   frequency = 2 $\frac{\text{waves}}{\text{second}}$

   wavelength = 3 $\frac{\text{meters}}{\text{wave}}$

   Solve for the speed.

   speed = 2 $\frac{\text{waves}}{\text{second}}$ × 3 $\frac{\text{meters}}{\text{waves}}$ = 6 $\frac{\text{meters}}{\text{second}}$

   Wave speed is expressed in meters per second (m/s), which is the SI unit for speed.

2. The speed of the approaching ocean waves is 4 meters per second. The length between two wave crests is 2 meters. What is the frequency in waves/second, or Hz?

   Plan Use the formula

   frequency = $\frac{\text{speed}}{\text{wavelength}}$

   Gather Data wavelength = 2 m
   speed = 4 m/s

   Solution Divide speed by wavelength.

   frequency = $\frac{4 \text{ m/s}}{2 \text{ m}}$

   frequency = $\frac{2 \text{ waves}}{\text{s}}$ = 2 Hz

Practice Problems

1. You are holding one end of a jump rope while your friend is flicking the other end up and down. The waves have a frequency of 3 Hz and a wavelength of 1.2 m. What is the speed of the waves in the rope?

2. A sound wave traveling toward you from a rock concert has a frequency of 680 Hz and a wavelength of 0.5 m in air. What is the speed of the sound wave?

3. The wake of a boat is moving at 3 m/s. The waves are 1.5 m apart. What is the frequency?

4. You are standing in the ocean 8 m from the beach. You see a big wave heading toward you. The wave is 200 m from the beach. Its frequency is 0.2 Hz, and its wavelength is 100 m. You can move an average of 2 m/s in water. Can you reach the beach before the wave hits you? Explain.

Multicultural Perspectives

Over 2,000 years ago the Chinese designed a device that detected earthquakes and their direction. The device was designed to resemble eight dragons with spheres carefully balanced inside their mouths. Have students find how this device worked and if it would still work today. (When the earth shook, a sphere fell from the mouth of one of the dragons, indicating the direction of the earthquake. It would still work.)

Science and Society
Earthquake-Proof Buildings

Earthquakes are caused by waves produced when the rocks deep within the earth move. The energy that is released travels through the earth. The amount of damage done by an earthquake depends on the strength of the waves and the design of the building.

People in ancient cultures who lived in earthquake areas built earthquake-resistant buildings. A Buddhist pagoda in Japan is shown in the bottom of Figure 14.9. The central shaft is sunk into the ground. Flexible joints attach the roof sections to the central shaft. The shaft sways during an earthquake, but the roof doesn't fall.

Chinese architects designed tentlike structures. Each building had a sloping, tiled roof. A central wooden beam supported the length of the roof. Each end of the beam had vertical shafts driven deep into rock. Lightweight bamboo walls hung from the roof, almost like curtains. The walls absorbed energy by swaying, since they were supported by the roof and not by the ground.

In the American Southwest and in Central America, adobe buildings remain standing after numerous earthquakes. Adobe walls are made of clay bricks with a crisscross network of twigs. This construction gives flexibility to each wall. The walls absorb the energy of earthquake waves to remain standing.

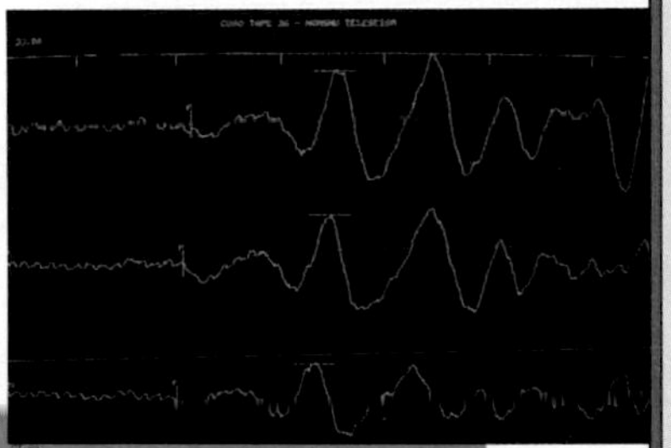

Figure 14.9 ▲
Seismographs (top) measure speed, strength, and arrival time of an earthquake. A pagoda (bottom) is a Buddhist shrine.

Check and Explain

1. Draw a transverse wave and a longitudinal wave. Label the parts of each wave.

2. An earthquake wave has a frequency of 20 Hz and a wavelength of 50 km. How fast is the wave?

3. **Predict** How does adding energy to a wave affect its amplitude?

4. **Compare** The height of a wave is the vertical distance between a crest and a trough. Compare wave height to amplitude for a transverse wave.

Skills Development

Infer Ask students how they think the early Japanese, Chinese, and Native Americans learned to make earthquake-resistant buildings. (They would notice the types of buildings that survived earthquakes and those that did not.)

WrapUp

Reteach Have students draw pictures of longitudinal waves along a spring. Ask them to show how they would increase the amplitude of the waves, then the frequency, then the wavelength. (Check students' drawings for accuracy.) How could they change the speed? (By stretching the spring tighter)

Use Review Worksheet 14.2.

Check and Explain

1. Check students' drawings for accuracy.

2. Speed = 20 wave/s × 50 km/waves = 1000 km/s

3. Amplitude will increase.

4. Wave height is twice the amplitude.

Section Objectives
For a list of section objectives, see the Student Edition page.

Skills Objectives
Students should be able to:

Observe destructive interference in a transverse wave.

Observe the motion of a wave around a barrier.

Predict how a wave would be affected as it passed from air into water.

Vocabulary
reflection, diffraction, refraction, interference

▶ MOTIVATE

Skills WarmUp

To help students understand wave interactions, have them do the Skills WarmUp.
Answer The waves in the rope should disappear as the troughs of the waves going in one direction meet the crests of the waves going in the other direction.

Misconceptions

Students watching waves meet at the center of a rope or string may think the waves reflect off one another and turn back to their source. Help students understand that the waves pass through one another and each continues to move in its original direction.

Answers to In-Text Questions

① **The energy is being absorbed by the shoreline, which causes the waves to form breakers.**

② **The crests become higher and they break against the rocks. Some slow down and some change direction.**

348

Themes in Science

Systems and Interactions Waves interact with objects by reflecting from surfaces, moving around barriers, and changing as they travel from one medium into another. Waves also interact with one another, producing new waves whose properties are related to the original waves. During these interactions, a wave moves in a predictable manner.

Patterns of Change/Cycles The behavior of waves is consistent. When wave interference occurs, ship captains and sailors are able to predict the behavior of a ship in a storm. Have students discuss how these predictions might be possible.

▼ ACTIVITY

Observing

Making Waves

Obtain a jump rope.
1. Hold one end of the rope perfectly still.
2. Have a person at the other end make waves in the rope by moving it up and down.
3. Now move your end of the rope up and down in the opposite direction.
What happens to the waves in the rope?

SKILLS WARMUP

Figure 14.10 ▲
Where is the energy from these waves being absorbed? How do you know? ①

14.3 Wave Interactions

Objectives

▶ **Describe** four kinds of wave interactions.

▶ **Explain** the relationship between the angle of incidence and the angle of reflection.

▶ **Compare** and **contrast** constructive and destructive interference.

▶ **Predict** how a wave will behave if it moves from air into water.

Did you ever watch the waves caused by a motorboat? You probably saw a series of waves rolling towards you. You might have noticed that many things change the direction or behavior of the waves. Waves change when they run into a sharp-edged rock jutting out of the water or when they meet a smooth sandbar arching above the water's surface. You might have wondered what happens if two different waves run into each other far out in the water. Perhaps a bigger wave forms, or maybe the collision will suddenly make the water flat.

Interaction, Energy, and Change

You learned that a wave carries energy through a medium. Recall that when an object with energy interacts with another object, energy is either lost or gained. When a wave interacts with an object or other waves, the amount of energy in the wave changes. The change in energy affects the wave's properties.

Look at Figure 14.10. How do the properties of the waves change when they reach the rocky shoreline? If some of the wave's energy is ② absorbed by another object, the amplitude, speed, or wavelength of the wave may change.

Sometimes the wave's behavior is altered. The direction of the moving wave may change. The wave may also break apart or pass the structure, and then re-form.

Art Connection

Show students examples of image reflection depicted in paintings, such as *Arnolfini and His Wife* by Jan van Eyck, *Water-Meadows Near Salisbury* by John Constable, *Fur Traders Descending the Missouri* by George Caleb Bingham, *The River* by Claude Monet, *A Bar at the Folies-Bergere* by Edouard Manet, or *Metamorphosis of Narcissus* by Salvador Dalí. Ask students to find the reflections in each of the paintings. Discuss how reflection contributes to the composition or theme of the painting. (It may reveal information that can't be seen directly or help give the painting a sense of symmetry.)

Reflection

The next time you see raindrops fall into a water fountain, observe the ripples. The ripples move outward, hit the fountain wall, and bounce off. The interaction between the ripples and the fountain wall is called **reflection**. Reflection occurs when a wave bounces off a surface. Look at Figure 14.11 to learn how waves reflect.

Reflected waves carry energy. The amount of energy depends on how much energy is absorbed by the surface that the wave hits. The energy not absorbed by the surface is carried by the reflected waves.

Figure 14.11
Reflection of a Wave ▼

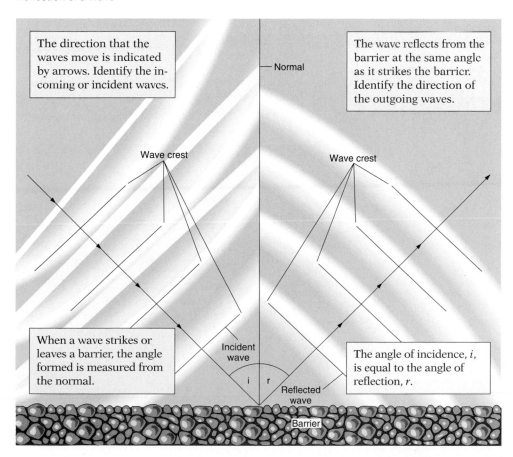

The direction that the waves move is indicated by arrows. Identify the incoming or incident waves.

The wave reflects from the barrier at the same angle as it strikes the barrier. Identify the direction of the outgoing waves.

Normal

Wave crest

Wave crest

When a wave strikes or leaves a barrier, the angle formed is measured from the normal.

The angle of incidence, *i*, is equal to the angle of reflection, *r*.

Incident wave

i   r

Reflected wave

Barrier

Chapter 14   Waves   **349**

Directed Inquiry

Have students study Figure 14.11. Draw the incident portion of the diagram on the chalkboard. Then ask:

▶ What are incident waves? In what direction are they moving? (Incoming waves; waves move toward the barrier)

▶ What is the normal and where is it located? (A line at 90° to the surface)

▶ What is the angle of incidence? (The angle at which the incident waves reach the barrier, measured from the normal)

▶ What is the angle of reflection? How does it compare to the angle of incidence? (The angle at which the reflected waves leave the barrier; their measures are the same)

Skills Development

Measure Have students use a protractor to show how *i* is equal to *r* with a drawing. Ask students to measure each angle. (Angles should be equal.)

Enrich

Use Enrich Worksheet 14.3.

 The Living Textbook: Physical Science Side 3

Chapter 26   Frame 08837
Reflection of Waves (Movie)
Search: Play:

 The Living Textbook: Physical Science Sides 1-4

Chapter 13   Frame 02115
Angle of Reflection/Incidence (3 Frames)
Search: Step:

TEACH ▪ *Continued*

Skills WorkOut

To help students observe the effect of a wave barrier, have them do the Skills WorkOut.

Answer The waves reflect from the barrier and bend around the barrier.

Skills Development

Communicate Have students make a diagram of reflection and one of diffraction. Ask students to record the following information under the appropriate diagram:
a. Waves bounce off a barrier.
b. Waves bend around a barrier.
c. Waves change direction.
d. Speed and frequency of the wave does not change.
e. Angle of incidence and reflection are of equal measure.
(a, c, and d apply to both; b applies to diffraction; e applies to reflection.)

The Living Textbook: Physical Science Sides 1-4

Chapter 11   Frame 01943
Diffraction in Ripple Tank (4 Frames)
Search: Step:

The Living Textbook: Physical Science Sides 1-4

Chapter 11   Frame 01927
Refraction in Shallow Water (1 Frame)
Search:

350

STS Connection

Explain to students that diffraction occurs not only as waves move around an obstacle but also as waves pass through a narrow gap. As waves move through the gap, they spread apart. The narrower the gap, the farther apart the waves spread. A diffraction grating is a series of narrow gaps etched on a flat glass plate. Many gratings consist of lines etched into an aluminum-coated sheet of glass. The lines are parallel, the same distance from one another, and very close—from 100 to 6,000 lines per millimeter are possible. Have students find out what kinds of instruments use diffraction gratings and what information is obtained. (Examples: spectroscope, elements in stars)

Diffraction

When you stand in a shallow pool of water facing into the breeze, you can look down and see waves reflected by your shins. If you look behind you, you'll see that the waves have reformed. They appear to have gone right through your legs! How can that be?

If you look closely, you'll see that sections of the wave near the sides of your legs begin to bend as they pass by your legs. They bend so much that they come together a short distance behind your legs to re-form the wave. This bending makes it appear that the wave passes right through you. The bending of a wave as a result of the interaction between a wave and the edge of an object is called **diffraction**.

Look at Figure 14.12. The waves move at an angle toward the rock. You can see the waves bend around the sharp rock that juts farthest into the sea. How do the waves spread into the area behind the rock? As you can see, the wavelength didn't change. The waves before, next to, and behind the rock travel at the same speed and frequency. The only change is the direction of waves as they pass by the rock's edge.

▼ **ACTIVITY**

Observing

Wave Barriers

Obtain a small block of wood and a pie pan.
1. Fill the pan half full with water.
2. Place the wood in the center of the pan of water.
3. Tap one side of the pan sharply to create waves.

Describe how the waves are affected by the barrier.

SKILLS WORKOUT

Figure 14.12 ▲
The waves bend around the angular rock, but the wavelength remains unchanged. Notice how the energy of waves erodes the shoreline.

Integrating the Sciences

Integrating the Sciences

Earth Science Tell students that wave refraction changes the shapes of shorelines. Ask them to research these changes and make a diagram that shows wave action on islands, inlets, and bays. Have them discuss how the action of the waves affects organisms living in the area. (Organisms living on the shores of islands, which are exposed to more forceful waves, would have to be well anchored to rocks or be able to float with the surges of the waves.)

Refraction

Waves passing undisturbed through a single medium, such as water, don't change properties or direction. However, waves can change as they pass from one medium to another. A wave entering a new medium at an angle changes direction, as shown in Figure 14.13. In air, the light waves move in a straight line. When light waves enter the new medium, they bend. Bending occurs because the wave speed is different for each medium. The bending of a wave as a result of a change in speed is called **refraction**.

To better understand refraction, imagine mowing a lawn. The wheels of the lawn mower represent a wave. One wheel moves into grass while the other continues to roll on a sidewalk. The wheels move at different speeds because they are on different mediums.

Look at what happens to the lawn mower in Figure 14.14. When the mower enters the grass at an angle, only one of the wheels is on the grass. The wheel on the grass slows down. The wheel on the sidewalk does not. The mower turns. If both wheels enter the grass at the same time, each would be affected equally, and the mower wouldn't change direction.

Figure 14.13 ▲
The beam of light bends when it moves from air into water. What causes the light waves to change direction? ①

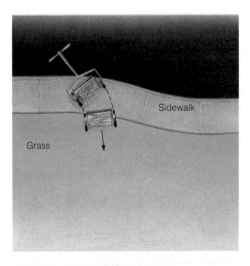

Figure 14.14 ▲
When one wheel slows down before the other wheel does, the lawnmower changes direction. This is a model of refraction.

TEACH ▪ *Continued*

Directed Inquiry

After students have read the page and studied Figure 14.15, ask the following questions:

▶ When waves constructively interfere, how are the speed and frequency of the resulting waves changed? (They are not affected; interference affects the amplitude of the wave only.)

▶ What two possibilities can result from destructive interference? (A wave with an amplitude smaller than one of the incoming waves or no wave at all)

▶ **Infer** Can interference occur in reflected waves? Explain. (Yes; two reflected waves, or an incident and reflected wave, can interact with each other.)

Portfolio

Have students make models of constructive and destructive interference using yarn glued to construction paper. Suggest that they use three different colors of yarn to show incoming and resultant waves. Students should use a metric ruler to measure each wave's amplitude to insure that the resultant wave is accurate for each pair of incoming waves. Students may keep their work in their portfolios.

The Living Textbook:
Physical Science Side 3

Chapter 27   Frame 09253
Interference in Ripple Tank (Movie)
Search: Play:

STS Connection

Tell students that architects and engineers often study standing waves and torsional waves. Have students use references to find out what standing waves and torsional waves are. Have them find out how these waves are generated and whether they are longitudinal or transverse. (Both are transverse)

Interference

Waves change when they interact with a surface, an edge, or a boundary. Waves also change when they interact with each other. The effect of two or more waves interacting is called **interference**. The interaction between two waves when they meet may produce a large single wave or no wave at all.

What happens as two wave crests meet? A single wave forms as the two crests begin to overlap. When two crests are at the same location at the same time, constructive interference takes place. A single wave with a crest of maximum amplitude is produced. The amplitude of the wave formed is the sum of the amplitudes of the interfering crests.

What happens when a crest of one wave meets a trough of another wave? The crest and trough subtract from each other to form a single wave, or possibly, no wave. Destructive interference takes place. Destructive interference produces water waves with a reduced amplitude. If the amplitudes of the crest and the trough were equal, the waves would cancel out one another.

Figure 14.15
When the water waves from the two boats meet, the amplitude of the resulting waves will change. ▼

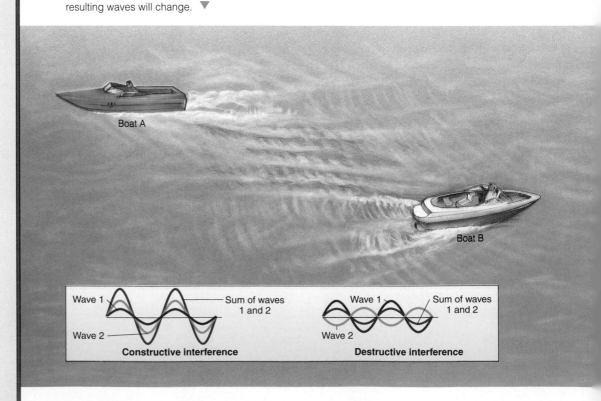

Boat A

Boat B

Wave 1 — Sum of waves 1 and 2
Wave 2
Constructive interference

Wave 1 — Sum of waves 1 and 2
Wave 2
Destructive interference

Social Studies Connection

Even the strongest breakwaters cannot protect shorelines from tsunamis. The countries and islands with coastlines along the Pacific and Indian Oceans are particularly vulnerable to tsunamis. One of the world's worst tsunamis occurred after the eruption of a volcano on the island of Krakatoa near Indonesia. Have students find out about the destruction caused by the tsunami.

Multicultural Perspectives

Many cultures have developed legends surrounding important events, such as earthquakes and tsunamis. Have students research several cultural explanations of tsunamis. Then ask students to write a report about how the legends explain these giant waves.

Consider This

Should Breakwaters and Wave Barriers Be Built?

Walk barefoot along the edge of the surf and you can feel the sand shifting constantly beneath your feet. The movement of the water causes the sand to move. Waves, tides, and water currents cause the natural formation and erosion of beaches.

Breakwaters and wave barriers are long walls built near harbors or along the shoreline. Breakwaters and wave barriers protect areas such as harbors, recreational areas, and private homes from erosion by forcing incoming waves to break farther from the shore. Breakwaters also prevent

damage to the harbor during heavy storms.

By changing wave action and redirecting water currents, these barriers cause sand deposits and beach erosion elsewhere. These changes affect the ecology of the shoreline. Often the habitat of wildlife is destroyed as a result of these changes.

Construction costs of breakwaters and wave barriers are high. Because of the force of the waves against them, they are also expensive to maintain.

Think About It What are the benefits of these structures?

Should nature be left to take its course or should people interfere with the natural processes?

Write About It Write a paper stating your position for or against building breakwaters and wave barriers. Include your reasons for choosing your position.

Science and Technology
Computer Models of Waveforms

A wind can create dangerous vibrations in a bridge spanning a river. Earthquake waves shake the surface of the earth. Overhead power lines release electromagnetic waves into the air. Heat waves spread away from the hot metal of a car exhaust. All these waves affect people's lives in some way. To better understand waves, scientists and engineers use computers to construct models of waves.

Computers produce complex waves by adding two or more simple waves. Computers also analyze the makeup of complex waves. Most complex waves that occur naturally are produced by the interference of many waves. To analyze complex waves, the computer generates a series of simple waves that make up the complex wave. By studying the simple waves produced by the computer, scientists are able to determine the behavior of complex waves. By understanding how complex waves interact,

Students can make a model of a shoreline using sand and a shallow pan. Before placing the sand in the pan, have students use a grease pencil to draw a line representing the shoreline. Then have them spread the sand to conform to the line. Have students gently add water at one end of the jar and observe what happens to the sand. Ask them to explain their observations.

Think About It Students may list some benefits of breakwaters as protection against storm damage and beach erosion. Students may disagree about whether or not people should interfere with natural processes.

Write About It Have students give reasons for their opinions.

Skills Development

Make a Model Have students discuss the computer models used to solve construction problems. Ask what complex waves have to do with the construction of buildings and bridges. (High winds can damage buildings if stress caused by winds isn't taken into account during construction; the effects of earthquake waves should be considered as buildings or bridges are constructed.)

 The Living Textbook: Physical Science Sides 1-4

Chapter 9   Frame 01547
Interference in Ripple Tank (1 Frame)
Search:

 The Living Textbook: Physical Science Sides 1-4

Chapter 11   Frame 01940
Interference in Rippple Tank (1 Frame)
Search:

Critical Thinking

Reason and Conclude Have students study the text and Figure 14.16 on this page. Ask students why researchers may wish to work with a series of simple waveforms rather than a single complex wave. (Individual waveforms can be analyzed much more easily. The interference displayed in a complex wave includes information on the frequency, wavelength, and amplitude of each energy input in the interference.)

EVALUATE

WrapUp

Portfolio Ask students to list several examples of each kind of wave interaction. Have them choose one example of each, and describe them using words and diagrams. Ask students to explain how they could demonstrate each wave interaction. Students can keep their diagrams in their portfolios.

Use Review Worksheet 14.3.

Check and Explain

1. **a.** Wave bounces off barrier, changes direction—amplitude, speed, frequency may be changed; **b.** wave bends around barrier, changes direction—amplitude, speed, frequency may be changed; **c.** wave bends as the result of a change in speed caused by moving from one medium to another; **d.** waves interact with each other to form a wave of greater, lesser, or no amplitude

2. Their measures are equal.

3. Constructive: resulting wave has amplitude larger than either incoming wave; destructive: resulting wave has amplitude smaller than incoming waves

4. It will bend. It will move more slowly in water.

STS Connection

Explain to students that linguists and speech therapists use spectrograms and computers to study the sound wave patterns of human speech. Have students find out what these studies are used for and how they help students learning languages. Have students make a bulletin board display showing their findings.

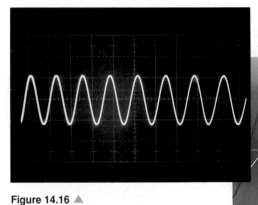

Figure 14.16 ▲
(left) The computer screen shows an image of a wave. (right) Computers can separate complex waves into a series of simple waves.

engineers and designers can solve problems that arise during the design and construction of buildings and bridges.

Look at the picture of a transverse wave on the left, in Figure 14.16. This curved line was actually produced on a computer screen. The computer calculated the position of each point on the curved line. The screen displayed each position to produce the curved line. This curved line is called a waveform. Some waveforms are very complex. Look at the waves shown on the right in Figure 14.16. These waves are examples of simple waves which make up complex waves.

Check and Explain

1. Explain how the motion of a wave is affected by each of the following interactions.

    a. reflection   b. diffraction
    c. refraction   d. interference

2. In wave reflection, how does the angle of incidence compare to the angle of reflection?

3. **Compare and Contrast** How do constructive and destructive wave interference differ?

4. **Predict** How would a light wave be affected as it passes from air into water at an angle?

Check Your Vocabulary

1. crest
2. refraction
3. rarefaction
4. wave
5. trough
6. amplitude
7. frequency
8. reflection
9. transverse wave
10. interference
11. longitudinal
12. refraction
13. wavelength
14. compression

Chapter 14 Review

Concept Summary

14.1 Nature of Waves
▶ Waves are a means by which energy travels through a medium.
▶ Only the energy carried by a wave moves forward through the medium.
▶ Waves are classified as either transverse or longitudinal, depending on how the medium is disturbed.

14.2 Wave Properties
▶ The parts of a transverse wave include crests and troughs.
▶ The parts of a longitudinal wave include compressions and rarefactions.
▶ Both transverse and longitudinal waves have wavelengths.

▶ A wave amplitude is the distance from the line of origin to the crest or trough. Amplitude is related to wave energy.
▶ The speed of a wave is the product of frequency multiplied by wavelength.

14.3 Wave Interactions
▶ Reflection, diffraction, refraction, and interference occur when waves interact.
▶ During reflection, diffraction, and refraction, waves change direction.
▶ During refraction a wave changes speed and bends as it moves from one medium to another.
▶ Wave amplitude increases during constructive interference and decreases during destructive interference.

Chapter Vocabulary

wave (p. 335)
crest (p. 336)
trough (p. 336)
transverse wave (p. 336)
longitudinal wave (p. 337)
compression (p. 337)
rarefaction (p. 337)
wavelength (p. 343)
amplitude (p. 344)
frequency (p. 344)
reflection (p. 349)
diffraction (p. 350)
refraction (p. 351)
interference (p. 352)

Check Your Vocabulary

Use the vocabulary words above to complete the following sentences correctly.

1. The top of a transverse wave is called the ____ .
2. A light wave bending as it passes from air to water is called ____ .
3. Matter spreads out in the ____ of a longitudinal wave.
4. Energy moves through a medium as a(n) ____ .
5. The lowest point of a transverse wave is a(n) ____ .
6. The distance from the line of origin to a crest is the ____ of a transverse wave.
7. The number of waves per unit time is ____ .
8. Angle of incidence applies to ____ .

9. The medium moves at right angles to the wave direction in a(n) ____ .
10. Waves interact with each other to produce ____ .
11. A wave that moves in the same direction as the disturbance in the medium is a(n) ____ .
12. The bending of a wave is called ____ .
13. The distance between two consecutive crests is ____ .
14. Matter in a longitudinal wave is close together in a(n) ____ .

Write Your Vocabulary

Write sentences using the vocabulary words above. Show that you know what each word means.

Write Your Vocabulary

Students' sentences should show that they know the meaning of each word as well as how to use it in a sentence.

Use Vocabulary Worksheet for Chapter 14.

Check Your Knowledge

1. When the pebble hits the water, kinetic energy is transferred to nearby water molecules. These molecules collide with others, transferring their energy outward. The disturbance is seen on the pond surface in the form of water waves.

2. Friction between the bottom of the wave and the sea bottom causes the lower part of the wave to move more slowly than the top, the crest gets higher, and the wave falls forward.

3. The crests of a transverse wave correspond to the compressions in a longitudinal wave; the troughs to the rarefactions.

4. The angle of incidence and the angle of reflection are equal.

5. A beam of light changes direction because wave speed is slower in water than it is in air.

6. When a crest and a trough meet at the same place, destructive interference takes place.

7. compressions and rarefactions

8. wind

9. frequency

10. 6 m/s

11. decreases

Check Your Understanding

1. 1 m
2. a. longitudinal
   b. transverse
   c. transverse
3. It is possible that the wind is stronger off-shore.
4. You can infer that the water is shallow out to about that distance or the waves are very high.
5. The frequency will increase.
6. To withstand earthquakes, buildings should be built in such a way that they absorb some of the energy of the quake waves.
7. The wake of the motorboat will spread out from the path of the boat as transverse waves. When the waves pass your location, your boat will rise and fall with the waves.
8. When the point at the center of the ripples is disturbed, kinetic energy is transferred to nearby water molecules, transferring their energy outward as surface waves.

Chapter 14 Review

Check Your Knowledge

Answer the following in complete sentences.

1. Why does a pebble dropped into a pond produce waves?

2. What causes an ocean wave to curl or break?

3. How do parts of transverse waves correspond to parts of longitudinal waves?

4. When a wave reflects from a surface, what is the relationship between the angle of incidence and the angle of reflection?

5. Why does a beam of light change direction when it passes from air into water?

6. What happens when a crest and a trough of two waves of equal amplitude meet at the same place?

Choose the answer that best completes each sentence.

7. Longitudinal waves have (crests and compressions, troughs and rarefactions, crests and troughs, compressions and rarefactions).

8. The motion of ocean waves is started by friction between surface water and (the seafloor, wind, water, rocks).

9. The number of waves that pass a point in a given time is a measure of (wavelength, frequency, trough, amplitude).

10. If a wave's frequency is 2 Hz and its wavelength is 3 m, its speed is (5 m/s, 5 Hz/s, 6 m/s, 6 Hz/s).

11. If a wave's frequency increases but its speed stays the same, you can assume that its wavelength (stays the same, increases, decreases, is zero).

Check Your Understanding

Apply the concepts you have learned to answer each question.

1. **Application** If the crest of a wave whose amplitude is 4 m meets the trough of a wave whose amplitude is 3 m, what is the amplitude of the resulting wave?

2. Which of the following describes a transverse wave? Which describes a longitudinal wave?

   a. close together, spread out
   b. up and down
   c. wind blowing grass

3. You go to the beach on a calm day to find large waves pounding the shore. What can you infer from this observation?

4. You go to the beach and see waves breaking about 300 m from the shore. What can you infer about the slope of the sea bottom?

5. If the wavelength stays the same, but the speed of a wave slows, how will the frequency of the wave be affected?

6. When building a structure in an area where earthquakes occur frequently, what general principle of construction should be followed?

7. **Application** You are fishing in the middle of a lake from an anchored rowboat. A motorboat 100 m away passes you at a high speed. Describe how the wake of the motorboat will affect the rowboat in which you are sitting.

8. **Mystery Photo** The photograph on page 334 shows surface waves forming in water. Describe in scientific terms the cause of the ripples in the water.

Develop Your Skills

1. a. Sound 3 has the largest frequency; 1 has the smallest.

   b. Sound 1 has the longest wavelength; 3 has the shortest.

   c. The longer the wavelength the lower the frequency.

   d. Sound 1: 1125 m/s; sound 2: 1169 m/s; sound 3: 1089 m/s

2. a. Short wave AM has the highest frequency; VHF has the lowest.

   b. VHF has the shortest wavelength; long wave AM has the longest.

   c. The longer the wavelength the lower the frequency if the wave moves at the same speed.

3. Student designs will vary. Note the method suggested for measuring wave height. Most will probably want to clearly mark the sides of the container in which waves are produced.

Make Connections

1.

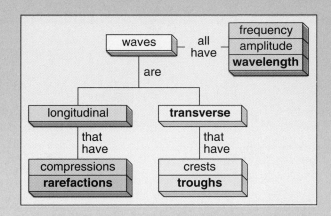

2. Student reports will vary.

3. Students may use a lake, river, or other water environment for their surveys. Review students' surveys to be sure they focus on the use and protection of the area they are studying.

4. Student models will vary. Make sure they are accurate depictions of the phenomena. Waves moving with the same energy over a shallower area will gain frequency.

Develop Your Skills

Use the skills you have developed in this chapter to complete each activity.

1. Interpret Data The table below shows the relationship between the frequency and the wavelength of three sounds.

Sound	Frequency (Hz)	Wavelength (m)
1	750	1.5
2	975	1.2
3	990	1.1

a. Which sound has the largest frequency? The smallest?

b. Which sound has the longest wavelength? The shortest?

c. How does the wavelength affect the frequency of each sound?

d. Calculate the speed of each sound.

2. Data Bank Use the information on page 638 to answer the following questions.

a. Which type of wave has the highest frequency? The lowest?

b. Which type of wave has the shortest wavelength? The longest?

c. What is the relationship between frequency and wavelength?

3. Hypothesize Recall how ocean waves are produced. Design a simple experiment to test the effect of wind speed on the amplitude of surface waves. Describe the problem, materials, procedure, expected observations, and conclusion.

Make Connections

1. Link the Concepts Below is a concept map showing how some of the main concepts in this chapter link together. Only part of the map is filled in. Finish the map, using words and ideas you find on the previous pages.

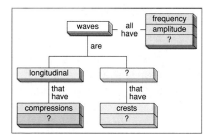

2. Science and You Surfing with a board or with just your body can be great fun, but it also can cause injury. Do research to find out how to ride the surf safely. Find out how competitive surfers train to reduce their chances of injury.

3. Science and Society The opinions of citizens affect how laws are written and whether they are passed. Design a survey addressing the use and protection of a local beach or other ecologically-sensitive area. Ask people in your community or school to fill in the survey sheets. Analyze the data. Based on your analysis, suggest regulations that reflect the views of the local citizens.

4. Science and Art Using clay, make a model of a wave as it approaches shore. Show how the shape of the wave changes as the water depth changes.

CHAPTER 15

Overview

This chapter discusses the nature of sound. The structure, characteristics, and motion of sound waves is described in the first section. The second section explains intensity and pitch, their relation to amplitude and frequency, and the measurement of sound in decibels and hertz. The chapter ends with a description of sound wave reflection, refraction, diffraction, interference, and resonance.

Advance Planner

► Provide flexible springs and a meter stick for TE page 360.

► Collect timers, metal and plastic rods, newspapers, glasses, and spoons for TE and glass bottles for SE page 363.

► Obtain a copy of Tom Wolfe's book for TE page 364.

► Supply dinner forks for SE page 365.

► Provide cotton and cups for TE page 367.

► Obtain recordings of the musical pieces and a tuning fork or pitch pipe and opaque screen for TE page 370.

► Provide trays and sticks for TE page 374.

► Gather materials for SE activity 15, page 380.

Skills Development Chart

Sections	Communicate	Generalize	Infer	Model	Observe	Predict	Research
15.1 Skills WarmUp					●		
SkillBuilder			●				
Skills WorkOut		●					
15.2 Skills WarmUp						●	
Skills WorkOut				●			
15.3 Skills WarmUp			●				
Skills WorkOut			●		●		
Historical Notebook	●			●	●		●
Activity			●	●	●	●	

Individual Needs

► **Limited English Proficiency Students** Make a tape recording of the definitions and pronunciations of the chapter's boldface terms. Tell students which figures and definitions in the text describe the term. Have them use the tape recorder to listen to the information about each term; then have them record a sound illustration for each. For example, to illustrate *intensity* they might record some loud music, some conversation, and then some whispering. They could narrate the illustration, giving the decibel range for each sound, using the information in Table 15.2. Have them use the tapes during their chapter review.

► **At-Risk Students** Write the terms *pitch, loudness,* and *tone quality* on the chalkboard. Have students copy each term onto a page of their portfolio. Provide soundmakers, such as whistles, bells, kazoos, horns, alarm clocks, and timers, for students to test. Ask students to write a description of each object's sound, placing the description of its pitch, loudness, and tone quality under the appropriate heading. After the soundmakers have been tested, have students compare their descriptions.

► **Gifted Students** Have students work in groups of four to use resonance to find the wavelength. Provide a long, glass or clear plastic tube with a diameter of about 7 cm, a stopper to fit the tube, sawdust, a tuning fork, a thermometer, and a table giving the speed of sound in air at different temperatures. They should hold the tube on its side and study the patterns made by sawdust along the tube when it resonates. Groups may assign specific tasks to their members: one student might prepare drawings showing what happens during the experiment. A second student might be responsible for measuring the distance between repeated patterns in the sawdust, and the third for measuring the air temperature and finding the speed of sound at that temperature. The fourth student might calculate the wavelength. You may need to tell students that the distance between repeated patterns (piles of sawdust) is 1/2 wavelength.

Resource Bank

► **Bulletin Board** Title the bulletin board *Sound Waves*. Prepare labels on index cards of the sound-related vocabulary words from the wave chapter (amplitude, compression, frequency, rarefaction, and longitudinal wave). Have students make drawings or find and cut out photographs that illustrate each of the vocabulary terms in this chapter. Randomly attach all cards to the bulletin board. Ask students to supply photographs that illustrate the term and encourage them to arrange the cards so that related terms are near one another.

► **Field Trip** Take students to a radio station or recording studio while it is in session. Ask the guide to tell you how sound is controlled and amplified by the equipment.

Section	Core	Standard	Enriched	Section	Core	Standard	Enriched
15.1 Wave Model of Sound pp. 359–365				**Blackline Masters** Review Worksheet 15.2 Enrich Worksheet 15.2 Skills Worksheet 15.2 Integrating Worksheet 15.2	● ● ●	● ● ● ●	● ● ●
Section Features Skills WarmUp, p. 359 Skills WorkOut, p. 365 SkillBuilder, p. 363	● ● ●	● ● ●	● ● ●	**Overhead Blackline Transparencies** Overhead Blackline Master 13 and Student Worksheet		●	●
Blackline Masters Review Worksheet 15.1 Skills Worksheet 15.1a Skills Worksheet 15.1b Integrating Worksheet 15.1	● ● ●	● ● ● ●	● ●	**Color Transparencies** Transparency 56	●	●	●
Ancillary Options *One-Minute Readings,* pp. 80–81	●	●	●	**15.3 Sound-Wave Interactions** pp. 372–380			
Color Transparencies Transparency 55	●	●	●	**Section Features** Skills WarmUp, p. 372 Skills WorkOut, p. 375 Historical Notebook, p. 378 Activity, p. 380	● ● ● ●	● ● ● ●	● ● ● ●
Laboratory Program Investigation 29 Investigation 30	● ●	● ●		**Blackline Masters** Review Worksheet 15.3 Vocabulary Worksheet 15	● ●	● ●	
15.2 Properties of Sound pp. 366–371				**Overhead Blackline Transparencies** Overhead Blackline Master 14 and Student Worksheet	●	●	●
Section Features Skills WarmUp, p. 366 Skills WorkOut, p. 371	● ●	● ●	● ●	**Laboratory Program** Investigation 31	●	●	●

Bibliography

The following resources can be used for teaching the chapter. See page T-46 for supplier codes.

Library Resources

Berman, Paul. *Light and Sound.* New York: Marshall Cavendish, 1988.

The Diagram Group. *Comparisons.* New York: St. Martin's Press, 1980.

Lampton, Christopher F. *Sound: More Than What You Hear.* Hillside, NJ: Enslow Publishers, Inc., 1992.

Sherwood, Martin, and Christine Sutton. *The Physical World.* New York: Oxford University Press, 1988.

White, Jack R. *The Hidden World of Forces.* New York: Dodd, Mead & Company, 1987.

Technology Resources

Software

Learning All About Heat and Sound. Mac, Win. LS.
Learning All About Matter. Mac, Win. LS.
Science in Your Ear. Mac, Win. ER.
Sound Waves. Mac. ESI.

Laserdiscs

Living Textbook. (See barcodes on pages in this chapter.) Optical Data.

Videos

The World of Sound Energy. FM.

Audio-Visual Resources

A Look at Sound. Film. T-L.

Writing Connection

Have students write a paragraph about a musical instrument. Have them describe the instrument, how to play it, and the sound it makes—without using the name of the instrument. Students can exchange paragraphs and try to identify the instruments based on the descriptions.

Introducing the Chapter

Have students read the description of the photograph. Ask if they agree or disagree with the description. Students may want to add that the area of the instrument where the player would press the strings is not shown in the picture.

Directed Inquiry

Have students study the photograph. Ask:

▶ What is shown in the photograph? (Students should say that the photograph shows a guitarlike stringed instrument.)

▶ How does the player of this instrument make sounds? (By picking, strumming, or plucking the strings to make them vibrate.)

▶ What accounts for the different sounds made by the strings? (Students may mention the string thickness, or changing the strings' lengths by pressing them against the instrument's neck.)

Chapter Vocabulary

constructive interference	hertz
decibel	pitch
destructive interference	resonance
Doppler effect	sound wave
	timbre

 The Living Textbook: Physical Science Side 3

Chapter 39   Frame 27396
Guitar String Vibrating (2 Movies)
Search: Play:

Chapter 15   Sound

Chapter Sections

15.1   **Wave Model of Sound**

15.2   **Properties of Sound**

15.3   **Sound-Wave Interactions**

What do you see?

❝I see strings that are tough and strong. This instrument works by plucking the strings with your fingers to make sounds. If you press on any of the shiny bars on which the strings lay, the sound will change. A person would use this wooden instrument by plucking and running her fingers across the strings while the other hand presses down on the parallel and shiny bars.❞

*Elizabeth Hayes
Santa Fe High School
Santa Fe, New Mexico*

To find out more about the photograph, look on page 382. As you read this chapter, you will learn about sound and how different sounds are made.

15.1 Wave Model of Sound

Objectives

▶ **Describe** the characteristics of a sound wave.

▶ **Identify** two factors that affect the speed of sound.

▶ **Compare** and **contrast** the behavior of sound before and during a sonic boom.

▶ **Make a model** to show how the speed of sound differs in the three phases of matter.

▼ **ACTIVITY**

Observing

Thwang!

Obtain a plastic ruler.

1. Place the plastic ruler on your desk so that 15 to 20 cm of the ruler extends over the edge.

2. Hold the ruler tightly against the edge of the desk with your hand.

3. Pluck the extended part of the ruler several times with a finger.

Observe the motion of the ruler. Describe the feeling in your hand holding the ruler while the ruler is vibrating.

SKILLS WARMUP

W hat do the twang of a guitar and the boom of a bass drum have in common? They are sounds. All sounds have a source. In a guitar, the sound comes from a plucked string. In a drum, the sound comes from the vibration of the drumhead.

How does sound get from its source to your ears? Recall that sound is a form of energy, and it travels as a wave. While some forms of energy can move through a vacuum, sound waves only move through matter. Sound travels through solids, liquids, and gases.

Sound Waves

When you strum guitar strings, they move rapidly back and forth. You cause the strings to vibrate. Often this back-and-forth motion is too fast for you to see. Each string blurs and looks like two or more strings. Look at the vibrating strings of the guitar in Figure 15.1.

Sound moves from its source through matter in the form of **sound waves**. A sound wave is produced in matter by a vibrating object. For example, you can make a sound by plucking a stretched rubber band. The rubber band pushes on the molecules in the surrounding air. This motion produces a series of compressions and rarefactions through the air.

Recall that a series of compressions and rarefactions forms a longitudinal wave. Molecules of matter are close together in a compression and spread apart in a rarefaction. Since the motion of the molecules is parallel to the direction of the wave, sound waves are longitudinal waves.

Figure 15.1 ▲
Vibrating guitar strings are a source of sound.

TEACH

Explore Visually

Have students study Figure 15.2. Ask:

- ▶ Which part of the spring is like the compression of a longitudinal wave? (The part where the springs are close together)

- ▶ What part of a longitudinal wave corresponds to a crest in a transverse wave? (Compression)

- ▶ How would you describe the rarefaction in a longitudinal wave? (The place where the springs move farther apart)

- ▶ What part of the transverse wave corresponds to the rarefaction? (Trough)

- ▶ What influences the amplitude of a longitudinal wave? (The size of its compressions)

- ▶ How can you describe the wavelength in a longitudinal wave? (The distance between two compressions or two rarefactions)

The Living Textbook:
Physical Science Sides 1-4

Chapter 11   Frame 01920
Slinky (3 Frames)
Search: Step:

The Living Textbook:
Physical Science Side 3

Chapter 23   Frame 06345
Mechanical Waves (Movie)
Search: Play:

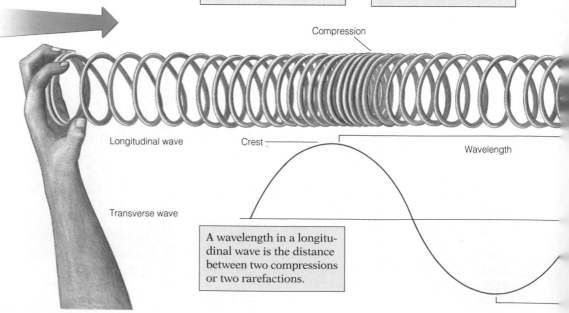

Cooperative Learning

Have students work in cooperative pairs to make a model of sound waves. Give each pair a flexible spring like the one shown on pages 360 and 361. Suggest that students put the spring on the floor to keep it horizontal. Have students hold one end of the spring stationary. Tell them to observe what happens as the other end is first pulled, then released. Ask, What happens to the individual coils of the spring? Have students make a diagram that shows the movement of the coils. Have students move the coils with different amounts of energy. Draw the size of the compressions and rarefactions for both amounts of energy. Have them label their diagrams to show how the spring coil is a model for sound waves. Students may add their diagrams to their portfolios.

How Sound Waves Travel

The stretched spring in Figure 15.2 is a good model of how sound energy moves through matter. When the spring is stretched and then released, energy moves from coil to coil. Because each vibrating coil pushes and is pushed by neighboring coils, energy moves through the spring. As sound energy moves through matter, the particles of matter move back and forth in a similar manner.

The compressions and rarefactions of a longitudinal sound wave can be compared to the parts of a transverse wave. Look at Figure 15.2. Compressions correspond to crests. Rarefactions correspond to troughs. The size of a compression indicates how much energy the sound wave has and corresponds to the amplitude of a transverse wave. For example, a sound wave with a high amplitude will have large compressions. A sound wave with a low amplitude will have small compressions.

Figure 15.2
Comparing Waves ▼

A sound wave travels in much the same way as a pulse of energy expands and contracts the coils of a spring.

The compression in a longitudinal wave corresponds to the crest in a transverse wave.

A wavelength in a longitudinal wave is the distance between two compressions or two rarefactions.

360   Chapter 15   Sound

STS Connection

In about 1650, Otto von Guericke invented a device called an air pump that could create a partial vacuum. In one of his experiments he sucked all the air from a jar that contained a bell. He could see the clapper striking the bell in the vacuum, but heard no sound. He showed that sound, unlike light, would not travel through a vacuum. Ask students to research and describe Guericke and the Magdeburg pump.

Math Connection

Explain to students that the speed of light is about 300 000 km/s, and the speed of sound, through air at 20°C, is about 344 m/s. If an observer sees a flash of lightning and hears a thunder clap 5 seconds later, how far away is the thunderstorm? (Assuming that the temperature of the air is 20°C, 344 m/s × 5 s = 1720 m.)

Did you ever notice that several seconds pass between the time you see lightning and you hear thunder. Actually, lightning and thunder occur at the same time. What's happening during this time lapse? Both light and sound are moving through the air toward you. However, light travels faster than sound does, so you see the lightning flash before you hear the thunder.

Factors Affecting the Speed of Sound

Sound waves can only move through matter, either solids, liquids, or gases. If you put your ear to a solid door, you can hear a conversation on the other side. Dolphins and many other marine mammals communicate by sending sound waves through water. When your teacher speaks to the class, the sound waves travel through air. Since there's no matter in outer space, sound can't move through it.

The speed at which sound waves move depends on the matter, or medium, through which they move, and not on the source. Notice that when a band begins to play in a large stadium, the sounds of the tuba and the drums reach your ears at the same time. Sound from both instruments is moving through the same medium. Several factors influence the speed of sound through a medium, including the temperature, elasticity, and density of the medium.

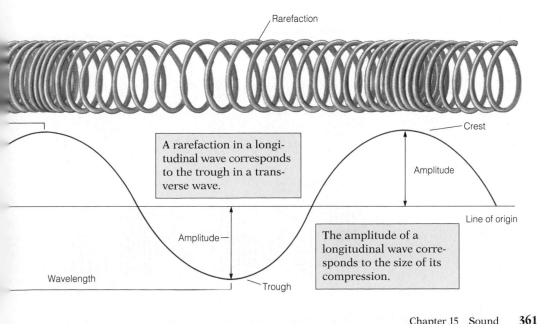

Rarefaction

A rarefaction in a longitudinal wave corresponds to the trough in a transverse wave.

Crest

Amplitude

Line of origin

Amplitude

Wavelength

Trough

The amplitude of a longitudinal wave corresponds to the size of its compression.

Skills Development

Predict   Copy the longitudinal wave onto the chalkboard. Beneath it draw a transverse wave. Ask, How can a transverse wave in the spring coil be made? (By moving one end of the coil up and down) Have students test their predictions.

Critical Thinking

Compare and Contrast   Draw a longitudinal wave on the chalkboard and ask students to indicate the direction in which the wave and particles of matter in the medium move. Ask them to give the wavelength and amplitude as well. Pose the same questions for a transverse wave. Then ask, How are the waves similar? How are they different? (They both transfer energy, they both have wavelength and amplitude; in longitudinal waves particles move in the same direction as the wave, in transverse waves, they move at an angle to the wave.)

Reteach

Have students make a diagram to show why the following statements are incorrect:

▶ Sound can travel through outer space. (Sound is vibrating matter, there's no matter in space.)

▶ The louder the sound, the faster it moves. (Speed of sound depends on the characteristics of the matter, not how loud it is.)

▶ The amplitude of wave depends on how fast it's moving. (The amplitude depends on the energy carried by the wave, not its speed.)

 **The Living Textbook:
Physical Science Side 3**

Chapter 19   Frame 03447
Longitudinal and Transverse Waves
(Movie)
Search: Play:

TEACH ▪ Continued

Directed Inquiry

Have students examine Figure 15.3. Ask the following questions:

▶ Are the compressions longer in cold air or in warm air? (Warm)

▶ Which has longer rarefactions, sound in cold air or sound in warm air? (Warm air)

▶ Does sound move faster through warm air or cold air? Why? (Warm air; as the temperature increases, the molecules collide more often because they are moving faster.)

Apply

Have students imagine that they are to design a music room for the library. They should design it so that the sounds are not heard in the library. Ask, Which of the following—a sheet of metal, a thin wall of water, or air—would you place between the inside and outside walls of the music room? Have students explain their choices. (Air; gases are poor transmitters of sound.)

Portfolio

Have the students copy Figure 15.3 by hand, plotting each diagram on a separate sheet of paper. Under each diagram have them draw a transverse wave showing crests and troughs that correspond to the compressions and rarefactions. Students should keep their drawings in their portfolios.

Answer to In-Text Question

① **Sound moves more quickly through the more active molecules in warm air than through the less active molecules in cold air.**

Answer to Link

The tap was noticeably louder when heard underwater. Water transmits sound better than air, allowing the whale's sound to travel vast distances and still be heard.

362

Math Connection

Explain to students that the speed of sound in air can vary. At normal pressure, V increases by 0.6 m/s for each degree-Centigrade increase in air temperature. Have them use the equation $V = [331 + 0.6x]$ m/s to compute the speed of sound through air at 0°C, –10°C, and 25°C. Explain that $x = $ °C. (331 m/s; 325 m/s; 346 m/s)

Social Studies Connection

The sound of a bell is determined by the metal in it. In the early history of the United States, bells were cast in Europe and sent to the New World. Have students find out which countries made bells, what they were made of, and why the sound of the bell was important.

Life Science LINK

Have you ever wondered how whales can communicate across vast distances of ocean? You can investigate how sound travels in water when you take a bath.

1. Sitting in the tub of water, tap lightly on a part of the bathtub that is above the water. Note how loud the sound is.

2. Lower yourself into the water so both ears are just below the surface. Tap lightly on a part of the bathtub that is underwater. Note how loud the sound is.

Describe your results. How do your results help explain how whales are able to communicate across long distances?

ACTIVITY

Elasticity and Density Sound waves move quickly through matter that is elastic. Matter is elastic if its molecules return quickly to their original position when disturbed. Some metals, like iron and nickel, are very elastic and transmit sound as well. Most liquids aren't very elastic, so they don't transmit sound as well. Gases are the least elastic and are poor transmitters of sound.

Sound moves well through a dense material, such as metal or wood, because the molecules are close together. Air density also affects the speed of sound. Because of the pressure of the air above it, air at sea level is denser than it is at high altitudes. At high altitudes, the air molecules are spread out and sound doesn't move as fast as it does through air at low altitudes.

Temperature When the temperature of air increases, the speed of sound also increases. Sound moves 344 m/s through 20°C air. However, if the air temperature is 0°C, sound moves through it at a speed of 331 m/s. Why? A sound wave moves through air when vibrating particles come into contact with other particles. As the temperature of air increases, molecules of air collide more often because they're moving around faster. As a result, a sound wave moves through warm air faster than it moves through cool air. Since molecules in liquids and solids are close together, temperature has less effect on the speed of sound through them.

Figure 15.3 ▶
The dots represent air molecules. Molecules are more active in warm air than in cold air. How does this fact affect the speed of sound? ①

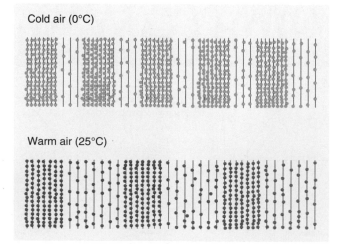

Cold air (0°C)

Warm air (25°C)

Cooperative Learning

Have students work in cooperative pairs to test the transmission of a sound through various materials. Have students use a ticking kitchen timer as the source of sound, and test a variety of materials, such as air, a wooden meter stick, a metal curtain rod, a plastic rod, and a tightly rolled newspaper.

Students should keep the distance from the timer to their ears the same for each material tested. Have them rate the sound transmission on a scale of one to five for each material tested. Ask, What can you conclude about the types of materials that can be used to conduct sound? (Answers will vary, but students should find that most metals transmit sound better than wood or air does.)

Material The speed of sound varies in different materials, or media. Look at the information in Table 15.1. The table lists the speed of sound through different kinds of material that are at the same temperature. Examine the table to locate at least one solid, liquid, and gas. Through which material does sound move fastest? The speed of sound in a fence rail made of oak at 20°C is 3,850 m/s. In an iron rail at the same temperature, the speed of sound soars to 5,130 m/s. Through which of these mediums does sound travel the slowest? What inferences can you make about how fast sound travels through different materials around you?

Listen, while a friend who is some distance away from where you are, hammers on an iron or wooden fence rail. Touch a portion of the rail with your hand. You might be surprised to discover that you can feel vibrations in the rail before you hear the sound. What accounts for this difference? ②

Table 15.1
Speed of Sound

Medium	Speed of Sound at 20°C (m/s)
Iron	5,130
Glass	4,540
Wood (oak)	3,850
Water	1,500
Alcohol	1,240
Cork	500
Air	344

SkillBuilder Inferring

Musical Bottles

Sounds can be produced in many different ways. All of them involve vibrations moving through some medium. Musical instruments cause vibrations in the air.

When you blow across the mouth of a bottle that is partly filled with liquid, air vibrates and you can make a sound. By increasing or decreasing the amount of liquid in the bottle, you can change the pitch of the sound it produces. How does the sound change when there are different amounts of liquid in the bottle?

1. Locate four glass bottles of approximately the same size and type. The bottles should have narrow necks.

2. Fill each bottle with decreasing amounts of water at room-temperature.

3. Use masking tape and markers to label your bottles A through D. Bottle A should have the most water in it. Bottle D should have the least amount of water in it.

4. Blow across each bottle to make a sound. Listen to the sound each one makes, and identify the pitch of each sound as high, medium, or low.

Answer the following questions.

1. Which bottle emits the lowest sound? Which emits the highest sound?

2. How does the pitch of each sound relate to the amount of water in the bottle?

3. Infer what would happen to the sound the bottles produced if you changed the temperature of the water in the bottles. Test your prediction.

Skills Development

Make a Graph Have students use the information in Table 15.1 to make a bar graph of the speed of sound through different materials. Have them use three different colored pencils: one for the solids— iron, glass, wood, and cork; the second color for the liquids—water and alcohol; and the third color for the gas— air. Ask them to label the bars with a *D* for dense materials and with an *E* for elastic.

Class Activity

Have students work in groups of four. Provide a glass, a spoon, and a water source for each group. Have one student in each group pour water into the glass while another constantly taps the spoon against the side of the glass. Ask students to describe how the tapping sounds change. Ask them to explain why. (The pitch rises as air height decreases, because the wave in the air produces the sound.)

SkillBuilder

Answers

1. Bottle *D*, with the least water, emits the lowest sound. Bottle *A*, with the most water, emits the highest sound.

2. The more water, the higher the pitch

3. The sound gets lower as the water temperature increases.

Answer to In-Text Question

② **Sound moves faster through wood or iron than through air.**

TEACH ■ Continued

Directed Inquiry

Have students study Figure 15.5. Point out that air compressions are spread out, or elongated, if the plane is moving faster than the speed of sound. Discuss the following:

▶ At what point on the drawing does the sonic boom occur? (Where the compressions meet the air, at the "V")

▶ Have students describe what makes the noise. (As the compression waves meet the air, the wave crests overlap to form constructive interference. A shock wave results. The shock wave is the sonic boom.)

Portfolio

Ask students to research the speeds of several different types of aircraft. Have them make a table that identifies at least three aircraft, their speeds, whether or not they fly faster than the speed of sound, and the uses of each plane. Students may add the tables to their portfolios.

Answer to In-Text Question

① Compressions build up in the air and the air expands and creates a sonic boom.

The Living Textbook: Physical Science Sides 1-4

Chapter 14 Frame 02268
Sonic Boom/Shock Wave (2 Frames)
Search: Step:

The Living Textbook: Physical Science Side 3

Chapter 40 Frame 29797
Shock Wave (Movie)
Search: Play:

Literature Connection

Ask students to describe what they think it would be like to travel faster than sound. Then read aloud an excerpt about breaking the sound barrier from the book *The Right Stuff,* by Tom Wolfe, or some other book about supersonic flight. Have the class compare their descriptions with the pilots'.

The Sound Barrier

The speed of sound in air probably seems fast to you. However, many jet planes, such as the one shown in Figure 15.4, cruise at even faster speeds. When a jet reaches a speed that is as fast or faster than sound, it produces a loud, thunderlike sound called a sonic boom.

By traveling faster than the speed of sound, a jet moves past the sound waves it creates in the air. A pattern of wave crests build up like those in Figure 15.5 (left). Where the wave crests overlap, constructive interference occurs and a conical shell results (right). The conical shell is the shock wave, or sonic boom, you hear when the jet passes.

Before the first jet plane broke the sound barrier, many engineers claimed it would be impossible to fly a plane faster than the speed of sound. They thought a plane going that fast would be destroyed. The first sonic boom produced by human beings "shattered" the air over California's Mojave (mo HAH vay) Desert on October 14, 1947. On that historic day, test pilot Chuck Yeager, flying in the experimental rocket plane called the X-1, reached the speed of sound. As the X-1 passed the speed of sound, observers could hear and feel the sound vibrations.

Figure 15.4 ▶
The Concorde is a supersonic jet.

Figure 15.5
What happens when a jet plane like the Concorde flies faster than the speed of sound? ▼ ①

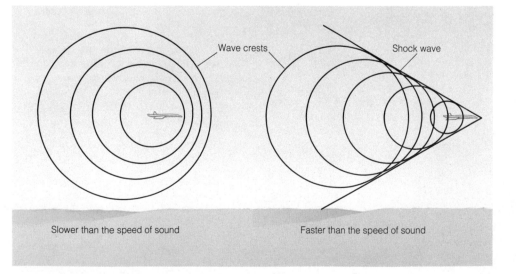

Wave crests Shock wave

Slower than the speed of sound Faster than the speed of sound

Integrating the Sciences

Health Point out to students that when a physician examines you, he or she sometimes thumps on your back. The purpose of this is to hear how the sound is conducted. A hollow sound means the lungs are clear of fluid. If you had pneumonia, for example, the physician would not hear a hollow sound, and would know to X-ray the lungs and to treat you with medication. Ask students if they have ever had this simple test.

Science and You
Listening Through Your Bones

Crunch! Crunch! Chewing a crisp apple is a noisy activity. You probably think that most students in the cafeteria can hear you. Don't worry. Your chewing is much noisier to you than it is to those around you.

When you chew something crunchy, the sound of your chewing is carried directly to your inner ear through the bones of your skull. Sound energy conducted through your bones bypasses your eardrum. For others to hear you crunch the apple, the sound waves created by your chewing must move through the air to reach them. Some energy is lost when the sound waves move through the air, and when they vibrate the listener's eardrums.

By the time sound waves from your chewing reach the eardrums of those around you, they have lost energy. Sound waves that carry less energy vibrate your inner ear with less force. The sound you hear as you crunch the apple is louder than the sound others hear because your eardrum will vibrate more.

Most of the sounds you hear come into your ear from the air. For example, when someone is speaking to you, the sound energy moves through the air before it enters your outer ear and causes your eardrum to vibrate. The vibration is transferred to your inner ear. When you create sounds in your mouth by eating, however, the sound energy is conducted directly to your inner ear. You are listening through your bones.

▼ ACTIVITY

Generalizing

Listening Outside

Obtain a dinner fork.

1. Hit the prongs of the fork on a table without damaging the table.

2. Quickly place the fork's handle against a bone behind your ear.

3. Repeat several times, placing the fork on a different bone near your ear each time.

How can you explain your observations?

SKILLS WORKOUT

Check and Explain

1. Describe the rarefactions and compressions of a sound wave.

2. Explain how temperature affects the speed of sound in air.

3. **Compare and Contrast** How do sound waves during a sonic boom compare with sound waves traveling at a slower speed?

4. **Make a Model** Use a drawing to illustrate how the compressions and rarefactions of a sound wave change when they travel through air, water, and solids.

Skills WorkOut

To help students recognize that bones conduct sound, have them do the Skills WorkOut.

Answer Answers will vary, but students should recognize that different bones conduct sound differently.

EVALUATE

WrapUp

Reteach Have students make two diagrams that show how sound travels to their ears. In one diagram, the sound source is their own singing; in the second diagram, someone is talking to them. The diagrams should show each step. Have students label parts of the diagrams to show sound waves, their movement, and the movement of the particles they affect. (Check students' diagrams for accuracy.)

Use Review Worksheet 15.1.

Check and Explain

1. The molecules in the compressions are close together, and are spread apart in a rarefaction.

2. Sound moves faster through warmer air because the molecules are moving faster and bump into one another more often.

3. Because a jet moves faster than the sound it makes, a pattern of wave crests builds up. Constructive interference causes a conical shock wave. Sound waves from aircraft moving slower than the speed of sound simply move out in front of the aircraft.

4. Check students' drawings for accuracy.

Section Objectives

For a list of section objectives, see the Student Edition page.

Skills Objectives

Students should be able to:

Predict how different variables affect sound.

Make a Model of a sound-effects machine.

Infer how loudness, pitch, and timbre relate to intensity, frequency and quality.

Define Operationally what is observed during the Doppler effect.

Vocabulary

decibel, pitch, hertz, Doppler effect, timbre

MOTIVATE

Skills WarmUp

To help students understand the properties of sound, have them do the Skills WarmUp.

Answer Faster rips produce louder sounds and different papers produce different sounds.

Misconceptions

Because *high* and *low* often describe both loudness and pitch, students may think of high pitches as always being loud. Explain that *high* and *low* refer only to pitch, not to intensity.

Answer to In-Text Question

① **The sound from the fork struck hard.**

The Living Textbook: Physical Science Side 3

Chapter 37	Frame 24680
Sound Waves (Movie)	
Search:	Play:

Themes in Science

Energy The intensity of a sound depends on the energy of the sound wave. As the distance between a source and a listener increases, the intensity of the sound decreases. Remind students that energy must be conserved. Have them explain what happens to the "miss-ing" or "lost" energy. (The sound waves spread their energy over an increasingly larger area, so the energy per unit area decreases. In addition, some of the energy is converted to other forms of energy, such as heat energy.)

▼ ACTIVITY

Predicting

Let It Rip

Obtain two 5-cm by 30-cm pieces of paper.

1. Listen as you rip one piece of paper lengthwise.

2. Predict what will happen to the sound if you rip the second piece of paper faster. Test your prediction.

Try this with different kinds of paper.

SKILLS WARMUP

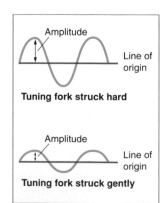

Figure 15.6 ▲
Which sound wave has greater amplitude? ①

15.2 Properties of Sound

Objectives

▶ **Identify** three properties of sound.

▶ **Estimate** the intensity of some familiar sounds.

▶ **Infer** how loudness, pitch, and timbre relate to the properties of sound waves.

▶ **Define operationally** how movement affects the pitch of sound.

Think of all the things you can do with your voice. You can shout, sing, talk, and whisper. You can even imitate the sounds of machines and nature. What makes the sound waves of a whisper different from those of a shout? Why is the sound of a singing voice different from that of a speaking voice?

If you think of how you made some of these sounds, you can understand how properties of sound waves can affect what you hear. The properties of sound waves include intensity, frequency, and quality. The effects of these three properties are loudness, pitch, and timbre.

Intensity of Sound

You're reading your report to the class. Because you're a little nervous, you speak softly. When the teacher asks you to speak louder, you force more air from your lungs. Your voice becomes louder because you use more energy to speak. When a sound wave has more energy, the amplitude is greater. Recall that the amplitude of a longitudinal wave depends on its energy.

Two sound waves produced by the same tuning fork are shown in Figure 15.6. The tuning fork at the top has more energy because it was struck harder than the one at the bottom. Except for their amplitudes, the two sound waves are similar. Which tuning fork in Figure 15.6 makes the louder sound?

The sound wave from the tuning fork that was struck hard has a high amplitude. The sound is louder because the sound wave has more energy and does more work to vibrate your eardrum. Loudness depends on your sensitivity to sound and the amplitude of the sound wave.

Think about making sound with a stretched rubber band. When you pull it, the work you do on it gives it energy. When you release the rubber band, its energy does work on the molecules of air in the form of a sound wave.

Decibels

Everyone might not agree when music is too loud. However, loudness can be measured. The **decibel** (dB) is the unit used to measure sound intensity or loudness. The sound of a leaf falling on the ground has a loudness of about 10 dB. A rock concert can produce sounds of 100 dB or more. Look at Table 15.2 for the decibel level of different common sounds.

You might see a jackhammer operator or an airport worker wearing ear protectors. These protectors decrease the loudness, or energy, of the sounds the worker hears. Your ears need protection because very loud sounds can be harmful. Sounds greater than 120 dB can cause pain. They can also cause vibrations that are intense enough to rupture an eardrum. Constant or daily exposure to high decibel sound, such as very loud music, can cause permanent hearing loss. The delicate bones and nerves that carry sound through your ears to your brain can be damaged by the intense compressions caused by very loud sound.

Table 15.2
Loudness of Common Sounds

Sound	Decibels (dB)
Jet engine	170
Rock concert	100–125
Thunderstorm	90–110
Vacuum cleaner	75–80
Conversation	60–70
Classroom	35
Whispering	10–20
Falling leaves	10

◀ **Figure 15.7**
How loud is the sound each of these objects makes? ②

Frequency and Pitch

When you sing the "Happy Birthday" song, you change your voice to sing the tune. The loudness of your voice doesn't change. The **pitch** does. Pitch describes how high or low a sound is. When you sing the word *birthday,* you raise the pitch of your voice.

TEACH ▪ *Continued*

Discuss

Have students work in pairs to write one or two sentences that describe the relationship of pitch and frequency. (Answers may vary. For example, if pitch increases, frequency increases; pitch depends on frequency.)

Directed Inquiry

Have students examine Table 15.3. Ask the following questions:

▶ What animal has the largest frequency range? What does having the largest frequency range mean? (Porpoise; the porpoise can produce sound with the greatest range of frequencies, or pitches.)

▶ In what units are frequency and pitch measured? (Both are measured in hertz, or Hz.)

▶ Which sound sources can produce frequencies above the range of human hearing? (Porpoises, bats, stereo systems, and dog whistles)

Enrich

Use Enrich Worksheet 15.2.

Answer to In-Text Question

① It is greater.

The Living Textbook: Physical Science Side 3

Chapter 24　　Frame 07406
Frequency (Movie)
Search:　　　　Play:

The Living Textbook: Physical Science Sides 1-4

Chapter 17　　Frame 03054
Hertz (2 Frames)
Search:　　　　Step:

368

Integrating the Sciences

Life Science Explain to students that the human voice is produced by tightening and relaxing the vocal cords in the larynx. As air from the lungs is forced past the vocal cords, the cords vibrate. The tongue, teeth, and lips help shape sounds. Ask students how sounds of higher pitch are produced. (By tightening the vocal cords)

STS Connection

The energy carried by ultrasonic sound waves can be harnessed to clean industrial machine parts and even delicate watches and jewelry. Have students use their knowledge of sound waves and particle motion to suggest how ultrasonic cleaning devices work. (The high-frequency vibrations convert electric energy to mechanical energy. The mechanical energy can be a vibrating liquid or a vibrating solid, such as a drill bit.)

Figure 15.8
How is the frequency of a high-pitch sound different from that of a low-pitch sound? ▶

①

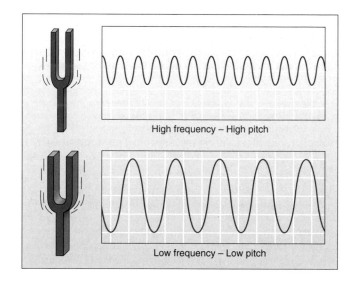

Table 15.3
Frequency Range of Some Sounds

Sound Source	Frequency Range (Hz)
Porpoise	7,000–120,000
Bat	10,000–120,000
Stereo system	15–30,000
Dog whistle	20,000–24,000
Frog	50–8,000
Piano	30–4,100
Dog	450–1,800
Human	85–1,100
Trumpet	190–990

When you change the pitch of your voice, you're changing the frequency of the sound waves you produce. The pitch of a sound depends on its frequency. Sound frequency is the number of sound waves that pass a point in a certain amount of time, such as one second.

The greater the frequency of a wave, the higher is its pitch. You hear high-pitch sounds, such as a bird's chirp, when high-frequency sound waves strike your eardrum. Low-frequency sound waves are heard as low-pitch sounds. One example of a low-pitch, low-frequency sound is a note played on a tuba. Give an example of a high-pitch sound.

The **hertz** is a unit used to measure frequency. Because a sound's pitch depends on the frequency of the sound waves, pitch is measured in hertz (Hz), also. The frequency of some common sounds are shown in Table 15.3.

If you have perfect hearing, you can hear sounds ranging from 20 to 20 000 Hz. You can hear a much wider range of frequencies than you can produce with your vocal cords. Many animals can hear sounds that are well beyond the range of human hearing.

Sound above the human range of hearing is called ultrasonic sound. Not only do many kinds of dolphins and bats hear ultrasonic sounds, they also produce them. Some of these animals produce ultrasonic sound to navigate and to find food.

The Doppler Effect

The increasing loudness of a wailing siren acts as a warning that an emergency vehicle is approaching. If you listen closely to the siren of an ambulance, you'll notice that the pitch of its siren decreases as the ambulance passes you. As the ambulance moves away, you notice that the pitch of the siren is lower. The noticeable difference in pitch is caused by the movement of the ambulance in relation to the listener.

A change in the frequency and pitch of a sound that is caused by either the movement of the source or the listener is known as the **Doppler effect**. Look at Figure 15.9. The Doppler effect explains the change in the frequency and pitch of the ambulance siren as it moves toward and then away from the listener.

You observe the Doppler effect often. Have you ever been on a train that was moving past a railroad crossing? The pitch of the warning bells decreases as you pass them. It decreases as you go by. In Figure 15.9, the sound source is moving and the listener is stationary.

Figure 15.9
The Doppler Effect ▼

The sound waves ahead of the ambulance are close together. The frequency and pitch of the siren is higher as it approaches the girl.

As the ambulance moves away, the sound waves are farther apart and reach the girl later. The frequency and pitch are lower.

TEACH ▪ *Continued*

Class Activity

For this activity you'll need three volunteers, a tuning fork or pitch pipe, and a screen to obscure the volunteers from the class.

▶ Have the volunteers leave the classroom and practice saying the same sentence, for example, "This is the timbre of my voice." Tell them to say the sentence as close to the same volume and pitch as possible.

▶ Have the volunteers return to the classroom and speak their phrases while hidden from view.

▶ Ask the class to identify the speakers by name. Discuss the results. (Each voice will have a distinguishing timbre.)

Answer to In-Text Question

① **The wave patterns have different amplitudes and frequencies.**

Music Connection

Play a recording of *Peter and the Wolf* by Sergey Prokofiev, *Carnival of the Animals* by Camille Saint-Saëns, or *Pictures at an Exhibition* by Modest Mussorgsky. Discuss the qualities of the sounds produced by each of the instruments that made them appropriate for the objects the composer wished to describe.

STS Connection

Music synthesizers can create almost any sound electronically. An early electronic synthesizer was a large instrument developed in 1955 for research into the properties of sound. In the 1960s, more compact synthesizers became commercially available. Most synthesizers have pianolike keyboards. Have students find out how a simple synthesizer works and make a diagram to show how it produces sounds of different qualities.

Sound Quality

The next time you're listening to a band or an orchestra, pay attention to the sounds of the individual instruments. Can you distinguish between them? If the instruments are playing the same note, you must use the *quality* of the sounds to make the distinction.

An instrument produces sound by vibrating air at a certain frequency. Musical instruments actually vibrate air at several different frequencies at the same time. Each frequency produces sound with a different pitch. The pitches produced by an instrument blend and give sound its quality, or timbre. The **timbre** (TIHM bur) of a sound is the blending of different-frequency sound waves that produce sound quality. If you listen carefully, you can hear that a sound produced by one instrument has a different quality than the same-pitch sound produced by another instrument.

The timbre of a sound can fool you about its source. For example, sound synthezisers can produce sounds electronically that have the same timbre as sounds produced by almost any sound source. A synthesizer can duplicate sounds that match the loudness, pitch, and timbre of every instrument in an orchestra. One synthesizer can sound like an entire orchestra.

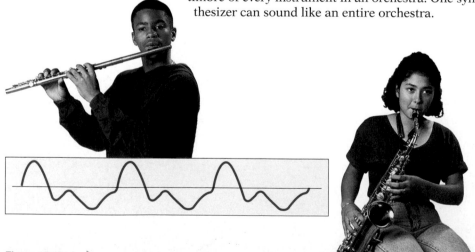

The Living Textbook:
Physical Science Sides 1-4

Chapter 14   Frame 02289
Musical Instruments (14 Frames)
Search: Step:

370

Figure 15.10 ▲ ▶
The wave patterns show what each instrument's sound would look like if you could see it. How are the wave patterns different? ①

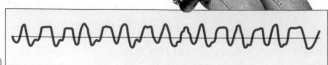

Cooperative Learning

Have students work in cooperative groups of four and choose a short story they would like to produce as a radio play. Encourage groups to choose stories that require several sound effects. Have students assign the roles of sound-maker and sound-collector among themselves. Have the groups record their play and present it to the rest of the class.
Use Integrating Worksheet 15.2b.

Science and Technology
Sound-Effects Machines

When you hear a scary groan in a play or booming thunder in a radio show, you're probably hearing a sound-effects machine that can imitate a certain sound. For example, a radio show can't depend on a thunderstorm to appear on cue, but a thunder machine can produce a similar sound and it is more reliable.

What kind of machine sounds like thunder? One way to create the sound of a distant rumble is to fill a cart with bricks and stones. The cart should have uneven wheels. When the cart is pushed across the floor, the uneven wheels cause the bricks and stones to shift in the cart. The resulting sound is a constant rumble, resembling an approaching storm.

Another kind of sound-effects machine can produce the sound of rainfall. The rain machine is made with a zigzag-shaped metal chute. Dried peas create the sound when poured through the top of the chute. As they make their way through the chute, the peas sound like rain falling on a roof.

An open-ended wooden barrel can create groans, creaks, and squeals. The barrel has a piece of rope fitted into the bottom. In order to produce sounds, the rope is held tightly, and a piece of leather is rubbed against the rope. The barrel acts to reinforce and prolong sounds. This machine can produce a variety of sounds, depending on how and where the leather is rubbed along the rope.

Check and Explain

1. Identify and describe three properties of sound.

2. Estimate the sound intensity of a pencil falling on a tile floor, an accelerating motorcycle, a barking dog, and the siren on an ambulance. Use Table 15.2 as a reference.

3. **Infer** How do loudness, pitch, and timbre relate to a sound's intensity, frequency, and quality?

4. **Define Operationally** Someone in a parked car is honking the horn. As you drive by, you notice that the pitch of the horn becomes lower. How might you account for your observation?

▼ ACTIVITY

Making a Model

Sound Device

Use every-day objects at home or in your classroom to create a simple device that makes a sound effect. Try it out on your classmates. See if they can guess what sound you're trying to simulate.

SKILLS WORKOUT

EVALUATE

WrapUp

Reinforce Write two columns of words on the board. In Column A include words and phrases, such as *pitch, frequency, decibel, hertz, amplitude, loudness, timbre,* and *Doppler effect.* In Column B include words and phrases, such as *increases, decreases, measure,* and *is related to.* Have students work in pairs to write sentences that use at least two words from Column A and one from Column B. Have pairs exchange sentences to check each other's work.
Use Review Worksheet 15.2.

Check and Explain

1. Intensity—measures loudness or the amount of energy in a wave; frequency—a measure of a sound's pitch; quality— produced by timbre, a blend of pitches

2. Answers will vary. Examples: pencil, 50 dB; motorcycle, 120 dB; dog, 80 dB; siren, 100 dB.

3. Answers will vary. Examples: Intensity is a measure of loudness, frequency is a measure of pitch, quality is defined by timbre.

4. The horn sounds lower because as you drive away, fewer sound waves reach you and are less frequent, so the pitch you hear is lower.

15.3

Section Objectives
For a list of section objectives, see the Student Edition page.

Skills Objectives
Students should be able to:

Infer how sound waves respond to interference.

Observe how sound differs during night and day.

Generalize about sound reflected as an echo.

Infer how sound waves reflect.

Vocabulary
destructive interference, constructive interference, resonance

---

MOTIVATE

Skills WarmUp
To help students understand sound-wave interaction, have them do the Skills WarmUp.
Answer Students should find that the noises are louder. They should say that cupping the hand behind the ear helps capture the sound waves emitted by the source.

Prior Knowledge
To gauge how much students know about sound-wave interactions, ask:

▶ What do you think can happen to sound waves once they leave the source?

▶ What affects the intensity and direction of sound?

▶ What is resonance?

Answer to In-Text Question
① Answers may vary, but should refer to a place with a reflective surface.

STS Connection
Have students find out about whispering galleries, such as the rotunda in the Capitol building in Washington, D.C. In a whispering gallery, a sound whispered at one end of the room can be heard clearly at the other end. Have students make a diagram and write captions that tell how sounds are reflected in these rooms. (The rooms are elliptical, sounds made at one focal point are reflected toward the opposite focal point.)

Answer to Link
The waves are reflected back toward the source of the waves. Bats send out high frequency sound waves which are reflected off insects in flight back toward the bat. These reflected waves allow the bat to locate the insect without being able to see it.

▼ ACTIVITY

Inferring

Sound Cup

Listen to the sounds in your classroom. Now cup your hands and place them behind each of your ears. How are sounds different? What do you think is happening to the sound waves?

SKILLS WARMUP

Figure 15.11
Think of where you were the last time you heard an echo. How was that place like the auditorium shown here? ▼
①

15.3 Sound-Wave Interactions

Objectives

▶ **Identify** five types of sound-wave interaction.

▶ **Define** resonance.

▶ **Generalize** about the behavior of echoes.

▶ **Infer** how sound waves interact to affect sound.

How do movie sound directors make a hallway seem long and empty? They add sound effects, such as the distant echo of footsteps. Sound directors know how a sound changes in different surroundings. They can change the sound of the footsteps so that they seem to be on a wooden floor or on concrete stairs.

Reflection of Sound

You've probably noticed that a shout sounds different in a vacant gym than it does in a cluttered classroom. When you shout, the sound of your voice moves away from your mouth. But what happens if the sound waves strike a hard, flat surface, such as a wall? As you can see in Figure 15.11, the sound waves of the singer's voice bounce back into the auditorium when they reflect off of the back wall.

Reflected sound waves

Sound waves

Math Connection

Have students solve the following problem: A hiker yells toward the back wall of a cave and hears the echo 1.5 seconds later. If the speed of sound is 344 m/s, how far away is the back wall of the cave? (344 m/s × 1.5 s = 516 m; 516 m is a round-trip distance; 258 m is the distance to the back wall.)

Art Connection

Have students draw a picture of a place that will produce an echo. Have them label the distance from the sound source to the reflecting surface. Then ask them to change the drawing to show how the echo could be eliminated. (To eliminate the echo, students might suggest covering up the surface, cluttering up the area, or moving the sound source closer than 17 m from the reflecting surface.)

Some energy from the sound wave passes through or is absorbed by the wall, but most of the sound is reflected. If you're sitting in the audience, the first sound you hear comes directly from its source, the speaker. A fraction of a second later, you hear the reflected sound wave. The reflected sound is an echo.

Why would you hear an echo in some auditoriums and not in others? The properties of the reflecting surface and the distance of the reflecting surface from the sound source affect echoes. Look at Figure 15.12. Notice that a curtain hangs from the back wall of the auditorium. Also notice that sound waves are not reflected off of the curtained wall as they are off of the hard, flat wall shown in Figure 15.11. Because the curtains at the back of the auditorium absorb most of the sound waves, very little sound is reflected into the auditorium. By changing a surface that reflects sound easily, echoes can be reduced or eliminated.

The distance of the reflecting surface from the sound source also determines if echoes are present. You can hear an echo if it comes at least 0.1 second after the original sound. For example, to hear an echo of your own voice, the reflected sound waves must reach your ears at least 0.1 second after you shout. During that time, sound waves travel about 34 m in air. To hear an echo of your voice, you must be at least 17 m from the reflecting surface. An echo can only occur naturally in an uncluttered space, such as a gymnasium. How would the amount of clutter affect sound waves?

Life Science

L I N K

Bats use reflected sound waves (echoes) to hunt insects. To investigate how echoes work, you need a brick, a ruler, and a sink.

1. Place the brick upright in the sink and fill the sink with water to about half the height of the brick.

2. With the length of the ruler parallel to one of the faces of the brick, quickly tap the surface of the water to create a series of waves. Observe how the waves are reflected off of the brick.

Describe the results. Explain how bats might use echoes to hunt for insects.

A C T I V I T Y

Figure 15.12
Think of an auditorium with curtains on the back wall. What will happen to the sound waves when they reach the back wall? ▼

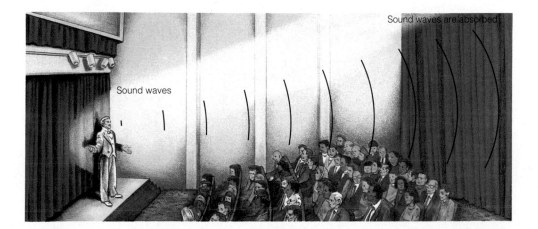

Sound waves are absorbed.

Sound waves

Class Activity

The temperature and humidity affect the speed at which sound travels. To demonstrate this, have students do the following activity. Have them line up facing a wall of the school building. The first line should be 25 m from the wall. Have one student clap while the rest listen for the echo. Have the line move a few meters closer and have a student clap again. Continue to do this until the students locate a distance at which they no longer hear an echo. Measure the distance from the wall at which no echo is heard. (About 17 m from the wall or less) Have students calculate the speed of sound. (They should double the distance from the wall and multiply by 10. This will give them a calculation for m/s.) Next have them measure the air temperature and humidity. Ask how the speed of sound they calculated is different from the information in the text. Explain that temperature and humidity affect the speed of sound.

Answer to In-Text Question

② **Sounds would be absorbed rather than reflected.**

 The Living Textbook: Physical Science Side 3

Chapter 26   Frame 08837
Reflection of Waves (Movie)
Search: Play:

 The Living Textbook: Physical Science Sides 1-4

Chapter 14   Frame 02271
Reflected Sound (1 Frame)
Search:

TEACH ▪ *Continued*

Explore Visually

Have students study Figure 15.13. Ask the following questions:

▶ How do sound waves get from the speakers to the ears of the listeners? (The waves move through the doorway and bend around the corner.)

▶ If the girl who is listening turned, faced her friend, and whispered something to him, would the other three students be able to hear her? Explain. (No, the sound waves wouldn't have enough energy, so her whisper would be inaudible over a long distance.)

Answer to In-Text Question

① Because the sound is diffracted through the doorway

The Living Textbook: Physical Science Sides 1-4

Chapter 11   Frame 01943
Diffraction (4 Frames)
Search: Step:

The Living Textbook: Physical Science Sides 1-4

Chapter 11   Frame 01942
Refraction (1 Frame)
Search:

Cooperative Learning

Have students work in cooperative pairs to explore wave diffraction using water waves as a model. Have them use a ripple tank to generate waves. (Students can make a ripple tank using a shallow tray filled with water and a long, flat stick, such as a ruler.) Have them use diagrams to record the wave patterns as the waves move around various barriers or pass through openings of various sizes.

Diffraction of Sound

Suppose you're standing in the hallway of your school. Can you hear a conversation around the corner? Of course you can. Sound waves diffract, or bend, around barriers like walls.

As waves move through an opening in a barrier, they fan out into the area beyond the barrier. Sound waves moving through an open hallway fan out similarly into the bend in the hallway. Because of the diffraction of sound waves, you can hear the sounds coming from places you can't see. You can see how sound waves diffract through an open door in Figure 15.13.

Wave diffraction is greatest when the wavelength of a wave is about the same as the width of the opening in the barrier. Most windows and doorways are about 0.75 to 1 m wide. In air, sounds that have a pitch between 350 to 400 Hz have a wavelength close to these values.

Lower-frequency sound waves diffract more than higher-frequency sound waves do. You're able to hear mostly low-pitch sounds, such as rumbling traffic, through an open window. High-pitch sounds, such as voices, are less noticeable.

Figure 15.13
Why can the students next to the door hear the people in the hallway? ▼ ①

Themes in Science

Systems and Interactions The interaction of sound waves with their surroundings as well as with other sound waves produces reflection, diffraction, refraction, interference, and resonance. Have students make tables in which they compare and contrast these interactions, and give an example of each. Students may include their tables in their portfolios.

Integrating the Sciences

Meteorology Several weather conditions can affect the behavior of sound waves. At night, the wind near the ground surface is lighter, so sound waves are not scattered. Also, if there is a temperature inversion, the air near the surface is more stable. Ask students to make a list of the sounds they hear at night and those they hear during the day. Have students compare lists. Also, have them observe the effect weather has on the sounds they hear.

Skills WorkOut

To help students understand more about refraction of sound, have them do the Skills WorkOut.

Answer At night, air is cooler, sound waves move directly toward the observer. During the day, air is warmer near the ground, sound waves are refracted upward.

Directed Inquiry

Have students study the text and Figure 15.14. Ask the following questions:

▶ What changes as sound waves move from one medium into another? (Their speed)

▶ How would you describe refraction? (The change in direction as sound travels from one material to another)

▶ What happens to sound waves as they move through air at different temperatures? (They bend.)

Refraction of Sound

Everyone knows that it's more difficult to see at night than during the day. But the reverse is true when it comes to the sounds you hear. Why is this so?

To answer this question, you first have to explore how waves behave when they travel from one medium to another. When the wave enters a new medium, its speed changes. If the wave enters the new medium at an angle, the change in its speed causes a change in its direction. The change in the direction of a wave moving from one material into another is called refraction. What does this have to do with hearing better at night?

The speed of sound waves in air increases as air temperature increases. If sound waves move through air at different temperatures, the sound waves bend or refract. The direction of sound waves traveling in air that is warmed by the ground, as it is during the day, is shown in Figure 15.14 on the left. The right side shows sound waves moving through air that is cooler near the ground. The air is cooler near the ground during the evening.

Study the art carefully to see how the direction of the sound waves differs when air temperature is different. When the air near the ground is cold, sound waves are directed toward the ground rather than away from it. Since you're on the ground, the sound waves get directed toward you rather than away from you. At night, the air is usually colder near the ground. So, you can usually hear sounds better at night than during the day.

▼ ACTIVITY

Observing

Listening Day and Night

1. During the day, stand 50 m away from a friend.

2. Have your friend ring a bell. Notice the volume of the sound.

3. Repeat this activity in exactly the same way at night. Compare the difference in the sounds.

SKILLS WORKOUT

Figure 15.14

Why are the children not aware of the passing car during the day? ▼ ②

Portfolio

Draw a sound source and a barrier representing a different medium on the chalkboard. Have volunteers draw the wave as it approaches the barrier at an angle, and the wave as it moves into the second medium. Ask another volunteer to explain the final drawing. Students may wish to include a similar drawing in their portfolios.

Answer to In-Text Question

② Because the sound is refracted upward

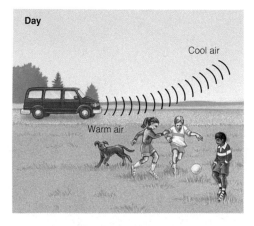

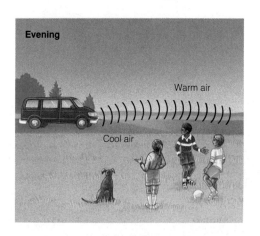

Explore Visually

Have students study Figure 15.15. Ask the following questions:

▶ What happens when the amplitude of one sound wave is subtracted from the amplitude of the other? (The sound is quieter than either of the two original sounds.)

▶ What happens to sound waves during constructive interference? (They combine, and the compressions and rarefactions are increased.)

▶ What is happening to the two sound waves on the right? (Constructive interference; the amplitudes of the two sound waves add to each other. The sound is louder.)

Cooperative Learning

Have students work in cooperative groups of three to explore sound interference. Each group will need two tuning forks. Have the groups work in different parts of the classroom. One student should strike the tuning fork and remain stationary while the other students move around to map out areas of destructive and constructive interference. Then have each group place their two tuning forks two meters apart. Again, students should move around to map out areas where the sound waves from the two prongs of the tuning fork interfere constructively (louder) and destructively (quieter). Have them describe any other changes they notice. (They may hear beats.)

Sound Interference

Sometimes it's harder to hear in some sections of an auditorium than in others. You wouldn't want to be sitting in these sections for a rock concert. You want to be in a seat where you can see *and* hear everything.

Why are sounds easier to hear in some locations than in others? The answer has to do with the interference of the sound waves. Sound waves can interfere in two ways. Look at Figure 15.15. The spacing of the dots represents compressions and rarefactions, or the amplitude, of the sound waves. On the left, the waves that combine result in **destructive interference**. On the right, the waves that combine result in **constructive interference**.

**Figure 15.15
Destructive and
Constructive Interference** ▼

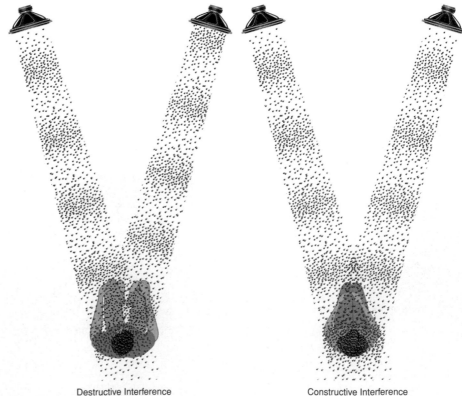

Destructive Interference　　　　　　Constructive Interference

Music Connection

The rich, colorful tones of an organ are the result of resonance. Have students find out how an instrument, such as an organ, flute, or violin, is designed to take advantage of resonance to amplify the sound it makes.

STS Connection

Destructive interference can be used to help solve noise pollution or other noise problems. An active noise control (ANC) device, produces a mirror image of the sound, that is, it duplicates the amplitude and frequency of the sound but the vibrations occur in the opposite direction. Ask students what part destructive interference plays in ANCs. (The combined sounds cancel one another.)

When the compressions of one sound wave overlap the compressions of another wave, the amplitudes of the waves add together and the resulting sound is louder. When the compressions of one wave overlap the rarefactions of another wave, the amplitudes subtract and the resulting sound is softer.

In most auditoriums, sound is amplified electronically. Sounds come from loudspeakers placed at different locations. If you are equally distant from speakers that emit identical sound waves at the same time, the sound is louder because the waves add. The compressions arrive in phase, or in step. If you move your seat so that the path the sound takes from each speaker to your ears differs by one-half wavelength, the waves destructively interfere and the sound intensity is reduced.

Resonance

A struck bell, a plucked guitar string, and a dropped table knife will vibrate and make sounds. Each object vibrates at a particular frequency, known as its natural frequency. The frequency of a sound wave corresponds to a particular pitch. The natural frequency of a small bell is higher than that of a large bell. When struck, the smaller bell will ring at a higher pitch.

A tuning fork is shown in Figure 15.16. When the tuning fork is struck, it makes a sound in a particular pitch.

◀ **Figure 15.16**
When the saxophonist plays at a certain frequency, the tuning fork resonates.

TEACH ▪ *Continued*

Reteach

To help students understand resonance, discuss the following situations:

▶ Sometimes when you hum a note, your lips tickle. Why? (The note you hum is the natural frequency of the space between your lips.)

▶ If you place a piece of waxed paper over a comb, it resonates when you hum a tune on the paper. Why? (You are humming at the natural frequency of the paper.)

▶ **Predict** What would happen if you used a heavier paper? (Depending on the thickness of the paper, it probably wouldn't vibrate.)

Historical Notebook

Research Have students research how engineers or architects work to avoid problems with natural frequency of bridges or buildings. Have them prepare a written report or make a three-dimensional model to explain the process.

Answers

1. A suspension bridge must be flexible enough to be elastic. Materials that are not elastic don't resonate.

2. Answers may vary. For example, the wind or rhythms produce frequencies that match the natural frequency of the bridge.

STS Connection

Point out that all materials have a natural frequency at which they will resonate, or vibrate. Ask students to explain why engineers must take resonance of each material into account when designing equipment, such as jet engines, helicopter blades, and airplane propellers. (Because the vibrations of these types of equipment could cause them to pull apart.)

Tuning forks are used to tune musical instruments. The musician plays a note on his instrument and compares its pitch to the pitch made by the tuning fork. He adjusts his instrument so the pitch of each note matches the pitch made by the tuning fork for that note.

When the saxophone player in Figure 15.16 plays at the natural frequency of the tuning fork, the vibrations create resonance (REHZ uh nuhnts) in the tuning fork. The vibration of an object at its natural frequency is called **resonance**. You can experiment with an instrument to find the natural frequency of an unlabeled tuning fork by playing different notes and seeing which one causes the tuning fork to resonate.

Finding the natural frequency of a tuning fork is just one example of resonance. Many objects have a natural frequency that is easily matched by other vibrating objects. The windows in your home rattle when the sound given off by a passing truck matches their natural frequency.

Historical Notebook

Incident at Tacoma Narrows Bridge

A marching band can create rhythmic vibrations even when it isn't playing music. Sometimes you can feel the ground vibrate from marching feet. Do you know why bands and military units don't march in step across suspension bridges?

The rhythm of the marching can cause the bridge to vibrate. If the frequency of the vibration caused by the marching matches the natural frequency of the bridge, resonance can occur. Resonance can cause the bridge to move up and down until its structure weakens and collapses.

English cavalry troops marching across a footbridge in 1831 caused the bridge to collapse when they marched in rhythm with the natural frequency of the bridge. Winds can also cause vibrations in suspension bridges. On November 7, 1940, vibrations caused by a mild gale produced resonance in the Tacoma Narrows Bridge in the state of Washington. In a few hours, the flexible

suspension bridge was torn apart and collapsed. Engineers now design suspension bridges with heavier, less-flexible roadbeds that aren't affected by wind.

1. Why is the flexibility of a suspension bridge important for developing resonance?

2. Explain how the wind or the rhythm of marching feet can cause a bridge to vibrate at its natural frequency.

Science and Technology
Acoustics—Sound Control

You might go to your school auditorium to hear a speaker, watch a play, or listen to a concert by the school chorus or band. If you can hear most of the sound from the stage in any location, the auditorium has good acoustics (uh KOO stihks). The concert hall in Figure 15.17 has a special design. Acoustics engineers design concert halls, theaters, and recording studios to control sound waves.

Reflected sound waves can add richness to sounds. Reflected sound waves in a room make sounds lively by making them last a little longer. To be heard, speech sounds should be reflected about a second in a small auditorium. The sound of music should be reflected one to two seconds in a concert hall. If sounds last too long, they can become garbled.

Reflected sound waves can interfere with the acoustics of a room by creating loud spots and dead spots. If a room is large enough, reflected sound waves cause echoes. Acoustics engineers know how to control reflected sounds. They use hard surfaces to direct reflected sounds to the audience or in the direction of a recording microphone. Reflected sounds are controlled by covering hard surfaces with materials, such as fabric or cork, that absorb sound waves. Good acoustics are the result of the effective use of knowledge about sound.

Figure 15.17 ▲
How do you think the roof over the stage affects sound? ①

Check and Explain

1. Identify five types of sound-wave interactions.

2. What is resonance?

3. **Generalize** Why must a reflecting surface be at least 17 m away for you to hear an echo of your shout?

4. **Infer** On two consecutive nights, you attend concerts in an outdoor stadium. Each night you listen to the same entertainer sing the same songs. On the second night, you sit in a different seat. You can't hear the singer's voice as well as you did on the first night. What might cause the change?

Time 40 minutes   Group pairs

Materials

60 identical cardboard tubes

15 sheets of cardboard, 26 × 40 cm each

15 ticking clocks or watches

Prelab Discussion

Have students read the entire activity. Discuss some points with students before beginning:

▶ Ask students to identify the purpose of the clock, the board, and the tubes.

▶ Have students recall the law of reflection for waves (Chapter 14).

▶ Be sure students tape the tubes together so they are straight.

▶ Substitute long tubes if they are available.

Analysis

1. The ticking should have sounded loudest when the angle of tube A to the board matched the angle of tube B to the board.

2. The ticking should have sounded softest when the angles of A to the board and B to the board were very different from each other.

Conclusion

Sound waves reflect off a surface at the same angle with which they strike the surface, therefore, the reflected sound will be loudest when tube B is at the same angle to the board as tube A.

Application

Echoes can be produced most easily from hard, smooth surfaces, like walls. Soft objects, such as furniture or curtains, will not produce echoes.

Activity 15 *How do sound waves reflect?*

Skills Observe; Model; Predict; Infer

Task 1 Prelab Prep
Collect the following items: paper, pencil, 4 identical cardboard tubes, tape, 26 × 40 cm sheet of cardboard, a protractor, and a ticking clock or watch.

Task 2 Data Record
1. At the top of a sheet of paper, write *Observations*.
2. Copy Table 15.4. Include 5 empty rows to record your data.
3. Notice in the figure shown that tube *A* and tube *B* form an angle. You will adjust this angle for each of the five trials of the experiment. To record the position of the tubes in each trial, draw the angle they form in the appropriate row in the table, using two straight lines.
4. Record the loudness you observe in each trial, using a scale from 1–10. Use 1 for a very faint sound and 10 for a very loud sound.

Task 3 Procedure
1. Make two long tubes by taping two of the short tubes together. Label the tubes *A* and *B*.
2. Have a classmate hold the sheet of cardboard perpendicular to a table top. Arrange the ticking clock and the two tubes in the positions shown in the figure.

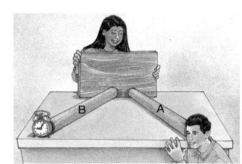

3. Cover one ear with your hand. Place your other ear near the opening of tube *A* and listen. Record the position of the tube and the loudness of the ticking sound.
4. Move tube *B* and the clock to a new position. Don't move tube *A*. Predict the position of tube *B* where the ticking will be loudest. Record your prediction. Repeat step 3.
5. Repeat steps 3 and 4 four more times.

Task 4 Analysis
1. Identify the angle of tubes *A* and *B* when the ticking of the clock was loudest.
2. Identify the angle of tubes *A* and *B* when the ticking of the clock was faintest.
3. How did your predictions compare to the actual result in each trial?

Task 5 Conclusion
How did the position of tube *B* influence the volume of the sound? Explain why the angle of the tube influences the amount of sound energy reflected. On what did you base your prediction about the position of the tube?

Application

Observe reflected sound in and around your home or school. Make a list of places where you can create echoes with your voice. Make a list of places where your voice won't echo. Describe the best surfaces for reflecting sound.

Table 15.4 Loudness of Ticking

Position of Tubes	Loudness (1-10)	Prediction

Chapter 15 *Review*

Concept Summary

15.1 Wave Model of Sound
▶ Sound waves are produced by a vibrating object
▶ A sound wave is a longitudinal wave composed of compressions and rarefactions that move through matter in the direction of the sound.
▶ The speed of sound depends on the elasticity, density, and temperature of the material through which sound waves travel.
▶ A sonic boom occurs when an object moves faster than the speed of sound.

15.2 Properties of Sound
▶ The unit for loudness, or intensity, is the decibel. The unit for pitch, or frequency, is called the hertz.
▶ Some animals can hear sound beyond the range of human hearing.
▶ The amplitude of a sound wave is a measure of its loudness, or intensity.
▶ The frequency of a sound wave is a measure of its pitch.
▶ The timbre of a sound is the sound quality produced by a mixture of different frequency sound waves.

15.3 Sound-Wave Interactions
▶ Sound waves interact to produce sound reflection, diffraction, refraction, interference, and resonance.
▶ Resonance occurs when the vibration of an object at its natural frequency is caused by another object vibrating at the same frequency.
▶ Echoes are produced when sound waves reflect from a surface.

Chapter Vocabulary

sound wave (p. 359)	hertz (p. 368)	destructive interference (p. 376)
decibel (p. 367)	Doppler effect (p. 369)	constructive interference (p. 376)
pitch (p. 367)	timbre (p. 370)	resonance (p. 378)

Check Your Vocabulary

Use the vocabulary words above to complete the following sentences correctly.

1. The unit used to measure sound frequency is the _____ .

2. When two sound waves interact in _____ , one amplitude is subtracted from the other.

3. Sound travels through matter as a(n) _____ .

4. The unit used to measure the loudness of sound is the _____ .

5. An increase in frequency will cause an increase in the _____ of the sound.

6. The change in pitch of an approaching siren is due to the _____ .

7. When the amplitudes of two sound waves add to each other, the result is _____ .

8. Sound quality, or _____ , is the blending of different-frequency sound waves.

9. An object vibrating at its natural frequency is also known as _____ .

Write Your Vocabulary

Write sentences using the vocabulary words above. Show that you know what each word means.

Check Your Vocabulary

1. hertz
2. destructive interference
3. sound wave
4. decibel
5. pitch
6. Doppler effect
7. constructive interference
8. timbre
9. resonance

Write Your Vocabulary

Students' sentences should show that they know the meaning of each word as well as how to use it in a sentence.
   Use Vocabulary Worksheet for Chapter 15.

Check Your Knowledge

1. Amplitude, frequency, and wavelength are characteristics of sound waves.

2. Sound waves are produced by vibrating objects.

3. Sound waves cannot travel through a vacuum because there are no molecules of matter to transmit the vibrations.

4. High-frequency sound waves produce high-pitched sounds.

5. The Doppler effect is the shift in the pitch of sound that results from the movement of the source of the sound relative to the listener. The Doppler effect occurs when the source and/or the listener move past each other.

6. A sound wave changes speed and sometimes direction when it is refracted, or moves from one medium to another.

7. Destructive interference of two sound waves identical in frequency and amplitude results in no sound.

8. False; rarefaction

9. True

10. False; higher

11. False; absorb

12. True

13. False; refraction

14. True

Check Your Understanding

1. Prolonged exposure to loud noises or a single exposure to a very loud sound can lead to hearing loss.

2. $\dfrac{700 \text{ m}}{344 \text{ m/s}} = 2.03 \text{ s}$

3. Sound waves of higher and lower-pitched sounds will have corresponding higher and lower frequencies. For loudness, the louder the sound, the greater the wave amplitude.

4. a. high
   b. high
   c. low
   d. high
   e. high
   f. low

5. The density of the medium and the temperature affect the speed of sound.

6. a. The sound would have a higher pitch.
   b. Sound intensity is increased as it echoes through the hollow body of the instrument.

Chapter 15 Review

Check Your Knowledge

Answer the following in complete sentences.

1. What are the characteristics of a sound wave?

2. How are sound waves produced?

3. Why doesn't sound travel through a vacuum?

4. What kind of sound waves produce a high pitch?

5. What is the Doppler effect? When does it occur?

6. What happens to a sound wave when it is refracted?

7. What causes two sound waves to combine and produce no sound?

Determine whether each statement is true or false. Write *true* if it is true. If it is false, change the underlined term(s) to make the statement true.

8. The compression in a sound wave compares to the trough in a transverse wave.

9. Planes that fly faster than the speed of sound can create a sonic boom.

10. If the frequency of a sound wave increases, its pitch becomes lower.

11. Drapes, furniture, and carpeting reflect most sound waves.

12. When sounds in a large room are garbled, the cause is probably caused by the constructive interference of sound waves.

13. You can hear better at night because of a sound-wave interaction called destructive interference.

14. The loudness of a sound depends on the amplitude of its sound wave.

Check Your Understanding

Apply the concepts you have learned to answer each question.

1. **Application** Describe two situations where a person might suffer hearing loss. What could a person do to avoid damage to their hearing in these situations?

2. If you are 700 m from a batter when you see her hit a ball, how long will you wait to hear the sound of the bat hitting the ball? The temperature of the air is 20°C.

3. Draw sound waves which compare and contrast the concepts of loudness and pitch.

4. Classify each of the following as having a high pitch or a low pitch.

   a. siren
   b. human infant voice
   c. bass fiddle
   d. flute
   e. whistle
   f. thunder

5. What variables might affect the measurement of the speed of sound at any particular location? Describe a location and its variables.

6. **Mystery Photo** The photograph on page 358 shows a Chinese stringed instrument called a liuyen ch'in. Different pitches are possible because the strings are of different thicknesses. The wavelength of a particular string can be shortened by pressing it against a fret, or ridge, located on the neck of the instrument. The sound is amplified in the hollow body of the instrument.

   a. If a player shortened the length of a string, how would that influence the sound when the string is plucked?

   b. How does the shape of its hollow body affect the sound of the instrument?

Develop Your Skills

1. a. *c*

b. *b*

c. *a*

d. amplitude

2. Student models will vary. In general, the closer together the particles of a substance are, the faster the sound will travel.

3. The denser the substance, the faster the sound will travel through it.

Make Connections

1.

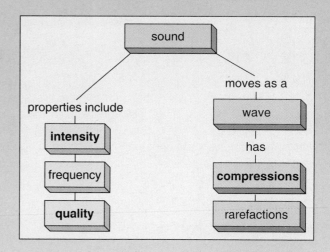

2. Student answers may vary, but the metaphor from Shakespeare makes the sound properties of a resonating air column, which resonates more "deeply," or at a lower pitch, as it increases. An empty vase (or goblet) resonates a larger air column (when you speak or hum into it) than the same vase does when it is full.

3. Student reports will vary. Most hearing aid technology relies on amplification or filtering of frequencies. Researchers are looking for ways to restore hearing to those whose loss is not treatable by amplification, by somehow converting sound directly into nerve impulses, as the cochlea does normally.

Develop Your Skills

Use the skills you have developed in this chapter to complete each activity.

1. Interpret Data Study the illustrations shown below.

a. Which represents the loudest sound?

b. Which represents the next-loudest sound?

c. Which represents the least-loud sound?

d. Which characteristic of a sound wave is associated with loudness?

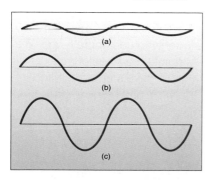

2. Make a Model Gather bits of paper or coins. These items will represent molecules. Make models of the molecules in a gas, a liquid, and a solid. Demonstrate how the speed of sound varies in each of these states of matter.

3. Data Bank Examine the table on page 640. Based on the data, answer the following question: What relationship exists between the density of a substance and the speed at which sound travels through it?

Make Connections

1. Link the Concepts Below is a concept map showing how some of the main concepts in this chapter link together. Only part of the map is filled in. Finish the map, using words and ideas you find on the previous pages.

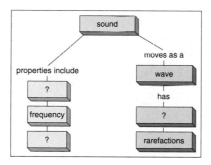

2. Science and Literature Many writers have used the word *sound* to create poetic images or to communicate ideas and emotions. Below is a reference to sound from William Shakespeare's play *Henry V*. In your own words state what you think Shakespeare wished to communicate.

"But the saying is true, 'The empty vessel makes the greatest sound.'"

3. Science and Technology Hearing impairment is neither new nor uncommon. New technology has developed devices that improve the impaired hearing of many people. Research the history of hearing aids and other audio devices. Write a report on the development of the hearing aid used inside the ear. Include current research for new and better devices and techniques.

Overview

This chapter explains how sound is used. The structure and function of the human ear is described in the first section. The next section discusses the characteristics of musical sounds and instruments, and noise. Sound technologies, such as ultrasound, sonar, and echolocation, are presented in the last section.

Advance Planner

▶ Obtain musical recordings for TE page 391.

▶ Collect photographs or drawings of instruments for TE page 393.

▶ Provide drinking straws for TE page 393.

▶ Gather shoe boxes, rubber hose, funnels, straws, rolls of masking tape, small metal cans with lids, beans, bottle tops, paper plates, bells, tongue depressors, smooth round stones, heavy cord, metal forks and trays, socks, broom handles, walnut shells, coat buttons, and yarn for SE Activity 16, page 397.

Skills Development Chart

Sections	Classify	Communicate	Compare	Infer	Interpret Data	Model	Observe	Research
16.1 Skills WarmUp							●	
Consider This		●						
16.2 Skills WarmUp	●							
Skills WorkOut							●	
Historical Notebook								●
Skills WorkOut	●							
Activity		●	●	●	●	●	●	
16.3 Skills WarmUp				●				

Individual Needs

▶ **Limited English Proficiency Students** As students read the chapter, have them make a list of the boldface terms. Then encourage them to study the concept summary on page 405 and use it as a guide in preparing a "news program" about using sound. Their program should include definitions of the boldface terms—given in their own words—and they should present their own summaries for the chapter's concepts. They may want to use diagrams to illustrate the terms and concepts. Have students make audiotapes of their news programs, and use the tapes as part of the chapter review.

▶ **At-Risk Students** Invite a studio or concert sound engineer, a television sound technician, or a medical professional familiar with ultrasound to talk with students. Have students prepare a list of questions for the speaker in advance. They may ask about the training and skills required for this type of work and about the latest technology available. Students may also want to know how the engineer or technician determines what adjustments are needed to obtain clear sound or image.

▶ **Gifted Students** Have students research and build a model of a glass harmonica, an instrument invented by Benjamin Franklin. They may use a series of water-filled bowls, glasses, or test tubes to make a model of the instrument. Encourage them to experiment with different kinds of bowls and glasses or test tubes to produce different sounds. Have them make diagrams that explain the principles of sound involved in this instrument and then give a demonstration or "concert" with their model to the class.

Resource Bank

▶ **Bulletin Board** Attach the title *Music Around the World* to the bulletin board. Encourage students to contribute magazine pictures, photocopies, and original drawings of musical instruments from a variety of cultures. Have them write information about their instruments on cards and place them beside the pictures. If they have a recording of the instrument, they might want to contribute a short sample of its sound to a class audiotape.

▶ **Field Trip** Have the class attend an orchestra or band concert. Before the concert, ask students to choose an instrument in the orchestra or band, and write the name of the instrument on a page in their portfolio. Ask students to concentrate on the sounds made by their instrument during the concert's last selection. Have them make notes about the instrument's part in the selection, the kind of sound it made, and how the sound made them feel. After the concert, have a class discussion, allowing students to share their views.

Section	Core	Standard	Enriched
16.1 How You Hear pp. 385–389			
Section Features Skills WarmUp, p. 385; Consider This, p. 388	● ●	● ●	● ●
Blackline Masters Review Worksheet 16.1	●	●	
Ancillary Options One-Minute Readings, pp. 87–88	●	●	●
Overhead Blackline Transparencies Overhead Blackline Master 15 and Student Worksheet	●	●	●
16.2 Sounds You Hear pp. 390–397			
Section Features Skills WarmUp, p. 390; Skills WorkOut, p. 391; Historical Notebook, p. 394; Skills WorkOut, p. 395; Activity, p. 397	● ● ● ● ●	● ● ● ● ●	● ● ● ● ●

Section	Core	Standard	Enriched
Blackline Masters Review Worksheet 16.2; Reteach Worksheet 16.2; Integrating Worksheet 16.2	● ● ●	● ● ●	● ●
Laboratory Program Investigation 32	●	●	
Color Transparencies Transparency 57	●	●	●
16.3 Sound Technology pp. 398–404			
Section Features Skills WarmUp, p. 398	●	●	●
Blackline Masters Review Worksheet 16.3; Skills Worksheet 16.3; Integrating Worksheet 16.3; Vocabulary Worksheet 16	● ● ● ●	● ● ●	●

Bibliography

The following resources can be used for teaching the chapter. See page T-46 for supplier codes.

Library Resources

Berman, Paul. *Light and Sound.* New York: Marshall Cavendish, 1988.

Gardner, Robert. *Experimenting with Sound.* New York: Franklin Watts, 1988.

Lampton, Christopher F. *Sound: More Than What You Hear.* Hillside, NJ: Enslow Publishers, Inc., 1992.

Technology Resources

Software

Science in Your Ear. Mac, Win. ER.

Laserdiscs

Living Textbook. (See barcodes on pages in this chapter.) Optical Data.

Ears and Hearing/Eyes and Seeing. EB.

Videos

Noise Pollution. LCA.

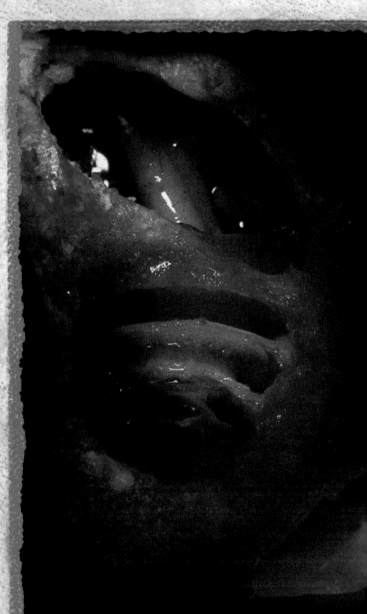

Writing Connection

Have students think about the sounds in a favorite place. Have them write a paragraph describing the place, using only the sense of hearing to provide details.

Introducing the Chapter

Have students read the description of the photograph. Ask if they agree or disagree with the description.

Directed Inquiry

Have students study the photograph. Ask:

► What part of an organism does the photograph show? (Students should say the ear.)

► What part of the ear do you think this is? (Students may respond that it is part of the inner ear.)

► What do you think happens when sound waves reach these structures? (They make the structures send sound to the brain.)

► What do we hear if the vibration changes? (We hear a different sound.)

Chapter Vocabulary

echolocation   overtone
inner ear   sonar
middle ear   ultrasound
outer ear

Chapter **16**   Using Sound

Chapter Sections

16.1   How You Hear

16.2   Sounds You Hear

16.3   Sound Technology

What do you see?

❝It looks like the ear canal of a human. It is located near the brain on each side of the head. It is part of the human sense of hearing. When sound goes through the ear, it causes the ear bones to vibrate, and nerves send messages to the brain registering the sound. That is why you can hear.❞

Jason Ko
Durham Academy
Durham, North Carolina

To find out more about the photograph, look on page 406. As you read this chapter, you will learn about how you use sound.

16.1 How You Hear

Objectives

▶ **Describe** the structure and functions of the ear.

▶ **Trace** the path of a sound wave through the ear.

▶ **Infer** how hearing can be damaged by exposure to sound.

▶ **Make a model** of the ear.

▼ **ACTIVITY**

Observing

Hear! Hear!

1. Use one hand to cover one ear. Close your eyes.

2. Have someone clap or whistle from a location about 5 m away.

3. Try to guess the location of the sound. Record your response. Repeat two more times.

4. Uncover your ear and repeat the procedure.

Are two ears better than one?

SKILLS WARMUP

What you probably enjoy most at a fireworks display are the spectacular bursts of color. You also hear whistling and booming sounds as the fireworks explode high in the sky. The sounds you hear heighten your awareness of the world around you.

Sounds you hear also give you information. What would movies and TV shows be like without sound? You'd have to guess what the actors were saying. There wouldn't be any music, sound effects, or applause.

Hearing and Balance

Sound surrounds you all the time, but you can't hear every sound. Your ears aren't sensitive enough to hear sounds outside a certain range. However, your ears can detect the tiny vibrations a pin makes when it falls to the floor. Your ears also detect large vibrations, such as the crash of thunder or a pounding bass drum. Look at Figure 16.1. What sound would your ears detect if you were standing nearby?

You can hear your friend's voice as you carry on a conversation in a noisy crowd. You can detect that sound although other sounds interfere. You hear all the many different sounds your friend's voice makes when forming words. When you listen to music, you hear the different sounds of the various instruments.

In addition to detecting sounds, your ears have another function. Part of your ear controls your sense of balance. The semicircular canals in your ears are filled with liquid. They also contain hair cells. The hair cells respond to changes in the position of your head. You are able to detect which direction is up and which is down, and to maintain your balance.

Figure 16.1 ▲
What is the vibrating sound source? What sound does it make? ①

Explore Visually

Have students study Figure 16.2. Ask the following questions:

▶ How do sounds get to the eardrum? (Via the air to the outer ear, ear canal, and eardrum)

▶ What is the stirrup? What does it do? (One of the bones in the middle ear; it vibrates the oval window, which transfers energy to the fluid in the cochlea.)

▶ What happens in the auditory nerve? (The nerve transmits sound information to the brain as electric impulses.)

Class Activity

Have students create a flowchart that describes how hearing works. Ask them to use boxes and arrows. Each box should include an organ or a place and the verb for what occurs there. Arrows should be labeled with the form of sound transferred (sound waves, ear canal, eardrum, hammer, anvil, stirrup, semicircular canal, cochlea, auditory nerve, electric signal).

Reteach

Use Reteach Worksheet 16.1.

The Living Textbook: Physical Science Side 3

Chapter 39   Frame 28362
Guitar String Vibrating (Movie)
Search: Play:

The Living Textbook: Physical Science Sides 1-4

Chapter 39   Frame 29201
Diagram of Ear (2 Frames)
Search: Step:

386

Themes in Science

Energy Remind students that sound is a form of energy. Have students make a diagram that traces the movement of sound from a source, such as a portable radio, to the brain.

STS Connection

Explain to students that several Italian scientists made important discoveries about the ear. Have students pick one of the following early anatomists and write a report about his discoveries: Gian Filippo Ingrassia, Bartolommeo Eustachio, Gabriello Fallopio, and Alfonso Corti.

The Human Ear

The human ear is divided into three sections—the outer, middle, and inner ear. As you read about the parts of the human ear, find each one in Figure 16.2. The part of your ear that you can see and the ear canal make up your **outer ear**. The ear canal ends with a tightly stretched membrane called the eardrum.

Behind the eardrum is the **middle ear**. The middle ear contains the three smallest bones in the human body—the hammer, the anvil, and the stirrup. Find these bones in Figure 16.2. The stirrup presses against another membrane called the oval window.

The oval window separates your middle ear from your **inner ear**. The semicircular canals and the cochlea (KOHK-lee-uh) are part of the inner ear. Find the cochlea. It is the coiled organ in the inner ear.

You can't see inside the cochlea in Figure 16.2, but if you could, you would see tiny hair cells lining it. The cochlea is filled with liquid. Motion of the cochlea causes the liquid to move and stimulate the hair cells. The hair cells send signals to the auditory nerve. The auditory nerve relays the signals to your brain. Your brain interprets the signals as sound.

How does your ear detect sound? Sound must travel to reach your ear. Sound travels in waves caused by a series of compressions and rarefactions in the air. When sound waves reach your ears, a series of events occurs allowing you to hear a sound. Study these events in Figure 16.2.

Figure 16.2
How You Hear ▼

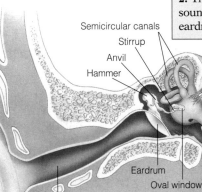

1. Sound waves travel through the air and enter the outer ear, passing through the ear canal.

2. The energy of the sound waves causes the eardrum to vibrate.

3. The vibrations of the eardrum cause the hammer, anvil, and stirrup bones to vibrate.

4. The stirrup vibrates the oval window, transferring the energy to the fluid in the cochlea. The vibrating hair cells in the cochlea stimulate the auditory nerve.

5. Sound energy is changed to an electrical signal, which travels through the auditory nerve to the brain. The brain interprets the electric signal as sound.

Hearing Range

How well you hear a sound depends on its frequency and intensity. Recall that frequency is the number of waves that passes a certain point every second. Frequency determines the pitch of sound. High-frequency sound waves have a high pitch. Low-frequency sounds have a low pitch. You hear a range of sounds from frequencies as low as 20 cycles per second, or 20 Hz, up to 20,000 cycles per second, or 20,000 Hz. Sounds with frequencies below 20 Hz or above 20,000 Hz are beyond the range of human hearing. Study Table 16.1. How does the range of human hearing compare to that of other animals?

Your hearing is also sensitive to the loudness, or intensity, of sound. Recall that the unit used to measure sound intensity is the decibel (dB). A sound of 0 dB is the least sound humans can hear. Sounds above 120 dB, such as the sound of a jet plane at takeoff, can actually rupture your eardrums and cause permanent hearing loss.

The substance through which a sound travels can also affect what you hear. For example, you may not hear sound waves coming through the air from your neighbor's stereo. However, you may hear sound traveling through a solid wall. Look at Figure 16.3. Will the sound travel farther through water or through air? How ① is the speed of a sound related to the phase of the medium through which it travels?

Table 16.1
Ranges of Hearing

Organism	Frequency (in Hz)
Dolphin	150–150,000
Bat	1,000–120,000
Cat	60–70,000
Dog	15–50,000
Human	20–20,000

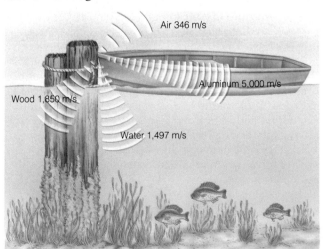

◀ **Figure 16.3**
Sound moves at different speeds and distances through water, air, aluminum, and wood. As a sound wave travels faster, its energy can travel farther.

TEACH ▪ Continued

Consider This

Portfolio Have students record sounds they notice in each place they go for one full day. Then have them research the frequency of four of the sounds. Ask them to put an asterisk by any sounds they think cause noise pollution.

Think About It Answers should reflect an understanding of the harmful effects of loud noise.

Write About It Check papers for supportive reasons.

Discuss

Point out that both loud sounds and constant moderately loud sounds can damage hearing. Ask students to think of situations in which they might be exposed to dangerous sound levels. (For example, rock concerts, living or working near a construction site, loud radios, loud TV)

Class Activity

Have students test their hearing. Have them sit in a circle and close their eyes and listen for sounds. Sit in the center and make high- and low-pitched sounds. Start with loud sounds and finish with soft ones.

Decision Making

If you have classroom sets of *One-Minute Readings*, have students read Issue 51 "Loud Sounds" on pages 87 and 88. Discuss the questions.

STS Connection

Explain that an audiologist can test a person for hearing loss by checking the lowest level at which he or she can detect a sound. Have students find out how a device called an audiometer is used in such tests. (An audiometer presents pure tones from 125 Hz to 10 000 Hz in intensity increments of 5 dB, starting at 100 dB. The patient indicates when the tone is just audible.)

Consider This

Should There Be More Regulation of Noise Pollution?

In 1972, Congress enacted the Noise Control Act to protect people from "noise that jeopardizes their health and welfare." The Environmental Protection Agency, or EPA, estimated that 34 million people experience noise levels that cause hearing loss in locations other than the workplace.

Even noise that isn't loud enough to damage your hearing can be harmful to your health. Some noise is linked to headaches, ulcers, stress, and high blood pressure. It can upset sleep patterns and the ability to learn for some people.

Some people believe that any restriction on noise interferes with their rights. Some feel that music must be loud to be fully appreciated. Representatives of industry claim that noisy machinery is unavoidable.

Think About It Is your ability to concentrate affected by loud noise? Do loudness levels affect you? Do you enjoy the sound of loud music? Should you be prevented from turning up the volume of your radio or stereo?

Write About It Write a paper stating your position for or against laws that control noise. Explain your reasons for your opinion.

Science and You *Hearing Protectors*

Exposure to loud sounds can damage your hearing. You can avoid damage by using devices called hearing protectors. Hearing protectors can prevent both temporary and permanent hearing loss.

In many workplaces, noise levels are carefully monitored. If the sound is too loud, it can rupture a worker's eardrums. If the sound level isn't very loud, but continues over a long period of time, hearing loss can result. The hearing loss occurs because the hair cells inside the cochlea become damaged by overuse. Constant noise levels at lower volumes can also affect a worker's health by causing stress.

Two basic kinds of hearing protectors are available. One kind is earplugs, made of a material that absorbs sound-wave energy. To protect yourself from loud sounds, you insert the earplugs directly into the ear canal. Earplugs are custom fit to your ear canal to

Cooperative Learning

Have students work in cooperative groups of four to debate the pros and cons of noise pollution regulation. Have pairs within each group take opposing sides in the debate and work together to prepare arguments. After the debates, have students identify the arguments they found most persuasive.

Portfolio

Have students research the kinds of earplugs available in drugstores. Students can write a report that includes price, value, content of earplugs, and instructions for use. You may wish to have them include the report in their portfolios.

Critical Thinking

Find Causes Ask students, Why are earmuff-type hearing protectors designed to enclose the outer ears? (To stop sound waves from entering the ear canal)

WrapUp

Reteach Pose these questions for students to discuss: If listening to sounds that are too loud can damage hearing, what about straining to hear sounds that are too soft? Could that damage your hearing? Why or why not? Have students give reasons based on the hearing process.

Use Review Worksheet 16.1.

Check and Explain

1. Outer ear: visible ear, ear canal, eardrum; middle ear: hammer, anvil, stirrup, oval window; inner ear: semicircular canals, cochlea

2. Answers should include all parts of the ear, the auditory nerve, and the brain.

3. Sound that is too loud can rupture the eardrum. Examples will vary.

4. Models should include all parts of the ear shown on page 386.

Answer to In-Text Question

① Answers may vary. For example, in a small airplane, in a helicopter, or at a rock concert

◀ **Figure 16.4**
Workers near jet aircraft usually wear both earplugs and earmuffs to protect their ears from the extremely loud noise of jet engines.

block the most sound possible. Many different kinds of earplugs are available in drug stores at low cost.

Another kind of hearing protector looks like a pair of earmuffs. When you put on the earmuffs, they completely enclose your outer ears. The earmuffs are filled with a foamlike material that absorbs sound-wave energy. The earmuffs usually block sound better than earplugs do.

Look at Figure 16.4. Airport employees working near jet aircraft wear hearing protectors to block the roar of a jet engine. The sound from a jet engine can measure 170 dB. Human hearing can be damaged easily by sound this intense. In what other situations might it be important to use hearing protectors? ①

Check and Explain

1. List the parts of the ear that play a role in hearing. Identify whether each part is located in the outer, middle, or inner ear.

2. Describe the path a sound wave travels before you hear a whistle being blown.

3. **Infer** How could sound damage your hearing? Give examples of dangerous sounds.

4. **Make a Model** Use paper and pencil, or materials of your choice, to make a model of the ear.

Section Objectives
For a list of section objectives, see the Student Edition page.

Skills Objectives
Students should be able to:

Classify musical instruments and sounds.

Observe instruments' sounds.

Compare and Contrast music and noise.

Make a Model of a musical instrument.

Vocabulary
overtone

MOTIVATE

Skills WarmUp
To help students understand sounds they hear, have them do the Skills WarmUp.
Answer Lists will vary. Students could use classification systems, such as what makes the sound (strings, wind); pitch of sound; and the role in performance (melody, harmony, accompaniment).

Prior Knowledge
Gauge how much students know about sound by asking:

▶ What are the differences between music and noise?

▶ What are the three main types of musical instrument?

▶ What kinds of instruments are in a band? In an orchestra?

The Living Textbook: Physical Science Side 3

Chapter 36   Frame 23485
Generating Sound Waves (Movie)
Search: Play:

Themes in Science
Diversity and Unity Explain that there are many different kinds of music and musical instruments, but they all rely on sound energy. The variety results from the manipulation of sound's properties: frequency, intensity, and timbre. Have students describe how the characteristics of a musical instrument might vary these properties. (Students may mention that changes in length of the string or air column give different pitches.)

▼ ACTIVITY
Classifying

Musical Listing
Make a list of all the musical instruments you can think of. Study your list and devise a way to classify the instruments. What characteristics did you use to classify the instruments?

SKILLS WARMUP

16.2 Sounds You Hear

Objectives

▶ **Explain** how musical instruments make sound.

▶ **Distinguish** between stringed, wind, and percussion instruments.

▶ **Compare** and **contrast** musical sounds with noise.

▶ **Make a model** of a musical instrument.

You recognize many different kinds of sound. On the radio or TV, you hear many kinds of music. You may hear rock or country bands that perform with electric guitars or other kinds of instruments.

For thousands of years, people all over the world have invented their own instruments and musical styles. Look at the instruments in Figure 16.5. In Australia, people play a long instrument called a *didjeridoo*, made from a tree trunk. It produces a raspy, low, twangy sound. In China, people invented many stringed instruments. One instrument, the *ch'in*, looks like a long, narrow Greek lyre and sounds like a mandolin. In West Africa, people developed the *cora*. The cora looks like a banjo, but it sounds like a harp. All musical instruments produce and amplify vibrations. These vibrations produce sound waves that people recognize as music.

**Figure 16.5
Musical Instruments from Around the World** ▼

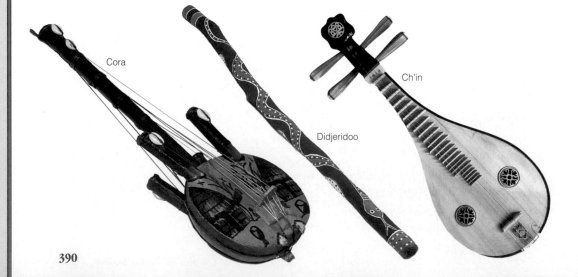
Cora

Didjeridoo

Ch'in

Music

People like music because it has an interesting beat and it produces pleasing sounds. The characteristics of musical sounds are pitch, intensity, rhythm, melody, harmony, and quality. A sound played at a specific frequency is called a note.

Pitch is the highness or lowness of the note, or the tone. Intensity is the loudness of the note. Because notes last different lengths of time, music also has rhythm. Rhythm is a repeating pattern of beats, or accents. The repeating pattern makes it possible for you to keep time to the music.

Each piece of music has a different melody, or series of pitches. Look at Figure 16.6. The melody of a song is easy to remember. You can hum or sing it. Most musical pieces also have harmony. Harmony occurs when three or more notes are played together to produce a pleasing sound. The note combinations selected for harmonics vary for different cultures and styles of music.

Music usually has several pitches that blend together. For example, a violin string vibrates at a certain frequency to produce its main tone. If parts of the string also vibrate at a different rate, you hear higher tones, or **overtones**.

Each musical instrument produces a different combination of overtones. The combination of overtones help to give each instrument a distinctive sound. For example, a flute and a clarinet can play a note with the same pitch. However, the sound of the note will be different for each instrument due to the overtones.

▼ ACTIVITY

Observing

Sound Instruments

Using a sound recording, listen to sounds made by the three different kinds of instruments. How do the sounds relate to the size of each instrument? Do your observations apply to other kinds of instruments? Explain.

SKILLS WORKOUT

Figure 16.6
The notes on the top staff indicate the melody. The notes on the bottom staff are a harmony that fits with the melody. ▼

O say, can you see, by the dawn's ear - ly light,

TEACH ▪ Continued

Explore Visually

Have students study the text and photographs on pages 392 and 393. Then discuss the following:

▶ What is a koto? How is it played? (A Japanese instrument; it's played by plucking the 13 waxed silk strings with three ivory picks.)

▶ How many strings does a violin have? How does a player make the violin strings vibrate? (4; by moving a bow across them or by plucking them)

▶ Name two ways a keyboard instrument can produce sound and give examples. (By striking different-length strings, as on a piano, by vibrating different-length air columns, as on an organ, or electronically, as on a synthesizer)

▶ Describe the strings in a piano or a violin that produce the lowest sounds. (The long, thick strings)

▶ Compare the trumpet and the saxophone. How are they alike? How are they different? (Both are wind instruments. Saxophones have reeds and trumpets are made of brass. Each has a different number of keys, and the shapes are different.)

▶ What type of instrument is a drum? How is it played? (Percussion; by striking the drumhead with a stick or with the hands)

The Living Textbook:
Physical Science Sides 1-4

Chapter 14	Frame 02282
Guitar (5 Frames)	
Search:	Step:

Multicultural Perspectives

Have students choose a family of instruments—string, wind, or percussion—and find an example of that family in the music of three different cultures. Ask them to write a description of each instrument telling how it is played and what kind of sound it makes. Students may wish to illustrate their descriptions with drawings of the instruments.

Use Integrating Worksheet 16.2a.

History Connection

Explain to students that some musicians can use their skills and talent to change the way an instrument makes sounds. Have students research talents, such as Louis Armstrong, Vladimir Horowitz, Gene Krupa, Benny Goodman, or Ravi Shankar, to learn how these musicians changed listeners' expectations of the instruments they played.

Musical Instruments

Musical instruments look very different. They are classified into three main groups: string, wind, and percussion. String instruments, such as the guitar, violin, and piano, produce a tone when their strings vibrate. Long, thick strings make low-pitch sounds. Short, thin strings have a higher pitch. When the strings vibrate with more amplitude, the volume of sound increases. String instruments usually have a wooden sound box that amplifies the sounds of the vibrating strings.

Wind instruments, such as the flute, trumpet, and saxophone, contain a column of air that vibrates when you blow into the instrument. Varying the length of the air column changes the pitch. A long air column

Violin ▲

A violin has four strings. Different notes are played by pressing a finger on the strings to change their lengths. If the string is shortened, a higher pitch is produced. The violinist draws a bow across the strings to make them vibrate. The bow is made of tightly stretched horsehair attached to a flexible stick.

Koto

A koto is an example of a stringed instrument from a different culture. In Japan, people play the koto in traditional orchestras. The 2 m-long wooden sound box rests on the floor. The player uses three ivory picks worn on her fingers to pluck the waxed silk strings. The 13 strings are tuned to different pitches. ▼

Keyboard Instruments ▲

Keyboard instruments differ in how they produce sound. Each key of a piano causes a string or a set of strings to vibrate and make a tone. Strings of different length and thickness produce different pitches. Each key of a pipe organ opens a pipe with a column of air. Each different-size pipe produces a different pitch. Each key of a synthesizer keyboard triggers a different internal-tone generator.

Cooperative Learning

Have students work in cooperative groups of three to explore the relationship between pitch and the length of a column of air in a wind instrument. Give each group several paper drinking straws. Have students flatten one end of each straw and then cut the corners off at an angle to form a point. Have students blow on the flattened ends of the straws until they produce a sound.

Have students experiment with various lengths of straws to see the different pitches they can produce. Ask students to explain what instruments their straws resemble. (Double-reed instruments, such as the oboe or bassoon)

---

produces a low note, while a shorter air column produces a high note. If you blow harder into the instrument, the volume of sound increases.

You can play a percussion instrument, such as a drum or cymbal, by striking it. You control the sound intensity by how hard you strike. The covering can be tightened or loosened so that it vibrates at different frequencies. The tension on the drum covering affects pitch.

Look at the different instruments on these pages. Read about how each instrument works. What other string, wind, or percussion instruments can you name? ①

Physical Science
L I N K

Make your own instrument. Obtain five straws and tape.
1. Tape the straws together, side-by-side.
2. Cut off each straw so it is shorter than the next one.
3. Blow across the top.
   What is vibrating and producing the sound?

A C T I V I T Y

Trumpet ▲

A trumpet player blows a stream of air into the trumpet mouthpiece. The column of air inside the trumpet vibrates and produces a tone. To change the pitch, the player opens and closes valves that change the length of the air column.

Saxophone ▲

A saxophonist blows across a reed in the mouthpiece. The vibrating reed vibrates the air inside the instrument to produce sound. The saxophone also has holes along the side that can be opened and closed to produce different notes. Opening and closing the holes changes the length of the vibrating air column. Sound frequency depends on the length of the air column.

Drums

A drummer striking the drumhead, or skin, of a drum causes vibrations. The body of the drum amplifies these vibrations. Drums of different sizes and materials produce different sounds. Also, the placement of the drumstick on the head and the force of the drumstick striking the head changes the sounds produced. ▼

Skills Development

Infer Ask students, How would a saxophone sound if it were missing its reed? Why? (Answers may vary. Students may say that the reed causes the air in the instrument to vibrate, and a reedless saxophone would probably not produce sound.)

Critical Thinking

Classify List a variety of instruments, such as the tuba, sitar, harp, maraca, glockenspiel, marimba, bagpipes, and soft-drink bottle, on the chalkboard. You may want to provide a photograph or sketch of any unfamiliar instruments. Ask students to classify the instruments as wind (tuba, bagpipes), stringed (sitar, harp), or percussion (maraca, glockenspiel, marimba). (The soft-drink bottle can be a wind instrument if the player blows across the top, or a percussion instrument if the player taps it or shakes stones in it.)

Answer to In-Text Question

① **Answers may vary. For example, string: cello, guitar; wind: flute, recorder; percussion: tambourine, cymbals**

Answer to Link

A series of notes are produced by the straws. The air column inside each straw vibrates creating a note.

The Living Textbook:
Physical Science Sides 1-4

Chapter 14   Frame 02292
Flute/Clarinet/Percussion (11 Frames)
Search: Step:

TEACH ▪ *Continued*

Class Activity

Have students work in groups of four to list the sounds they think of as noise. Remind them that everyone has their own ideas about what sounds are noise, and all suggestions should be included on the list. Have groups compare lists to see if there are any sounds that the entire class considers as noise. Then have them discuss the sounds they listed to see if there is anything similar about them. (Answers may vary.)

Historical Notebook

Enrich Point out that music is a form of artistic expression and listening to music provides pleasure and enjoyment. In addition, some cultures consider music an important part of their religious ceremonies. Others use music for communication. Ask students to identify occasions or events that are usually accompanied by music. (Answers may vary. Students may mention weddings, funerals, inaugurations, and dance performances.)

Answers

1. Answers will vary. Be sure students explain their answers.

2. Answers may vary. For example, people may have had common needs for music, or people may have had common materials, such as logs, sticks, metal, and clay.

3. Check students' timelines for accuracy.

 The Living Textbook: Physical Science Sides 1-4

Chapter 17   Frame 03188
Noise (2 Frames)
Search: Step:

 Language Arts Connection

Have students write a poem about sounds that they consider to be noise. Have them use onomatopoeia—words or syllables in which the sounds suggest their meanings, such as a buzzing bee.

Noise

Imagine being stuck in a big-city traffic jam. The city streets are clogged with stalled traffic. The motors of the cars, buses, and trucks make a constant rumbling sound. Drivers begin to lean on their horns. Some drivers shout from their car windows. Other drivers try to block out the sounds by turning up the volume on their car radios. The streets are filled with annoying, unwanted sounds—noise.

Noise has been a concern to people for a long time. For example, the Roman ruler Julius Caesar was so upset by the street noise in Rome that he banned chariots from the city. In general, any sound that disturbs or threatens your mental or physical health is noise. However, people don't always agree on what noise is.

Everyone agrees that sounds loud enough to burst a person's eardrums are noise. However, not everyone agrees on when a sound is too loud. Loud music from a

Historical Notebook

History of Musical Instruments

People have played music and danced since prehistoric times. The first musical instruments probably involved tapping the ground, special rocks, hollow logs, or the human body itself. By 10,000 B.C., people were making flutes from hollow bones. Perhaps stringed instruments began when a hunter picked up a bow and began to play notes. A 5,000-year-old image of a harp has been found in Sumer, near Iraq and Iran. Stringed instruments existed even earlier in Africa.

Flutes and musical pipes were used in Egypt more than 6,000 years ago. In many parts of the world, people made flutelike instruments by drilling holes in cow horns. Such flutes later became a part of the bagpipe. Slender pipes made of wood or cane were played by the Etruscans long before the Romans ruled Italy. In North and South America, people made a variety of flutes long before the arrival of the Europeans.

In ancient China, people understood that sound is made by vibrations and that it is carried through the air to the ear. They tuned drums and bells to make different sounds. In ancient Rome, people played metal trumpets during ceremonies and parades. Early Muslim leaders, called Caliphs, had vast military bands that played trumpets, drums, and cymbals.

1. Study this short history of musical instruments. What ideas most surprised you? Explain why.

2. Musical instruments from different parts of the world show many similarities. How do you explain this?

3. Do library research on the history of a musical instrument. Make an illustrated timeline showing the development of the instrument.

Integrating the Sciences

Zoology Explain to students that many birds use song for communication. Young birds can be "imprinted," or taught to sing a song that is species-specific and identifies them as a member of that species. Have students find out what might happen if a chick does not learn the song of its species. (It may not recognize its mother or be recognized by other members of its species.)

Use Integrating Worksheet 16.2b.

radio may be pleasing to some people, but it may be noise to others. You might even classify soft music or conversation that disturbs your sleep as noise.

Most sounds that people classify as noise lack pleasing sound quality, definite pitch, rhythm, and pattern. Look at Figure 16.7a and 16.7b. Compare the sound waves produced by music to the sound waves produced by noise. Notice that the music waves have a regular pattern. In contrast, the waves produced by noise are random and irregular.

Some modern composers deliberately blur the distinction between noise and music. They blend sounds of machines or other noisy objects into their compositions. For example, the sound of helicopters could be used to introduce a song and later fade into the music. Although the sound of helicopters is considered noise, the effect would be dramatic, and it might serve to make the words and feelings of the song more meaningful. Musicians can use electronic keyboards to record noises, such as a door slamming or glass breaking. Electronic keyboards can reproduce these noises in a variety of pitches. What music can you name that uses sound this way? ①

▼ ACTIVITY

Classifying

Noise

List all the sounds you hear in three different places, such as a school hall, the inside of a bus, your dinner table, or a street corner. Identify the sounds you would classify as noise. Explain your choices.

SKILLS WORKOUT

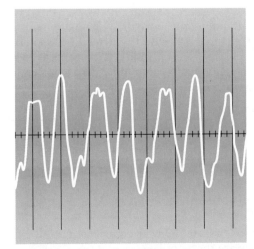

Figure 16.7a ▲
Study the pattern of sound waves made by a clarinet. Compare them to the pattern of sound waves in Figure 16.7b.

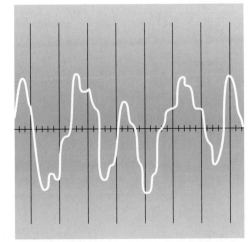

Figure 16.7b ▲
These sound waves are random and irregular. Sounds classified as noise often make sound waves like these.

Directed Inquiry

Have students study Figures 16.7a and 16.7b. Ask the following questions:

▶ What is regular about the pattern of sound waves in Figure 16.7a? (The amplitude and wavelengths)

▶ What is irregular about the sound waves in Figure 16.7b? (The wavelengths and shape of the crests)

▶ Can you tell by looking at the patterns in the illustrations which is music and which is noise? Explain. (Yes, there is a perceived regularity to the sound made by a musical instrument.)

Research

Have students use magazines, books, and video resources to write a report on a composer, such as John Cage, who uses "noise" in his or her work. If possible, have them find any quotes or explanations for using noise in the compositions.

Answer to In-Text Question

① Electronically generated sounds are used in both popular and classical styles of music and can often be heard in movie soundtracks.

395

Skills Development

Make a Graph Have students make a line graph using the information in Table 16.2. Ask them what the variable is. (Time) Ask on which axis the variable is shown. (Y-axis) They should place sound level on the X-axis and maximum time duration on the Y-axis. Ask them what generalizations they can make using their graphs. (Students should recognize that maximum duration drops quickly as decibel level rises.)

EVALUATE

WrapUp

Reteach Ask students to design a musical instrument. Have them use diagrams to show how the instrument works, and descriptions to tell about its pitch and sound quality.
Use Review Worksheet 16.2.

Check and Explain

1. A violinist presses against the violin strings to make them shorter; a trumpeter opens and closes valves that change the length of the air column.

2. Stringed: produce sound when string vibrates; wind: produce sound when column of air vibrates; percussion: produce sound when struck

3. Music and noise are both forms of sound energy. Noise threatens or disturbs mental health; music is pleasing and provides enjoyment.

4. Check students' models for accuracy.

STS Connection

Tell students that "white noise" is used to mask unwanted noises. White noise is usually made up of a wide range of different frequencies. Ask students to define white noise and to give some examples. (Moving water or waves breaking against a surf) Have students find out about the uses of white noise.

Table 16.2
Noise Exposure Limits

Sound Level (decibels)	Maximum Duration Per Day (in hours)
90	8
92	6
95	4
97	3
100	2
102	1 1/4
105	1
110	1/2
115	1/4

Science and Society *Noise Pollution*

Loud sounds that harm your hearing, interfere with your ability to concentrate, or make you feel stressed are examples of noise pollution. Noise can prevent you from carrying on a conversation or keep you from sleeping. Studies show that constant noise can cause high blood pressure. In addition, it may cause headaches, digestive problems, ulcers, and asthma. Because of these problems, people are taking steps to control noise pollution.

You can do something about noise pollution by controlling the noise you make and by encouraging others to do the same. When you have to do a noisy job, you can warn people nearby. Most people can accept some noise if they know it won't last too long. You can also choose a time to do your work that will be less disturbing to other people. Encourage your family to choose quiet models of machines, such as vacuum cleaners, blow dryers, or power saws. Also, you can encourage your peers to consider others when adjusting the stereo or TV volume.

U.S. government agencies set limits for exposure to loud noises for all federal employees. These limits are shown in Table 16.2. The sound of an auto horn is 110 dB. According to federal regulations, no worker should endure sounds that loud for more than one-half hour at a time. What is the maximum duration a worker should be exposed to a 115 dB sound? Find out about local laws concerning noise. Does your community have a process for reporting sources of disturbing noise?

Check and Explain

1. How does a violinist make different sounds? How does a trumpeter make sounds?

2. How do string, wind, and percussion instruments differ from one another?

3. **Compare and Contrast** How are music and noise different? How are they similar?

4. **Make a Model** Using materials of your choice, make a model of a musical instrument. Explain how it makes sound.

Prelab Discussion

Have students read the entire activity. Tell them that they will be working in groups of four and that there should be enough supplies for each group to make one of each instrument. Discuss a few points before beginning:

▶ Review the difference between tone and pitch.

▶ Ask students to describe the tones made by each type of instrument listed in the table.

▶ Explain that students trying to construct a guitar may be frustrated with the result if they do not include a resonance box in their designs.

Time 2 class periods   **Group** 4

Materials

100 paper fasteners, smooth round stones

50 rubber bands, drinking straws, bottle tops

40 bells, walnut shells, coat buttons

16 index cards, paper plates

10 safety pins, 2 cups of beans, 1 skein of yarn rolled into 8 small balls

8 shoe boxes, 0.5-m pieces of rubber hose, funnels, rolls of masking tape, scissors, small metal cans with lids, tongue depressors, 0.5 m sections of heavy cord, metal forks, metal trays, socks, wooden broom handles

---

Activity 16 *What musical instruments can be made from common materials?*

Skills Model; Observe; Compare; Infer; Interpret Data

Task 1 Prelab Prep

1. Collect the following items: shoe box, index card, 6 rubber bands, 12 paper fasteners, 0.5 meter piece of rubber hose, funnel, 5 drinking straws, masking tape, scissors, small metal can with a lid, a handful of seeds or beads, 6 metal bottle tops, 2 paper plates, 5 bells, safety pins, tongue depressor, 12 smooth round stones, 0.5 meter piece of heavy cord, metal fork, metal tray, sock, wooden broom handle, 5 walnut shells, 5 coat buttons, and a ball of yarn.
2. Study the list of instruments in the table. Use reference sources, if needed, to find out what each instrument looks like.

Task 2 Data Record

1. On a separate sheet of paper, draw the data table shown.
2. Record what you know about the sounds the instruments make.

Table 16.1   Homemade Instruments

Instrument	Observations
Castanets	
Guitar	
Kettledrum	
Panpipe	
Shaker	
Stone bells	
Tambourine	
Trumpet	

Task 3 Procedure

1. Decide which materials you can use to make each of the instruments listed in the data table.
2. Work to make each instrument play as many clear tones as possible. If the instrument is used simply to produce a rhythm, it may not have a tone.
3. After completing an instrument, try to play a tune. Record your observations about the sound the instrument makes.

Task 4 Analysis

1. Identify the variables in this activity.
2. How does the tone quality of each instrument vary?
3. How did you change the pitch of your instruments?
4. How are your homemade instruments different from the actual instruments? How are they alike?
5. Explain how you might improve your homemade instruments.

Task 5 Conclusion

Explain how common materials are used to make a musical instrument. Identify the type of sounds you made with your instrument and explain how the sound was made and changed.

Everyday Application

Test ordinary objects in your home to see if they have a musical tone. Make a list and describe the tone they make.

Extension

Visit a museum that has a section on musical instruments. Observe the materials used to make different instruments. Write a report comparing the musical instruments of various cultures.

Analysis

1. Various dimensions of the instruments and the materials used to make them

2. Tone varies among different instruments because their different structures vary the way sound is produced.

3. In general pitch of: wind instruments change by modifying air column length; string instruments, by changing string length; percussion instruments, by changing objects' size; drums, by altering the head tension

4. Different in sound quality; alike in producing sound

5. Better construction and materials

Conclusion

Common materials can be put together to make instruments that can be plucked, blown, or struck and produce a variety of sounds.

Everyday Application

Student responses will depend on the objects that are chosen.

Section Objectives
For a list of section objectives, see the Student Edition page.

Skills Objectives
Students should be able to:

Infer how dog whistles work.

Make an Analogy between sonar and lightning.

Vocabulary
ultrasound, sonar, echolocation

► MOTIVATE

Skills WarmUp
To help students understand sound technology, have them do the Skills WarmUp.
Answer The whistle produces sound frequencies out of the range of human hearing, but within the range of a dog's hearing.

Prior Knowledge
Gauge how much students know about sound technology by asking the following questions:

► What is ultrasound? When is it used?

► How do ships locate other ships that are underwater?

► How do sightless animals use sound?

The Living Textbook:
Physical Science Sides 1-4

Chapter 17   Frame 03400
Ultrasonic (2 Frames)
Search: Step:

Themes in Science
Scale and Structure Explain that ultrasonic waves have relatively short wavelengths. Ask students why shorter waves are useful in detecting smaller objects. (Shorter wavelengths are subject to less diffraction and produce a sharper picture.)

Language Arts Connection
Point out that the term *ultrasonic* comes from *ultra* meaning "beyond" and *sonic* meaning "sound." Have students infer what the prefix *infra* means if infrasonic sounds are those below the range of human hearing. (Below)

▼ **ACTIVITY**

Inferring

Silent Noise?
    Some people use a "silent" dog whistle to call their dog. Why is the dog whistle silent to people but not to dogs?

SKILLS WARMUP

Figure 16.8 ▲
The images on this sonar screen are made by reflected sound waves or echoes.

16.3 Sound Technology

Objectives

► **Identify** the medical and industrial uses of ultrasound.

► **Explain** how sonar works.

► **Compare** animal echolocation with sonar.

► **Make an analogy** between using sonar to find the depth of the ocean and making other distance measurements.

A ship slowly plows through the ocean far from shore. Below deck, a group of scientists and technicians huddles around a screen like the one shown in Figure 16.8. The ship is a floating laboratory. The people on board are on a voyage of discovery. Their goal is to map the ocean floor that is thousands of meters below the ship. Their tools are sound waves. They send the sound waves where they can't go themselves. The sound waves enable the scientists to "see" the ocean bottom.

Scientists aren't the only people to use this kind of sound technology. Prospectors use sound waves to hunt for oil. Dentists use sound waves to drill and clean teeth. Sound has many uses that you probably never thought about!

Ultrasound

Some sounds are too high pitched for people to hear. Most people can't hear frequencies greater than 20,000 Hz. Sounds above the range of human hearing are called **ultrasound**. Even though you can't hear ultrasound, it has many important medical and commercial uses. You may have experienced ultrasound without being aware of it.

Scientists produce ultrasound by changing electric or magnetic energy into mechanical energy. They use a device called an ultrasonic transducer. The transducer has a quartz or ceramic disk that can be charged with electricity. When charged, the disk vibrates very rapidly. The high-frequency vibration produces ultrasonic waves.

Integrating the Sciences

Earth Science Explain to students that infrasonic waves are produced by waterfalls, earthquakes, and volcanoes. Have students find out how artificially produced infrasonic waves can be used to locate oil and mineral deposits. Have them make diagrams of their findings. (Researchers compare patterns of waves traveling through unknown materials to those from a version containing oil and mineral deposits.)

STS Connection

Explain to students that many industries depend on ultrasound to detect flaws in metals, such as cracks, holes, and dirt. In some cases, the energy from ultrasound is used in welding. Have students suggest how ultrasound is used in industry. (Flaws in metal affect the ultrasound waves differently than unflawed metal; in welding, sound energy is converted to thermal energy.)

Skills Development

Infer Ask students to explain why ultrasound may offer advantages over X-rays to check on fetal development. (X-rays use radiation, which may pose a danger to the woman and the fetus. Sonograms use ultrasound and show soft tissues that are almost invisible in X-rays.)

Critical Thinking

Find Causes Have students make a diagram to show how ultrasound can produce a warming effect in muscles and sprains. (Answers will vary, but diagrams should indicate that ultrasound sets molecules in motion and the increased motion of the molecules in a muscle results in an increase in temperature. So, sound energy is converted to thermal energy. The heating effect of a microwave oven is based on the same principle: Electromagnetic waves produce kinetic energy in the particles of the substance they pass through, heating it up from the inside.)

Answer to In-Text Question

① **The sonogram in Figure 16.9 shows the stage of development of a fetus.**

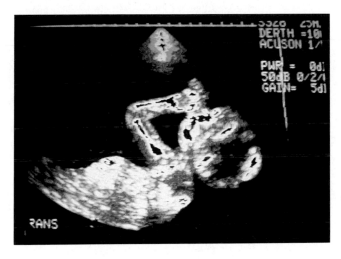

◀ **Figure 16.9**
This sonogram of a developing fetus shows the imaging power of ultrasound.

Medical Uses Doctors use ultrasound to observe soft tissues in the human body. Soft tissues, such as those that make up the liver, are almost invisible on an X-ray picture. However, ultrasonic waves reflect off soft tissues. A computer transforms the reflected waves into a picture on a computer screen. The picture is called a *sonogram*. Using a sonogram, a surgeon can detect a tumor or examine valves in the heart. Pregnant women routinely have sonograms to determine the development of the fetus. How is ultrasound being used in Figure 16.9? ①

Other medical professionals also use ultrasonic devices. Physicians use ultrasonic vibrations to get rid of stones that form in the kidney and gall bladder. The ultrasonic vibrations break the stones into very small pieces so they can pass out of the body naturally. Dental hygienists use high-frequency vibrations to loosen plaque deposits on teeth. Physical therapists use ultrasound to produce a deep-heating effect for muscle spasms and sprains.

Commercial Uses Ultrasound is used to clean small, intricate metal items, such as jewelry and small machine parts. The item to be cleaned is placed in a liquid bath. Ultrasonic vibrations travel through the liquid bath to loosen and remove dirt and corrosion. Ultrasound makes it easy to clean cracks and crevices that can't be reached by hand-polishing methods.

**The Living Textbook:
Physical Science Sides 1-4**

Chapter 14   Frame 02312
Ultrasonic (1 Frame)
Search:

**The Living Textbook:
Physical Science Sides 1-4**

Chapter 14   Frame 02313
Sonograms (6 Frames)
Search: Step:

TEACH ▪ *Continued*

Reteach

Draw a ship and the ocean floor on the chalkboard. Have several volunteers draw a step in sonar navigation. (An ultrasonic beam is sent into the ocean and then reflected back.) Ask another volunteer to write the equation used to determine the distance to the ocean floor. ($\frac{\text{round trip time}}{2} \times 1{,}500$ m)

◆ *Explore Visually*

Have students study Figure 16.10. Ask the following questions:

▶ How do commercial fishers use sonar? (To detect schools of fish)

▶ Why is sonar useful for mapping the ocean floor? (It can travel many kilometers through water. By timing the reflection, distance can be calculated.)

▶ What else might the signal detect besides the ocean floor? (Answers may vary, but students may mention fish, sea mounts, shipwrecks, or submarines.)

▶ What is Alvin, and what does it do? (Alvin is an undersea research vessel that uses sonar to help it navigate underwater.)

▶ How did oceanographers map the Mid-Atlantic Ridge? (Sonar was used to map the Mid-Atlantic Ridge.)

Answers to In-Text Questions

① (17 s ÷ 2) × 1,500 m/s = 12,750 m

② (4 s ÷ 2) × 1,500 m/s = 3,000 m

Integrating the Sciences

Oceanography Inform students that only about 5 percent of the ocean floor has been mapped in detail. In 1993, researchers found more than 1,000 previously unknown volcanoes on the ocean floor in the South Pacific. Some of the volcanoes were more than 2,100 m high. Ask students to explain how sonar may be useful in studying undersea volcanoes. (Sonar would reveal changes in elevation and shape in the volcanoes.)

Sonar

Ultrasound is used to locate underwater objects. Ultrasonic waves travel for many kilometers underwater. When the ultrasonic waves strike an obstacle, the waves are reflected. The technique of using sound waves to locate underwater objects is called **sonar**. The word *sonar* comes from "**so**und **na**vigation and **r**anging."

Sonar helps oceanographers and ship captains determine the depth of the ocean. Look at Figure 16.10. A ship sends ultrasonic waves downward. When the sound waves reach the ocean floor, they are reflected back to the ship. The time it takes for the signals to

**Figure 16.10
Uses of Sonar** ▼

By taking continuous depth readings as a ship moves along, the shape of the ocean floor can be mapped.

Signal from ship

Echo

If it takes 17 s for the ultrasound signal to go from the ship to the bottom and back, how deep is the ocean at this location? ①

If it takes 4 s for the ultrasound signal to go from the ship to the bottom and back, how deep is the ocean at this location? ②

Seamount

Ocean floor

return is used to calculate the depth of the water below the ship. Since sound travels at about 1,500 m/s in ocean water, the depth of the ocean can be calculated using this formula:

$$\frac{\text{round trip time (s)}}{2} \times \frac{1{,}500 \text{ m}}{\text{s}} = \text{distance to ocean bottom}$$

The French scientist Paul Langevin invented sonar in 1915 to help ships detect icebergs. In 1925, scientists discovered the Mid-Atlantic Ridge with the aid of an echo sounder. The Mid-Atlantic Ridge is an undersea mountain range that runs down the middle of the Atlantic Ocean. Its discovery helped to explain how the continents move.

Commercial fishers use sonar to detect schools of fish.

The undersea research vessel *Alvin* uses sonar to help navigate underwater. Echo sounders tell the pilot how far the craft is from the seafloor, the surface, and approaching objects.

Sonar was used to determine the height and shape of the mountains in the Mid-Atlantic Ridge.

TEACH ▪ Continued

Explore Visually

Have students study the photographs and text on pages 402 and 403. Ask the following questions:

▶ What kind of frequency does a dolphin use for echolocation? Why? (Low frequencies to detect an object; high frequencies to get a more accurate picture)

▶ For what kinds of communication does a dolphin use echolocation? (Navigation, distress, and recognition)

▶ What does echolocation enable dolphins to detect? (Differences in shape, size, thickness, and location of objects)

▶ How do some moths interfere with the echolocation systems of bats? (Some moths produce high-pitched clicks at the same frequency as the bats' clicks for echolocation.)

▶ How do bats differ in their use of sound? (Each emits a different sound from between the relatively broad range of 10 000–120 000 Hz.)

Cooperative Learning

Have students work in cooperative groups to determine if they can use sound to locate an object. Have pairs of students stand about one meter from a wall in a gym or school playground. Students should be about two meters apart. Have one student blindfold the other. Blindfolded students should take small steps toward the wall while tapping the ground with a stick or clapping their hands. Have them observe the difference in sound as they approach the wall. Have them repeat the activity several times and reverse roles as well. Challenge students to use the sound to tell when they have come within 30 centimeters of the wall.

Animal Echolocation

Many animals live in environments where their sense of vision is of little use. Some live in dark caves or deep within the sea where there is no sunlight. Others are active only at night. Some of these animals use high-frequency sound waves to guide them in the dark. They use a system that is similar to sonar, called **echolocation** (EHK oh loh KAY shuhn). Echolocation involves sending out sounds to judge the location, size, and motion of objects from the returning echoes. Look at the dolphins below to find out how they use echolocation.

▲ Dolphins use both a high- and low-frequency sound for echolocation. Since low-frequency sound travels farthest, a dolphin uses low frequencies first to detect an object. The dolphin then switches to a high-frequency sound, which gives a more accurate picture of the object. Dolphins have a hearing range between 150 Hz and 150,000 Hz.

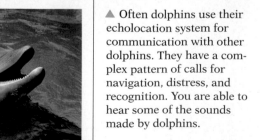

▲ Often dolphins use their echolocation system for communication with other dolphins. They have a complex pattern of calls for navigation, distress, and recognition. You are able to hear some of the sounds made by dolphins.

Echolocation allows dolphins to detect small differences in the shape, size, and thickness of objects. ▶

Dolphins also use echolocation for navigation and to locate prey and avoid predators. Dolphins have a very advanced echolocation system. Many of their sounds have frequencies between 120,000 to 150,000 Hz, which are well beyond the range of human hearing.

Using echolocation, bats can fly in total darkness through caves with many obstacles without running into anything. They emit high-pitch clicks and listen for the returning echoes. Moths use high-pitch sounds for defense and for communication. Look at the bat and the moths below to find out how they use high-frequency sound.

◀ Bats emit high frequencies that range between 10,000 and 120,000 Hz. Each species of bat emits its own distinctive sounds. The echoes from these sounds help bats to navigate and to locate their prey.

▲ In addition to using echolocation for defense, some moths communicate with each other by emitting ultrasounds. What kinds of information do you think moths communicate?

Some moths, a favorite food animal of bats, have the ability to produce high-pitch clicks like those of bats. These sounds seem to interfere with the bats' echolocation system. Thus, the moths can sometimes evade a bat on the hunt for a meal. ▶

TEACH ▪ *Continued*

Directed Inquiry

Have students study Figure 16.11. Ask the following questions:

▶ What are the parts of a hearing aid? (Earphone, amplifier, microphone, and battery)

▶ Make a flowchart that shows how sound is processed through a hearing aid. (Check students' charts for accuracy.)

EVALUATE

WrapUp

Reinforce Have students work in groups of four to design a portable machine that uses ultrasound to help sight-deficient people to move about without canes or other aids. Remind students to consider the features that users would want and how the machine would get and transmit information to the user. Have each group present its machine to the rest of the class.

Use Review Worksheet 16.3.

Check and Explain

1. Answers will vary. Students may say that ultrasound could be used to examine heart valves, break up kidney stones, clean teeth, and find objects underwater.

2. An ultrasonic wave is sent to and reflects from an object. The round trip time and the speed of sound in water are used to calculate the object's location and to find size and shape.

3. They both rely on the reflection of sound waves from an object to determine its distance and shape. Both the animals and the sonar equipment usually cannot see and have large antennae or ears to receive sound.

4. Both use the time it takes for sound to travel to determine the distance that the sound travels.

STS Connection

Explain to students that most hearing aids, such as the one shown in Figure 16.11, rely on the amplification of sound. They can be used as long as the person's inner ear is healthy. In cases in which the middle ear is damaged, a person may use a bone-conduction hearing aid. In this type of hearing aid, the vibrations of sound waves are conducted by bone behind the ear to the cochlea and the auditory nerves.

Art Connection

Tell students that people who are hearing impaired use the American manual alphabet to communicate. Have students research this alphabet. Have them draw pictures of some of the hand signals. They can share their drawings with the class.

Science and Technology
High-Tech Hearing Aids

Recall how sound waves move through your ear. What would happen if the movement of the stirrup bone were limited? It wouldn't transmit much sound energy to the fluid in the inner ear. Hair cells in the cochlea wouldn't move very much. The nerve impulses to the brain would be weaker. The person's hearing would be impaired. As long as the person's inner ear is healthy, problems with the stirrup bone can be corrected with a hearing aid.

A hearing aid is a device that increases the loudness, or intensity, of incoming sound waves. A hearing aid has three main parts, as shown in Figure 16.11.

▶ A microphone picks up sounds and changes the sound waves into electric signals.

▶ An amplifier makes the electric signal stronger.

▶ An earphone, or speaker, changes the electric signal back into sound waves.

A hearing aid is similar to a telephone because it changes sound energy into electric energy and then back into sound energy. At low frequencies, the performance of a hearing aid is limited by the quality of the microphone. At high frequencies, the earphone is the limiting factor.

Small hearing aids can be worn behind the ear, in eyeglass frames, or completely inside the outer ear. Larger hearing aids that can be attached to clothing are more effective but not as convenient to use.

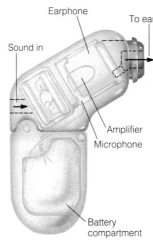

Earphone
To ear
Sound in
Amplifier
Microphone
Battery compartment

Figure 16.11 ▲
A hearing aid can be designed to amplify all incoming sounds or to boost certain frequencies.

Check and Explain

1. Give three examples of medical and other uses of ultrasound.

2. How does sonar work?

3. **Compare and Contrast** How does echolocation in animals compare with sonar?

4. **Make an Analogy** How does using sonar to determine the depth of the ocean compare to using the sound of thunder to determine the distance of a lightning flash?

Chapter 16 Review

Concept Summary

16.1 How You Hear
▶ The ear consists of three major regions: the outer ear, the middle ear, and the inner ear.
▶ The energy of sound waves is transferred from the eardrum in the outer ear, then to the three bones of the middle ear, and finally to the cochlea and auditory nerve of the inner ear.
▶ Sounds with an intensity over 120 dB can damage structures in the ear and impair hearing.

16.2 Sounds You Hear
▶ Musical instruments produce sounds that have pitch, intensity, rhythm, harmony, quality, and overtones.
▶ Musical instruments are classified as string, wind, or percussion.

▶ Noise is unwanted, annoying, or sometimes unhealthy sound. Noise often has irregular sound-wave patterns.

16.3 Sound Technology
▶ Ultrasound waves have frequencies above 20,000 Hz. These frequencies are beyond the range that humans can hear.
▶ Ultrasound waves are used to produce images of organs and tissues inside the body. These images are called sonograms.
▶ Sonar is a device that reflects sound waves off undersea objects. Sonar was used to map the ocean floor.
▶ Echolocation is used by animals such as dolphins, bats, and moths for communication, defense, and to locate objects underwater or in darkness.

Chapter Vocabulary

outer ear (p. 386)   overtone (p. 391)   sonar (p. 400)
middle ear (p. 386)   ultrasound (p. 398)   echolocation (p. 402)
inner ear (p. 386)

Check Your Vocabulary

Use the vocabulary words above to complete the following sentences correctly.

1. Ships use ___ to map the ocean floor.
2. Sound waves with a frequency exceeding 20,000 Hz are called ___ .
3. The ear canal is part of the ___ .
4. A second frequency sound produced by a violin string is called a(n) ___ .
5. The anvil bone is located in the ___ .
6. Bats avoid obstacles in total darkness by using ___ .
7. The semicircular canals are located in the ___ .

Pair each numbered word with a vocabulary term. Explain in a complete sentence how the words relate.

8. hammer
9. high frequency
10. semicircular canals
11. oval window
12. irregular
13. Mid-Atlantic Ridge

Write Your Vocabulary

Write sentences using the vocabulary words above. Show that you know what each word means.

Check Your Vocabulary
1. sonar
2. ultrasound
3. outer ear
4. overtone
5. middle ear
6. echolocation
7. inner ear
8. The hammer is one of the bones of the middle ear.
9. High-frequency sound waves are used for ultrasound.
10. The semicircular canals are part of the inner ear.
11. The oval window separates the middle ear from the inner ear.
12. Sonar can detect items with irregular shapes.
13. The Mid-Atlantic Ridge was discovered with sonar.

Write Your Vocabulary
Students' sentences should show that they know the meaning of each word as well as how to use it in a sentence.
   Use Vocabulary Worksheet for Chapter 16.

Check Your Knowledge

1. Vibrations of the eardrum are transmitted through the hammer, anvil, and stirrup to the oval window and into the fluid of the inner ear.

2. Hair cells convert vibrations in the fluid of the inner ear into nerve impulses.

3. Sounds of 120 dB can rupture the eardrum and damage hair cells, causing hearing loss.

4. Pitch, intensity, rhythm, overtone, harmony, and melody.

5. Noise is any sound that disturbs people or threatens mental or physical health.

6. Ultrasound is used to observe tissue too soft to show up on X-ray images.

7. Sound waves travel at a constant rate in specific media; they travel long distances in water, and the relatively short wavelength of the waves determines how clearly the image produced will be—sonar pictures can in effect be "focused."

8. stirrup

9. brain

10. 20–20,000 Hz

11. intensity

12. string

13. **so**und **na**vigation and **r**anging

14. dolphins and bats

Check Your Understanding

1. In general, noise lacks quality, definite pitch, and rhythm.

2. Sonar is technology for range-finding and navigation that is based on the echolocation system used by animals.

3. Noise can interfere with the ability to concentrate on tasks and can cause health problems.

4. One moth might be able to produce sounds that interfere with the bat's echolocation.

5. a. cochlea
   b. conducts vibrations from the stirrup to the hair cells
   c. Students may be able to distinguish semicircular canals and the auditory nerve.

6. Students might suggest that humans do not have hair cells that respond to those frequencies, or that the eardrum/middle ear bones will not vibrate at those frequencies.

7. The higher pitch comes from an instrument with a shorter air column.

8. The hair cells will be damaged, leading to hearing loss.

Chapter 16 Review

Check Your Knowledge

Answer the following in complete sentences.

1. How do incoming sound waves reach the inner ear?

2. What is the role of hair cells during the process of hearing?

3. How do sounds that measure more than 120 dB affect hearing?

4. What are the six characteristics of musical sounds?

5. How would you describe noise?

6. In medical technology, when are ultrasonic waves used instead of X-rays?

7. What properties of ultrasonic waves make them useful in sonar?

Check the answer that best completes each sentence.

8. The bone nearest the oval window is the (hammer, anvil, stirrup, cochlea).

9. The auditory nerve leads from the ear to the (eardrum, cochlea, hair cells, brain).

10. The range of human hearing is (10 to 20,000 Hz, 20 to 20,000 Hz, 20 to 30,000 Hz, 0 to120 dB).

11. The loudness of a musical note is the same as its (pitch, intensity, melody, quality).

12. A piano is a (wind, string, percussion, plucked) instrument.

13. Sonar stands for (sound arrival and reflection, sound notes and reflection, sound navigation and ranging, sound navy and ranging).

14. Echolocation is used by (people and bats, dolphins and bats, dogs and dolphins, moths and people).

Check Your Understanding

Apply the concepts you have learned to answer each question.

1. How do music sound waves differ from noise sound waves? Explain the differences in terms of sound waves.

2. Compare echolocation to sonar.

3. Why are there laws limiting noise exposure in the workplace?

4. **Critical Thinking** You observe a bat chasing two different kinds of moths. The bat always catches one kind of moth but has difficulty catching the second kind. Explain why the bat has trouble catching the one kind of moth.

5. **Mystery Photo** The photograph on page 384 shows a human inner ear.
   a. What is the spiral structure?
   b. How does the spiral structure function in hearing?
   c. What other structures can you identify? Give the function of each.

6. Based on what you know about the structure of the ear, give a possible explanation of why people can't hear sounds with frequencies higher than 20,000 Hz.

7. **Application** You hear the sound from two wind instruments. One instrument tends to produce higher pitch sounds than the other. What might you conclude about the length of the air column in each instrument?

8. **Application** Many people listen to music with headphones. Sometimes the volume is so loud that people around them can hear it. What can happen to their inner ear if people do this regularly?

Develop Your Skills

1. a. *a; d*

   b. *d; a*

2. The fish are moving away (diving).

3. Echolocation would be as effective in the daytime as at night, because it does not involve light.

4. a. underwater signaling

   b. thunder; birdsong

Make Connections

1.

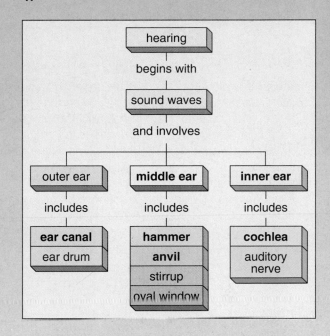

2. You will feel dizzy because while you spun, the fluid in your semicircular canals was moving, and takes a few moments to settle down.

3. Students' ads should all involve some form of persuasion.

4. Students' descriptions of unfamiliar music forms will vary.

Develop Your Skills

Use the skills you have developed in this chapter to complete each activity.

1. Interpret Data The screens below show wave patterns representing four different sounds.

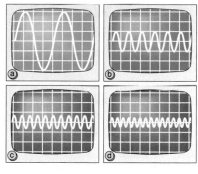

  a. Which screen shows the loudest sound? The softest sound?

  b. Which image shows the highest pitch? The lowest pitch?

2. Infer You are using sonar to locate a school of fish. Your first set of sonar waves returns in 2.4 seconds. The second set takes 2.6 seconds. What does this tell you about the fish?

3. Predict If bats were active during the day, would echolocation be as useful for catching prey? Explain.

4. Data Bank The graph on page 639 shows the frequency and intensity of different sounds.

  a. Which sound has the greatest intensity?

  b. Which sound has the widest range of frequencies? The narrowest range?

Make Connections

1. Link the Concepts Below is a concept map showing how some of the main concepts in this chapter link together. Only part of the map is filled in. Finish the map, using words and ideas you find on the previous pages.

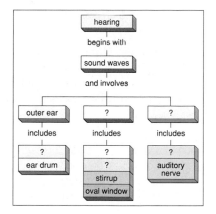

2. Science and You Close your eyes and spin around for several minutes. Record how you feel when you stop spinning. Why does this occur?

3. Science and Society Design a TV or newspaper ad that convinces people to use hearing protectors.

4. Science and Social Studies People in different cultures use many kinds of musical styles and harmonies. Do library research on the musical scales and harmonies used in different styles of music. Listen to examples from library record and tape collections. Find out about the cultures from which the music comes. Prepare a class presentation.

Overview

This chapter explores the nature and characteristics of light. The first section discusses both the wave and the particle models of light and presents information about the intensity and speed of light. The next section describes the characteristics and uses of the visible and invisible regions on the electromagnetic spectrum. The last section explains the relationship between light and color. It also includes a description of light wave interactions—reflection, refraction, diffraction, and interference.

Advance Planner

▶ Supply yarn for TE page 410.

▶ Provide tennis or golf balls for TE page 412.

▶ Obtain broom straw or spaghetti bundle for TE page 412.

▶ Supply materials for SE Activity 17, page 415.

▶ Obtain a prism for TE page 417.

▶ Obtain a full spectrum of colored pencils, markers, or crayons for TE page 418.

▶ Supply dishwashing liquid, glycerin, wire hangers, and a rimmed cookie sheet for TE page 424.

▶ Provide water-based paints for TE page 427.

Skills Development Chart

Sections	Communicate	Compare	Control Variables	Estimate	Generalize	Infer	Model	Observe	Research
17.1 Skills WarmUp					●				
SkillBuilder		●	●						
Skills WorkOut							●		
Skills WorkOut				●					
Activity						●		●	
17.2 Skills WarmUp								●	
17.3 Skills WarmUp								●	
Historical Notebook	●								●

Individual Needs

▶ **Limited English Proficiency Students** As students read the chapter, ask them to list the boldface terms and other unfamiliar words in their portfolio, placing two or three on a page. Have them cut out pictures from magazines or catalogs that illustrate each term, and paste them on the pages to make a picture dictionary for the chapter.

▶ **At-Risk Students** Write the titles of the three chapter sections on the chalkboard. Have students copy each title onto a page in their portfolio. As students read each section, provide a photograph from a magazine or newspaper that relates to the main idea or concepts in each subsection—except the Science and Society, and Science and Technology features. Have them write a sentence that tells how the photograph connects to the content in the subsection. You may wish to have students use their sentences and the pictures as part of their chapter review.

▶ **Gifted Students** Invite students to stage a *Wave vs. Particle Debate* for the class. Have the students form two groups, and assign "Light as a Wave" to one, and "Light as a Particle" to the other. Ask each group to research their topic from its first proposal to the most recent evidence. Group members should take turns presenting arguments for each side. Encourage students to use demonstrations to support their arguments: for instance, they may shine light through a double slit to demonstrate the interference pattern that supports the wave theory.

Resource Bank

▶ **Bulletin Board** Write several different terms and concepts presented in the chapter on index cards. Hang these on a bulletin board titled *Light and Color Treasure Hunt*. Add pictures to illustrate the concept. Encourage students to find examples of the terms and concepts in their own lives. For example, for *translucent* a student might mention the frosted glass windows in the school gym. Have them record their examples on cards, attaching them to the bulletin board under the appropriate term or concept. At the end of the chapter, discuss the examples.

Section	Core	Standard	Enriched	Section	Core	Standard	Enriched
17.1 The Nature of Light pp. 408–415				**Overhead Blackline Transparencies** Overhead Blackline Master 16 and Student Worksheet	•	•	•
Section Features Skills WarmUp, p. 409	•	•	•	**Color Transparencies** Transparencies 58, 59a, 59b	•	•	•
Skills WorkOut, p. 412		•	•	**17.3 Light and Color** pp. 422–428			
Skills WorkOut, p. 414		•	•				
SkillBuilder, p. 411		•	•	**Section Features** Skills WarmUp, p. 422	•	•	•
Activity, p. 415	•	•	•	Historical Notebook, p. 427	•	•	•
Blackline Masters Review Worksheet 17.1	•	•	•	**Blackline Masters** Review Worksheet 17.3	•	•	
Integrating Worksheet 17.1	•	•	•	Skills Worksheet 17.3	•	•	
17.2 The Electromagnetic Spectrum pp. 416–421				Integrating Worksheet 17.3a	•	•	•
				Integrating Worksheet 17.3b	•	•	•
Section Features Skills WarmUp, p. 416	•	•	•	Vocabulary Worksheet 17	•	•	
Blackline Masters Review Worksheet 17.2	•	•	•	**Color Transparencies** Transparency 60	•	•	•
Reteach Worksheet 17.2	•	•	•	**Laboratory Program** Investigation 33	•	•	•
Skills Worksheet 17.2a	•	•					
Skills Worksheet 17.2b		•	•				
Integrating Worksheet 17.2	•	•	•				

Bibliography

The following resources can be used for teaching the chapter. See page T-46 for supplier codes.

Library Resources

Berman, Paul. Light and Sound. New York: Marshall Cavendish, 1988.

The Diagram Group. Comparisons. New York: St. Martin's Press, 1980.

Lafferty, Peter. Energy and Light. New York: Gloucester Press, 1989.

Science Universe Series: Sight, Light and Color. New York: Arco Publishing, Inc., 1984.

Sherwood, Martin, and Christine Sutton. The Physical World. New York: Oxford University Press, 1988.

Technology Resources

Internet

PLANETDIARY at http://www.planetdiary.com
- Discover more about astronomy and space in Astronomy/Space by clicking on Phenomena Backgrounders and Current Phenomena.

Software

Learning All About Lights and Lasers. Mac, Win. LS.

Laserdiscs

Living Textbook. (See barcodes on pages in this chapter.) Optical Data.

Videos

Color from Light. EB.
How Does Light Travel? EB.
Light Science: You Can Do It! EB.
What Is Light? EB.
The World of Light Energy. FM.

Writing Connection

Have students write about the use of color in a painting or drawing. They should focus on how color gives a painting or drawing depth and reality. Some students may wish to describe how color is used for effect in a commercial ad.

Themes in Science

Energy Light is a form of energy emitted as electrons in an atom change energy levels. The range, or spectrum, of light energy extends beyond the range of light humans can see.

▶ Introducing the Chapter

Have students read the description of the photograph. Ask if they agree or disagree with the description. Explain to students that the photograph is not "just color."

Directed Inquiry

Have students study the photograph. Ask the following questions:

▶ What does this photograph show? (A surface covered with three different colors of paint)

▶ How do you know that light was shining on the surface when it was photographed? (The surface would not be visible without light; the shiny white spots are reflected light.)

▶ What does the photograph have to do with light? (Light enables us to see objects and colors.)

▶ Why are the colors different? (Paints are made up of materials called pigments, which reflect different colors of light.)

▶ Chapter Vocabulary

electromagnetic spectrum	photon
gamma ray	polarized
infrared	translucent
opaque	transparent
photoelectric effect	ultraviolet
	X-ray

Chapter 17 Light

Chapter Sections

17.1 The Nature of Light

17.2 The Electromagnetic Spectrum

17.3 Light and Color

What do you see?

❝ I think this photograph is just color, nothing in particular. The reason for the different colors is that different light waves are reflected off of the paint. Certain light waves are absorbed by it, and some are reflected. For example, all colors are absorbed except the primaries, that is what we see as red, blue, and yellow. ❞

Aashish Mewada
Carman Ainsworth Junior
High School
Flint, Michigan

To find out more about the photograph, look on page 430. As you read this chapter, you will learn about light and color.

Integrating the Sciences

Oceanography Mention to students that some deep-sea creatures emit light as a result of chemical reactions in their bodies. This process is called *bioluminescence*. Have students find out which creatures are capable of bioluminescence and identify some of its functions in the animal world.

Language Arts Connection

Ask students to list several words beginning with the prefix *photo-*, such as *photocopy*, *photograph*, *photoelectric*, and *photosynthesis*. Ask volunteers to look up the meanings in the dictionary and share them with the class. Ask students to identify what the meanings have in common. (The prefix *photo-* means "light." All the words mentioned involve light.)

Section Objectives
For a list of section objectives, see the Student Edition page.

Skills Objectives
Students should be able to:

Generalize about the nature of light.

Control Variables in an experiment with polarized lenses.

Make a Model showing the two theories of light.

Calculate light reflection in light-years from Venus to Earth and from Mars to Earth.

Vocabulary
photon, polarized, photoelectric effect

17.1 Nature of Light

Objectives

▶ **Identify** three sources of light.

▶ **Describe** how light is produced.

▶ **Compare** the wave model and particle model of light.

▶ **Calculate** time and distance using the speed of light.

▼ **ACTIVITY**

Generalizing

Thin Light

1. Hold two fingers close together to form a slit.
2. Look at a light bulb through the slit. Describe the pattern of light you see.
3. Vary the size of the slit. How does the size of the slit affect what you see?

SKILLS WARMUP

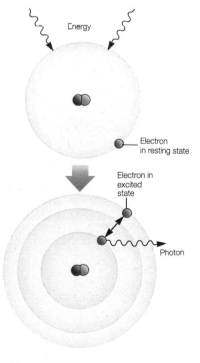

H ave you ever walked into a darkened room late at night? If so, you probably walked slowly and carefully to keep from bumping into things. When you found the light and switched it on, everything changed. Things you couldn't see were suddenly visible. Light was reflected off of objects to make them visible. You could see form, shape, and color.

Light affects your life in many ways. You need light to read this book. When you look at a clear sky at night, you can see the light from distant stars. By making things visible, light links you to objects that are close by or far away!

Light Energy

Light is a form of energy that your eyes can detect. Where does light come from, and how does it reach your eyes? Objects that produce light are sources of light. The sun, a light bulb, and flames all produce light. Most objects don't produce their own light, they reflect light from some source. You can't see the furniture in a dark room until you switch on the lights. Only when light is reflected by the furniture can you see it.

Light is produced when electrons change energy levels in an atom. The electrons moving around the nucleus of an atom have different amounts of energy. The energy of an electron depends on its distance from the nucleus. Look at Figure 17.1. If an electron absorbs extra energy, it jumps to a higher energy level away from the nucleus. When the electron falls back to a lower energy level, it gives off the added energy as a packet of light. A packet of light energy is called a **photon** (FOH tahn).

Figure 17.1 ▲
The electron absorbs energy added to the atom (top). The electron moves to a higher energy level. As the electron falls back to its original position, photons are released (bottom).

MOTIVATE

Skills WarmUp
To help students understand the nature of light, have them do the Skills WarmUp.
Answer Students should see some small, dark vertical lines crossing the light that are parallel to the slit. They will see fewer lines through a wider slit.

Prior Knowledge
To gauge how much students know about the nature of light, ask:

▶ Where are the energy levels in an atom?

▶ How long are the days at the North Pole during the summer?

 The Living Textbook:
Physical Science Side 3

Chapter 35   Frame 22613
Emission of Light (Animation)
Search: Play:

TEACH

TEACH

Discuss

After students read pages 409 and 410, ask the following questions:

▶ How is light produced? (Light is the energy released as an electron in an atom returns to a lower energy level.)

▶ How can you describe a photon? (It's a packet of light energy that acts like a particle.)

▶ How does light act like a wave? (It bends around objects, it can produce interference patterns, and one light beam can pass through another.)

Skills Development

Make a Model Have students use construction-paper slits and lengths of yarn to make a model of a polarizing filter. The yarn will represent waves that interact with the construction-paper polarizing filter. (Models will vary but should show that the filter blocks out light waves vibrating in several directions—light that passes through the filter is parallel and vibrates in the same direction.)

Answer to In-Text Question

① Right: red, green, blue; left: blue, green, red

The Living Textbook: Physical Science Sides 1-4

Chapter 9   Frame 01547
Wave Interference (1 Frame)
Search:

The Living Textbook: Physical Science Sides 1-4

Chapter 13   Frame 02222
Light Polarization (18 Frames)
Search: Step:

410

Models of Light

In the late 1600s, Isaac Newton reasoned that because light travels in straight lines and casts sharp shadows, it must behave like a tiny stream of particles. Other scientists disagreed. They argued that light traveled in waves, because it bends slightly around objects and two light beams can pass through one another. This could only happen if light traveled in waves.

The controversy ended when it was demonstrated that light displayed an interference pattern. Since only waves exhibit interference patterns, light must be waves. A hundred years later, Albert Einstein challenged this theory after studying the behavior of light striking metal objects. Einstein stated that light was tiny energy packages, or photons.

Is light composed of waves or particles? Scientists have concluded that light has the properties of both waves and particles. When it travels, light acts like a wave. When it is given off or absorbed by objects, light acts like a particle.

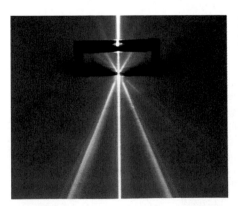

Figure 17.2 ▲
Light waves projected through this diffraction grating produce an interference pattern. What colors are between the bands of interference? ①

Light as a Wave Interference patterns that prove light is a wave can be shown with a diffraction grating like the one in Figure 17.2. A diffraction grating is a glass plate that has thousands of tiny grooves in it. When light passes through the spaces between the grooves, it spreads out. The images from each groove interfere with each other to produce bands of light.

Recall that there are two kinds of waves, longitudinal waves and transverse waves. Light behaves as a transverse wave. Transverse waves, such as sunlight, vibrate in all directions as they travel.

Light waves can be aligned so they all vibrate in the same direction by passing the light through a special filter. The filter works by only allowing light waves that vibrate in a single direction to pass through the filter. The rest of the light waves are blocked. After passing through the filter, the light waves are all parallel and vibrate in the same direction. These waves are said to be **polarized**. Some sunglasses contain polarizing filters for reducing glare.

Social Studies Connection

Explain to students that aviator sunglasses were designed in the 1930s to protect pilots from high-altitude glare. The aviator glasses were the first sunglasses and a flying necessity. Invite students to discuss how sunglasses are used today both as protection and fashion. Discuss the types of lenses used, and their coloring.

STS Connection

"Electric eyes," such as those that turn on street or house lights at dusk, rely on the photoelectric effect. They produce a current or close a switch when light shines on them. Have students learn how solar cells turn on streetlights. (When the light level drops, the solar cell quits generating electricity. A switch kept open by the electric current closes, and turns on the streetlight.)

SkillBuilder

Ask students to explain why their first observation involved looking at an object in ordinary light. (Answers will vary but should indicate students' understanding of a control with which to compare their observations during the activity.)

Answers

1. Answers may vary. The light waves were blocked by both polarized lenses.

2. To protect your eyes from harmful rays

3. The amount of light on the object

SkillBuilder *Comparing, Controlling Variables*

ACTIVITY

Polarized Sunglasses

The lenses in some sunglasses contain polarized filters. Compare the difference in light when viewing an object without a polarized lens, with a polarized lens, and with two polarized lenses. Record what you see in all three observations.

1. Observe a light-colored object in full sunlight or under the light from a 100-watt light bulb. **CAUTION! Never look directly at the sun.**

2. Put on a pair of polarized glasses. Observe the object under the same light.

3. Position a second pair of polarized glasses so one lens is perpendicular to a lens of the first pair of glasses. Observe the object under the same light.

Complete the following questions.

1. Use the diagrams to explain what happened to the light waves when you held two polarized lenses perpendicular to each other.

2. Why might you choose to wear polarized sunglasses?

3. Identify the control in the experiment?

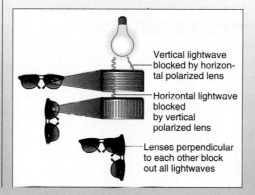

Vertical lightwave blocked by horizontal polarized lens

Horizontal lightwave blocked by vertical polarized lens

Lenses perpendicular to each other block out all lightwaves

Portfolio

Have students work in small groups to make a diagram showing the photoelectric effect. Have them draw light striking a metal plate; show high energy photons traveling and being absorbed and electrons escaping from the plate. (Drawings may vary, but should show all the steps mentioned above.) Have students keep their diagrams in their portfolios.

Integrated Learning

Use Integrating Worksheet 17.1.

Light as a Particle Evidence also supports the idea that light acts like a particle. When a beam of high-energy light strikes a metal plate, electrons are released from the metal atoms. Enough electrons are released to produce an electric current that can be measured. The release of electrons when high-energy light strikes a metal is called the **photoelectric effect**.

In 1905, Albert Einstein offered an explanation of the photoelectric effect. He suggested that light is a stream of tiny packets of energy, or photons. When a photon strikes an atom in a metal plate, an electron in the atom absorbs energy from the photon. If the photon carries enough energy, an electron can escape from the metal plate.

Metals that release electrons are said to be photosensitive, that is, they are sensitive to light. Only high-frequency light, such as violet light, will supply enough energy to release electrons from metals. Low frequency light, such as red light, does not have enough energy to release electrons when it strikes a photoelectric metal.

 The Living Textbook: Physical Science Sides 1-4

Chapter 13   Frame 02036
Rays of Light (2 Frames)
Search: Step:

Skills WorkOut

To help students understand models of light, have them do the Skills WorkOut.

Answer Models may vary. Students should use their particle model of light to explain the photoelectric effect. Be sure the students' models are accurate.

Reteach

Discuss light intensity using models, such as a bundle of straw from a broom or a bundle of spaghetti. Have one student hold the bundle tightly at one end. Ask another student to compare the diameter of the bundle close to the student's hand to the diameter at the loose end of the bundle. (The diameter is larger farther from the hand.) Ask students to explain how this is a model for the intensity of light. (Light spreads out farther from the source.)

**The Living Textbook:
Physical Science Sides 1-4**

Chapter 13   Frame 02000
Light Intensity (2 Frames)
Search: Step:

412

Integrating the Sciences

Astronomy Point out to students that differences in the intensity of light from heavenly bodies do not necessarily indicate differences in their distances from the earth. Some stars emit more light energy than others. Have students find two or three different measurements that astronomers use to determine a star's distance from the earth.

Writing Connection

Have students write a short mystery story in which light intensity and shadows play a part in solving the mystery. Encourage students to be descriptive and to share their stories with the class.

▼ ACTIVITY

Making a Model

Light

Make two models. One to represent the particle model of light and the other to represent the wave model of light. You should be able to explain the photoelectric effect using your particle model.

SKILLS WORKOUT

**The Photoelectric Effect
Figure 17.3** ▶

A low-frequency photon may not have enough energy to eject an electron.

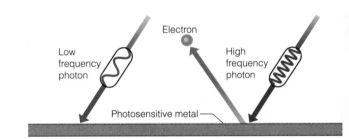

A higher-frequency photon has more energy and can eject an electron.

Light Intensity

As you walk toward a light in the distance, the light source becomes brighter as you get closer. The particle nature of light explains why the brightness, or intensity, of light varies with distance. Particles of light travel in a straight line from the light source. At the source, all of the light particles are very close together. This makes the light bright. As the distance from the source increases, the light spreads out. The light seems dim because the distance between the straight line paths increases as well.

A change in light intensity is similar to using paint from a spray can. If you were to spray the paint when the nozzle is very close to a piece of paper, a small dense painted area would result. As you increase your distance from the paper, the paint on the paper spreads over a large area. Like the paint on the paper, the intensity of light decreases with distance. However, the amount of light released from the source remains the same.

Speed of Light

During ancient times, people thought the speed of light was infinite. Actually, the instruments and measuring techniques couldn't measure such a high speed. In 1926, physicist Albert Michelson performed an experiment in California to measure the speed of light.

Michelson measured the distance between a location on Mount Wilson and a second location on Mount San Antonio. The distance was 35.4 km. A beam of light was sent from a special mirror on Mount Wilson to a mirror on Mount San Antonio, as shown in Figure 17.4.

Michelson used a rotating multi-sided mirror to measure the amount of time the light took to travel the 35.4 km distance. He divided the distance, by the time, to get a speed of 299 798 km/s. Today, using modern instruments, scientists determined that Michelson's measurement was very close to the actual speed of light.

The speed of light varies, depending on the medium it passes through. In space, which is a vacuum, light travels at about 299 793 km/s. In air, light moves at about 99 percent of its speed in space. In water, light slows to about 223 000 km/s. Through glass, light slows down to about 200 000 km/s. The time it takes light to travel between various locations is shown in Table 17.1.

Table 17.1   Travel Time of Light

Location 1	Location 2	Distance (km)	Travel Time Between Locations
Mountain 1	Mountain 2	35.4	0.0001180795 s
Los Angeles	New York	4 025	0.013435 s
Moon	Earth	384 365	1 min 20 s
Sun	Earth	149 596 000	8 min 20 s
Pluto	Earth	5 750 098 000	5 h 20 s

Figure 17.4

Timing a light beam as it traveled between two mountains was the first accurate measurement of the speed of light. ▼

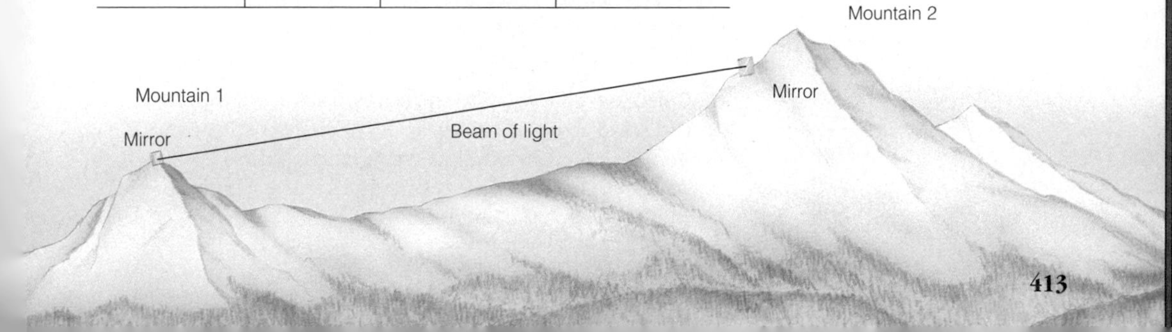

Mountain 2

Mountain 1

Mirror

Beam of light

Mirror

The Living Textbook: Physical Science Sides 1-4

Chapter 13   Frame 02002
Speed of Light (4 Frames)
Search: Step:

TEACH ▪ *Continued*

Skills WorkOut

To help students estimate how long it takes light to travel to a distant star, have them do the Skills WorkOut.

Answer 4.197 light-years

EVALUATE

WrapUp

Reinforce Have the class form five groups. Have members of each group prepare light-game cards. Each card should have a diagram or picture showing a characteristic of light on one side. On the other side, there should be an explanation using either the particle model or wave model of light. Invite groups to play a game with these cards. They can either pick the diagram side and give an explanation or pick the explanation side and make a diagram.

Use Review Worksheet 17.1.

Check and Explain

1. Answers will vary. Answers may include fluorescent light, incandescent light, or sunlight.

2. Light is the energy released as an electron in an atom moves to a lower energy level.

3. Light acts like a wave when it travels and bends around barriers. Light acts like a particle when it is given off or absorbed by objects.

4. Venus: 2.25 minutes; Mars: 4.36 minutes

Answer to In-Text Question

① Since people living far from the equator have less exposure time to light during the winter months, the symptoms of SAD would be worse.

Language Arts Connection

Students may be familiar with phrases, such as "light-years away" or "light-years apart." Ask them to use their knowledge of light to explain these terms. (Very, very, far apart)

Integrating the Sciences

Life Science Ask students to give explanations for why birds migrate in the fall, and plants bloom in the spring. Then ask them to find out about *photoperiodism*. (An organism's ability to respond to relative lengths of daily light and dark) Finally, have students explain bird migration and the blooming of poinsettias in terms of photoperiodism.

▼ **ACTIVITY**

Estimating

Traveling Light

The nearest star is 39 707 876 380 000 km away. How long would it take a message traveling at light-speed to reach there?

SKILLS WORKOUT

Since distances beyond the solar system are so large, kilometer measurements are not practical. For example, the distance between the earth and its nearest star beyond the solar system is 39 707 876 380 000 km. Instead of kilometers, astronomers measure large distances in light-years. A light-year is the distance light travels through space in one year. This distance is 9.46 trillion km (9.46×10^{12} km).

Science and Society *Light Cures SADness*

Do you know someone who feels depressed as the days grow shorter? A condition called Seasonal Affective Disorder, or SAD, is a change in a person's emotional state caused by a change in seasons. People with SAD sleep more and can become severely depressed. They may also overeat and gain weight.

Why does light affect a person's mood? Light triggers the release of chemicals that the body needs to function. During the seasonal change from summer to autumn and winter, the amount of daylight decreases. A winter day has fewer hours of daylight than a summer day. Most people aren't greatly affected by the chemical changes that occur in their bodies during the winter months. However, those with SAD don't adjust easily. Explain why you think the symptoms of SAD are better or worse for people with this condition living far away from the equator. ①

Luckily for SAD sufferers, strong artificial lighting can bring relief. The brightness of the light must be similar to the light in the sky 40 minutes after sunrise. After an hour or so of exposure to such light, many SAD victims find that their depression disappears.

Check and Explain

1. Identify three sources of light that you use everyday.

2. Describe how light is produced in an atom.

3. **Compare and Contrast** Discuss how light behaves both as a wave and as a particle.

4. **Calculate** How many minutes does it take light reflected from Venus to reach Earth? From Mars? Venus is 40 200 000 km from Earth. Mars is 78 390 000 km away. (Hint: Divide the distance by the speed of light.)

Prelab Discussion

Have students read the entire activity before beginning. Discuss the following:

▶ Explain that the effects of diffraction are negligible in this activity. The size of the opening would have to be close to the average wavelength of the light for diffraction to occur.

▶ Disuss how a pinhole camera captures an image. Then have students predict what will happen when light is shone through the holes in the cards in this activity.

Time 40 minutes   Group 4

Materials

3 m shelf paper

32 3 × 5 cards

32 slit rubber stoppers

8 hole punches

8 small flashlights

8 metric rulers

Activity 17   Does light travel in a straight line?

Skills   Observe; Infer

Task 1   Prelab Prep

1. Collect a sheet of white shelf paper 30 cm long, pencil, four index cards, metric ruler, hole punch, 4 rubber stoppers slit in the center, small flashlight or penlight.
2. Use the ruler to draw a line lengthwise down the center of the paper. Start at one end of the line and mark a point at 6 cm, 12 cm, 18 cm, and 24 cm.
3. On one of the index cards, mark a point 3.2 cm from the bottom and 2 cm from the left side. Put the marked card on top of 2 cards and punch a hole over the mark through all 3 cards.
4. Place a card in the slit of each stopper.

Task 2   Data Record

1. On a separate piece of paper, copy the data table shown below.
2. Record all of your observations for each index card.

Table 17.2   Behavior of Light Beam

Index card	Observation
6 cm	
12 cm	
18 cm	
24 cm	

Task 3   Procedure

1. Place a card without a hole at the 24 cm mark and the others at the 6 cm, 12 cm, and 18 cm marks.
2. Line up the holes as shown.
3. Darken the room and shine the beam of the flashlight directly through the hole on the first card.

4. Observe the path of light and the size of the beam on each card. Record your observations.
5. Move the light at a 45° angle and shine it through the hole of the first card. Observe the path of the light. Record your observations.

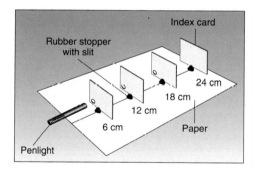

Task 4   Analysis

1. How is the size of the light beam different on each card?
2. What happened when you changed the angle of the light?
3. What evidence shows that light travels in a straight line?

Task 5   Conclusion

Explain how you showed that light travels in a straight line.

Everyday Application

Go into a dark room at night and leave the door slightly ajar. Describe the light pattern on the floor. How is the light pattern similar or different from the light on the cards? Explain.

Extension

Try setting the cards in different positions so that the light beam will still pass through all three holes. Did you show that light does not travel in a straight line by doing this? Explain.

Analysis

1. The spot of light around the hole in each card gets progressively smaller the farther away it is from the light source. The spot also gets dimmer.
2. When the light is aimed at 45 degrees, no light strikes the second, third, or last cards.
3. The observation in question 2 shows that light travels in straight lines.

Conclusion

Only when the light source was aligned with the straight line path through the index card holes did light reach the last card.

Everyday Application

The light spreads out wider than the gap in the doorway. It also is dimmer and the edges of the shadow get fuzzier the farther it is from the crack. Because light rays travel in straight lines, light rays reflected from all points in a particular area outside the room pass through the opening and reflect from corresponding points on the floor inside the room.

Extension

It is possible for other arrangements to allow light to pass all the way through to the fourth card, but the light source would still have to be in line with portions of all the holes.

Section Objectives

For a list of section objectives, see the Student Edition page.

Skills Objectives

Students should be able to:

Observe colors in the visible spectrum.

Infer how the colors of light combine.

Vocabulary

electromagnetic spectrum, infrared, X-ray, ultraviolet, gamma ray

---

MOTIVATE

Skills WarmUp

To help students understand the visible portion of the electromagnetic spectrum, have them do the Skills WarmUp.

Answer Students should see the visible spectrum, in order: red, orange, yellow, green, blue, and violet. (Students may not be able to identify *indigo*. Tell them it's a color in the spectrum that is positioned between blue and violet. Note that indigo is shown in Figure 17.8.)

Prior Knowledge

To gauge how much students know about the electromagnetic spectrum, ask the following questions:

▶ Can humans see every kind of light?

▶ Why does light have different colors?

▶ Can you see infrared and ultraviolet light?

▶ Who is Roy G. Biv? (See Language Arts Connection on page 418.)

▶ What's the difference between wavelength and wave frequency?

Themes in Science

Diversity and Unity Like other forms of energy, light energy moves in waves. Unlike other waves, however, the electromagnetic waves of light energy don't require a medium. Ask students what other forms of energy travel in waves. (Sound and seismic energy both travel in waves, and require a medium. Other electromagnetic energy forms, such as radio waves and X-rays, do not require a medium.)

▼ **ACTIVITY**

Observing

Light Through Glass

Obtain a drinking glass and a pad of white paper.

1. Fill the glass to the top with water.

2. Place the glass in a sunny window or outside in the sun.

3. Place the pad of paper so that the sun shines through the glass onto the paper.

What colors do you see on the paper? List the colors in the correct order.

SKILLS WARMUP

17.2 The Electromagnetic Spectrum

Objectives

▶ **Identify** six kinds of invisible electromagnetic waves.

▶ **Relate** wavelength to the colors of visible light.

▶ **Compare** and **contrast** visible and invisible electromagnetic waves.

▶ **Infer** how different colors of light combine to produce new colors.

When you hear the word *light,* you probably think about sunlight or the light that fills a room when you switch on a lamp. You may also think of the many colors that can be seen when sunlight is separated by a prism or in a rainbow. But did you know that light is just a small part of a broad family of mostly invisible waves? Electromagnetic waves form a continuous spectrum of waves, extending from large radio waves to tiny gamma waves. Visible light comprises a small portion of the spectrum.

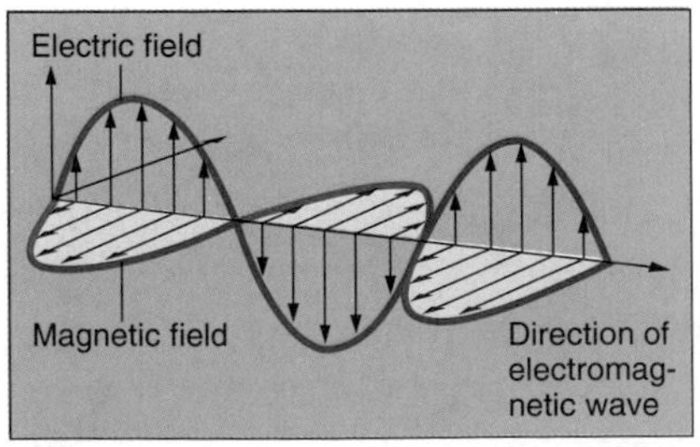

Electromagnetic Waves

Figure 17.5 ▲
In an electromagnetic wave, the electric field and the magnetic field are at 90° angles.

You are surrounded by electromagnetic waves. In addition to sunlight and artificial light, familiar forms of electromagnetic waves include X-rays, radar, television, and radio waves. Even your body gives off heat in the form of electromagnetic radiation.

Electromagnetic waves are transverse waves, composed of alternating electric and magnetic fields. You can see in Figure 17.5 that both the electric and the magnetic fields are at a right angle to the direction the wave travels, and perpendicular to each other. Electromagnetic waves are created by accelerating charges or changing magnetic fields. All electromagnetic waves have characteristics of both particles and waves.

Electromagnetic waves can travel through a vacuum. Unlike sound waves, they do not need a medium to travel through. For example, sunlight travels through a near vacuum to reach the earth. All electromagnetic waves travel at the speed of light.

Social Studies Connection

In 1666, Isaac Newton (1642–1727) used two prisms to show that white light is made up of colored light. He shone a white light on the first prism that separated the light into its visible color spectrum. He directed the color spectrum to a second prism, which combined the colors to form white light. Invite interested students to research and recreate Newton's simple experiment.

Themes in Science

Patterns of Change/Cycles The order in which the colors appear in the visible spectrum is always the same. In addition, combinations of colored light produce predictable colors. Ask students to use their observations of white light passing through a prism to predict colors and their order in the spectrum produced by sunlight passing through raindrops. (Red, orange, yellow, green, blue, indigo, violet)

TEACH

Directed Inquiry

Have students study Figure 17.6. Ask the following questions:

▶ Do all electromagnetic waves have the same frequency? (No; frequency ranges from 10^2 to 10^{24} Hz.)

▶ What determines the frequency of the electromagnetic wave? (The number of wavelengths that pass a point in one second)

▶ Which of the three waves in Figure 17.6 has the greatest frequency? (The one on the bottom)

▶ **Infer** What are the frequencies of the waves shown in Figure 17.6? (From top to bottom: 2 Hz, 4 Hz, 6 Hz)

Portfolio

Have students draw a line representing the electromagnetic spectrum. Have them label one end *radio waves, 10^6 Hz* and the other end *gamma rays, 10^{-19} Hz.* Ask, Where is the visible portion of the spectrum? (Near the center of the line) Have them save their drawings as part of their portfolios.

Class Activity

If you have access to a prism, you may want to use it to show how white light can be bent to show colors, as in Figure 17.7.

Answer to In Text Question

① Red, orange, yellow, green, blue, indigo, and violet

The Living Textbook: Physical Science Sides 1-4

Chapter 12   Frame 01948
Electromagnetic Spectrum (38 Frames)
Search: Step:

All electromagnetic waves are not the same. Recall that the energy of the photons varies for different kinds of electromagnetic waves. The wavelength and frequency of electromagnetic waves also varies.

Wavelength Wavelength varies for different kinds of electromagnetic waves. Very long electromagnetic wavelengths, called radio frequencies, reach 300 km. The shortest waves are gamma rays, which are 3.0×10^{-14} km, or 0.0000003 nanometers (3.0×10^{-7}) nm long. One nanometer is equal to one trillionth of a kilometer.

Frequency Recall that the wave frequency is the number of waves that pass a point in one second. When the wavelength is short, the frequency is high because more waves pass a point in one second. The relationship between frequency and the wavelength is shown in Figure 17.6. The unit for the frequency of electromagnetic waves is hertz (Hz). The frequencies for electromagnetic waves range from 1×10^2 to 1×10^{24} hertz.

Electromagnetic Spectrum

Electromagnetic waves arranged in order of their wavelength and frequency, are called the **electromagnetic spectrum**. Radio waves with a frequency of 1×10^6 hertz are low on the electromagnetic spectrum. X-rays with a frequency of 1×10^{19} hertz are high on the electromagnetic spectrum. Electromagnetic waves that can be seen by the human eye are a small band called the visible spectrum, which is near the center. Light bent by the prism in Figure 17.7 shows the colors of light in the visible spectrum.

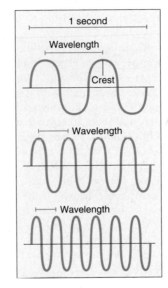

Figure 17.6 ▲
The greater the number of wavelengths that pass a point in one second, the greater is the frequency.

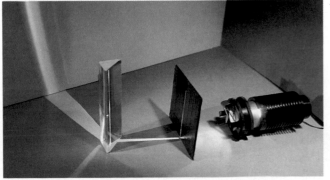

◀ **Figure 17.7**
The prism bends white light to show the visible colors in part of the electromagnetic spectrum. What colors of light do you see? ①

TEACH ▪ *Continued*

Explore Visually

Have students study Figure 17.8. Ask the following questions:

▶ From left to right on the spectrum, or from radio waves to gamma rays, how does wavelength change? Frequency? (Wavelength decreases; frequency increases.)

▶ What is the visible spectrum? (The part of the spectrum that contains all the colors of light that you can see)

▶ Can you see infrared waves, waves with wavelengths longer than red light? (No)

▶ Do television waves or radio waves have greater wavelengths? (Radio waves)

▶ Which have higher frequencies, FM radio waves or AM radio waves? (FM radio waves)

Integrated Learning

Use Integrating Worksheet 17.2.

**The Living Textbook:
Physical Science Sides 1-4**

Chapter 13   Frame 01991
Visible Spectrum (5 Frames)
Search: Step:

**The Living Textbook:
Physical Science Sides 1-4**

Chapter 13   Frame 02018
Mixing Colored Light/Color Wheel
(8 Frames)
Search: Step:

418

Integrating the Sciences

Astronomy Astronomers learn about the stars by observing the spectrum of color they give off. Different types of stars, such as red giants and white dwarfs, produce color spectrums with different proportions of colors. Narrow black lines in the stars' spectrums indicate which elements are present in the stars. Have students find out what element is most common in stars. (Hydrogen)

Language Arts Connection

Share the mnemonic device *Roy G. Biv* with the students. Ask students what they think the letters stand for. (The order of the colors in the visible spectrum) Have students make up another mnemonic to help them remember that violet light has shorter wavelengths and red light has longer wavelengths. (Answers will vary. Example: Violet made short waves at the long red light.)

Visible Spectrum

Each color in the visible spectrum—red orange, yellow, green, blue, indigo, and violet—has a different frequency. For example, the frequency of the shortest wave length is 750 trillion hertz (7.5×10^{14} Hz) and produces violet light. The frequency of the longest wavelength is 430 trillion hertz (4.3×10^{14} Hz) and produces red light.

When all the colors of light are combined, you see white light. Sunlight is one example of white light. Use Figure 17.8 to locate the colors in the visible spectrum.

Red, green, and blue are called the primary colors of light. These colors combine in different amounts to produce other colors of light. For example, red and blue light mixed in equal amounts produces the color magenta. Green and blue light combine to make a color called cyan. Any two colors of light that mix to form white light are called complementary colors. For example, cyan and red light mix to produce white light.

Not all animals see the same colors you do. For example, bees can see blue, yellow, and ultraviolet light. Ultraviolet light is high-energy electromagnetic waves that your eyes can't see. Some animals see only black and white. Monkeys and apes see the same colors you do. Since birds have brightly colored feathers that attract a mate, they probably also see color.

**Figure 17.8
The Electromagnetic Spectrum** ▼

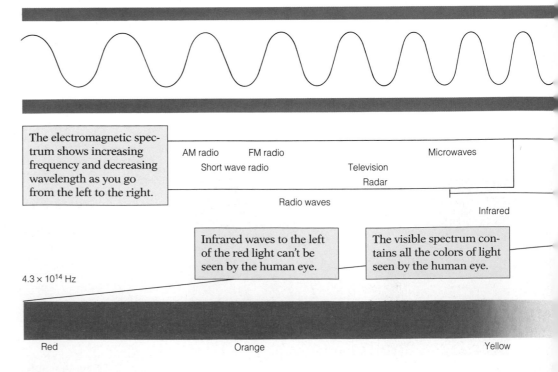

The electromagnetic spectrum shows increasing frequency and decreasing wavelength as you go from the left to the right.

AM radio   FM radio   Microwaves
Short wave radio   Television
                                   Radar
                Radio waves
                                        Infrared

Infrared waves to the left of the red light can't be seen by the human eye.

The visible spectrum contains all the colors of light seen by the human eye.

4.3×10^{14} Hz

Red   Orange   Yellow

Invisible Spectrum

The waves on both sides of the visible spectrum make up the invisible spectrum. You can't see wavelengths shorter than 430 nm or longer than 750 nm. Locate the invisible spectrum in Figure 17.8.

Radio Waves Radio waves sent through the air from radio stations carry the music you hear on the radio. To pick up a signal, you must tune your radio to the same wave frequency as the waves from the radio station. Radio stations transmit radio waves by amplitude modulation (AM) or by frequency modulation (FM). AM radio waves have a pattern of amplitude changes. FM changes the pattern of radio wave frequency.

FM waves carry the picture portion of most television shows. The sound portion of most television shows is on AM waves. AM waves are longer than FM waves, so AM waves can bend around objects more easily. This explains why sometimes you receive the sound but not the picture for a TV program.

Microwaves High energy radio waves are called microwaves. They have wavelengths between 100 mm and 30 cm. Like other radio waves, microwaves are used in communications. Since microwaves reflect off certain substances, such as metal or wood, radar uses microwaves to locate objects and to determine their speed. Because some substances absorb microwaves, they are also used for cooking.

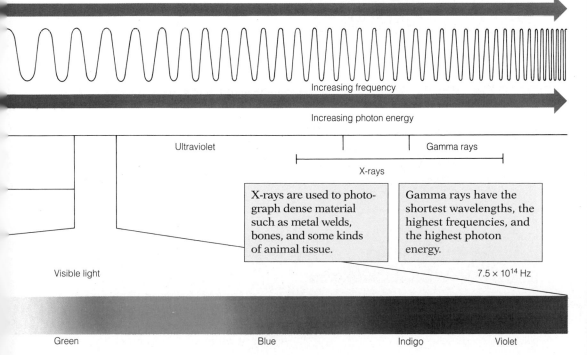

Decreasing wavelength

Increasing frequency

Increasing photon energy

Ultraviolet

Gamma rays

X-rays

X-rays are used to photograph dense material such as metal welds, bones, and some kinds of animal tissue.

Gamma rays have the shortest wavelengths, the highest frequencies, and the highest photon energy.

Visible light

7.5×10^{14} Hz

Green   Blue   Indigo   Violet

TEACH ▪ *Continued*

Critical Thinking

Compare and Contrast Write the headings for four columns on the chalkboard: *infrared rays, X-rays, ultraviolet rays,* and *gamma rays.* For each column, have students fill in wavelengths and features or uses. (Infrared rays: 750 nm to 30 000 nm, causes objects' molecules to vibrate and produce heat; X-rays: 0.001 nm to 10 nm, can travel through matter; ultraviolet: 10 nm to 430 nm, destroys viruses and bacteria; gamma: 0.0000003 nm to 0.003 nm, can harm living cells, used to destroy cancer cells)

Discuss

Have students study Figures 17.9 to 17.11. Ask the following questions:

► What does Figure 17.9 show? What does it tell you? How do you know? (An infrared picture; the image shows areas of degrees of heat.)

► How can you tell the difference between bone and the soft tissue in the X-ray? (Bone is clearly outlined but tissue has a faded, fuzzy appearance.)

► What is happening in Figure 17.11? (Cancer treatment using gamma rays)

Reteach

Use Reteach Worksheet 17.2.

Answers to In-Text Questions

① The blue areas

② The whitest areas contain the most calcium; the calcium absorbs X-rays.

The Living Textbook:
Physical Science Sides 1-4

Chapter 12   Frame 01950
X-rays/Ultraviolet Rays (9 Frames)
Search: Step:

Social Studies Connection

The first Nobel Prize in physics was awarded in 1901 to Wilhelm Roentgen (1845–1923) of Germany. Roentgen discovered the X-ray in 1895. Because he did not know what kind of rays they were, he called them "X rays." Roentgen's discovery revolutionized medicine. In Germany, X-rays were named Roentgen rays in his honor. Suggest that students study other Nobel Prize winners in physics.

STS Connection

Infrared photography is often used for surveillance cameras and nighttime photography of animals in the wild. Ask students why it works without daylight. (Infrared radiation imprints the film.) Ask students to discuss the value of infrared photography.

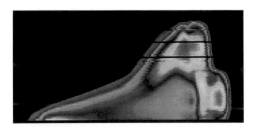

Figure 17.9 ▲
The red area in the film indicates the location of the highest temperature. Which areas are the coolest? ①

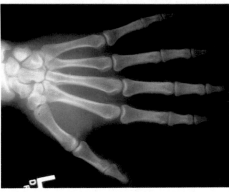

Figure 17.10 ▲
What areas of the bones shown in the X-ray of the person's hand contain the most calcium? How do you know? ②

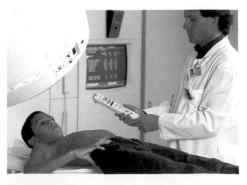

Figure 17.11 ▲
The technician avoids destroying healthy cells by controlling the amount of gamma rays and by targeting only cancer cells.

Infrared Rays Electromagnetic waves with wavelengths between 750 nm and 30 000 nm are **infrared** rays. They are called "infrared" because their wavelengths are slightly longer than those of visible red light. You detect infrared rays with your skin when you feel heat. Infrared radiation causes the molecules in an object to vibrate more rapidly. The vibrations produce heat and cause the temperature of the object to rise. Certain camera film can take a picture like the one in Figure 17.9 that only shows the heat given off by objects. Such films are sensitive to infrared rays but not to visible light.

X-rays High energy waves with lengths from 0.001 nm to 10 nm are **X-rays**. X-rays travel through most matter. Look at the X-ray of a hand in Figure 17.10. The calcium in the bones of the hand absorbs X-rays better than muscle or skin does. That's why the bones show up as light areas on an X-ray photograph.

Ultraviolet Rays Waves between 10 nm and 430 nm in length are called **ultraviolet** rays. The main source of ultraviolet rays is sunlight. Ultraviolet rays destroy bacteria and viruses. They also stimulate your body to produce vitamin D, which you need for healthy bones. However, overexposure to ultraviolet rays can burn your skin and is one cause of skin cancer. Sunscreen reduces absorption of ultraviolet rays.

Gamma Rays The waves with the shortest wavelengths are **gamma rays**. Their wavelengths range from 0.0000003 nm (3.0×10^{-7}) to 0.003 nm (3.0×10^{-3}). Radioactive materials and nuclear reactions give off gamma rays. Gamma rays can harm living cells. They are used in cancer treatment to destroy cancer cells.

Cooperative Learning

Have students work in cooperative groups. Ask students when they think microwave ovens were first available, and when they came into widespread use. (1950, 1970s) Have groups of three students work together to prepare a poster or bulletin board display on microwave ovens. One student could survey the class on how many households have a microwave oven. Another student might report on the growth in popularity of microwaves in the past 25 years. The third could report on the possible hazards of microwave radiation. Encourage students to list any sources they consult such as the U.S. Census Bureau, Statistical Abstracts, or consumer periodicals.

Critical Thinking

Find Causes Ask students how microwave energy generates heat energy. (It excites the molecules and they move faster. The movement creates heat energy.)

WrapUp

Reinforce Ask students to work together to create a large classroom display illustrating the electromagnetic spectrum. Remind them that most of their experience is with the visible portion of the spectrum, so they may want to give this portion of the spectrum the greatest attention. Encourage students to include details about wavelength, frequency, and uses of the different kinds of electromagnetic waves. If students make a rainbow, make sure the progression of color is accurate.

Use Review Worksheet 17.2.

Check and Explain

1. Radio waves—to carry picture and sound transmission; microwaves—communication, radar to locate objects and determine their speed, and cooking; infrared rays—in combination with infrared sensitive film to locate heat-producing objects; X-rays—produce internal pictures of bones, welds, and teeth; ultraviolet rays—destroy bacteria and viruses; gamma rays—cancer treatment

2. Each color is associated with a particular wavelength of electromagnetic waves.

3. Humans cannot see light with wavelengths shorter than 430 nm or longer than 750 nm.

4. Use the colored glass to produce colored light, and combine two or three sheets to make different shades, if necessary.

Science and Technology
Using A Microwave Oven

Suppose there's leftover pizza in the refrigerator. You're in a hurry, and you don't have time to wait for your conventional oven to heat the pizza. What can you do? With a microwave oven, you have hot pizza in two minutes!

A microwave oven heats food quickly by using high-energy microwaves. All foods, including your pizza, contain water molecules. Microwaves excite the water molecules so that they move very quickly. This rapid movement produces heat.

Notice in Figure 17.12 that a device called a magnetron (MAG nuh trahn) generates microwaves. A magnetron is a special vacuum tube. When the oven switches on, the magnetron develops a large potential difference between its electrodes. The negative electrode sends out microwaves. Uneven hot spots may occur because microwaves tend not to spread out evenly. A fan in the oven helps to deflect the microwaves to all parts of the food.

Heating food in a microwave oven differs from heating food in a regular oven. In a regular oven, heat radiates from inside the oven to the food. In a microwave oven, the heat is produced right inside the food when its water molecules begin to vibrate.

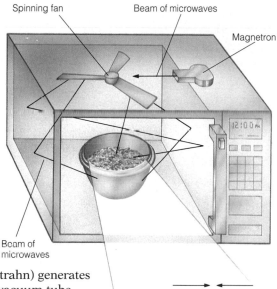

Spinning fan

Beam of microwaves

Magnetron

Beam of microwaves

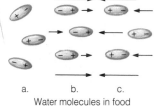

a.   b.   c.
Water molecules in food

Figure 17.12 ▲

The poles of water molecules in food are not aligned (a). Microwaves cause the poles to line up (b) and reverse direction rapidly (c), producing heat.

Check and Explain

1. List the electromagnetic waves in the invisible spectrum and give one use for each kind of wave.

2. Explain how colors are related to wavelength.

3. **Compare and Contrast** What portions of the electromagnetic spectrum are not visible to humans?

4. **Infer** To light the stage for a school play, you need yellow, cyan, and magenta beams of light. Unfortunately, you have only one spotlight and three sheets of glass. The glass sheets are cyan, magenta, and yellow. What can you do?

Section Objectives
For a list of section objectives, see the Student Edition page.

Skills Objectives
Students should be able to:

Observe qualities of colors.

Infer how color interacts with light.

Predict how colors mix.

Vocabulary
transparent, translucent, opaque

MOTIVATE

Skills WarmUp
To help students understand light and color, have them do the Skills WarmUp.
Answer Answers will vary. Students may be able to see that the picture is composed of dots of only four colors: magenta, blue-green (cyan), yellow, and black. They should mention that the density of the dots in a given area helps to determine the darkness of the colors.

Misconceptions
Students may think that they can see objects in a lighted room simply because light is present. Help students recognize that the light must reflect off the objects and into their eyes for them to be able to see the objects.

Answer to In-Text Question
① Red

Themes in Science
Systems and Interactions The interaction of light waves with materials determines whether the materials appear transparent, translucent, or opaque. Whether or not an organism can see certain colors depends on the light reflected from an object and the organism's ability to see the light waves.

Integrating the Sciences
Life Science Inform students that brightly colored, sweet-smelling flowers are not the most attractive to all pollinators. Hummingbirds and butterflies are attracted to red flowers, but bees aren't because they can't see red. Bats are attracted to dull-colored, foul-smelling flowers. Have students name some pollinators that can see colors humans can't. (One example: bees can see ultraviolet light.)
Use Integrating Worksheet 17.3.

▼ ACTIVITY

Observing

Up Close

Look at the color picture in Figure 17.13 through a hand lens. Describe what each color looks like. Notice which colors seem to be combinations of more than one color. Why do some colors seem darker or lighter?

SKILLS WARMUP

Figure 17.13
What color must be seen by the bee in order for it to be aware of the flower? ▼ ①

17.3 Light and Color

Objectives

▶ **Identify** three surfaces that interact with light.

▶ **Explain** why the daytime sky appears blue.

▶ **Infer** how dark and light objects reflect light.

▶ **Predict** the colors that will be produced when pigments of various colors are mixed.

Imagine a world of black, white, and gray. It would not be as interesting or as beautiful as the world that surrounds you every day. Did you know that colors can also affect your mood and behavior? Bright colors tend to make you feel happy. Gray or drab colors tend to make a scene somber and sad.

Colors are important in nature. The color of flowering plants attracts insects and other animals, which helps the flowering plants to reproduce. For example, pollen from a flower will stick to a bee as it gathers nectar. The bee will carry the pollen to another flower, which uses the pollen to reproduce. At every visit, the bee picks up pollen from one flower and drops off pollen from other flowers.

Plant colors help some animals identify food. The bright color of the flower helps the bee locate nectar. Animals, such as deer, use color to blend into their surroundings. The deer is not easily seen by its predators. Color helps some animals to find and select mates. In many species of birds, the female chooses the male bird with the brightest feathers.

Light from a Surface

Look at the objects around you. Depending upon the material the object is made of, the light may be transmitted, absorbed, or reflected. When light is transmitted through a window, it passes through the material it strikes. A black object, such as charcoal, absorbs all the light that strikes it. Colored objects such as flowers reflect light. A red flower absorbs all colors but red. The reflected color is the color you see.

Objects can be classified as transparent, opaque, or translucent, depending on how the material reacts with light. Objects that transmit almost all the light that strikes them are **transparent**. Transparent materials reflect some light from their surface. Otherwise, you wouldn't see them at all. Have you ever accidentally bumped into a sliding glass door that reflected so little light that you didn't see it?

Materials that transmit light and scatter it are **translucent** (tranz LOOS uhnt). An image is difficult to see through a translucent material. The image is unclear and lacks detail. Wax paper and shower doors are translucent materials.

Materials that block the transmission of light are **opaque** (oh PAYK). An opaque object absorbs most of the light that strikes it. You can't see through opaque objects. Look around the room. What objects do you see that are opaque? ②

Life Science LINK

Obtain blue paper, green paper, scissors, small containers, and sugar water.

1. Cut flower shapes (about 5 cm in diameter) from blue and green paper.

2. Arrange the flowers outside in small containers with sugar water at the centers.

What happened? Does color affect whether bees are attracted to a flower?

ACTIVITY

Transparent ▲
Light passes through clear glass and water in straight lines. These materials are transparent. Notice that the outline of the glass and the water line are visible. Even transparent materials reflect some light.

Translucent
Light reflects off the strawberries at the bottom of the bowl. The reflected light does not pass through the translucent glass in straight lines. As the light passes through the bowl, it scatters and looks fuzzy. How much detail can you see through the bowl? ▼

Opaque ▲
The vacuum bottle is opaque because the light that strikes it is either absorbed or reflected. Because light is reflected from its surface, the cap of the bottle looks shiny.

TEACH ▪ *Continued*

◆ *Explore Visually*

Have students study the art and photographs on this page. Ask the following questions:

► Why is an image reflected from a mirror? (The mirror's smooth surface doesn't scatter light.)

► What makes light waves refract? (They slow down and bend when they move from one medium to another.)

► What results from interference in light waves? (Bands of light)

► Why does the pencil in the water appear to be in two pieces? (Light travels more slowly through water than air, so the pencil looks broken.)

Class Activity

Demonstrate to students the colors that result from interference by using soap bubbles. A solution of three parts water, one part dishwashing detergent, and one part glycerin, which can be purchased at drug stores, works well. Bend wire hangers into loops. Put the bubble solution into a rimmed cookie sheet. Have students dip the loops into the solution and observe the interference patterns in the colors of the bubble solution. Ask them to notice the bands of color. Ask them what happens to the color as the soap film becomes thinner. (The red bands of color become larger.)

 The Living Textbook: Physical Science Sides 1-4

Chapter 13   Frame 02090
Refraction (6 Frames)
Search: Step:

Integrating the Sciences

Life Science Interference occurs not only in inanimate objects like soap bubbles and compact disks, but also in several organisms. The iridescent colors of pearl, mother-of-pearl, and peacock feathers are a result of light wave interference within thin structural layers. Have students find out how the thickness of the layer affects the colors in the interference pattern. (As the thickness decreases, the amount of red visible increases.)

Interactions of Light

Light waves that are reflected interact with the surface of an object. Light waves are reflected when they bounce off an object. Because light reflected from an uneven surface scatters, it is called a diffuse reflection. Light reflected off the moon's surface is a diffuse reflection.

Refraction occurs as light waves pass from one medium to another. The light wave slows down and is bent, or refracted. When they strike a barrier, light waves spread out, or diffract. As light diffracts around the edge of an object, it forms a shadow that appears fuzzy.

Interference occurs when two waves arrive at the same point at the same time. Interference in light waves produces bands of bright light and bands of no light. The bands of color seen on a compact disc are due to the interference of light waves.

Reflection
Light waves bounce off the girl's face into the mirror. A clear image is reflected from the mirror because it has a very smooth surface. The smooth surface does not scatter light. ▼

Refraction ▲
The speed of light depends on the medium. Light slows down in water, so the part of the pencil in water looks bent, or refracted.

Interference
Constructive interference results in a larger wave. Destructive interference cancels out the light waves. So, interference produces bands of light. ▼

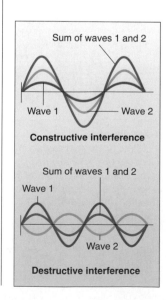

Sum of waves 1 and 2

Wave 1   Wave 2

Constructive interference

Sum of waves 1 and 2

Wave 1

Wave 2

Destructive interference

Diffraction ▶
When light waves move past a barrier, they bend or diffract. Why will the area directly behind the barrier be dark?

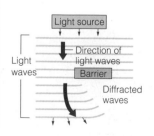

Light source
Direction of light waves
Light waves
Barrier
Diffracted waves

Writing Connection

Color of the Sky

On a bright sunny day the sky appears blue. A blue sky is caused by the interaction of lightwaves with particles in the atmosphere. These particles include molecules of gases and water, and tiny specks of dust. When light strikes a particle in the atmosphere, it is scattered.

Remember that sunlight contains the wavelength of every color in the visible spectrum. When light of a particular wavelength strikes an atmospheric particle, the wavelength is scattered in all directions. The particles in the atmosphere scatter the short wavelengths more than the long wavelengths. Since blue and violet have short wavelengths, more blue and violet light reaches your eyes from all directions in the atmosphere. To you the sky appears blue.

The sky in Figure 17.14 doesn't appear blue. Instead, it is various shades of red and orange. This color change occurs only at sunrise and sunset when the sun is low on the horizon. Light rays must travel a greater distance through the atmosphere before reaching your eye. At this greater distance, the particles in the air scatter the blue, yellow, and green wavelengths. By the time the light reaches your eyes, the only wavelengths left for you to see are the red and orange ones.

Figure 17.14

What does the sky at sunset tell you about the wavelengths of light you see? ▼ ①

 The Living Textbook: Physical Science Sides 1-4

Chapter 13   Frame 02195
Colors at Sunset (11 Frames)
Search: Step:

TEACH ▪ *Continued*

Skills Development

Predict Ask students to make predictions based on what they have learned about the color of objects. Ask them to imagine they are wearing white shirts and red shoes in rooms with different colored lights. Then ask the following:

▶ What color does your shirt appear to be when yellow light shines on it? (Yellow) Blue light? (Blue) Explain. (White reflects all the wavelengths of light.)

▶ What color would your shoes appear to be in green light? (Predictions may vary. The shoes would appear black.)

Enrich

Have students stare at a brightly colored object for a minute. Then have them look at a clean, white sheet of paper. Ask them to explain what they see. (They will see an afterimage of the object in a complementary color; a color "opposite" to the color they were staring at.)

Explain that when you look at the white paper, receptors send a weak signal to the brain. If all the color receptors send a signal, the brain interprets the color as white. If the eye's receptors get tired from looking at an intense color, the signal will be missing the sign for that color. Therefore, the brain interprets the color as the complementary color.

Answers to In-Text Questions

① Red

② It absorbed the blue light.

**The Living Textbook:
Physical Science Sides 1–4**

Chapter 13   Frame 02105
Retina (1 Frame)
Search:

Integrating the Sciences

Biology Explain to students that animals that lack color vision still have both rods and cones in their eyes. The rods are adapted for low light conditions (night) and the cones for bright light (day). Although humans possess color vision, our cones detect color only in relatively bright light. Ask students to describe a twilight landscape from memory. (They should note that color is less vivid at this time of day.)

Multicultural Perspectives

Several cultures assign meanings or values to colors. For instance, the Pueblo use colors to represent compass directions: white—east, yellow—north, blue—west, and red—south. For the Cherokee, red symbolizes success, blue stands for trouble, black is the symbol for death, and white means happiness. Have students find out what cultures use white to symbolize mourning. (Some Asian cultures such as the Chinese)

Color Vision

Unlike humans, many animals do not see color. Your eyes have special cells called cones that enable you to see a red apple or the green grass. To see color, light enters your eye through an opening called the pupil. Light focuses on the retina at the back of your eye. The retina is made of two kinds of cells called rods and cones. Rods are very sensitive but cannot detect color. The cones, however, are sensitive to color.

Chemicals in the cones are sensitive to red, green, or blue light. Each cone is sensitive to a particular primary color. When a mixture of different colored light enters your eye, you see the mixture as a single color.

You see a plum as purple when reflected red and blue light enters your eyes. Each color stimulates an electric signal in the cones. These signals travel to the brain through the optic nerve. The brain unscrambles the signals. Instead of interpreting each color separately, the signals for red light and blue light combine to form purple. Most of the colors you see are combined signals.

Color of Objects

Look at the object in Figure 17.15. What color do you see? You see the color red because all of the colors in white light are absorbed except red. The red surface reflects only red light.

Look at the same object shown in Figure 17.16. What color is it? If you shine a blue light on the same object, it appears purple. The object absorbs some wavelengths of the blue light, but reflects purple light. Black is the absence of all color.

A white shirt reflects all the wavelengths of light. That's why it looks white. You feel cooler when you wear a white shirt than when you wear a black shirt. The white shirt reflects sunlight. However, a black shirt absorbs sunlight. The light energy from the sun's rays changes to heat energy and you feel warm.

Look out the window. You can see colored objects through the window because the clear glass transmits all wavelengths of the visible spectrum. However, tinted glass is not transparent to all wavelengths. For example, glass tinted green absorbs all the colors of white light except green. Green glass transmits green light.

Figure 17.16
Why does the same origami bird shown under blue light appear purple? ▼ ②

Figure 17.15 ▲
What color is reflected by the origami bird shown under white light? ①

Cooperative Learning

Have students work in cooperative groups of four. Explain to students that natural plant materials can provide a variety of colors for dyes. Have students research the colors they can find in easily available plants. Encourage them to prepare the dye, choose something to dye, and present their dyed projects in a class display. (Projects will vary. Some colors may include: blue from beets; red from teas or oregano leaves; brown from onion skins or teas; and green from spinach or carrot tops. Eggs or old scraps of cotton fabric dye well.)

Paint and Pigments

Paint is made of coloring particles, called pigments, mixed in a liquid. Each pigment absorbs and reflects different colors of light. The colors you see depend on which colors the pigments absorb and which colors they reflect.

The primary colors of light are red, green, and blue. Similarly, there are three primary pigments. The three primary pigments are magenta, yellow, and cyan. Recall that when primary colors combine, they produce white light. The primary pigments behave differently than the primary colors of light. Mixing equal amounts of the three primary pigments produces black. Combinations of the primary pigments produce different colors. Figure 17.17 illustrates what color results when you mix two primary pigments. When you mix yellow and cyan, you get green. Mixing magenta and cyan produces purple. How does this compare to combining red and blue light? ③

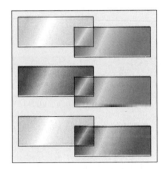

Figure 17.17 ▲
Combining pigments forms new colors. What color is formed from the combination of cyan and yellow pigments?

Historical Notebook

Color and Impressionism

Imagine you are visiting an art museum. You see many different paintings. There are paintings of people, nature, and objects. Then you come to another painting and see nothing but dots of colors. You step back and a beautiful picture emerges on the canvas. In the late 19th century, a group of innovative painters developed this creative use of color.

The painting by Georges Seurat illustrates how these painters used color in a unique way. They built up their painting with many colored points instead of using brush strokes. When viewed from a distance, the points of color blend to form images.

This technique, known as pointillism, set these artists apart from other painters. They did not try to tell a story with their painting. Instead, they tried to capture a moment in the lives of ordinary people.

1. How was the use of color by pointillists different from the way other painters employed color?

2. Do library research to locate works of other pointillist painters. Which painter's use of color do you think is most effective?

Apply

Have students use water-based paints on white paper to show how colors combine. Have them paint three overlapping circles: a magenta circle, a yellow circle, and a cyan circle. Have students label the combinations of colors.

Historical Notebook

Research Have students use books, videotapes, computer resources, and, if possible, museum exhibits to write a report on how a particular artist or schools of artists, such as impressionists or color-field painters, use color. Ask them to include how the work, and the colors in it, makes them feel.

Answers

1. Pointillists built up paintings with many colored points whose colors blend when seen at a distance. Other painters blended colors on their palettes and applied them to the canvas.

2. Answers will vary.

Integrated Learning

Use Integrating Worksheet 17.3b.

Answers to In-Text Questions

③ It's the same; you see purple.

④ Green

The Living Textbook: Physical Science Sides 1-4

Chapter 13   Frame 02020
Combining Colors (11 Frames)
Search: Step:

The Living Textbook: Physical Science Sides 1-4

Chapter 13   Frame 01994
Paint Pigments (2 Frames)
Search: Step:

INTEGRATED LEARNING

TEACH ▪ *Continued*

Portfolio

Have students collect several pictures produced by the four-color printing process. They can use a magnifying glass and compare the quality of the printing. Have them describe each printing example and make a generalization about dots and printing quality. Students may need to use reference materials for more information. (Students should recognize that increased dot density, or smaller dot size, improves image quality.)

EVALUATE

WrapUp

Reteach Ask students to draw and label a scene illustrating the various ways light behaves. They should trace the path of the light from its source, to objects, to the eyes of an observer. Remind them to show what light does when it strikes transparent and translucent objects, how light produces color, and how light waves interact.

Use Review Worksheet 17.3.

Check and Explain

1. Opaque: reflects or is absorbed; translucent: passes through but scatters; transparent: travels in straight lines

2. Particles in the atmosphere scatter light with short wavelengths (blue light).

3. White clothing reflects all colors of light and is more visible at night than other colors.

4. Orange; reddish blue

Multicultural Perspectives

Remind students that before color printing, all printed images were produced in shades of black or white. The reader needed to be able to interpret a large range of blacks and whites. The Inuit have developed 17 words for white to describe the wide variety of snow they experience. Have students describe as many different shades of black as possible. (Answers will vary.)

Science and Technology
Four-Color Printing

This book has colored pictures on many pages. To print a photograph like the one shown in Figure 17.18 requires several steps. The printer first separates the colors in the photograph. To do this, four pictures of the original photograph are taken. For each shot, the photographer puts a different color filter over the camera lens.

In addition, the photographer takes each picture through a screen that causes the colors to appear as tiny dots. The position of the screen is changed slightly for each different color. One filter blocks out all colors except yellow. This produces a photographic negative with only a yellow color. The process is repeated using different filters to produce three more negatives—a magenta, a cyan, and a black negative. Recall that magenta, cyan, and yellow are all primary pigments.

Next, the four dot negatives are used to make separate pictures on metal plates coated with photographic chemicals. The plates are then treated with an acid to make the dots higher than the rest of the plate. During the printing process, each plate distributes ink of a matching color on paper. As the paper moves from one plate to the next, it picks up each color. The final product is a full-color picture. The combinations of primary colored dot patterns give an illusion of different colors. Notice the magnified dot pattern of the four-color picture shown in Figure 17.18.

Figure 17.18 ▲
Locate four different colors used to print this photograph.

Check and Explain

1. How does a light wave react when it strikes an opaque surface? A translucent surface? A transparent surface?

2. Why does the daytime sky look blue?

3. **Infer** Explain why is it wise for people walking along a road at night to wear white clothing.

4. **Predict** What colors are produced by mixing the following pigments: one part magenta and three parts yellow; one part cyan and three parts magenta? You may wish to test your predictions.

428

Chapter 17 Review

Concept Summary

17.1 The Nature of Light
▶ Objects are visible because they produce, reflect, or transmit light.
▶ Light has the properties of both waves and particles.
▶ Light is produced when electrons change energy levels in an atom.
▶ The speed of light is 299 793 km/s.

17.2 The Electromagnetic Spectrum
▶ The electromagnetic spectrum contains radio waves, microwaves, infrared rays, visible light waves, ultraviolet rays, X-rays, and gamma rays.
▶ The color of visible light is determined by its wavelength. White light is composed of all the colors in the visible spectrum.

▶ Electromagnetic waves can travel through a vacuum.

17.3 Light and Color
▶ Surfaces can be opaque, translucent, or transparent.
▶ When light waves strike a material, they change direction by reflection, refraction, or diffraction.
▶ When light strikes a surface, the color you see is the color reflected by the surface.
▶ The primary colors of light are red, green, and blue.
▶ Primary colors combine to produce white. Primary pigments combine to produce black.

Chapter Vocabulary

photon (p. 409)
polarized (p. 410)
photoelectric effect (p. 411)
electromagnetic spectrum (p. 417)

infrared (p. 420)
X-ray (p. 420)
ultraviolet (p. 420)
gamma ray (p. 420)

transparent (p. 423)
translucent (p. 423)
opaque (p. 423)

Check Your Vocabulary

Use the vocabulary words above to complete the following sentences correctly.

1. A packet of light energy is called a(n) ____ .

2. Objects look fuzzy when viewed through ____ materials, such as wax paper or frosted glass.

3. Heat can be felt when your skin is exposed to ____ rays.

4. Some sunglasses have ____ lenses that reduce glare.

5. Doctors use a(n) ____ to take a picture of bones.

6. The glass in the window of an automobile is ____ .

7. In the invisible electromagnetic spectrum, a(n) ____ has the shortest wavelength.

8. A(n) ____ object blocks the passage of all light.

9. Visible and invisible wavelengths combine to make up the ____ .

10. The ____ supports the idea that light behaves like a particle.

11. Sunburn and skin cancer are caused by ____ waves.

Write Your Vocabulary

Write sentences using the vocabulary words above. Show that you know what each word means.

Check Your Vocabulary

1. photon
2. translucent
3. infrared
4. polarized
5. X-ray
6. transparent
7. gamma ray
8. opaque
9. electromagnetic spectrum
10. photoelectric effect
11. ultraviolet

Write Your Vocabulary

Students' sentences should show that they know the meaning of each word as well as how to use it in a sentence.

Use Vocabulary Worksheet for Chapter 17.

Check Your Knowledge

1. The ability of light to create interference patterns is evidence that light is a wave.

2. Photons striking the plate cause electrons to be knocked off metal atoms, creating a current.

3. Electromagnetic waves differ from each other in wavelength and frequency.

4. Microwave energy is absorbed by molecules in food; it increases the molecular activity and heats the food from the inside out.

5. Ultraviolet waves interact with chemicals in the skin to produce vitamin D. Overexposure causes changes in the skin that can lead to cancer.

6. Different colors are produced by different wavelengths.

7. Short wavelengths (toward the blue end of the visible spectrum) are scattered and reflected more by particles in the atmosphere, so more of this color light reaches the eye.

8. False; energy

9. True

10. False; violet

11. False; distance

12. False; transverse

13. True

14. False; black

15. False; translucent

16. True

Check Your Understanding

1. Violet light is the only visible light listed.

2. The source of the primary colors of light is the wavelength and frequency of the electromagnetic wave. The pigment colors' source is the reflected light of only one color. All other light is absorbed.

3. All parts of the EM spectrum are waves of energy; all are transverse waves.

4. Because light rays travel in straight lines and spread out with distance.

5. Ancient peoples believed that the speed of light was infinite because they had not found a way to measure it.

6. People suffer from SAD during winter months when there are fewer daylight hours. Strong artificial light can treat the disorder.

7. Pigments in the ink absorb some colors of light and reflect others. We see the reflected light as colors.

8. Red, orange, yellow, green, blue, indigo, violet; white light refracts as it passes into water droplets, reflects off the inside surface, and finally refracts again as it reemerges from the droplet. Different wavelengths of light are refracted to different degrees, and are separated. You could form a rainbow by spraying water from a hose into the air when the sun is behind you.

9. Extending outward from violet would be the wavelengths of ultraviolet through gamma rays; extending out from red would be infrared through short wave radio.

10. gamma rays, X-rays, ultraviolet waves, visible light, infrared waves, microwaves, radio waves

---

Chapter 17 Review

Check Your Knowledge

Answer the following in complete sentences.

1. What evidence did scientists give to support that light is a wave?

2. During the photoelectric effect, what happens when a photon strikes a metal plate?

3. How do electromagnetic waves differ from one another?

4. How do microwaves increase the temperature of food?

5. How are ultraviolet rays both good and bad for you?

6. What accounts for the difference between one color and another?

7. Why does the sky appear to be blue?

Determine whether each statement is true or false. Write *true* if it is true. If it is false, change the underlined term to make the statement true.

8. Light is a form of <u>matter</u>.

9. When light is <u>refracted</u>, it changes direction.

10. The photoelectric effect is caused by <u>infrared</u> waves.

11. A light-year is a measure of <u>time</u>.

12. All electromagnetic waves are <u>longitudinal</u>.

13. The <u>shortest</u> waves possess the greatest energy.

14. When the primary pigments are mixed in equal amounts, they produce <u>white</u>.

15. Materials that are <u>transparent</u> transmit light but scatter it so that clear images can't be seen.

16. A prism separates <u>white</u> light into colors.

Check Your Understanding

Apply the concepts you have learned to answer each question.

1. Identify which of the following are visible parts of the electromagnetic spectrum and which aren't: violet light, infrared rays, radio waves, microwaves, ultraviolet rays, and gamma rays.

2. How do the sources of the primary colors of light and the primary pigments differ?

3. What characteristics do all parts of the electromagnetic spectrum share?

4. Why does light passing through a pinhole project a circle that is a larger circle than the pinhole itself?

5. Why did ancient people assume that the speed of light was infinite?

6. **Critical Thinking** What evidence supports the conclusion that the condition called Seasonal Affective Disorder is caused by a reduction in daylight?

7. **Mystery Photo** The photograph on page 408 shows paints containing different pigments. Explain why you see various colors.

8. **Application** Sometimes you see a rainbow after a rainstorm. List the colors of a rainbow in order of their appearance. Explain how the moisture in the air forms a rainbow. How could you form a rainbow in your own backyard?

9. **Extension** Draw a rainbow, then extend it to show where each wavelength of the invisible spectrum would be placed. Show each wavelength of the invisible spectrum.

10. Rank the photon energy of the following parts of the electromagnetic spectrum from highest to lowest: ultraviolet waves, visible light waves, X-rays, radio waves, gamma rays, microwaves.

Develop Your Skills

1. a. radio waves

b. gamma rays

c. Frequency and wavelength are inversely related.

2. Radio waves, microwaves, and infrared waves do not have enough energy to knock electrons loose.

3. blue—orange; red—green; yellow—purple

Make Connections

1.

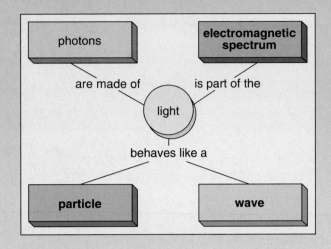

2. Distance = x light-years x

$$\frac{365 \cancel{d}}{1 \cancel{y}} \times \frac{24 \cancel{h}}{1 \cancel{d}} \times \frac{60 \cancel{min}}{1 \cancel{h}} \times \frac{60 \cancel{s}}{1 \cancel{min}} \times \frac{300\,000 \text{ km}}{\cancel{s}}$$

or: Distance = x light-years x (9.5×10^{12})

a. 8.6 light-years = 8.2×10^{13} km

b. 4.3 light-years = 4.1×10^{13} km

c. 26 light-years = 2.4×10^{14} km

3. SPF is a ratio that compares time spent in the sun with and without sunscreen. If you are using sunscreen with SPF 4, you can stay in the sun 4 times as long as you could without the sunscreen. People with fair skin react to sunlight differently than those with dark skin. However, *all* skin will burn with overexposure. Students' personal choice of SPF will vary.

Develop Your Skills

Use the skills you have developed to complete each activity.

1. Interpreting Data Study the table and answer the following questions.

a. Which source has the longest waves?

b. Which has the shortest?

c. What is the relationship between wavelength and wave frequency?

Energy Source	Wavelength	Wave Frequency (Hz)
Radio waves	1 m – 30 km	$10^4 – 10^8$
Microwaves	1 mm – 30 cm	$10^9 – 10^{12}$
Infrared rays	750 nm – 30 000 nm	$10^{12} – 4.3 \times 10^{14}$
Visible light	430 nm – 750 nm	$4.3 \times 10^{14} – 7.5 \times 10^{14}$
Ultraviolet rays	10 nm – 430 nm	$7.6 \times 10^{14} – 4.0 \times 10^{17}$
X-rays	0.001 nm – 10 nm	$4.0 \times 10^{17} – 10^{19}$
Gamma rays	0.0000003 – 0.003 nm	$10^{19} – 10^{24}$

2. Hypothesize Suggest an explanation for the fact that radio waves, microwaves, and infrared waves don't produce a photoelectric effect, but ultraviolet waves, X-rays, and gamma rays do.

3. Data Bank Use the informaton on page 640 to answer the following question. What is the complementary color of each primary color?

Make Connections

1. Link the Concepts Below is a concept map showing how some of the main concepts in this chapter link together. Only part of the map is filled in. Finish the map, using words and ideas you find on the previous pages.

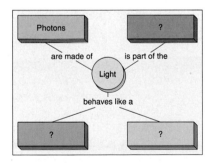

2. Science and Math Below are the names of some stars and their distances from the earth in light-years. Calculate the distance of each in kilometers. Use 300 000 km/s for the speed of light. Express your results in scientific notation.

a. Sirius   8.6 light-years

b. Alpha Centauri   4.3 light-years

c. Vega   26 light-years

3. Science and You The containers of all sunscreen products have a number written on them. This number stands for the **s**un **p**rotection **f**actor, or SPF. Do research to find out the practical meaning of this number. Also find out what variables affect a person's reaction to exposure to sunlight. Based on this data, determine what SPF is best for you.

Overview

This chapter describes the uses of light. Illuminated and luminous objects are compared and three sources of artificial light are distinguished in the first section. Light reflections from plane and curved mirrors are discussed next, followed by a discussion of the refraction of light in concave and convex lenses. The chapter also explains various light technologies such as cameras, microscopes, lasers, and optical fibers.

Advance Planner

► Supply flashlights and table-tennis balls for TE page 433.

► Obtain copies of artwork for TE page 439.

► Obtain a copy of Andre Gide's book for TE page 440.

► Supply plane mirrors and shiny spoons for TE page 443.

► Obtain concave and convex lenses for TE pages 446 and 447.

► Provide hand lenses for SE Activity 18, page 450.

► Obtain a pair of binoculars for TE page 453.

► Collect cardboard tubes, aluminum foil, plastic wrap, and yarn for TE page 458.

Skills Development Chart

Sections	Calculate	Classify	Collect Data	Communicate	Compare	Infer	Measure	Observe	Predict
18.1 Skills WarmUp Skills WorkOut			●		●				
18.2 Skills WarmUp Skills WorkOut					●			●	
18.3 Skills WarmUp Skills WorkOut						●			●
18.4 Skills WarmUp Activity	●						●	●	●
18.5 Skills WarmUp Consider This		● ●		●					

Individual Needs

► **Limited English Proficiency Students** Have students make a light log. At the top of each page have them name a light or lighting device with which they are familiar. Below the name have them list the boldface vocabulary words that describe that device. Remind them to include any vocabulary words from Chapters 14 and 17 that apply as well. Ask them to draw a diagram to show how light beams act or interact with the devices. Discuss the light logs individually with students, or have them share their logs with the class.

► **At-Risk Students** Provide students with 10 index cards and 10 sheets of paper. Have them write one of the chapter terms and its definition on each index card. Photocopy the photographs on pages 434–435, Figures 18.8, 18.12, 18.14, 18.18, 18.19, 18.20, 18.21, 18.23, and 18.24. Then have students paste the drawing or diagram for each term on each sheet of paper. Ask them to paste the index cards to the correct drawings.

► **Gifted Students** Encourage students to find out about the cameras, lenses, and projectors used in filming and projecting movies. Suggest that they learn something about the history of motion pictures and make their own version of a 19th-century device called a *zoetrope*. Have students present their findings and demonstrate their zoetropes to the rest of the class.

Resource Bank

► **Bulletin Board** Label sections of the bulletin board with kinds of "state-of-the art" light technology, such as lasers, holography, and fiber optics. Ask students to bring in articles and pictures showing industrial, medical, or novel uses for these technologies. Encourage students to find as many new applications for each technology as possible. Invite students who have their own ideas for applications to add them to the board.

► **Field Trip** Visit a museum or art gallery that has a display of holograms, telescopes, cameras, or old movie equipment. If possible, have students bring cameras to take pictures of the displays and add them to the bulletin board.

Section	Core	Standard	Enriched	Section	Core	Standard	Enriched
18.1 Light Sources pp. 433–436				**Blackline Masters** Review Worksheet 18.3 Integrating Worksheet 18.3	● ●	● ●	●
Section Features Skills WarmUp, p. 433 Skills WorkOut, p. 436	● ●	● ●	●	**18.4 Refraction and Lenses** pp. 445–450			
Blackline Masters Review Worksheet 18.1 Integrating Worksheet 18.1	●	● ●	● ●	**Section Features** Skills WarmUp, p. 445 Career Corner, p. 449 Activity, p. 450	● ● ●	● ● ●	● ● ●
18.2 Vision pp. 437–440				**Blackline Masters** Review Worksheet 18.4 Skills Worksheet 18.4	●	● ●	● ●
Section Features Skills WarmUp, p. 437 Skills WorkOut, p. 439	● ●	● ●	● ●	**Color Transparencies** Transparencies 62, 63	●	●	●
Blackline Masters Review Worksheet 18.2 Intergrating Worksheet 18.2	●	● ●	●	**18.5 Light Technology** pp. 451–458			
Overhead Blackline Transparencies Overhead Blackline Master 17 and Student Worksheet	●	●	●	**Section Features** Skills WarmUp, p. 451 Consider This, p. 454	● ●	● ●	● ●
Laboratory Program Investigation 34	●	●	●	**Blackline Masters** Review Worksheet 18.5 Enrich Worksheet 18.5 Skills Worksheet 18.5 Vocabulary Worksheet 18	● ●	● ● ● ●	● ● ● ●
Color Transparencies Transparency 61	●	●	●	**Ancillary Options** *One-Minute Readings,* p. 89	●	●	●
18.3 Reflection and Mirrors pp. 441–444				**Color Transparencies** Transparencies 64, 65, 66, 67, 68,	●	●	●
Section Features Skills WarmUp, p. 441 Skills WorkOut, p. 444	● ●	● ●	●				

Bibliography

The following resources can be used for teaching the chapter. See page T-46 for supplier codes.

Library Resources

Asimov, Isaac. *How Did We Find Out About Lasers?* New York: Walker and Company, 1990.

Burkig, Valerie. *Photonics: The New Science of Light.* Hillside, NJ: Enslow Publishers, Inc., 1986.

Gardner, Robert. *Experimenting with Light.* New York: Franklin Watts, 1991.

Hecht, Jeff. *Optics: Light for a New Age.* New York: Charles Scribner's Sons, 1987.

Technology Resources

Internet

PLANETDIARY at *http://www.planetdiary.com*
• Learn more about astronomy and space in *Astronomy/Space* by clicking on *Phenomena Backgrounders* and *Current Phenomena.*

Software

Experiment City. Mac, Win. ESI.
Learning All About Lights and Lasers. Mac, Win. LS.
Learning All Matter. Mac, Win. LS.

CD-ROMs

hip Physics. Mac. ESI.

Laserdiscs

Living Textbook. (See barcodes on pages in this chapter.) *Optical Data.*

Videos

The World of Light Energy. FM.

Audio-Visual Resources

Light and Lenses. Film. JF.

Introducing the Chapter

Have students read the description of the photograph. Ask if they agree or disagree with the description.

Directed Inquiry

Have students study the photograph. Ask the following questions:

► How would you describe the image in the picture? (It looks like shiny wires or tubes.)

► What are the round shapes? (Students may say that each is the end of a cut wire or tube.)

► Why are the ends of the wirelike objects bright? (The surfaces could be reflecting light, or perhaps they are a light source themselves.)

► How do you think these objects might help people use light? (They may transmit light signals or images in some way; they may reflect light. Some students may recognize them as a bundle of optical fibers.)

Chapter Vocabulary

concave	laser
convex	lens
fluorescent	luminous
hologram	optical fiber
incandescent	virtual image

**The Living Textbook:
Physical Science Side 3**

Chapter 35   Frame 22613
Electron Light Emission (Animation)
Search: Play:

Writing Connection

Ask students to imagine that they are small enough to ride on a beam of light. Have them write a story describing the experience. Students' stories might answer the following questions: Where does the trip begin? How fast can they go? Where can or can't they travel? What will they experience when the beam strikes a surface or passes through a substance like glass or water? Where can they travel that they can't go in their human size? Where will they be when the trip is over?

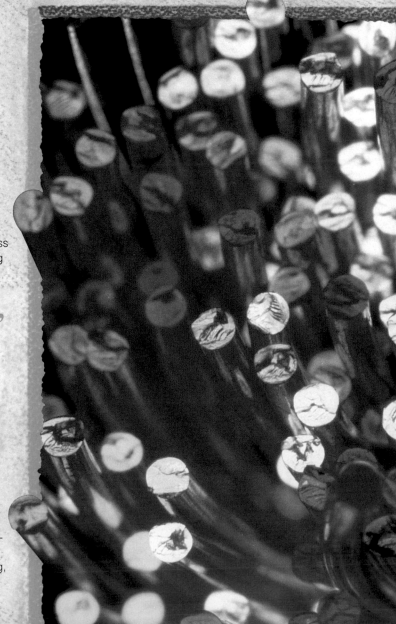

Chapter 18   Using Light

Chapter Sections

What do you see?

❝This looks like many glass cylinders. Instead of having smooth tops, they are cut unevenly. Perhaps light is shined through them in a certain way that is useful.❞

*Tahsha Scott
Milton High School
Milton, Massachusetts*

To find out more about the photograph, look on page 460. As you read this chapter, you will learn about the many ways, such as seeing, that you use light.

Cooperative Learning

Students can work in cooperative pairs to do an activity about the illumination of the moon during its phases. Remind them that the moon regularly orbits the earth. Have each pair use a flashlight (for the sun) and two table tennis balls (for the earth and moon). While one student holds the flashlight steady about 40 cm above a desktop, the other should orbit the earth with the moon. With the flashlight aimed at the moon, what would people at 6, 3, 12, and 9 o'clock on the earth see? Have each pair prepare a drawing of the moon based on the experiment that explains the new, full, and quarter moons. Have students explain why the whole moon isn't fully lighted all the time. **Use Integrating Worksheet 18.1.**

Section Objectives
For a list of section objectives, see the Student Edition page.

Skills Objectives:
Students should be able to:

Compare how different objects reflect light.

Observe light reflection.

Collect Data about light sources.

Infer why fluorescent light is preferred in some situations.

Vocabulary
luminous, incandescent, fluorescent

18.1 Light Sources

Objectives

▶ **Name** and **describe** three types of artificial light.

▶ **Distinguish** between lighted and luminous objects.

▶ **Compare** the efficiency of fluorescent and incandescent lights.

▶ **Infer** why one kind of artificial light may be more useful than another.

▼ ACTIVITY

Comparing

Reflecting on Light

Observe how three different objects or surfaces in your classroom reflect light. Compare how much light the objects reflect to you. Do any of the surfaces reflect an image to you? Do any reflect no light?

SKILLS WARMUP

Light comes from a variety of sources and has a variety of uses. You come in contact with many sources of light each day. In fact, the beginning of each day is marked by the rise of the sun—the earth's main source of light.

You use light to see things, but light also has other uses. For example, light is used during the filming of a movie, both to brighten the movie set and to help set the mood of a scene. Light is also used to communicate, as in neon signs and traffic signals.

People aren't the only living things that use light. You may have seen a firefly's light at night. Fireflies use light to attract and identify a mate.

Lighted Objects

Although all light is a form of energy, it doesn't come from the same source. The sun, neon lights, candles, and fireflies are all sources of light. Any object that produces its own light is referred to as **luminous** (LOO muh nuhs). Recall that an object produces light when the electrons in its atoms give off energy.

You've probably looked at stars and the moon in the nighttime sky. Each star, like the sun, is a luminous object—it produces its own light. The moon, however, isn't a luminous object. Look at the moon in Figure 18.1. Although the moon appears to be luminous, the light from the moon is actually light from the sun that is reflected by the moon. The moon is an example of an *illuminated* object. An illuminated object reflects light.

Figure 18.1 ▲
The moon is illuminated by light from the sun. Why does the moon sometimes appear fully illuminated and sometimes only partially illuminated? ①

MOTIVATE

Skills WarmUp

To help students understand light sources, have them do the Skills WarmUp.
Answer Answers may vary. Students should note that dark, rough objects tend to reflect less light than light, smooth objects do. Shiny, metallic objects may reflect most of the light. Transparent objects, such as glass, will reflect very little light.

Answer to In-Text Question
① **Students may reason that this is due to the relative positions of the sun, the earth, and moon.**

 The Living Textbook:
Physical Science Sides 1-4

Chapter 13   Frame 02206
Moonrise over Ocean (10 Frames)
Search: Step:

Critical Thinking

Compare and Contrast Ask students to compare fluorescent and incandescent lighting in terms of their energy sources and efficiency. Tell them fluorescent bulbs are more expensive, but long lasting. Ask, Which kind of lighting is better for the school? (Answers may vary. Incandescent bulbs are cheaper, but fluorescent lighting is more efficient and a better buy in the long run.)

Explore Visually

Have students study the photographs and descriptions on pages 434 and 435. Ask the following questions:

▶ How does the method of producing light differ between incandescent light and fluorescent light? (Incandescent light is produced by heating an object, while fluorescent light is produced when electrons and gas molecules collide)

▶ What is the source of bioluminescence? (Chemical reactions inside organisms)

▶ In what location is light given off in an incandescent light? A fluorescent light? (Only the filament gives off light in an incandescent bulb. The entire surface area of the fluorescent bulb gives off light.)

Answer to In-Text Question

① Answers may include: to scare predators, attract mates, or find food.

The Living Textbook: Physical Science Side 2

Chapter 29   Frame 23601
Incandescence (Animation)
Search: Play:

Integrating the Sciences

Life Science Point out that animals can be sources of light. At Phosphorescent Bay in Puerto Rico, for example, the water shines at night as microscopic invertebrates secrete luminescent fluids. In the Pacific Ocean, luminous single-celled dinoflagellates can light up the water at night when a ship's wake disturbs them.

STS Connection

Tell students that fluorescent lamps use concepts of electricity and atomic structure. An electric current passes through the fluorescent tube and causes free electrons to strike atoms of mercury gas. When this happens, the atoms emit ultraviolet rays. These energize atoms of phosphor that coat the tube, and they emit white light.

Light from Luminous Objects

You use several types of artificial light. For example, the light in your classroom is probably fluorescent light. Fluorescent light is produced in glass tubes that contain gases. How do fluorescent lights compare to the kinds of lights you have in your home? Although you may have some fluorescent lights in your home, most of the light is probably produced from ordinary incandescent

Fluorescent Light

Electrons collide with gas molecules contained at low pressure to produce **fluorescent** light. The phosphor-coated glass tube contains mercury and argon gas. When excited, the gas molecules give off photons of ultraviolet light.

When the UV light strikes the phosphor coating, it changes to visible light. Fluorescent bulbs are cool. They are more energy efficient than incandescent bulbs. ▼

Incandescent Light

◀ Light that is produced by heating an object until it glows is **incandescent** light. An incandescent light bulb gives off light when a thin piece of tungsten wire inside the bulb, called the filament, is heated until it glows by a flow of electricity.

A vacuum inside the bulb helps to keep the filament from burning in two, which would cause the bulb to burn out. Incandescent lights are not efficient. Most of their energy is given off as heat.

Animal Light ▶

A firefly gives off cool light when chemicals in its abdomen react. The ability of living things to give off light is called *bioluminescence* (BY oh LOO muh NES uhns). Some kinds of fish, some protists, and some fungi can also produce light. How do you think these organisms use bioluminescence? ①

light bulbs. The kind of light produced from these bulbs is called incandescent light.

Another kind of light that may be familiar to you is "neon" light. Neon light is often seen in brightly colored lighted signs and storefronts. It is produced by passing electrons through neon or other gases inside a thin, glass tube. Different gases produce different colors of light. Study the different types of artificial light shown. How is each type of light produced? ②

Tungsten-Halogen Light ▲

A *tungsten-halogen* bulb has a tungsten filament and is filled with a halogen gas, such as iodine, bromine, or fluorine. The gas reduces wear on the filament. A tungsten-halogen bulb doesn't "burn out" for a long time. Tungsten-halogen bulbs give off very bright incandescent light. They also produce a large amount of heat.

Neon Light ▲

The color of the light given off depends on the gas in the tube. Neon gives off bright red light. Mercury vapor gives off a greenish-blue light. Krypton produces purple light, and helium gives off yellow light.

Sodium-Vapor Light ▲

When electrons are passed through a sodium-vapor lamp, the lamp gives off a yellow-orange light. Sodium-vapor lamps are energy efficient and give off very bright light with little glare. These characteristics make sodium-vapor lights especially useful as streetlights.

TEACH ▪ *Continued*

Skills WorkOut

To help students collect data about light sources, have them do the Skills WorkOut.
Answer Students should include sunlight along with many artificial light sources.

EVALUATE

WrapUp

Reteach Ask students to imagine they are setting up lights for an evening art display in a large room. Have them develop a lighting plan that allows people to move easily around the room and view the lit art pieces. Students' plans should identify the types of lights used and the positions of the lights.
Use Review Worksheet 18.1

Check and Explain

1. Electrified tubes of neon, krypton, and helium gas, fluorescent or incandescent, incandescent, fluorescent (UV)

2. Illuminated objects reflect light (car, moon, spoon); luminous objects emit light (sun, light bulb, fire)

3. Fluorescent because it uses less energy over time and gives off less heat

4. It gives off UV light, which plants can use. Also gives off very little heat—air temperature won't increase too much.

Integrating the Sciences

Earth Science All organisms on the earth need energy to survive, and almost all get it from photosynthesis. Tell students that less than one percent of all radiant energy reaching the earth is captured in photosynthesis, but the process literally makes life on earth possible. Ask students to discuss how energy efficient photosynthesis is.

STS Connection

Companies have developed a variety of incandescent light bulbs to meet consumer needs. Examples are three-way bulbs, semi-transparent bulbs, tinted bulbs, large theatrical bulbs, flashlight, and new energy-saving bulbs. Have each student research two kinds of lights and compare the amounts of light and heat they emit.

Science and Society
Energy-Saving Light Bulbs

Scientists and engineers are developing new kinds of lights that use less energy than the incandescent light bulbs used in most homes. One of these new developments is the compact fluorescent light bulb. Unlike ordinary fluorescent bulbs, the compact fluorescent bulb can be used in place of ordinary incandescent light bulbs. These bulbs are also useful for growing plants because they give off UV light.

Compact fluorescent bulbs cost more to buy than incandescent bulbs, but they cost less to use. For example, an 18-watt compact fluorescent bulb gives off as much light as a 75-watt incandescent bulb. The cost of electricity to use an 18-watt compact fluorescent bulb three hours each day for a year is about $2.00. The cost of electricity for using a 75-watt incandescent bulb is about $8.50 per year. The fluorescent bulb also lasts 5 to 13 times longer than an incandescent bulb does.

Tungsten-halogen bulbs are also new. Because of their brightness, tungsten-halogen bulbs are common in automobiles, stadiums, and parking areas, as well as in the home. These bulbs have several advantages over ordinary incandescent light bulbs. They are small, use less electricity, and give off more light. One disadvantage to tungsten-halogen bulbs is the large amount of heat they give off. Fixtures that use these bulbs require thick, glass heat shields. The heat shields prevent objects from touching the bulb and catching fire.

▼ ACTIVITY

Collecting Data

Tracking Lighting

During the day, count the different kinds of light sources you see. Keep track of how many of each kind you see. What kind did you see the most? What kinds didn't you see?

SKILLS WORKOUT

Check and Explain

1. Identify the kind of light produced by each of the following: the red, purple, and yellow lights of an advertising sign, the lights in your classroom, a tungsten-halogen light bulb, and a plant light.

2. How does an illuminated object differ from a luminous object? Give two examples for each.

3. **Compare** Which is more energy efficient, fluorescent light or incandescent light? Explain.

4. **Infer** Why would fluorescent light be the best artificial light for a terrarium?

436

Themes in Science

Scale and Structure While eye structure is basically the same in all animals, many variations have developed as a result of each creature's environment and survival needs. Discuss with students the different eye structures of insects, birds, fish, and mammals, and suggest the survival value of each variation.

Evolution As organisms evolved, the pigments that led to photosynthesis may have evolved and allowed the organisms to adapt in special ways to light. Today for example, some flatworms have eyespots that can sense light and dark but can't form images. In other many-celled animals, specialized groups of cells (eyes) have evolved that can obtain more information from light.

18.2 Vision

Objectives

▶ **Identify** each part of the eye and explain its function.

▶ **Trace** the path of light through the eye.

▶ **Compare** where light rays focus for normal, nearsighted, and farsighted vision.

▶ **Make a model** to show how each part of the eye helps to focus light on the retina.

▼ ACTIVITY

Observing

How Much Can You See?

Cup your hands around your eyes. Look straight forward. Observe what you can see out of the corner of your eyes. What do you see out of the corners of your eyes when you remove your hands?

SKILLS WARMUP

Living things can see because of the structure of their eyes. The field of vision for living things depends on the location of their eyes. Your eyes are located at the front of your head at a distance of about 3 to 7 cm apart. Because of the position of your eyes, you see nearly the same image with each eye. Seeing the same image with both eyes helps you to judge distances, but it also gives you a relatively narrow field of vision.

You've probably noticed that a bird's eyes are located at the sides of its head. Because its eyes are so far apart, a bird's field of vision is much wider than yours. A bird sees a different image with each of its eyes, as shown in Figure 18.2. Only a small portion of the bird's field of vision is covered by both eyes.

Parts of the Eye

If you look at your eyes or the eyes of someone else, you can easily observe three different parts. At the center of your eye is a black circle, called the *pupil*. The pupil is actually an opening through which light enters your eye. Surrounding the pupil is a colored disk called the *iris*. The iris is surrounded by the white part of the eye, called the *sclera*. The pupil, iris, and sclera aren't the only parts of the eye. It has other parts that aren't easily observed. All the parts of your eye work together with your brain to allow you to see.

Your eyes are covered by eyelids. The eyelids keep dirt and harmful substances from entering your eyes. Eyelids also spread tears over the eyes when you blink.

 One eye   Both eyes

Figure 18.2 ▲

Identify the area the bird sees with its right eye, its left eye, and with both eyes. In what way is this field of vision useful to the bird?

SECTION

18.2

Section Objectives
For a list of section objectives, see the Student Edition page.

Skills Objectives
Students should be able to:

Observe peripheral vision.

Compare the effects of light and dark on the pupil of the eye.

Make a Model of the human eye.

MOTIVATE

Skills WarmUp

To help students understand fields of vision, have them do the Skills WarmUp

Answer Students should see much more when they remove their hands. Their field of vision extends on each side.

Prior Knowledge

Gauge how much students know about vision by asking the following questions:

▶ What three parts of your eyes can you observe?

▶ Why can you see different colors?

▶ What is meant by nearsightedness and farsightedness?

Answer to In-Text Question

① It can see predators and obstacles more easily. The light-shaded sections are seen by only the right or left eye. The dark-colored section in front of the bird is seen with both eyes.

The Living Textbook: Physical Science Sides 1-4

Chapter 13   Frame 02111
Human Eye (2 Frames)
Search: Step:

Directed Inquiry

Have students study the text and Figure 18.3. Ask the following questions:

▶ What are rods and cones? Where are they? (Light-sensitive cells in the retina, which is at the back of the eye)

▶ What is the function of each part of the eye, starting with the cornea? (Cornea—covers and protects the pupil and iris, lets light into the eye; iris—adjusts pupil size to control amount of light entering the eye; pupil—adjusts to allow light into the eye; lens—bends light rays to focus an image on the retina; retina—provides surface on which light rays form an image, contains rods and cones that facilitate seeing black, white, and colors; optic nerve—carries electric signals formed in the retina to the brain.)

▶ How do signals from your eye get to your brain? (Through the optic nerve)

Answer to In-Text Question

① **To avoid damage to the retina and to allow enough light into the eye for vision to occur.**

The Living Textbook: Physical Science Sides 1-4

Chapter 13   Frame 02104
Structure of Eye (2 Frames)
Search: Step:

The Living Textbook: Physical Science Sides 1-4

Chapter 13   Frame 02026
Colorblindness Test (2 Frames)
Search: Step:

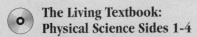

Integrating the Sciences

Life Science The human eye contains about 7 million cones that are highly concentrated in the center of the retina. Cones help perceive sharp, detailed images, as well as color. They require bright light to function properly. The 150 million rods are more abundant around the edges of the retina and can detect a single photon of light. This arrangement allows the eye to adapt to darkening conditions. Have students look at pieces of red, blue, green, grey, and purple cloth. Darken the room until the colors are hard to distinguish. Put the cloths in a box, mix them up, and ask students to identify the colors. Have students explain what they see in terms of the use of rods and cones in the eyes.

Iris and Pupil The iris adjusts the size of the pupil to control the amount of light that enters your eye. Locate the iris and the pupil in Figure 18.3. When light is bright, the muscles of the iris contract to make the pupil smaller. Less light enters the eye. In the dim light, the muscles of the iris relax and let in more light. Why is it important for the eye to control the amount of light that enters your eye? ①

Cornea and Lens A transparent structure, called the *cornea*, covers and protects the pupil and the iris. The cornea lets light into your eye. Look carefully at Figure 18.3. You will see that the cornea is part of the sclera.

Another transparent structure, called the lens, is located behind the pupil. Your eye's lens bends light rays to focus an image on your retina. The shape of the lens changes in order to focus the image. Find the cornea and the lens in Figure 18.3.

Retina The *retina* is the inner layer of the back of your eye. Look at Figure 18.3. Light passing through the lens forms an image on the retina.

The retina contains light-sensitive cells, called rods and cones. Rods allow you to see black and white. The rods can function in dim light. Cones allow you to see colors. The cones require bright light. Three kinds of cones are needed to see each of the primary colors of light. Some people are color deficient. They don't have all three kinds of cones, so they don't see all colors.

Optic Nerve Nerve fibers connected to the rods and cones of the retina form the *optic nerve*. When the rod and cone cells in the retina absorb light rays, the energy in the light changes to electric signals. The optic nerve carries the electric signals formed in the retina to your brain. Your brain interprets these signals as vision.

Figure 18.3 ▶
This cross section of the eye shows its main parts. Trace the path of light through the eye.

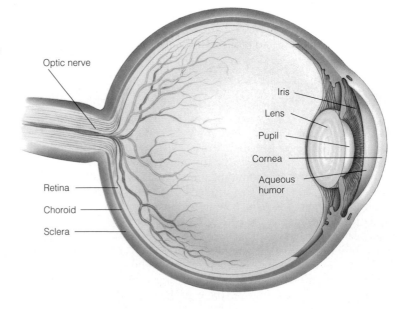

The Path of Light

For perfect vision, light travels through the cornea, the pupil, and the lens, and focuses directly on the retina. Not everyone has eyes that function perfectly. However, most vision disorders can be corrected.

Like a camera, your eye can adjust in order to focus on things near or far. Unlike a camera lens, your eye's lens has muscles around it that change its shape to adjust to different distances. When the lens is unable to adjust to make an image focus directly on the retina, a person is either nearsighted or farsighted.

Look at Figure 18.4 to see how an image can focus in the eye. A nearsighted person sees nearby objects clearly, but far-off objects appear blurred. Light rays from distant objects focus in front of the retina, as shown in the center.

For a farsighted person, light rays from distant objects focus correctly on the retina. However, close-up objects appear blurred. Light rays from nearby objects focus behind the retina, as shown at the bottom.

If the cornea of the eye isn't correctly shaped, light entering the eye may bend more in one direction than in another. This problem is called *astigmatism*. People with astigmatism can't focus light rays on the retina— all images appear blurred.

▼ ACTIVITY

Comparing

Eyes

Collect the following items: 10 sheets of white paper, a rubber band, printed text and a mirror.

1. Make a roll with the sheets of paper, and secure it with a rubber band.

2. Stand the roll on printed text so that no light enters the roll.

3. Close one eye and look at the print through the rolled paper with the other eye for at least two minutes.

4. As soon as you are able to read the words, look at your eye in the mirror.

What do you observe?

SKILLS WORKOUT

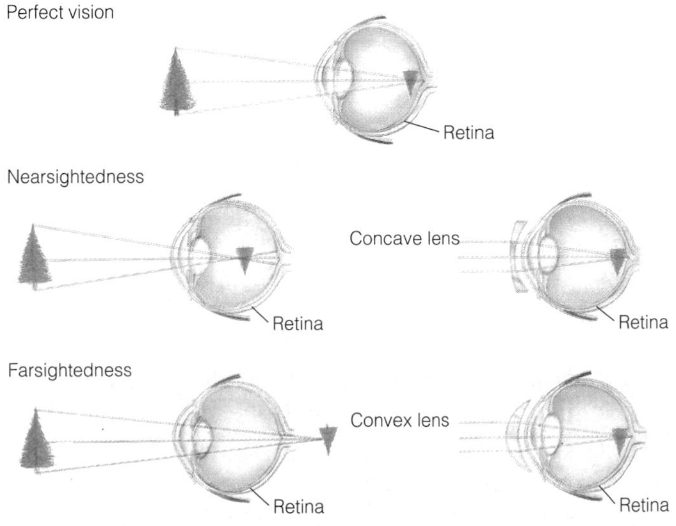

**Figure 18.4
Correcting Vision Problems**
▼

Perfect vision

Retina

Nearsightedness

Concave lens

Retina | Retina

Farsightedness

Convex lens

Retina | Retina

To correct nearsighted vision, a concave lens in front of the eye bends light rays so that light focuses on the retina.

To correct farsighted vision, a convex lens in front of the eye bends light rays so that light focuses on the retina.

TEACH ▪ *Continued*

Critical Thinking

Uncover Assumptions Ask students to think about the five senses. Then choose a common scenario—having lunch with friends, watching a sports event, shopping—and discuss what one would miss with a vision impairment and what parts of the experience would be the same. Ask, How much would your life change if your vision were impaired?

EVALUATE

WrapUp

Reinforce Have a class discussion in which students compare the eye to a camera. What part is like the film? What part is like the lens? What is like the lens cover? What role does light play in each? How many other similarities can they see? Students can turn their conclusions into a class poster.

Use Review Worksheet 18.2.

Check and Explain

1. The pupil lets in light; the iris adjusts pupil size; the lens focuses light; the cornea covers and protects the pupil and the iris; the retina perceives light and sends signals to the optic nerve.

2. Answers should follow light through the parts listed in answer 1.

3. In normal vision, light is focused directly on the retina; in nearsightedness, it is in front; in farsightedness, it is behind.

4. Diagrams should resemble Figure 18.4.

Answer to In-Text Question

① Answers will vary. The dog guides the woman on steps and around obstacles, and lets her know when it is safe to cross streets.

Literature Connection

Read the passage in Andre Gide's *Pastoral Symphony* in which a man describes a scene to a sightless woman using the metaphor of a symphony. Have students discuss ways in which this method succeeds and fails. Challenge students to describe a familiar object as if the person they are speaking to has been sightless since birth.

STS Connection

Communication companies try to develop products and services for people with different impairments. Ask students to imagine what it would be like to use a telephone if they could see little or nothing. What would make it easier to use? (Answers may include keypads and numbers, Braille keypads, and recording devices.)

Figure 18.5 ▲
Name some ways the seeing-eye dog helps the woman find her way around. ①

Science and You *Living Without Light*

How would your life be different if you couldn't see light? For millions of people, living in darkness is part of their daily life. These people were either born unable to see or lost their sight as a result of illness or injury.

Imagine trying to get to class or to the store without using your eyes. Sight-impaired people face such challenges every day. Some use canes or trained dogs to help them get around. They also memorize the number of steps between objects in familiar places.

In the early 1800s, a 15-year-old French boy named Louis Braille created an alphabet blind people could use. The braille system uses patterns of raised dots to represent numbers and letters. People who have lost their sight can enjoy books written in braille that are available at many libraries. Machines called braille writers also allow people to communicate in braille. Many elevators and ATMs now have instructions in braille.

Some disorders that cause sight loss are diabetes, cataracts, and glaucoma. Diabetics can help to prevent sight loss with medication and special diets. Cataracts are a condition that clouds the eye's lens. Cataracts can be corrected surgically by replacing the clouded lens with an artificial one. Glaucoma is caused by pressure within the eyeball. It is treated with drugs or surgery.

Eye injuries can occur if chemicals or objects enter the eyes. Such injuries are prevented with safety goggles. Athletes at risk for eye injury can wear helmets or protective eye wear. Protecting your eyes can be as simple as wearing sunglasses.

Check and Explain

1. Describe the functions of the following parts of the eye: pupil, iris, cornea, lens, retina, and optic nerve.

2. Explain how vision occurs: begin with light entering the eye and end with the role of the brain.

3. **Compare** Compare how light rays focus on the retina for normal, nearsighted, and farsighted vision.

4. **Make a Model** Draw a diagram showing light focusing on the retina. Show all the parts of the eye and include two light rays reflected from an object.

Geography Connection

Surveyors and topographers use mirrors with lasers to determine elevation and distance. Very precise measurements can be made by timing the journey of a beam of light that is "bounced" from a distant point back to the sender.

Literature Connection

Greek mythology tells of a mountain sprite, Echo, who loved a beautiful youth named Narcissus. Narcissus ignored her, choosing instead to stare at his own image in a pond. Eventually, he tried to touch the image, fell into the pond, and drowned. Invite students to read more about Narcissus and to find other stories in which mirrors or reflections play an important role. (For example, Snow White, Medusa, and Dracula)

Section Objectives
For a list of section objectives, see the Student Edition page.

Skills Objectives
Students should be able to:

Infer how mirrors affect images.

Predict the angle of reflection of a ball bounced off a wall.

Measure the area reflected by convex and concave mirrors.

Vocabulary
virtual image, concave, convex

18.3 Reflection and Mirrors

Objectives

▶ **Explain** how light interacts with three types of mirrors.

▶ **Identify** two uses for a plane, a concave, and a convex mirror.

▶ **Compare** and **contrast** the image formed by each of the three types of mirrors.

▶ **Measure** the areas reflected by a concave mirror and a convex mirror.

▼ **ACTIVITY**

Inferring

AMBULANCE

The word AMBULANCE is often printed backward on the front of the vehicle. Why do you think the word is printed backward?

SKILLS WARMUP

Have you ever looked at yourself in a pool of water? When the surface of the water is calm, light bounces off your body to form your image on the water. You see a reflection of yourself. When there are ripples on the water, you don't see your reflection. You only see the surface of the water.

Look at the water in Figure 18.6. Notice that the surface of the water acts like a mirror to create a perfect image of the surroundings. Why does the surface of a body of water reflect an image when the water is perfectly still? ②

Reflection

A reflection occurs when light rays from some light source directed at an object bounce off the object. The light rays that approach an object are called *incident rays*. Light rays that bounce off and are directed away from a surface are called *reflected rays*. Because a perfectly calm lake, or a mirror, reflects most of the incident rays and doesn't scatter the reflected rays, it produces a clear, sharp image.

Most objects you see reflect light rays to your eyes. Cars, walls, windows, and even people reflect some amount of light rays. Otherwise, you would not be able to see them. Smooth, shiny surfaces, such as metals, glass, polished wood, and the surface of liquids reflect light easily. In what other kinds of surfaces can you see your reflection? ③

Figure 18.6 ▲
How does the detail in the reflection differ from the actual scene? Try looking at the photo upside down. ④

MOTIVATE

Skills WarmUp

To help students understand the reversed reflection in mirrors, have them do the Skills WarmUp.
Answer The word is visible correctly in the rearview mirror of a car in front of the ambulance.

Answers to In-Text Questions

② It's a flat, reflective surface that reflects many of the incident rays and doesn't scatter reflected rays.

③ Answers will vary, but may include mirrors, other people's eyes, high-glaze ceramics, and shiny surfaces.

④ The details are nearly the same in the actual and in the reflected scene.

 The Living Textbook: Physical Science Sides 1-4

Chapter 13   Frame 02115
Light Ray Reflection (5 Frames)
Search: Step:

TEACH

Explore Visually

Have students study Figure 18.7 and discuss the following:

▶ Describe the angle of incidence. (The angle made by the incident light ray and the normal)

▶ What is formed when the normal and a reflected ray meet? (Angle of reflection)

▶ How do the angle of incidence and the angle of reflection compare? (Their measures are equal.)

Class Activity

Ask, why do babies look behind a mirror? (Babies think another baby is looking back at them from behind the mirror.) Have a volunteer make a diagram on the chalkboard of a plane mirror, an object, and its image behind the mirror. Ask students to explain why the image is called a virtual image. (It isn't where it appears to be.) Ask, What is a virtual image and where can you see one? (A virtual image is seen in a plane mirror.)

Critical Thinking

Reason and Conclude Explain to students that images projected onto a screen are considered to be *real* images. Ask them to describe what they would see if images were first projected onto a mirror, then to a screen. Why? (A virtual image; it would be reversed and would not result from converging rays.)

**The Living Textbook:
Physical Science Sides 1-4**

Chapter 13   Frame 02127
Angles of Incidence/Reflection
(13 Frames)
Search: Step:

Multicultural Perspectives

Abu Ali Mohamed ibn al-Hasan Ign al-Haytham, known among Europeans as Alhazen, was among the first to formally study light and vision. Al-Hasan (935–1039), who lived in Baghdad, recognized that light originates in sources, reflects off objects, and enters the eye to create vision. Have students learn more about Al-Hasan and make a diagram of the device he used to show that light travels in straight lines. (Camera obscura)

History Connection

According to legend, Archimedes knew enough about mirrors to use sunlight as a weapon against the Roman fleet that invaded Sicily in 212 B.C. Huge curved mirrors focused sunlight on the sails of the ships, creating so much heat that the sails burst into flames. Ask students to find out if mirrors are used for any similar purposes today. (Parabolic mirrors are used to collect sunlight and cook food.)

Mirrors

A common mirror is a flat or curved piece of glass. It has been painted on the back with a thin coating of metal. The metal gives the glass a shiny surface that reflects most of the light rays that strike it.

Images in a mirror appear to be reversed left to right. Light rays from the right side of an object reflect off the mirror and appear to be on the left. The way a mirror reflects light depends on the shape of its surface. Mirrors are classified as plane, concave, or convex.

Plane Mirrors A mirror with a flat surface is a plane mirror. The image appears to be behind a plane mirror. Also, the image appears to be the same size and distance behind the mirror as the object is in front of it.

The image that you see in a plane mirror is called a **virtual image.** A virtual image is not where it appears to be and is seen only in a mirror. A virtual image can be compared to another type of image, called a real image, which is formed by converging light rays. A real image can be projected onto a surface. A virtual image, however, can't be projected onto a surface.

**Figure 18.7
A Light Beam Reflected Off a
Plane Mirror** ▼

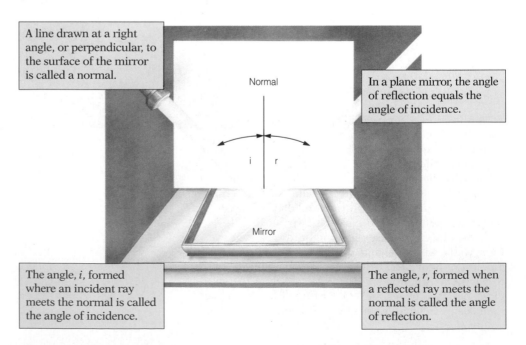

A line drawn at a right angle, or perpendicular, to the surface of the mirror is called a normal.

In a plane mirror, the angle of reflection equals the angle of incidence.

The angle, *i*, formed where an incident ray meets the normal is called the angle of incidence.

The angle, *r*, formed when a reflected ray meets the normal is called the angle of reflection.

Cooperative Learning

Have students work in cooperative pairs to study the effect of different mirrors. Give each pair a plane mirror and a shiny spoon. Have each student print his or her name on a notecard and look at it in the mirror. Challenge students to print a message on the paper so that their partners can read it in the mirror. Then have each student use the bowl of the spoon as a mirror. Starting with the spoon close to their faces, have them move the spoon slowly away from their faces. Ask them to describe what happens to the image. (It turns upside down as the spoon passes through the focal point.) Have students repeat the activity looking at the back of the spoon. (The image stays upright.)

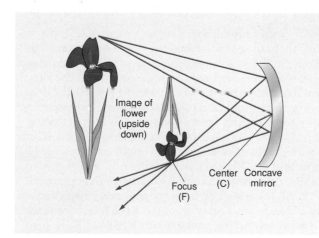

Concave Mirrors A mirror that curves inward, like the bowl of the spoon in Figure 18.8, is a **concave** mirror. Unlike the image produced by a plane mirror, a concave mirror can produce a real image as well as a virtual image. A real image forms when light rays pass through it and can be projected onto a surface.

The distance between an object and a concave mirror determines the kind of image that forms. If an object is close to the concave surface of the mirror, the reflected image is virtual and appears larger than the object. People sometimes use these mirrors when applying cosmetics or shaving. If the object is farther away from the mirror than the place where the reflected rays meet, or converge, the image is real, upside down, and smaller than the object. This kind of image is seen in Figure 18.8.

Convex Mirrors A mirror that curves outward, like the back side of the spoon, shown in Figure 18.9, is a **convex** mirror. A convex mirror forms a virtual image that appears to be behind the mirror. The focus for a convex mirror lies behind the mirror and rays appear to spread out from this point. The image is always upright and smaller than the object being reflected.

Convex mirrors provide a very wide angle of view, so a large area can be seen. They are often used in stores to prevent shoplifting. The side-view mirrors on some cars are often convex mirrors. Where have you used a convex mirror?

Figure 18.8 ▲
The diagram shows how the concave bowl of the spoon reflects the image of the flowers. What kind of an image appears in the spoon? ①

Figure 18.9 ▲
Explain how the image of the flowers on the back of the spoon differs from the image on the bowl of the spoon. ②

Critical Thinking
Reason and Conclude If an automobile mirror label reads: "Objects in mirror are closer than they appear," what kind of mirror is it? (Convex)

Reteach
Use hand mirrors to show students how plane mirror reflection distance works. Have students prop up or hold up the mirrors, and use tape to mark the top and bottom of the reflection of their faces. Then have the students step back from the mirror. Ask students to compare the sizes of the two images. (Same size) (Note that the mirror must be one half of the size of the student's head in order to see the full facial reflection.)

Misconceptions
Students may be confused as to why a real image can also be a reflected image. Explain that the light rays must *converge* to form a real image. This can occur with a concave mirror. It does not occur with plane or convex mirrors because the light rays don't converge at a given point in front of the mirror.

Answers to In-Text Questions
① Real, upside-down and smaller than the object.

② The image on the back of the spoon is a virtual image from a convex mirror, rather than a real image from a concave mirror.

③ Answers may vary. A car side-view mirror is one example.

**The Living Textbook:
Physical Science Side 3**

Chapter 31   Frame 18408
Concave Mirrors (Movie)
Search: Play:

TEACH ▪ Continued

Skills WorkOut

To help students understand the angle of incidence and the angle of reflection, have them do the Skills WorkOut.

Answer Answers will vary. Students should recognize that the angle of incidence and the angle of reflection have the same measure.

EVALUATE

WrapUp

Reteach Provide convex, concave, and plane mirrors. Ask students to view their images in the three mirrors, holding them near and far from their faces. Discuss the different images students see based on what they know about reflections and real and virtual images.
Use Review Worksheet 18.3.

Check and Explain

1. Plane: virtual/same size and upright/reversed left to right; concave: virtual/larger and upright or real/smaller and upside-down, depending on the distance to the mirror; convex: virtual/upright and smaller

2. Plane: looking glass, to see around corners; concave: applying cosmetics or shaving; convex: car or store mirrors

3. It's always the same size, upright and behind the mirror.

4. The area reflected in the convex mirror should be larger.

The Living Textbook: Physical Science Sides 1-4

Chapter 13   Frame 02122
Concave/Convex Mirrors (5 Frames)
Search: Step:

444

Math Connection

The Keck telescope can identify the light of a candle 804,500 km away. Light travels at 300,000 km/s. How long would it take the light from the candle to reach the telescope? (804,500 km ÷ 300,000 km/s = 2.6 s) The sun is 148,000,000 km from the earth. How long, in minutes, does it take light from the sun to reach the earth? (148,000,000 km ÷ 300,000 km/s = 500 or 8.3 min.)

STS Connection

Explain to students that *silvering* is the process of applying a thin layer of silver to the back of a plate of glass to make a mirror. This chemical process was discovered in 1835. Mirrors today are glass plates coated on the back with a thin layer of aluminum or silver. Ask students to infer why silver and aluminum are used. (Malleable metals create a thin coat. Aluminum and silver are highly reflective when polished.)

▼ **ACTIVITY**

Predicting

Learning the Angles

Obtain a ball.
1. Predict at which angle the ball will bounce back if you throw it against a wall from a certain angle.
2. Use a different angle each time you throw the ball.
How well did you predict the angle at which the ball bounces back? What did you learn about the angle at which the ball bounces back?

SKILLS WORKOUT

Science and Technology *Super Telescopes*

Astronomers are using new super telescopes that allow them to see far beyond the range of any previous telescope. The main component of a super telescope is a concave mirror. The slightest imperfection on the surface of a super telescope's mirror badly distorts the image.

The mirror of one new telescope was designed to be so smooth that if it were as wide as the United States, there would be no rise on its surface higher than 10 cm. Unfortunately, after six years of construction, a major imperfection was discovered when the mirror was put into use. So, the telescope is far less effective than planned.

The Keck telescope is one of this new generation of super telescopes. The heart of the Keck telescope is what scientists are calling an ingenious design of 36 hexagonal mirrors. These adjustable mirrors join to form the telescope's concave mirror. The Keck telescope's mirror measures almost 10 m in diameter and is the largest ever built.

With the completion of the construction of the Keck telescope, scientists can study eight times more of the universe than is visible with other telescopes. A super telescope, such as the Keck, can identify the light of a candle 800,000 km away. The Keck telescope also provides a look back in time as well as across space. The light it sees was given off billions of years ago, traveling across space for all this time.

Check and Explain

1. What kind of image can each of the three types of mirrors form?

2. Describe two uses each for plane mirrors, concave mirrors, and convex mirrors.

3. **Compare and Contrast** How does the image formed by a plane mirror differ from that formed by concave and convex mirrors?

4. **Measure** Look at a concave mirror, observe the reflected area. Measure the reflected area with a measuring tape. Repeat the procedure with a convex mirror of the same size. How do the sizes of the reflected areas compare?

Themes in Science

Diversity and Unity Light refracts as it passes through transparent materials and converges or diverges. A variety of images, real, virtual, or larger or smaller than the actual object, can be produced by lenses. For any lens, the characteristics of the images that will be produced can be predicted if the distance between the object and the lens's focal point is known.

Integrating the Sciences

Astronomy Explain to students that sunlight is refracted as it passes from space into the earth's atmosphere. As the sun moves lower in the sky, the angle at which sunlight strikes the earth's atmosphere becomes smaller, or more acute, and the amount of refraction increases. At sunset, when the sun appears to be on the horizon, it has already set. Have students make a diagram of the refraction of light at sunset.

Section Objectives
For a list of section objectives, see the Student Edition page.

Skills Objectives
Students should be able to:

Calculate the percentage of eyeglass-wearing parents.

Infer why light refracts through a lens.

Make a Model to show how focal length changes the image formed by a convex lens.

Vocabulary
lens

18.4 Refraction and Lenses

Objectives

▶ **Explain** how convex and concave lenses affect light rays.

▶ **Identify** two uses for convex and concave lenses.

▶ **Infer** why lenses refract light.

▶ **Make a model** that shows how focal length affects an object being observed through a convex lens.

▼ **ACTIVITY**

Calculating

Glasses Survey

Survey the other students in your class to find out how many of their parents wear eyeglasses. Divide the number of parents who wear eyeglasses by the total number of parents. Multiply the answer you get by 100 to find out what percentage of the students' parents wear eyeglasses.

SKILLS WARMUP

I f you've ever tried to use a net to catch a fish in an aquarium, you've probably found that the fish was harder to catch than you expected. Light rays bend when they enter water. So, the fish appears to be in a location where it isn't.

You can see this same effect in Figure 18.10. Water bends the light from the straws. As a result, the straws appear to be broken at the place where they meet the surface of the water.

Refraction

You know that the straws in Figure 18.10 aren't really bent. The straws appear to be bent because light rays bend as they enter the water. The bending of light rays is called *refraction*.

Light usually travels in straight lines and at a constant speed. However, when light passes from one medium to another medium with a different density, the speed and the direction of light change. Use Figure 18.10 to see what happens when light passes from air to water. The light slows down and bends, or refracts. The light changes direction again when it passes from the water to the air. As a result, the straw appears to be in different positions above and below the water's surface. How else is the appearance of the straws different?

If you wear eyeglasses, you're probably familiar with refraction. The density of the glass is greater than the density of air. Eyeglasses bend the light entering your eye. The light from an object refracts and focuses correctly on your retina. How do you think a hand lens affects light? ①

Figure 18.10 ▲
Light rays bend when they pass from air into water. Bending light rays make these straws appear to be bent.

MOTIVATE

Skills WarmUp

To help students determine the percentage of students' parents who wear glasses, have them do the Skills WarmUp.
Answer The answers will vary. Data collection can be done as a whole-class activity, but students can calculate individually the percentage of parents who wear glasses.

Misconceptions

Students may think that all lenses produce an image that is larger than the original object. Explain to them that lenses can also be used to reduce images. Ask if students have ever looked through the wrong end of binoculars or a telescope, and have them describe what they saw.

Answer to In-Text Question

① It bends light and changes the size of an image.

Directed Inquiry

After students study the text and Figures 18.11 and 18.12, discuss the following:

▶ Describe a lens. (A transparent material that refracts light passing through it)

▶ What determines the image of a convex lens? (Distance between the object and the lens)

Class Activity

Have students work in pairs and use a convex lens to examine the photograph on page 432. Have them move the lens closer to, and farther from, the photograph. Be sure students see and identify both a smaller and a larger real image. Discuss why the images are different sizes.

Critical Thinking

Reason and Conclude Ask students to explain why an image would look very large through a thick convex lens. (Light is refracted at a more acute angle.)

Answers to In-Text Questions

① It's thicker in the center than the edges, and light rays that pass through bend toward the thickest part.

② The flowers appear upside-down and larger because they are between one and two focal lengths from the convex lens.

The Living Textbook: Physical Science Sides 1-4

Chapter 13   Frame 02039
Concave and Convex Lenses
(24 Frames)
Search: Step:

Integrating the Sciences

Biology The eye sends images to the brain that are inverted from the actual object. The brain interprets the images upright. If a person wore lenses that inverted images before they reached the eye, the world would appear upside down—but only temporarily. After several days, the brain would adapt to the new condition and interpret the images as upright. Ask students to suggest why this ability to adapt is useful to humans.

Lenses

Figure 18.11 ▲
How is the drop of water on the leaf similar to the convex lens in the diagram? ①

An optical **lens** is a transparent material that refracts light passing through it. Lenses may have one or more curved surfaces. Most lenses are made of glass or plastic. Eyeglasses, cameras, microscopes, and telescopes all use lenses.

Recall that mirrors reflect light rays. Lenses differ from mirrors because they transmit light. Lenses allow light to pass through rather than reflecting it. There are two types of lenses: convex and concave. Each type of lens refracts light differently.

Convex Lenses A convex lens is thicker in the center than at the edges. As parallel light rays pass through a convex lens, the rays bend toward the thickest part, or center, of the lens. The point at which the light rays come together, or converge, is called the point of focus. The distance from a lens to its point of focus is called *focal length*. The diagram in Figure 18.12 shows an image that is one focal length from the object.

The image a convex lens forms is determined by distance of the object from the lens. An object that is between one and two focal lengths from the lens forms a real image. The image is enlarged and upside-down as shown in Figure 18.12. The convex lens in a microscope or slide projector forms this type of image.

An object more than two focal lengths from a convex lens also forms a real image. It is an upside-down image that is smaller than the object. The lens of a camera and the lens in your eye form this kind of image.

Figure 18.12 ▶
Why do the flowers in the diagram appear upside down and larger in this ray diagram? ②

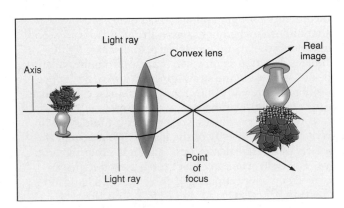

Cooperative Learning

Have students work in cooperative groups of three to study the effects of various lenses. Give each group an assortment of concave and convex lenses. Allow each student an opportunity to look at a photograph or object through each of the different lenses. Then have one student look through a lens and describe the image. Have the other two students identify the lens being used. Each member of the group should have a turn describing an image. Ask students to work together to make a diagram similar to Figure 18.12 and Figure18.14 for each lens and image. Have students add the diagrams to their portfolios.

A convex lens forms a virtual image if an object is placed between the lens and its focal point. The virtual image is right-side up and enlarged. The image you see in a magnifying glass is a virtual image.

Concave Lenses A lens that is thinner at the center than it is at the edges is a concave lens. Parallel light rays passing through a concave lens bend toward the thickest part of the lens. Instead of coming together at a point of focus, light rays passing through a concave lens spread apart, or diverge. The point of focus is behind the image. Find the point of focus in the diagram in Figure 18.14.

Notice what happens to the light rays as they pass through a concave lens in the diagram. The light rays spread out, or diverge, behind the lens. How is this different from the light rays passing through a convex lens?

Concave lenses form images that are right side up and smaller than the object. An image observed through a concave lens is virtual. Explain why a concave lens forms a virtual image. ④

Recall that for a nearsighted person, light rays from distant objects converge in front of the retina instead of on it. A concave lens in front of the eye makes the light rays diverge. The natural lens of the eye, which is convex, can then converge the light rays correctly on the retina.

Concave lenses are used in some kinds of optical equipment. Together with convex lenses, concave lenses are used to focus telescopes. Concave lenses are also used in optical targets.

Figure 18.13 ▲
Is more or less area of the stamp visible in the concave lense? Explain ③

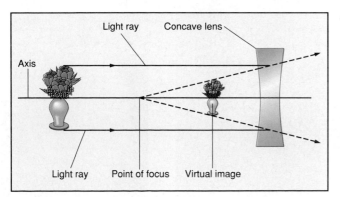

◀ **Figure 18.14**
Which image of the flowers would you see if you were looking through the concave lens from the right? ⑤

Figure labels: Light ray, Concave lens, Axis, Light ray, Point of focus, Virtual image

Chapter 18   Using Light   **447**

Directed Inquiry

Have students study Figure 18.14. Ask the following questions:

▶ What kind of image does a concave lens form? What does it look like? (Virtual; right-side up and smaller than the object)

▶ Where is the point of focus? (Between the image and the object)

▶ What happens to the light rays as they pass through the concave lens? (They diverge behind the lens.)

Skills Development

Predict List the following items on the chalkboard. Have students tell which type of lens the item uses, if the image is smaller or larger than the original, and if it is a real or virtual image. Have students explain their choices, and use references to check their predictions. Slide projector (Convex/larger and real image); camera (Convex/smaller and real image); eye (Convex/smaller and real image); land telescope (Concave and convex/smaller, then larger image); microscope (Convex/larger image); eyeglasses (Concave or convex/converge or diverge light rays so they focus on the retina; magnifying glass (Convex/larger image)

Answers to In-Text Questions

③ **More area**

④ **Because the image does not contain real light rays so it can be seen but not projected onto a screen**

⑤ **A smaller, virtual image**

**The Living Textbook:
Physical Science Sides 1-4**

Chapter 13   Frame 02107
Concave Lens Correction (1 Frame)
Search:

447

TEACH ▪ *Continued*

Portfolio

Have students work in groups of four to make diagrams that show how lenses are used in eyeglasses or contact lenses to correct nearsightedness and far-sightedness. Remind them that their diagrams should show and label the types of lenses used, and how they change focal points.

Research

Have students investigate prices of glasses and contact lenses. Assign each student a vision problem (nearsightedness, farsightedness, or astigmatism), and have them determine the price of glasses or contact lenses for one year. Then have them prepare a list of pros and cons for glasses and for contact lenses.

Answer to In-Text Question

① (Left to right) trifocal lens, bifocal lens, single vision lens

Answer to Link

The Hubble telescope performed poorly due to flaws in its optical system. It was repaired by fitting it with corrective lenses. In a similar way, we "repair" people who have flaws in their optical systems.

Social Studies Connection

The earliest eyeglasses were made of gemstones. Eyeglasses have been used in both Europe and China since at least the thirteenth century. Historians disagree over whether they were invented in China and carried to Europe, or the other way around. Either way, the travels of Marco Polo in the 13th century played a role in the exchange.

STS Connection

Contact lenses are fitted by a process of mapping the contour of the cornea with an ophtalmometer, an instrument that measures the accuracy of the image reflected from the cornea. For this reason, most contact lenses don't correct astigmatism, which is an abnormality in the cornea's shape. Glass lenses that hold an irregular shape are used to "smooth out" the shape of the cornea.

Astronomy
LINK

Obtain a kaleidoscope.

1. Ask a classmate who wears glasses to remove her glasses, look through the kaleidoscope, and tell what she sees.

2. Now ask the student to replace her glasses and look through the kaleidoscope. What are the differences?

The repairs made to the Hubble Telescope included the placement of corrective lenses. Research this topic and write a paragraph comparing glasses with the lenses placed on the Hubble.

ACTIVITY

Science and Technology
Correcting Your Vision

About 50% of the population of the United States wears corrective lenses. Advances in technology have made it possible for corrective lenses to correct many different vision problems. Prescription eyeglasses or contact lenses correct common vision problems, such as near-sightedness, farsightedness, and astigmatism.

A bifocal lens has one corrective lens on the top half and another on the bottom half. The top half corrects distance vision and the bottom half corrects close vision. Before bifocals were developed, to a farsighted person wearing a pair of glasses to see close-up objects, distant objects were blurred.

With bifocals, a person doesn't need to switch eyeglasses to see both far and near. Scientists have also developed trifocal lenses. With three different lenses, a person can see distant, middle-range, and close-up objects clearly without switching glasses.

Contact lenses replaced eyeglasses for many people. Hard contact lenses, made of glass or plastic, float on a thin layer of tears on the cornea. They were developed in the 1950s.

Soft contact lenses were developed in the 1970s. Soft contacts are more comfortable to wear because they absorb moisture and contain water. Because they are more likely to cause infection, most soft contacts must be cleaned and sterilized daily.

Figure 18.15
Use what you learned to identify the type of lens in each photo. ▼ ①

Integrating the Sciences

Medicine Old age, disease, side effects from prescription medicines, and genetic disposition can produce cataracts. As a cataract develops, the lens becomes opaque. The clouded lens can be removed surgically and replaced with a plastic lens that is permanently implanted. Cataract surgery is usually done on an outpatient basis. Have students find out more about cataract replacement.

Career Corner Optician

Who Makes and Fits Your Glasses?

Suppose you have a prescription for new eyeglasses or contact lenses. You can purchase your new glasses or contact lenses from an optician. An optician makes the glasses or contact lenses you need according to your eyeglass prescription.

The optician will also measure and record the distance between the center of one pupil to the center of the other pupil. This distance is important to make sure your new lenses form a sharp, clear image. She can help you to select eyeglass frames that fit you well and look good on you.

The optician will order lenses that match your prescription. She cuts the lenses to fit your frames. Once your eyeglasses are made, the optician adjusts them to make sure your glasses fit properly.

To work as an optician requires good math skills and the ability to make accurate measurements. You should have an interest in both physical and life sciences. You should also enjoy working with people.

In some states, high-school graduates may receive on-the-

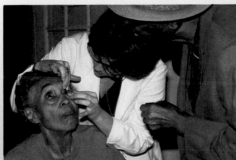

job training as opticians. Others receive formal training in a trade school. Many states require candidates to take a state board exam to obtain a medical assurance certificate before they can practice as an optician.

Extended-wear lenses and disposable contacts are special soft contacts that can be worn for a week without cleaning. A person can wear disposable contacts for a week, throw them away, and replace them with another pair. Some special soft contact lenses change the color of the wearer's iris. Another type can treat diseases by slowly releasing medicine into the eye.

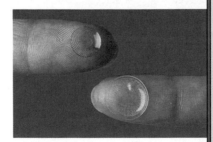

Figure 18.16 ▲
The contact lens at the top is a hard lens. The contact lens at the bottom is a soft lens. Describe how they are different. ②

Check and Explain

1. How do convex and concave lenses affect incoming parallel light rays?

2. Describe two uses for convex and concave lenses.

3. **Infer** Why does light refract when it passes through a lens?

4. **Make a Model** Draw ray diagrams that show how an image formed by a convex lens changes as focal length changes.

Career Corner

Class Activity Collect newspapers or magazines with job listings and bring them to class. Have students clip job listings for different kinds of eye-care professionals. List the job titles on the bulletin board, and compare the experience and training needed for each. Have students discuss the supply and demand for eye-care professionals.

EVALUATE

WrapUp

Portfolio Have students use parallel rays to represent sunlight. Have them make a diagram to show how a convex lens can be used to focus light from the sun onto one spot to make intense light. Have them draw a second diagram to show what happens to light from the sun as it passes through a concave lens. Students can add the diagrams to their portfolios.

Use Review Worksheet 18.4.

Check and Explain

1. Convex rays converge incoming rays at a point behind the lens; a concave lens diverges incoming rays as though they started from a point in front of the lens.

2. Convex: microscope, slide projector; concave: telescope, correction for nearsightedness

3. The light changes speed as it travels from the air into the lens and from the lens out into the air.

4. Check students' diagrams for accuracy.

Answer to In-Text Question

② Hard contact lenses are thicker and less flexible than soft contact lenses, which are pliable and larger.

ACTIVITY 18

Time 40 minutes   **Group** pairs

Materials

15 hand lenses

15 metric rulers

15 plain white sheets of paper

Analysis

1. If students have identical hand lenses, the image distance should be similar for each group.

2. The image formed is smaller than the object and is inverted. Distance will vary. Actual distance depends on the hand lens being used.

Conclusion

Both the image formed with the hand lens and the image formed on the retina of the eye are real images. They are the same kind of image because the lens of the eye, like the hand lens, is a convex lens.

Prelab Discussion

Have students read the entire activity. Before beginning, discuss the following:

▶ Discuss where the light rays that form the image come from.

▶ Review the differences between a real image and a virtual image.

▶ Discuss the fact that the object distance is as far as the eye can see.

Activity 18 *Is a convex hand lens like an eye?*

Skills Observe; Predict; Measure

Task 1 Prelab Prep

Collect the following items: paper, hand lens, and a metric ruler.

Task 2 Data Record

1. Prepare a ray diagram similar to the one below to record your observations. Look through the window. Choose one object, such as a tree, on which to focus your lens.

2. Draw a side view of a convex lens in the center of a sheet of paper. To the right of the lens, draw a horizontal line to the center of the lens. Choose a spot along the line that represents the focus, and write an *F* at that spot.

3. To the left of the diagram, at a distance greater from the lens than the focus is on the right, draw the object on which you have chosen to focus the lens.

Task 3 Procedure

1. On a bright or sunny day, darken all the windows in a room except for one.

2. Hold the hand lens about 1.5 m from the window at the same level as the object outside.

3. Hold up the piece of paper on the opposite side of the lens from the window. Line the paper up with the object. Predict where a focused image of the object will appear on the paper and what the image will look like.

4. Move the paper back and forth until an image of the object appears on the paper. Measure the distance between the lens and the paper.

5. Complete your ray diagram by drawing the image you observed in the proper place.

Task 4 Analysis

1. How far from the lens did the image appear? How close was your prediction?

2. Describe the image that formed on the paper. Explain why it appeared as it did.

Task 5 Conclusion

Explain how the image you formed with the convex lens is like an image formed on the retina of the eye.

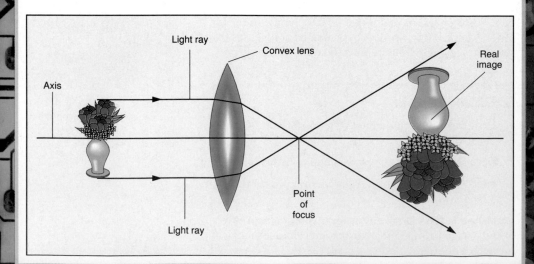

Themes in Science

Scale and Structure The predictable interactions of light and lenses produce images that differ in scale from the original object yet preserve the object's structure. Ask students to describe how a camera can produce images that are smaller or larger than the original object.

Section Objectives
For a list of section objectives, see the Student Edition page.

Skills Objectives
Students should be able to:

Classify instruments and devices that use mirrors and/or lenses.

Infer uses of lasers.

Make a Model of a camera.

Vocabulary
laser, hologram, optical fiber

18.5 Light Technology

Objectives

▶ **Explain** how cameras, telescopes, and microscopes work.

▶ **Compare** the technology in lasers, holography, and fiber optics.

▶ **Infer** about new ways to use lasers.

▶ **Make a model** to explain how a camera forms an image on film.

▼ ACTIVITY

Classifying

Lenses and Mirrors

Make three columns on a sheet of paper with the headings *mirrors, lenses,* and *mirrors and lenses.* Below each heading, list as many objects or devices as you can think of that contain each of these optical devices. Compare your list to those of two of your classmates.

SKILLS WARMUP

Y ou know that light allows you to see. Did you know that light can also help you to hear? It sounds unbelievable, but the voices you hear on the telephone actually travel as light.

New technology makes it possible to change the sound energy of a human voice into light signals. These light signals are carried through glass fibers over very long distances to all parts of the country. The light signals are changed back into sound before they reach your telephone. As a result, you are able to pick up the telephone and talk to people anywhere. This amazing technology is part of the science of fiber optics.

Using Mirrors and Lenses

You know that mirrors reflect and that lenses refract, or bend, light. The ability of mirrors and lenses to focus light and form images makes them very useful. For example, people use mirrors to check their appearance, put on makeup, shave, or to check traffic when driving a car. Lenses are used in eyeglasses and optical instruments.

Cameras, telescopes, and microscopes are optical instruments that have many uses. Each of these instruments uses mirrors or lenses, or both. Surgeons can now use light instead of a scalpel to perform delicate surgeries. Artists use light to create three-dimensional images on a two-dimensional surface. As technology develops, scientists and engineers continue to find new and better ways to make light work for you. More powerful cameras, telescopes, and microscopes are being developed.

Figure 18.17 ▲
The microscope's mirror reflects light through the object being viewed. The lenses magnify the object.

Skills WarmUp

To help students understand the many uses of light technology, have them do the Skills WarmUp.

Answer Answers may vary. For example, mirrors: car mirrors, dental mirrors, periscopes, lasers; lenses: eyeglasses, binoculars, cameras, video cameras; mirrors and lenses: astronomers' telescopes, light microscopes.

Prior Knowledge

To gauge how much students know about light technology ask the following questions:

▶ What instruments, other than lenses and mirrors, use light technology?

▶ What is the difference between white light and laser light?

▶ Why does a hologram look different from different angles?

TEACH

Explore Visually

Have students study Figure 18.18, then ask the following questions:

▶ How is the camera's aperture like the pupil in your eye? (They're both openings that change in area to control how much light enters the camera or the eye.)

▶ What kind of lens does a camera use? (convex)

▶ How does the photographic film record the image? (Light striking the film reacts with the film's chemicals to record the image.)

▶ Which part of your eye is like the camera shutter? Why? (The eyelid; it opens and closes to let in light.)

Skills Development

Communicate Have students make a flowchart that outlines the details of how light travels through a camera. (Charts may vary. They should include: shutter opens, light enters through lens, passes through aperture, strikes film, reacts with chemicals to record image.)

Answer to In-Text Question

① You focus a camera by changing the distance between the lens and the film; your eye focuses by changing the shape of the lens.

The Living Textbook:
Physical Science Sides 1-4

Chapter 13   Frame 02162
Cameras (15 Frames)
Search: Step:

452

Social Studies Connection

Have students look up the contributions to photography of Nicephore Niépce, Louis Daguerre, Fox Talbot, George Eastman, James Clerk Maxwell, and Thomas Edison. (Niépce—first permanent photo, Daguerre—improved permanent photo with shorter exposure time, Talbot—paper negative, Eastman—Kodak camera and celluloid film, Maxwell—color photograph, and Edison—movie camera.)
Use Integrating Worksheet 18.5a.

STS Connection

Advances in photomicrography and stop-action allow us to see in detail objects invisible to the unaided eye. The motion of a bullet in flight, or a splash of water, can be frozen in time. Have students identify the objects in images made with new technologies, such as those in *The Secret House* or *The Secret Garden,* both by David Bodanis.

Cameras You know that a camera uses light and lenses to record images on film. In many ways, a camera is like your eye. Both have structures that control the amount of light that enters. They each have a convex lens that produces a real and upside-down image.

Look at Figure 18.18. Notice how a camera and an eye are different. Instead of forming an image on the retina, a camera records an image on film that is sensitive to light. The image on the film is then reproduced on paper as a photograph. What are some other ways a camera and an eye are different? ①

Figure 18.18
How a Camera Works ▼

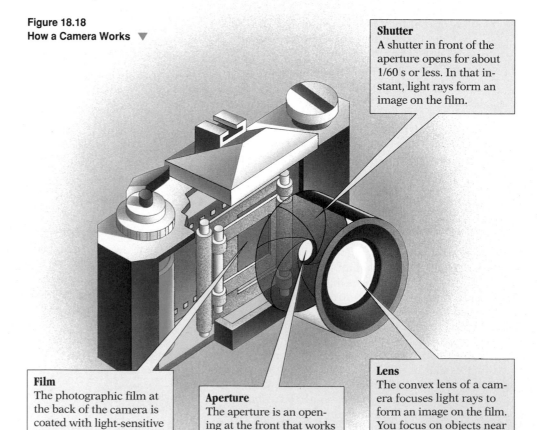

Shutter
A shutter in front of the aperture opens for about 1/60 s or less. In that instant, light rays form an image on the film.

Film
The photographic film at the back of the camera is coated with light-sensitive chemicals. When light strikes the film, it reacts with the chemicals.

Aperture
The aperture is an opening at the front that works like the pupil of the eye. The size of the opening controls how much light enters the camera.

Lens
The convex lens of a camera focuses light rays to form an image on the film. You focus on objects near or far by moving the lens closer to or farther from the film.

Telescopes If you have ever looked at the stars away from city lights, you probably noticed that the stars were much brighter. Even under ideal conditions, objects in outer space are too far away to study in detail without using a telescope. Two kinds of telescopes are used to see distant objects, a refracting telescope and a reflecting telescope.

A simple refracting telescope is shown on the left in Figure 18.19. It is used to see objects on land. It has two lenses: an objective lens and an eyepiece lens. An image from the objective lens is focused and enlarged by the eyepiece lens. The eyepiece lens is positioned within one focal length of the image made by the objective lens. What kind of image is formed by the eyepiece lens? ②

A reflecting telescope, which is used mostly by astronomers, is shown on the right in Figure 18.19. Light rays entering the telescope are reflected onto mirrors. The mirrors form a real image within one focal length of the eyepiece lens. The eyepiece lens forms the virtual image you see when you look into a telescope. Why do you think astronomers use a reflecting telescope? ③

Figure 18.19
Refracting and Reflecting Telescopes ▼

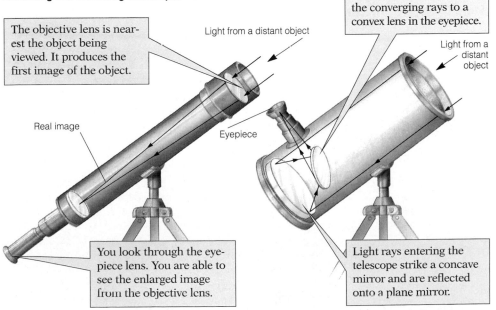

The objective lens is nearest the object being viewed. It produces the first image of the object.

Light from a distant object

Real image

Eyepiece

You look through the eyepiece lens. You are able to see the enlarged image from the objective lens.

The plane mirror directs the converging rays to a convex lens in the eyepiece.

Light from a distant object

Light rays entering the telescope strike a concave mirror and are reflected onto a plane mirror.

TEACH ▪ *Continued*

Discuss

Have students read the text and ask the following questions:

▶ What kind of image is formed by the objective lens? (Enlarged, real)

▶ How are the objective and the eyepiece alike? (They're both convex lenses.)

Decision Making

If you have classroom sets of *One-Minute Readings*, have students read Issue 52 "Scattering of Light: Light Pollution" on page 89. Discuss the questions.

Consider This

Classify Have students make a list of all the expenses involved with keeping office lights on 24 hours a day. (Answers will vary, but lists should include: electricity cost/hour, hours/day and days/week building is occupied; number of light bulbs, hours/light bulb, cost/light bulb, and cost of person to replace bulbs.) Have students list the advantages of leaving on lights.

Think About It Answers will vary. Students' opinions may include safety, conserving resources, and environment.

Write About It Be sure students give reasons for their positions.

 The Living Textbook: Physical Science Side 3

Chapter 32   Frame 19349
Kitt Peak Telescope (Movie)
Search: Play:

Integrating the Sciences

Environmental Science The many lights around populated areas contribute light pollution. The lights from cities are even visible to the astronauts in the Space Shuttle. People who live in big cities are often amazed at the number of stars visible in the night sky when they visit the desert or the mountains. Have students discuss what might happen as cities spread to the remote areas where astronomical telescopes are located.

Math Connection

The magnifying power of a microscope is determined by multiplying the magnification of the objective lens by the magnification of the eyepiece lens. Ask students to write this information in an equation using variables, and then have them compute the magnification of a microscope with an eyepiece that magnifies 8 times and an objective that magnifies 16 times. ($M_m = M_o \times M_e$; 128) Explain the subscripts and why they are used.

Light Microscopes Have you used a microscope to study a very small object? Actually, a hand lens is a microscope. It is a simple microscope because it has only one lens. A microscope with two or more lenses is called a compound microscope. It is called a light microscope because light is needed to view very small objects.

Light enters a compound microscope from a light source, which may be an electric light bulb. Some microscopes have mirrors that reflect light from a window. Light travels from its source, through the object being viewed, and into the objective lens. The objective lens is a convex lens which forms an enlarged, real image.

The eyepiece lens of a microscope is also a convex lens. The eyepiece lens further magnifies the image formed by the objective lens. The eyepiece lens forms the virtual image you see when you look into the microscope. The total magnification of the virtual image is the product of the magnification of the objective and the eyepiece.

Consider This

Should Office Buildings Leave Lights On at Night?

To conserve electricity, most people turn off unneeded lights in their homes. However, this is not done in many stores and office buildings. It is more common to keep lights on 24 hours a day.

One reason people who manage stores and offices leave the lights on at night is security. Lights inside a building make it possible to see into the building from the outside. This practice of keeping the lights on helps to prevent crime. The lights also reduce the risk of injury for anyone working at night in the building.

Leaving lights on can save money. Light bulbs undergo less wear and last longer when they are not turned on and off frequently. The cost of the electricity needed to keep the bulbs on at night is less than the cost of replacing burned-out bulbs.

Buildings that use large amounts of electricity pay for electricity at a lower rate than individuals do. The electricity to keep lights on in a large building is cheaper than replacing the bulbs more often. The additional electricity used to keep the lights on at night increases the use of fossil fuels, which can't be replaced.

Greater usage of electricity also increases the amount of pollution caused by burning fossil fuels.

Think About It Are there greater benefits or drawbacks to keeping lights on in large buildings day and night? Which is more important, security and saving money now or preserving resources for the future?

Write About It Write a paper stating your position on leaving office lights on all day and night. Include your reasons for choosing your position.

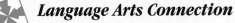

Integrating the Sciences

Medicine A team of Texas researchers has developed a method of treating stored blood with a light-absorbing dye and then exposing the blood to a low-intensity laser beam. They found that the laser kills any viruses in the blood, such as those associated with measles, herpes simplex type 1, and acquired immune deficiency syndrome. Have students use news reports and references to make a list of the medical uses for lasers.

Language Arts Connection

Words such as *laser, sonar,* and *radar* are acronyms. Have students use a dictionary to find the meaning of *acronym,* as well as the meanings for these specific three given. Invite students to add any other acronyms they are familiar with to the list. (A word formed by the initial letter(s) of a compound term; Light Amplification by Stimulated Emission of Radiation, SOund NAvigation & Ranging, RAdio Detection And Ranging)

Explore Visually

Have students study the text and Figure 18.20. Ask the following questions:

▶ How would you describe the light from a laser? (One wavelength, all the waves are moving in one direction, and the crests and troughs are in line)

▶ How are the light waves in a laser amplified? (Photons of light reflect off mirrors at each end of the rod; there is a chain reaction and more atoms are involved, releasing more photons.)

▶ What provides energy in the laser? (The flashtube)

▶ What is a laser beam? (Photons that have the same frequency, wavelength, and color and coherence)

▶ What are the parts of a ruby crystal laser? (Flashtube, mirrors, and ruby crystal rod)

Critical Thinking

Reason and Conclude Ask, Does laser technology rely on light acting like a particle or acting like a wave? (Both—photons act like particles; the light is all one color, moves in one direction, and crests and troughs reinforce each other.)

Integrated Learning

Use Integrating Worksheet 18.5b.

Lasers

You know that white light spreads out equally in all directions as it travels. A beam of light that doesn't spread out as it travels can be produced by a **laser**. The word *laser* is an acronym for **l**ight **a**mplification by **s**timulated **e**missions of **r**adiation.

Laser light is unique. In addition to traveling in one direction, it is generally of one wavelength, and it is coherent. Light is coherent when all its waves move in the same direction and the crests and troughs of the light waves match up.

A laser is made of a flashtube, mirrors, and a rod that is usually made of ruby crystals. The rod is closed off at each end with a mirror. Look at Figure 18.20 to see how a laser works.

Light from the coiled tube focuses on the rod to excite the electrons in it. The electrons give off photons. These photons travel in the same direction and have the same wavelength. The photons reflect off the mirrors at each end of the rod. They strike other atoms and set off a chain reaction that releases more photons. The laser increases, or amplifies, the strength of the light waves. Some amplified light leaves the laser as a beam of laser light.

Surveyors use lasers to measure land distances. In industry, lasers are used to cut through metals. Surgeons use the cutting power of lasers to replace the scalpel.

The Living Textbook:
Physical Science Sides 1-4

Chapter 13   Frame 02243
Lasers (10 Frame)
Search: Step:

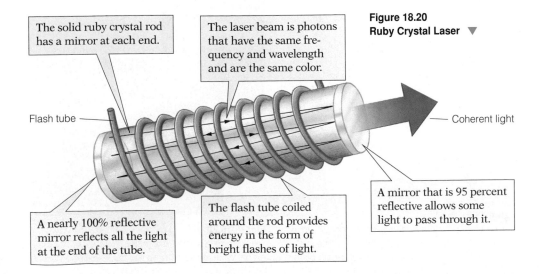

The solid ruby crystal rod has a mirror at each end.

The laser beam is photons that have the same frequency and wavelength and are the same color.

Flash tube

Coherent light

A nearly 100% reflective mirror reflects all the light at the end of the tube.

The flash tube coiled around the rod provides energy in the form of bright flashes of light.

A mirror that is 95 percent reflective allows some light to pass through it.

Figure 18.20
Ruby Crystal Laser ▼

455

TEACH ▪ *Continued*

Explore Visually

Have students study how a hologram is made and look at Figures 18.21 and 18.22. Ask the following questions:

▶ What kind of wave interaction is used to make a hologram? (Interference pattern)

▶ Describe the path the reference beam takes from the laser to the photographic plate. (Reference beam leaves laser, passes through convex lens, and travels to plate)

▶ Is the path of the object beam to the plate more or less direct than the reference beam? Explain. (Less direct; beam is split, is reflected from mirror, passes through convex lens, reflects from object, and travels to plate.)

▶ What happens at the photographic plate that produces the hologram? (Waves from the reference and object beam interact to form the interference pattern on the plate.)

Discuss

Explain that when light strikes the completed hologram, the light diffracts, producing two images, a virtual and a real image. The virtual image is visible *through* the hologram, like seeing something through a window. The real image is in front of the hologram, but is often not seen clearly since the hologram is flat. Have students list the characteristics of light waves that are used to produce and see a hologram. (Reflection, refraction, and interference to make the hologram; refraction to view it.)

Answer to In-Text Question

① **Answers may vary. Examples: educational tools, trading card, credit cards, special effects, and even currency**

Art Connection

A hologram's three-dimensional nature provides opportunities for artistic interpretation, and a growing number of artists work with holograms. In addition, technology has been developed for printing holograms on a variety of surfaces. Invite students to bring in examples of holograms on items such as paper weights, trading cards, or jewelry.

STS Connection

Combat pilots need to look at both the instrument panel and out the window at the target. The aircraft travels so fast that, in the time it takes a pilot to look from a target, to the controls, and back, the plane may have flown past the target. Some aircraft now have a "Heads-up" display that projects a three-dimensional holographic image of the target at eye level. This eliminates the need for a pilot to look back and forth.

Holography

Have you ever seen an exhibit or a movie in which a three-dimensional figure seemed to appear from nowhere? The effect may seem like magic, but it is more likely that the image is a product of holography. Holography is a technology that uses lasers to make the three-dimensional image called a **hologram**.

Hologram Uses Holograms have many applications. They are now used as special effects in movies and plays. Holograms may someday be used to produce three-dimensional television.

Because they are difficult to duplicate, holograms are used as security devices. For example, some credit-card companies now put holograms on their credit cards. The holograms help to prevent the forgery of credit cards.

Holograms can also be used as educational tools. For example, holograms can be used to display a three-dimensional image of internal body organs. Medical students can use the images as a model to study the human body.

Hologram Technology Now that you know about lasers, you can learn how a hologram is formed. Refer to Figure 18.21 as you read about the process for making a hologram.

1. A laser beam is split into two beams. One beam, called the reference beam, is focused on a photographic plate. The other beam is focused on an object and is reflected onto the photographic plate. An interference pattern forms where the reference beam and the reflected light meet.

2. The photographic plate is developed, but it doesn't appear any different from the way it did before developing. However, chemicals in the developing fluid have etched a pattern on the plate.

3. A laser beam aimed at the developed plate produces a three-dimensional image of the object. The image produced is a hologram, like the ones in Figure 18.22.

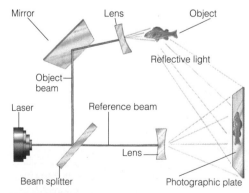

Figure 18.21 ▲
An interference pattern is formed where the reference beam meets light reflected from the fish. A holographic image is etched on the photographic plate.

Figure 18.22 ▲
A hologram is a three-dimensional version of a photograph. What are some ways you could use holograms? ①

Integrating the Sciences

Medicine Students may have heard of arthroscopic surgery, often used to examine and repair injured joints. The arthroscope is a type of endoscope. Explain to students that an endoscope is a tubular instrument that uses optical fibers. The instrument contains fibers that carry light down the tube and under the skin. Other fibers carry images back to an eyepiece. Other tiny tubes provide water and a vacuum to clear the visual pathway. The instrument is used to examine or to operate on the inside of cavities or hollow organs of the body, such as the lungs, the ear, and female reproductive structures. An endoscope can also be equipped with a laser that can vaporize, coagulate, or cut structures with more flexibility than a knife. Have students find out other uses for endoscopes. (Example: biopsies)

Fiber Optics

Through the technology of fiber optics, a doctor can now look at organs inside your body without performing surgery. Fiber optics involves the transmission of light signals through thin, flexible, transparent fibers made of glass or plastic. Each fiber is called an **optical fiber**.

Internal Reflection How do optical fibers work? Look at Figure 18.23. Think of an optical fiber as a "light pipe." Imagine that you aimed a flashlight into one end of a straight piece of pipe. What would happen to the light? It would pass through the pipe and come out the other end.

What do you think would happen to the light if the pipe were bent instead of straight? If the inside of the pipe is highly reflective, the light reflects off the inner walls of the pipe. The reflection of light within the pipe is called *internal reflection*.

Because of internal reflection, light can be piped from one location to another within glass or plastic fibers. Light is aimed inside one end of the fiber. When the light reaches a bend in the transparent fiber, it doesn't pass through the fiber. Instead it bounces off the walls of the fiber, as shown in Figure 18.23. The light travels through the fiber, reflecting off the walls within the fiber, until it reaches the end.

Uses of Fiber Optics When two sets of optical fibers are placed side by side, light signals sent through one set can be returned along the other set. This idea is used in a fiberscope. Doctors use fiberscopes to view organs inside the body. Mechanics can also use fiberscopes to look at the inside of a machine.

In some places, optical fibers are used for telephone communication instead of wires. The fibers are more efficient because a single fiber can carry as much information as a large bundle of wires.

Figure 18.23 ▲
Light rays travel in the confined space of an optical fiber in much the same way as light waves travel through a pipe.

Light rays

Reflective pipe

Light source

Figure 18.24 ▲
Each of the thin optical fibers is small enough to fit through the eye of a needle. Why is the size of the fiber important? ②

Make a Model Have students make a drawing that shows how light rays travel around a bend or corner in an optical fiber. (Drawings should show how light enters fiber, bounces off walls, and reaches the end.)

Infer Remind students that the fibers used in fiber optics are flexible and transparent. Ask, What other property or characteristic must the fibers have? (They have to be reflective on the inside.)

Portfolio

Have students create a list and collect photographs, articles, advertisements, and diagrams that illustrate new uses of fiber optics. Have them add these examples to their portfolios.

Answer to In-Text Question

② Smaller fibers are more efficient and can be used in smaller spaces.

 The Living Textbook: Physical Science Sides 1-4

Chapter 13   Frame 02253
Fiber Optics (6 Frames)
Search: Step:

TEACH ▪ Continued

TEACH ▪ Continued

Critical Thinking

Decision Making Have students work as a class to list the pros and cons of videophones. Examples might be: security problems (cons) and enhanced communication quality (pros).

EVALUATE

WrapUp

Review Have students work in small groups. Each group should prepare a card that has a written description of a use of light technology, such as "reproducing a three-dimensional image of the White House." Have groups exchange cards and ask students to prepare a diagram or a written explanation of how the technology works.

Use Review Worksheet 18.5.

Check and Explain

1. Cameras: lens produces reduced image on film; telescopes: mirrors or lens collects and focuses light, lens produces enlarged image; microscope: mirror collects light, lenses produce enlarged image.

2. All three technologies depend on the wave characteristics of light.

3. They produce a small, accurate cutting point, reducing damage to surrounding tissue.

4. Chart should include the following steps: shutter opens, light enters through lens then passes through aperture, light strikes film, reacts with chemicals to record image.

Answer to In-Text Question

① Answers will vary. Examples: modeling agencies, law enforcement agencies, retail sales businesses

458

Cooperative Learning

Have students work in cooperative groups of four to make a model of one of the optical instruments discussed in this section. One student might make or collect drawings of how the instrument works. Another might collect materials such as cardboard tubes, aluminum foil for mirrors, plastic wrap for lenses, and yarn or string for light waves. A third student might collect pictures or diagrams showing how the instrument is used, and examples of the instrument's uses. The fourth could explain the model to the rest of the class. Allow students time to stage a light show, at which they present and explain their models.

Science and Society
New Communication Age

Optical fibers are changing the way people communicate. Optical fibers are replacing old telephone wires worldwide. Light sent through the fibers does the same job as electric signals sent through wires. However, optical fibers do the job more efficiently.

Today optical fibers make it possible for people to use their computers for shopping and banking. People can use their phone to "visit" libraries across the country. When they find information they want, they can have the information sent over fiber-optic phone lines to their home computer. They then use their computer to print out the information.

In the future, other kinds of communication will be carried through optical fibers. For example, optical fibers will be used to deliver television signals to your home. Programs from around the world will be available to you.

Scientists have also developed a fiber-optics communication system that combines video and computer technologies. Using this technology, a person working at a computer can speak with a person in another city on the telephone about information appearing on both computer screens. At the same time, these people can see each other's faces in a window on their computers. This device, called a videophone, is shown in Figure 18.25. Some day this same kind of conferencing could allow people in three or four different places to have a "face to face" conversation by videophone.

Figure 18.25 ▲
The woman is able to see and be seen by the person she's talking to. What kinds of businesses would benefit from videophones?

Check and Explain

1. Describe the role of the lenses used in cameras, telescopes, and microscopes.

2. How is the technology used in lasers, holography, and fiber optics similar?

3. **Infer** Why are lasers useful as surgical instruments?

4. **Make a Model** Using the figure on page 452 as a guide, create a flowchart that traces the path of light through a camera to form an image on film.

Check Your Vocabulary

1. hologram
2. incandescence
3. concave
4. convex
5. luminous
6. laser
7. virtual image
8. optical fiber
9. fluorescent
10. lens

Write Your Vocabulary

Students' sentences should show that they know the meaning of each word as well as how to use it in a sentence.

Use Vocabulary Worksheet for Chapter 18.

Chapter 18 Review

Concept Summary

18.1 Light Sources
▶ A luminous object makes its own light.
▶ An illuminated object reflects light.
▶ Three types of artificial light are fluorescent, incandescent, and neon light.

18.2 Vision
▶ Light enters your eye through the cornea and the pupil, and is focused by the lens on the retina. The optic nerve carries signals from the retina to the brain.
▶ Nearsightedness and farsightedness result when the lens doesn't focus light rays on the retina.

18.3 Reflection and Mirrors
▶ Light is reflected when it bounces off a surface.
▶ A flat, or plane, mirror forms a virtual image that is right side up and reversed.
▶ A concave mirror bends inward at the center and forms a real image.

▶ A convex mirror curves outward at the center and forms a virtual image.

18.4 Refraction and Lenses
▶ Refraction is the bending of light.
▶ The image formed by a convex lens depends on the object's distance from the lens.
▶ A concave lens forms a virtual, upright image that is smaller than the object.

18.5 Light Technology
▶ Cameras, telescopes, and microscopes are optical instruments that use mirrors, lenses, or both.
▶ A laser produces a beam of coherent light of only one wavelength.
▶ A hologram is a three-dimensional image made with a laser.
▶ Fiber optics are glass or plastic rods that are used to transmit information in the form of light.

Chapter Vocabulary

luminous (p. 433)	virtual image (p. 442)	lens (p. 446)	optical fiber (p. 457)
fluorescent (p. 434)	concave (p. 443)	laser (p. 455)	
incandescent (p. 434)	convex (p. 443)	hologram (p. 456)	

Check Your Vocabulary

Use the vocabulary words above to complete the following sentences correctly.

1. A three-dimensional image produced with laser technology is a(n) _____ .

2. Light produced by heating an object until it glows is _____ .

3. Close-up objects are magnified by a(n) _____ mirror.

4. The kind of mirror that provides a wide angle of view is a(n) _____ mirror.

5. An object producing its own light is _____ .

6. A device that produces an intense beam of coherent light is a(n) _____ .

7. A concave lens produces a(n) _____ .

8. A fiber that transmits light is a(n) _____ .

9. Passing electrons through a phosphor-coated tube produces _____ light.

10. A curved piece of glass is a(n) _____ .

Write Your Vocabulary

Write sentences using the vocabulary words above. Show that you know what each word means.

Check Your Knowledge

1. mirrors and lenses
2. holography
3. incandescent
4. a mirror
5. False; heat
6. False; retina
7. True
8. True
9. True
10. True
11. False; lens

Check Your Understanding

1. a, c, d, g, h are luminous
2. A convex lens bends light toward a point on the side opposite from the image. A concave lens spreads light out.
3. a. The object is farther from the mirror than the focus.
   b. The object is between the mirror and the focus.
4. A light bulb that produces a large amount of heat and uses a larger amount of electricity is less efficient than one that burns cooler and uses less electricity. The neon light is more efficient than the tungsten-halogen light.
5. When light from inside an optical fiber strikes the inside surface of the fiber at a sufficiently large angle of incidence, the light is reflected back into the fiber, where it continues to reflect off the inside surface as it travels the length of the fiber. If internal reflection did not occur, the light would simply exit the fiber without being transmitted from one end to the other.
6. The person is farsighted.

Chapter 18 Review

Check Your Knowledge

Choose the answer that best completes each sentence.

1. A reflecting telescope makes use of (mirrors, lasers, lenses, mirrors and lenses).
2. The technology that uses lasers to produce a three-dimensional image is (fiber optics, holography, bioluminescence, refraction).
3. A tungsten-halogen light bulb produces (incandescent, neon, coherent, fluorescent) light.
4. Of the following, all are luminous objects except (the sun, a campfire, a mirror, a flashlight).

Determine whether each statement is true or false. Write *true* if it is true. If it is false, change the underlined word(s) to make the statement true.

5. Most of the energy from an incandescent light is given off as <u>light</u>.
6. The film in a camera works like the <u>cornea</u> of the eye.
7. Light is <u>coherent</u> when the crests and troughs of the light waves match up and move in the same direction.
8. In a compound telescope or microscope, the lens nearest the object being viewed is the <u>objective</u> lens.
9. Light rays don't actually pass where a <u>virtual</u> image appears to be.
10. Rays that pass through a <u>concave</u> lens spread outward.
11. The part of the eye that focuses light on the retina is the <u>pupil</u>.

Check Your Understanding

Apply the concepts you have learned to answer each question.

1. Which of the following are luminous objects?

   a. stars
   b. plane mirrors
   c. fireflies
   d. sodium-vapor lights
   e. convex mirrors
   f. lenses
   g. neon lights
   h. some fishes

2. How does the way a convex lens bends light differ from the way a concave lens bends light?

3. When using a concave mirror, what is the position of the object in relation to the focal point when:

   a. a real, upside-down image is produced?
   b. a virtual image that is right-side up is produced?

4. What might you infer about the efficiency of the lights described? A neon light produces little heat and uses a small amount of electricity. A tungsten-halogen light uses more electricity than a neon light and produces a large amount of heat.

5. **Mystery Photo** The photograph on page 432 shows a bundle of optical fibers. Describe how fiber optics makes use of internal reflection. What would happen if light rays in an optical fiber weren't reflected internally?

6. **Application** You find a pair of eyeglasses that have convex lenses. Based on the shape of the lenses, what kind of vision does the owner of the glasses have?

Develop Your Skills

1. Student designs will vary. Make sure they choose the correct gas for each color they plan to use.

2. a. 2496 lumens

   b. 40 watt

   c. The fluorescent bulbs all last longer and produce more light than the incandescent bulbs.

   d. circular fluorescent bulb

3. 35 degrees; the angle of reflection equals the angle of incidence for any mirror.

4. The magnified image of a letter will reveal small imperfections and irregularities that cannot be seen by the unaided eye. The rods and cones in the eye limit the ability of the eye to resolve small details.

Make Connections

1. Concept maps will vary. You may wish to have students do the map below. First draw the map on the board, then add a few key terms. Have students draw and complete the map.

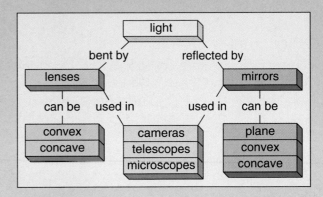

2. a. 3.75 mm

   b. 9 mm

   c. 20 mm

   d. 1.75 mm

3. Student reports will vary. Edison invented, among other things, the microphone, the phonograph, and an incandescent lamp. Using a simple microscope, van Leeuwenhoek was the first to view living cells. Kitt Peak Observatory has the world's largest collection of optical astronomical telescopes, and is used by 300 to 400 astronomers yearly.

4. Student opinions for and against making the switch will vary.

5. Lists will vary. Services include libraries and schools that carry talking books or Optacons; schools for the sight deficient and occupational training programs; peripatologists who assist sight deficient people in using a special cane and finding the best daily routes to travel; offices of U.S. agencies that help sight deficient people, such as the Bureau of Education for the Handicapped, the Office of the Blind Visually Handicapped, and trainers of guide dogs.

Develop Your Skills

Use the skills you have developed to complete each activity.

1. **Interpret Data** Design your own neon sign. Use the information in the table below to indicate which gases you would use to produce the colors you want.

Gas	Color of Light
Helium	Yellow
Krypton	Purple
Mercury vapor	Greenish-blue
Neon	Red

2. **Data Bank** Use the information on page 642 to answer the following questions.

   a. How much light (in lumens) do two 100-watt incandescent light bulbs produce?

   b. Which fluorescent bulb produces about the same amount of light as two 100-watt bulbs?

   c. Compare other incandescent and fluorescent bulbs that have about the same amount of watts. Which type is the most energy-efficient?

   d. Which type of light bulb will last the longest?

3. **Application** An incident ray strikes a plane mirror at a 35-degree angle. What is the angle of reflection? Why?

4. **Observe** Examine any single letter on this page both with and without a hand lens. Make careful drawings of your observations both with and without the lens. Describe any differences you may have observed. How can you explain these differences?

Make Connections

1. **Link the Concepts** Draw a concept map showing how the concepts below link together. Add terms to link, or connect, the concepts.

   light   lenses
   mirrors   convex
   concave   plane
   telescopes   microscopes

2. **Science and Math** How large would objects of the following sizes appear under a microscope at a magnification of 250 times?

   a. 0.015 mm   c. 0.08 mm
   b. 0.036 mm   d. 0.007 mm

3. **Science and Social Studies** Describe the impact one of the following had on society. Use the library for your research.

   Nicholas Copernicus
   Thomas Edison
   Anton van Leeuwenhoek
   Kitt Peak Observatory
   Palomar Observatory

4. **Science and You** Imagine videophones were available at the price of a regular telephone. Would you want to replace your family's phones with videophones? How would using the phone change if all telephones were videophones?

5. **Science and Society** Form a team of four students to find out about services available for sight-deficient people in your community. Make a list of the services available and the organization offering each service. Discuss your list as a group. Which services would you find most important if you were sight deficient? Identify any additional services you think should be available.

About the Literary Work

"Blue Tights" was adapted from the novel *Blue Tights* by Rita Williams-Garcia, copyright 1989 by Rita Williams-Garcia and Bantam Books. Reprinted by permission of Rita Williams-Garcia and Bantam Books.

Description of Change

Detailed passages were edited from a short section of the text for the sake of readability. The dialogue has been kept as true to the original as possible.

Rationale

This vocabulary and syntax are too difficult for the entry-level Limited English Proficiency student. However, the story itself is appropriate for the student level.

Vocabulary

kalimba, contralto, gourd, engrossed, nuptial, ardor

Teaching Strategies

Directed Inquiry

After students finish reading, discuss the story. Relate the story to the science lesson in this unit by discussing the sensations experienced by Joyce during the ceremony. Ask the following questions:

▶ What are some examples of the author's use of sound and light to suggest moods in this story? (In devices such as personification: "...bells ...sang...joyously"; and metaphor: "Joyce heard the drum within her.")

▶ What sources of sound and light helped to create the "stage magic"? (The drumbeat, human cries, the colors reflected from skin and costumes, and the sighs and shouts of the audience)

▶ How do the different amplitudes created by the instruments affect the stage ceremony? (Answers may vary. High amplitude sounds, like those from the congas and drums, create sound waves with more energy that do more work to vibrate eardrums. Perhaps the strongest effect is produced by the dancers' combined foot-striking, which "sent a tremor throughout the stands.")

Critical Thinking

Reason and Conclude   Ask students the following questions:

▶ How would you interpret the author's description of the sounds made by the audience? Use terms from the lesson to describe sound. (Answers will vary. Students may note that the author describes the audience as creating a variety of sounds: from a low, resounding sigh to a roar. Most students will say that the audience is moved, enthusiastic, and, finally, acclamatory.)

▶ What kind of wave interference do you think occurs in the sounds being made? (Most of these sounds illustrate destructive interference because they are simultaneous, but not in unison, and not organized by pitch.)

Science and Literature Connection

Blue Tights

The following excerpts are taken from the novel Blue Tights *by Rita Williams-Garcia*

The doors opened to the public and the seats began to fill. The lights dimmed shortly. Joyce watched everything from behind the makeshift wing, awaiting her cue.

Magic began. A kalimba tinkled an introduction and was accompanied by an elder, whose rich contralto linked the spiritual and the cries of the Congo. From the wings children appeared in number, doing a jumping dance. They formed a circle around the elder, answering her cries with a sweet, lyrical chant.

As the children disappeared, the sounds of gourd instruments and birdcalls were woven into the music. Maidens entered in three rows with baskets of fruit perched on their heads, all held high. Tamu led the magnificent spectrum of multicolored maidens, from the flawless ebonies and earthy cafés to the clay reds and creamy yellows. The bells around their ankles sang joyously as they stamped their feet into the ground.

They exited in threes, all bowing stage right where the men were to enter. The tinkling of the kalimba was overtaken by four drummers in dreadlocks. A thunder rolled off the congas while the warriors paraded

their oiled bodies in loincloths. They came at the audience, hurling powerful kicks and firm fists. Scott broke away from the male chorus to solo.

Joyce became so engrossed in the stage magic that Hassan had to eject her from the wings onto the floor when the time came. She jumped in like a wriggling salmon with the drumbeat as her mighty stream. She immediately felt at ease on the stage. It was finally her turn to dance.

The heavy percussion soothed into a slow samba as the nuptial couple neared center stage. The audience responded enthusiastically to their courtship ritual, consisting of subtle hip movements, winding torsos, and floating arms.

Her people had to be out in the crowd. All she heard was "Get it, Joyce!" and "Joy-ceeeee!" And that was music enough. She could burst from the sheer joy of it. . . .

In an effortless sweep, the groom perched his bride onto his shoulder. They focused longingly into each other's gaze in a moment of created stage ardor, and he whisked her off into the wings. A low sigh resounded from the audience.

Then the ensemble sprang onto the stage. The nuptial couple returned. The

Skills in Science

Reading Skills in Science

1. The passage depicts African tribal ceremonial dances. The performance takes place in a public auditorium.

2. Answers may vary. The kalimba makes a tinkling sound; the children's cries are sweet and lyrical; the bells sing; the congas sound like thunder; and one hundred feet sound like an earthquake tremor.

Writing Skills in Science

1. The "thundering" congas produce a sound with a longer wavelength and a greater amplitude than the "tinkling" kalimba.

2. The dancers' skin tones are multicolored as light is absorbed by or reflected in the skin. The skin of the "flawless ebonies and earth cafes" absorb more light than "the clay reds and creamy yellows."

Activities

Collect Data Students' work will vary. Students should note the size, shape, and other characteristics of the drums that produce the various sounds. Students may note the ceremonies that include specific drums.

Communicate Extend the activity by having students determine the ways other cultural groups celebrate similar ceremonies or events.

---

elder showered them with blessings of children, harvest, and old age. To consecrate the earth, the dancers began a vigorous funga. One hundred feet striking the stage sent a tremor throughout the stands.

Without warning, Clarke spun Joyce out into the center of the stage.

And that's when they took her hands and said "come, daughter. Come, child." The women in her back root, with warm and strong hands, broad hips, and loving bosoms. The Ibo and the Mali women, watching down at the Child dancing. Joyce

heard the drum within her and stirred a mighty passion of feet and hips and head. And oh! the Child couldn't stop dancing, beyond music, beyond limit. "Leave her be! She touched by the dance!" they mused, spinning her, turning her, smiling down at the Child, who was touched by their spirit.

She whirled and whirled to the sound of some three-hundred-odd home folks and others shouting her name. As the drums halted, the audience roared. The dancers bowed in turn, then in unison.

Skills in Science

Reading Skills in Science

1. **Use Context Clues** What kind of performance takes place in this passage? Where does it take place?

2. **Accurate Observations** List five sources of sound in this selection. Describe how each one makes sound.

Writing Skills in Science

1. **Compare and Contrast** Compare the sound waves of "the tinkling of the kalimba" and the "thunder" from the congas. Which has longer wavelength? Which has a greater amplitude?

2. **Find Causes** The passage describes "a spectrum of multicolored maidens." Describe how light reflects off the dancers to cause their skin tones to look different.

Activities

Collect Data Research two kinds of African drums. Describe the sound each drum produces. Explain how the drums are used, and the groups that use them.

Communicate Find out about the role of dance in the Ibo or the Mali culture. Describe the ceremonies in which dance is important.

Where to Read More

The Voyage of the Frog by Gary Paulsen. New York: Orchard Books, 1989. A teenager encounters a life-threatening storm when he sails to scatter his uncle's ashes.

A Boat to Nowhere by Maureen Wartski. New York: DAL-Dutton, 1981. Mai and her family leave Vietnam in search of a better life.

Introducing the Unit

Directed Inquiry

Have students examine the photograph. Ask:

▶ In what ways do the coins in the photograph vary? How are they similar? (They vary in color, patterns of wear, and date. They have the same basic shape and are made of copper.)

▶ How can you tell which pennies are worn and which underwent a chemical change? (The image is fading, the engraving is less clear, and the metal is dented on the worn pennies. The chemically changed pennies have a different overall color or have a different color on some areas.)

▶ What interactions might cause changes in a coin? (Handling and rubbing against other items in a pocket might cause physical changes in coins. Chemical change occurs when the copper penny oxidizes. Accept all reasonable answers.)

Writing About the Photograph

Encourage students to examine a quantity of matter, such as grains of rice, a crop in a field, or a stack of paper. Have students write about the observable differences in a group of items that seem alike at first glance, but are not exactly alike on second look.

nit 6 explores interactions of matter and introduces the basic concepts of chemistry. Chapter 19 explores three types of chemical bonding, ionic, covalent, and metallic, and describes and compares the formation and structure of these bonds. Chapter 20 describes the characteristics of chemical reactions and compares exothermic and endothermic reactions. The chapter provides directions for writing a chemical equation, then pre-sents four types of chemical reactions. It closes with a discussion of activation energy, catalysts, and factors affecting reaction rate. Chapter 21 identifies types of solutions and factors that affect the solution rate, the solubility, and the concentration of solutions. Suspensions and colloids are described. Chapter 21 closes with an explanation of the properties of acids, bases, and salts and introduces the pH scale. Chapter 22 discusses the

Unit **6**
Interactions of Matter

Chapters

structure of carbon compounds and their prevalence in nature. The chapter explains the chemistry of carbohydrates, lipids, and proteins and explains briefly their functions in the human body. It also explains the chemical processes of photosynthesis and respiration. Chapter 23 introduces radioactivity, compares stable and unstable nuclei, and defines radioactive isotopes. The chapter describes three types of radioactive decay, transmutation of elements, and carbon-14 dating. The chapter closes with a discussion on nuclear fission and nuclear fusion.

Data Bank

Use the information on pages 634 to 643 to answer the questions about topics explored in this unit.

Inferring

What kind of an ingredient is added to distilled water to make soda water?

Graphing

Make a graph showing the average yearly dosage of five sources of radiation.

Predicting

How would the energy per gram of fats, proteins, and carbohydrates influence the diet of a very active, thin person?

Interpreting Data

Which atom in periods 2 and 3 has the smallest radius? How does the radius of the ion of that element compare to the radius of the atom?

The photograph to the left shows how copper pennies change color as they age. What kind of a change affects the color of the pennies?

Data Bank Answers

Have students search the Data Bank on pages 634 to 643 for the answers to the questions on this page.

Inferring Soda water is a slightly acidic solution. The answer is found in the graph, The pH Scale, on page 643.

Extension Encourage students to explain why sodium bicarbonate helps calm an upset stomach. (An upset stomach is often overly acidic. Bicarbonate of soda has a slightly alkaline pH, which restores pH balance in the stomach.)

Graphing Students should create their graphs using information in the table, Radiation Exposure in the United States, on page 643.

Extension Ask students to consider the frequency of exposure and the avoidance of various radiation sources shown in the table, Radiation Exposure in the United States, on page 643. Ask them how they might lower their exposure to radiation. (Accept all reasonable answers.)

Predicting An active, thin person would require more fats and proteins than a sedentary, heavy person. The answer can be found using the graph, Energy Production, on page 637.

Interpreting Data Fluorine has the smallest radius of all atoms in periods 2 and 3. The fluorine ion has a radius that is more than double that of the fluorine atom. The answer is found in the table, Size of Atoms and Ions in Periods 2 and 3, on page 637.

Answer to In-Text Question

A chemical change caused by oxidation affects the color of the pennies.

Overview

Chapter 19 introduces chemical bonding. The first section describes the chemical bonding of atoms and classifies chemical bonds into three types—ionic, covalent, and metallic. The remaining two sections describe and compare the formation and the structure of these chemical bonds.

Advance Planner

▶ Display a wallchart of the Periodic Table for TE page 469.

▶ Obtain a recording of Edgard Varèse's music for TE page 472.

▶ Provide hand lenses, table salt, Epsom salt, calcite, quartz, feldspar, or mica for TE page 474.

▶ Supply index cards for activity on TE page 475.

▶ Supply table salt, sugar, distilled water, test tubes and holders, measuring cups, stirring rods, Bunsen burners, dry cells, small bulbs and sockets, timers, and safety goggles for SE Activity 19, page 484.

Skills Development Chart

Sections	Classify	Communicate	Compare and Contrast	Infer	Interpret Data	Measure	Model	Observe
19.1 Skills WarmUp	●							
19.2 Skills WarmUp SkillBuilder							●	●
19.3 Skills WarmUp Skills WorkOut Consider This Activity		● ●	●	●	●	●	●	●

Individual Needs

▶ **Limited English Proficiency Students** When students have read the first section, have them write the term *chemical bond* at the top of a page of their science journal and add a definition in their own words. As they read the rest of the chapter, ask them to make a simple concept map that shows how the other boldface vocabulary words relate to the topic *chemical bonds*. Then have them make a page each for *ionic, covalent,* and *metallic bonds.* Beneath each term, have them write a description and illustrate the term with two or three diagrams. On the most appropriate of the three pages, have them write *polyatomic ion,* and include its definition and a diagram.

▶ **At-Risk Students** Have students use foam balls of different colors and sizes to make models of the atoms, ions, and compounds shown in Figures 19.5, 19.10, 19.11, and 19.12. Have them explain what part electrons play in forming the bonds shown in the models and ask them to identify which models show ionic, covalent, or metallic bonds.

▶ **Gifted Students** Ask students to find out more about crystals. Encourage them to grow crystals from a solution of copper sulfate or alum and water. Suggest that they make three-dimensional models of several crystal shapes and, if possible, bring in some actual examples of crystalline rocks or other substances. Have them use the things they have made and found to create a classroom display about crystals.

Resource Bank

▶ **Bulletin Board** Divide the bulletin board into three sections titled *Ionic Bonds, Covalent Bonds,* and *Metallic Bonds.* Invite students to cut out or draw pictures that illustrate some aspect of chemical bonding and place it in the correct section of the bulletin board. Encourage them to be creative in selecting pictures, contributing such things as visual analogies as well as more literal representations. For example, a picture of a girl giving her little sister one of her cookies could illustrate ionic bonding. At the end of the chapter, use the bulletin board as a springboard for discussion and review of chapter concepts.

▶ **Field Trip** Take the students to a museum that has a geology display of natural crystals and gems. Have students make drawings of the shapes of the crystals for their portfolios.

Section	Core	Standard	Enriched	Section	Core	Standard	Enriched
19.1 Atoms and Bonding pp. 467–470				**Color Transparencies** Transparencies 70a, 70b, 71, 73	●	●	●
Section Features Skills WarmUp, p. 467	●	●	●	**19.3 Covalent Bonds** pp. 478–484			
Blackline Masters Review Worksheet 19.1	●	●	●	**Section Features** Skills WarmUp, p. 478 Skills WorkOut, p. 479 Consider This, p. 482 Activity, p. 484	● ●	● ● ● ●	● ● ● ●
Color Transparencies Transparency 69	●	●	●				
19.2 Ionic Bonds pp. 471–477				**Blackline Masters** Review Worksheet 19.3 Reteach Worksheet 19.3 Skills Worksheet 19.3 Integrating Worksheet 19.3 Vocabulary Worksheet 19	● ● ● ● ●	● ● ● ● ●	● ● ● ● ●
Section Features Skills WarmUp, p. 471 SkillBuilder, p. 476		● ●	● ●				
Blackline Masters Review Worksheet 19.2 Skills Worksheet 19.2a Skills Worksheet 19.2b Skills Worksheet 19.2c Integrating Worksheet 19.2	● ● ●	● ● ● ● ●	● ● ● ●	**Color Transparencies** Transparencies 72	●	●	●
Laboratory Program Investigation 35			●	**Overhead Blackline Transparencies** Overhead Blackline Master 18 and Student Worksheet		●	●

Bibliography

The following resources can be used for teaching the chapter. See page T-46 for supplier codes.

Library Resources

Ardley, Neil. *The World of the Atom*. New York: Gloucester Press, 1990.

Berger, Melvin. *Atoms, Molecules and Quarks*. New York: G.P. Putnam's Sons, 1986.

Sherwood, Martin, and Christine Sutton. *The Physical World.* New York: Oxford University Press, 1988.

Technology Resources

Software

All About Science I. Mac, Dos. ESI.
Learning All About Matter. Mac, Win. LS.
Matter. Mac, Dos. ESI.
Science Elements. Win. ER.

Laserdiscs

Living Textbook. (See barcodes on pages in this chapter.) Optical Data.

Videos

Models of the Atom. AVNA.

Audio-Visual Resources

Matter and Molecules: Into the Atom. Filmstrip and cassette. SVE.

Introducing the Chapter

Have students read the description of the photograph. Ask if they agree or disagree with the description. You might explain that these are actually salt crystals.

Directed Inquiry

Have students study the photograph. Ask:

▶ How would you describe the image in the picture? (Students will mention that the objects in the picture look like magnified cubes. They may recognize that they are looking at crystals.)

▶ What substances can you think of that are found as crystals? (Students might name sugar, salt, quartz, Epsom salts, and diamonds.)

▶ How are all crystals alike in shape? (Students should point out the regular, geometrical, angular forms of all crystals.)

▶ What do you think that these crystals might tell you about the way the atoms in this substance are joined to one another? (Students may suggest that the atoms themselves are joined in cubic patterns.)

Chapter Vocabulary

chemical bond   metallic bond
covalent bond   polyatomic ion
ionic bond

Writing Connection

Have students write a series of five descriptive clues about the photograph for another student who will use them to draw a picture like the photograph. Each clue should be brief and add one more piece of information. Students may wish to try out their clues on another class.

Math Connection

Have students calculate the magnification of the photograph. Note that an average crystal of table salt measures about 0.2 mm along each edge. Ask students to use a metric ruler to measure the edges of 10 of the crystals. Have students average these measurements, then use the following formula to calculate the magnification: magnification = average measurement ÷ 0.2 mm.

Chapter 19   Chemical Bonding

Chapter Sections

19.1 Atoms and Bonding
19.2 Ionic Bonds
19.3 Covalent Bonds

What do you see?

❝I think that these are magnified salt or sugar crystals with some type of coloring. They are composed of little particles that formed together. Chemical bonding holds the crystallized salt or sugar together.❞

Greg Sarbacher
Einstein Middle School
Sacramento, California

To find out more about the photograph, look on page 486. As you read this chapter, you will learn about chemical bonding.

19.1 Atoms and Bonding

Objectives

▶ **Describe** the role of electrons in chemical bonding.

▶ **Explain** why atoms form chemical bonds.

▶ **Infer** the relationship between chemical bonds and chemical changes.

▼ **ACTIVITY**

Classifying

Oil vs. Salt

Identify the properties of cooking oil and of table salt. Then make a list of ten other substances you could find in your kitchen. When you finish the list, consider the properties of each substance. If the substance is more like table salt than cooking oil, circle it. If it is more like oil than salt, draw a box around it. What do the circled items have in common? How are they different from the boxed items?

SKILLS WARMUP

What is water? You might answer that water is a compound, which is correct. You might also answer that water is made up of the elements oxygen and hydrogen. This answer is correct, too. But did you know that there is another compound made up of hydrogen and oxygen? Look at Figure 19.1. This compound, which is used as an antiseptic, is hydrogen peroxide. Hydrogen peroxide's properties differ from those of water.

Why can hydrogen and oxygen combine chemically to form two different compounds? The reason is that an oxygen atom can combine with more than one other atom. It can form a compound with either two hydrogen atoms, or two hydrogen atoms and another oxygen atom with its own hydrogen atom.

Atoms of different elements can combine with each other in many different ways. How an atom combines chemically with other atoms is its most important property. What happens to atoms when they combine? How are they held together?

Chemical Bonds

When atoms combine chemically, they create a **chemical bond**. A chemical bond is an attractive force that holds atoms or ions together. Chemical bonds exist between particles in most of the matter surrounding you and in most of the matter that makes up your body.

Electrons and Bonding To understand chemical bonding, recall what you have learned about atomic structure. An atom is made up of a small, positively charged nucleus surrounded by a cloud of negatively charged electrons. It is the electrons that are involved in bonding.

Figure 19.1 ▲
The oxygen and hydrogen atoms in water (H_2O) and hydrogen peroxide (H_2O_2) are bonded together in different ways.

467

TEACH

Discuss

You may wish to refer students to the Periodic Table of the Elements on pages 634 and 635 in the Data Bank and to the discussion of the noble gases on page 197. Have them note that the noble gases are described as six colorless gases in Group 18, and that they are sometimes called *inert gases* because they don't react easily with other elements. The noble gases are helium, neon, argon, krypton, xenon, and radon.

Explore Visually

Have students study Figure 19.2. Ask:

► Where do the electrons of an atom move? (In a cloud around the nucleus)

► What is a shell diagram designed to show? (The arrangement of electrons in an atom; each energy level is drawn as a layer, or shell, containing a certain number of electrons.)

► How many electrons does an oxygen atom have and how many of these are in the outer electron shell? (Eight electrons; six of them in the outer shell)

► What are valence electrons? (They are the outer electrons, or electrons in the highest occupied energy level.)

► Why are the valence electrons important? (They are the electrons involved in chemical bonding.)

The Living Textbook: Physical Science Side 1

Chapter 20   Frame 10669
Valence Electrons (Movie)
Search: Play:

Themes in Science

Energy Electrons in an atom are arranged in energy levels, or shells. Each energy level is characterized by a certain number of electrons. The shells closer to the nucleus hold electrons at the lowest energy level. Those farther from the nucleus have electrons at higher energy levels. The number of electrons in the outermost energy level determines how the atom will bond with other atoms.

Electrons in an atom occupy different energy levels. Think of each level as a layer, or shell, like those shown in Figure 19.2 below. Each level holds a specific number of electrons. The first energy level can hold two electrons, and the second has room for eight. As the elements increase in atomic number, electrons fill the energy levels in an orderly way. Lower energy levels tend to fill with electrons before higher levels are filled. A carbon atom, for example, has its first energy level filled with two electrons, leaving just four in the second level.

The number of electrons in an atom's highest, or outer, energy level determines how it will bond with other atoms. All the elements with *unfilled* outer energy levels can form chemical bonds. The noble gases do not readily form bonds because their highest energy levels are filled with electrons.

**Figure 19.2
Electron Shell Diagram
of an Atom**
▼

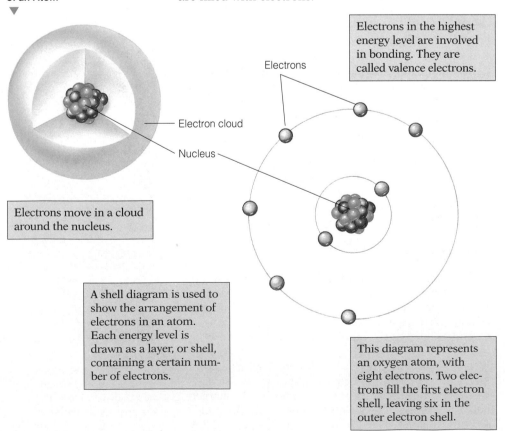

Electrons in the highest energy level are involved in bonding. They are called valence electrons.

Electrons

Electron cloud

Nucleus

Electrons move in a cloud around the nucleus.

A shell diagram is used to show the arrangement of electrons in an atom. Each energy level is drawn as a layer, or shell, containing a certain number of electrons.

This diagram represents an oxygen atom, with eight electrons. Two electrons fill the first electron shell, leaving six in the outer electron shell.

Themes in Science

Stability and Equilibrium

Bonding is related to the stability of atoms. Atoms are most stable when their outermost occupied energy level is completely filled. The first energy level holds a maximum of two electrons, the second holds a maximum of eight. Bonding with other atoms in ionic or covalent bonds is one way that atoms fill their outermost energy levels.

Language Arts Connection

Ask students to look up the meaning of the term *valence*. Mention that *valence* is derived from a Latin term that means "capacity." Ask how valence electrons give atoms a *combining capacity*. (They determine how reactive an atom is.) Then discuss the prefix *co-*. Explain to them that atoms forming a *co*valent bond *co*operate in using some of their valence electrons.

Critical Thinking

Reason and Conclude Which group of atoms in the periodic table is most stable and the least reactive? What can you conclude about their outer energy level? (Noble gases, Group 18; it is filled.)

Portfolio

Show the class a wall chart of the periodic table of the elements that provides valence numbers for each element. Explain that this information tells the number of electrons in the outermost energy level, the valence electrons, of each element. Disregard the rare earth elements. Have students make a table showing the groups in order of increasing valence electrons. Students may keep their tables in their portfolios.

Chemical Bonds and Stability Why do atoms form bonds? Recall that all matter tends to exist in its lowest possible energy state. Matter in its lowest energy state is more *stable* than it is in a higher energy state. The more stable matter is, the less likely it is to undergo a change. Having a partially filled outer energy level is a higher energy state than having a full one. Therefore, an atom with a full outer energy level is more stable than an atom with an unfilled outer level.

An atom with an unfilled outer energy level can become more stable if the right number of electrons are added to fill the level. Where can these electrons come from? They come from other atoms! Atoms interact in ways that give them the electrons they "need" to have full outer energy levels. These interactions cause chemical bonds to form.

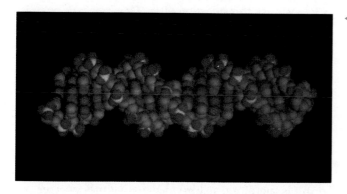

◀ **Figure 19.3**
Scientists often make models of chemical compounds, showing how the atoms that make them up are bonded. This model was made on a computer.

Picture two atoms of hydrogen as an example. Each hydrogen atom has only one electron, and each needs one more electron to fill its only energy level. If the atoms come near enough for their electron clouds to overlap, they can share their two electrons. The fast-moving electrons will spend time around both atoms. Each atom will have a full outer energy level. They will form a chemical bond because when bonded together, they are more stable than if they remained separate.

As you will see, there are three different kinds of chemical bonds: ionic (eye AHN ihk), covalent (KOH vay lehnt), and metallic. In ionic bonds, electrons are transferred from atom to atom. In covalent bonds, electrons are shared. Metallic bonds involve the sharing of electrons among many atoms.

 The Living Textbook: Physical Science Sides 1-4

Chapter 4   Frame 00935
Electron Energy Level Diagrams
(2 Frames)
Search: Step:

TEACH ▪ *Continued*

Discuss

Have students study Table 19.1. Explain that chemists develop sweeteners by changing the bonding of molecules. The new products are called *nonnutritive sweeteners.* Ask, Why would chemists develop new sweeteners? (People want things to taste sweet with fewer calories.)

EVALUATE

WrapUp

Reteach Elements with atomic numbers 3 through 10 on the periodic table, lithium, beryllium, boron, carbon, nitrogen, oxygen, fluorine, and neon, have two energy levels to hold their electrons. Have students make a diagram of each atom showing the electrons in the two levels. Ask, Which of these elements are most likely to bond with others? Why? (Elements 3–9 can bond with other elements; 10, a noble gas, won't.)
Use Review Worksheet 19.1.

Check and Explain

1. Chemical bonds occur at the outer energy level where electrons are shared or transferred.

2. Unfilled outer energy levels of some atoms attract electrons from other atoms.

3. Yes; students' models should show 6 valence electrons.

4. The original bonds are broken. New bonds form, producing the new substance.

 The Living Textbook:
Physical Science Sides 1-4

Chapter 4   Frame 01013
Sucrose Model (1 Frame)
Search:

 Multicultural Perspectives

People around the world have discovered ways to alter the sense of taste to make eating more pleasurable. West Africans sometimes chew a berry from the *Synsepalum dulcificum* bush that grows locally before they eat something sour. The berry contains sugar molecules that are chemically released by sour foods, making even lemons taste sweet.

Integrating the Sciences

Health Explain to students that many people with diabetes use artificial sweeteners because they must restrict their sugar intake. There are two types of diabetes. In Type I, the body lacks glucose-processing insulin. Treatment involves insulin injections and a strict diet. In Type II, the body produces insulin but can't use it properly. Often, this type can be controlled by diet alone. In both cases, sugar intake must be carefully regulated.

Table 19.1
Sweetness and Sweeteners

Sweetener	Relative Sweetness*
Sucrose (cane sugar)	1
Cyclamate	30–80
Aspartame	100–200
Saccharine	500–700
Sucralose	650

*Relative sweetness depends on the taste tester. For example, some people find aspartame 200 times sweeter than sugar, others do not.

Science and Technology
Designer Molecules

Imagine that you have a big pile of plastic foam balls, all different colors and sizes, and a box of toothpicks. What would you do? You might start building some kind of object with the balls, sticking them together with the toothpicks.

Building a spaceship or a funny giraffe with plastic foam balls and toothpicks is similar to what some chemists do in their laboratories. The chemists, however, work with atoms and molecules instead of foam balls. They assemble custom-made molecules that have some desirable set of properties. They put together the pieces of these molecules not with toothpicks but by breaking and forming chemical bonds.

What kind of molecule would you want to design? Chemists ask this question often. One molecule chemists have wanted to create is a sweet-tasting substance with fewer calories than sugar. Several sugar substitutes, such as saccharin and cyclamate, have been known for many years. Even though they have different structures from the sugar molecule sucrose, they taste sweet. Most sugar substitutes, however, have drawbacks ranging from a bitter aftertaste to possible health risks.

Recently, some chemists turned to the sucrose molecule itself as a model for a better artificial sweetener. They started with sucrose and simply changed some of the atoms bonded to the main part of the molecule. The result is sucralose, a substance many times sweeter than sucrose itself.

Check and Explain

1. How are electrons involved in chemical bonding?

2. Why do atoms form chemical bonds?

3. **Predict** Will an oxygen atom, with eight total electrons, form a bond with other atoms? Make a model on paper to explain your answer.

4. **Infer** You combine two compounds, and a chemical change occurs, producing a new substance. Infer what happened to the chemical bonds between the atoms in the original compounds.

Math Connection

Introduce the formula $2n^2$ for finding the maximum number of electrons in each of five energy levels, where n is the energy level. Make a chart on the chalkboard that shows the relationship between energy level and the number of electrons in that energy level. Have students choose an element and find its valence number, using the formula $2n^2$. They can use the periodic table to get atomic numbers for their elements. For example, the atomic number for zinc is 30. Applying the formula, the first energy shell contains 2 electrons $(2[1]^2)$, leaving 28. The second energy shell contains 8 electrons $(2[2]^2)$, leaving 20. The third contains 18, leaving an extra 2 valence electrons. Point out that the zinc ion has a charge of +2. Some atoms to use would be Cu, H, Ag, K, Na, Fe, Mg, Zn, Cl, F, I, O, and S.

19.2 Ionic Bonds

Objectives

▶ **Explain** how an ionic bond forms.

▶ **Describe** the structure of solid ionic compounds.

▶ **Make a model** that explains ionic bonding.

▼ **ACTIVITY**

Making a Model

Shell Diagram

Draw a shell diagram for the element lithium, which has three electrons. How would you describe lithium's outer electron shell?

SKILLS WARMUP

It's a hot summer day and you want to go swimming with a friend. But you find out that your friend has no bathing suit. Then you remember that you have several bathing suits and so you give one to your friend. You both go swimming and have fun cooling off. By giving up your extra suit, both of you benefit.

Transfer of Electrons

In ionic bonding, atoms of two different elements make an exchange similar to the one between you and your friend. One atom gives up one or more electrons, and another accepts them. Why does this transfer of electrons happen?

Remember that an atom is more stable with a full outer energy level, or electron shell. If an atom has just a few electrons in its outer shell, it can release these electrons. The original outer shell disappears, making the shell next to it the new outer shell. This new outer shell is full. The opposite also happens. An atom needing just a few electrons to fill its outer shell can get these electrons from another atom.

When an atom with "extra" electrons interacts with an atom "needing" electrons, one or more electrons may be transferred. The atom that released electrons becomes a positive ion. The atom that accepted the electrons becomes a negative ion. The two ions are attracted because they have opposite charges. They form an **ionic bond**. An ionic bond is an electrostatic attraction between oppositely charged ions.

Ionic compounds are made up of ions bonded together with ionic bonds. You may recall that sodium chloride, which is common table salt, is an ionic compound. Many other common and useful substances are ionic compounds.

Figure 19.4 ▲
The particles making up concrete are held together by ionic bonds.

Section Objectives
For a list of section objectives see the Student Edition page.

Skills Objectives
Students should be able to:

Make a Model by drawing a shell diagram.

Observe properties of ionic solids.

Predict whether atoms will give up electrons in chemical reactions.

Vocabulary
ionic bond

MOTIVATE

Skills WarmUp
To help students understand ionic bonds, have them do the Skills WarmUp.
Answer Lithium has two electrons in the inner shell and only one in the outer. This shell could be described as nearly empty because it can hold eight electrons.

Prior Knowledge
Gauge how much students know about ionic bonds by asking:

▶ What is the difference between an atom and an ion?

▶ Why do the ions that make up compounds stay together?

TEACH

Critical Thinking
Compare and Contrast Have students compare how likely some pairs of elements are to form ionic bonds, for example, potassium and chlorine and potassium and iodine. (Both are about equally likely to form ionic bonds. The alkali metal has an "extra" electron and both halogens "need" one electron.)

Directed Inquiry

Have students read these pages. Then lead a discussion using some or all of the following questions:

▶ How many electrons does a sodium atom have in its highest energy level, or outer electron shell? (One)

▶ How many electrons does a chlorine atom have in its outer electron shell? (Seven)

▶ How does a sodium atom become a sodium ion? (It gives up the one outer-shell electron.)

▶ How does a chlorine atom become a chloride ion? (It gains one electron.)

▶ What is the charge of the sodium ion, and what is its symbol? (1+; Na+)

▶ What is the charge of the chloride ion, and what is its symbol? (1−; Cl−)

The Living Textbook: Physical Science Sides 1–4

Chapter 17   Frame 03088
Ionic Bond (2 Frames)
Search: Step:

 The Living Textbook: Physical Science Sides 1–4

Chapter 17   Frame 03086
Ion (2 Frames)
Search: Step:

472

Music Connection

Students might be interested in listening to a recording of *Ionization*, a modern work for percussion by French-American composer Edgard Varèse (1883–1965). This work was written in 1931. Let students give their reactions to the music. Ask them to discuss how appropriate the title is for this piece of music.

Language Arts Connection

Explain to students that the rule governing how atoms form compounds to achieve a stable state is called the *octet rule*. Have students look up the word *octet* in a dictionary to find the origin, meaning, and another use of the word. Then ask students to infer what the octet rule is. (In general, atoms will bond with each other if the bonding causes both atoms to have eight electrons in their outer energy levels.)

Forming an Ionic Bond

Look at the sodium and chlorine atoms in Figure 19.5. Sodium has only one electron in its outer electron shell. If it empties this outer shell by releasing the electron, it will become more stable. Chlorine needs only one electron to fill its outer shell. If it gains an electron, it will become more stable. Notice that before any transfer of electrons takes place, each of the two atoms is electrically neutral. The positive charge of the nucleus cancels out the negative charge of the electrons.

Now look on the next page. The sodium atom has transferred its outer electron to the chlorine atom. The sodium atom has become a sodium ion. It has a charge of 1+. Look at the calculation below to check that this is true. A sodium ion has the symbol Na+.

**Figure 19.5
Ionic Bonding in Sodium Chloride** ▼

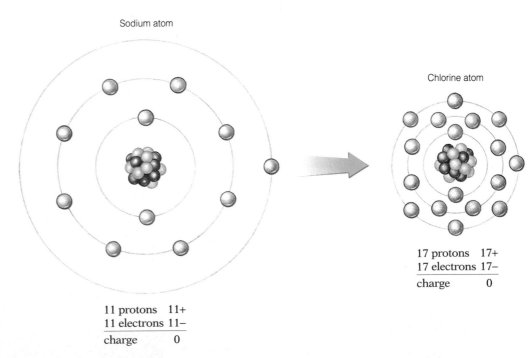

Sodium has only one electron in its highest energy level. If this electron is given up, a full outer electron shell will remain.

The outer shell of chlorine has seven electrons. An additional electron from the sodium atom will fill the outer shell.

Having gained an electron, the chlorine atom has become a chlor*ide* ion. It has a charge of 1-, as you can see in the calculation below. The symbol for the chloride ion is Cl^-. Both ions now have eight electrons in their outer electron shells. Both are stable because their outer shells are full.

Notice that the sodium ion is smaller than the sodium atom. Notice also that the chloride ion is larger than the chlorine atom. Why do you think ions and atoms of the same element differ in size? ①

The chloride ion and the sodium ion have opposite charges and so are attracted to each other. They are partners in an ionic bond. The positive charge of the sodium ion and the negative charge of the chloride ion cancel each other out. Together, they are electrically neutral. What is the name of the ionic compound they have formed? What is its chemical formula? ②

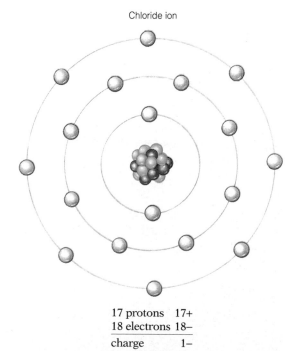

Chloride ion

Sodium ion

11 protons   11+
10 electrons 10–
charge   1+

17 protons   17+
18 electrons 18–
charge   1–

After the sodium atom loses its outer electron, it becomes a more stable sodium ion with a charge of 1+.

After the chlorine atom gains the electron from the sodium atom, its outer shell is filled. It is now a chloride ion with a charge of 1-.

TEACH ▪ *Continued*

Class Activity

Have students work in small groups to look at the crystals of table salt under a hand lens. Have students note the shape of the grains. If possible, have them look at other crystals as well. They could look at Epsom salt, calcite, quartz, feldspar, or mica. Have them answer the question, How would you describe the shapes of each of these crystals? (Cubic— Epsom salt; rhombohedral—6 equal parallelogram faces—calcite and quartz; monoclinic—2 equal rhombus faces and 4 rectangular faces—mica and feldspar)

Integrated Learning

Use Integrating Worksheet 19.2.

Answers to In-Text Questions

① Crystals grow equally in all directions; people change in shape as they grow. Also, crystals grow from without, by addition, organisms grow from within.

② Cubic

The Living Textbook: Physical Science Sides 1-4

Chapter 7   Frame 01242
Crystal Growth: Potassium Ferricyanide
(4 Frames)
Search: Step:

474

Integrating the Sciences

Earth Science Suggest that interested students research crystal shapes from geology. Students can draw and label the seven general crystal shapes and find pictures of mineral crystals of each shape. Construct the shapes from toothpicks, glue, and cut paper. Suggest that students label and combine their work in a class display.

STS Connection

In the late 1800s, Swedish scientist Svante Arrhenius proposed that ions carried electricity through solutions. He also developed the theory of ionization to explain freezing points of certain solutions. Although considered strange at first, his theories eventually won him the Nobel Prize. Among his later accomplishments was the surprising discovery that light exerts pressure.

The Crystal Lattice

A grain of salt contains many millions of ions. How are these ions arranged? Each ion is bonded not with just one other oppositely charged ion, but with several others. Look at Figure 19.6. Notice how chloride and sodium ions alternate with each other. In a grain of salt, six sodium ions surround each chloride ion, and six chloride ions surround each sodium ion.

The ions in table salt and in other ionic solids are arranged in an orderly three-dimensional pattern that repeats itself over and over again. This structure is called a *crystal lattice*. Each ion is bonded with all the oppositely charged ions that directly surround it.

Look at Figure 19.6. The salt particles have a cube shape. The shape of these visible particles is the same cube shape formed by the sodium and chloride ions in the crystal lattice.

Crystal Shapes The cube shape of the sodium chloride crystal is just one of seven crystal shapes taken on by ionic solids. In a cubic crystal, all the sides meet at right angles. Other crystal shapes have corners in which one or more of the angles are not right angles.

You can find many beautiful examples of crystals in nature. Epsom salt, a compound of magnesium, sulfur, oxygen, and hydrogen, forms long needle-shaped crystals. Crystals of calcite, a mineral found in limestone, look like parallelograms. In each case, the shape of the crystal you can see is determined by how the ions are arranged in the crystal lattice.

Crystal Formation Crystals form in several ways. One way they form is when a solution containing a dissolved ionic compound is allowed to evaporate. As the water vaporizes, the ions fall into their lattice structure. A second way crystals form is when an ionic solid is heated until it melts and the liquid is allowed to cool. The crystals in igneous rocks are formed in this way.

A crystal grows by regularly adding ions to all of its sides. This means that under the right conditions a crystal will keep the same shape no matter how large it becomes. How do crystals grow differently than you do? ①

◀ **Figure 19.6**
Crystals of table salt appear as cubes under a hand lens (far left). The sodium and chloride ions in table salt are arranged in a crystal lattice. What is the shape of this lattice structure? ②

Portfolio

Assign each student one atom that forms a single positive ion and one that forms a single negative ion. Have them draw and label the atom and the ion of each. (Negative ions should be bigger and positive ions smaller than their atoms. The drawings should also show the correct number of electrons in each shell.)

Cooperative Learning

Have students work in cooperative groups to create a classroom set of *Ionic Pursuit* cards using index cards. Each card should cover one atom that is either a metal or a nonmetal. One side should name the atom and list four categories of color-keyed questions: What is the periodic group? What is the name of the ion? What is the ion's charge? What is the other ion in this compound:_____? Color key the answers on the other side of the card.

Enrich

Give students an example of an ionic compound in which more than one atom of an element is combined with another atom, as in calcium chloride, $CaCl_2$. Remind students that the charges in an ionic compound cancel each other. In $CaCl_2$, the total negative charge $(-1) + (-1) = -2$ equals the total positive charge $(+2)$. Ask students, How many atoms of a halogen do you think it would take to combine with one atom of an alkaline earth metal to make an ionic compound? Why? (Two atoms of the halogen; the alkaline earth metal gives up two electrons but each halogen atom needs only one electron to become stable.)

Critical Thinking

Reason and Conclude Ask, How does an atom that loses one electron compare in size to an identical atom that loses three electrons? (The atom that loses three electrons is smaller because there are fewer electrons repelling one another.)

Answer to In-Text Question

③ **The magnesium ion is smaller than the atom because after the atom loses two electrons, there is less repulsion between the remaining electrons.**

Answer to Link

Answers will vary. Students should report being able to pick up unusual stations, perhaps from some distance.

Ions

Look at the periodic table on pages 186 to 187 and find the metals. These elements have few electrons in their highest energy levels. Metals tend to lose electrons and become positive ions. Now find the nonmetals. Most of these elements have nearly full outer energy levels. Nonmetals tend to gain electrons and become negative ions. As you may infer, ionic bonds form between metallic elements and nonmetallic elements.

Within a group in the periodic table, all the elements form ions with the same charge. The halogens, for example, all form ions with a 1- charge. The alkali metals all form ions with a 1+ charge. The alkaline earth metals all form 2+ ions.

Size of Ions Recall that when an atom becomes an ion, it changes in size. Look at the magnesium atom in Figure 19.7 below. Notice that when it loses the two electrons in its outer shell, it becomes much smaller. Positive ions are always smaller than the atoms from which they are formed, because the nucleus holds the remaining electrons more tightly. Negative ions, in contrast, are larger than their corresponding atoms, because the nucleus cannot hold a larger number of electrons as tightly. The chloride ion, for example, has nearly twice the radius of the chlorine atom!

The size of ions varies with atomic number. The size of ions decreases from left to right across the metallic elements in a period. The size of ions also decreases from left to right across the nonmetallic elements in a period. This decrease in size occurs because of the increase in the positive charge of the nucleus and its pull on the electrons.

Astronomy LINK

The ionosphere is a layer of air in the atmosphere where the electrons have been stripped off the atoms to form ions. Because of the charge in the ionosphere, radio waves bounce off it.

Obtain a radio. On a clear night, tune the radio in-between two local stations. Take the radio outside, and see what stations you pick up.

How many and what kinds of stations did you pick up?

ACTIVITY

Figure 19.7
The nitrogen ion is much larger than the nitrogen atom. Why is the magnesium ion smaller than the magnesium atom? ▼

+3 Electrons   −2 Electrons

Nitrogen atom, N   Nitrogen ion, N^{3-} Magnesium atom, Mg   Magnesium ion, Mg^{2+}

The Living Textbook:
Physical Science Sides 1-4

Chapter 4   Frame 00939
Electron Dot Models (1 Frame)
Search:

TEACH ▪ Continued

Discuss

Students may be familiar with *plasma* as a medical term. Explain that one of the main parts of blood is called *plasma*. Blood plasma is a clear, yellow fluid in which all the parts of the blood are either dissolved or suspended. Ask, Why are plasma transfusions given when whole blood is not available? (The chemicals in the plasma include dissolved ions that the body needs.)

SkillBuilder

Answers

1. Each compound dissolves in water. The crystal structure has broken down into individual ions.

2. All four ionic compounds dissolve and the ions spread throughout the water. They differ in the amount of time each takes to dissolve, the appearance of the resulting solution, and the by-products of dissolving. (Fizzing indicates that the sodium bicarbonate releases a gas as it dissolves.)

3. More can be learned about each compound by observing the solution over time, applying heat, or evaporating the water to see what kind of crystals form.

Integrating the Sciences

Astronomy Ask volunteers to find out about plasmas in the sun and in fusion reactions and lightning. Have them find out why plasmas can form in these places and situations, and how astronomers discovered plasmas. (The formation of plasmas requires very high temperatures, 50 000°C, or very large electric current. Plasmas usually give off light due to the energy released when electrons and positive ions come in contact with one another.)

Life Science Students may know that people and animals can't survive without water inside their bodies. Explain that one function of ions in body fluids is to reduce the amount of water lost to the surrounding air or water. Tell students that the concentration of ions in the body fluids for people and all animals with backbones is roughly the same.

Dissolved Ions What happens when you put table salt in water? The table salt, like many ionic compounds, will dissolve in water. When an ionic compound dissolves, each ion is surrounded by molecules of water. The crystal lattice structure of the solid breaks down.

Dissolved ions are very important to all living things. Plants take up the ions dissolved in water and use them as nutrients. Ions help your nerve cells to communicate with each other. Your blood contains many different kinds of dissolved ions. All your body cells contain many dissolved ions.

Ions in Plasma Plasma, the fourth state of matter, is a mixture of electrons and positively charged ions. Except in lightning bolts, natural plasmas do not exist on the earth. They exist only in stars, where the temperature is high enough to strip the electrons off atoms and prevent them from rejoining.

SkillBuilder Observing

Properties of Ionic Solids

Many products in your home are ionic compounds or mixtures of ionic compounds. You can learn about some of the properties of ionic compounds by observing some familiar examples. Copy the table shown here on a separate sheet of paper. Using a hand lens, observe the color, size, and shape of particles of sodium chloride (table salt), potassium chloride (salt substitute), sodium bicarbonate (baking soda), and magnesium sulfate (Epsom salt). Record your observations in the table.

Make a solution of each ionic compound by adding about a spoonful to about 50mL of water. Label each solution. Then answer the following questions.

1. What happened to each compound when placed in water? Record this information in the table. What does the behavior of these compounds in water tell you about them?

2. What properties do all four ionic compounds have in common? In what ways are they different?

3. How could you learn more about each compound? Suggest an experiment that might provide data about an additional property of these elements.

Common Ionic Compounds		
Name	**Description of Particles**	**Behavior in Water**
Sodium chloride		
Potassium chloride		
Sodium bicarbonate		
Magnesium sulfate		

Integrating the Sciences

Biology The transmission of nerve impulses depends on the movement of sodium and potassium ions across the membrane of a nerve cell. Explain how this wave of polarization works. Different concentrations of the ions on either side of the membrane cause the polarity. (Ions moving across the cell membrane reverse the polarity. Ions moving as parts of the membrane are "excited" in sequence along the nerve cell from the point at which a stimulus is received.)

Science and You *Trading in Ions*

Our drinking water naturally contains a variety of dissolved ions, both positive and negative. Water containing calcium and magnesium ions is called hard water. Soap lathers poorly in hard water and is less effective at cleaning. For these reasons, people have developed ways of softening water.

In one early method of water softening, a compound known as washing soda was added, along with soap, to the water used for washing clothes. Washing soda reacts with hard-water ions, forming compounds that do not dissolve in water. The rinse water carried away these insoluble compounds.

Today, many homes have devices that soften water by an ion-exchange process. In this process, water filters through mineral substances called zeolites, or through ion-exchange resins. Both zeolites and ion-exchange resins contain sodium ions.

As hard water flows through the ion exchange resin, sodium ions from the resin dissolve in the water. Calcium and magnesium ions from the hard water replace the sodium ions and become caught in the exchanger. When the exchanger can hold no more calcium and magnesium ions, a concentrated solution of sodium chloride can be pumped through it to reverse the ion-exchange process. Sodium ions again fill the ion exchanger. The hard-water ions are removed with the waste water.

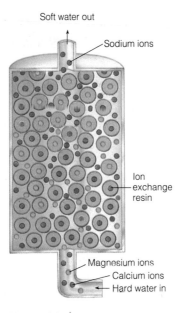

Soft water out
Sodium ions
Ion exchange resin
Magnesium ions
Calcium ions
Hard water in

Figure 19.8 ▲
A home water softener removes calcium and magnesium ions from water, replacing them with sodium ions.

Check and Explain

1. How does an ionic bond form?

2. How are the ions arranged in a solid ionic compound? Give an example.

3. **Predict** Find potassium (K) and iodine (I) in the periodic table. When an atom of potassium reacts with an atom of iodine, which atom will give up electrons? How many electrons will be transferred?

4. **Make a Model** Draw shell diagrams to show ionic bonding between magnesium and oxygen. Refer to the periodic table to determine the number of electrons in the outer electron shells of these elements.

EVALUATE

WrapUp

Review Have students look at the list of ionic compounds in the SkillBuilder data table on page 476. Ask them to name the elements that make up each compound. Tell them bicarbonate is the polyatomic ion $(HCO_3)^{-1}$. Using the periodic table, have them identify and compare the charge and size of the ion for each element. You may wish to list additional ionic compounds for this analysis.

Use Review Worksheet 19.2.

Check and Explain

1. When an electron is transferred from one atom to another, completing both atoms' outer shells and giving the ions opposite charges, an ionic bond is formed.

2. In a crystal lattice; salt crystals, which are cubic

3. One electron is transferred from potassium to iodine.

4. Students' diagrams should indicate that both ions hold eight electrons in their outer shells; O is 2− and Mg is 2+.

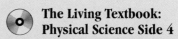

The Living Textbook: Physical Science Side 4

Chapter 29   Frame 30902
Hardness of Water (Movie)
Search: Play:

Art Connection

Have students draw cartoons of two atoms that would form a covalent bond. Cartoons should include dialog balloons that show why and how the elements would share their electrons.

Themes in Science

Diversity and Unity Close to four million different kinds of compounds are based on the carbon atom. Explain that an entire branch of chemistry, called *organic chemistry*, is devoted to the study of carbon-based compounds.

Section Objectives
For a list of section objectives, see the Student Edition page.

Skills Objectives
Students should be able to:

Compare and Contrast the ionic compound table salt with covalently-bonded substances.

Make a Model that shows covalent bonding.

Observe how the properties of salt and sugar relate to how their atoms bond.

Vocabulary
covalent bond, polyatomic ion, metallic bond

MOTIVATE

Skills WarmUp

To help students understand covalent bonds, have them do the Skills WarmUp.
Answer Students may note the following differences: water, oil, and alcohol are liquids, while salt is a solid; rubber and plastic wrap are solids and not crystals, as salt is; cornstarch particles are less hard than salt particles; sugar looks like salt but tastes different.

Prior Knowledge

Gauge how much students know about covalent bonds by asking the following questions:

▶ Why do people form *bonds* of friendship?

▶ Name some ways in which things can be shared.

▶ What are molecules?

▼ **ACTIVITY**

Contrasting

Like Salt?

Water, vegetable oil, sugar, cornstarch, rubbing alcohol, plastic wrap, and rubber are all made up of atoms held together by covalent bonds. For each substance, describe at least one way in which it differs from the ionic compound table salt.

SKILLS WARMUP

Figure 19.9 ▲
Two seat belt ends, when joined, become useful. In a similar way, unpaired electrons from two atoms come together to form a covalent bond.

19.3 Covalent Bonds

Objectives

▶ **Describe** a covalent bond.

▶ **Identify** three covalently-bonded substances.

▶ **Relate** metallic bonding to properties of metals.

▶ **Make a model** that explains covalent bonding.

W hat would you do if you and a friend were caught in the rain with only one umbrella? You would probably share it. The umbrella would keep both of you reasonably dry. Sharing is a good way to solve many problems because it can help more than one person at the same time.

Shared Electron Bonding

You have just learned that atoms may transfer electrons from one to another, becoming ions joined by an ionic bond. This bonding occurs when one atom has extra electrons and the other needs electrons. But what happens between two atoms that both "need" a small number of electrons to have full outer electron shells? Like two people with one umbrella, they share.

Look at the chlorine atom on page 472. Its outer electron shell is one electron short of being full. If two chlorine atoms come together, they can share a pair of electrons. Each atom gives up one electron to the pair. The two electrons in the pair give both atoms a full outer shell. The shared pair of electrons makes up a **covalent bond**, the second major type of chemical bond.

Recall that ionic bonds form between the metals and nonmetals. Covalent bonds, in contrast, form between the atoms of nonmetallic elements. These are elements with outer electron shells that are at least half full. Covalent bonds can form not only between different nonmetals, but also between atoms of the same nonmetal. A covalent bond, for example, holds together two oxygen atoms in O_2, the oxygen molecule in the air we breathe.

Atoms joined with covalent bonds form molecules. Molecules are very different from the rigid network of

Portfolio

Have students draw electron dot diagrams for the nonmetal atoms. They have already listed the valence numbers of these atoms in a table for their portfolios. Draw a diagram for one of the noble gases with students. Ask, Which elements will have the same diagram? (The other noble gases, Group 18) Have students draw the rest of the diagrams.

Skills WorkOut

To help students use models to understand covalent bonding, have them do the Skills WorkOut. **Answer** Check students' diagrams for accuracy.

Directed Inquiry

Have students study the text on this page and Figure 19.10. Discuss the following questions:

► How many pairs of dots are there in the diagram of argon? (Four)

► How are electrons shared in covalent bonds? (In pairs)

► Why does argon have a stable arrangement of electrons? (All eight electrons are paired.)

► What does an atom's unpaired valence electron do in a covalent bond? (Joins with another atom's unpaired valence electron, forming a covalent bond)

► Why do hydrogen and chlorine atoms form a covalent bond? (Hydrogen has one unpaired valence electron and chlorine has one unpaired valence electron. The unpaired electrons form a covalent bond.)

ions in an ionic compound. The definite size of a molecule contrasts with the unlimited size of an ionic solid. Molecules may exist as liquids, gases, or solids depending on their size. Ionic compounds, in contrast, are nearly always solids.

Covalent bonding among atoms can be shown with electron dot diagrams. These diagrams are similar to shell diagrams, except that only the valence electrons are shown. Look at the electron dot diagrams below. Because covalent bonds are *pairs* of shared electrons, the electrons in an atom's outer shell are shown as paired and unpaired dots. Each unpaired electron around an atom can join with another atom's unpaired electron to form a covalent bond. Atoms bond covalently to achieve the stable arrangement of electrons found in a noble gas atom.

 ACTIVITY

Making a Model

Methane Model

Draw an electron dot diagram for carbon. Carbon has four electrons in its outer shell. Then draw an electron dot diagram for the simple carbon compound called methane. The formula for methane is CH_4.

SKILLS WORKOUT

Figure 19.10
Forming Covalent Bonds

The noble gas, argon, has a full outer electron shell. All eight electrons are paired, so argon can't form a covalent bond.

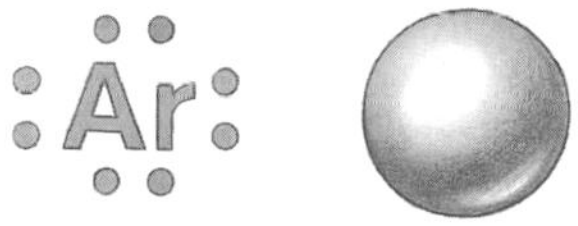

▲ Hydrogen's single electron is shown as an unpaired dot. Six of chlorine's seven outer electrons are paired, leaving one unpaired.

The unpaired electrons from hydrogen and chlorine come together to form a pair. This pair of electrons is the covalent bond in the HCl molecule.

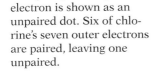    

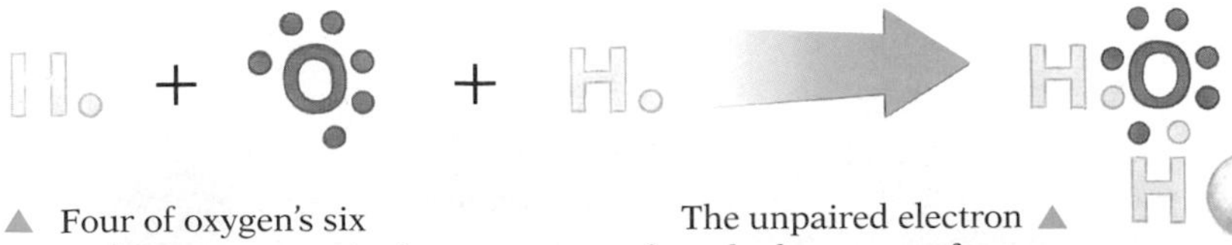

▲ Four of oxygen's six outer electrons are paired, leaving two unpaired electrons. Each unpaired electron can form a bond.

The unpaired electron ▲ from hydrogen can form a covalent bond with each of oxygen's unpaired electrons.

 The Living Textbook: Physical Science Sides 1-4

Chapter 17   Frame 02918
Covalent Bond (2 Frames)
Search: Step:

 The Living Textbook: Physical Science Sides 1-4

Chapter 4   Frame 00954
Covalent Bonds of Water (5 Frames)
Search: Step:

TEACH ▪ *Continued*

Skills Development

Infer Explain that carbon exists in two crystalline solid forms. One form, diamond, is the hardest naturally occurring substance on the earth. Graphite, the other form, is quite soft and is mixed with clay and used as pencil lead. Ask students to explain if graphite is a network solid. (Answers may vary. Graphite's crystalline structure and high melting point make it a network solid; it is soft because its layers slide easily across each other.)

Infer Explain that the polyatomic ion sulfate has a charge of 2⁻. Ask, Does sulfate have more or fewer protons than electrons? (Fewer)

Misconceptions

Students may think that, because of their name, polyatomic ions form via ionic bonds. Use dot diagrams to explain that the groups of atoms result from covalent bonds.

Reteach

Use Reteach Worksheet 9.3.

Answer to In-Text Question

① **Covalent bonds**

**The Living Textbook:
Physical Science Sides 1-4**

Chapter 4   Frame 00993
Ammonia and Methane Models
(2 Frames)
Search: Step:

**The Living Textbook:
Physical Science Sides 1-4**

Chapter 4   Frame 00987
Graphite and Diamond Crystals
(5 Frames)
Search: Step:

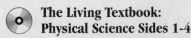

Geography Connection

Have students find out where diamonds, sapphires, emeralds, and rubies are mined. Point out that all of these gems are network solids. For a classroom display, ask students to place pins or labels on a large world map to show where each gemstone is mined.

Language Arts Connection

Go over the word parts of *polyatomic*. Have students look up the meaning of *poly-* in the dictionary. (Many) Ask students to write a definition of *polyatomic*. (*Polyatomic* means "more than one atom present.")

Compounds formed from covalently bonded atoms are far more common than ionic compounds. For example, the millions of carbon compounds found in living things are held together with covalent bonds. The major nutrients in your food, including carbohydrates, proteins, fats, and vitamins, are also covalent compounds. Even the oxygen molecules you breathe in and the carbon dioxide you breathe out are covalently bonded.

Network Solids Atoms joined by covalent bonds usually form molecules, but certain substances held together by covalent bonds are not molecules. These substances have a structure like that of an ionic solid. They are called network solids because all of their atoms are connected in a network by covalent bonds.

Diamond is a good example of a network solid. It is made up of carbon atoms, each bonded covalently to four neighboring carbon atoms. Quartz, sapphire, emerald, and ruby are also network solids. Network solids are generally hard but not malleable. They melt only at very high temperatures.

Covalently Bonded Ions Certain molecules held together by covalent bonds tend to gain or lose electrons as a unit. The whole group of atoms becomes an ion with a positive or negative charge. These groups of covalently bonded atoms are called **polyatomic ions**. Polyatomic ions form ionic bonds with other ions just like single ions do. One example of a polyatomic ion is the carbonate ion, CO_3^{2-}. It bonds with a calcium ion to form calcium carbonate, which makes up limestone. Other examples of polyatomic ions are shown in Figure 19.11 below. Polyatomic ions are contained in many common substances, such as baking soda and Epsom salts.

Figure 19.11
Some polyatomic ions have a negative charge, and others have a positive charge. How are the atoms that make up each ion held together? ▼ ①

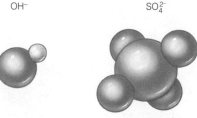  

OH⁻	SO_4^{2-}	NO_3^-	NH_4^+
Hydroxide ion	Sulfate ion	Nitrate ion	Ammonium ion

Answer to Link

The paperclips should be left in the can. The erosion of the earth and creation of holes that would be significant on a large scale are two aspects of environmental impact.

Metallic Bonds

Metallic bonds, as you have probably guessed, occur in metals. Like covalent bonds, they involve the sharing of electrons. In a covalent bond, two atoms share a pair of electrons. However, in a **metallic bond**, many atoms share many electrons.

In a sample of a pure metal, such as silver or copper, the valence electrons make up a "sea" of electrons that can flow freely through the piece of metal. Because the valence electrons do not belong to individual atoms, the atoms actually exist as positive ions. The positive charges of all the ions in a sample of metal are canceled out by the negative charges of all the electrons.

Look at Figure 19.12. You can see that the positive silver ions are arranged in a lattice structure and surrounded by loose electrons. Because they are attracted to all the metal ions, the moving electrons serve as the bond that holds the metal lattice together.

This model of bonding in a metal helps explain many of the properties of metals. Most metals have a high density. The high density is caused by the lattice structure of a metal. Actually, there is very little empty space between the positive ions. Metals are also malleable. In a malleable substance, the electrons are free to move and keep the ions bonded to each other when a stress changes the positions of the ions. The malleability of metals contrasts with the brittleness of other crystalline solids. The freely-moving electrons also account for the ability of metals to conduct electricity.

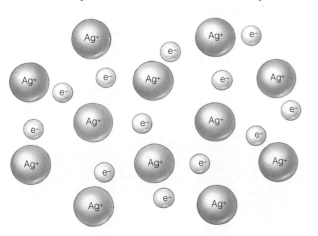

Environmental Science LINK

Hydraulic mining is one method for extracting metal ores from the earth. Mining has an impact on the environment. Obtain an empty can, 10 paper clips, a cup of dirt, and a garden hose with a spray nozzle.

1. Place the paper clips and dirt in the can. Mix them up.

2. Spray water from the hose into the can until the overflowing water is clean.

What was left in the can? What kind of impact do you think this kind of mining has on the environment?

ACTIVITY

◀ **Figure 19.12**
Metallic bonding allows metal ions to change position without breaking apart from each other. The spoon is made of malleable metal.

Discuss

Have students read about metallic bonds and study Figure 19.12. Ask:

▶ Because the valence electrons of the metals are "free," in what form do the atoms actually exist? (As positive ions)

▶ What holds the metal ions together in a metallic bond? (The attraction of the moving electrons)

▶ How is metallic bonding related to the density of metals? (High density is caused by the closeness of the metal ions in the lattice structure. Very little empty space exists between the positive ions.)

▶ How would you explain malleability in terms of metallic bonding? (The electrons are free to move, but they still keep the metal ions bonded when stress changes the positions of the ions.)

▶ **Infer** How might metallic bonds help explain how electricity may be conducted through a metal wire? (Accept all logical answers. The freely moving electrons are organized into a current that moves along the atoms in the wire.)

The Living Textbook: Physical Science Sides 1-4

Chapter 4   Frame 00941
Metallic Bonds (1 Frame)
Search:

The Living Textbook: Physical Science Sides 1-4

Chapter 3   Frame 00897
Malleability of Lead (1 Frame)
Search:

TEACH ▪ *Continued*

Class Activity

Have students bring in packages of different kinds of adhesive, glue, and tape that they use at home or in art class. They should organize and arrange their samples for display. Have students label the exhibits and give the history, composition, uses, advantages, and drawbacks of each type of adhesive.

Enrich

Help students understand how glue is formed and how it works. Many kinds of glue are formed when materials, such as hides and bones, that come from vertebrates are cooked in water. The proteins from these materials form glues, or sticky substances that fit into tiny spaces between the materials being glued. When the glue hardens, materials are closely bonded together.

Consider This

Write About It Answers will vary, but students should give reasons in their papers for their opinions about food additives.
Research Have students research one of the common food additives from the following list: *sweetener,* aspartame; *coloring,* carotene; *flavoring,* vanilla; *flavor enhancer,* MSG; *leavener,* calcium phosphate; *stabilizer,* cellulose; *emulsifier,* diglyceride; *preservative,* BHT; *fortifier,* iron. Challenge students to explain how a food containing the substance, or their reaction to the food, would change without the additive.

STS Connection

Explain to students that adhesives play a major role in the manufacture of aircraft, cars, books, and furniture as well as in the construction of buildings and roads. Since ancient times, people have made adhesives from such things as tree sap and animal skins. Today, adhesives are made from such substances as nylon, polyethylene, and silicone rubber. Adhesives vary in the way they are applied and how they bond. For example, thermosetting adhesives require heat and pressure to bond. These adhesives are among the strongest and are used to secure the tails on jet aircraft.
Use Integrating Worksheet 19.3.

Science and You *A Sticky Problem*

How many times in the past week have you made two things stick together? Maybe you pasted together some cardboard or sealed an envelope. Or possibly you stuck a sticker somewhere or fixed something with glue. Substances that make things stick, called adhesives, are important in our daily lives. But did you know that things tend to stick together even without adhesives?

Most substances are slightly sticky because the molecules that make them up are attracted to other molecules. This attraction occurs in part because the electrons in many molecules are not evenly distributed throughout the molecule. Certain atoms hold shared electrons more tightly than the atoms to which they are bonded. As a result, parts of the molecules are *slightly* positive, and parts are *slightly* negative. The negative parts of one molecule attract the positive parts of other

Consider This

Stricter Regulations for Food Additives?

Look on the label of a packaged food, and you'll probably see some ingredients with strange names such as BHA, sodium benzoate, and diglyceride. These are food additives. Substances are added to foods to improve nutrition, flavor, or consistency, or as preservatives.

About 3,000 different food additives are commonly used today. Many additives are synthetic compounds. People manufacture them by breaking chemical bonds in raw materials and reforming new bonds. The use of all food additives is regulated by the Food and Drug Administration, or FDA.

Food additives make food taste better and keep it from spoiling. But are food additives safe? Even though the FDA must test and approve all new additives, many additives in use before 1958 have never been tested for approval.

In addition, some people are concerned that many approved food additives may still be dangerous. Tests may not be able to determine all possible health risks over a lifetime of eating the additive.

Food companies claim all their products are safe. They believe the FDA's current rules are more than strict enough to ensure consumer safety. They don't feel there is enough evidence to prove that food additives are harmful.

Think About It When foods contain certain additives, warning labels are required. Should more additives be treated in this way? Should food labels give the *amounts* of all food additives? Should the FDA test all the additives now used in foods?

Write About It Write a short paper describing how the FDA should regulate food additives, giving reasons for your position.

Integrating the Sciences

Oceanography The "glue" secreted by barnacles contains calcium carbonate, and hardens to form one of the most durable adhesives in the world. Ship owners spend a great deal of time and money cleaning barnacles from the hulls of ships. Point out to students that because barnacles attach themselves permanently to an object or organism, they must find a place where their needs for survival will always be met. Some locations are interesting. Barnacles may live on the backs of whales, for example, gaining constant access to fresh food sources and good water circulation.

Figure 19.13 ▲
Adhesives are found in nature as well as in tubes of glue. Barnacles (above) secrete an adhesive that permanently attaches them to a surface. A sticky substance in the spider web helps to trap the moth.

molecules, and the positive parts attract other molecules' negative parts. Each attraction is relatively weak, but they combine to create a stickiness.

Usually you don't notice this stickiness, called intermolecular attraction, because most surfaces aren't really flat or clean at a microscopic level. When two surfaces touch, air molecules, dirt, and surface roughness prevent most molecules in the two surfaces from coming close enough to be attracted. That's why an adhesive, such as glue, comes in handy.

Glue can flow into the microscopic valleys of a surface, coming in contact with all the surface molecules. The molecules in the glue are attracted to the surface molecules, causing them to stick together. The same thing occurs when another surface is pressed onto the glue. As long as the glue holds itself together, the two surfaces will stick together.

Check and Explain

1. What is a covalent bond?

2. Describe the covalent bond in three molecules identified in this chapter.

3. **Relate** Explain how metallic bonding accounts for two properties of metals.

4. **Make a Model** Draw an electron dot diagram to show covalent bonding between one nitrogen atom and three hydrogen atoms in an NH_3 molecule.

Time 60 minutes   **Group** 4–5

Materials

table salt

sugar

distilled water

16 test tubes

7 measuring cups

14 stirring rods

7 test-tube holders

7 Bunsen burners

7 circuit setups (dry cell, small bulb and socket, connecting wires)

7 timers

Analysis

1. The melting point of sugar is lower than that of salt.

2. The salt; the light lit up.

3. The salt is an ionic compound, and the sugar is covalently bonded. The salt solution conducts electricity. Ions must be present for a solution to conduct electricity.

Conclusion

The sugar melts at a lower temperature because covalent compounds have weak intermolecular bonds that break at relatively low temperatures. Ionic compounds, such as salt, are held together by ionic bonds, which break at relatively high temperatures. The salt solution conducts electricity because the ions that are released in the water carry the electric charge from one wire to the other.

Extension

Students' hypotheses and tests should take into account the fact that any ions already present in the water might make the solution conduct electricity.

Prelab Discussion

Have students read the entire activity. Discuss the following points before beginning:

► Ask students to identify salt and sugar as types of compounds.

► Review the principles of electric conductivity as they apply to this situation.

► Ask students why it is important to use a different stirring rod for each solution.

Activity 19 *How do ionic and covalent compounds differ?*

Skills Measure; Observe; Infer; Interpret Data

Task 1 Prelab Prep

1. Collect the following items: table salt, sugar, distilled water, 2 test tubes, 2 measuring cups, stirring rod, test-tube holder, 4 small labels, Bunsen burner, low-voltage dry cell, small light bulb and socket, 3 connecting wires, timer, safety goggles. Make sure the wires can be attached to both the light bulb socket and the terminals of the dry cell.

2. Label a test tube and a measuring cup *Salt*. Label the other test tube and measuring cup *Sugar*.

Task 2 Data Record

1. Copy Table 19.2 on a sheet of paper.
2. Record all your observations about the properties of salt and sugar in the table.

Table 19.2   Properties of Salt and Sugar

Substance	Did it Melt?	Did it Conduct?
Salt		
Sugar		

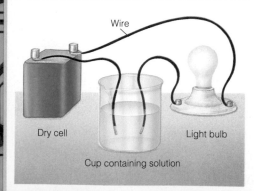

Wire

Dry cell   Light bulb

Cup containing solution

Task 3 Procedure

1. Put a small amount of salt in the test tube labeled *Salt*. Put an equal amount of sugar in the second test tube.

2. Note the time, then, using the test-tube holder, heat the test tube of salt over the Bunsen burner. **CAUTION: Wear goggles and point the test tube away from you and others.** Observe whether the salt melts within two minutes. Record the result in Table 19.2.

3. Repeat step 2, using sugar instead of salt.

4. Pour 50 mL of distilled water into the measuring cup labeled *Salt*. Add salt and stir until it is dissolved. Repeat the procedure using the same amount of sugar.

5. Set up a circuit as shown, using the measuring cup of salt water. Observe whether the solution will conduct electricity and record the results. Repeat the procedure using the sugar solution.

Task 4 Analysis

1. From your data, what can you infer about the melting point of the compounds?

2. Which compound is a better conductor of electricity? How could you tell?

3. Which compound is ionic and which is covalently bonded? How do you know?

Task 5 Conclusion

Write a short paragraph explaining how the properties you observed relate to the type of bonding in each compound.

Extension

Develop a hypothesis that explains why you used distilled water to make the salt and sugar solutions. How would you test your hypothesis?

Chapter 19 Review

Concept Summary

19.1 Atoms and Bonding
▶ A chemical bond is an attractive force that holds the atoms of a compound together.
▶ Atoms of elements with unfilled outer energy levels can form bonds.
▶ When atoms form chemical bonds they fill their outer energy levels with electrons and become more stable.
▶ There are three main types of chemical bonds: ionic, covalent, and metallic.

19.2 Ionic Bonds
▶ An ionic bond forms when electrons are transferred from one atom to another.
▶ An ionic bond is an electrostatic attraction between ions that have opposite charges.

▶ Ionic bonds form between the atoms of metallic and nonmetallic elements.
▶ The ions that make up ionic solids are arranged in a three-dimensional structure called a crystal lattice.

19.3 Covalent Bonds
▶ A shared pair of electrons makes up a covalent bond between two atoms.
▶ Covalently bonded atoms form either molecules or network solids.
▶ Polyatomic ions, such as ammonium and sulfate ions, are groups of covalently bonded atoms with an overall charge.
▶ Metallic bonds occur in metals, where a sea of shared electrons surrounds positive metal ions arranged in a lattice structure.

Chapter Vocabulary

chemical bond (p. 467)   covalent bond (p. 478)   metallic bond (p. 481)
ionic bond (p. 471)   polyatomic ion (p. 480)

Check Your Vocabulary

Use the vocabulary words above to complete the following sentences correctly.

1. An attachment between atoms that involves the sharing of electrons is called a(n) _____ .

2. A charged particle such as NH_4^+ is called a(n) _____ .

3. A(n) _____ is the result of an electrostatic attraction that forms between oppositely charged ions.

4. Many atoms share many electrons in a(n) _____ .

5. A general term that is used to describe the force that holds together the atoms or ions in a molecule is a(n) _____ .

Pair each numbered word or words with a vocabulary term. Explain in a complete sentence how the words are related.

6. Nonmetallic elements

7. NO_3^-

8. Sodium chloride

9. Transfer

10. Network solid

11. Lattice

12. Electron dot diagram

Write Your Vocabulary

Write sentences using the vocabulary words above. Show that you know what each word means.

Check Your Vocabulary

1. covalent bond

2. polyatomic ion

3. ionic bond

4. metallic bond

5. chemical bond

6. covalent bonds: Covalent bonds form between non-metallic elements.

7. polyatomic ion: NO_3^- is an example of a polyatomic ion.

8. ionic bond: In sodium chloride, sodium ions are held together with chloride ions by ionic bonds.

9. ionic bond: In an ionic bond, one or more electrons are transferred from one atom to another.

10. covalent bond: A network solid forms by certain atoms that are joined by strong, directional covalent bonds.

11. ionic bond: A lattice is the name for the structure of a crystalline ionic solid.

12. covalent bond: Covalent bonding between atoms is usually shown with electron dot diagrams.

Write Your Vocabulary

Students' sentences should show that they know the meaning of each word as well as how to use it in a sentence.

Use Vocabulary Worksheet for Chapter 19.

Check Your Knowledge

1. A network solid is a solid formed by atoms that are joined by strong, directional covalent bonds.

2. Noble gases have filled outer energy levels.

3. The outermost, or valence, electrons are involved in bonding.

4. An atom becomes an ion by gaining or losing one or more electrons.

5. A negative ion is generally larger than an atom.

6. A crystal lattice is a regular, repeating structure found in ionic solids and network solids.

7. The innermost energy levels are the first to fill with electrons.

8. False; valence electrons

9. False; ion

10. True

11. False; nonmetals

12. True

13. False; network

14. False; metals

Check Your Understanding

1. Diagrams should show the following valences: magnesium—2 single dots; aluminum—3 single dots; silicon—4 single dots; phosphorus—3 single dots and a pair; sulfur—2 pairs and 2 single dots.

2. metallic, ionic; covalent

3. a. Ne; b. Xe; c. Ar; d. Ar

4. Sodium chloride is an ionic solid. The sodium and chloride ions form a cubic crystal lattice when they crystallize.

5. The substance is likely a metal, having electrons floating freely among atoms in metallic bonds.

6. Polyatomic ions are ions made up of covalently bonded atoms. They behave as ions, forming ionic compounds, but are themselves covalent compounds.

Chapter 19 Review

Check Your Knowledge

Answer the following in complete sentences.

1. What is a network solid?

2. Why do noble gases not form compounds under ordinary circumstances?

3. Which electrons in an atom are involved in chemical bonding?

4. How does an atom become an ion?

5. Which is generally larger, an atom or its negative ion?

6. What is a crystal lattice? What kinds of substances have a crystal lattice?

7. Which energy levels are the first to fill with electrons.

Determine whether each statement is true or false. Write *true* if it is true. If it is false, change the underlined word or words to make the statement true.

8. Elements in the same group of the periodic table have similar properties because they have the same number of <u>neutrons</u>.

9. An atom losing two electrons becomes a <u>molecule</u> with a 2+ charge.

10. During ionic bonding, <u>electrons</u> are transferred from atom to atom.

11. Covalent bonds usually form between the atoms of <u>metals</u>.

12. In an electron dot diagram of an atom, only the <u>valence</u> electrons are shown.

13. Diamond and quartz are examples of <u>ionic</u> solids.

14. In <u>covalent compounds</u>, atoms are held together by a sea of electrons.

Check Your Understanding

Apply the concepts you have learned to answer each question.

1. Draw electron dot diagrams for each of the following atoms: magnesium, aluminum, silicon, phosphorus, and sulfur. Refer to the periodic table on pages 186 to 187 for the information you need.

2. **Generalize** Copy and complete this table describing the kind of bonding that occurs between elements.

Substance	Metal	Nonmetal
Metal	?	?
Nonmetal	Ionic	?

3. **Interpret Data** Use the periodic table to determine which noble gas has the same number of electrons as each of the following ions.

    a. N^{3-} b. I^- c. S^{2-} d. K^+

4. **Mystery Photo** The photograph on page 466 shows crystals of table salt, sodium chloride (NaCl). Explain why sodium chloride crystals have this appearance.

5. **Infer** A substance is found to be flexible and to conduct heat and electricity well. What can you infer about the chemical bonds that hold it together?

6. **Compare and Contrast** How do polyatomic ions compare with ordinary ions? How do they compare with covalently bonded molecules?

Develop Your Skills

1. a. decreasing ionic radius with increasing atomic number

   b. Ionic radius increases dramatically from 14 to 15, because Si loses its 4 valence electrons to form an ion, while P gains 3 electrons.

2. Students should realize that the physical arrangement of the foam balls (atoms) is as important as the numerical ratios of atoms.

3. a. 0.031 nanometers

   b. 0.058 nanometers smaller

   c. magnesium

Make Connections

1.

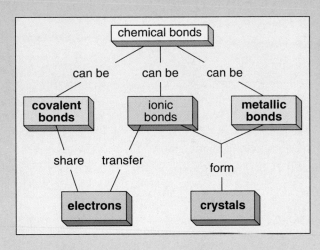

2. Hydrogen and oxygen will form covalent bonds; magnesium and chlorine will form ionic bonds.

3. Answers will vary depending on region and community. Common ions present in drinking water are chloride (Cl^-), fluoride (F^-), calcium (Ca^{2+}), and (Mg^{2+}).

Develop Your Skills

Use the skills you have developed in this chapter to complete each activity.

1. Interpret Data The graph below shows how the radius of different ions varies with their atomic number.

a. What trend do you see among the sizes of the four positive ions shown?

b. What happens to ionic radii as atomic number increases from 14 to 15? Why does this occur?

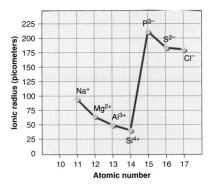

2. Make a Model Use plastic foam balls and toothpicks to make models of water (H_2O), diamond, and potassium chloride (KCl). Use a different color ball for each element.

3. Data Bank Use the information on page 637 to answer the following questions.

a. What is the radius of a beryllium ion?

b. How much smaller is a beryllium ion than a beryllium atom?

c. Name an element with atoms that are the same size as the fluoride ion.

Make Connections

1. Link the Concepts Below is a concept map that shows connections between some of the main concepts in this chapter. Only part of the map has been filled in. Copy the map and complete it, using words and ideas from the chapter.

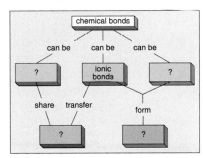

2. Science and Art Cut disks out of heavy paper to represent the outer electron shells of hydrogen, magnesium, oxygen, and chlorine atoms. Make the disks different sizes to account for the different numbers of electron shells in the elements. Draw inner circles to represent inner shells. Then, place pennies on the disks to represent the electrons in each atom. Decide which atoms will form an ionic bond and use the pennies to show how the bond forms. Do the same for atoms that will form covalent bonds.

3. Science and You Find out what dissolved ions your drinking water contains. The utility company or government agency that supplies your water will have this information. Determine if your water is hard, and if any of the ions are present in unusually high amounts.

Overview

This chapter discusses chemical reactions. The first section describes the changes, evidence, mechanics, and energy in chemical reactions. The second section presents guidelines for writing chemical equations. The next section presents the four types of chemical reactions. The chapter ends with a discussion of activation energy, catalysts, and factors affecting reaction rate.

Advance Planner

▶ Provide glasses, thermometers, and ice cubes for TE page 492.

▶ Obtain coins and buttons for TE page 499.

▶ Obtain colored paper clips and colored pencils for TE page 500.

▶ Supply colored pencils for TE page 501.

▶ Prepare sugar, cigarette ashes, and matches for TE page 506.

▶ Collect iron nails, beakers, test tubes and holders, Bunsen burners, copper sulfate solution, sugar, and goggles for SE Activity 20, page 510.

Skills Development Chart

Sections	Calculate	Classify	Communicate	Hypothesize	Infer	Interpret Data	Model	Observe
20.1 Skills WarmUp Skills WorkOut					●		●	
20.2 Skills WarmUp Skills WorkOut SkillBuilder	●		● ●					
20.3 Skills WarmUp Skills WorkOut		●					●	
20.4 Skills WarmUp Skills WorkOut Activity				● ●	●	●		●

Individual Needs

▶ **Limited English Proficiency Students** Have students work in cooperative groups of three. Each group should use index cards to make a deck of chemical reaction cards. Have them draw and color shapes to represent chemicals and compounds in chemical reactions. Groups should prepare three cards for each type of reaction: one for reactants, one for product or products, and one with an arrow for "yield." Have groups match the cards with definitions and diagrams, or pick a card and give the information on the other two cards. Have them use these cards during the chapter review.

▶ **At-Risk Students** Write the titles of the four chapter sections on the chalkboard. Have students copy each title onto a page in their science journals. As students read each section, have them find a photograph in a magazine or newspaper that relates to the main idea or concepts in each subsection—except the Science and You, Science and Society, and Science and Technology features. Have them write a sentence that tells how the photograph connects to the content in the subsection.

▶ **Gifted Students** Ask a fire department representative to come to class to discuss the types of chemicals and procedures used in fire fighting. Also, have them discuss the safe disposal of hazardous chemicals.

Resource Bank

▶ **Bulletin Board** Title the bulletin board *Puzzling Reactions* and prepare several index cards with numbers (coefficients) and yield arrows. Invite students to choose equations for various chemical reactions. They should write the chemical symbol for each reactant and product on separate cards. Scatter the symbols, coefficients, and arrows on the bulletin board. Encourage students to use the cards to assemble balanced equations.

Section	Core	Standard	Enriched
20.1 Characteristics of Chemical Reactions pp. 489–493			
Section Features Skills WarmUp, p. 489 / Skills WorkOut, p. 491	•	• •	• •
Blackline Masters Review Worksheet 20.1 / Skills Worksheet 20.1	•	• •	• •
Color Transparencies Transparency 74	•	•	•
Laboratory Program Investigation 36		•	•
20.2 Chemical Equations pp. 494–498			
Section Features Skills WarmUp, p. 494 / Skills WorkOut, p. 495 / SkillBuilder, p. 497	• •	• • •	• • •
Blackline Masters Review Worksheet 20.2	•	•	
Color Transparencies Transparency 75	•	•	•
20.3 Types of Chemical Reactions pp. 499–502			
Section Features Skills WarmUp, p. 499 / Skills WorkOut, p. 502	•	• •	• •

Section	Core	Standard	Enriched
Blackline Masters Review Worksheet 20.3 / Skills Worksheet 20.3 / Integrating Worksheet 20.3	•	• • •	• • •
Color Transparencies Transparencies 76, 77	•	•	•
20.4 Energy and Reaction Rate pp. 503–510			
Section Features Skills WarmUp, p. 503 / Skills WorkOut, p. 508 / Career Corner, p. 507 / Activity, p. 510	• •	• • • •	• • • •
Blackline Masters Review Worksheet 20.4 / Enrich Worksheet 20.4 / Integrating Worksheet 20.4a / Integrating Worksheet 20.4b / Vocabulary Worksheet 20	• •	• • • • •	• • • • •
Ancillary Options *CEPUP,* Activities 1–2 in Solutions and Pollution	•	•	•
Overhead Blackline Transparencies Overhead Blackline Master 19 and Student Worksheet		•	•
Color Transparencies Transparency 78	•	•	•

Bibliography

The following resources can be used for teaching the chapter. See page T-46 for supplier codes.

Library Resources

Ardley, Neil. The World of the Atom. New York: Gloucester Press, 1990.

Sherwood, Martin, and Christine Sutton. The Physical World. New York: Oxford University Press, 1988.

Technology Resources

Internet

PLANETDIARY at *http://www.planetdiary.com*
- Learn more about the atmosphere in *Atmosphere* by clicking on *Phenomena Backgrounders.*
- Find out more about fire in *Fire* by clicking on *Phenomena Backgrounders.*
- Find meteorological news in *Current Phenomena.*

Software

All About Science I. Mac, Dos. ESI.
Learning All About Matter. Mac, Win. LS.
Superstar Science. Mac, Win. LS.

Laserdiscs

Living Textbook. (See barcodes on pages in this chapter.) Optical Data.

Videos

Special Topics in Chemistry. FM.

Audio-Visual Resources

Chemical Reactions. Still frame. FM.
Investigating Matter, Chemical Reaction. Filmstrip and cassette. EB.

 Writing Connection

Have students imagine they're on a walk with a friend who is sight deficient. They come to a rusty metal door. Students should write a brief description of the door as though they were describing it to their friend. Encourage them to use as many metaphors as possible. They should use images that relate to touch, sound, smell, and temperature.

Introducing the Chapter

Have students read the description of the photograph. Ask if they agree or disagree with the description.

Directed Inquiry

Have students study the photograph. Ask:

▶ What do you think the photograph shows? (It shows metal sheets partly covered with rust.)

▶ Where do you think the rust has come from? (Students may say that the metal and air or oxygen made the rust.)

▶ Why is some of the metal completely free of rust? (Students may respond that it has some coating to keep the air away.)

▶ Why do you think this photograph is used for a chapter about chemical reactions? (The formation of rust is a chemical reaction.)

Chapter Vocabulary

activation energy	endothermic
catalyst	reaction
chemical	enzyme
equation	exothermic
chemical reaction	reaction
coefficient	product
decomposition	reactant
reaction	single-replace-
double-replace-	ment reaction
ment reaction	synthesis reaction

 **The Living Textbook:**
Physical Science Sides 1-4

Chapter 17   Frame 02846
Chemical Change (2 Frames)
Search: Step:

488

Chapter 20   Chemical Reactions

What do you see?

❝I see what looks like small sheets of metal overlapping to form one large piece of metal with ridges. The metal is covered with an orangish-brown substance. I think the orangish-brown substance is rust, and it formed by the metal being exposed to oxygen. Rust is composed of iron and oxygen.❞

Bridget Dunne
Swanson Middle School
Arlington, Virginia

To find out more about the photograph, look on page 512. As you read this chapter, you will learn about chemical reactions.

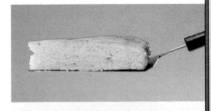

Themes in Science

Patterns of Change/Cycles

Explain that all chemical reactions cause substances to change in ways that can be predicted. As they read this chapter, have students look for patterns in the ways elements combine and separate in chemical reactions. Ask students to think about an image they could use to express patterns or cycles.

Section Objectives
For a list of section objectives, see the Student Edition page.

Skills Objectives
Students should be able to:

Infer from observations.

Make a Model showing a chemical reaction.

Classify endothermic and exothermic reactions.

Vocabulary
chemical reaction, exothermic reaction, endothermic reaction

20.1 Characteristics of Chemical Reactions

Objectives

▶ **Identify** everyday chemical reactions.

▶ **Describe** four kinds of evidence for chemical reactions.

▶ **Distinguish** between exothermic and endothermic chemical reactions.

▶ **Make a model** that shows bonding changes in a chemical reaction.

▼ **ACTIVITY**

Inferring

New Substances

Make a list of substances created from other substances. What evidence do you have that each is a new substance or that a chemical change took place when the substance was produced?

SKILLS WARMUP

W hat ingredients do you need to bake a cake? Include flour, eggs, sugar, water—and don't forget the baking powder! The person who baked the cake in the top of Figure 20.1 forgot to add baking powder, and look what happened. The cake didn't rise. What is it about baking powder that makes a cake rise?

Baking powder contains substances that begin to undergo a chemical change when they are mixed with water. The substances combine to produce bubbles of carbon dioxide gas. When these gas bubbles are trapped in the cake batter, they cause a cake to rise.

Chemical Changes and Chemical Reactions

If you think about it, chemical changes similar to what happens to baking powder occur all the time. Recall that a chemical change in matter results in a new substance being formed. New substances are produced when you fry an egg, eat a piece of pizza, operate a power mower, snap a photograph, or light a candle. Even as you read these words, the cells in your body are creating new substances that you need to survive.

What is actually happening to atoms and molecules when a chemical change occurs? Every chemical change involves a **chemical reaction**. When a chemical reaction occurs, chemical bonds between atoms or ions break, and new bonds form between different atoms or ions. A chemical reaction creates one or more new substances. The new substance has properties that are different from the properties of the original substances.

Figure 20.1 ▲

Which of these cakes was baked without baking powder?

MOTIVATE

Skills WarmUp
To help students understand characteristics of chemical reactions, have them do the Skills WarmUp.
Answer Answers will vary. Students may respond that chemical changes have taken place when the new substances are different in color or texture (rust compared to iron), when bubbles of gas are produced (baking powder and water), or when heat or light is given off (burning occurs).

Prior Knowledge

Gauge what students know about the difference between physical and chemical reactions by asking, What is a physical change and a chemical change?

Answer to In-Text Question

① The cake at the top

The Living Textbook:
Physical Science Sides 1-4

Chapter 17   Frame 02856
Chemical Reaction (2 Frames)
Search: Step:

489

Discuss

Have students read about chemical reactions, then discuss the contrast between chemical changes and physical changes. (Chemical reactions create new substances; physical changes alter only the physical appearance.)

Directed Inquiry

After students have read about the evidence for chemical reactions, have them discuss the following:

▶ What are four changes that indicate a new substance is being produced? (There is a precipitate, a color change, a release of energy, or formation of a gas.)

▶ Briefly describe a precipitate. (It is a solid that separates from the liquids.)

▶ How can you tell if energy is released during a chemical reaction? (See light or feel heat)

▶ What does the color change indicate when you mix two colorless solutions together and a bright yellow product forms? (The color change shows a chemical reaction occurred.)

▶ Give an example of a gas formed in cooking. (The holes in bread are formed by gas given off during rising.)

 The Living Textbook: Physical Science Side 4

Chapter 34   Frame 39862
Color Changes (Movie)
Search: Play:

 The Living Textbook: Physical Science Side 4

Chapter 32   Frame 38360
Precipitation (Movie)
Search: Play:

Integrating the Sciences

Earth Science Remind students that fossil fuels, such as oil and coal, are the result of chemical changes that occurred when plants and animals decayed. Ask students to discuss why methane gas (swamp gas) is given off in a swamp. (The rotting vegetation is a chemical reaction that gives off methane gas.)

Evidence for Chemical Reactions

You can't see chemical bonds breaking or forming. So how do you know when a chemical change is happening? If you have a window in your oven, you can watch a cake bake and see little bubbles break the surface. These bubbles are evidence that a chemical reaction is taking place in the cake batter. Most chemical reactions give you very good clues that a new substance is being produced. Here are four of the most important kinds of clues.

Precipitate
A white substance forms when household ammonia is added to a solution of alum. The white substance is called a *precipitate* (pree SIHP uh TAYT). The appearance of a precipitate is a sign of a chemical reaction. ▼

Color Change ▲
The colorful substance is a clue that a chemical reaction occurred. Here a colorless solution is added to another colorless solution to form a bright yellow product.

Release of Energy
Many chemical reactions give off some form of energy. Here you can see light energy given off by burning magnesium. Other reactions release heat energy alone. ▼

Gas Formation
◀ The release of gas indicates that a chemical reaction is taking place. Hydrogen gas bubbles form as zinc reacts with hydrochloric acid.

Integrating the Sciences

Life Science Explain to students that color changes in autumn leaves are the result of chemical reactions. Plants produce chlorophyll, a green pigment, in order to absorb light energy for photosynthesis. In autumn, as the amount of sunlight decreases, the amount of chlorophyll decreases, allowing the plants' other pigments to be visible. Have students find out what part the pigments *carotenoids*, *xanthophylls*, and *anthocyanins* play in autumn leaf displays. (Carotenoids—orange, yellow, red; xanthophylls—yellow; anthocyanins—purple, scarlet, blue)

Mechanics of Chemical Reactions

During a chemical reaction, at least one new substance with different properties is produced. Look at Figure 20.2 below. It shows a chemical reaction. The original substances are on the left. What are they? What elements make them up? How are the atoms bonded? The new substance produced in the reaction is on the right. What has changed during the reaction? How did these changes occur?

Notice that in the original substances on the left, chemical bonds join atoms of the same element. When the two different molecules come together with enough energy, the bonds that hold the atoms together begin to break. At the same time, new bonds form. Take a look at Figure 20.2. Each chlorine atom begins to form a bond with a hydrogen atom. New hydrogen chloride molecules are produced when the old bonds break. Now the chemical bonds are between atoms of different elements. Hydrogen chloride molecules have been formed. All this takes place in a very short, almost immeasurable, period of time.

As you will see, there are many kinds of chemical reactions. Compounds can break down into elements, and elements can join to form compounds. Compounds can react with elements or other compounds to form one, two, or more new substances. The substances involved in a chemical reaction can be pure metals, ionic solids, or covalently bonded molecules. They can be solids, liquids, or gases.

In all chemical reactions, however, old bonds break and new bonds form. The same elements present in the original substances are also present in the new substances. The atoms or ions are simply rearranged during the reaction. Why do you think the atoms remain as either an element or in a compound? ①

▼ ACTIVITY

Making a Model

Reaction Model

Using Figure 20.2 as an example, draw a model that shows how atoms are rearranged in the following reaction. A molecule of CH_4 reacts with two molecules of O_2 to form a molecule of CO_2 and two molecules of H_2O.

SKILLS WORKOUT

Figure 20.2
In a chemical reaction, bonds between atoms break and re-form between different atoms.
▼

A chlorine molecule (Cl_2) and a hydrogen molecule (H_2) are about to collide.

The molecules collide, and the reaction occurs.

The reaction produces two hydrogen chloride (HCl) molecules.

Skills WorkOut

To help students make a model to show how atoms are arranged in a reaction, have them do the Skills WorkOut.

Answer Be sure students rearrange the atoms to produce the products CO_2 and $2H_2O$.

Discuss

You may wish to clarify for students what the results of a chemical reaction are. Stress that if a reaction occurs, at least one new substance is always created. A new substance is recognizable because it will have different properties than the original substances.

Directed Inquiry

After students have studied Figure 20.2, ask:

▶ What are the elements and compounds in this reaction? (The elements are chlorine and hydrogen; the compound is hydrogen chloride.)

▶ Look at bonds in the original substances. How do the bonds in the chlorine and hydrogen change as a result of the reaction? (Chlorine atoms bond together and hydrogen atoms bond together in the original substances. In the chemical reaction, hydrogen bonds to chlorine, forming hydrogen chloride molecules.)

Answer to In-Text Question

① **The outer energy levels tend to become filled as a result of the reaction. Atoms remain as elements and compounds if they are stable.**

**The Living Textbook:
Physical Science Sides 1-4**

Chapter 8   Frame 01268
Chemical Reaction (1 Frame)
Search:

491

TEACH ▪ *Continued*

Directed Inquiry

Have students study this page. Then lead a discussion using the following questions:

▶ How does the law of conservation of mass and energy apply to an exothermic reaction? (Any energy released in an exothermic reaction was present in the chemical bonds of the reacting substances. Any energy absorbed becomes part of the new chemical bonds formed. Mass is also conserved; it is rearranged.)

▶ Can you think of any exothermic or endothermic reactions that occur in animals? (Accept answers that reflect an understanding of energy release and energy absorption.)

▶ **Infer** Suppose two liquids are combined in a beaker, and you pick up the beaker and find that it is warm. What kind of reaction has taken place? Why? (Exothermic; heat was given off.)

Answer to In-Text Question

① Heat energy is absorbed.

 The Living Textbook: Physical Science Side 4

Chapter 33   Frame 39426
Exothermic Reaction (Movie)
Search: Play:

492

Integrating the Sciences

Life Science Ask students to think about chemical reactions that result in new substances in plants. Point out that photosynthesis (the process by which plants manufacture glucose using light energy) is an endothermic reaction, one that absorbs energy. Respiration (the process by which plants take in oxygen from the air, use it to make glucose, and then return the by-products—carbon dioxide and water—to the air) is exothermic because the breakdown of the molecules during respiration produces energy.

Energy and Chemical Reactions

Energy changes occur whenever chemical bonds break or form. Some chemical reactions release energy; others absorb energy. The law of conservation of mass and energy, however, applies to chemical reactions.

In other words, chemical reactions do not create or destroy energy. Any energy released in a reaction was present in the chemical bonds of the original substances. Any energy absorbed in a reaction becomes part of the chemical bonds of the new substances.

Exothermic Reactions You probably can think of several chemical reactions that release energy. Such reactions heat your home, cook your food, and run your family's car. The explosion in Figure 20.3 is a chemical reaction that released a large amount of energy.

A reaction that releases energy is called an **exothermic** (EHK soh THER mihk) **reaction**. All exothermic reactions fit this chemical description.

$$\text{original substances} \longrightarrow \text{new substances} + \text{energy}$$

Figure 20.3 ▲
An explosion is a very exothermic chemical reaction.

Exothermic reactions most often produce energy in the form of heat, light, or electricity.

Endothermic Reactions Chemical reactions that absorb energy, called **endothermic** (EHN doh THER mihk) **reactions**, are probably less familiar to you. Here is the chemical description for an endothermic reaction.

$$\text{original substances} + \text{energy} \longrightarrow \text{new substances}$$

Look at Figure 20.4. If you could feel the glass, you would notice the water becomes colder as the antacid tablet disappears. The chemical reaction that is taking place absorbs heat energy from the water.

Some reactions absorb energy in the form of light or electricity. For example, when you take a photograph, light energy enters the camera. The light energy is absorbed by the film and molecules in the film undergo a chemical change. When an electric current passes through water, the water molecules absorb the energy. The water molecules undergo a chemical change, breaking apart into hydrogen and oxygen.

Figure 20.4 ▲
What kind of energy is absorbed in this endothermic reaction? ①

Multicultural Perspectives

Tell students that gunpowder was developed by the Chinese. Early gunpowder, called black powder, was a mixture of potassium nitrate, charcoal, and sulfur. This form of gunpowder produced large amounts of smoke. Smokeless gunpowder was developed in the 1800s, but it was dangerous to manufacture. Around 1887, Swedish chemist Alfred Nobel made the smokeless powder in general use today. Ask students to find out more about Nobel's work and his reasons for establishing the Nobel Prize.

Science and You
Chemistry Celebration: The Fourth of July

You probably see fireworks every Fourth of July. Have you ever wondered how the dazzling colors and thunderous sounds of fireworks are made? They are carefully controlled exothermic reactions. Safety is a major concern in making fireworks.

Modern fireworks are shells launched from tubes on the ground. A fast-burning fuse ignites a charge of black powder that propels the shell skyward. When the shell is high in the air, a slower-burning fuse ignites other compartments filled with flash powder. Pellets inside these charges produce colors. Usually, another charge explodes in a final big bang.

Making fireworks is both a science and an art. It requires a great deal of knowledge of chemistry. Each color, for example, is the result of a certain mixture of elements or compounds in the pellets. Green stars come from barium compounds, red from strontium, and blue from copper. Because the color-producing compounds aren't very stable, they must be created during the explosion of the charge. Making the right chemical reactions occur in the correct way is one of the biggest challenges of building fireworks.

Each pattern you see when a fireworks shell explodes is the result of a different arrangement of the color-producing pellets inside the flash-powder charges. A fireworks company carefully guards its secret "recipes" for packing its fireworks shells.

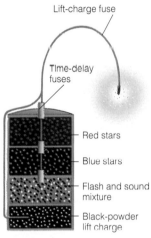

Lift-charge fuse

Time-delay fuses

Red stars

Blue stars

Flash and sound mixture

Black-powder lift charge

Figure 20.5 ▲
Which of the compartments in a fireworks shell ignites first? ②

Check and Explain

1. Describe three everyday chemical reactions.

2. What kinds of evidence can tell you that a chemical reaction is taking place in a beaker?

3. **Compare and Contrast** What is the difference between exothermic and endothermic reactions? How can you identify a reaction as one or the other?

4. **Make a Model** On paper, draw a model that shows how you think the chemical bonds change when an atom of sulfur (S) and a molecule of oxygen (O_2) react to form a molecule of sulfur dioxide (SO_2).

Critical Thinking

Reason and Conclude Have students think about how fireworks ignite. Ask, What kind of reactions cause the exothermic reactions in the shell? Why? (Fuses ignite the lift charge, the color display, and the flash and sound mixture.)

EVALUATE

WrapUp

Reteach Ask if a physical or chemical change occurs in the following: (1) dissolving a powder drink mix in water; (2) using a gasoline-powered mower; (3) lighting a campfire. Students should identify the chemical changes as exothermic or endothermic. (Physical change; chemical change, exothermic; chemical change, endothermic to start fire, then exothermic)

Use Review Worksheet 20.1.

Check and Explain

1. Examples: frying an egg, eating a cookie, and operating a power mower

2. A precipitate, a color change, a release of energy or a gas

3. Both create new substances. An exothermic reaction uses original substances to release energy. An endothermic reaction absorbs energy.

4. Models should show that bonds holding atoms together break, and the sulfur atom bonds with oxygen atoms.

Answer to In-Text Question
② The lift charge compartment

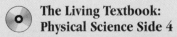

The Living Textbook: Physical Science Side 4

Chapter 25   Frame 14938
Endothermic Reaction (Movie)
Search: Play:

20.2

Section Objectives
For a list of section objectives, see the Student Edition page.

Skills Objectives
Students should be able to:

Communicate in symbols and equations.

Calculate by balancing chemical equations.

Vocabulary
chemical equation, reactant, product, coefficient

MOTIVATE

Skills WarmUp

To help students understand how symbols are used in chemical equations, have them do the Skills WarmUp.

Answer Answers will vary. Encourage students to use clear, simple symbols rather than complicated ones to convey their messages.

Prior Knowledge

Gauge how much students know about chemical equations by asking the following questions:

► How do chemical equations relate to the periodic table?

► What do chemical equations tell you about chemical reactions?

► Why would scientists use chemical equations instead of words?

**The Living Textbook:
Physical Science Sides 1-4**

Chapter 17   Frame 02850
Chemical Equation (2 Frames)
Search: Step:

494

Language Arts Connection

Just as chemists use symbols as shorthand to describe chemical reactions, people in other fields use descriptive symbols. In astronomy, the following symbols are common: Neptune = Ψ, Earth = ⊕, New Moon = ●, and Sun = ☉. In biology, a male organism is ♂ and a female is ♀. Ask students about symbols they see every day. (Various road signs, symbols on maps, weather symbols, and so on)

▼ **ACTIVITY**

Communicating

Secret Code

Write two or three messages to a friend using different pictures as symbols for words.

SKILLS WARMUP

20.2 Chemical Equations

Objectives

► **Identify** the reactants and products of a chemical reaction.

► **Distinguish** between subscripts and coefficients.

► **Communicate** what happens during a chemical change by writing a balanced chemical equation.

Have you ever written a message in a secret code? In one example of a simple number code, 1 represents *A*, 2 represents *B*, and so on. The words *secret code* are written in this code as 19-5-3-18-5-20 3-15-4-5. Pictures can also represent words. What does the picture message ☎ ♥ U mean?

Numbers and pictures are symbols. You use symbols every day because they are very useful. In math, for example, you substitute symbols for words when you solve word problems. What other kinds of symbols do you use regularly?

Chemists use symbols to show what happens during a chemical reaction. Many of these symbols you already know. As you will see, describing a chemical reaction with symbols is much like writing a word puzzle.

Equations in Chemistry

Suppose you want to describe the chemical reaction that occurs when baking soda and vinegar are mixed together. You could say, "Sodium bicarbonate reacts with a solution of acetic acid to produce carbon dioxide gas, sodium acetate, and water." This statement says exactly what you mean, but it takes up a lot of space.

You need a short, precise way to state what happens in a chemical reaction. The way to do this is to write a **chemical equation**. A chemical equation is an expression that uses symbols to describe a chemical reaction. Because the same chemical symbols are used worldwide, a chemical equation can be understood in any country in the world.

An equation is like a sentence in chemical terms. The sentence begins at the left with the formulas for the starting materials, called **reactants** (ree AK tuhnts).

TEACH

Language Arts Connection

Discuss the meaning of the word *equation*. (An expression, algebraic or chemical, stating that two quantities are equal) The root word is *equal*. What does *equal* mean? (That one thing is the same as or like another thing) After students read the page, discuss the word *coefficient*. (A number placed before and multiplied by another number; for example, in $2H_2O$, the number 2 *before* the H.)

Writing Connection

Have students write a letter to a friend using symbols, abbreviations, and pictures. Students can trade letters and see if they can figure out the meaning of each symbol used.

TEACH

Explore Visually

Have students study the symbols and their meanings in Figure 20.6. Have them note that the direction of the reaction is from the left to right. Also, have them observe that all the elements, which are color coded, are on both sides of the equation. Ask the following questions:

▶ On which side of the equation are the starting materials, or reactants? (The left side)

▶ What does the yield sign mean? How is it like the equals sign in mathematics? (It means *yield* or *produce*. In math, the equals sign follows the added numbers and precedes the results.)

▶ Do all chemical reactions involve two or more products? Explain. (No. Help students understand that reactants can sometimes combine into a single product.)

Skills WorkOut

To help students write a chemical equation by means of symbols, have them do the Skills WorkOut.
Answer $S + O_2 \rightarrow SO_2$

Answer to In-Text Question

① **Energy is neither a reactant nor a product because it is not a substance.**

Reactants

Compounds or elements on the left side of the equation are the starting materials, or reactants. When more than one reactant is present, a plus sign separates them.

Yield Sign

As its name implies, the yield sign means "yield" or "produce." It is similar to the equal sign in a mathematical equation.

Products

New substances formed in a reaction are its products. They are placed to the right of the yield sign. A plus sign separates different products when there is more than one.

Figure 20.6 ▲
Parts of a Chemical Equation

The reactants are the substances that undergo a chemical change. When combined, the reactants begin the chemical equation. Look at the chemical equation shown in Figure 20.6. In this equation, the reactants are sodium hydroxide (NaOH) and hydrochloric acid (HCl).

An arrow, called a yield sign, connects the two sides of the equation. The yield sign acts like the verb of the sentence. When you read the chemical equation you read the arrow as "yield." The yield sign also shows the direction of the reaction. The sentence ends with the formulas for the new substances formed by the reaction. The substances formed are called the **products**. As Figure 20.6 shows, the products of this reaction are sodium chloride (NaCl) and water (H_2O).

To show whether a reaction is exothermic or endothermic, the word *energy* is sometimes added to the appropriate side of an equation. Energy, however, is neither a reactant nor a product. Can you explain why? ①

Chemical equations are always written to represent one set of reactants and one set of products. Thus, one equation describes equally well what happens to two molecules or to a beaker full of those molecules. But, as you will see, equations must sometimes be written to include more than one molecule or unit of the same substance.

▼ **ACTIVITY**

Communicating

The Right Equation

Write a chemical equation for the following reaction: Silicon (Si) reacts with oxygen (O_2) to form silicon dioxide (SiO_2).

SKILLS WORKOUT

 The Living Textbook: Physical Science Sides 1-4

Chapter 4   Frame 00971
Models of Reactions (1 Frame)
Search:

Reteach

Help students understand that a balanced chemical equation is like the math equation $3x + 2y + 2x + y = 5x + 3y$. Ask, How many ys are on each side of the equation? (3) How many xs? (5) Students can generalize about the number of each kind of letter. (The number of each letter on both sides of the equal sign must be the same.)

Explore Visually

Have students study the unbalanced and balanced equations in Figure 20.7. Ask:

▶ What does each molecule on the left side of the unbalanced equation contain? (Two hydrogen and two oxygen atoms)

▶ What does the molecule on the right side of the unbalanced equation contain? (One oxygen atom and two hydrogen atoms)

▶ What atom is left in the unbalanced equation? (One oxygen atom)

▶ Ask the same questions for the balanced equation. (Four hydrogen atoms and two oxygen atoms on the left; two hydrogen atoms and one oxygen atom in each molecule on the right)

The Living Textbook: Physical Science Sides 1-4

Chapter 4   Frame 00980
Balanced Equation Model (1 Frame)
Search:

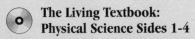

The Living Textbook: Physical Science Sides 1-4

Chapter 4   Frame 00978
Ammonia: Balanced Equation (1 Frame)
Search:

Themes in Science

Energy In all chemical reactions, energy is conserved. Balancing a chemical equation shows conservation of energy by accounting for the total mass and energy involved in a chemical reaction.

Answer to Link

The balanced equation for photosynthesis is as follows:
$$6CO_2 + 6H_2O + \text{light} \rightarrow C_6H_{12}O_6 + 6O_2$$

Life Science LINK

Photosynthesis is the process by which plants use the energy of the sun to make food. A chemical equation shows how this works:

$$CO_2 + H_2O + \text{light} \rightarrow C_6H_{12}O_6 + O_2$$

Rewrite the photosynthesis equation and balance it.

ACTIVITY

Balanced Chemical Equations

Look again at Figure 20.6. How many atoms of sodium are on the left side of the equation? How many are on the right side? Also, count the numbers of hydrogen, oxygen, and chlorine atoms. You should come up with an equal number of atoms for each element on each side of the equation. Why?

The law of conservation of mass and energy states that mass can't be lost or gained in a chemical reaction. The atoms present in the reactants must also be present in the products. Chemical equations, therefore, are often written so that the numbers of each kind of atom on one side equal the numbers of each kind of atom on the other side. A chemical equation written in this way is called a *balanced* chemical equation.

The equation in Figure 20.6 is already balanced. You will come across many chemical equations, however, in which you know the *kinds* of substances involved but not *how many* molecules or atoms of each are present. These equations must be balanced.

When you balance an equation, you write numbers in front of the formulas where they are needed. These numbers, called **coefficients** (KOH eh FIHSH uhnts),

Figure 20.7 ▼
Balancing a Chemical Equation

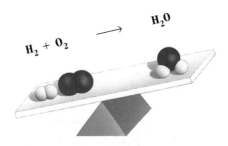

Unbalanced Chemical Equation ▲
Why is this equation unbalanced? Count the number of hydrogen atoms. You'll find there are two on each side. The number of oxygen atoms, however, are not equal on each side. There are two oxygen atoms on the left and only one on the right.

Balanced Chemical Equation
The equation is balanced when the coefficient 2 is placed in front of the formula for water on the right and the formula for hydrogen on the left. You can see that there are now two oxygen atoms on the left and two on the right. There are four hydrogen atoms on the left and four on the right. ▼

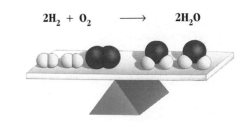

Portfolio

Have students list common substances that have chemical formulas, such as vinegar, cement, sugar, salt, rust, bronze, brass, and water. Have them use the dictionary and record the chemical formula for each substance. Students should add to this list as they study the chapters in this unit.

Critical Thinking

If . . . Then Arguments Point out that hydrogen and oxygen are both gases. Ask, if you were separating water into the two gases, which gas would you collect the bigger volume of? Why? (Hydrogen; there are two hydrogen atoms to one oxygen atom.)

Skills Development

Infer Have students consider how to write the chemical reaction that would separate water into hydrogen and oxygen. (The reaction would be just the opposite of the equation on page 496: $2H_2O \rightarrow 2H_2 + O_2$.)

SkillBuilder

Answers

1. $Ca + 2HCl \rightarrow CaCl_2 + H_2$
2. $2Mg + O_2 \rightarrow 2MgO$
3. $2Na + 2H_2O \rightarrow 2NaOH + H_2$
4. $Br_2 + 2KI \rightarrow 2KBr + I_2$
5. $Zn + 2HCl \rightarrow ZnCl_2 + H_2$
6. $2Fe + 3Cl_2 \rightarrow 2FeCl_3$
7. $2HCl + CaCO_3 \rightarrow CaCl_2 + CO_2 + H_2O$

indicate how many atoms or molecules of a substance are involved in a reaction. For example, $2H_2O$ means there are two molecules of water. Be careful not to confuse coefficients and subscripts. A subscript, which shows how many *atoms* of an element are present in a molecule, can't be changed to balance an equation. Only the coefficient can be changed.

Look at Figure 20.7. The equation on the left needs balancing. Count the number of atoms of hydrogen and oxygen on each side of the equation. As you can see, the hydrogens balance, but the oxygens don't.

How can you make the number of oxygen atoms on the right side equal the number on the left side while keeping the hydrogens balanced? You can put a 2 in front of the formula for hydrogen and a 2 in front of the formula for water. With these coefficients, the equation says that two molecules of hydrogen and one molecule of oxygen react to form two molecules of water.

SkillBuilder *Calculating*

Writing Chemical Equations

Writing chemical equations is an important skill that you learn through practice. Write chemical equations for the word equations that follow. Each problem includes the formulas you need to write the equation.

1. Calcium and hydrochloric acid yield calcium chloride and hydrogen.

   hydrochloric acid: HCl
   calcium chloride: $CaCl_2$ hydrogen: H_2

2. Magnesium and oxygen yield magnesium oxide.

   oxygen: O_2
   magnesium oxide: MgO

3. Sodium and water yield sodium hydroxide and hydrogen.

   sodium hydroxide: NaOH

Remember that an equation is not finished until it is balanced. Go back and balance each of the equations you've just written by following these steps.

a. Count the number of atoms of each element on each side of the equation.
b. Use coefficients to balance the numbers of atoms.
c. Check your work by repeating step a.

Are you getting better at balancing equations? Sharpen your skill even more by balancing the equations below.

4. $Br_2 + KI \longrightarrow KBr + I_2$
5. $Zn + HCl \longrightarrow ZnCl_2 + H_2$
6. $Fe + Cl_2 \longrightarrow FeCl_3$
7. $HCl + CaCO_3 \longrightarrow CaCl_2 + CO_2 + H_2O$

Research

Have students use reference books to find out how ozone is produced naturally. Have them research the history of the depletion of ozone in the atmosphere.

EVALUATE

WrapUp

Reinforce Ask students how they could represent chemical reactions using disks punched or cut from colored paper. Have them assign different colors to the elements that appear in the text equations. Each student can choose two equations and make diagrams, using colored disks to represent the elements' atoms and lines for the bonds between them. Remind them that their diagrams must be balanced. Have pairs exchange diagrams and "translate" them into conventional chemical equations. Discuss how the diagrams relate to the equations.
   Use Review Worksheet 20.2.

Check and Explain

1. Ca and HCl are the reactants; $CaCl_2$ and H_2 are the products.

2. $2NaCl + H_2SO_4 \rightarrow Na_2SO_4 + 2HCl$

3. Subscripts represent the number of atoms in a molecule. Coefficients represent the number of molecules in the reaction. Coefficients can be changed to balance an equation; subscripts cannot be changed.

4. $4Fe + 3O_2 \rightarrow 2Fe_2O_3$

Integrating the Sciences

Meteorology Discuss the altitude of the ozone layer and how it relates to the other layers of the earth's atmosphere. The earth's atmosphere has five basic layers. The *troposphere* extends from the earth's surface to an altitude of 10 km to 16 km. The *stratosphere* extends from the edge of the troposphere to about 50 km. A concentrated layer of ozone between 20 km and 45 km in the stratosphere protects the earth from excess UV light. The *mesosphere* is above the stratosphere and extends to 80 km. Next is the *thermosphere*, which is between 80 km and 600 km above the earth. The final layer is the *exosphere*, which is beyond 600 km.

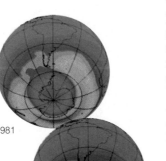
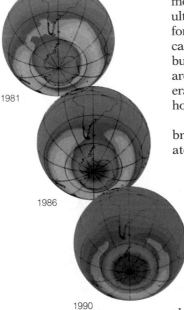

1981

1986

1990

Figure 20.8 ▲
In these computer images, yellow shows areas where the ozone layer is thick. Blue and purple areas have a very thin layer of ozone.

 ## Science and Society
Chain Reactions in the Ozone Layer

High above the earth's surface, a thin layer of ozone molecules protects all life on earth from the sun's harmful ultraviolet radiation. Ozone is a form of oxygen with the formula O_3. In 1974, scientists discovered that substances called chlorofluorocarbons (CLOR oh FLOR oh KAR buhns), or CFCs, were destroying the ozone layer. CFCs are synthetic gases used in some spray cans and in refrigerators and air conditioners. Look at Figure 20.8 to see how the ozone layer over the South Pole has thinned.
   As CFCs rise in the atmosphere, ultraviolet radiation breaks the bonds between their carbon and chlorine atoms.

$$2CF_2Cl_2 \longrightarrow 2CF_2Cl + Cl_2$$

The chlorine molecules produced in this reaction are split apart by ultraviolet radiation to form chlorine atoms.

$$Cl_2 \longrightarrow 2Cl$$

The chlorine atoms then attack ozone molecules.

$$Cl + O_3 \longrightarrow ClO + O_2$$

The ordinary oxygen molecules that result from this chain of reactions don't prevent ultraviolet radiation from reaching the earth's surface. Many people are worried because too much ultraviolet radiation can cause skin cancer and damage food crops. In 1990, 93 nations agreed to stop using CFCs by the year 2000. This action, however, may not be enough to stop the gradual destruction of ozone.

Check and Explain

1. Identify the reactants and the products in this equation: $Ca + 2HCl \longrightarrow CaCl_2 + H_2$.

2. Balance this equation: $NaCl + H_2SO_4 \longrightarrow Na_2SO_4 + HCl$.

3. **Compare and Contrast** How are coefficients and subscripts alike? How are they different?

4. **Communicate** Write a balanced equation for this reaction: iron + oxygen yields iron oxide. The formula for iron oxide is Fe_2O_3.

Integrating the Sciences

Environmental Science Tell students that one air pollutant, sulfur trioxide, combines with water in the air to form sulfuric acid. The acid dissolves the marble, changing it to calcite and gypsum, which crumbles. If the sulfur dioxide in the air does this to marble, ask students what it might do to living things.

Themes in Science

Diversity and Unity There are many types of chemical reactions, but all chemical reactions produce new substances and redistribute energy.

Section Objectives
For a list of section objectives, see the Student Edition page.

Skills Objectives
Students should be able to:

Make a Model to study types of chemical reactions.

Classify chemical reactions by type.

Vocabulary
synthesis reaction, decomposition reaction, single-replacement reaction, double-replacement reaction

20.3 Types of Chemical Reactions

Objectives

▶ **Name** four types of chemical reactions.

▶ **Describe** each type of chemical reaction and give an example of each.

▶ **Classify** chemical equations by reaction type.

▶ **Make a model** that describes the generalized form of each type of chemical reaction.

▼ **ACTIVITY**

Making a Model

Coinage Molecules

Collect a penny, a quarter, a dime, a nickel, and a button.

1. Put the penny and the quarter together on a flat surface to represent a molecule.

2. Make another molecule with a nickel and a dime.

3. Experiment with ways in which these "molecules" can react and form new chemical bonds.

4. Finally, add a button to represent a separate atom and see how it can react with each of the other two molecules.

SKILLS WARMUP

MOTIVATE

Skills WarmUp

To help students understand types of chemical reactions, have them do the Skills WarmUp.

Answer The two "molecules" can each be divided into two "atoms." These atoms can recombine to form 4 new two-atom molecules, 4 new three-atom molecules, or 1 four-atom molecule. Adding a button to a pair could yield 2 new two-atom molecules or 1 three-atom molecule.

As you probably realized when you wrote and balanced chemical equations, there are a great variety of chemical reactions. The number of reactants and products both vary. The substances involved in reactions can be elements or compounds, atoms or molecules. And in different reactions, atoms rearrange themselves in different ways.

Patterns in Chemistry

Scientists have observed and described millions of different chemical reactions. Although each one is unique, there are similarities between reactions. For example, did you notice in the equations you just studied that in several reactions two atoms traded places? The atoms that moved were different each time, but the process of chemical reaction was the same. The closer you look, the more similarities you see. Long ago, scientists realized that when substances react, they follow some basic patterns.

Most chemical reactions can be divided into four main types, depending on the pattern they follow. These reaction types are synthesis reactions, decomposition reactions, single-replacement reactions, and double-replacement reactions. By carefully examining the equation for a reaction, you can determine which of the four types it is. Classifying reactions by type is useful because it helps make sense of the huge variety of chemical reactions in nature.

Prior Knowledge

Gauge how much students know about types of chemical reactions by asking the following questions:

▶ What characteristics could you use to sort chemical reactions into types?

▶ What are some examples of the kinds of substances a chemical reaction produces?

▶ Do chemical reactions involve breaking down substances, combining substances, or both?

Figure 20.9 ▲
Chlorine gas reacts with the iron in steel wool to form a single substance.

Explore Visually

Have students study Figures 20.10 and 20.11. Discuss:

▶ Look at the synthesis reaction. Identify the atoms in each molecule on the left side of the equation. (Nitrogen molecule contains two N atoms; oxygen molecule contains two O atoms.)

▶ Identify the atoms in each product molecule in the synthesis reaction. (Each molecule contains one O and one N atom.)

▶ Look at the decomposition reaction. How are the product molecules different from those in the synthesis reaction? (Each product molecule in the decomposition reaction has the same kind of atom. In the synthesis reaction, they contain different kinds of atoms.)

Skills Development

Infer What usually makes decomposition reactions start? (They start when heat or some other form of energy is applied to the reactant.)

Enrich

Use Enrich Worksheet 20.3.

The Living Textbook: Physical Science Side 4

Chapter 35   Frame 45048
Metals React to Chlorine (Movie)
Search: Play:

The Living Textbook: Physical Science Side 4

Chapter 23   Frame 08683
Decomposition (Movie)
Search: Play:

Art Connection

Have students use geometric shapes, such as triangles or squares, and patterns, such as dots or grids, to make models of synthesis and decomposition reactions. Then have them make models of single-replacement and double-replacement reactions. Have them glue the geometric shapes to paper and present their models to the class.

Language Arts Connection

Ask students to write simple definitions of the terms *synthesize, decomposition,* and *replace.* Have them explain why each term is appropriate for the kind of chemical reaction it describes. (To synthesize is to make a new thing; to decompose is to break apart; to replace is to switch or substitute.)
Use Integrating Worksheet 20.3.

Synthesis Reactions

When two simple substances combine to form a third, more complex substance, a **synthesis reaction** has occurred. The word *synthesize* means "to put together or combine." Synthesis reactions are also called combination, or composition, reactions.

An example of a synthesis reaction is shown in Figure 20.10. Nitrogen combines with oxygen to form nitric oxide. Many other synthesis reactions involve two elements that combine to form a compound. When you heat a mixture of iron (Fe) and sulfur (S), for example, these elements combine to form iron sulfide (FeS).

$$Fe + S \longrightarrow FeS$$

Two compounds can also combine in a synthesis reaction to form a single product. For example, calcium oxide combines with water to form calcium hydroxide.

$$CaO + H_2O \longrightarrow Ca(OH)_2$$

Many synthesis reactions, such as the burning of coal, are exothermic.

$$C + O_2 \longrightarrow CO_2 + heat + light$$

Decomposition Reactions

When a leaf decomposes, it breaks down into simpler substances. The word *decomposition* is used in a similar way in chemistry. In a **decomposition reaction**, a single reactant breaks down into elements or simpler compounds.

Look at the equation in Figure 20.11. It shows the decomposition of water into hydrogen and oxygen. Like many decomposition reactions, the decomposition of water is endothermic. Electric energy must be added to make the reaction happen.

The decomposition of many compounds is triggered by heat. For example, mercury oxide (HgO) decomposes when heated in a test tube. Oxygen gas and silvery beads of mercury are formed.

$$2HgO + heat \longrightarrow 2Hg + O_2$$

If you reverse the arrow of a decomposition reaction, it becomes a synthesis reaction. So, synthesis and decomposition reactions are opposites. Notice that if you reverse the equation for the decomposition of water in Figure 20.11, it becomes the equation for the synthesis of water shown in Figure 20.7.

Figure 20.10 ▶
Synthesis Reaction

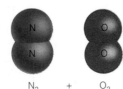

N₂   +   O₂   yield   2NO

Figure 20.11 ▶
Decomposition Reaction

2H₂O   yield   O₂   +   2H₂

Single-Replacement Reactions

Look at the equation in Figure 20.12. It shows the reaction between iron and copper sulfate. The reactants are an element and a compound. The products are a different element and a different compound. If you look closely at the equation, you can see that iron has replaced the copper in copper sulfate. This kind of chemical reaction, in which atoms of one element replace atoms of another element in a compound, is called a **single-replacement reaction**.

Three kinds of single-replacement reactions are possible. In the first, a nonmetal replaces another nonmetal. In the second, a metal atom replaces a hydrogen atom. In the third and most common, a metal replaces another metal.

You can predict if one metal will replace another by comparing their reactivity. Iron replaces copper in the above reaction because iron is more reactive than copper. Gold doesn't react with copper sulfate because gold is less reactive than copper. A list of metals arranged by reactivity is called an activity series of metals.

Double-Replacement Reactions

The reaction in Figure 20.13 shows what happens when silver nitrate and potassium chloride react. These two compounds react to form two new compounds, silver chloride and potassium nitrate. This is an example of a **double-replacement reaction**, in which two positive ions trade places between different ionic compounds.

One common product of a double-replacement reaction is a precipitate. Remember that a precipitate is an insoluble solid that forms in a solution. In the reaction in Figure 20.13, for example, the product silver chloride is a precipitate. The other product, potassium nitrate, stays dissolved in solution. In another reaction, iron chloride combines with ammonium hydroxide to form the precipitate iron hydroxide.

$$FeCl_3 + 3NH_4OH \longrightarrow Fe(OH)_3 + 3NH_4Cl$$

Another common product of a double-replacement reaction is a gas. Sodium chloride combined with sulfuric acid forms sodium hydrogen sulfate and hydrogen chloride gas.

$$NaCl + H_2SO_4 \longrightarrow NaHSO_4 + HCl$$

Figure 20.12 ▼
Single-Replacement Reaction

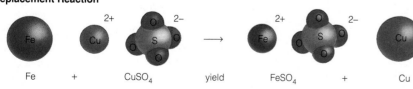

Fe + CuSO₄ yield FeSO₄ + Cu

Figure 20.13 ▼
Double-Replacement Reaction

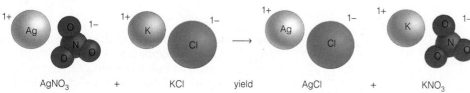

AgNO₃ + KCl yield AgCl + KNO₃

Skills WorkOut

To help students classify a type of reaction, have them do the Skills WorkOut.
Answer It is a double-replacement reaction because two positive ions trade places.

Skills Development

Infer Suppose that a farmer's soil is analyzed and the soil contains too much acid. What might the farmer do to neutralize the acid? (Add a base, such as lime, to the soil.)

EVALUATE

WrapUp

Portfolio Ask students to draw an example of each type of chemical reaction using circles of different colors to represent different atoms and lines to represent bonds. Students should write the chemical equation under each drawing and identify the reaction type. Students can add the drawings to their portfolios.
Use Review Worksheet 20.30.

Check and Explain

1–2. Answers may vary. Synthesis—burning coal: $C + O_2 \rightarrow CO_2$; Decomposition—mercury decomposition: $2HgO + heat \rightarrow 2Hg + O_2$; Single-replacement—reaction of iron and copper sulfate: $Fe + CuSO_4 \rightarrow FeSO_4 + Cu$; Double-replacement—reaction of silver nitrate and potassium chloride: $AgNO_3 + KCl \rightarrow AgCl + KNO_3$

3. a. double-replacement; **b.** synthesis; **c.** single-replacement; **d.** decomposition

4. Answers may vary. Students' models should note the ways elements combine, break down, replace other elements, and create new compounds.

Integrating the Sciences

Life Science Remind students that digestion involves many decomposition reactions. Now that students have learned more about these reactions, ask them what the reactants and products might be in human digestion. (Reactants come from food, and products include molecules used in cells, as well as wastes.)

▼ **ACTIVITY**

Classifying

Reaction Type
The equation to the right shows the reaction between an acid and a base. What type of reaction is it? How do you know?

SKILLS WORKOUT

 Science and You
How Antacids Work

Have you ever had a burning sensation in your chest? It's probably caused by stomach acid backing up into your esophagus, the tube between your throat and stomach. You take an antacid tablet. Soon, you're better. What's the chemistry of your relief?

An antacid contains a base. Bases combine with and neutralize acids. For example, when magnesium hydroxide, which is a base, combines with hydrochloric acid, the following reaction occurs:

$$Mg(OH)_2 + 2HCl \longrightarrow MgCl_2 + 2H_2O$$

The products, magnesium chloride and water, are neither acidic nor basic. The products form a harmless solution of a salt in water.

Of the many bases that can neutralize acids, only a few weak bases are safe enough to be used in antacids. The labels on over-the-counter antacids tell you which weak base they contain. Common weak bases in antacids include magnesium hydroxide and calcium carbonate. Each compound differs in the amount of acid it can neutralize and the rate at which it acts.

Check and Explain

1. List the four types of chemical reactions. Give an example of each.

2. Write a balanced equation that describes each type of chemical reaction.

3. **Classify** Classify each of the following reactions as one of the four types of chemical reactions:

   a. $3KOH + AlCl_3 \longrightarrow Al(OH)_3 + 3KCl$

   b. $2Na + Cl_2 \longrightarrow 2NaCl$

   c. $2Na + 2H_2O \longrightarrow 2NaOH + H_2$

   d. $NH_4NO_2 \longrightarrow N_2 + 2H_2O$

4. **Make a Model** You could describe all synthesis reactions with a general equation like $A + B \longrightarrow AB$. Use your own set of symbols to create similar general equations for each of the four types of reactions.

20.4 Energy and Reaction Rate

Objectives

▶ **Define** activation energy and explain its role in getting a reaction started.

▶ **Identify** three factors that affect the rate of a chemical reaction.

▶ **Describe** how enzymes contribute to body processes.

▶ **Make** a graph showing how a catalyst lowers the activation energy of a chemical reaction.

You may wish it weren't true, but your homework won't get done if you just put your book, paper, and a pencil together on your desk. Nor will your room get clean unless you put some energy into it. Just like any activity, chemical reactions also need energy to happen. Breaking and forming chemical bonds requires energy.

Getting a Reaction Started

Some reactions, as you have seen, occur at room temperature when the reactants are mixed. For example, if you put a piece of sodium in water, the sodium will leap around the water as it reacts violently. It produces a sizzle of hydrogen bubbles, sodium hydroxide, and heat. Other reactions, however, do not occur unless some condition is changed. Heat must be added or pressure must increase.

You may be tempted to think that exothermic reactions always happen by themselves; they don't need any added energy. This inference is logical, but incorrect.

Many familiar reactions, in fact, are exothermic but need added energy before they will happen. The burning of paper, for example, is exothermic. But paper doesn't burst into flame when exposed to air. To get the reaction started, you need to add the heat energy from a lighted match. More than just the energy change of a reaction is needed to explain whether a reaction will start under a certain set of conditions. The key factor for any chemical reaction is how much energy is needed to drive its first step: the breaking of chemical bonds in the reactants.

Figure 20.14 ▲
What is needed to start this reaction between paper and oxygen? ①

Explore Visually

Have students read the page and study the diagram. Then lead a discussion using the following questions:

▶ How is activation energy related to chemical bonds? (The energy is needed to break bonds in a chemical reaction.)

▶ What happens when sufficient activation energy is supplied? (A reaction takes place.)

▶ Why do endothermic reactions need a constant supply of energy? (The reactants absorb energy that must be replaced for the products to keep forming.)

▶ How does the activation energy compare to the energy released by the reaction in the diagram? (The activation energy is slightly greater.)

Discuss

Have students discuss what happens when they push a wagon to the top of a hill and let go. Relate the energy they use to push the wagon to the energy released when the wagon goes downhill.

Ancillary Options

If you are using CEPUP modules in your classroom for additional hands-on activities, experiments, and exercises, have students do Activities one and two in Solutions and Pollution of *Chemical Survey & Solutions and Pollution.*

Social Studies Connection

Point out to students that a small amount of energy can cause a disaster. In 1937, a hydrogen-filled German dirigible, called the Hindenburg, landed in the United States during a thunderstorm. When ignited by lightning, the hydrogen inside the blimp exploded as it combined with oxygen from the air, killing many passengers. Ask students to write an equation for the chemical reaction. ($2H_2 + O_2 \rightarrow 2H_2O$)

STS Connection

Tell students that burning is a very rapid oxidation reaction—a chemical reaction in which substances react with oxygen. Ask students to explain why a blanket wrapped around a small burning object can help put out the flames. (The amount of oxygen available for the reaction is eliminated.)

Activation Energy

The flame of a match provides the energy needed to get the reactants in paper and air to begin to combine. This start-up energy is called **activation energy**. All chemical reactions need some amount of activation energy.

Look at the graph in Figure 20.15. It is an energy graph, a way of showing the energy changes that occur as a reaction goes from reactants to products. The "hill" in the graph shows the activation energy for the reaction.

$$2H_2 + O_2 \longrightarrow 2H_2O$$

The energy it takes to get the reactants over the activation-energy hill can be compared to the energy it would take to push a boulder up a real hill.

The height of the "energy hill" determines the amount of energy needed to get a reaction started. Reactions that happen by themselves at room temperature have a low activation energy.

The energy needed to start the reaction is contained in the energy of the reactants themselves, as measured by their temperature.

Once a reaction has started, the energy level of its products compared to its reactants determines whether it needs a continuous supply of added energy to keep going. An endothermic reaction needs a constant supply of added energy, even if it has a low activation energy.

An exothermic reaction, in contrast, will keep going on its own. The burning of paper is a good example. The energy released as some molecules react provides the activation energy other molecules need to start reacting.

Figure 20.15
An Energy Graph ▼

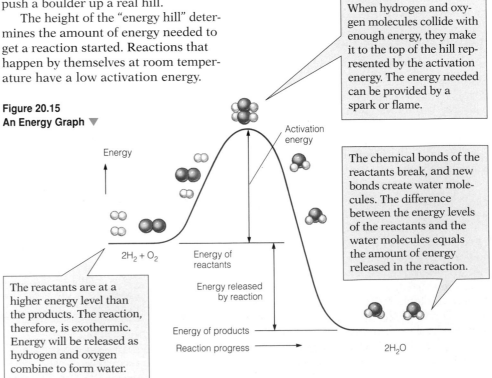

When hydrogen and oxygen molecules collide with enough energy, they make it to the top of the hill represented by the activation energy. The energy needed can be provided by a spark or flame.

The chemical bonds of the reactants break, and new bonds create water molecules. The difference between the energy levels of the reactants and the water molecules equals the amount of energy released in the reaction.

The reactants are at a higher energy level than the products. The reaction, therefore, is exothermic. Energy will be released as hydrogen and oxygen combine to form water.

Energy

Activation energy

$2H_2 + O_2$

Energy of reactants

Energy released by reaction

Energy of products

Reaction progress

$2H_2O$

Cooperative Learning

Have students work in cooperative pairs. Each pair should have two sheets of paper and a metric ruler. One student in each pair should roll a sheet of paper into a tight ball. Have students figure out a way to compare the surface areas of the sheet of paper and the ball of paper. Ask each pair to share its results with the class.

Reaction Rate

A chemical reaction occurs when reactant particles collide with enough energy to break and form chemical bonds. The more reactant particles there are, the more collisions there will be. With more reactant particles, the speed, or rate, of a reaction increases. The reaction rate also increases when the force of the collisions between reacting particles increases. You can control the rate of a reaction, therefore, by changing factors that affect the collisions between reacting particles.

Temperature

An increase in temperature makes particles move faster. They collide more often and with more energy. As a result, more particles react. You can see that the reaction causing a light stick to glow happens faster at a higher temperature. ▼

Surface Area

◄ Have you ever made a fire in a fireplace? Several small pieces of wood ignite faster than one big piece. Why? The total surface area of several small objects is much greater than that of one object with the same volume. Greater surface area means more reactant particles come in contact with each other, causing an increase in the rate of reaction. Solids, for example, react much faster as powders because powders have a very large surface area.

Concentration ▲

A candle burns much faster in pure oxygen than it does in air. The difference is in the number of oxygen molecules available to react with the candle wax. When more particles are packed into a certain space, the number of collisions increases. Therefore, an increase in the concentration of one or more reactants increases the reaction rate.

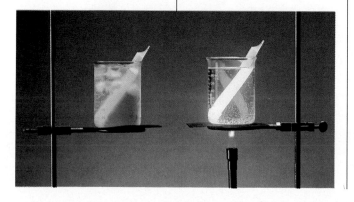

Directed Inquiry

Have students read the page and study the pictures. Then ask:

► What happens to a reaction when more particles collide? (The rate, or speed, of the reaction increases.)

► How do the particles in a reaction behave when the temperature increases? (Absorb energy, move faster, and collide more)

► Why will many small surfaces react more quickly than a few large surfaces? (Many small surfaces have a greater total surface area; the larger the surface, the quicker the reaction.)

► When the concentration of one or more reactants increases, what happens? (The rate of reaction increases because more reactant particles come in contact with one another, providing there is a sufficient amount of all the reactants.)

► **Infer** Suppose the temperature and concentration are lowered, and the surface area is decreased. What would happen to the rate of reaction? Why? (It would decrease because the reactant particles would not collide as often.)

Integrated Learning

Use Integrating Worksheet 20.4a.

The Living Textbook: Physical Science Side 4

Chapter 30   Frame 34138
Temperature and Reaction Rate (Movie)
Search: Play:

The Living Textbook: Physical Science Sides 1-4

Chapter 8   Frame 01299
Concentration (2 Frames)
Search: Step:

TEACH ▪ Continued

Skills Development

Infer Demonstrate how a catalyst works by applying a match flame to two small amounts of sugar, one of which has fine ashes mixed in. The sugar with the ash in it will ignite. Ask students to identify the catalyst and describe its effect. (The ashes lower the activation energy of the mixture to the point where it ignites at the temperature of a match flame.)

Explore Visually

Have students study Figure 20.16, then ask the following questions:

▶ How does this figure resemble an energy graph? (More energy is required to start the reaction, or go over the mountain, without the catalyst, or tunnel.)

▶ What does a catalyst do for the entire reaction? (It changes the rate of the chemical reaction.)

▶ How does the catalyst affect the reaction rate? (By lowering the activation energy, it allows collisions among reactant particles to occur sooner and more frequently.)

Integrated Learning

Use Integrating Worksheet 20.4b.

Answer to In-Text Question

① **A catalyst lowers the amount of activation energy needed for a reaction to occur.**

The Living Textbook: Physical Science Sides 1-4

Chapter 17	Frame 02834
Catalyst (2 Frames)	
Search:	Step:

506

Integrating the Sciences

Biology Compounds called enzymes are biological catalysts. Apple slices dipped in lemon juice do not brown because the lemon changes the enzyme that catalyzes browning. Bromoline in pineapple is an enzyme that breaks down animal tissue. Uncooked pineapple juice is used to tenderize meat.

Social Studies Connection

A *catalyst* can be anything that causes change or makes things happen. Can a person be a catalyst? (Yes. For example, Dr. Martin Luther King, Jr., caused many changes in the United States.) Ask the class for examples of people who were catalysts. (For example, Clara Barton, in the development of nursing; Christopher Columbus, whose voyages changed history. Accept all reasonable answers.)

Catalysts

Many chemical reactions can be made to go much more rapidly without raising the temperature, and without increasing the surface area or concentration of the reactants. All that's necessary is to add a small amount of a substance that speeds up a reaction without being used up in the process, a **catalyst** (CAT uh lihst).

The effect of a catalyst is often very dramatic. If you pour a solution of the common disinfectant, hydrogen peroxide, into a beaker, it will take months for a small amount to decompose quietly into water and oxygen. Add a pinch of the catalyst manganese dioxide (MnO_2), however, and the hydrogen peroxide will decompose so rapidly that oxygen gas fizzes out. How does a catalyst produce such results? ①

Recall that for a chemical reaction to proceed, it needs a certain amount of activation energy. A catalyst lowers the amount of activation energy needed for a reaction to take place. A catalyst does this by providing the necessary energy.

Look at Figure 20.16. It compares a chemical reaction to driving over a hill. Both actions require energy.

**Figure 20.16
Effect of a Catalyst ▼**

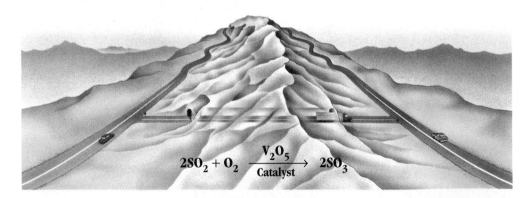

$$2SO_2 + O_2 \xrightarrow[\text{Catalyst}]{V_2O_5} 2SO_3$$

Colliding oxygen and sulfur dioxide molecules must overcome a large activation energy to react and form sulfur trioxide. It is as if they must climb a steep mountain.

The addition of the catalyst V_2O_5 lowers the activation energy of the reaction. It's like using a tunnel through a mountain. Colliding reactants don't need as much energy to react.

With the catalyst, the reaction proceeds rapidly. Large amounts of the product, sulfur trioxide, can be produced because more reactants have the energy needed to react.

Integrating the Sciences

Health Tell students that many substances, such as BHT, are added to foods to preserve freshness. Have students compare the effect of some preservatives and describe how they are alike and different.

Generalize Ask students, What are some of the products that you use that require the work of a quality-control chemist? Explain what you think the chemist needs to test. (Examples might include gym shoes—testing the rubber for durability; snack foods—testing the amount of preservatives in each portion, and their effects; medicine tablets—making sure the tablet dosage doesn't vary.) This may lead students to ask who sets the standards that guide the work of the quality-control chemist. Explain that most standards are set by the United States Food and Drug Administration. Point out that the FDA requires new and proposed products to go through a period of strict testing that often takes years to complete.

Answer to Link

$$starch \xrightarrow{salivary\ amylase} glucose + maltose$$

Once energy has been used to get up the hill, going downhill is easy. A catalyst is compared to a shortcut through the mountain tunnel. It reduces the energy required and allows the reaction to take place.

A catalyst is neither a reactant nor a product in a chemical reaction. When the reaction is over, all the added catalyst can be recovered. When you write an equation for a reaction that uses a catalyst, the catalyst is written above the yield sign. Look at Figure 20.16 to see how this is done.

Catalysts are vital in the manufacturing of many products. Using a catalyst saves energy and reduces costs. A small amount of catalyst can be used over and over. Catalysts are especially useful when changing the factors of temperature, surface area, or concentration is impractical or expensive. Some of the common products that require the aid of catalysts are ammonia, polyester, margarine, and gasoline.

Life Science LINK

There are many catalysts that speed up reactions in the human body. One of these is salivary amylase, which is produced in the mouth. Salivary amylase breaks down starches into sugars called glucose and maltose.

Obtain some saltine crackers. Put one in your mouth and chew it until it tastes sweet.

Write a word equation for the breakdown of starch in your mouth.

ACTIVITY

Career Corner *Quality-Control Chemist*

Who Checks the Quality of Products?

When you wash your hair, how do you know the shampoo won't damage it? Most chemical products used by people are tested for harmful side effects before they are put on the market. Thus, you can be fairly confident that the products won't hurt you.

What if something goes wrong, however, in the manufacturing process? Could a bad batch of a product harm you? Not if the quality-control chemists do their jobs.

Quality-control chemists work in laboratories where they test samples of the different products that people buy.

These chemists make sure that the products contain just the right kinds and amounts of chemicals they are supposed to contain.

If you want to be a quality-control chemist, you need to be good at math. You should also like to work with electronic instruments. A quality-control chemist needs to pay careful attention to a great number of details. A single wrong calculation or missed reading of a number on a computer screen could endanger the health of many consumers.

To get a job as a quality-control chemist, you need a

bachelor's degree in chemistry. In high school, you should take classes in biology, chemistry, physics, algebra, and geometry. English composition and computer classes are also good preparation for this career.

TEACH ▪ *Continued*

Skills WorkOut

To help students hypothesize about catalysts in chemical reactions, have them do the Skills WorkOut.
Answer Answers should reflect an understanding of the particle model of matter that students learned in Chapter 6.

Research

Have students use references to find out about some enzymes that have commercial uses, in addition to the enzymes *rennin* and *invertase*. Ask them to discuss the possible advantages of using these enzymes.

Integrating the Sciences

Life Science Some students in your class may be lactose-intolerant. This intolerance affects many adults, particularly in Asia and Africa, where people seldom drink milk after infancy. Lactose-intolerant people are unable to digest the sugar, lactose, in milk. Their digestive systems do not produce *lactase*, which is the enzyme needed to catalyze the reaction that breaks down lactose. Have students find out why these people are usually able to digest cheese and yogurt. (Cheese: lactose is in the form of lactic acid; yogurt: has active enzymes)

▼ ACTIVITY

Hypothesizing

Catalysts

Using the particle model of matter, form a hypothesis that explains how a catalyst can take part in a chemical reaction but not be changed in the process.

SKILLS WORKOUT

Enzymes: Biological Catalysts

If you chew a potato for a few minutes, you will begin to taste something sweet. Since there is no sugar in the potato, where does the sweet taste come from? The salivary glands in your mouth produce a catalyst that helps split starch molecules in the potato into sugar molecules.

Organisms produce many such catalysts. These biological catalysts are called **enzymes**. Enzymes are protein molecules that control the rate of chemical reactions that occur in living things. Each enzyme affects a specific reaction. These reactions occur thousands or even millions of times faster with enzymes than they would without them.

Some enzymes, such as the one that converts starch to sugar, play a role in the digestion of foods. Other enzymes help in the conduction of nerve impulses, the clotting of blood, the contraction of muscle tissue, and the everyday functioning of cells, tissues, and organs.

Of the more than 2,000 enzymes known to be produced by various living things, about 150 have commercial uses. Cheese, for example, is made with the aid of an enzyme called rennin. Candy makers use an enzyme called invertase to create liquid-centered candies, such as chocolate-covered cherries.

Figure 20.17 ▶
A cheesemaker checks the consistency of milk that has been curdled by rennin.

Integrating the Sciences

Life Science Carbon monoxide is extremely dangerous because when it is inhaled, it replaces the oxygen in the blood. The cells throughout the body do not receive enough oxygen. Ask students to compare carbon monoxide (CO), carbon dioxide (CO_2), and molecular oxygen (O_2). Point out that human blood carries both oxygen and carbon dioxide.

STS Connection

Point out that the two main types of automobile gasoline are leaded and unleaded. Leaded gasoline releases lead compounds when burned. Lead in a car's exhaust fumes destroys catalytic converters. Inside the catalytic converter, lead compounds coat the surface of the catalyst, which is a blend of metals, making the catalytic converter ineffective.

Science and Technology
Catalytic Converters and Smog Reduction

Explosive chemical reactions inside a car's engine are what make the crankshaft turn and the wheels go around. Gasoline reacts with oxygen in the air forming water and carbon dioxide, and releasing energy. In the high temperatures that exist in an engine, other reactions also occur. Nitrogen in the air reacts with the oxygen to form various oxides of nitrogen. Some of the gasoline doesn't burn completely, producing carbon monoxide (CO) and other substances that are known to be harmful to people.

Over the past 20 years, efforts have been made to reduce the amount of harmful gases in automobile exhaust. One of the most important anti-smog devices is the catalytic converter introduced in 1975. A catalytic converter is a mufflerlike reaction chamber installed in a vehicle's exhaust system. It contains several catalysts, usually finely divided metals, such as platinum, palladium, and rhodium.

Look at the diagram of a catalytic converter in Figure 20.18. When a mixture of exhaust gases from the engine and outside air passes over the catalysts, several chemical reactions occur. These reactions change harmful gases into compounds that are safe for both people and the environment.

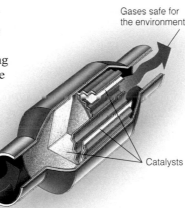

Gases safe for the environment

Catalysts

Harmful gases

Figure 20.18 ▲
What is the purpose of an automobile's catalytic converter? ①

Check and Explain

1. What is activation energy? Draw an energy graph and identify the activation energy.

2. Name three ways to increase the rate of a reaction. Explain how each works.

3. **Reason and Conclude** Use an everyday example to explain why the surface area, temperature, and concentration of reactants affect the rate of a reaction

4. **Make a Graph** A catalyst lowers the activation energy of a certain exothermic reaction by 50 percent. Draw an energy graph showing both the catalyzed and uncatalyzed reactions. Label all of the parts of your graph.

WrapUp

Reinforce Have a class discussion about why an open flame or a spark near a grain storage elevator or in a hospital operating room might cause a disaster. (The grain dust in the elevator and ether in an operating room need a small amount of activation energy to explode.)

Use Review Worksheet 20.4.

Check and Explain

1. Activation energy is the start-up energy that makes reactants combine. Students' graphs should indicate activation energy as it rises up to the tops of their graphs.

2. An increase in temperature allows particles to move faster, increasing collision rates. An increase in surface area provides more reactant particles to make more contact with one another and causes more reactions. An increase in concentration also increases the collision rates of reactants.

3. Answers may vary. For example, the greater surface area of a large piece of firewood increases the rate of reaction for burning the wood; an increase in temperature in the fire causes the wood to burn faster; an increase in the concentration of the particles of some woods causes them to burn longer.

4. Students' graphs should include a large dip in the level of activation energy for a catalyzed reaction and a large rise in activation energy in an uncatalyzed reaction.

Answer to In-Text Question

① **The catalytic converter changes harmful gases into environmentally safe compounds.**

Time 40 minutes **Group** pairs

Materials

15 iron nails

15 beakers

15 test tubes and holders

15 Bunsen burners

copper sulfate solution ($CuSO_4$)

sugar

Analysis

1. The sugar melted first, then burned.

2. The actual products of the combustion of sugar are CO_2, H_2O, and carbon. Students will likely observe only water vapor inside the test tube (although there will also be water vapor on the outside from the Bunsen burner), and smoke. The CO_2 is invisible.

3. A decomposition reaction occurred.

4. The color of the solution fades, while a dark substance (copper) appears on the nail.

5. Copper

6. Single-replacement; one element (Fe) replaces the copper in copper sulfate.

Conclusion

$C_{12}H_{22}O_{11} + O_2 \rightarrow CO_2 + H_2O$ + energy

$Fe + CuSO_4 \rightarrow FeSO_4 + Cu$

The two reactions differ in that the iron-and-copper sulfate reaction is a single-replacement while the burning sugar is a decomposition reaction.

Everyday Application

When food is overcooked, it burns. To prevent burning, keep food below its combustion temperature.

Extension

$C_{12}H_{22}O_{11} + 12O_2 \rightarrow 12CO_2 + 11H_2O$ + energy

$Fe + CuSO_4 \rightarrow FeSO_4 + Cu$

Prelab Discussion

Have students read the entire activity before beginning the discussion. Explain that you have made sure that the nails in this activity are not galvanized. Ask the following questions:

▶ What is galvanization? Why should the nails not be galvanized?

▶ Explain what copper chloride solution contains and how to dispose of it.

Activity 20 *How do some everyday substances react chemically?*

Skills Observe; Infer; Interpret Data

Task 1 Prelab Prep

Collect the following items: iron nail, beaker or glass jar, test tube, copper sulfate solution, sugar, test-tube holder, Bunsen burner.

Task 2 Data Record

On a separate sheet of paper, copy the data table shown. Use the table to record your observations of the chemical reactions.

Task 3 Procedure

1. Put the iron nail in the beaker or jar.

2. Add enough copper sulfate solution to the beaker to cover the nail. Set the beaker aside while you do the next two steps.

3. Place about 1 cm of sugar into the test tube. Light the Bunsen burner. Using the test-tube holder, hold the test tube over the tip of the Bunsen burner flame. Move the test tube around in the flame in order to heat the sugar evenly. **CAUTION! Wear your goggles. Be careful around the open flame. When heating a test tube, hold the open end away from you.**

4. Record in your data table what happens as the sugar is heated.

5. Observe the nail in the copper sulfate solution. Has any change occurred? If not, wait 5 minutes or more.

6. Record in your data table the changes you observe in the nail and the copper sulfate solution.

Task 4 Analysis

1. What changes occurred when you heated the sugar?

2. The formula for sugar is $C_{12}H_{22}O_{11}$. Based on this information and your observations, how many new substances do you think were formed when the sugar was heated? Give reasons for your answer.

3. What type of chemical reaction do you think took place in the sugar?

4. What changes did you observe in the nail or copper sulfate?

5. The formula for copper sulfate is $CuSO_4$. Iron (Fe) replaces the copper in copper sulfate. Knowing this, what do you think makes up the coating you observed on the nail?

6. What type of chemical reaction occurred between the nail and the copper sulfate? How do you know?

Task 5 Conclusion

Describe the two chemical reactions. Explain how they differ.

Everyday Application

What happens when food is heated too hot or for too long? What chemical change occurs? How do you prevent this from happening when you cook your food?

Extension

Write balanced equations for both reactions in this activity.

Reactants	Evidence of Chemical Reaction
Heated sugar	
Copper sulfate and iron	

Chapter 20 Review

Concept Summary

20.1 Characteristics of Chemical Reactions
▶ Evidence of a chemical reaction is formation of a gas or precipitate, energy release, or color change.
▶ During a chemical reaction, bonds among reactants break and new bonds form.
▶ Exothermic reactions release energy; endothermic reactions absorb energy.

20.2 Chemical Equations
▶ In a chemical equation, reactants are on the left and products on the right.
▶ The number of atoms on each side of a chemical equation must be equal.
▶ Coefficients balance an equation.

20.3 Types of Chemical Reactions
▶ In a synthesis reaction, two substances combine to form a third substance. In a decomposition reaction, one substance breaks down to form two or more substances.
▶ In a single-replacement reaction, one element replaces another in a compound; in a double-replacement reaction, the metal elements of two ionic compounds change places.

20.4 Energy and Reaction Rate
▶ All chemical reactions require energy.
▶ A catalyst speeds up a reaction.
▶ Enzymes are catalysts.

Chapter Vocabulary

chemical reaction (p. 489)   product (p. 495)   double-replacement reaction (p. 501)
exothermic reaction (p. 492)   coefficient (p. 496)
endothermic reaction (p. 492) synthesis reaction (p. 500)   activation energy (p. 504)
chemical equation (p. 494)   decomposition reaction (p. 500) catalyst (p. 506)
reactant (p. 494)   single-replacement reaction (p. 501) enzyme (p. 508)

Check Your Vocabulary

Use the vocabulary words above to complete the following sentences correctly.

1. Biological catalysts are called ____ .
2. In a(n) ____ , two elements exchange places in two compounds.
3. In general, a process that causes a chemical change is called a(n) ____ .
4. In a(n) ____ , a metal atom replaces another metal atom.
5. In a(n) ____ , symbols are used to represent a reaction.
6. Reactions that absorb energy are ____ .
7. The left side of a chemical equation contains the ____ .
8. To speed up certain reactions, a(n) ____ can be used.
9. In a(n) ____ , a substance breaks down to form two new substances.
10. Reactions that release energy are ____ .
11. Colliding reactant particles must overcome the ____ to react.
12. The opposite of a decomposition reaction is a(n) ____ .
13. Balanced equations may have ____ .
14. A reaction produces ____ .

Write Your Vocabulary

Write sentences using the vocabulary words above. Show that you know what each word means.

Check Your Knowledge

1. The formation of a precipitate, a gas, a color change, or the release of energy as heat or light shows that a chemical reaction has occurred.

2. When an equation is balanced, there are the same number of atoms of each element on each side of the equation. All the matter on the reactant side of the equation is present on the product side.

3. The atoms in reactant molecules are rearranged in a chemical reaction, creating products.

4. Subscripts indicate the number of atoms of a particular kind of element in each molecule of a compound. Coefficients indicate the numbers of each type of molecule involved in a chemical reaction.

5. In a synthesis reaction, two simpler compounds combine to form a more complex compound, often releasing energy in the process. In a decomposition reaction, a compound breaks apart into two or more simpler compounds, often using energy.

6. In both reactions, atoms in one compound are replaced by atoms of another element. In a single-replacement reaction, one element replaces an element in another compound. In a double-replacement reaction, two positive ions trade places between two different ionic compounds.

7. Once you get the ball to the top of the hill, it will roll down the other side by itself. Once the molecules in a chemical reaction have been given enough energy, the reaction will continue on its own.

8. For a reaction to occur, the reactants must be brought into physical contact and sufficient energy must be available.

9. precipitate

10. absorbed

11. coefficients

12. releases energy

13. speeds up

Check Your Understanding

1. a. endothermic
   b. exothermic
   c. exothermic

2. a. zinc in concentrated hydrochloric acid
   b. zinc in sulfuric acid at 20°C

3. The zinc itself is more reactive than the iron and actually oxidizes, preventing oxygen from reaching the iron.

4. a. synthesis
   b. single-replacement
   c. decomposition
   d. double-replacement

5. a. $BaCl_2 + Na_2SO_4 \longrightarrow BaSO_4 + 2NaCl$
   b. $2PbO_2 \longrightarrow 2PbO + O_2$

6. The chemical processes slow down because of a lowered body temperature.

Chapter 20 Review

Check Your Knowledge

Answer the following in complete sentences.

1. What observations might lead you to conclude that a chemical reaction has occurred?

2. In what way does a balanced chemical equation relate to the law of conservation of mass and energy?

3. Describe how reactants are related to products.

4. What is the difference between a subscript and a coefficient?

5. Compare synthesis and decomposition reactions.

6. How are single- and double-replacement reactions similar and how are they different?

7. Why is activation energy like rolling a ball to the top of a hill?

8. What must occur if two reactant particles are to react?

Choose the answer that best completes each sentence.

9. The production of a (catalyst, enzyme, precipitate, coefficient) is evidence of a chemical reaction.

10. During a chemical reaction, energy may be (created, absorbed, destroyed, changed into matter).

11. To balance a chemical equation, you add (coefficients, subscripts, formulas, atoms).

12. An exothermic reaction (releases energy, creates a radioactive substance, creates matter, absorbs energy).

13. A catalyst (slows down, stops, speeds up, reverses) a chemical reaction.

Check Your Understanding

Apply the concepts you have learned to answer each question.

1. **Classify** Identify each of the following reactions as exothermic or endothermic.

   a. $2H_2O + electricity \rightarrow 2H_2 + O_2$
   b. $2Na + 2H_2O \rightarrow 2NaOH + H_2 + heat$
   c. $2H_2 + O_2 \rightarrow 2H_2O + heat, light, and sound$

2. **Predict** In each pair of reactions, which will go faster?

   a. Zinc in concentrated hydrochloric acid or zinc in dilute hydrochloric acid?

   b. Zinc in sulfuric acid at 15°C or zinc in sulfuric acid at 20°C?

3. **Mystery Photo** The photograph on page 488 shows iron siding that was protected with a thin layer of zinc to prevent rusting. In places where the zinc is gone, rust has formed. Hypothesize why zinc prevents iron from rusting.

4. Classify each reaction below as synthesis, decomposition, single replacement, or double replacement.

   a. $Zn + S \rightarrow ZnS$
   b. $MgBr_2 + 2K \rightarrow Mg + 2KBr$
   c. $C_{12}H_{22}O_{11} \rightarrow 12C + 11H_2O$
   d. $BaCl_2 + H_2SO_4 \rightarrow BaSO_4 + 2HCl$

5. Balance the following equations.

   a. $BaCl_2 + Na_2SO_4 \rightarrow BaSO_4 + NaCl$
   b. $PbO_2 \rightarrow PbO + O_2$

6. **Find Causes** Why do you think chemical processes slow down in hibernating animals?

Develop Your Skills

1. a. Endothermic; the energy of the products is greater than that of the reactants.

   b. the products

   c. *A* represents the activation energy for the reaction; *B* represents the amount of energy absorbed.

2. a. sodium

   b. Yes; aluminum is slightly more active than iron.

   c. No; the copper will not replace the magnesium because the magnesium is higher in the activity series.

Make Connections

1.

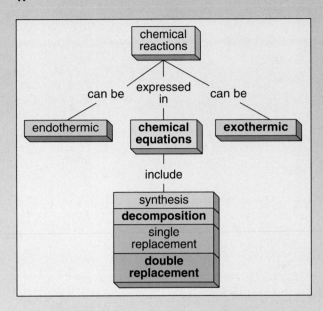

2. Student stories will vary. Make sure they demonstrate an understanding of the role of catalysts in chemical reactions.

3. Student responses will vary. Most major efforts have involved finding environmentally safe chemicals that have the same function as CFCs in consumer products.

Develop Your Skills

Use the skills you have developed in this chapter to complete each activity.

1. Interpret Data The energy graph below shows the energy level of the reactants and products of a certain chemical reaction.

   a. Does this graph represent an exothermic or an endothermic reaction? How do you know?

   b. Which has the greater amount of energy, the reactants or the products?

   c. What does *A* represent? What does *B* represent?

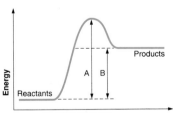

2. Data Bank Use the information on page 638 to answer the following questions.

   a. Which is more reactive, sodium or magnesium?

   b. Zinc replaces copper in a certain single-replacement reaction because zinc is more reactive than copper. Will aluminum replace iron in Fe_2O_3? Explain.

   c. Will copper replace magnesium in $MgBr_2$? Explain.

Make Connections

1. Link the Concepts Below is a concept map showing how some of the main concepts in this chapter link together. Only parts of the map are filled in. Copy the map. Using words and ideas from the chapter, complete the map.

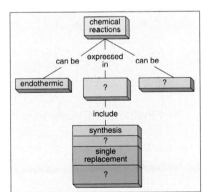

2. Science and Literature Write a short story using the title "The Catalyst." The story should be about a relationship among three people and how one "catalyzes" a change in the other two. Try to explain the human interaction so that it is similar in some way to chemical reactions.

3. Science and Society Do research to find out how the uses and production of CFCs are being regulated to protect the ozone layer. Suggest additional laws or regulations you think would be effective. Find out what substances are being developed to replace CFCs.

Overview

This chapter focuses on solution chemistry. The first section identifies types of solutions, the factors that affect solution rate and solubility, and the concentration of solutions. The next section describes suspensions and five kinds of colloids. The final section discusses the properties of acids, bases, and salts. The pH scale is also discussed.

Advance Planner

▶ Supply sugar, salt, and other ionic salts for TE pages 515 and 516.

▶ Supply some common mixtures and solutions, and flashlights for activity on TE page 523.

▶ Provide red and blue litmus paper for TE page 529.

▶ Obtain distilled water, glass containers, baking soda, colorless vinegar, red and blue litmus paper, phenolphthalein solution, and samples for testing for SE Activity 21, page 532.

Skills Development Chart

Sections	Classify	Communicate	Compare and Contrast	Define Operationally	Infer	Interpret Data	Observe
21.1 Skills WarmUp Skills WorkOut SkillBuilder		●		●		●	●
21.2 Skills WarmUp Skills WorkOut	●						●
21.3 Skills WarmUp Consider This Activity		● ●	●		●	●	●

Individual Needs

▶ **Limited English Proficiency Students** Write the titles of the three chapter sections on the chalkboard. Have students copy each title onto a page in their portfolio. As students read each section, have them write the boldface chapter terms on the appropriate pages, leaving space between the terms. Ask them to define each term in their own words. Have students identify a substance that relates in some way to each term. Where appropriate, students should use chemical formulas in their sentences.

▶ **At-Risk Students** Write the terms *solutions and concentrates, colloids,* and *acids and bases* on the chalkboard. Have students copy each term onto a page of their science journal. Then ask them to find advertisements in magazines and newspapers for products in each of these categories. Have them make a collage of the products in their portfolio.

▶ **Gifted Students** Invite students to write a news release or a science fiction story about the discovery of a substance that dissolves every other kind of matter. Remind them to explore the problems that would accompany such a universal solvent.

Resource Bank

▶ **Bulletin Board** Use thick strips of construction paper to divide the bulletin board into three parts, one for each section of the chapter. Encourage students to create a collage for each of the three sections by attaching photos, diagrams, original drawings, symbols, formulas, and equations to the appropriate areas of the board. Have students add labels listing the chemicals in the products illustrated. Students with access to computers may wish to experiment with different programs in making symbols, formulas, and equations.

▶ **Field Trip** Take students to a manufacturing plant that includes emulsifiers in their products. This might be a food processing plant that makes products such as mayonnaise, salad dressing, or chocolate candy, or a manufacturing plant that makes cleaning products such as liquid soap or shampoo. Be certain to tell the guide that the students will be interested in seeing the products before and after emulsifiers are added.

Section	Core	Standard	Enriched	Section	Core	Standard	Enriched
21.1 Solutions pp. 515–521				**21.3 Acids, Bases, and Salts** pp. 527–532			
Section Features Skills WarmUp, p. 515 Skills WorkOut, p. 517 SkillBuilder, p. 520	● ●	● ● ●	● ● ●	**Section Features** Skills WarmUp, p. 527 Consider This, p. 530 Activity, p. 532	● ●	● ● ●	● ● ●
Blackline Masters Review Worksheet 21.1 Skills Worksheet 21.1a Skills Worksheet 21.1b Integrating Worksheet 21.1	● ● ●	● ● ● ●	● ● ● ●	**Blackline Masters** Review Worksheet 21.3 Skills Worksheet 21.3 Integrating Worksheet 21.3a Integrating Worksheet 21.3b Vocabulary Worksheet 21	● ● ●	● ● ● ● ●	● ● ● ● ●
Laboratory Program Investigation 37		●	●	**Ancillary Options** *CEPUP*, Activities 3–7 in Solutions and Pollution *Multiculturalism in Mathematics, Science, and Technology*, p. 41	● ●	● ●	● ●
21.2 Suspensions and Colloids pp. 522–526							
Section Features Skills WarmUp, p. 522 Skills WorkOut, p. 526		● ●	● ●	**Overhead Blackline Transparencies** Overhead Blackline Master 20 and Student Worksheet	●	●	●
Blackline Masters Review Worksheet 21.2 Reteach Worksheet 21.2 Integrating Worksheet 21.2	● ● ●	● ● ●	● ● ●	**Laboratory Program** Investigation 38 Investigation 39	●	● ●	● ●

Bibliography

The following resources can be used for teaching the chapter. See page T-46 for supplier codes.

Library Resources

Ardley, Neil. The World of the Atom. New York: Gloucester Press, 1990.

Corrick, James A. Recent Revolutions in Chemistry. New York: Franklin Watts, 1986.

The Diagram Group. Comparisons. New York: St. Martin's Press, 1980.

Technology Resources

Software

All about Science I. Mac, Dos. ESI.
Great Physical Science Knowledge Race. Dos. ESI.
Molecules. Dos. ESI.
Superstar Science. Mac, Win. LS.

CD-ROMs

An Odyssey of Discovery for Science Insights: Encourage students to try the activity *Aquarium* on the Living Science Disk. *SFAW.*

Laserdiscs

Living Textbook. (See barcodes on pages in this chapter.) Optical Data.

Videos

All About Acids and Bases. FM.

Audio-Visual Resources

Acids, Bases, and Salts. Film. C/MTI.

21

INTEGRATED LEARNING

Writing Connection

Ask students to write a description of a scene in which people are making a secret solution that looks like the one in the picture. Who are these people? What does their solution do? Encourage students to be creative.

Introducing the Chapter

Have students read the description of the photograph. Ask if they agree or disagree with the description.

Directed Inquiry

Have students study the photograph. Ask:

▶ What is happening in this photograph? (Two colored liquids are mixing together in water or another colorless liquid.)

▶ What do you think will happen eventually? (Students should say that the colored liquids will spread evenly throughout the water, turning it purple.)

▶ Is this an example of a chemical reaction that forms new substances or is it something else? (It's not a chemical reaction because new substances are not formed. A physical change is taking place. A solution, which is a kind of mixture, is forming.)

▶ What do you think is happening to the ions of the substances shown in the picture? (They are mixing evenly with those of the water as the solution forms.)

Chapter Vocabulary

acid	solubility
base	solute
colloid	solution
concentration	solvent
pH	supersaturated
salt	suspension
saturated	unsaturated

Chapter 21 Solution Chemistry

Chapter Sections

21.1 Solutions

21.2 Suspensions and Colloids

21.3 Acids, Bases, and Salts

What do you see?

66 I see two or three different water colors dropped in a beaker of water. The water is changing colors as the colors dissolve in it. Some of the colors are mixing with each other. It looks like a mixture of water and a solute. So they make a solution. 99

Eric Jacobs
South High School
Minneapolis, Minnesota

To find out more about the photograph, look on page 534. As you read this chapter, you will learn about solution chemistry.

Themes in Science

Systems and Interactions The three phases of matter interact in various ways. For example, solutions can be made by combining forms of matter in any of their three phases—solid, liquid, or gas. The combinations may differ, but each kind of solution is homogeneous. Ask students to identify the phases of matter in fog, a blizzard, and a rainstorm. (Liquid in gas, solid in gas, liquid in gas)

Integrating the Sciences

Earth Science Explain to students that the air they breathe is a solution of oxygen, argon, neon, helium, water vapor, carbon dioxide, ozone, and other gases dissolved in nitrogen. The layer of the atmosphere in which we live is called the *troposphere*.

Section Objectives
For a list of section objectives, see the Student Edition page.

Skills Objectives
Students should be able to:

Define Operationally a solution.

Observe the properties of water and compare them to common liquids.

Interpret Data on a table.

Calculate the concentration of a solution at a given temperature.

Vocabulary
solution, solvent, solute, solubility, concentration, saturated, unsaturated, supersaturated

21.1 Solutions

Objectives

▶ **List** the nine types of solutions and give an example of each.

▶ **Identify** the factors that affect solution rate and solubility.

▶ **Compare** and **contrast** the difference between saturated, unsaturated, and supersaturated solutions.

▶ **Calculate** the concentration of a solution.

▼ **ACTIVITY**

Defining Operationally

Solutions

Based on your own observations and experiences, explain what a solution is. Give examples.

SKILLS WARMUP

MOTIVATE

Skills WarmUp
To help students understand solutions, have them do the Skills WarmUp.
Answer Students will probably answer that a solution is a solid or liquid mixed thoroughly in a liquid. They may also recall from Chapter 19 that substances in solutions are often broken into individual ions. Examples of solutions will vary. Have students save this Skills WarmUp and use it with the WrapUp at the end of this section.

Misconceptions
Students may think that solutions are always made up of liquids. Emphasize that this is not true. Air is a solution of gases dissolved in a gas. Metal alloys are solutions made up of one melted solid dissolved in another melted solid and cooled.

Answer to In-Text Question
① The salt was dissolved in the water and was left behind when the water dissolved.

What happens when you put a spoonful of table salt into a glass of water? The solid crystals disappear. They seem to be swallowed up by the liquid. But even though you can't see it, you know the salt is still there because you can taste it.

Salt water is an example of a **solution**. A solution is the same as a homogeneous mixture. Remember that in a homogeneous mixture, two or more different substances are mixed evenly together.

Types of Solutions

The two substances that make up a solution have different chemical roles. One role is that of the **solvent**. A solvent is the substance that takes in, or dissolves, the other substance or substances. Usually the solvent is present in the greater amount. The other role is that of the **solute**. A solute is what gets taken in, or dissolved by, the solvent. A solution is usually described as something *dissolved* in something else. In salt water, salt is dissolved in water.

You are most familiar with solutions, such as salt water, in which the solvent is a liquid. However, according to the definition above, a solution doesn't have to be a liquid. The air you breathe, for example, is a solution made up of gases dissolved in a gas. Metal alloys are solutions of a solid dissolved in a solid. A liquid dissolved in a solid, a liquid dissolved in a gas, and a gas dissolved in a solid are other possible kinds of solutions. In fact, the three phases of matter can be paired together in nine different ways to make solutions. Thus, there are a total of nine different kinds of solutions.

Figure 21.1 ▲
The salt in these piles was once part of a solution—the salty ocean water of a lagoon. How do you think the salt was separated from the water? ①

TEACH

Discuss

Have students study Table 21.1 and then discuss the following:

▶ What do you notice about the combinations of gas, liquid, and solid solutes and solvents in the first two columns? (Each solute is combined with each kind of solvent.)

▶ Have students name solutions they have seen. Put the list of solutions on the board. Ask them to identify the phase of matter of the solute and solvent and the ingredients in each solution. Write this information on the board as an extension of Table 21.1.

Integrated Learning

Use Integrating Worksheet 21.1.

Answers to In-Text Questions

① Answers will vary, but examples of a solid dissolved in a liquid include sugar or a drink mix dissolved in water. Bronze is a solid made of tin dissolved in copper.

② Solvent: water; solutes: carbon dioxide, sugar, and flavorings

Answer to Link

The exhaled breath fogged the mirror. The fog condensed on the mirror to form small droplets of water.

**The Living Textbook:
Physical Science Sides 1–4**

Chapter 6   Frame 01179
Carbon Dioxide in Solution (3 Frames)
Search: Step:

516

Themes in Science

Stability and Equilibrium Have students make models of a solution, such as sugar water. Tell them to show an even distribution of solute particles in the solvent. (For example, they could mix two colors of jelly beans in a jar.) Have them explain why a solution is a stable, homogeneous mixture. (Because of the attractions between particles)

Integrating the Sciences

Biology Point out that blood is an example of a solution in which gases are dissolved in a liquid. Both oxygen and carbon dioxide are dissolved in blood. Point out that solids, such as nutrients and fats, are also in solution in blood.

Figure 21.2 ▲
What is the solvent in a carbonated drink? What are the solutes?
②

Life Science
L I N K

Your breath is a solution of water vapor in air. Obtain a hand mirror. Hold the mirror up to your mouth. Breathe on the mirror.

What happened? Describe what you observe.

A C T I V I T Y

The nine different types of solutions are shown in Table 21.1. As you can see, each type of solution is a different combination of two of the three phases of matter. Some types are more common than others. A gas dissolved in a liquid is one common type of solution. You can find such a solution in a can of soda, for example. Solutions of one liquid dissolved in another liquid are also common. A familiar example is automobile antifreeze, a mixture of ethylene glycol and water. Give an example of a solid dissolved in a liquid. Give an example of a solid dissolved in a solid. ①

In a solution, solvent particles surround each particle of solute. Attractions between solute particles and solvent particles keep this arrangement stable, even though the particles move. This stable relationship between solvent and solute particles is what makes a solution a homogeneous mixture.

For solvent particles to surround solute particles in a solution, the solute particles must be extremely small. Solute particles are so small that they can't be separated from a solution by filtering. The molecules or ions of the solute simply pass through even the tiniest pores in a filter. For example, tea is a solution in which neither the solute nor the solvent particles can be filtered out. All liquid solutions share this property of being nonfilterable.

Table 21.1 Types of Solutions

Solute	Solvent	Example
Gas	Gas	Air (oxygen in nitrogen)
Gas	Liquid	Carbonated beverages (CO_2 in water)
Gas	Solid	Hydrogen fuel storage (hydrogen in metal hydrides)
Liquid	Gas	Humid air (water in air)
Liquid	Liquid	Vinegar (acetic acid in water)
Liquid	Solid	Dental fillings (mercury in silver)
Solid	Gas	Air surrounding mothballs (naphthalene in air)
Solid	Liquid	Salt water
Solid	Solid	Stainless steel (carbon in iron)

Integrating the Sciences

Biology Explain to students that the human body is primarily a water solution. Various types of ions, amino acids, fats, proteins, glucose, and other substances are dissolved in water, which makes up about 65 percent of the body.

Chemistry Point out that salt (NaCl) is an example of an ionic solid. Explain that ionic bonds are strong. To overcome the attraction between the positive sodium ions and the negative chloride ions in salt, several water molecules must surround each ion and dissolve the salt.

Skills WorkOut

To help students observe the properties of water, have them do the Skills WorkOut.
Answer Answers will vary, but students might say that water is an excellent solvent; that it reacts with many substances; is less dense as a solid than as a liquid; and that people use it to drink, cook, and wash.

Water as a Solvent

Of all the different substances that can be solvents, water is the most important. Water carries dissolved nutrients in the body fluids of living things.

Water can dissolve so many different substances that it is often called the *universal solvent*. What makes water so special? Look at Figure 21.3. The oxygen atom of a water molecule holds electrons more strongly than the hydrogen atoms do. The shared electrons in the two covalent bonds, therefore, are drawn closer to the oxygen. As a result, the oxygen takes on a slightly negative charge and the hydrogens a slightly positive charge. Because of the molecule's shape, one end is positive and the other end negative.

As you can see in Figure 21.3, the positive ends of water molecules are attracted to solute particles that have a negative charge. The negative ends of water molecules are attracted to positively-charged solute particles.

Water dissolves most ionic solids because its molecules pull apart the ions that make up the solid. Water can also dissolve molecules that have slightly negative and slightly positive parts. However, because molecules of fats and oils have few positive or negative parts, water molecules are not attracted to them. Therefore, fats and oils do not dissolve in water.

Class Activity

Have students make one or more solutions with water. You might have them mix sodium chloride with one or more other ionic salts in water. Tell students that such a solution can be found in the ocean. Also have students make a sugar solution. Have students note that the solutes in each solution cannot be observed with the unaided eye.

Directed Inquiry

Have students look at Figure 21.3. Explain that it shows water dissolving a grain of salt. Ask, Which ions are attracted to the negative ends of the water molecules and which are attracted to the positive ends? (Sodium ions are attracted to the negative ends; chloride ions are attracted to the positive ends.) Point out the dipolar structure of the water molecule gives it a negative end and a positive end, making it a good solvent.

▼ **ACTIVITY**

Observing

Water's Properties

Based on your experience with water, make a list of its properties and uses. Then use each item on your list to compare water with other common substances. What unique properties does water have?

SKILLS WORKOUT

Figure 21.3
Water dissolves many substances because of the structure of water molecules. Water molecules are slightly positive at one end and slightly negative at the other. ▼

Slightly negative

Slightly positive

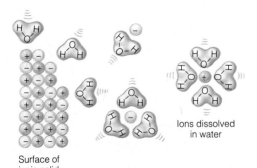
Surface of ionic solid

Ions dissolved in water

 The Living Textbook: Physical Science Sides 1-4

Chapter 4   Frame 00954
Covalent Bonds of Water (5 Frames)
Search: Step:

 The Living Textbook: Physical Science Sides 1-4

Chapter 6   Frame 01198
Oil on Water (1 Frame)
Search:

TEACH ▪ *Continued*

Directed Inquiry

Have students look at the photographs and read about the factors affecting solution rate. Ask:

▶ Why does sugar dissolve faster in hot tea? (Molecules of hot water move faster and contact the surface of the sugar granules more frequently.)

▶ Which would dissolve faster—a bouillon cube or a crushed bouillon cube? Why? (The crushed bouillon cube, because it presents more surface area to the water)

▶ Why is the solid in the test tube not evenly dissolved in the water? (The solid has limited contact with the water, slowing the dissolving process.)

▶ What happens when the water in the test tube is stirred? (Regions of high solute concentration are broken up. As more water molecules come into contact with the solid, dissolving speeds up.)

The Living Textbook: Physical Science Sides 1-4

Chapter 6   Frame 01194
Food Coloring Dissolving (2 Frames)
Search: Step:

The Living Textbook: Physical Science Sides 1-4

Chapter 6   Frame 01173
Sugar Dissolving (4 Frames)
Search: Step:

Home Economics Connection

Explain that most dirt is soluble in water. Have students use what they know about factors that affect solution rate to explain how to use water to remove dirt from clothes. (Most types of dirt are more soluble at higher temperatures, so hot water helps to remove dirt from clothes. Scrubbing clothes brings water molecules into contact with dirt particles, speeding the dissolving process.)

Math Connection

An object's surface area increases when it is broken into smaller pieces. Have students calculate the surface area of a 10-cm cube. [Surface area = number of faces × area of each face = 600 cm^2] This cube can be divided into 1,000 1-cm cubes. What is the combined surface area of the smaller cubes? [6000 cm^2] Relate this to exposure of surface area of a solid in a solvent.

Factors Affecting Solution Rate

Dissolving a solid in a liquid is an everyday experience for many people. You create this kind of solution, for example, when you make up a powdered drink mix. Scientists also commonly dissolve solids in liquids to make solutions. How does this dissolving process take place?

Think of what happens when you dissolve a powdered drink mix in water. The solid doesn't disappear instantly in the liquid. The process of dissolving takes a certain amount of time. The particles making up the solid must be pulled apart by the solvent particles. Such action can only occur at the surface of the solid, where it contacts the solvent. The rate at which a solid dissolves in a liquid depends on temperature, particle size, and movement.

Particle Size

Which will dissolve faster, the large salt crystals or the same mass of salt in powdered form? Since the process of dissolving takes place at the surface of a solid, the larger the surface, the more rapidly it will dissolve. The surface area of an object increases greatly when it is broken down into smaller and smaller bits. ▼

Temperature ▲

You probably know that hot water will dissolve a solid faster than cold water. When you make tea, for example, you always use hot water. Molecules of hot water have more kinetic energy than those of cold water. They move around faster and come in contact more frequently with the substance to be dissolved.

Movement ▲

Water molecules attract the ions of an ionic solid and pull them into solution. These ions fill the available spaces between the closest water molecules, slowing the dissolving process. If you stirred this solution, however, water molecules with empty spaces around them could contact the surface of the ionic solid, causing the solid to dissolve faster.

Math Connection

Give students the following problems: Suppose you add 60 g of lead nitrate $Pb(NO_3)_2$ to 100 g of water at room temperature. After you stir it, 6 g of lead nitrate remains undissolved. What is the solubility of lead nitrate at room temperature? (54 g per 100 g of water) If you add 44 g of salt to 100 g of water at room temperature, how many grams will remain undissolved? (8 g)

Integrating the Sciences

Biology Explain that gases dissolved in blood increase in solubility as air pressure increases. This fact creates a problem for scuba divers. As a diver swims deeper and breathes pressurized air, more gases dissolve in the blood. If the diver rises to the surface too quickly, the gases decrease in solubility and form bubbles in the blood vessels. This causes a life-threatening condition called the *bends*.

Factors Affecting Solubility

No matter how fast you can make something dissolve, there is a limit to *how much* of it you can dissolve in a certain amount of liquid. What happens when you add sugar, a spoonful at a time, to a glass of water? At some point, the sugar no longer dissolves. Some of it remains on the bottom of the glass no matter how long you stir. The ability of one substance to dissolve in another is called its **solubility**.

The solubility of different substances in water varies greatly. In fact, many substances aren't soluble at all. Solubility is usually expressed as the grams (g) of solute that will dissolve in 100 g of water at a certain temperature. At room temperature, the solubility of sugar is about 200 g per 100 g of water; and the solubility of table salt is only about 36 g per 100 g of water.

Solubility varies with temperature. It is important that a measurement of solubility always includes a temperature. For most solids, an increase in temperature causes an increase in solubility.

Gases, however, behave differently. The solubility of a gas in water *decreases* as the temperature increases. For example, more than twice as much oxygen will dissolve in water at 23°C, than will dissolve in water at 60°C.

In addition to temperature, the solubility of a gas depends on its pressure. When you reduce the pressure in a bottle of soda by removing the cap, bubbles of carbon dioxide fizz to the top. The lower pressure forces carbon dioxide out of the solution. In general, increasing the pressure of a gas increases the amount that will dissolve in a liquid. The particle model of matter helps to explain why pressure affects the solubility of a gas.

Particles of a gas dissolved in a liquid are constantly being pushed out of the liquid by movement of the liquid particles. At the same time, particles of the gas above the liquid are constantly being pushed into the liquid. This exchange of particles is balanced, or in equilibrium, at a particular pressure. Increasing the pressure of the gas squeezes the gas particles closer together, and pushes more of them into the liquid.

◀ **Figure 21.4**
The fish in this aquarium depend on oxygen dissolved in the water. If the aquarium water is heated above room temperature, how will the oxygen content in the water change? ①

TEACH ▪ *Continued*

Discuss

Have students think about dilute and concentrated solutions. Then discuss the following:

▶ On a hot day you make a pitcher of iced tea using two tea bags. The tea tastes weak. Is the solution you've made dilute, concentrated, unsaturated, or saturated? Explain. (It's an unsaturated solution that is dilute.)

▶ What kind of solution do you want the iced tea to be? What can you do to make this kind of solution? (Concentrated; add more tea bags.)

SkillBuilder

Interpret Data Have students practice reading the table to find the solubility of compounds. Ask them to name the compounds that can be made with aluminum. (Aluminum bromide, hydroxide, nitrate, and oxide)

Answers

1. Insoluble; soluble

2. Magnesium carbonate, magnesium hydroxide, or magnesium oxide

3. Ammonium hydroxide or sodium hydroxide

4. Nitrate ion
   Answers will vary, but students should say sodium and nitrate compounds are always soluble, and that bromide and ammonium compounds are usually soluble.

The Living Textbook: Physical Science Sides 1-4

Chapter 17   Frame 02940
Dilute Solution (2 Frames)
Search: Step:

520

Math Connection

Tell students that the solubility of sodium hydroxide (NaOH) is 109 g per 100 g of water at 20°C. Ask what concentration they would have if they dissolved 209 g of NaOH in 200 g of water at 20°C. (Unsaturated) Ask what concentration they would have if they added 9 g more of NaOH. (Saturated)

Answer to Link

The water evaporates slowly, leaving frosty salt crystals on the edge of the bowl. The slow evaporation allows larger, cubic salt crystals to form at the bottom of the bowl.

Earth Science
L I N K

Pools of water near the ocean usually contain salt. As the water in the pools evaporates, the concentration of the salt solution changes and salt beds or deposits are left. Collect the following items: 2-L glass bowl, 1-cup measure, tablespoon, and salt.

1. Mix 1 c of water and 4 T of salt in the bowl.

2. Leave the solution untouched until the water evaporates. (about 3 weeks)

Write a paragraph describing what you observed.

A C T I V I T Y

Concentration of Solutions

If you add too much water when you make up a can of frozen juice, it tastes weak. In other words, there aren't enough solute particles for the amount of solvent to provide a pleasing taste. Whenever you express a relationship between the amount of solute and the amount of solvent in a solution, you are identifying its **concentration**. Concentration is the amount of solute per given volume of solvent.

To compare the concentration of different solutions, you can use the words *concentrated* and *dilute*. A dilute solution contains very little solute. A concentrated solution contains a large amount of solute. These terms are not precise, since they can refer to a wide range of actual concentrations.

You can also classify solutions as **saturated**, **unsaturated**, or **supersaturated**. When you add salt to water until no more will dissolve, the solution is saturated.

SkillBuilder *Interpreting Data*

Soluble or Insoluble?

Scientists often want to know how soluble a substance is and how its solubility changes with temperature. Even more basic is knowing whether a substance is soluble at all. The solubility table to the right describes various ionic compounds as either soluble or insoluble in water.

Positive ions appear in the column down the left side and negative ions in the row across the top. To find the solubility of aluminum oxide, look at the aluminum row and the oxide column, then find where they meet. Use the table to answer the questions.

1. Is aluminum oxide soluble or insoluble? How about copper bromide?

2. Name an insoluble compound of magnesium.

3. Name a soluble hydroxide compound.

4. Which negative ion listed in the table forms only soluble compounds?

In a short paragraph, make generalizations about the solubility patterns you see in the table.

Solubilities of Compounds					
	bromide	carbonate	hydroxide	nitrate	oxide
aluminum	S	—	I	S	I
ammonium	S	S	S	S	—
copper	S	—	I	S	I
magnesium	S	I	I	S	I
silver	I	I	—	S	I
sodium	S	S	S	S	S

Key: S = Soluble   I = Insoluble   — = No such compound

Cooperative Learning

To help students learn more about the diversity of solutions, have students work in three groups, and assign each group a category of products. Examples might be household cleaners, foods, or cosmetics. Have each group research the ingredients that make up ten products in their categories. To find information, students can look at product labels at home or at the grocery. Have each group make a bulletin board display about its product category using photographs and the information they gathered.

A saturated solution contains all the solute a solvent will dissolve at a certain temperature and pressure. A solution that contains less solute than this amount is called unsaturated. An unsaturated solution can range from dilute to concentrated.

In some cases, you can create a supersaturated solution—one that goes beyond the point of saturation. You make a saturated solution at a high temperature and then cool it very slowly. If the solution isn't disturbed, all the solute will stay dissolved. At room temperature the solution contains more solute than it could normally dissolve at that temperature.

Science and You *Kitchen Solutions*

You don't have to look beyond your kitchen to find all sorts of different solutions. Vanilla extract, vinegar, and maple syrup are just a few of the many solutions that are probably sitting on your kitchen shelves.

Vanilla extract is made by dissolving oil from the vanilla bean in alcohol. This solution is then dissolved in water. Vanilla extract flavors many of the foods you eat.

Vinegar is one of the most versatile kitchen solutions. It is a dilute solution of acetic acid. Vinegar flavors and preserves many foods, such as pickles. Maple syrup is a concentrated solution of sugars from maple-tree sap. The sap is heated to boil away most of the water, leaving it thick and syrupy.

Figure 21.5 ▲
Maple tree sap is a solution of sugars in water. How is it turned into maple syrup? ①

Check and Explain

1. Give examples of three types of solutions and tell the phase of matter of each solute and solvent.

2. What three things could you do if you wanted to increase the rate at which sugar dissolves in water?

3. **Compare and Contrast** Is a dilute solution always unsaturated? Is an unsaturated solution always dilute? Explain.

4. **Calculate** The solubility of $AgNO_3$ is 222.0 g per 100 g of water at 20°C. What kind of solution will you create if you add 110.99 g of $AgNO_3$ to 50 g of water at 20°C? What kind of solution will it become if you add 10 g more of $AgNO_3$?

Skills Development

Communicate Ask students to define the terms *unsaturated*, *saturated*, and *supersaturated*.

Portfolio

Students can prepare reports about the quantity of water needed to make various fruit juices from frozen concentrate. Have them calculate the concentration for each resulting juice. (For example: If 236.5 mL of juice concentrate dissolved in water equals 946 mL of solution, the solution concentration amounts to 25 percent.) Students can also compare the price per milliliter of different frozen juice brands. They can add their reports and findings to their portfolios.

EVALUATE

WrapUp

Reinforce Have students reread the descriptions of a solution they wrote at the beginning of this chapter. Ask them to rewrite their descriptions based on what they learned.

Use Review Worksheet 21.1.

Check and Explain

1. Air: gases dissolved in gas; metal alloy: solid dissolved in solid; salt water: solid dissolved in water. Answers may also include gas dissolved in liquid or solid; solid in gas; liquid in gas or solid.

2. Heat water, stir water, or reduce the size of sugar particles

3. No, a slightly soluble solute can produce a dilute solution that is saturated. Unsaturated solutions are not always dilute; they can be concentrated.

4. Unsaturated; saturated

Answer to In-Text Question
① The water is boiled away.

Section Objectives
For a list of section objectives, see the Student Edition page.

Skills Objectives
Students should be able to:

Classify foods into different types of mixtures.

Observe how an emulsifier functions.

Classify sols, gels, emulsions, foams, and aerosols and give examples of each.

Vocabulary
suspension, colloid

► MOTIVATE

Skills WarmUp

To help students understand what suspensions and colloids are, have them do the Skills WarmUp.
Answer Answers will vary. Mixtures with particles that will separate out include salad dressing and soup. Mixtures with particles that won't separate include milk, ice cream, and drinks made from mixes.

Prior Knowledge

Gauge how much students know about suspensions and colloids by asking the following questions:

► Do you think all mixtures are solutions? Why?

► What types of mixtures can you name?

► What are the characteristics of each type of mixture?

► What is a Venn diagram?

Answer to In-Text Question

① **They settle out when the water slows down.**

Writing Connection

Have students write their own versions of "Honey, I Shrunk the Kids." Have them imagine that they have shrunk to the size of a molecule. Then tell them to describe their adventures through a variety of suspensions and colloids, such as a glass of milk, a tube of toothpaste, a jar of jelly, or a mud puddle.

Integrating the Sciences

Earth Science Explain that the motion of a river keeps its "load" of soil, sand, and clay in suspension. However, as the river nears the ocean, it slows down and the particles settle, forming a delta. Tell students that the Mississippi River carries so much soil that its delta grows about 1.6 km into the Gulf of Mexico every 16 years. Today, the Mississippi River Delta covers nearly 34,000 square kilometers.

▼ ACTIVITY

Classifying

Mixing it Up

List all the foods you ate yesterday that were mixtures. Classify them as mixtures with particles that could be separated out, and mixtures with particles that could not be separated out.

SKILLS WARMUP

21.2 Suspensions and Colloids

Objectives

► **Describe** what a suspension is and give common examples.

► **Compare** and **contrast** colloids, solutions, and suspensions.

► **Classify** five kinds of colloids.

Is milk a solution? What about a fruit jelly? Muddy water? Shaving cream? To tell if these mixtures are solutions, you have to be a kind of microscopic detective. The size of their particles makes some substances mixtures, but not solutions.

Imagine you have been shrunk to the size of a molecule. If you are placed in a mixture in which the particles are your size or smaller, you're in a solution. If you find yourself in a mixture with particles much larger than you, you're not in a solution. Mixtures with large particles can't be completely homogeneous. So, they can't be solutions. These mixtures have their own special names and properties.

Suspensions

What happens when you shake a mixture of soil and water in a jar and then let it stand? The soil particles slowly settle at the bottom of the jar. A mixture in which some of the particles will settle out is called a **suspension**.

The particles in a suspension are relatively large and are usually visible. They settle out because they aren't strongly attracted to water molecules. Over time, the force of gravity makes them sink to the bottom. Unlike the particles of solute in a solution, the particles in a suspension are large enough to be filtered out.

What common mixtures do you think are suspensions? A medicine or food product labeled "shake well" probably contains a suspension. You must shake it to distribute its contents evenly. After it sits for a while, the particles settle to the bottom. In a solution, the particles are always evenly distributed and don't settle out.

Rapidly moving rivers and streams often carry a load of suspended particles called *silt*. The larger particles gradually settle out as the water slows down along its

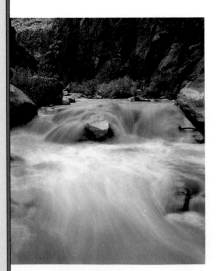

Figure 21.6 ▲
What happens to the particles of soil carried in muddy river water?
①

Portfolio

Have students make a chart comparing and contrasting solutions, suspensions, and colloids. Have them describe the properties of each type of mixture and find pictures to illustrate each type. Have students also list foods labeled *shake well* and explain what the label implies. They can keep their charts and photographs in their portfolios.

Cooperative Learning

Have students work in cooperative groups of three. Have students choose several mixtures and use a beam of light to test whether the mixtures are solutions or colloids. Have each student predict the outcome of the tests. Then have the students prepare samples of the mixtures and use a beam of light to test them. Have them compare the test results with their predictions.

Skills Development

Infer Have students think about dust on the furniture at home. Ask, Where does the dust come from? (It's in suspension in the air. When the air is still, the dust settles out.)
Discuss Ask students to explain how they would test salt water to find out if it is a solution, a suspension, or a colloid. (Shine a light through it; if a beam is visible, it is a colloid. If the salt settles out, it's a suspension. If neither happens, it's a solution.)

Integrated Learning

Use Integrating Worksheet 21.2.

Answer to In-Text Question

② The particles of colloids and suspensions are large enough to reflect light.

③ The air contains small particles of dust and water vapor. When the air contains enough of these particles and a beam of light is passed through it, the path of the light beam is visible.

---

course. You may have seen silt built up on the banks of a river. Air also often contains suspended particles. City air usually contains soot, which are tiny carbon particles that form when fuels burn. These particles settle out of the air, leaving a black coating on buildings.

Colloids

Solutions and suspensions are very different kinds of mixtures. Solutions are homogeneous mixtures with very small particles. Suspensions are heterogeneous mixtures with large particles. As you may have guessed, there are also mixtures that are halfway between solutions and suspensions. These mixtures, called **colloids** (KAHL oydz), have particles that are larger than the particles in solutions and smaller than those in a suspension. The properties of colloids differ from the properties of solutions and suspensions.

A colloid can be clear, just like a liquid solution. So, how do you tell the difference between a colloid and a solution? The simple test shown in Figure 21.7 provides the answer. Although colloidal particles are too small to be seen by the unaided eye, they are large enough to reflect light off their surfaces. When you pass a beam of light through a colloid, the beam becomes visible, just as it does in a suspension. A beam of light isn't visible as it passes through a solution. Why is it possible to see a beam of sunlight between a cloud and the ground? ③

Figure 21.7
Why is the beam of light visible in the colloid and suspension but not in the solution? ▼ ②

Light source   Solution   Dilute colloid   Suspension

The Living Textbook:
Physical Science Sides 1-4

Chapter 6   Frame 01203
Salad Dressing (2 Frames)
Search: Step:

The Living Textbook:
Physical Science Sides 1-4

Chapter 16   Frame 02674
Smoke Stacks (1 Frame)
Search:

TEACH ▪ *Continued*

Discuss

Have students study the definitions of each type of colloid on pages 524 and 525. Ask:

▶ What is the difference between a colloid and a suspension? (Suspensions settle, colloids do not; Suspensions can be filtered out, colloids cannot.)

▶ What kind of colloid is ink? Explain. (Sol; it has solid pigments dispersed in a liquid.)

▶ List the properties of styling gel. What gives it these properties? (As a gel it has long, branching particles that trap liquids.)

▶ Is rain an aerosol? Explain. (No; the water droplets are not dispersed in air, but fall to the ground.)

Skills Development

Classify Have students prepare a list of products they use daily that are suspensions or colloids. Ask them to classify each colloid as a sol, gel, or aerosol. (Answers will vary. Students should list different kinds of hair preparations, cosmetics, and foods.)

Answer to In-Text Question

① Fog is an aerosol.

 The Living Textbook: Physical Science Sides 1-4

Chapter 6   Frame 01206
Colloids (6 Frames)
Search: Step:

 The Living Textbook: Physical Science Sides 1-4

Chapter 8   Frame 01447
Colloidal Sol: Milk of Magnesia (1 Frame)
Search:

524

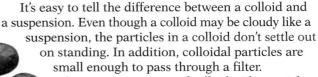

STS Connection

Explain that spray cans contain solid or liquid particles dispersed in propellants, such as compressed gas. When the spray-can valve is opened, the pressurized contents escape. Because it is known that propellants called *chlorofluorocarbons*, or CFCs, destroy the ozone layer, they are no longer used in aerosol cans. In 1978, the U.S. government banned the use of some CFCs. Now the gases carbon dioxide and nitrous oxide are commonly used as propellants.

Figure 21.9
A colloidal mixture of two solids produces the opalescence of opals. ▼

Figure 21.8 ▲
What type of colloid is fog? ①

It's easy to tell the difference between a colloid and a suspension. Even though a colloid may be cloudy like a suspension, the particles in a colloid don't settle out on standing. In addition, colloidal particles are small enough to pass through a filter.

There are many types of colloids. The particles in a colloid may be grains of solid, droplets of liquid, or bubbles of gas. The material in which the particles are spread out, or dispersed, may also be a solid, liquid, or a gas. Five common types of colloids are sols, gels, aerosols, foams, and emulsions.

Sols A colloid composed of a solid dispersed in either a solid or a liquid is called a sol (SAHL). Many paints and inks are liquid sols. They contain tiny particles of pigment dispersed in a liquid. Putty, potter's clay, milk of magnesia, and toothpaste all belong to this group of colloids. Some red glass is an example of a solid sol. The red color comes from tiny bits of gold dispersed in the glass. Pearls and the gemstones called opals are also solid sols. Because they are sols, opals do not have a crystal structure like other gemstones.

Gels A gel is a jellylike colloid in which long particles form a branching structure that traps a liquid inside. Gels behave like flexible solids. In many gels, the branching structure is made of gelatin, a protein obtained from the skin and bones of animals. Gelatin dessert mixes contain powdered gelatin, flavorings, and a sweetener. Jams and jellies are other familiar gels. They are made with pectin, a substance found in the skins and cores of fruit. Pectin causes the fruit juice to "jell." Campers sometimes ignite a can of a jellylike substance to use for cooking. This gel is a mixture of alcohol and calcium acetate.

Aerosols Smoke, clouds, fog, and mist are natural colloids called aerosols (AIR oh SAHLZ). They are made up of solid or liquid particles dispersed in air. The particles in smoke are solids. In clouds, fog, and mist, the particles are water droplets. Some spray cans contain artificial aerosols. The fine mist they produce consists of liquid or solid particles dispersed in a gas. Name some different kinds of aerosols you use.

STS Connection

Have students find out about different types of fire extinguishers. Explain that extinguishers put out fires by cutting off the oxygen needed for combustion. Depending upon the kind of fire, pressurized water, foam, chemical powder, or carbon dioxide may be used. Most home fire extinguishers have labels telling what kinds of fires they can put out. Some extinguishers can only be used on trash, wood, and paper fires. Others work on liquid and grease fires or electrical fires. Some extinguishers can be used on all types of fires.

◀ **Figure 21.10**
Why do you think foams are used to put out fires?

Foams Foam is a colloid of gas bubbles dispersed in liquid. Chemical foams are used to put out fires. Whipped cream, marshmallows, and shaving cream are some common examples of foam.

Emulsions A colloid made up of tiny droplets of a liquid dispersed in another liquid is an emulsion (ee MUHL shuhn). Because the particles in an emulsion cling to each other, individual particles don't settle out. Many of the foods you eat are emulsions. Homogenized milk, butter, and margarine are all emulsions of oil in water. Most of the creams and ointments used in cosmetics and medicine are also emulsions.

Table 21.2   Properties of Solutions, Colloids, and Suspensions

	Solution	Suspension	Colloid
Size of particles	Molecules or ions	Large enough to be seen	Between that of solutions and suspensions
Type of mixture	Homogeneous	Heterogeneous	Borderline
Do particles settle out?	No	Yes	No
Can particles be separated by filtering?	No	Yes	No
Do particles scatter light?	No	Yes	Yes

Critical Thinking
Compare and Contrast Ask students:

▶ What is the difference between aerosols and foams? (Aerosols are solid or liquid particles dispersed in air; foams are gas bubbles dispersed in liquids.)

▶ How is the contents in a tube of toothpaste a different colloid than the contents in a tube of styling gel? (The toothpaste is a sol, the styling gel is a gel.)

▶ How are solutions and colloids alike and different? (In both solutions and colloids, particles don't settle out and can't be separated by filtering. However, particles in colloids are large enough to scatter light while particles in solutions aren't.)

▶ How are solutions and suspensions alike? (Both are mixtures.)

Reteach
Use Reteach Worksheet 21.2.

Answer to In-Text Question
② Because the gas bubbles in foam disperse quickly and evenly, the foam shuts off the oxygen supply and smothers the fire.

The Living Textbook: Physical Science Sides 1-4

Chapter 6   Frame 01207
Emulsion: Glass of Milk (1 Frame)
Search:

The Living Textbook: Physical Science Sides 1-4

Chapter 6   Frame 01208
Colloidal Aerosol: Fog (2 Frames)
Search: Step:

Chapter 21   Solution Chemistry   **525**

TEACH ▪ *Continued*

Skills WorkOut

To help students observe what happens when mayonnaise is made, have them do the Skills WorkOut.

Answer Students should observe that the beater breaks up the yolk, which functions as an emulsifier to disperse particles.

EVALUATE

WrapUp

Reinforce On a large sheet of paper, have each student draw a Venn diagram with three overlapping circles labeled *solutions, suspensions,* and *colloids.* Have students list properties common to all three groups where all circles overlap, properties common to two groups where two overlap, and individual properties and examples in nonoverlapping parts of each circle.

Use Review Worksheet 21.2.

Check and Explain

1. Example: A particle is drifting in liquid surrounded by other large particles that slowly sink.

2. Sol—paint, milk of magnesia, red glass; gel—gelatin desserts, jellies; aerosols— clouds, sprays; foams— whipped cream, marshmallows; emulsions—milk, butter, creams

3. Solutions, suspensions and colloids are mixtures. Solutions are homogeneous, stable mixtures; suspensions have large particles that settle or can be filtered out; colloids have larger particles than solutions but smaller ones than suspensions.

4. Check students' tables.

Answer to In-Text Question

① Emulsifiers are identified in the ingredients list on food labels; egg yolk is a natural emulsifier.

Integrating the Sciences

Health Help students understand how soap molecules act as emulsifiers to wash away dirt. Explain that dirt usually sticks to the body because it combines with body oils. Since water doesn't dissolve oil, washing with water alone won't remove dirt and oil. Then explain the structure of soap molecules. Explain that one end of each molecule dissolves in water and the other end dissolves in oils. In this way, soap molecules act as emulsifiers that break down the oil into droplets that disperse through the water. After the oil is removed from the dirt, water can wash the dirt away.

Science and Technology
Smooth and Creamy Foods

You know what happens when you try to mix oil and water: The two liquids quickly separate into layers. If you add a few drops of egg yolk to the mixture before shaking, however, the liquids separate more slowly. The egg yolk breaks up the oil into tiny droplets that mix more easily with water.

Egg yolk is a natural *emulsifier* (ee MUHL suh FY er), a substance that helps disperse tiny particles of one liquid in another. Emulsifiers improve the uniformity, consistency, stability, and texture of food products. Recipes for homemade mayonnaise always include egg yolks, because an emulsifier is needed to keep the oil and water in mayonnaise from separating.

Peanut butter is a common food that usually contains an emulsifier. To get an idea of its effect, examine a jar of "natural" peanut butter, which contains only peanuts and salt. A layer of oil will probably be on the top. In peanut butter with an added emulsifier, the oil doesn't separate.

Emulsifiers are found in many other foods. When solid chocolate undergoes a temperature change, its surface tends to change color because the cocoa butter separates from the rest of the chocolate. An emulsifier keeps the cocoa butter in a more stable emulsion within the chocolate. Most ice creams and many other frozen desserts owe much of their smoothness and consistency to added emulsifiers. Look at the labels of different food products. Which foods contain emulsifiers? ①

▼ **ACTIVITY**

Observing

Heavy on the Mayo

Find a recipe for mayonnaise and make some. Observe what happens during the process.

What kind of tool do you need to make mayonnaise? What does this tool do to the oil and egg yolk ingredients?

SKILLS WORKOUT

Check and Explain

1. Describe a suspension from the point of view of one of its particles.

2. What are the five types of colloids you learned about in this chapter? Give one example of each.

3. **Compare and Contrast** How are solutions, suspensions, and colloids alike? How are they different?

4. **Classify** Draw a table to classify sols, gels, emulsions, foams, and aerosols. Identify the states of matter involved in each and give an example.

Integrating the Sciences

Biology Explain that the stomach contains a dilute solution of hydrochloric acid. Have students find out how this acid helps the digestive process. Have them make a diagram showing digestion in the stomach, and have them list foods digested by stomach acid. (Stomach acid works with enzymes to help break down proteins. Contraction of stomach muscles helps to mix the foods, acid, and enzymes, turning food into a semiliquid.)

21.3 Acids, Bases, and Salts

Objectives

▶ **Compare** the properties of acids, bases, and salts.

▶ **Interpret** measurements on the pH scale.

▶ **Predict** what salt will be formed by a neutralization reaction.

▼ ACTIVITY

Comparing

Lemons and Vinegar

What properties do lemon juice and vinegar share? How are they different from other substances?

SKILLS WARMUP

What do you think of when you hear the word *acid*? Many people think all acids are harsh liquids that burn your skin and eat away at metal and stone. However, this is true of only a few acids in their concentrated forms. In fact, you put acids into your body whenever you eat pickles or sauerkraut, or drink orange juice.

In chemical terms, an **acid** is a substance that produces hydrogen ions (H^+) in a water solution. This characteristic makes acids chemically active. The chemical activity of acids is shared by another group of substances, **bases**. A base is a substance that produces hydroxide (OH^-) ions in a water solution. Both acids and bases are important in the manufacture of many products, in food making, and in the life processes of organisms.

Properties of Acids

What do vinegar and lemon juice have in common? They both taste sour because they both contain acids. In addition to a sour taste, acids have a number of other common properties. Acids turn blue litmus paper red, for example. They react with bases in a process called *neutralization*. The process is termed neutralization because its products are neither acids nor bases. Acids also react with metals, to form hydrogen gas, and with baking soda and limestone, to form carbon dioxide gas.

Acids are classified as strong or weak. Only strong acids, such as sulfuric acid, nitric acid, and hydrochloric acid, have the properties many people associate with acids. These acids can burn your skin and make holes in your clothes. You must handle them very carefully. Weak acids are common in many foods and plants. Citrus fruits and tomatoes contain citric acid, for example.

Figure 21.11 ▲
The acid in lemon juice can keep apples from turning brown.

SECTION

21.3

Section Objectives
For a list of section objectives, see the Student Edition page.

Skills Objectives
Students should be able to:

Compare and Contrast the properties of lemon juice, vinegar, and other substances.

Predict the salts that form from NaOH and HNO_3 and KOH and HCl.

Vocabulary
acid, base, salt, pH

MOTIVATE

Skills WarmUp
To help students understand acids and bases, have them do the Skills WarmUp.
Answer Students will probably mention that both lemon juice and vinegar are liquids and have a sour taste. Some might mention that both are acids.

Misconceptions
Students may tend to think that all acids are harmful and that all harmful chemicals are acids. Ask students to think about foods they eat that might contain acids. (Orange juice contains ascorbic acid—Vitamin C.) Ask if they know of any acid that exists normally in their bodies. (The stomach makes hydrochloric acid that aids digestion.) Explain that many bases, such as drain cleaner, are also dangerous.

The Living Textbook:
Physical Science Sides 1-4

Chapter 8   Frame 01426
Blue Litmus Test for Acids (1 Frame)
Search:

TEACH

Directed Inquiry

Have students study Table 21.3. Ask:

▶ Which of these acids have you taken into your body? (Answers will vary, but students have probably ingested vinegar, an acetic acid; carbonic acid, which is formed in carbonated drinks; and acetylsalicylic acid, or aspirin.)

▶ What element do all of these acids contain? (Hydrogen)

▶ Which acids are strong acids? Why? (HCl, H_2SO_4, HNO_3; because they have the properties commonly associated with acids. They can burn skin and eat holes in clothing.)

Skills Development

Infer Ask students how aspirin can be an acid when it comes in the form of a pill. (When the pill dissolves in water, it releases hydrogen ions into solution.)

Critical Thinking

Compare and Contrast Ask students how acids and bases are alike. (They are chemically active in a water solution.) How are they different? (Acids produce hydrogen ions [H+] in water solutions; bases produce hydroxide ions [OH-] in water solutions. Acids turn blue litmus paper red. Bases turn red litmus paper blue.)

Answer to In-Text Question

① The solution is acidic because acids turn blue litmus paper red.

**The Living Textbook:
Physical Science Sides 1-4**

Chapter 8   Frame 01425
Red Litmus Test for Bases (1 Frame)
Search:

Art Connection

Explain that acid rain harms marble and limestone sculptures. Burning coal releases sulfur oxides into the air. In time, some of these gases react with water to form sulfuric acid (H_2SO_4), which mixes with rain. Ask students to collect photographs of damaged sculptures and use them to make a poster. Have them research an explanation of how acid rain dissolves marble and limestone and add these explanations to their posters.

STS Connection

Explain that litmus is a combination of several organic compounds that come from a species of lichen, called *canary weed*. Originally, litmus was used as a dye.

Use Integrating Worksheet 21.3a.

Figure 21.12 ▲
What does this change in the color of the litmus paper indicate?
①

Table 21.3   Common Acids and Their Uses

Name of Acid	Formula	Uses
Acetic acid (vinegar)	CH_3COOH	Seasons and preserves foods; cleans and deodorizes
Hydrochloric acid	HCl	Produced by stomach and aids digestion; used in toilet-bowl cleaners and for cleaning metal surfaces
Sulfuric acid	H_2SO_4	Used in automobile batteries and in making fertilizers, dyes, and plastics
Nitric acid	HNO_3	Used in making explosives and fertilizers
Phosphoric acid	H_3PO_4	Removes hard-water deposits; used in making fertilizer
Carbonic acid	H_2CO_3	Formed in carbonated drinks
Acetylsalicylic acid (aspirin)	$C_9H_8O_4$	Reduces pain and inflammation

Look at the formulas for the acids listed in Table 21.3. All of these acids contain one or more hydrogen atoms that can form ions when the acid is in a water solution. The presence of hydrogen ions in acid solutions is responsible for most of the properties of acids.

Properties of Bases

In some ways, bases are just the opposite of acids. Bases turn red litmus paper blue, and they neutralize acids. Bases taste bitter. They feel slippery because they react with oils in your skin to form soap. A solution containing a base is said to be *basic*.

Look at the formulas for the bases listed in Table 21.4. Except for baking soda, they all contain hydroxide ions that are given off when they are dissolved in water. The presence of these ions in water is responsible for most of the properties of bases.

Sodium hydroxide and potassium hydroxide are strong bases. Like strong acids, they are very dangerous and must be handled with care. Products such as oven and drain cleaners contain these bases because they can break down greases that make ovens grimy and clog drains.

Cooperative Learning

Have students work in three co-operative groups. Give each group a category of common products, such as household cleaners, beverages, or non-prescription medicines. Ask each group to use red and blue litmus paper to test for acids and bases in these products at home. Tell each group to organize its findings into a table illustrated with photographs.

Use Integrating Worksheet 21.3b.

Table 21.4   Common Bases and Their Uses

Name of Base	Formula	Uses
Sodium hydroxide	NaOH	Used in making soaps, detergents, drain and oven cleaners
Calcium hydroxide	Ca(OH)$_2$	Softens water; neutralizes acid in soil, used in making mortar, plaster, and cement
Magnesium hydroxide	Mg(OH)$_2$	Used in antacids
Ammonium hydroxide	NH$_4$OH	Used in cleaning solutions
Sodium bicarbonate (baking soda)	NaHCO$_3$	Used in baking and cleaning

Figure 21.13 ▲
The litmus paper shows that this solution is basic.

Forming a Salt

When an acid and a base react, the hydrogen ion from the acid and the hydroxide ion from the base combine to form water. What happens, then, to the rest of the acid and the rest of the base? They combine to form a **salt**. A salt is an ionic compound made up of the positive ion of the base, and the negative ion of the acid. The positive ion is often a metal, and the negative ion is usually composed of nonmetals. The equation below shows a typical neutralization reaction.

$$\underset{\text{(acid)}}{\text{HNO}_3} + \underset{\text{(base)}}{\text{KOH}} \rightarrow \underset{\text{(salt)}}{\text{KNO}_3} + \underset{\text{(water)}}{\text{HOH}}$$

The salt formed in this reaction, potassium nitrate, (KNO$_3$) contains the K$^+$ ion from the base and the NO$_3^-$ ion from the acid. By writing the water molecule as HOH, it's easier to see that the H and the OH come from different substances. You can make a wide variety of salts by mixing different acids and bases.

The pH Scale

You know that both acids and bases vary in strength. Likewise, solutions of acids and bases can be strong or weak. A measurement called **pH** tells how acidic or basic a solution is.

When measuring pH, the same scale of numbers is used for both acids and bases. Look at the pH scale in

Directed Inquiry

Have students study Table 21.4. Ask the following questions:

► What base would you use to open a clogged drain? Why? (Sodium hydroxide; it changes grease into soap.)

► What base would you use to help your plants grow by reducing acid in garden soil? (Calcium hydroxide)

► What base would you find in medicine for an upset stomach? (Magnesium hydroxide)

► What base is in cake mix? (Sodium bicarbonate)

Apply

Ask students to use their knowledge of acids and bases to explain how an antacid containing Mg(OH)$_2$ relieves an overly acid stomach. (Antacids are basic compounds. The hydroxide ions from the base neutralize the hydrogen ions from the stomach acid.)

Reteach

Give students the following neutralization reaction and help them determine the outcome: NaOH + HCl → H$_2$O + NaCl. (Sodium hydroxide, a base, is mixed with hydrochloric acid to form water and salt. The salt contains the positive [Na$^+$] ion from the base and the negative [Cl$^-$] ion from the acid.)

Ancillary Options

If you are using CEPUP modules in your classroom for additional hands-on activities, experiments, and exercises, have students do Activities three to seven in Solutions and Pollution of *Chemical Survey & Solutions and Pollution*.

 The Living Textbook: Physical Science Sides 1-4

Chapter 8   Frame 01452
Neutralization Reaction (1 Frame)
Search:

TEACH ▪ Continued

Directed Inquiry

Have students study Figure 21.14. Ask the following questions:

▶ What is a solution that has a pH of 4? (weakly acidic)

▶ A solution has a pH of 11. What is it? (weakly basic)

▶ What is a solution that tests in the 6 to 8 range? (A nearly neutral solution)

▶ What would you expect the pH of dilute hydrochloric acid to be? (1 even if it is diluted)

▶ The pH of human blood is about 7.4. What is it? (A slightly basic solution)

Ancillary Options

If you are using the blackline masters from *Multiculturalism in Mathematics, Science, and Technology*, have students read about the Celts on page 41. Complete pages 42 to 44.

Consider This

Infer Ask students to identify the pH of acid rain. (Below 5.6) Ask them to infer whether pure rainwater is neutral, acidic, or basic. (Acidic, because a solution of 5.7 to 7 is slightly acidic.) Explain to students that water droplets in the air interact with CO_2 to form carbonic acid, making pure rainwater slightly acidic.

Write About It Answers will vary, but students should give reasons for the positions they take.

The Living Textbook:
Physical Science Side 4

Chapter 27   Frame 20800
pH of Common Substances (Movie)
Search: Play:

Integrating the Sciences

Botany Have students test the pH of soil in plant pots at home or at school. Explain that soil pH is important to healthy plant growth. Soil that is near neutral or just slightly acidic is considered best for most plants. Scientists have found that certain nutrients in the soil are only available to plants when the pH of the soil is within that range.

Multicultural Perspectives

Explain that the pH system was invented in 1909 by S.P.L. Sorensen, a Danish scientist. Have students do research to find out what the designation *pH* means. (power of the hydrogen ion)

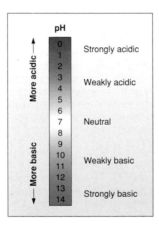

Figure 21.14 ▲
The pH scale is used to describe the strength of acids and bases.

Figure 21.14. Notice the numbers on the scale range from 0 to 14. The midpoint, 7, represents the pH of pure water and is called neutral. Solutions with a pH below 7 are acidic; the smaller the number, the stronger the acid. Solutions with a pH above 7 are basic. The larger the number, the stronger the base.

You can measure the pH of a solution with a substance called an indicator. An indicator changes color depending on a solution's pH. Each color corresponds to a pH number shown on a color chart for that indicator. Some indicators are solutions, such as phenolphthalein (FEE nohl THAL een). Other indicators are added to strips of paper. These strips, called pH papers, are then used for testing substances.

The indicators in pH paper, for example, turn a bright pink in a strong acid, such as hydrochloric acid. In sodium hydroxide, pH paper turns a dark blue. In a neutral solution, the paper turns greenish yellow.

Consider This

Should the pH of lakes be adjusted?

When fossil fuels are burned, sulfur oxides and nitrogen oxides are released into the atmosphere. These gases combine with water in the atmosphere to form sulfuric and nitric acids. Their presence reduces the pH of rain. When its pH falls below 5.6, rain is called *acid* rain.

Acid rain can concentrate in lakes and decrease the pH. When a lake's pH drops below 6, many of the plants and animals living in it begin to die. If enough plants and animals die, the entire body of water can become polluted. This is a problem in many of the lakes

in the northeast region of the United States.

It is possible, however, to artificially raise the pH of a lake that has become too acidic. The base calcium carbonate is added to the lake in the form of powdered limestone. The calcium carbonate reacts with and neutralizes the acids in the lake. This process is called liming.

Many people who enjoy fishing, boating, and the beauty of lakes believe lakes damaged by acid rain should be limed to keep them healthy. Other people say this procedure of raising the pH is too expensive. It

only treats the effects of the acid rain problem. It does not eliminate the causes. They also point out that poorly controlled liming can make a lake too basic.

Think About It How important to you is saving fish and other living things in lakes? Is it worth the cost of liming? Should the acid rain problem be solved in another way?

Write About It Write a paper stating your position for or against liming lakes. Include your reasons for choosing your position.

Themes in Science

Stability and Equilibrium Point out to students that the body keeps the pH of the blood stable between 7.35 and 7.45. Have students explain how biking uphill might affect the pH of the blood and how the body would bring the pH back into normal range. (This exercise would increase the amount of carbon dioxide in the blood and thus lower the pH. To decrease the amount of carbon dioxide and raise the blood pH, the body would respond with deeper and faster breathing, eliminating the extra carbon dioxide.)

Science and You *The pH of Your Blood*

Right now, something quite amazing is happening inside you. All sorts of adjustments are taking place automatically and continuously. One thing your body adjusts is the pH of your blood. Your body keeps the pH of your blood and other body fluids between 7.35 and 7.45.

The chemical reactions that occur in your body don't work very well in solutions with a pH below 7.35 or above 7.45. Your daily activities, however, can begin to push the pH of your blood out of this narrow range of safety. Eating certain foods, exercising, and becoming ill can change your blood pH.

The concentration of carbon dioxide in your blood is the main factor that determines the blood's pH. Carbon dioxide is carried in your blood as waste from cell respiration. It reacts with water in the blood to form carbonic acid. The greater the amount of carbon dioxide in the blood, the lower is the pH. Usually, the amount of carbon dioxide that enters the bloodstream is balanced by the amount removed through the lungs.

Whenever the amount of carbon dioxide in the blood changes, your body makes adjustments to bring it back in line. When your blood pH falls too low, you automatically exhale larger amounts of carbon dioxide. The concentration of carbonic acid in your blood goes down, and the pH goes up. When the pH of your blood gets too high, the opposite action brings the pH back down.

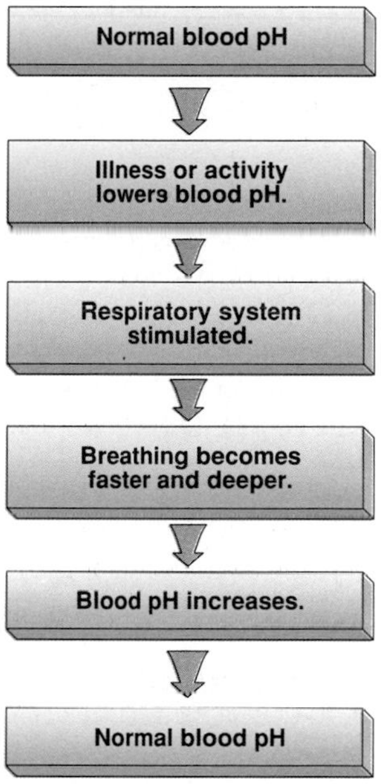

Figure 21.15 ▲
What does your body do when the pH of your blood gets too high? ①

Normal blood pH
↓
Illness or activity lowers blood pH.
↓
Respiratory system stimulated.
↓
Breathing becomes faster and deeper.
↓
Blood pH increases.
↓
Normal blood pH

Check and Explain

1. List two properties of acids and two properties of bases.

2. Describe two different ways you can tell whether a solution is acidic or basic.

3. **Classify** You test eight solutions and get the following pH measurements: 2.0, 6.5, 7.7, 8.0, 11.1, 1.7, 12.3, and 5.5. Classify these measurements into four groups.

4. **Predict** What salt forms when sodium hydroxide (NaOH) reacts with nitric acid (HNO_3)? What salt forms when potassium hydroxide (KOH) reacts with hydrochloric acid (HCl)?

Time 40 minutes   **Group** 3

Materials

distilled water

40 small glass containers

baking soda

colorless vinegar

red and blue litmus paper

phenolphthalein solution

samples of at least 4 substances

Analysis

1. Baking soda turned red litmus paper blue, had no effect on blue litmus, and caused the phenolphthalein to turn pink. Vinegar turned blue litmus red, did not affect red litmus, and made phenolphthalein colorless. Conclusion: baking soda solution is basic; vinegar is acidic.

2. Distilled water is neutral—pH close to 7. Water that is too acidic or too basic could be harmful. A water inspector would use an indicator to make sure that the drinking water was safe.

3. Answer depends on substance tested. Basic samples will test like the baking soda.

4. Answer depends on substance tested. Acidic samples will test like the vinegar.

5. Answer depends on substance tested. Neutral samples will test like the distilled water.

Conclusion

Conclusions should follow from students' recorded observations. Because of its pH range, phenolphthalein can give an indication of the strength of a basic solution. Litmus paper can only categorize solutions as either acidic or basic.

Everyday Application

Food can be either acidic or basic. Many cleaning products are basic.

Prelab Discussion

Have students read the entire activity. Discuss the following points before beginning the activity:

▶ Discuss the function of indicators.

▶ Discuss why the baking soda must be dissolved in water before it can be tested.

▶ Discuss the fact that phenolphthalein has a useful range of only pH 8 to 10.

Activity 21 *What's an acid and what's a base?*

Skills Observe; Infer; Interpret Data

Task 1 Prelab Prep

Collect the following items: distilled water, 4 small glass containers, baking soda, colorless vinegar, red and blue litmus paper, phenolphthalein solution, and samples of at least four substances to be tested for pH. **CAUTION: Handle glassware carefully. Keep all chemicals away from your face.**

Task 2 Data Record

1. On a separate sheet of paper, copy Table 21.5. Add an extra line for each sample.

2. Record all your observations.

Task 3 Procedure

1. Put 5 mL of distilled water into three of the containers. Add a small amount of baking soda to the first container and stir. Label it *Baking Soda*. Add a small amount of vinegar to the second container and stir. Label it *Vinegar*. Don't add anything to the third container. Label it *Distilled Water*.

2. Test the liquids in the three containers with red and blue litmus paper. Record your observations. Then add 2 drops of phenolphthalein to the liquid in each container. Record your observations.

3. Put a small amount of the first sample to be tested in the fourth container. Test the sample with the litmus papers first and then with phenolphthalein. You may want to compare

the test colors with those of the vinegar and baking soda solutions. Record your observations.

4. Test each of the remaining samples by repeating step 3.

Task 4 Analysis

1. How does baking soda affect litmus paper and phenolphthalein? How does vinegar affect these indicators? What can you conclude from your observations?

2. What kind of substance is distilled water? Why might a water inspector test a sample of drinking water with an indicator?

3. Which substances affected the indicators in the same way as baking soda? Are these substances acids or bases?

4. Which substances tested the same as vinegar? Are these substances acids or bases?

5. Which substances tested the same as distilled water? Classify these substances.

Task 5 Conclusion

Write a paragraph summarizing your findings. Which test method gave the clearer results? Can you use your data to determine the strength of each acid and base?

Everyday Application

What generalizations can you make about the pH of foods? Of cleaning products?

Table 21.5   pH Tests

Substance	Red Litmus-Paper Test	Blue Litmus-Paper Test	Phenolphthalein Test
Baking soda			
Vinegar			
Distilled water			

1. supersaturated
2. acid
3. suspension
4. solvent
5. base
6. salt
7. colloid
8. solute
9. pH
10. saturated
11. solubility
12. unsaturated
13. concentration
14. solution

Write Your Vocabulary

Students' sentences should show
that they know the meaning of
each word as well as how to use it
in a sentence.

Use Vocabulary Worksheet for
Chapter 21.

Chapter 21 Review

Concept Summary

21.1 Solutions
▶ A solution is a homogeneous mixture of
two or more evenly mixed substances.
▶ The rate at which a solid dissolves
in a liquid is affected by movement,
temperature, and particle size.
▶ The solubility of one substance in
another varies with temperature and,
in the case of gases, pressure.
▶ A saturated solution contains as much
solute as will dissolve at a certain temperature and pressure.

21.2 Suspensions and Colloids
▶ A suspension contains large particles
that settle out on standing.

▶ A colloid contains particles smaller
than those in a suspension but larger
than those in a solution. The particles
in a colloid don't settle out.

21.3 Acids, Bases, and Salts
▶ Acids are sour and turn blue litmus
paper red.
▶ Bases are bitter, slippery, and turn red
litmus paper blue.
▶ A salt forms when an acid and base
neutralize each other.
▶ The pH of a solution indicates if it is
an acid, a base, or neutral. A pH of 7
indicates a neutral solution.

Chapter Vocabulary

solution (p. 515)	concentration (p. 520)	suspension (p. 522)	salt (p. 529)
solvent (p. 515)	saturated (p. 520)	colloid (p. 523)	pH (p. 529)
solute (p. 515)	unsaturated (p. 520)	acid (p. 527)	
solubility (p. 519)	supersaturated (p. 520)	base (p. 527)	

Check Your Vocabulary

Use the vocabulary words above to complete
the following sentences correctly.

1. A(n)____solution holds more solute
than usual at a certain temperature.
2. A pH of 5.0 indicates a(n)____solution.
3. Particles settle out of a(n)____.
4. Water is a(n)____.
5. A solution that feels soapy is a(n)____.
6. When an acid reacts with a base, water
and a(n)____are formed.
7. The particles in a(n)____scatter light
but don't settle out.
8. A substance that dissolves in a solvent
becomes a(n)____.
9. You can compare the strength of acids
and bases by measuring their____.

10. When more solute is added to a(n)
____solution, the additional solute
won't dissolve.
11. If a large amount of a substance will
dissolve in water, it has a high____.
12. You can dissolve more solute in a(n)
____solution.
13. The amount of solute in a certain
volume of solvent is called the
solute's____.
14. Another name for a homogeneous
mixture is a(n)____.

Write Your Vocabulary
Write sentences using the vocabulary
words above. Show that you know what
each word means.

Check Your Knowledge

1. Solute particles in a solution cannot be separated by filtering.

2. The uneven distribution of positive and negative charge between the ends of the water molecule make it a good solvent.

3. Stirring allows solute molecules to become surrounded by water molecules faster. Heating causes all the molecules in the solution to move around faster and come in contact more frequently. When a solid is broken apart into smaller particles, the total surface area of the solid increases.

4. The particles in a suspension will settle out if the mixture is allowed to remain undisturbed. The particles in a colloid will not settle out.

5. The particles in a solution are too small to scatter light, while those in a colloid will scatter light that is passed through it.

6. When dissolved in water, molecules of an acid produce hydrogen ions (H^+), while basic molecules produce hydroxide ions (OH^-).

7. A salt is an ionic compound made up of a metal and a nonmetal.

8. The lower the pH number, the more acidic the solution.

9. False; less

10. False; will not

11. False; visible

12. False; suspension

13. True

14. False; salt

Check Your Understanding

1. a. solid solute in a liquid solvent

   b. solid solute in a liquid solvent

   c. solid solute in a solid solvent

   d. gaseous solute in a liquid solvent

   e. gaseous solute in a solid solvent

   f. gaseous solute in a gaseous solvent

2. The water is the solute and the alcohol is the solvent.

3. The particles of a gas are too small to form a colloid.

4. As temperature increases, the motion of all particles increases, increasing the ability of solvent molecules to surround solute molecules. This increases both the rate of dissolving and the amount of solute that may be dissolved.

5. All are mixtures of at least two substances, with one present in a larger quantity.

6. The dye will have spread throughout the beaker, leaving the liquid a uniform color.

7. The water molecules are smaller than the alcohol molecules, so they are able to occupy small spaces between alcohol molecules.

8. Twenty-five grams of KBr dissolved in 50 g of water is more concentrated.

Chapter 21 Review

Check Your Knowledge

Answer the following in complete sentences.

1. How do particles behave in a solution?

2. Why can water dissolve so many different substances?

3. Why do stirring, heating, and smaller particle size increase solution rate?

4. How does a colloid differ from a suspension?

5. Why does a beam of light become visible in a colloid but not in a solution?

6. What is the major difference between the molecules of acids and bases?

7. How would you describe a salt?

8. How does a solution's pH number relate to how acidic or basic it is?

Determine whether each statement is true or false. Write *true* if it is true. If it is false, change the underlined term to make the statement true.

9. A solution that holds 2 g of NaCl in 100 mL of water is <u>more</u> dilute than a solution that holds 1 g of NaCl in 100 mL of water.

10. If you add a crystal of solute to a supersaturated solution, the crystal <u>will</u> dissolve in the solution.

11. If you were to shine a beam of light through dusty air, the beam would be <u>invisible</u>.

12. Silt deposited by a river tells you that river water is a <u>colloid</u>.

13. A solution with a pH of 3.5 is an <u>acid</u>.

14. A neutralization reaction produces water and a <u>base</u>.

Check Your Understanding

Apply the concepts you have learned to answer each question.

1. In each of the following, what phases of matter make up the solute and the solvent?

   a. Ocean water

   b. Sweetened tea

   c. Gold jewelry

   d. Oxygen in an aquarium

   e. Poison gas sticking to charcoal

   f. Air

2. In a solution of 25 mL of water and 75 mL of alcohol, which substance is the solute and which is the solvent?

3. Colloids include many different mixtures of phases of matter but not gases dispersed in gases. Why?

4. Temperature affects both the rate at which a substance will dissolve and its solubility. Explain.

5. In what ways are solutions, suspensions, and colloids similar?

6. **Mystery Photo** The photograph on page 514 shows a dye in water. If you stirred the mixture and took another photo a few minutes later, what would it look like?

7. **Application** If you mix 100 mL of water and 100 mL of alcohol, the resulting solution has a volume of less than 200 mL! Explain this fact based on what you know about solutions and the particle model of matter.

8. Which is more concentrated? A solution of 10 g of KBr in 25 g of water or a solution of 25 g of KBr in 50 g of water?

Develop Your Skills

1. Student models will vary. Make sure they have accurately modeled each type of mixture.

2. a. About 40 g/100 g H₂0; About 40 more grams of chemical 2 can be dissolved per 100 g of water at 100°C.

b. no

3. a. about 10

b. Digestive juices

c. Dark purple

Make Connections

1.

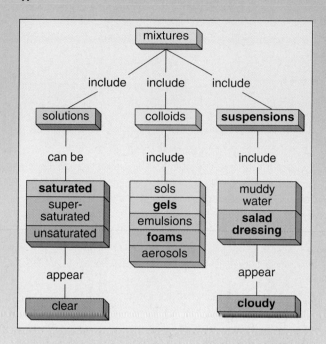

2. Defoe uses the word to mean postpone or delay. In chemistry, the word *suspend* means to hold up or support.

3. Student reports will vary. Check students' use of new terms about air pollution technology, such as *fluidized-bed combustion* and *flue-gas desulfurization*.

Develop Your Skills

Use the skills you have developed in this chapter to complete each activity.

1. Model Obtain blocks of clay and small objects of different colors and sizes, such as BBs, peas, or marbles. Embed the objects on the surface of the three blocks of clay to represent a solution, a suspension, and a colloid.

2. Interpret Data The graph below compares the amounts of three different substances that can dissolve in 100 g of water at temperatures between 0°C and 100°C.

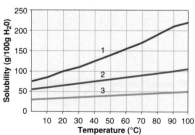

a. What is the difference in the solubility of chemical 2 at 20°C and at 100°C? How many more grams of chemical 2 can be dissolved in water at 100°C than at 20°C?

b. Is chemical 3 more soluble at 100°C than chemical 2 is at 0°C?

3. Data Bank Use the information on page 643 to answer the following questions.

a. What is the pH of toothpaste?

b. Which substance produced by the body is more acidic? Blood or digestive juices in the stomach?

c. What color does universal indicator become when added to a solution of sodium hydroxide?

Make Connections

1. Link the Concepts Below is a concept map showing how some of the main concepts in this chapter link together. Only parts of the map are filled in. Copy the map. Using words and ideas from the chapter, complete the map.

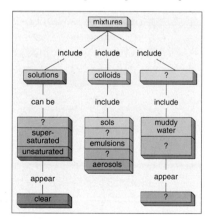

2. Science and Literature Expressing his feelings about the death of a friend, Daniel Defoe, author of *Robinson Crusoe*, wrote these lines:

> The best of men cannot suspend their fate
>
> The good die early, and the bad die late.

Compare Defoe's use of the word *suspend* with what you have learned about suspensions.

3. Science and Technology Find out what is being done to lower the emissions of nitrogen and sulfur oxides from power plants in order to reduce acid rain. What methods have been developed?

Overview

Chapter 22 describes carbon compounds and carbon's importance in the chemistry of living things. The first section explains why the structure of the carbon makes it possible for it to combine with other atoms. The second section explains the chemistry of carbohydrates, lipids, and proteins, as well as what these substances provide for the human body. The role of carbon bonds in photosynthesis and respiration in living cells is described in the last section.

Advance Planner

▶ Provide colored chalk for TE page 539.

▶ Obtain gumdrops and toothpicks for TE page 541.

▶ Supply acetic, butyric, and salicylic acids; ethanol, isopentanol, octanol, and methanol; and a dropper for TE page 542.

▶ Provide labels, small jars with lids, whole cloves, and rubbing alcohol for SE Activity 22, page 544.

▶ Obtain heat-proof beakers; one stick each margarine, butter, and reduced-fat butter substitute; tub; and small burner for TE page 547.

▶ Collect newspapers for TE page 549.

Skills Development Chart

Sections	Apply	Communicate	Compare	Compare and Contrast	Infer	Interpret Data	Make a Table	Measure	Observe
22.1 Skills WarmUp			●						
Skills WorkOut	●								
Activity		●			●			●	●
22.2 Skills WarmUp		●							
Skills WorkOut							●		
22.3 Skills WarmUp				●					
SkillBuilder		●				●			

Individual Needs

▶ **Limited English Proficiency Students** Write the following terms on the chalkboard: *straight chain, branched chain, ring, methane, butane and methyl propane, alcohol, glucose, triglyceride, glycine;* and write the equations for photosynthesis and respiration. Have students list each item in their science journals as they read each section. Beneath each term they should copy the diagram that illustrates it. Where appropriate, students should also write its chemical formula. Ask them to identify each compound, using the terms presented in the chapter. For photosynthesis and respiration, have students write the equations in words and write a sentence or two explaining the differences between the two processes. Have students use this information during their chapter review.

▶ **At-Risk Students** Invite a food scientist to speak with students. Have students prepare a list of questions for the speaker beforehand. They may ask about the training and skills required for this type of work, the problems and challenges associated with food chemistry and food additives, and the latest foods available. Students may also ask how a new food product or flavor is developed and how a scientist or technician determines what ingredients should be part of the product. Be sure to alert the speaker to the students' questions.

▶ **Gifted Students** Ask students to do some research to learn more about food chemistry, nutrition, and metabolism. Have each student use the information to design a week's worth of detailed personal menus that provide the correct balance of nutrients, including vitamins, and the number of calories he or she needs. Then have each student plan a week's worth of menus for someone quite different—a friend on the swim team or an elderly aunt in a wheelchair. Students should be able to describe each food in terms of its nutrients and vitamins and its benefits.

Resource Bank

▶ **Bulletin Board** Title the bulletin board *Carbon Rules.* Along the left side of the board, list the names of several useful organic compounds. Encourage students to find the chemical formula for each compound, write it on a card, and attach the card to the right of the compound's name. Encourage students to provide pictures illustrating the uses and importance of these compounds.

Section	Core	Standard	Enriched	Section	Core	Standard	Enriched
22.1 A World of Carbon pp. 537–544				**Blackline Masters** Review Worksheet 22.2 Skills Worksheet 22.2 Integrating Worksheet 22.2a Integrating Worksheet 22.2b	• • • •	• • • •	• •
Section Features Skills WarmUp, p. 537 Skills WorkOut, p. 543 Activity, p. 544	• • •	• • •	• • •	**Laboratory Program** Investigation 40		•	•
Blackline Masters Review Worksheet 22.1 Reteach Worksheet 22.1 Integrating Worksheet 22.1	• •	• • •	• • •	**22.3 Energy in Living Things** pp. 551–556			
Overhead Blackline Transparencies Overhead Blackline Master 21 and Student Worksheet		•	•	**Section Features** Skills WarmUp, p. 551 SkillBuilder, p. 554	•	• •	• •
Color Transparencies Transparency 79	•	•	•	**Blackline Masters** Review Worksheet 22.3 Skills Worksheet 22.3 Vocabulary Worksheet 22	• • •	• • •	
22.2 Food Chemistry pp. 545–550				**Color Transparencies** Transparencies 80a, 80b	•	•	•
Section Features Skills WarmUp, p. 545 Career Corner, p. 549 Skills WorkOut, p. 550	• • •	• • •	• • •				

Bibliography

The following resources can be used for teaching the chapter. See page T-46 for supplier codes.

Library Resources

Ardley, Neil. The World of the Atom. New York: Gloucester Press, 1990.

The Diagram Group. Comparisons. New York: St. Martin's Press, 1980.

Newton, David E. Consumer Chemistry: Projects for Young Scientists. New York: Franklin Watts, 1991.

Sherwood, Martin, and Christine Sutton. The Physical World. New York: Oxford University Press, 1988.

Technology Resources

Software

All about Science I. Mac, Dos. ESI.
Body and Mind. Win. ESI.
Photosynthesis: Unlocking the Power of the Sun. Dos. ESI.

CD-ROMs

An Odyssey of Discovery for Science Insights: Have students try the activity Aquarium on the Living Science Disk. SFAW.

Laserdiscs

Living Textbook. (See barcodes on pages in this chapter.) Optical Data.

Videos

The Resource Revolution. CSWS.

Audio-Visual Resources

Carbon and Its Compounds, 2nd Edition. Film. C/MTI.

Writing Connection

Have students imagine that the photograph on this page shows the surface of an unexplored world and that they are in a spaceship hovering above that surface. Have them describe what they observe in their ship's log.

Introducing the Chapter

Have students read the description of the photograph. Ask if they agree or disagree with the description.

Directed Inquiry

Have students study the photograph. Ask:

▶ How would you describe the image? (Students should mention that the long bodies form a network.)

▶ What do you think the function of the item in the photograph might be? (Students might say that the network could support the material covering it or connect objects that aren't visible in the photograph.)

▶ Do you think this image is life-size or magnified? (Magnified)

▶ How might this picture be related to the subject of this chapter? (Students will probably suggest that the picture shows particles of a carbon compound or some microscopic structure in a living thing.)

Chapter Vocabulary

carbohydrate	protein
hydrocarbon	respiration
isomer	saturated
lipids	hydrocarbon
organic	substituted
compound	hydrocarbon
photosynthesis	unsaturated
polymer	hydrocarbon

Chapter 22 Carbon Compounds and the Chemistry of Life

Chapter Sections

What do you see?

❝I see a tangle of lines. It looks like it could be inside of a cell. It could also be ropes tied together. It could be used to make a net or web of some kind, like a net hanging on a basketball rim.❞

Steven Duke
Washington High School
Fremont, California

To find out more about the photograph, look on page 558. As you read this chapter, you will learn about carbon compounds in living things.

Themes in Science

Diversity and Unity Have students give examples of living things as well as things that were once alive. Emphasize that although many different kinds of organisms exist, all organisms have something in common: they all contain carbon compounds. In fact, carbon compounds account for about 18 percent of the matter in all living things.

Integrating the Sciences

Chemistry Tell students that organic chemistry is the study of carbon compounds; inorganic chemistry is the study of compounds containing elements other than carbon. One reason an entire branch of chemistry is devoted to a single element is that carbon compounds greatly outnumber the compounds formed by all the other elements combined.

Section Objectives
For a list of section objectives, see the Student Edition page.

Skills Objectives
Students should be able to:

Classify substances as carbon compounds.

Make a Model of simple hydrocarbons.

Observe esters in solvents.

Vocabulary
organic compound, hydrocarbon, saturated hydrocarbon, unsaturated hydrocarbon, polymer, isomer, substituted hydrocarbon

22.1 A World of Carbon

Objectives

▶ **Explain** why carbon can form many different compounds.

▶ **Distinguish** between saturated and unsaturated hydrocarbon molecules.

▶ **Describe** and give examples of isomers.

▶ **Make models** of simple hydrocarbons.

▼ **ACTIVITY**

Comparing

Substance of Life

List ten substances that you think came from, or were produced by, a living thing. Then write down similarities that any of these substances have.

SKILLS WARMUP

W hat has four arms and is found in hamburgers, clothing, oil, blood, trees, and plastics? The answer to this chemical riddle is in the title of this chapter—carbon. An atom of carbon doesn't really have four arms, but four is the number of bonds it can form with other atoms. This special characteristic makes carbon one of the most important elements. It is also the reason you can find carbon in things as different as hamburgers and trees.

Carbon and Living Things

Carbon compounds are the chemicals of life. Every organism, dead or alive, and almost any substance produced by an organism, contain large numbers of carbon atoms. To carry on their life processes, organisms manufacture large carbon-containing molecules out of smaller molecules containing carbon. The main purpose of eating, in fact, is to provide your body with a source of carbon. Every cell in the giraffe's body, in Figure 22.1, is made of carbon compounds. The giraffe is consuming carbon as well.

The early scientists found carbon compounds only in organisms. They thought that organisms alone had the ability to produce carbon compounds. Today, carbon compounds are made daily in laboratories and in factories.

The direct connection between carbon and the living, or organic, world has survived in the scientific name originally given to carbon compounds. Nearly all compounds that contain carbon are still classified as **organic compounds**. Many organic compounds are not produced directly by organisms.

MOTIVATE

Skills WarmUp

To help students understand carbon compounds, have them do the Skills WarmUp.
Answer Answers will vary. Students might group substances by whether they came from animals or from plants, or are edible. A few students might suggest that the compounds that form the substances might be similar in chemical structure.

Misconceptions

Students may think that the elements of a compound are solely responsible for the compound's properties. You may wish to tell students that the caffeine in coffee and the aspartame in diet sodas are each made of the same four elements. Stress to students that the structure of an organic compound may be more important than which elements make up the compound.

Answer to In-Text Question

① **Eating leaves provides both a giraffe and a human with a source of carbon compounds.**

Figure 22.1 ▲
All organisms need carbon compounds. How is the giraffe's eating leaves like your eating a salad? ①

TEACH

Apply

Draw a ball-and-stick model of each carbon backbone shape on the chalkboard. Ask students to identify each shape and describe the differences among the bonds. (In a straight chain, each carbon atom is bonded to two other carbon atoms except for the end carbon atoms, which are bonded to only one other carbon atom. In a branched chain, some carbon atoms are bonded to three or four other carbon atoms. In a ring that has only single covalent bonds, each carbon atom is bonded to two other carbon atoms, and the chain forms a circle.)

Skills Development

Make a Model Ask students to draw hexane (C_6H_{14}) as both a straight-chain polymer and a branched-chain polymer. (Both drawings should show all bonds as single bonds, with 6 carbon and 14 hydrogen atoms. On the branched-chain polymer, the branch can attach to any carbon except the ones on the ends.)

Critical Thinking

Classify Gather items for students to classify as either *organic* or *inorganic* on the chalkboard. Items could include fruit, water, nylon, charcoal, rock, hair, pictures of animals, a plant, and so on.

Social Studies Connection

Tell students that one of the major breakthroughs in organic chemistry was the result of a dream. Until the late 1800s, chemists thought that carbon compounds existed only in straight or branched chains. However, neither of these structures explained the behavior of benzene, C_6H_6. In 1865, August Kekulé (1829–1896) dreamed of a snake that had seized its own tail. Ask students to explain how Kekulé's dream suggested a third model for a carbon chain.

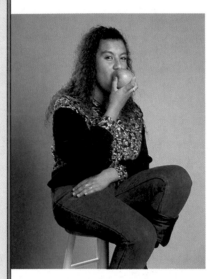

Figure 22.2 ▲
Carbon compounds make up many common items. This girl, the apple she's eating, and even her clothes are made up of carbon compounds.

Structure of Organic Compounds

Carbon is essential to living things because its atoms can form the "backbone" of large molecules. Reach around and feel your backbone. It is made up of units called vertebrae (VUR tuh bree). In your upper back, each vertebra is attached to two other vertebrae and two ribs. The vertebrae thus form the core of your skeleton—the framework that holds your body together. Carbon atoms function very much like vertebrae when they form a molecule's "backbone."

A carbon atom has four electrons in its outer electron shell. These electrons can be shared in four covalent bonds with other atoms. For example, since a carbon atom can form four chemical bonds, it can bond with two other carbon atoms and still have two bonds left over to bond with other atoms.

Carbon Backbone Shapes The basic backbone shape formed by carbon atoms is a straight chain. Like a string of beads, a molecule with a chain of carbon atoms can be any length. Many common organic compounds have chains dozens of carbon atoms long.

$$-\overset{|}{\underset{|}{C}}-\overset{|}{\underset{|}{C}}-\overset{|}{\underset{|}{C}}-\overset{|}{\underset{|}{C}}-\overset{|}{\underset{|}{C}}-$$ Straight chain

A second kind of carbon backbone is a branched chain. A different shape of molecules occurs when a carbon atom is bonded to three or four other carbons instead of only two. What other branched-chain shapes can you imagine?

$$-\overset{|}{\underset{|}{C}}-\overset{|}{\underset{|}{C}}-\overset{|}{\underset{|}{C}}-\overset{|}{\underset{|}{C}}-$$ Branched chain
$$-\overset{|}{\underset{|}{C}}-$$

In a third kind of arrangement, the ends of a carbon chain can be joined to form a circle, or ring. You can see a model of a carbon ring below.

Ring

Integrating the Sciences

Earth Science Explain that fossil fuels, such as oil and natural gas, formed from the remains of microorganisms that lived in oceans millions of years ago. Organisms died, and were covered by sediment. Heat and pressure caused chemical changes that turned the remains into fossil fuels. What can you infer about the molecular structure of fossil fuels? (They are organic, or made of carbon compounds.)

Multicultural Perspectives

In the first century B.C., Chinese engineers developed a method for extracting a fuel, methane gas, from the earth. The Chinese used bamboo cables for the derricks; the bamboo could withstand pressures over 5×10^7 Pa. This allowed the miners to drill wells as deep as 1440 m to reach the methane. They used the fuel for cooking and heating.

Use Integrating Worksheet 22.1.

Carbon-Carbon Bonds A carbon atom can share four pairs of electrons with other atoms. But, it doesn't have to share these electron pairs in four separate bonds. Two or even three pairs of electrons can be shared in bonding between two carbons.

When two atoms share two pairs of electrons, they form a *double covalent bond*. When they share three pairs, they form a *triple covalent bond*. The way to represent these types of carbon-carbon bonds on paper is shown in the figure below. Double and triple bonds can occur almost anywhere in a carbon chain, branched chain, or ring.

Single bond   Double bond   Triple bond

Double bonds in a chain

Double bond in a ring

Double and triple bond in a chain

Hydrocarbons

Many materials you use contain only hydrogen and carbon atoms. Compounds with only hydrogen and carbon atoms are **hydrocarbons** (HY droh KAR buhnz). Hydrocarbons are made up of straight chains, branched chains, or rings of carbon atoms with hydrogen atoms attached.

Bonds that aren't carbon-carbon bonds in a hydrocarbon are carbon-hydrogen bonds. Hydrocarbons, such as oil and natural gas, are a major source of energy for heating buildings and running machines. Gasoline is made up of several different hydrocarbons. Other hydrocarbons are the raw materials used for making plastics, medicines, and synthetic materials, such as nylon and acrylic fibers.

Environmental Science

L I N K

To identify the carbon compounds that make up recyclable plastics, a code system has been developed. Collect several different kinds of plastic containers. Look for a number in a triangle and some capital letters on each container. Make a list of the capital letter combinations. These letters are abbreviations of the compound's name. Match the ones you found with the name below.

◆ PETE (polyethylene-terephthalate)
◆ HDPE (high-density polyethylene)
◆ V (vinyl or polyvinyl chloride)
◆ PP (polypropylene)
◆ PS (polystyrene)

Which recyclable plastic was used most often at your house?

A C T I V I T Y

TEACH ▪ *Continued*

Class Activity

Have students work in groups of three or four. Tell each group to copy Table 22.1 onto a sheet of paper. Have them leave room for a large drawing at the bottom of each column. Have the groups draw a space-filling model of each hydrocarbon in the table. Allow groups to exchange drawings with one another and compare and correct the models. Students should explain any corrections.

Research

Have students use references such as books or computer data bases (if available) to make a chart of hydrocarbons. For each hydrocarbon listed, students should include an example of how it is used. (Example: propane and butane can be used as cooking and heating fuels, and isobutane is often used in aerosol sprays.)

Answers to In-Text Questions

① CH_4

② Ethane—two large spheres in the center with three smaller spheres attached to each; methane—one large sphere in the center with four smaller spheres attached to it

③ Two bonded carbon atoms with two hydrogens each

 The Living Textbook: Physical Science Sides 1-4

Chapter 4   Frame 00973
Methane (1 Frame)
Search:

 The Living Textbook: Physical Science Sides 1-4

Chapter 4   Frame 00983
Ethene (1 Frame)
Search:

540

Language Arts Connection

Tell students that prefixes in the names of carbon compounds indicate how many carbon atoms are contained in the compounds. Have them use Table 22.1 to determine the number associated with the prefixes *meth-, eth-, prop-, and but-*. (One, two, three, four; respectively) Ask students what they think the prefixes *pent-, hex-,* and *hept-* mean. How could they check their answers? (Five, six, seven; check a dictionary)

STS Connection

Explain to students that as fruit ripens, it gives off ethene gas. Explain that some fruit-growers harvest fruit and ship it to stores before it is ripe. The stores may treat the fruit with ethene, imitating the fruit's own process and ripening the fruit. Ask students what they think are the advantages of this practice. (Unripe fruit can be transported farther and stay on the shelf longer.)

The simplest hydrocarbon is the compound methane (MEHTH ayn). You can see in Figure 22.3 that a methane molecule has only a single carbon atom. How do you write the formula for methane? ①

A hydrocarbon with two carbon atoms is ethane. The two carbon atoms in ethane share one bond with each other. That leaves each carbon atom with three bonds left to share with hydrogen atoms. The formula for ethane is C_2H_6. How would a space-filling model for ethane differ from the methane molecule shown? ②

Some hydrocarbons contain double or triple bonds between carbon atoms. The simplest hydrocarbon with a double bond is ethene (EHTH een). Find ethene's formula and structure in Table 22.1. How is ethene different from ethane? A special property of a double bond, such as the one in ethene, is that it prevents the two carbon atoms that share it from rotating around one another. What would a space-filling model of an ethene molecule look like? ③

Figure 22.3   Methane ▼

Methane is one carbon atom bonded with four hydrogen atoms. Each shared pair of electrons making up a bond is shown as a single line.

A space-filling model of a methane molecule shows how it looks in three dimensions.

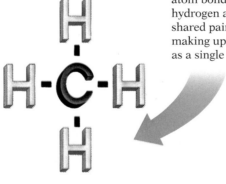

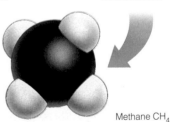

Methane CH_4

Table 22.1   Common Hydrocarbons

Name, Formula, and Structure				
Methane CH_4	Ethane C_2H_6	Propane C_3H_8	Butane C_4H_{10}	Ethene C_2H_4
H │ H—C—H │ H	H H │ │ H—C—C—H │ │ H H	H H H │ │ │ H—C—C—C—H │ │ │ H H H	H H H H │ │ │ │ H—C—C—C—C—H │ │ │ │ H H H H	H H \\ / C=C / \\ H H

Portfolio

Have students prepare an illustrated catalog of products that contain organic compounds. For each product pictured, both the name and formula of the organic ingredient should be given. Examples include insecticides, paint removers, aspirin, detergents, and all types of plastics.

Unsaturated Hydrocarbons

Hydrocarbons in which all the carbon atoms are joined to one another by single covalent bonds are called **saturated hydrocarbons**. Hydrogen atoms are bonded to all of the other bonding sites on the carbon atoms.

In contrast, hydrocarbons that contain carbon-carbon double or triple bonds are called **unsaturated hydrocarbons**. All their carbon atoms aren't "saturated" with other atoms. Each double or triple carbon-carbon bond can be turned into a single carbon bond, making it possible to add additional atoms to the molecule.

Polymers

Plastics are made up of very long carbon-containing molecules. They are created by joining together large numbers of much smaller organic molecules. Any similar type of molecule, formed from the covalent bonding of smaller repeated units, is called a **polymer** (PAHL uh muhr). The molecules from which a polymer is made are called *monomers*.

Isomers

What's the structure of the hydrocarbon with the formula C_4H_{10}? If you think it is a molecule with four carbons in a row, you're right. But, that isn't the only correct answer!

Actually, two different compounds have the formula C_4H_{10}. You can see what they look like in Figure 22.4. When more than one structure exists for one chemical formula, each structure is called an **isomer** (EYE soh mur) of the other. Isomers have different properties because their atoms are arranged differently. The greater the number of carbon atoms in a molecule, the more isomers it's likely to have. How many isomers can you draw for C_5H_{12}? ④

Look at Figure 22.5. It shows another kind of isomer, a geometric isomer. Geometric isomers have the same atoms and bonds in the same order. However, they have a different arrangement of atoms around a double bond. Remember that the carbons sharing a double bond can't rotate. Therefore, the two molecules in Figure 22.5 can't become the same.

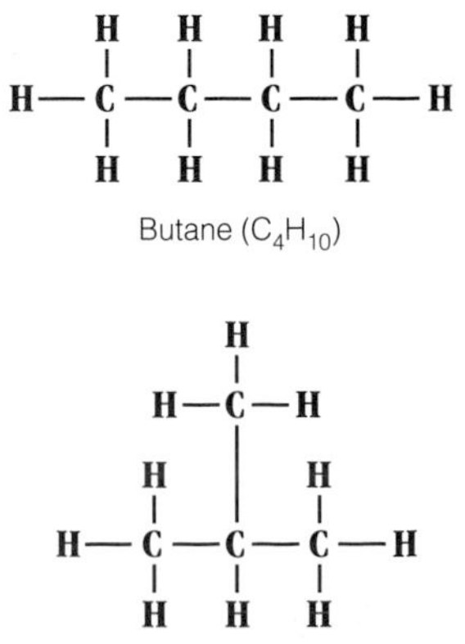

Butane (C_4H_{10})

Methylpropane (C_4H_{10})

Figure 22.4 ▲
How do the structures of these isomers differ? ⑤

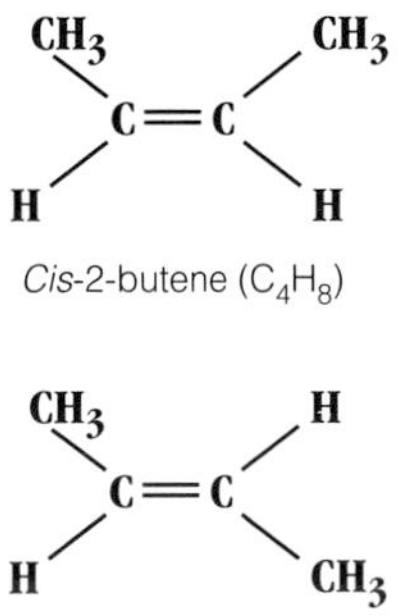

Cis-2-butene (C_4H_8)

Trans-2-butene (C_4H_8)

Figure 22.5 ▲
What is the difference between these two geometric isomers? ⑥

Critical Thinking

Reason by Analogy Remind students that a solution that contains the maximum solute for a certain amount of solvent is a saturated solution. Then discuss the following:

▶ How is a saturated compound like a saturated solution? (Answers will vary but students should point out that a saturated compound is a hydrocarbon that has the maximum number of hydrogen or other atoms bonded to its carbon atoms.)

▶ Describe an unsaturated hydrocarbon. (It has double or triple bonds; these bonds could be changed into single carbon bonds if other atoms are added to the molecule.)

Skills Development

Make a Model Use gumdrops and toothpicks to make models of the four isomers on this page. Use the models for butane and methylpropane to stress that isomers have different structures for the same chemical formula. Use the models for the molecules in Figure 22.5 to reinforce the concept of geometric isomers. Ask students to draw two isomers for C_5H_{12} and two geometric isomers for an imaginary carbon compound. (Check students' drawings for accuracy.)

Answers to In-Text Questions

④ **Three**

⑤ **Methylpropane is a three-carbon chain that has a CH₃ molecule attached to the middle carbon. But butane is a four-carbon chain and is saturated with hydrogen.**

⑥ **The *cis* form has two CH₃ molecules at consecutive "corners" of the molecule, the *trans* form has two CH₃ molecules at alternate "corners" of the molecule.**

Reteach

Review with students the halogen group of the Periodic Table on page 197 in Chapter 8. Ask:

▶ What one term other than *halogen* can describe these elements? (Nonmetals)

▶ What elements are in the halogen group? (Fluorine, chlorine, bromine, iodine, and astatine)

Class Activity

Write the words *substituted hydrocarbon* on the chalkboard. Then ask students to create a catalog of types of substituted hydrocarbons. Ask volunteers to describe the substitution and to give an example of each compound. (Alcohols in which an –OH group has been substituted for a hydrogen atom, such as methanol; carboxylic acids in which a –COOH group has been substituted for a hydrogen atom, such as acetic acid in vinegar. Halocarbons form when an atom of the halogen group substitutes for a hydrogen atom; chloroform.)

Enrich

A demonstration using acetic acid, ethanol, and a dropper can provide experience with synthetic esters. Produce fragrances by adding a few drops of acetic acid to ethanol. Ask students to describe the resulting odor. (Apple) Other common esters you may make include:
butyric acid + ethanol→pineapple
acetic acid + isopentanol→banana
acetic acid + 1-octanol→orange
salicylic acid + methanol→wintergreen

STS Connection

Explain to students that naturally occurring esters such as isopentyl acetate and ethyl butyrate are the compounds responsible for the scents associated with bananas and pineapples, respectively. These esters, as well as hundreds of others, can be produced artificially and used as synthetic fragrances and flavors. Have students keep a record of foods they eat that contain artificial flavors. Then have them use reference sources to discover which esters might be responsible for these flavors. Students may wish to place their observations in their portfolios.

Figure 22.6 ▲
Many different esters combine to produce the aromas that you recognize as banana, pineapple, or grape.

Substituted Hydrocarbons

What happens when you remove one of the hydrogen atoms of a hydrocarbon and replace it with another kind of atom or group of atoms? You create a **substituted hydrocarbon**. The atom or group of atoms substituted for hydrogen is called a *functional group*. Common functional groups are single atoms of a halogen, and other groups such as hydroxyls (-OH) and amines ($-NH_2$). Each functional group brings a certain set of chemical properties to its molecule.

Among the substituted hydrocarbons are alcohols. In alcohols, an -OH group has been substituted for a hydrogen atom. The simplest alcohol is methanol. Look at Table 22.2 to see the formula and structure of methanol.

The carboxylic (KAR bahk SIHL ihk) acids are another group of substituted hydrocarbons. They contain the functional group -COOH, the structure of which is shown in Table 22.2. The acid in vinegar, acetic acid, is a carboxylic acid.

When a carboxylic acid and an alcohol react, they form an ester (EHS tur). Most esters have a pleasant smell and taste. Esters produce the aromas of pineapples, apples, oranges, bananas, and apricots.

When a halogen atom, such as a chlorine or a bromine, substitutes for a hydrogen atom in a hydrocarbon, a halocarbon (HAL uh KAR buhn) forms. Very few halocarbons are found in nature. They are manufactured and used for many different purposes. Examples of halocarbons include chloroform ($CHCl_3$), which is used as a general anesthetic, and carbon tetrachloride, (CCl_4), which is used in dry cleaning.

Table 22.2   Common Substituted Hydrocarbons

Name, Type, Formula, and Structure			
Methanol	**Acetic acid**	**Ethyl acetate**	**Methyl chloride**
Alcohol CH_3OH	Carboxylic acid CH_3COOH	Ester $CH_3COOC_2H_5$	Halocarbon CH_3Cl
H | H—C—OH | H	H O | || H—C—C—OH | H	H O H H | || | | H—C—C—O—C—C—H | | | H H H	H | H—C—Cl | H

Language Arts Connection

Have students find out about the uses of polymers such as polyethylene, polystyrene, and polyvinylidene chloride. Have them organize their information in the form of a chart and include pictures that illustrate a use of each polymer. (Polyethylene—tubing, kitchen utensils; polystyrene—insulation, boats; polyvinylidene chloride—clinging food wraps) Explain to students that the word polymer comes from the Greek words *poly,* meaning "many," and *meros,* meaning "parts." Polymers are giant molecules made up of many smaller molecules.

Science and Technology   *Presto! Plastics!*

A student in the laboratory holds a large beaker. It contains two liquids, one is clear and one is translucent. The liquids are layered in the beaker, one above the other. The student explains that the two liquids have been heated but don't mix. The student dips tweezers to where the two solutions meet. She pulls the tweezers up, and to everyone's astonishment, a solid fiber clings to them. The fiber is nylon, a synthetic polymer.

The two liquids in the beaker are solutions of different organic compounds. Each compound has a certain functional group on each end. The functional groups of the two compounds react with each other at the boundary between the two solutions. Monomers link together in long strings to form nylon. The long strings of monomers make up the nylon polymer.

Synthetic polymers such as nylon have many useful features. They are strong, light, and very durable. When researchers tested materials to use for artificial body parts, such as knee joints and heart valves, they chose synthetic polymers.

Synthetic polymers are used in many other products. For example, automobiles are becoming lighter and more fuel efficient because polymers are quickly replacing heavy metal parts. Polymers also turn up in such various items as telephones, toothbrushes, pop bottles, and tennis rackets. Name other items you use daily that are made from polymers.

▼ **ACTIVITY**

Applying

Plastic

List all the plastic objects that you used or came across today. For each object, give a reason why it is made from plastic and not another material.

SKILLS WORKOUT

Check and Explain

1. Why can carbon form more compounds than other elements?

2. What is the difference between a saturated hydrocarbon and an unsaturated hydrocarbon?

3. **Predict** How many isomers exist for the formula C_6H_{14}?

4. **Make a Model** Make three-dimensional models of simple hydrocarbons. Use polystyrene balls of two different sizes to represent carbon and hydrogen atoms. Use toothpicks to represent the bonds. Base your models on structural diagrams in this chapter.

Skills WorkOut

To help students grasp the large number of plastics available, have them do the Skills WorkOut.
Answer Check students' lists for accuracy. Examples include: toothbrush, automobile, clothing, soft-drink bottle.

Discuss

After students read this page, ask:

▶ How is a synthetic polymer made? (By combining solutions of different organic compounds with certain functional groups)

▶ What synthetic fabrics do you wear? (Answers will vary.)

EVALUATE

WrapUp

Reinforce Ask students to make a concept map that summarizes the substances in this section. The chart should include carbon backbone shapes and bonds, and various hydrocarbons. Students should draw a diagram for each structure or molecule in the chart.
Use Review Worksheet 22.1.

Check and Explain

1. Because carbon can form four bonds with other atoms and long, branching chains

2. In a saturated hydrocarbon, all the carbons are joined by four single bonds. In an unsaturated hydrocarbon there are double or triple bonds between carbon atoms leaving fewer electrons to bond with hydrogen atoms.

3. Five

4. Check students' models.

 The Living Textbook: Physical Science Sides 1-4

Chapter 36   Frame 047779
Making Nylon (Movie)
Search: Play:

Time 1 week   Group pairs

Materials

30 labels

30 small jars with lids

450 whole cloves

rubbing alcohol

water

Analysis

1. The cloves in alcohol

2. They both are liquids in which a smaller amount of a different substance is dissolved.

3. Clove oil; yes

Conclusion

Some of the fragrant oils from the cloves dissolve in the water. However, as the molecules contributing to the scent of the cloves are primarily alcohols, they readily dissolve in the alcohol solvent.

Everyday Application

Alcohol is a common solvent in food colorings and flavors.

Extension

Grinding and crushing should make the perfume stronger because it exposes a larger surface area to the solvent. Because the fragrant oils dissolve more easily in rubbing alcohol than in water, rubbing alcohol would be a better solvent for perfumes; more scent could be contained in a smaller bottle.

Prelab Discussion

Have students read the entire activity. Discuss with students what an ester is and how it is formed. Ask students to predict the results of the activity. Have them give reasons for their predictions.

Activity 22 *How can you capture a scent?*

Skills   Measure; Observe; Infer

Task 1 Prelab Prep

1. Collect the following items: 2 labels, pen, 2 small jars with lids, 30 whole cloves, water, and rubbing alcohol. **CAUTION: Keep rubbing alcohol away from your mouth. It is a poison.**

2. On one label write *Water* and on the other write *Rubbing Alcohol*.

3. Attach a label to each jar.

Task 2 Data Record

1. On a separate sheet of paper, draw a data table like the one shown.

2. Record all your observations about the solutions in the data table like the one at the bottom of the page.

Task 3 Procedure

1. Place 15 whole cloves in each jar.

2. Fill one jar half full with water. Fill the other jar half full with rubbing alcohol.

3. Close both jars and screw the lids on tightly. Don't open the jars for one full week.

4. When the week is over, put a few drops of the liquid from the water jar on your left wrist. Put a few drops of the alcohol solution on your right wrist. When the liquids evaporate, smell each wrist.

Task 4 Analysis

1. Which liquid had the strongest scent?

2. Why are water and alcohol called solvents in this activity?

3. In the jar with the strongest scent, what substance do you think dissolved from the cloves? If you removed the cloves from the liquid, would the liquid still have the same scent a week from now? Give reasons for your answer.

Task 5 Conclusion

In a short paragraph explain how the scent from the cloves formed in the liquids. Hint: think of how this relates to the scent of fruits like pineapples and bananas.

Everyday Application

Many food colorings are made from the leaves of plants. Orange and vanilla and other liquid flavorings are made from other plant parts, such as peels and beans. Read the labels on bottles of such products. Based on what you read, what can you conclude about the solvents used to make food colorings and liquid flavors?

Extension

Experiment with various spices, herbs, and flower petals to make your own perfumes. Select both dry and fresh spices, herbs, and flower petals. Experiment by using the items whole and ground up. Identify any difference between fresh and dried materials. How does grinding or crushing affect the strength of the perfumes? Which solvent from this experiment is better to use for perfumes? Why?

Table 22.3 Clove Perfumes

Solvent	Observations
Water	
Alcohol	

Themes in Science
Systems and Interactions
Humans get most of their energy from carbohydrates. Chemical reactions break down more complex carbohydrates into glucose; energy is stored in the chemical bonds in glucose. Ask students what kind of energy is stored in the bonds. (Chemical, potential) Then ask what they think must happen before the body can use its stored energy. (A chemical reaction must break the bonds.)

Section Objectives
For a list of section objectives, see the Student Edition page.

Skills Objectives
Students should be able to:

Communicate about how food gets to consumers' tables.

Make a Table comparing carbohydrates, fats, and proteins.

Vocabulary
carbohydrates, lipids, proteins

22.2 Food Chemistry

Objectives

▶ **Give examples** of foods that are rich in carbohydrates, lipids, and proteins.

▶ **Describe** the general chemical structure of each group of nutrients.

▶ **Contrast** saturated and unsaturated lipids.

▶ **Make a table** comparing the roles of carbohydrates, lipids, and proteins in human nutrition.

 **ACTIVITY**

Communicating

Food Processing

Pick your favorite food. Draw a flow chart to describe how that food reaches your table from its source.

SKILLS WARMUP

MOTIVATE

Skills WarmUp

To help students understand food chemistry, have them do the Skills WarmUp.
Answer Flowcharts will vary. If students choose a food that has several parts, such as a hamburger, they should make a chart for each part. Encourage students to be as specific as possible. Flowcharts should begin with the sun.

Prior Knowledge

Gauge how much students know about food chemistry by asking the following questions:

▶ What do organic compounds have to do with food?

▶ What are the three main types of organic compounds in foods?

▶ What role does each group play in the body?

A re you getting hungry for some good, tasty organic compounds? When you eat your next meal, you will probably take into your body hundreds of different organic compounds. Your body will break down most of these compounds into simpler substances during the process of digestion. The products of digestion will then be used for energy and as building blocks for new substances you need to live and grow.

Organic compounds in foods are classified in three main groups: carbohydrates, lipids, and proteins. These organic compounds are called nutrients. Each group of nutrients plays a different role in the body.

Carbohydrates

The runners in Figure 22.7 are competing in a marathon. Since a marathon can take more than two hours to complete, a lot of energy will be needed. Much of the energy used during the race will be released from organic compounds stored in each athlete's body. These energy-providing compounds are called **carbohydrates** (KAR boh HY drats). Carbohydrates are organic compounds that contain hydrogen and oxygen atoms in a ratio of two to one.

About three days before a marathon, a runner begins "carbohydrate loading." The runner eats large amounts of breads, pasta, grains, and potatoes, which are all rich in carbohydrates. Carbohydrate loading provides the marathon runner with a supply of stored carbohydrates large enough to last the race.

Figure 22.7
These runners prepared to run this race by eating extra carbohydrates beforehand.

 The Living Textbook: Physical Science Sides 1-4

Chapter 4　　　　Frame 01012
Starch Monomer Model (1 Frame)
Search:

TEACH

Portfolio

Have students keep a journal of the kinds of foods they eat for a week. Have them list foods eaten during each day and categorize these foods as either carbohydrates, lipids, or proteins. Have students keep these journals as part of their portfolios.

Explore Visually

Have the students study the text and Figures 22.8 and 22.9. Discuss the following:

▶ Identify four specific foods that are high in carbohydrates. (Bread, bananas, apples, various grains)

▶ How many carbon atoms are in a single molecule of glucose? (Six)

▶ Identify four specific foods that are high in lipids. (Butter, sausage, avocado, hamburger)

▶ What are two ways that a glucose molecule is like a triglyceride? What two ways are they different? (Both contain many carbon and hydrogen atoms; the triglyceride molecule is larger and contains double bonds.)

Answer to In-Text Question

① **Possible answers include pasta and legumes.**

The Living Textbook: Physical Science Sides 1-4

Chapter 4   Frame 01013
Sucrose (1 Frame)
Search:

546

Multicultural Perspectives

Explain to students that starches make up the bulk of peoples' diets throughout the world. Most of these starches come from cereals, such as millet and wheat, or from plant tubers or roots, such as potatoes and cassava. Have students find out which starches are most common in different parts of the world.

Math Connection

Each gram of carbohydrate in food contains 4 Calories of energy. Have students bring in a food label and calculate the number of Calories that one serving of the food contains from carbohydrates. Ask students what percentage of the total Calories come from carbohydrates and whether a nutritionist would recommend this food item. Have them explain their answers.

Carbohydrates aren't just for athletes. Everyone relies on them as a basic source of energy for life processes. For most people, carbohydrates make up the largest part of their diet.

Most of the carbohydrates you eat are in the form of starch. A starch is a polymer made up of simpler carbohydrates called sugars. Your body breaks down starches into sugars because sugars are the carbohydrates your cells use for energy.

An important simple sugar is *glucose* (GLOO kohs). It has the formula $C_6H_{12}O_6$. Look at Figure 22.8 to see the structure of glucose. How is it different from other organic compounds you studied? Glucose is one of the main products of digestion of starches. Glucose is sent through your blood to all the cells in your body. Your cells break the chemical bonds in glucose to release the energy stored in them.

Although sugars are your cells' actual energy source, your body works best when it takes in starches and converts them to sugars. Nutritionists recommend that about 55 to 60 percent of the Calories you take in daily should be from starchy carbohydrates like those in Figure 22.8. What other foods do you think are high in starch? ①

Figure 22.8
Carbohydrates provide energy for your body the way wood fuels a fire. ▼

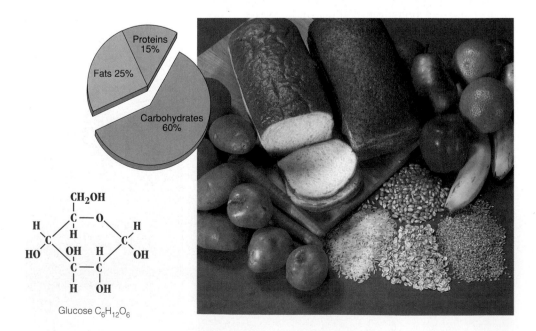

Glucose $C_6H_{12}O_6$

Integrating the Sciences

Health   Even though people are usually encouraged to avoid fats in their diet, these nutrients have an important role in the body. Fats not only store energy, they help the body absorb some vitamins, and supply an essential fatty acid (linoleic acid). Cholesterol in the body forms hormones and cell membranes. The U.S. Department of Health and Human Services recommends a diet in which 25 percent or less of Calorie intake is in the form of fats. A gram of fat contains 9 Calories of energy. Calculate with students the number of Calories that a sample meal contains, then find the percentage of Calories from fat. Use food labels to represent the sample meal. Have students look at the circle graph in Figure 22.9. Ask, Would a nutritionist recommend the meal you just analyzed?

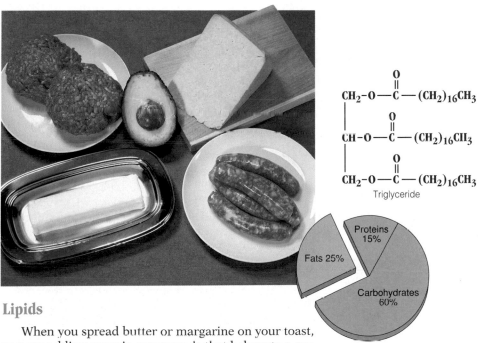

Triglyceride

Proteins 15%

Fats 25%

Carbohydrates 60%

Figure 22.9 ▲
Fats and oils help to insulate your body from cold the way a blanket does.

Lipids

When you spread butter or margarine on your toast, you are adding organic compounds that belong to a second group of nutrients. These nutrients, which include fats and oils, are called **lipids** (LIHP ihdz). Lipids are organic compounds that have long hydrocarbon chains and don't dissolve in water.

Your body uses lipids to produce substances that protect nerves, insulate you from the cold, and transmit messages among organs. Lipids, like carbohydrates, can also be used as an energy source. Gram for gram, however, lipids contain more energy than carbohydrates. Thus, when you take in a large amount of lipids, not all of them can be used. Excess lipids get stored as body fat. For this reason, less than 25 percent of the Calories you take in should come from fats and oils.

You should also be concerned about what kinds of lipids you eat. Lipids that contain only single bonds are called saturated lipids. These are found mostly in animal foods, such as meats, poultry, and dairy products. Eating large amounts of saturated lipids may be a major cause of heart disease. Unsaturated lipids, which have double bonds in their structures, are better for your body. Olive oil, peanut oil, canola oil, and other oils from plants all contain mostly unsaturated lipids.

Class Activity

Compare the lipid and water content of butter and margarine and a reduced-fat butter substitute. You will need three heat-proof beakers; a stick each of butter, margarine, and reduced-fat butter substitute; a tub full of cool water; a hot plate; and a metric ruler. Melt the spreads in separate beakers. Don't allow the spreads to boil or burn. Then place the beakers in a cool water bath. Two layers will form in each beaker: a top layer of lipids (either butterfat or oil) and a bottom aqueous layer. Ask students to measure the water and lipids in each, and calculate the percentage of water and lipids in each of the three spreads.

Critical Thinking

Compare and Contrast   Have students compare and contrast the *sources* of foods high in carbohydrates with foods high in lipids. (Carbohydrates usually come from plants; lipids usually from animals. Both trace back to the sun.)

Portfolio

Have students create a list of foods with more than 25 percent fat in them. Instruct them to read food labels, or use other resources. Ask them to label the foods in their list *Unsaturated Fats* or *Saturated Fats*. Students can add the lists to their portfolios.

Integrated Learning

Use Integrating Worksheet 22.2a.

TEACH ▪ *Continued*

Discuss

Have students make a concept map relating proteins, amino acids, and –COOH and –NH₂ groups. The map should include some of the functions of amino acids.

Research

The artificial sweetener aspartame (Nutrasweet® and Equal® are two brand names of aspartame) is made of two amino acids. Have students research what amino acids make up aspartame and how the sweetener is formed. Have them take notes and produce a "recipe" for making aspartame. Their recipes should show how the two amino acids bond to form the new compound. (Aspartame is made of aspartic acid and phenyl-alanine.)

Enrich

The body contains thousands of proteins, all from just 20 different amino acids. The eight essential amino acids that the body does not produce are leucine, isoleucine, lysine, methionine, phenylalanine, threonine, tryptophan, and valine. Have students look at Figure 22.10. Ask, Which part of the glycine molecule is the carboxyl group? Explain how you know. (CO_2H; it contains two oxygen and a hydrogen atom linked to a carbon.)

Portfolio

Have students use a biological textbook to prepare a list of the eight amino acids the body can't produce. Their lists should include possible dietary sources for these amino acids. (Meats and poultry) Have them draw the structure of one of these amino acids. They can add the lists to their portfolios.

Reteach

Use Reteach Worksheet 22.2.

Themes in Science

Energy Explain to students that carbohydrates, lipids, and proteins all provide energy to the human body. Each source produces a different amount of energy. Carbohydrates and proteins provide about the same amount of energy per gram. Lipids provide more than twice as much energy per gram as do the other two nutrients.

Use Integrating Worksheet 22.2b.

Multicultural Perspectives

Different cultures eat certain combinations of incomplete proteins that together provide their diet with all of the essential amino acids. A Mexican meal, for example, might consist of beans and rice. Grains and beans eaten together provide complete protein. Two other dishes that also provide complete protein when eaten together come from the Middle East: tabouli (a cracked wheat salad) and hummus (pureed chickpeas).

Proteins

What do dried beans, nuts, eggs, dairy products, and meats have in common? They are all rich in a third group of nutrients called **proteins** (PROH teenz). Proteins are large, complex molecules made up of 20 different building blocks called amino (uh MEE noh) acids. Amino acids are organic molecules that contain both a carboxyl group (–COOH) and an amine group (–NH₂). The structure of one of the amino acids is shown in Figure 22.10.

When you eat a protein, it is broken down into the amino acids that make it up. The cells in your body use these amino acids to build your body's own proteins. To make a protein, a cell links together different amino acids in a certain order, like beads on a string. Each protein has its own unique order of amino acids.

The proteins made by your cells serve many functions. They are the chief materials that make up new cells. They help transport oxygen throughout the body. As catalysts, or enzymes, they help digest food and make thousands of other vital chemical reactions possible.

Your body produces some, but not all, of the amino acids it needs. To obtain the amino acids your body doesn't make, you must eat foods that contain them. Eggs, dairy products, and meats contain all the amino acids your body needs. You can also get these amino acids by eating a combination of dried beans and grains.

Figure 22.10
Proteins are the materials that your body uses to build new cells, just as construction workers build a house out of wood or brick. ▼

$$H_2N - \overset{\overset{\displaystyle H}{|}}{\underset{\underset{\displaystyle H}{|}}{C}} - CO_2H$$

Glycine

Cooperative Learning

Have students work in cooperative groups of three to research, write, design, and produce an educational booklet. The booklet should explain the importance of the basic vitamins listed here and identify food sources that provide each vitamin. Encourage students to design the booklets so that they could be used to teach second and third graders about vitamins. If possible, share the booklets with elementary school students.

Science and You   *Essential Vitamins?*

You've probably seen row upon row of bottles of vitamin pills in the store. If you read the label of a multiple-vitamin product, you'll see it contains vitamins A, C, D, E, K, and several different B vitamins. What are vitamins and why are they essential?

Vitamins are special nutrients not classified as carbohydrates, lipids, or proteins. Their structures vary, but all vitamins are organic compounds necessary for your body to function properly. Most vitamins work together with enzymes to make possible the chemical reactions that occur in your body.

By eating a well-balanced diet, you can get all the vitamins you need. Meats, eggs, and dairy products contain B vitamins and vitamins A, D, and K. Citrus fruits and tomatoes are rich sources of vitamin C. Green, leafy vegetables have large amounts of vitamins A, E, and K. Dried beans and grains provide you with B vitamins.

Career Corner   Food Scientist

Who Develops New Food Products?

Almost every month a new food product comes to your market. Nonfat ice cream, sugarless cakes, and salt-free cereals are some examples. Who is responsible for these new foods? Researchers known as food scientists create them.

Food scientists often work to produce foods that are healthier for people to eat. They may find ways to make foods taste good, even though the foods have less fat, sugar, or salt.

Some food scientists may work with other scientists to test special diets on animals,

or even on people, to see how diet might prevent or cure certain diseases. Food scientists also search for ways to keep foods fresh longer so they won't spoil on supermarket shelves or soon after you bring them home.

Food scientists may also test foods to make sure they are safe. Safety standards for food are set by government agencies such as the Food and Drug Administration, or FDA. Some food scientists work for the FDA to monitor the quality of manufactured foods, such as meats, vegetables, fruits, and seafood.

A person with a bachelor's degree in biology or nutrition may work as a food scientist. But, food-science jobs related to creating new foods may require advanced degrees.

Skills Development

Communicate Ask students whether a person who generally eats a balanced diet needs to take daily vitamin supplements. Have them write a brief essay on this question. Student volunteers can share their essays with the class.

Critical Thinking

Classify Have students make a chart with a row for each of the following vitamins: A, B vitamins, C, D, E, and K. Have them bring food labels that list the vitamin contents of food to class. Then ask them to use the labels to fill in the chart with foods that are sources of each vitamin. (Possible answers—A: meats, eggs, dairy, and green, leafy vegetables; B vitamins: dried beans and grains; C: citrus fruits and tomatoes; D: meats, eggs, and dairy products; E: green, leafy vegetables; K: meats, eggs, dairy products, and green, leafy vegetables)

Career Corner

Portfolio Have students collect local newspaper "Help Wanted" sections as well as other job listings from professional periodicals. Ask them to cut out job advertisements for food scientists or nutritionists. (They can photocopy or hand copy if the listing can't be cut out.) Ask them to make a list of the skills and background required for each job.

 The Living Textbook: Physical Science Sides 1-4

Chapter 17   Frame 02835
Vitamins (1 Frame)
Search:

549

TEACH ▪ Continued

Skills WorkOut

To help students evaluate their vitamin diet, have them do the Skills WorkOut.

Answer Students' tables will vary.

EVALUATE

WrapUp

Reteach Have students discuss the following case and analyze it in terms of food chemistry: Sue Li dislikes meats and dairy products. Because she takes vitamins, she thinks she already gets what these foods provide.

Use Review Worksheet 22.2.

Check and Explain

1. Carbohydrates: pasta, grains; fats: avocados, olive oil; protein: eggs, meats.

2. Saturated fats contain only single carbon-carbon bonds; unsaturated fats contain some double carbon-carbon bonds.

3. All are organic compounds containing carbon, hydrogen, and oxygen atoms. Carbohydrates have a two to one hydrogen to oxygen ratio. Lipids usually consist of triglycerides containing three hydrocarbon chains. Proteins contain nitrogen atoms, and their structures include carboxylic acid groups, –COOH and amino groups, $-NH_2$.

4. Check students' tables for accuracy. Carbohydrates: supply glucose which the body breaks down for energy; fats: protect nerves, carry fat soluble compounds through bloodstream, supply energy, and insulate your body from the cold; proteins: provide materials to make new cells, help transport O_2 throughout the body, form enzymes that control chemical reactions in the body.

550

Social Studies Connection

Scurvy was once a serious problem on long sea journeys. Many sailors fell sick or died from this condition. Have students research the role of Scottish surgeon James Lind (1716–1794) in uncovering the connection between scurvy and vitamin C. Have them write a news story outlining Lind's findings and his suggestions for preventing scurvy.

Integrating the Sciences

Biology Tell students that the B vitamins and vitamin C are water-soluble, and that vitamins A and D are fat-soluble. Ask students why excessive amounts of vitamin A and vitamin D can be harmful to the body. (Vitamins that are not water-soluble are not eliminated in urine. A surplus of these vitamins can build up in the body, causing health problems.)

▼ ACTIVITY

Making a Table

Vitamins

List in a table the vitamins mentioned on this page. Next to each vitamin, write down the foods you ate today with that vitamin in it. Which vitamins are missing from your diet?

SKILLS WORKOUT

Your body doesn't need any of the essential vitamins in large amounts. However, some amount of each vitamin is important to your health. Many people in the world have diets that lack a sufficient amount of one or more vitamins. These people often suffer from what is called a deficiency disease.

Look at Table 22.4. It lists some essential vitamins, their function, and the deficiency disease caused by a lack of the vitamin. Some people take vitamin supplements to be sure they get enough vitamins. However, excessive amounts of some vitamins can be harmful.

Table 22.4 Vitamins

Vitamin	Function	Deficiency Disease
A	Maintains healthy skin, eyes, and bones	Night blindness; permanent blindness
B (complex)	Needed to break down carbohydrates, fats, and proteins, and to manufacture proteins	Beriberi; loss of appetite; skin disorders; anemia
C	Helps in the formation of bones	Scurvy; slow healing; gum disease
D	Promotes bone growth; helps the body use calcium	Rickets
E	Prevents damage to cell membranes	Breakdown of red blood cells; anemia
K	Helps blood to clot	Uncontrolled bleeding

Check and Explain

1. What are two foods that are a good source of carbohydrates? Of fats? Of protein?

2. What is the difference between a saturated and an unsaturated fat?

3. **Compare and Contrast** How are the chemical structures of carbohydrates, lipids, and proteins similar? How are they different?

4. **Make a Table** Compare the roles of carbohydrates, fats, and proteins in human nutrition.

Language Arts Connection

Have students look at Figure 22.11. Explain that the corn, the cow, and the boy occupy different trophic levels. Have students look up the meaning and origin of the word *trophic*. Then have them describe the trophic levels of the corn, the cow, and the boy.

Themes in Science

Energy Energy in any ecosystem flows from producers to consumers as shown in Figure 22.11. Explain to students that as energy passes through each stage, 90 percent of it is lost, mostly as heat. Ask, Which stage contains the highest percent of the original energy from the sun and therefore would feed the most people: ten square acres of land used to grow corn or ten square acres of land used to raise cattle? (The land used to grow corn)

Section Objectives
For a list of section objectives, see the Student Edition page.

Skills Objectives
Students should be able to:

Classify organisms as plants and animals.

Interpret Data about wavelengths and photosynthesis.

Infer how plants affect the earth.

Make a Model of respiration versus photosynthesis.

Vocabulary
photosynthesis, respiration

22.3 Energy in Living Things

Objectives

▶ **Describe** the flow of energy from the sun through plants and animals.

▶ **Summarize** the process of photosynthesis.

▶ **Explain** what occurs during cell respiration.

▶ **Make a model** that shows how respiration is the reverse of photosynthesis.

▼ **ACTIVITY**

Comparing

Plants vs. Animals

Write down as many differences between plants and animals as you can think of. Next write down the similarities. Add more similarities and differences to this list when you finish this chapter.

SKILLS WARMUP

Powered by contracting muscles, your feet, legs, arms, and torso move to the rhythm of the music at your school's dance. You're using energy stored in your body, energy that not only keeps you dancing but keeps you alive. Where does this all-important energy come from?

If you say your energy comes from food, you are right. But what is the source of the energy in food? The leaves, fruits, seeds, milk, meat, and eggs that you eat are made up of organic compounds. These compounds all contain energy in their chemical bonds.

Look at Figure 22.11. You can see that the original source of all the energy in the organic compounds you eat is the sun. Plants are an important link in this flow of energy. Plants are used as food by many animals. You use both plants and animals as food. Plants can capture the sun's energy and store it in the bonds of organic compounds. How are plants able to do this? ①

◀ **Figure 22.11**
The energy in a hamburger you eat originated from the sun.

Energy from the sun   Corn receives sun's energy   Cattle eat corn   People eat beef

MOTIVATE

Skills WarmUp

To help students understand energy use in living things, have them do the Skills WarmUp.
Answer Students should list similarities such as the ability to grow and reproduce. Differences include plants' inability to move from place to place under their own power and most plants' ability to manufacture their own food. Have students save their lists, adding more similarities and differences at the end of the chapter.

Prior Knowledge

Gauge how much students know about energy by asking the following questions:

▶ Why is the sun the original source of the energy your body gets from food?

▶ What is photosynthesis?

▶ How does the food we eat become energy?

Answer to In-Text Question
① Through photosynthesis

Explore Visually

Have students study the text and pictures on pages 552 and 553. Discuss the following:

▶ How does the plant grow in relation to the sun? (It grows toward the sun.)

▶ How is the structure of a leaf adapted to absorbing sunlight? (It exposes a large surface area to sunlight.)

▶ Describe the inside of a chloroplast. (Contains disklike structures and chlorophyll)

▶ How does a plant store energy from the sun? (The chemical process of photosynthesis traps energy in the chemical bonds of glucose.)

▶ What product of photosynthesis do plants use for food? (Glucose)

▶ In what form do plants store the food they make during photosynthesis? (Starch)

The Living Textbook:
Physical Science Sides 1-4

Chapter 8   Frame 01273
Photosynthesis Equation (1 Frame)
Search:

Themes in Science

Scale and Structure The basic structure of a plant consists of leaves, stems, and roots. Remove a houseplant from its soil and point out the plant parts to the class. Relate the structure of each part to its function. (Leaf: collects sunlight; stem: supports, lifts leaves toward sun, transports water and nutrients to the leaves; roots: absorb H_2O and nutrients, and anchor)

Integrating the Sciences

Chemistry Explain that plants get the carbon, hydrogen, and oxygen they need from the carbon dioxide in the air and from the water. Plants also need several other nutrients such as nitrogen, potassium, magnesium, calcium, phosphorus, and sulfur for healthy growth. Ask students to describe how plants get these nutrients from the soil. (Most are dissolved in water in the soil and absorbed by plant roots.)

**Figure 22.12
Photosynthesis** ▼

Photosynthesis: Storing Solar Energy

You know the sun beams energy to the earth. You can feel the energy as heat. You can see the energy as light. The energy from the sun feels good and lets you see everything around you. But, since you aren't a plant, you can't use the sun's energy directly to power your muscles or carry on all the other life processes in your body.

Plants capture the energy of the sun in a chemical process called **photosynthesis** (FOHT oh SIHN thuh sihs). During photosynthesis, water and carbon dioxide are combined to make glucose and oxygen. The glucose molecule produced in photosynthesis contains in its chemical bonds the energy absorbed from sunlight.

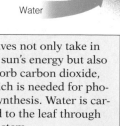
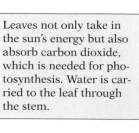

Sun

Energy

The sun radiates light energy to the earth. Plants absorb this light energy and convert it into stored chemical energy in the process of photosynthesis.

Plants grow toward the sun. Their leaves expose a large surface area to sunlight.

The roots of plants reach down into the soil where they absorb water and nutrients.

Water

Leaves not only take in the sun's energy but also absorb carbon dioxide, which is needed for photosynthesis. Water is carried to the leaf through the stem.

Plant cells

Oxygen

Carbon dioxide

Portfolio

Have students imagine they have toured a plant's glucose factory. Have them write a description of what they saw. Encourage them to illustrate their description with drawings of the factory. Students may want to include their paragraphs and drawings in their portfolios.

Cooperative Learning

Have students work in groups of four to design and carry out an experiment to show the importance of light in the process of photosynthesis. Ask the following question to help students focus their experiments: Can photosynthesis take place without light? Students may want to include the results of their experiment in their portfolios.

Critical Thinking

Uncover Assumptions Have students identify the assumption in the following statement: Because plant roots do not contain chlorophyll and do not take in sunlight, they do not play a part in photosynthesis. (Answers may vary but should indicate that the statement assumes [incorrectly] that only chlorophyll, sunlight, and leaves are essential for photosynthesis. Water and nutrients are also needed for photosynthesis.)

Apply

Ask students to make a list of things humans need to survive. (Lists may vary, but should include food, water, shelter, and oxygen.) Then have students draw a diagram showing which of the needs can be met by plants. (People eat plants; plant tissues contain water; parts of plants can be used for shelter, or to build shelter; plants produce oxygen.)

Plants carry on photosynthesis in the cells of their leaves. Each of these cells contains a kind of glucose factory, a chloroplast (KLOR uh PLAST). Chloroplasts have inside them all the compounds and structures needed to carry out the reactions needed for photosynthesis to take place.

Plants use the glucose they produce to make the larger organic compounds they need to live and grow. These organic compounds include carbohydrates, lipids, and proteins. Like glucose, the chemical bonds of these compounds store energy that originally came from the sun.

Cells near the top surface of the leaf are specialized for photosynthesis.

Chloroplast

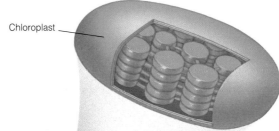

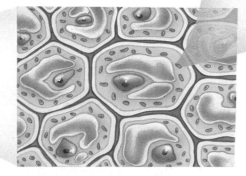

The chemical reactions of photosynthesis occur inside the cell's chloroplast. These cell structures contain chlorophyll, the green pigment that captures light energy from the sun.

$$6CO_2 \ + \ 6H_2O \ + \ \text{Light Energy} \longrightarrow C_6H_{12}O_6 \ + \ 6O_2$$

During photosynthesis, carbon dioxide, CO_2, from the air combines with water, H_2O, from the soil. Light energy from the sun creates chemical bonds.

Glucose, $C_6H_{12}O_6$, is the sugar the plant uses as food. The plant stores food as starch.

Oxygen, O_2, produced during photosynthesis is released into the atmosphere. Animals use oxygen to live.

Enrich

Tell students that *breathing* brings in a supply of oxygen, while *respiration* uses oxygen to break the bonds in glucose.

Skills Development

Communicate Have students make a flowchart showing how the carbohydrates they eat are broken down into glucose and then used by the body for energy. Tell them that the flowchart should indicate what processes occur and where they occur. Students may wish to title their flowcharts *Food to Energy,* and include them in their portfolios. (Flowcharts should cover the following steps: food is eaten, chewing and stomach contractions break food into small pieces, acids and enzymes further break down the food into glucose molecules. Glucose travels to cells through the bloodstream, oxygen is also carried by blood to cells. Glucose and oxygen are burned during respiration, and energy, carbon dioxide and water are released.)

SkillBuilder

Reteach Have students review the electromagnetic spectrum. Review that visible light is a small portion in the electromagnetic spectrum. Write the following sequence on the chalkboard: Radio waves, _____, infrared, _____, ultraviolet, _____, gamma rays. Have students fill in the blanks, naming the appropriate wavelength of light. (Microwaves, visible light, X-rays)

Answers

1. Violet and red, 400 nm and 680 nm

2. Yellow and green

3. Longer red wavelengths

4. The growth rate of the plant will be slow, because the rate of photosynthesis will be slow.

Integrating the Sciences

Environmental Science Explain to students that cell respiration in plants and animals, and most other organisms, depends on oxygen. Anaerobic bacteria, however, are poisoned by oxygen and grow only in oxygen-free environments.

These bacteria convert carbon dioxide (CO_2) and hydrogen (H_2) into methane gas (CH_4). Have students use references to determine what role anaerobic organisms can play in landfills and the production of fuel from waste materials.

Cell Respiration: Using Energy

How does your body get energy from food? The first step in the process is digestion. Chewing and stomach contractions help break the food you eat into small pieces. Acids and enzymes in the stomach work to break down the small pieces. Eventually, the food breaks down into the molecules it's made of. Some of those molecules are glucose molecules. After digestion, your bloodstream carries the glucose from your digestive system to all the cells of your body.

To harvest the energy in the chemical bonds of glucose, your cells need oxygen. This oxygen comes from the air you breathe. It is picked up from the lungs by red blood cells and then carried to your body cells.

With a supply of both oxygen and glucose, your cells carry out the process called **respiration**. During respiration, oxygen reacts with glucose, breaking the bonds in glucose and releasing their energy.

SkillBuilder *Interpreting Data*

The Best Light for Photosynthesis

You know that sunlight is actually made up of light of many different wavelengths. Each wavelength corresponds to a different color of light. Scientists have observed that plants can absorb light of certain wavelengths better than others. This infers that plants use only certain colors of light to manufacture glucose during photosynthesis.

The graph to the right shows how the rate of photosynthesis in a plant varies according to the wavelength of light that strikes it. Study the graph and answer the following questions.

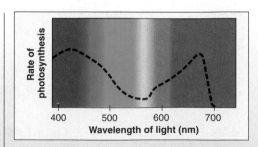

1. What colors of light produce the highest rate of photosynthesis? What are the approximate wavelengths of these colors?

2. What colors of light produce the lowest rate of photosynthesis?

3. What color of light has the sharpest drop rate?

4. If the only light a plant receives has wavelengths of between 500 and 600 nanometers (nm), what will happen to the growth rate of the plant? Why?

Write a paragraph describing how light of different wavelengths affects the growth of plants. Include an explanation of why the leaves of many plants appear green.

Energy Point out to students that the law of conservation of energy states that energy can neither be created nor destroyed. Have students explain how the processes of photosynthesis and respiration illustrate this law. (Energy is converted from one form to another: Energy taken in by plants is converted during photosynthesis and stored in the chemical bonds of glucose. During respiration, oxygen reacts with glucose, the chemical bonds break, and the stored energy is released and used to synthesize ATP. No energy is created or destroyed in the process.)

The equation below summarizes the respiration process.

$$C_6H_{12}O_6 + 6O_2 \longrightarrow 6CO_2 + 6H_2O + energy$$

The equation probably looks familiar to you. Actually, you've seen it before—in reverse. Respiration is, in many ways, the opposite of photosynthesis, as you can see in Table 22.5.

Table 22.5 Photosynthesis versus Respiration

Photosynthesis	Respiration
Uses water	Gives off water
Uses carbon dioxide	Gives off carbon dioxide
Makes glucose	Breaks down glucose
Gives off oxygen	Uses oxygen
Takes in energy (sunlight)	Releases energy
Occurs only in cells of plants and some bacteria and protists	Occurs in cells of all organisms

A major difference between photosynthesis and respiration is that respiration takes place constantly and photosynthesis doesn't. Study the formulas again. Notice that respiration gives off energy. Light energy is not needed for respiration to take place. However, for photosynthesis to take place, light energy must be present. Photosynthesis can't take place in the dark!

Much of the energy released during respiration is in the form of heat. The rest of the energy, however, is stored in the chemical bonds of a compound called adenosine triphosphate (ATP). Unlike glucose, a molecule of ATP easily gives up the energy stored in it. Molecules of ATP can move around the cell and power any chemical reaction. When you dance, for example, the energy of ATP molecules in your muscle cells is converted into kinetic energy.

Respiration, or some related process, occurs in all known organisms. Even plants, the makers of glucose, must respire to harness the energy they capture from the sun. Respiration and photosynthesis fit together to form the energy cycle of life on earth.

Environmental Science LINK

Carbon dioxide in the atmosphere is a greenhouse gas. It traps radiated heat which keeps the earth at a livable temperature. The main source of this gas is plant respiration. However, human sources of carbon dioxide, such as the combustion of gasoline, are enhancing the greenhouse effect and may cause an increase in temperatures worldwide called global warming. Write and balance the chemical equation for the reaction of octane (C_8H_{18}) with oxygen to form carbon dioxide and water. What else does this combustion form?

ACTIVITY

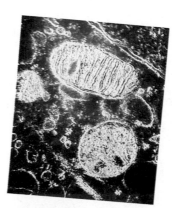

Figure 22.13 ▲
Mitochondria, like those shown here, are often called the powerhouses of a cell. ATP is produced in mitochondria by respiration.

Directed Inquiry

Have students examine Table 22.5. Ask the following questions:

▶ Do photosynthesis and respiration involve any of the same materials? Explain. (Yes; both processes involve oxygen, carbon dioxide, and glucose, but the roles are reversed.)

▶ Which products of photosynthesis and respiration are the same? (None)

▶ What generalization can you make about the substances produced by respiration and the substances used by photosynthesis? (One uses what the other makes.)

Skills Development

Communicate Ask students to describe how the energy released during respiration is stored. (In the bonds of ATP)

▶ Have students describe how ATP is different from glucose. (ATP easily gives up the energy stored in its bonds.)

▶ Have students add this energy storage information to their Carbohydrate to Energy flowcharts.

Answer to Link

$2C_8H_{18} + 25O_2 \rightarrow 16CO_2 + 18H_2O + energy$

This reaction produces energy, just as respiration does.

TEACH ▪ *Continued*

Discuss

Ask students to describe factors that affect the body's "energy budget." (Amount of Calories taken in, and amount of Calories used) Ask students how their bodies use energy. (Growth, movement, maintenance, and healing)

EVALUATE

WrapUp

Reinforce Ask students to imagine that a visitor from another planet wishes to learn the difference between green plants and animals. The visitor is particularly interested in how plants and animals obtain energy. Divide the class into pairs, and have one student play the visitor and ask questions as the other explains the processes. Tape record each encounter.

Use Review Worksheet 22.3.

Check and Explain

1. Carbon dioxide and water react in the presence of sunlight to produce glucose and oxygen.

2. Oxygen reacts with glucose, breaking its bonds and releasing energy in the form of ATP, along with carbon dioxide.

3. All animals and humans would have a greatly diminished food and oxygen supply.

4. Check students' drawings for accuracy.

Answer to In-Text Question

① **Knowing the rate of oxygen used can help a doctor determine how fast your body can change glucose into energy. The faster your metabolic rate, the more oxygen you use.**

 ### Math Connection

Tell students that riding a bicycle at about 16 km an hour uses up about 140 Calories per hour. Ask students to calculate how long a person would have to ride a bicycle to use up the 421 Calories found in one chocolate milkshake. (421/140 = about 3 hours)

Figure 22.14 ▲
A device called a respirometer measures how much oxygen your body uses. How does the amount of oxygen used relate to your metabolic rate? ①

Science and You
Your Body's Energy Budget

The amount of energy in the food you eat is usually in balance with the amount of energy your body uses. As you may know, the amount of energy you use varies with your level of activity. When you are resting, you use only 60 to 70 Calories per hour. During heavy exercise, you may use over 2,000 Calories per hour. To stay in balance, then, you should eat more if you're active and less if you're not.

If you take in more Calories than you use, excess Calories are stored as fat, and you gain weight. If you take in fewer Calories than you use, your body uses stored fat for energy, and you lose weight. However, each person extracts energy from food at a different rate. This rate is called your metabolic rate. Two people may eat and exercise exactly the same, but only one of them gains weight because their metabolic rates differ.

If you have a weight problem, a doctor may want to measure your metabolic rate. If your metabolic rate is fast, it might account for your being underweight. If your metabolic rate is slow, it may explain why you're overweight.

One way to determine metabolic rate is to measure the amount of oxygen used by your body in a given period of time. You breathe into a respirometer (REHS pur AH muh tur) like the one in Figure 22.14. Soda lime in the respirometer reacts with the carbon dioxide you exhale and removes it. Every molecule of oxygen used in respiration produces one molecule of carbon dioxide. By measuring the amount of carbon dioxide, your doctor can tell how much oxygen your body uses.

Check and Explain

1. Summarize the process of photosynthesis by writing a word equation.

2. What happens during cell respiration?

3. **Infer** What might happen if many of the plants on the earth died?

4. **Make a Model** Draw a diagram or other model that shows respiration is the reverse of photosynthesis.

Chapter 22 Review

Concept Summary

22.1 A World of Carbon

▶ Carbon is part of many different compounds because a carbon atom can form bonds with four other atoms.

▶ Carbon atoms form straight chains, branched chains, and rings.

▶ A saturated hydrocarbon has single bonds between all carbon atoms; an unsaturated hydrocarbon has at least one double or triple bond.

▶ When more than one structure exists for a formula, each structure is called an isomer.

22.2 Food Chemistry

▶ Carbohydrates serve as the body's main energy source.

▶ Lipids are used by the body to make substances that are necessary for its functioning. Some lipids are saturated, others are unsaturated.

▶ Proteins provide the body with the amino acids it needs to make other proteins.

22.3 Energy in Living Things

▶ Through photosynthesis, plants convert sunlight into chemical energy stored in the chemical bonds of glucose.

▶ Living things constantly release the energy stored in glucose through the process of respiration.

▶ Together, photosynthesis and respiration make it possible for organisms to use the sun's energy.

Chapter Vocabulary

organic compound (p. 537)	polymer (p. 541)	lipid (p. 547)
hydrocarbon (p. 539)	isomer (p. 541)	protein (p. 548)
saturated hydrocarbon (p. 541)	substituted hydrocarbon (p. 542)	photosynthesis (p. 552)
unsaturated hydrocarbon (p. 541)	carbohydrate (p. 545)	respiration (p. 554)

Check Your Vocabulary

Use the vocabulary words above to complete the following sentences correctly.

1. By replacing a hydrogen atom in a hydrocarbon with another kind of atom, you make a(n) _____ .

2. Only green plants can undergo _____ .

3. Nearly all compounds that contain carbon atoms are called _____ .

4. A(n) _____ is formed from the linking of many monomers.

5. A(n) _____ is made up of many amino acids.

6. Fats and oils are classified as _____ .

7. Glucose and starch are _____ .

8. A(n) _____ contains only carbon and hydrogen atoms.

9. Compounds with identical formulas but different structures are called _____ .

10. A(n) _____ contains only single bonds between carbon atoms.

11. Living things release the energy stored in glucose through the process of _____ .

12. An organic compound with a double or triple carbon bond is called a(n) _____ .

Write Your Vocabulary

Write sentences using the vocabulary words above. Show that you know what each word means.

Check Your Knowledge

1. Carbon is important because it has the ability to form many different types of long branching molecules that are necessary for life.

2. Hydrocarbons contain only hydrogen and carbon atoms. A substituted hydrocarbon will contain other elements besides carbon and hydrogen.

3. A carbohydrate molecule is made up of carbon, hydrogen, and oxygen, usually with approximately twice as many hydrogen atoms as carbon atoms.

4. Large amounts of saturated lipids may lead to heart disease.

5. Amino acids make up proteins. They contain a carboxyl group and an amine group.

6. Vitamins work together with enzymes in carrying out chemical reactions inside cells.

7. Photosynthesis is the process by which CO_2 and H_2O are combined to produce $C_6H_{12}O_6$ and O_2. Respiration is the process by which $C_6H_{12}O_6$ and O_2 react to form H_2O and CO_2.

8. four

9. methane

10. nitrogen

11. 2:1

12. glucose

13. water

14. single

Check Your Understanding

1. a, b, e, and f are organic compounds.

2. The compound must be unsaturated, because two carbon atoms could bond to as many as six hydrogen atoms, if they were single-bonded.

3. Both have a single, central carbon atom, but chloroform has three chlorine atoms replacing hydrogen atoms.

4. You might infer that the compound was either an amino acid or a protein.

5. Night blindness can be a symptom of a vitamin A deficiency. A doctor might ask about the person's diet to see whether vitamin A was lacking.

6. Starches and sugars are both carbohydrates. Starches are complex carbohydrates made up of simple sugars.

7. Width in picture: about 1 cm (0.01 m) ÷ 50,000 = 2×10^{-7} m.

Chapter 22 Review

Check Your Knowledge

Answer the following in complete sentences.

1. Why is carbon considered to be one of the most important elements on the earth?

2. How does a hydrocarbon differ from a substituted hydrocarbon?

3. What is the main identifying characteristic of a carbohydrate molecule?

4. Why should you limit your intake of saturated lipids?

5. What are the compounds that make up proteins? What functional groups do they contain?

6. Why are vitamins important nutrients?

7. Explain the relationship between photosynthesis and respiration.

Choose the answer that best completes each sentence.

8. A carbon atom can form (one, two, three, four) bonds.

9. The simplest hydrocarbon is (methane, ethane, propane, butane).

10. Proteins are the only nutrients that contain (oxygen, nitrogen, hydrogen, carbon).

11. The ratio of hydrogen to oxygen atoms in a carbohydrate is (1:1, 2:1, 3:1, 4:1).

12. During photosynthesis, energy is stored in the chemical bonds of (glucose, carbon dioxide, oxygen, water).

13. The products of respiration include carbon dioxide and (glucose, methane, oxygen, water).

14. A saturated hydrocarbon contains only (single, double, triple, protein) bonds.

Check Your Understanding

Apply the concepts you have learned to answer each question.

1. **Classify** Which of the following are organic compounds?

   a. CCl_4 d. HCl
   b. C_6H_6 e. CH_4
   c. $NaCl$ f. C_2H_5OH

2. **Infer** If you discovered that a particular hydrocarbon had two carbon atoms and two hydrogen atoms, would you conclude that it was saturated or unsaturated? Why?

3. **Compare and Contrast** How are methane and chloroform similar? How are they different?

4. **Infer** If you were given a mystery organic compound and found that it contained atoms of nitrogen, what might you infer?

5. **Hypothesize** If you were a doctor and a patient came to you complaining of difficulty seeing at night, what would you suspect to be the cause of the problem? What questions would you ask the patient?

6. **Compare and Contrast** How are starches and sugars similar? How do they differ?

7. **Mystery Photo** The photograph on page 536 shows collagen fibers magnified approximately 50,000 times. Collagen is a protein that provides a weblike structure for connective tissues, such as your skin. Using a metric ruler and a calculator, determine the approximate width of a real collagen fiber.

Develop Your Skills

1. Check student models: CH$_4$—1 carbon, 4 hydrogen; CHCl$_3$—1 carbon, 1 hydrogen, 3 chlorine; C$_2$H$_6$—2 carbon, 6 hydrogen; C$_2$H$_4$—2 carbon, 4 hydrogen, one double bond; C$_2$H$_2$—2 carbon, 2 hydrogen, one triple bond

2. a. 0.5°C
   b. pentane, hexane
   c. Boiling point increases as the number of carbon atoms increases

3. a. 3.5 Calories
   b. proteins
   c. almost 3 grams

Make Connections

1.

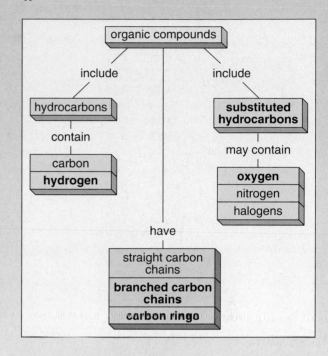

2. Eating plenty of carbohydrate-rich foods would be good preparation.

3. Students' reports will vary. Many companies are using recyclable paperboard instead of plastic and plastic-coated paper in packaging, or are simply reducing the amount of packaging for products. Packing "peanuts" made of corn-starch that actually dissolve in water are being used.

Develop Your Skills

Use the skills you have developed to complete each activity.

1. **Model** Draw models of the following molecules: CH$_4$, CHCl$_3$, C$_2$H$_6$, C$_2$H$_4$, C$_2$H$_2$.

2. **Interpret Data** The table below shows the boiling point of hydrocarbons.

Compound	Formula	Boiling Point (°C)
Methane	CH$_4$	-161.0
Ethane	C$_2$H$_6$	-88.5
Propane	C$_3$H$_8$	-42.0
Butane	C$_4$H$_{10}$	0.5
Pentane	C$_5$H$_{12}$	36.0
Hexane	C$_6$H$_{14}$	68.7

a. What is the boiling point of butane?
b. Which of the compounds are liquid at room temperature (25°C)?
c. Describe the pattern that you observe in the relationship between the boiling point and number of carbon atoms.

3. **Data Bank** Use the information on page 637 to answer the following questions.

a. How many Calories of energy can your body release from 1 g of carbohydrates?
b. Which provides more energy per gram, proteins or carbohydrates?
c. How many grams of carbohydrates does it take to equal the energy contained in 1 g of fat?

Make Connections

1. **Link the Concepts** Below is a concept map showing how some of the main concepts in this chapter link together. Only parts of the map are filled in. Copy the map. Using words and ideas from the chapter, complete the map.

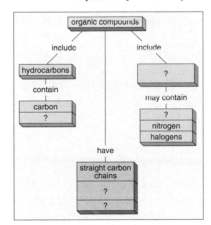

2. **Science and Physical Education** Your basketball team has lost all its substitutes because of injuries. You and four other players will have to go the distance in the upcoming championship game. Based on what you've learned in this chapter, how can you best prepare your body for the big game?

3. **Science and Technology** One problem of using synthetic polymers for packaging is that they are *too* durable. They fill up garbage dumps, pollute the environment, create litter, and harm living things. Find out what scientists are doing to develop biodegradable plastics—synthetic polymers that break down in the environment.

Overview

Nuclear chemistry is the subject of this chapter. The first section introduces the concept of radioactivity, compares stable and unstable nuclei, and defines isotopes. Section 2 describes the three types of radioactive decay and the transmutation of elements. Carbon-14 dating is described in this section. The final section explains what occurs during nuclear fission and nuclear fusion.

Advance Planner

▶ Provide foam balls and toothpicks for TE page 562.

▶ Supply unopened film and a smoke detector or a camping lamp mantle for TE page 563.

▶ Obtain coins and bags for SE Activity 23, page 570.

▶ Supply dominoes for TE page 572.

▶ Provide graph paper for the activity on TE page 573.

▶ Provide colored chalk for TE page 574.

Skills Development Chart

Sections	Classify	Communicate	Estimate	Graph	Infer	Interpret Data	Observe	Predict
23.1 Skills WarmUp Skills WorkOut SkillBuilder	●		●			●		
23.2 Skills WarmUp Activity		●		●	● ●	●	●	●
23.3 Skills WarmUp Consider This		● ●						

Individual Needs

▶ **Limited English Proficiency Students** Photocopy Figures 23.2, 23.5, 23.6, 23.9, and 23.10 with the labels masked. Draw arrows to the important parts of each figure. Have students make labels from strips of index cards and place the labels in the correct places on the photocopies. Have students refer to the text to check the placement of the labels. For each of the figures, students can write a description or caption telling how it relates to the chapter content. Students can remove and save the labels, and repeat the exercise as part of their chapter review.

▶ **At-Risk Students** Make three photocopies of Figure 23.5 with the paths of the particles masked for each student. Ask students to draw the path of a gamma ray as it passes through the magnetic field and then the paper and wood. Have them write a caption for the drawing that explains why the radiation did not bend and pass through the paper and wood. Have students repeat the activity on each of the remaining photocopies, first by drawing and describing the path of the alpha particles and then beta particles. You may want students to draw a model or symbol for each type of radiation.

▶ **Gifted Students** Invite students to research methods of dating that do not rely on carbon-14, such as potassium-argon, rubidium-strontium, radiation-damage, and fission-track. Have them consider such questions as how the method works, what materials it is most suited for, whether transmutation is involved, and how it differs from carbon-14 dating. Have students display their findings on a poster-sized chart.

Resource Bank

▶ **Bulletin Board** Ask students to bring in pictures and written descriptions of some practical applications of nuclear chemistry and radiation. Encourage them to find uses that are not mentioned in the chapter. Have them randomly attach their contributions to the bulletin board. Once several items have been contributed, lead a class discussion about ways of classifying and arranging the information. Ask volunteers to rearrange the material to reflect the arrangement the students liked best.

▶ **Field Trip** Plan a visit to a nuclear medical facility in your area. Have students prepare a list of questions for the guide. They may ask about the training and skills required for work at the facility. They may also want to know what safety features and procedures exist. Be sure to alert the guide to the students' questions and concerns.

Section	Core	Standard	Enriched	Section	Core	Standard	Enriched
23.1 Radioactivity pp. 561–564				**Overhead Blackline Transparencies** Overhead Blackline Master 22 and Student Worksheet		•	•
Section Features Skills WarmUp, p. 561 Skills WorkOut, p. 562 SkillBuilder, p. 563	•	• •	• • •	**Color Transparencies** Transparencies 81, 82	•	•	•
Blackline Masters Review Worksheet 23.1 Skills Worksheet 23.1	• •	• •	•	**Laboratory Program** Investigation 41		•	•
23.2 Radioactive Decay pp. 565–570				**23.3 Energy from the Nucleus** pp. 571–574			
Section Features Skills WarmUp, p. 565 Activity, p. 570	•	• •	• •	**Section Features** Skills WarmUp, p. 571 Consider This, p. 573		• •	• •
Blackline Masters Review Worksheet 23.2 Reteach Worksheet 23.2 Skills Worksheet 23.2 Integrating Worksheet 23.2	• • •	• • • •	• • •	**Blackline Masters** Review Worksheet 23.3 Vocabulary Worksheet 23		• •	• •
				Color Transparencies Transparency 83		•	•
				Laboratory Program Investigation 42	•	•	•

Bibliography

The following resources can be used for teaching the chapter. See page T-46 for supplier codes.

Library Resources

Asimov, Isaac. *How Did We Find Out About Superconductivity?* New York: Walker and Company, 1988.

Haines, Gail Kay. *The Great Nuclear Power Debate.* New York: Dodd, Mead & Company, 1985.

Lampton, Christopher F. *Superconductors.* Hillside, NJ: Enslow Publishers, Inc., 1989.

Milne, Lorus J., and Margery Milne. *Understanding Radioactivity.* New York: Atheneum, 1989.

Newton, David E. *Particle Accelerators: From Cyclotron to the Superconducting Supercollider.* New York: Franklin Watts, 1989.

Swertka, Albert. *Superconductors.* New York: Franklin Watts, 1991.

Technology Resources

Internet

PLANETDIARY at *http://www.planetdiary.com*
• Find out more about radioactivity in *Radioactivity* by clicking on *Phenomena Backgrounders.*

Software

Atomic Age. Mac, Dos. ESI.

CD-ROMs

hip Physics. Mac. ESI.
Interactive Earth. SFAW.

Laserdiscs

Living Textbook. (See barcodes on pages in this chapter.) Optical Data.

Videos

Fusion: Work in Progress. NGSES.
Nuclear Energy: The Question Before Us. NGSES.

Audio-Visual Resources

The World of Energy II. Filmstrip. NGSES.

Introducing the Chapter

Have students read the description of the photograph. Ask if they agree or disagree with the description.

Directed Inquiry

Have students study the photograph. Ask the following questions:

► Do you think someone drew or painted the image shown or was it made by a natural event? (Students may decide that a natural event made it.)

► What kind of event do you think this picture shows? (It looks like tracks or paths of moving objects.)

► What might a scientist learn from studying the tracks in this photograph? (How the objects move)

► What do you think this picture has to do with the subject of this chapter? (The tracks might be those of particles from atomic nuclei.)

Chapter Vocabulary

alpha decay	nuclear fission
beta decay	nuclear fusion
binding energy	radioactive decay
gamma decay	radioactivity
half-life	transmutation

The Living Textbook:
Physical Science Sides 1-4

Chapter 4   Frame 01032
Particle Tracks in Bubble Chamber
(3 Frames)
Search: Step:

Writing Connection

Point out to students that the image in the photograph, like many other images in nature, resembles other natural—and even some artificial—things. Have students write a short story about the image in the photograph. Students should use their imagination to compare the image to some other make-believe or natural occurrence or object.

Themes in Science

Energy The strong nuclear force binds the protons and neutrons in an atomic nucleus together. It is the strongest attractive force known; therefore, it requires a lot of energy to break apart a nucleus. Ask students to cite other examples of using energy to overcome an attractive force. (For example, jumping upward against the force of gravity, pulling two magnets apart.)

Chapter 23 Nuclear Chemistry

Chapter Sections

23.1 Radioactivity

23.2 Radioactive Decay

23.3 Energy from the Nucleus

What do you see?

❝This picture of subatomic particles looks sort of like a star chart made in 100 B.C. The tracks of the subatomic particles look like comets and falling stars making patterns in the sky. I know this picture was made in a bubble chamber, but it looks like it was painted. Scientists can use this to study the nature and interaction of subatomic particles.❞

Bobby Way
Iroquois Middle School
Grand Rapids, Michigan

To find out more about the photograph, look on page 576. As you read this chapter, you will learn about radioactivity and nuclear chemistry.

Integrating the Sciences

Health Marie and Pierre Curie's daughter Irène Joliot-Curie continued her parents' studies. In 1936, Irène and her husband Frédéric were awarded the Nobel Prize for their work with artificial radiation. Irène and her mother, Marie, both died of leukemia. Have students use periodicals and other references to find out about the relationship between cancer and exposure to radiation.

Earth Science Radon gas released naturally from the soil can help scientists to predict earthquakes. Cracks created by small earth movement release radon, which collects in well water. By monitoring the change in the amount of radon gas in well water, geologists are able to detect the location of the earth movement that precedes large earthquakes.

Section Objectives
For a list of section objectives, see the Student Edition page.

Skills Objectives
Students should be able to:

Classify sources of radiation.

Interpret Data by using a graph and table to identify the nuclear composition of elements.

Estimate the radiation dose students receive annually.

Make a Model of two isotopes of helium to identify radioactivity.

Vocabulary
radioactivity, binding energy

23.1 Radioactivity

Objectives

▶ **Describe** how radioactivity was discovered.

▶ **Identify** the source of radioactivity.

▶ **Compare** and **contrast** stable and unstable nuclei.

▶ **Make a model** representing different isotopes.

▼ **ACTIVITY**

Classifying

Radiant Things

Make a list of everything you can think of that produces radiation. Classify the items into groups according to some common characteristics.

SKILLS WARMUP

"**P**ress your chest against the metal plate. Turn your shoulders in. Hold it." Click! You don't feel a thing. Yet energy has passed through your body and created an image on film. When the film is developed, dense tissues, such as those in bones, will show up as white shadows. The energy that has allowed your doctor to see inside you is X-ray, a kind of radiation.

You've probably heard the word *radiation* many times. It can be used to describe many forms of energy, including heat and light. These common kinds of radiation carry relatively small amounts of energy. Other kinds of radiation are much more energetic. They come from the nuclei of atoms.

Discovery of Radioactivity

On March 1, 1896, French chemist Antoine Becquerel opened a desk drawer and removed a photographic plate he had been storing along with a sample of uranium ore. When he developed the film, he was amazed to see an image on it, even though it had never been exposed to light. The image was the shape of a key that had been lying on top of the film.

Becquerel hypothesized that the ore had given off invisible energy rays that had clouded the film except where the key had blocked them. Two of Becquerel's students, Marie and Pierre Curie, began studying this invisible energy. They found that the uranium atoms in the ore emitted the rays. They also discovered other elements with the same property. Marie Curie called this ability of certain elements to give off invisible energy **radioactivity**.

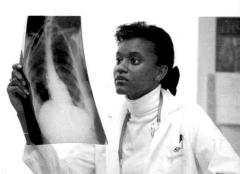

Figure 23.1 ▲
Doctors read X-rays by holding them up to the light. The dense tissues inside your body appear as white areas on the X-ray.

MOTIVATE

Skills WarmUp
To help students understand radioactivity, have them do the Skills WarmUp.
Answer Students may identify several types of nuclear weapons and group them together. They may also list X-ray machines, microwaves, and televisions.

Misconceptions
Students may think that radiation is related only to nuclear energy. A class discussion should help students recognize that sources of heat and light are also forms of radiation. Students may think all radiation is harmful. Be sure they understand that heat and light are not harmful forms of radiation under normal circumstances.

 The Living Textbook:
Physical Science Sides 1-4

Chapter 1   Frame 00703
Marie and Peter Curie (2 Frames)
Search: Step:

TEACH

TEACH

Skills WorkOut

To help students interpret the data in Figure 23.2, have them do the Skills WorkOut.

Answer Check students' graphs for accuracy. Stable nuclei of H, He, Li, Be, B, C, N, O, and F should be identified.

Class Activity

Have students use small foam balls and tape, glue, and toothpicks to make models of stable and unstable lithium and carbon atoms. Have them use the models to compare the binding energy of stable and unstable nuclei.

Directed Inquiry

Have students place a pencil over the nuclei that have equal numbers of protons and neutrons in Figure 23.2. Ask the following questions:

► Where are the stable nuclei in relation to the pencil? (Either on the pencil or close to it)

► What generalization can you make about stable nuclei? (They probably have equal or nearly equal numbers of protons and neutrons.)

► Do you think this generalization is true for all nuclei? Explain. (Answers will vary, but a check of the periodic table shows that the generalization is appropriate for atoms of low atomic mass.)

The Living Textbook: Physical Science Sides 1-4

Chapter 4   Frame 00930
Atomic Model/Strong Force (2 Frames)
Search: Step:

562

Themes in Science

Stability and Equilibrium Atoms with unstable nuclei release energy, or matter, until the forces inside the nucleus are balanced and the atom is stable. Ask students for an analogy from their own experience in which motion occurs until the forces acting on it are balanced. (A swing, a bouncing ball)

▼ **ACTIVITY**

Interpreting Data

Stable Nuclei

Copy the graph in Figure 23.2 on a sheet of paper. Using the periodic table on pages 634 to 635, find out which element is represented by each stable nucleus shown on the graph. On your graph, label each stable nucleus with its symbol.

SKILLS WORKOUT

Figure 23.2
Stable and Unstable Nuclei ▼

Stable and Unstable Nuclei

What is the source of the radiation in a radioactive element? It is the nuclei of the element's atoms. Radioactivity results from the release of energy or matter from nuclei. Only some atoms are radioactive.

As you know, the nucleus of an atom is made up of protons and neutrons. These particles are held together by a force called the *strong nuclear force*. This attractive force counteracts the repulsive forces between the protons in the nucleus. A large amount of energy is needed to overcome the strong nuclear force and break the nucleus into smaller particles. This amount of energy is called the **binding energy** of the nucleus.

Whether a nucleus is stable or unstable depends on its binding energy. The most stable nuclei have a large binding energy per nuclear particle. Stable nuclei do not change spontaneously over time. Unstable nuclei can change into different nuclei by releasing energy or matter, or both. It is this release of energy that Marie Curie called radioactivity.

Why are some nuclei radioactive while others are not? For each number of protons in a nucleus, there is a certain number of neutrons that make the nucleus stable. Atoms with equal numbers of protons and neutrons have stable nuclei. Unstable nuclei have too many or too few neutrons. In addition, all nuclei having more than 83 protons are radioactive. Thus, all elements with a greater atomic number than bismuth are radioactive.

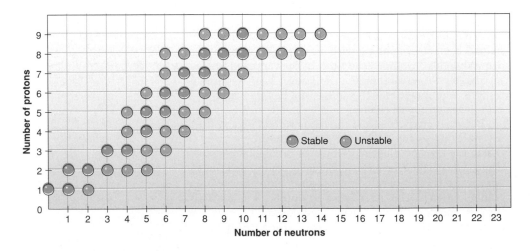

Integrating the Sciences

Astronomy Inform students that some of the radiation they receive daily is from cosmic rays from space. The atmosphere absorbs most of this radiation, and only a small percentage actually reaches the earth's surface. Have students find out the sources of cosmic rays and make a poster that shows their findings. (Most cosmic rays come from supernovas, pulsars, and solar flares.)

STS Connection

Explain to students that radiation has life-saving possibilities outside of medicine. Explain that the radioactive element americium-241 is part of most smoke detectors. Ask students to find out the part radioactivity plays in a smoke detector.

Radioactive Isotopes

The Curies discovered that in samples of some elements, all the atoms were radioactive. What they didn't know was that most elements have at least some radioactive atoms. Recall that atoms of the same element can differ in their number of neutrons. These different atoms of the same element are *isotopes*. If an isotope has too few or too many neutrons compared with its number of protons, it is unstable and radioactive.

Radioactive isotopes have many uses in industry and medicine. For example, radioactive iodine-131 is used to determine the health of the thyroid gland. The thyroid needs iodine to make a hormone. A healthy thyroid picks up as much iodine as it needs from the bloodstream. To test how much iodine a person's thyroid is picking up, the patient is given radioactive iodine. Special machines that detect radiation can measure how much radioactive iodine goes into the thyroid.

Table 23.1
Common Radioactive Isotopes

Stable Isotope	Radioactive Isotope
Hydrogen-1	Hydrogen-3
Carbon-12	Carbon-14
Sodium-23	Sodium-24
Iron-56	Iron-59
Cobalt-59	Cobalt-60
Iodine-127	Iodine-131

SkillBuilder *Estimating*

Your Annual Radiation Dose

You are exposed to nuclear radiation every day. Exposure to radiation, or radiation dosage, is measured in millirems (mrem). The National Council on Radiation Protection recommends that your total annual radiation dose not exceed 500 mrem. What is your annual dose of radiation? Use the table on page 643 of the Data Bank to estimate your radiation exposure from each possible source. Copy the table to the right, fill in your estimates, and add them up. Answer the following questions.

1. The average annual exposure per person in the United States is 230 mrem. How does your total compare with this number?

2. Why might your average radiation dose differ from year to year?

3. What source of radiation contributed the most to your annual exposure?

Source of Radiation	Annual Dose (mrem)
Radiation from space	
TV and computer screens	
Living in a brick or stone house	
Dental X-ray (whole mouth)	
Air travel	
Air, water, food	
Rocks and soil	
Smoke detectors, luminous watch dials	
Total	

The Living Textbook:
Physical Science Sides 1-4

Chapter 4   Frame 00940
Isotopes of Hydrogen (1 Frame)
Search:

EVALUATE

WrapUp

Review Ask a volunteer to diagram a stable boron atom on the chalkboard. Have another student change the drawing so it shows an unstable isotope of boron. Ask a third student to change the drawing to show an unstable isotope of carbon. Repeat the procedure suggesting students draw stable and unstable models for lithium and carbon.

Use Review Worksheet 23.1.

Check and Explain

1. Radioactivity was discovered when Antoine Becquerel found that uranium produced an image on a photographic plate.

2. The release of energy or matter from unstable nuclei of some atoms

3. A stable nucleus has an ideal number of neutrons for its number of protons. An unstable nucleus has either too few or too many neutrons.

4. Students' models should include nuclei with two protons and two neutrons in helium-4 and two protons and four neutrons in helium-6; helium-6 is radioactive.

The Living Textbook:
Physical Science Sides 1-4

Chapter 4   Frame 01017
Geiger Counter (1 Frame)
Search:

564

Language Arts Connection

Remind students that some units or scales of measurement, such as newtons or the Richter scale, are named after researchers. Ask students where the name *Geiger counter* came from. Have them use the encyclopedia or other references to learn more about the equipment and its inventor.

STS Connection

Explain to students that people who work with radiation must be protected from exposure. Thick concrete and lead shields around radioactive sources protect laboratory workers from high-energy radiation. In labs, people use robotic hands or remote-control devices to handle radioactive substances. A dosimeter is worn by anyone who works near radiation. This device measures radiation doses received over a period of time.

Science and Technology
Radiation Detectors

Figure 23.3 ▲
A worker who is exposed to radiation may be scanned with a Geiger counter. A film badge (right) may also be worn to monitor radiation on the job.

Click ... click ... click. This is the sound of a Geiger counter, a tool that detects and measures radiation. The number of clicks per second indicates the strength of radiation. Natural, or background, radiation causes a slow, random clicking. Background radiation is normal, but greater levels of radiation can be dangerous.

Radiation damages body cells by ionizing the atoms that make them up. Ionized atoms have different chemical properties than normal atoms and can cause harmful changes in a cell. Cancer is one possible result of exposure to radiation. Because radiation is so dangerous, it is important to monitor levels of radioactivity for people who may be exposed to more than background radiation.

Geiger counters test radiation levels at work sites where radiation levels may be high, such as nuclear power plants and radiation laboratories. Radiation enters a gas-filled tube in the counter and ionizes the gas by removing the electrons. The electrons are attracted to a positive wire and create a high-voltage discharge. The discharge produces a current that makes a click in the speaker.

Another instrument for monitoring radiation exposure is a film badge. People who work near sources of radiation wear the badges clipped to their clothes. The film is protected from exposure to normal light. High levels of radiation go through the protective cover and change the color of the film. A color change, therefore, alerts workers to possible radiation exposure.

Check and Explain

1. How was radioactivity discovered?

2. What is the cause of radioactivity?

3. **Compare** Describe how the stability of a nucleus is related to the number of neutrons and protons it contains.

4. **Make a Model** Make models of the nuclei of helium-4 and helium-6, both of which have an atomic number of 2. Which of these helium isotopes is radioactive?

Themes in Science

Patterns of Change/Cycles Many elements go through natural radioactive decay; many more elements decay artificially. There are three main kinds of radioactive decay. As students study this section, have them record each type of decay and its characteristics in their portfolios.

Literature Connection

Many stories describe alchemists' attempts to change one kind of element into another, such as lead into gold. Alchemists also searched for a universal cure for illnesses. Encourage students to find references to alchemy in ancient literature, such as in the works of Shakespeare.

Section Objectives
For a list of section objectives, see the Student Edition page.

Skills Objectives
Students should be able to:

Infer what happens to a nucleus as it releases energy or matter.

Graph radioactive decay showing the amount of matter left in a sample after each half-life.

Vocabulary
radioactive decay, alpha decay, beta decay, gamma decay, transmutation, half-life

23.2 Radioactive Decay

Objectives

▶ **Identify** three types of radioactive decay.

▶ **Describe** the role of radioactive decay in the transmutation of elements.

▶ **Compare** and **contrast** the three different types of radioactive decay.

▶ **Graph** the decay rate of a carbon-14 sample.

▼ **ACTIVITY**

Inferring

Nuclear Changes

You have read that radioactivity is the release of energy or matter from the nucleus. What do you think happens to a nucleus when it releases energy or matter? Write down your ideas.

SKILLS WARMUP

Imagine turning lead into gold! Centuries ago, alchemists tried to find ways to turn one element into another through chemical reactions. As you might guess, the alchemists didn't succeed in reaching this goal.

One element can't be turned into another by chemical means. However, elements do change into other elements in nature. In addition, scientists can now turn one element into another, and even create elements that never existed before. What the alchemists didn't know is that the process of one element turning into another isn't chemical. The change occurs in the nucleus of the atom itself.

Changes in the Nucleus

The release of radioactivity from an unstable atomic nucleus changes the nucleus. The result is a different kind of nucleus. It may have a different atomic mass than the original nucleus. The new nucleus may have a different atomic number than the original nucleus. The process by which this nuclear change occurs is called **radioactive decay**. Radioactive decay is the spontaneous breakdown of an unstable nucleus.

There are three common ways that unstable nuclei decay. In two kinds of decay, the nucleus releases particles. In the third kind of radioactive decay, the nucleus gives off energy. Each kind of decay produces a different type of radiation with a different level of energy. All three kinds of radiation, however, can be harmful to you and to other living things.

Figure 23.4 ▲
The alchemists were some of the first chemists. However, they worked on the wrong kinds of reactions to try to turn lead into gold.

MOTIVATE

Skills WarmUp
To help students understand radioactive decay, have them do the Skills WarmUp.
Answer Some particles in the nucleus may leave, a change in temperature may occur, released energy may then affect other atoms, or the atom may change from one element to another.

Prior Knowledge
Gauge how much students know about radioactive decay by asking the following questions:

▶ Could a chemical change convert one element into another? Why or why not?

▶ What kind of change would have to take place for one element to change into another?

 The Living Textbook:
Physical Science Side 1

Chapter 26   Frame 34028
Alpha, Beta, and Gamma Particles
(Movie)
Search: Play:

TEACH

Portfolio

Have students study the text and Figure 23.5. Then have them refer to the periodic table in the Data Bank on pages 634 and 635. On a sheet of paper labeled *Alpha Decay,* have students record the particles that are in a helium nucleus. (2 protons, 2 neutrons) On a sheet of paper labeled *Beta Decay,* have students make a diagram showing the neutron, proton, and beta particle involved in beta decay. Have them record the charge of the particle on the diagram. On a sheet of paper labeled *Gamma Decay,* have students record what they've learned about gamma decay. Have students keep their diagram and data in their portfolios.

Answer to In-Text Question

① **Some particles in the nucleus have a charge. Positively charged alpha particles are attracted to the negative pole of the magnet. Negatively charged beta particles are attracted to the positive pole. Gamma rays are not affected by the magnetic field. The atomic mass of the nucleus is less, because the nucleus gives off particles.**

The Living Textbook: Physical Science Sides 1-4

Chapter 4   Frame 01015
Alpha, Beta, and Gamma Penetration
(1 Frame)
Search:

Integrating the Sciences

Health Point out that people who work with radiation must be especially careful. Ask students to interview an X-ray technician, dentist, or nuclear power plant worker to find out what precautions they take to avoid excessive exposure to radiation. (Medical and industrial personnel are well protected by OSHA standards. The radiation limit per year is 500 mrem. Cancer treatments can require up to 5000 rem.)

Alpha Decay Some nuclei decay by releasing a package of particles made up of two protons and two neutrons. This package, called an alpha particle, is represented by the Greek letter alpha, α. You might recognize the alpha particle as being the positively charged nucleus of a helium atom. The release of an alpha particle is called **alpha decay**.

Alpha particles aren't very energetic. A few sheets of paper or light clothing will stop them. Alpha particles usually aren't very dangerous to living things. A source of alpha radiation, however, can be very harmful if taken into the body.

Beta Decay Other nuclei decay by giving off a negatively charged subatomic particle called a beta particle. A beta particle is represented by the Greek letter beta, β. Beta particles come from neutrons. When a neutron emits a beta particle, the neutron becomes a proton. This process is

called **beta decay**. Beta particles have more energy than alpha particles, but they travel less than 1 m in air. Beta radiation can be stopped by metal foil.

Gamma Decay Both alpha and beta decay involve the release of particles. The third kind of decay, **gamma decay**, is the release of energy alone. This energy is called gamma radiation or gamma rays. Gamma radiation is represented by the Greek letter gamma, γ. Gamma decay usually occurs along with alpha and beta decay.

Gamma rays are very energetic and can be blocked only by thick sheets of high-density materials, such as lead. These sheets must be several centimeters thick to block gamma rays. Gamma rays can penetrate deep into your body and damage vital cell materials. A high dose of gamma rays can cause radiation sickness, a life-threatening disease.

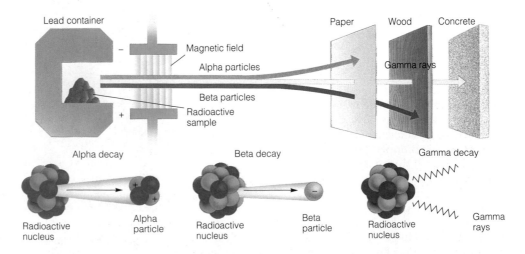

Figure 23.5 ▲
Why does the magnetic field affect the types of radiation differently? (above)
How is the nucleus affected when it gives off radiation? (below) ①

Transmutation of Elements

Both alpha decay and beta decay change the number of protons in a nucleus. Both forms of decay, therefore, change one element into another. The process of an element changing into a different element is called **transmutation** (TRANZ myoo TAY shuhn).

Look at Figure 23.6 below. It shows the series of transmutations that a nucleus of uranium-238 (U-238) goes through. The final product of these many steps is a stable nucleus of lead.

Find U-238 on the chart. This isotope undergoes alpha decay, losing two protons and two neutrons. Its atomic number, therefore, changes from 92 to 90. Its atomic mass drops by four, from 238 to 234. The element that results is thorium-234 (Th-234).

A transmutation can be shown as an equation by using special symbols. The atomic number of a nucleus is shown as a subscript to the left of its symbol: $_{92}U$. Its atomic mass is shown as a superscript: $_{92}^{238}U$. These numbers help you keep track of the protons and neutrons in a transmutation equation such as the one below.

$$_{92}^{238}U \rightarrow _{90}^{234}Th + _{2}^{4}He$$

What does $_{2}^{4}He$ represent in this equation?

Look again at Figure 23.6. What kind of decay does $_{90}^{234}Th$ undergo? Why does its atomic number increase by one? A beta particle can be written as $_{-1}^{0}e$. Can you write an equation for this transmutation?

With huge devices called particle accelerators, scientists can produce transmutations that don't occur in nature. In a particle accelerator, high-speed protons and neutrons are smashed into atomic nuclei. Some of the nuclei absorb one or more of these particles, creating a new element. All elements with an atomic number of 93 or higher were made in this way.

Figure 23.6   Radioactive Decay of Uranium-238 ▼

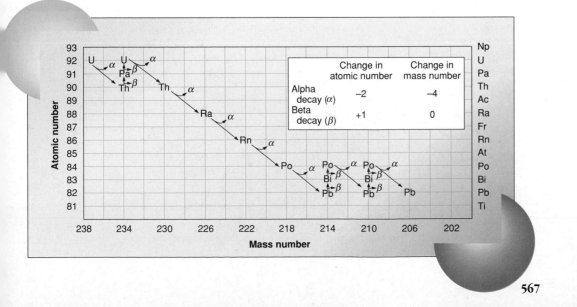

◄ TEACH ▪ *Continued*

Critical Thinking

If . . . Then Arguments Have students discuss the flaw in the following argument: If half the atoms in a sample decay in ten minutes, then all atoms will have decayed in 20 minutes. To aid the discussion, draw a large rectangle on the chalkboard and ask a volunteer to shade in half of the rectangle. Then ask another student to shade in half of the remaining area. Continue until the rectangle appears to be completely shaded.

◆ *Explore Visually*

Have students read the material on carbon-14 dating and study Figure 23.7. Ask:

► How does the plant get carbon-14? (The carbon-14 molecule is taken in from the CO_2 in the air.)

► How does an animal get carbon-14? (By eating the plant that contains carbon-14 or by eating plant-eating animals that do)

► How can carbon-14 be compared to a clock that works for thousands of years? (Its regular decay rate allows it to be used to date the remains of long-dead organisms.)

Decision Making

If you have classroom sets of *One-Minute Readings*, have students read Issue 35 "Radioactive Waste Disposal" on page 59. Discuss the questions.

Reteach

Use Reteach Worksheet 23.2.

Answer to In-Text Question

① **They decay at a constant rate to become nitrogen-14.**

✦ *Math Connection*

Point out to students that they can find the amount of radioactive substance in a sample if they know the half-life. Ask students to imagine that a patient has been given 100 mg of iodine-131, which has a half-life of eight days. Ask, How long will it be before only 25 mg of iodine-131 remains in the patient's body? Less than 1 mg? (16 days; 56 days)

✦ *Writing Connection*

Have students write a detective story in which the crime solvers want to use carbon-14 to tell if a vase is an original or a reproduction. Remind students that the crime solvers may want to know if the vase contains any organic compounds.

Use Integrating Worksheet 23.2.

Decay Rate

The chances that a single atom of uranium-238 will decay during a one-minute period are very low. In contrast, the chances that an atom of polonium-214 will decay in this same time period are very high. This difference in decay rate means that polonium-214 will decay at a much faster rate than uranium-238.

Each radioactive isotope has its own rate of decay. This rate is measured as a **half-life**. An isotope's half-life is the amount of time it takes for half of the atoms in a sample of the element to decay. Half-lives vary greatly, from milliseconds to billions of years.

The half-life of lead-214, for example, is 27 minutes. Every 27 minutes, half the nuclei in a sample of pure lead-214 will undergo beta decay to become bismuth-214. After the first 27-minute period, a 10-g sample of pure lead-214 will contain 5 g of lead-214 and 5 g of bismuth-214.

Figure 23.7
What happens to the atoms of the carbon-14 isotope when an organism dies? ▼ ①

Carbon-14 Dating

All living things contain many carbon compounds. A tiny amount of the carbon in these compounds is carbon-14. Carbon-14 is a radioactive isotope of carbon with a half-life of 5,730 years. The stable isotope carbon-12 makes up the rest of the carbon in organisms.

The amount of carbon-14 in an organism's tissues stays the same while the organism is alive. When an organism dies, the carbon-14 within its tissues decays to nitrogen-14. With each passing half-life of 5,730 years, the organism's remains have half as much carbon-14. However, the amount of carbon-12 does not change.

The decay of carbon-14 acts like a clock. By determining the ratio of carbon-12 to carbon-14 in its remains, a scientist can estimate when an organism died. This process, called carbon-14 dating, is used to estimate the age of organisms that lived on the earth thousands of years ago. Carbon-14 dating is limited to fossils 50,000 years old or less.

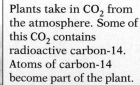

Plants take in CO_2 from the atmosphere. Some of this CO_2 contains radioactive carbon-14. Atoms of carbon-14 become part of the plant.

As a result of the animal eating the plant, carbon-14 becomes part of the animal.

The carbon-14 left in the remains of the animal decays at a constant rate.

Cooperative Learning

Tell students that radiology is a medical specialty that is helpful in diagnosing as well as treating illness. Have students work in cooperative groups of five to research, illustrate, and present a report on a technique, such as computerized tomography, fluoroscopy, magnetic resonance imaging, and positron emis-sion tomography. Ask the groups to find out if each technique relies on radiation, particle emission, or on the magnetic properties of the nucleus. (Radiation: ultrasound, fluoroscopy, computerized tomography; particle emission: positron emission; magnetic properties: magnetic resonance imaging)

Science and Technology *Nuclear Medicine*

Radiation, as you know, can be very harmful to organisms. Health professionals, however, use radiation and radioactive isotopes to help save lives. Nuclear medicine has become important in diagnosing and treating medical problems.

For diagnosing cancers and circulatory problems, health workers often use radioactive isotopes with short half-lives, called tracers. Patients are injected with or drink the tracer. Inside the body, tracers behave like atoms of the same element found naturally in the body.

Doctors can follow the movement of the tracers with radiation detectors. For example, to monitor the flow of blood in a patient, the radioactive isotope sodium-24 is injected into the bloodstream. Normal blood is about 1 percent sodium chloride. The tracer, sodium-24, flows through the blood just as normal sodium would. Its location is detected as the radiation from the decay of sodium-24 is picked up on X-ray film. Places where there is a narrowing or blockage in the circulatory system show up on the X-ray.

Radiation is also a common treatment for cancerous tumors. A beam of radiation directed at a tumor destroys the cancer cells. Like all serious medical procedures, however, radiation therapy carries risks. Radiation damages healthy tissue as well as cancerous tumors. Often it produces side effects, such as hair loss and nausea. Another problem is that many forms of nuclear medicine produce hazardous radioactive waste. This waste is difficult to dispose of safely.

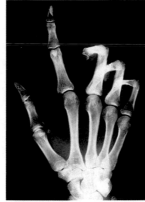

Figure 23.8 ▲
Which X-ray image provides more information about a patient's circulatory system?

Check and Explain

1. What are three types of radioactive decay?

2. What is transmutation? Describe a transmutation in words and with an equation.

3. **Compare and Contrast** How are the three different types of radioactive decay similar? How are they different?

4. **Graph** Make a bar graph that illustrates the mass of carbon-14 that remains in a 24-g sample at the end of each of its first five half-lives.

WrapUp

Reteach As students think about radioactive decay, ask:

▶ How do the nuclei of the isotopes of an element differ? (The number of neutrons is different.)

▶ Why is carbon-14 unstable if carbon-12 is stable? (The additional neutrons of C-14 make it unstable.)

▶ How do the number and kind of particles in a nucleus change during alpha decay? (Fewer protons *and* neutrons)

Use Review Worksheet 23.2.

Check and Explain

1. Alpha decay, beta decay, gamma decay

2. During transmutation, the nucleus of the atom changes from that of one element to that of another. Uranium ($^{238}_{92}$U) loses two protons and two neutrons in alpha decay and transmutes into thorium ($^{234}_{90}$Th) and a stable nucleus of lead ($^{206}_{82}$Pb).

3. All types of decay release energy or particles. Alpha and beta decay release particles; gamma decay releases energy.

4. Students' graphs should show half-lives at 12 g, 6 g, 3 g, 1.5 g, and 0.75 g.

 The Living Textbook: Physical Science Sides 1-4

Chapter 4   Frame 01018
Half-Life (2 Frames)
Search: Step:

ACTIVITY 23

Time 40 minutes **Group** 4

Materials

100 coins per group

8 durable bags

Analysis

1. Each coin represents an atom.

2. The number of rounds will vary, but should be between 6 and 9.

3. The sample decreased each time. Each group's actual data will vary. Make sure answers and graph match data.

4. The calculated half-lives may vary from group to group. It could be as few as one round or as many as several rounds, depending on chance.

5. If the activity were repeated and an average taken for each round, according to probability, the observed half-life should approach one round.

Conclusion

A coin has a 50 percent chance of showing heads, so in any one round you would expect approximately half the coins to show heads. This corresponds to the decay of half the atoms in a radioactive substance. For this reason, coins are a good model.

Extension

Similar variation would be observed in two identical radioactive samples, because whether a given atom in a sample does or does not decay at a given moment is a matter of chance.

Prelab Discussion

Have students read the entire activity. Discuss the following before beginning:

► Why are coins a good way to model half-lives?

► Would the model work as well with 1,000 coins? With four coins? Explain.

► At what point in this model does transmutation occur?

Activity 23 *How can you make a model of radioactive decay?*

Skills Observe; Interpret Data; Infer; Graph; Predict

Task 1 Prelab Prep

Collect the following items: pencil, paper, 100 coins, and a bag made of durable material.

Task 2 Data Record

1. On a separate sheet of paper, draw the data table shown.
2. Record the results of each round in the data table.

Table 23.2 "Radioactive Decay" of Coin Sample

Round	Coins Removed	Coins Remaining
0	0	100
1		
2		
3		
4		
5		
6		
7		
8		
9		

Task 3 Procedure

1. Clear the top of a desk or other smooth surface. Put the coins in the bag. Close the bag and shake it hard.
2. Carefully spill the coins out onto the desktop, making sure none fall onto the floor.
3. Collect all the coins that are showing heads. Count these coins and put them aside. Record this number of coins in the table

under the *Coins Removed* column. Calculate the number to put in the *Coins Remaining* column.

4. Put the coins that are showing tails back into the bag. Close the bag and shake it hard.
5. Repeat steps 2, 3, and 4 until there are no coins left to put back into the bag.
6. Use the data you have recorded in your table to draw a bar graph showing the change in the size of the coin sample over time.

Task 4 Analysis

1. In this activity, what does each coin represent?
2. How many rounds did it take for all the coins to "decay"?
3. What happened to the size of the coin sample during this activity? Describe the pattern you observed. How does the bar graph show this pattern?
4. If each round were equal to one year, what would be the "half-life" of your coin sample? How many half-lives does it take for your coin sample to "decay" completely?
5. If you repeated this activity, how do you think your results would vary?

Task 5 Conclusion

Write a short paragraph explaining why this activity is a model of radioactive decay. How is it similar to the actual decay of a radioactive substance? How is it different?

Extension

Repeat this activity to test the predictions you made in question 5 above. How do you account for the differences in the two trials? Do you think similar differences would occur in the decay of two identical samples of a radioactive substance? Explain.

Themes in Science

Energy The sun, the earth's primary source of energy, is the result of nuclear fusion reactions. This energy, which reaches the earth as sunlight, is converted into other forms of energy, such as heat and electricity.

Integrating the Sciences

Chemistry Have students locate the elements in Figure 23.9 on the periodic table. Have them identify each element as a metal, nonmetal, or transition metal and according to group and family. (U is an actinide metal, group 8; Ba is an alkaline earth metal, group 2; Kr is a nonmetal, group 18)

Section Objectives
For a list of section objectives, see the Student Edition page.

Skills Objectives
Students should be able to:

Communicate the meaning of $E=mc^2$.

Compare the processes of nuclear fusion and nuclear fission.

Vocabulary
nuclear fission, nuclear fusion

23.3 Energy from the Nucleus

Objectives

▶ **Summarize** the events of nuclear fission.

▶ **Describe** a nuclear chain reaction and the process of nuclear fusion.

▶ **Compare** and **contrast** fission and fusion reactors.

▶ **Communicate** the meaning of a nuclear equation.

If you could measure the mass of an unstable nucleus and the mass of its decay products, would the two masses be equal? If you remember that matter can't be created or destroyed, a logical answer is that the two masses will be the same. After radioactive decay, however, the mass of the products is less than the mass of the original nucleus! How can this be? Where did the missing matter go? The answer is that the "missing" matter was converted into energy.

Nuclear Fission

Radioactive decay is a natural process in which very small amounts of matter are converted into energy. Scientists, however, have learned how to create an artificial kind of radioactive decay. They split the nucleus of a heavy element into two smaller nuclei. This process converts some matter from the original nucleus into a large amount of energy. The process is called **nuclear fission**.

How is fission made to occur? Look at Figure 23.9. A neutron is smashed into a nucleus of uranium-235. The nucleus splits into two smaller nuclei of similar size. As it splits, the uranium-235 nucleus releases more neutrons and a great deal of energy. This process is fission.

If other uranium-235 nuclei are nearby, some of them are struck by neutrons from the first nucleus. These nuclei, in turn, undergo fission. The result is a *chain reaction*. If the chain reaction is controlled, the energy released can be used to do work. If the chain reaction isn't controlled, huge amounts of energy are released all at once. The explosion that takes place in an atomic bomb is an uncontrolled chain reaction.

▼ **ACTIVITY**

Communicating

Wording Energy

In Einstein's famous equation $E = mc^2$, E stands for energy, m stands for mass, and c is the speed of light. In your own words, explain what this equation means.

SKILLS WARMUP

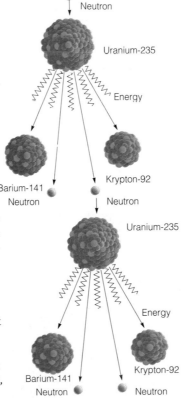

Neutron

Uranium-235

Energy

Krypton-92

Barium-141
Neutron

Neutron

Uranium-235

Energy

Krypton-92

Barium-141
Neutron

Neutron

Figure 23.9 ▲
The neutrons released when one nucleus is split during fission may cause other nuclei to undergo fission as well.

MOTIVATE

Skills WarmUp
To help students understand nuclear energy, have them do the Skills WarmUp.
Answer Because mass is a property of matter, students may recognize that the equation expresses a relationship between matter and energy. Students may also mention that the equation suggests that a small amount of mass can have a large amount of energy.

Prior Knowledge
To gauge what students know about nuclear changes, ask:

▶ What is the result of an atom's nucleus splitting apart?

▶ How is energy produced in the sun?

▶ What is the speed of light?

▶ State the law of conservation of mass and energy.

▶ What is an isotope?

 The Living Textbook:
Physical Science Sides 1-4

Chapter 9   Frame 01519
Atomic Bomb Explosion (3 Frames)
Search: Step:

571

Class Activity

Have students work in groups of three and use dominoes to make a model of a chain reaction. Ask them to design a way to slow the reaction and to speed up the reaction. Have groups share ideas.

Explore Visually

Have students study Figure 23.10. Have them explain how a nuclear fission reactor generates electricity. Ask the following questions:

▶ What are two uses of water in a nuclear reactor? (Water is heated and changed to steam which drives the turbines that generate electricity. Also, water is used to cool the steam, which condenses and recirculates through the reactor.)

▶ What is the function of the control rods? (They absorb neutrons from the fuel rods and control the speed of the nuclear reaction.)

▶ How are the two pumps used? (To pump water through the reactor, and to pump cool water through the condenser.)

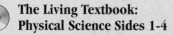

The Living Textbook:
Physical Science Sides 1-4

Chapter 4   Frame 01023
Nuclear Reactor Diagram (1 Frame)
Search:

The Living Textbook:
Physical Science Sides 1-4

Chapter 16   Frame 02710
Fuel Rod Pellets (1 Frame)
Search:

Social Studies Connection

Ask students to research and write a report on a serious nuclear accident. They may choose to research the accident at the Three Mile Island power plant near Harrisburg, Pennsylvania, in 1979 or the accident at Chernobyl in the Ukraine in 1986. Have students outline what effects each accident had on surrounding populations as well as on those farther away. Encourage them to include information on the cost, in money and time, of the cleanup. If the TV documentary on the Chernobyl accident is available, you may wish to show it to your class.

Fission Reactors

The energy produced by fission is harnessed in a device called a fission reactor. Look at the diagram of a typical fission reactor in Figure 23.10. Rods made of uranium-235 are positioned inside the reactor between movable rods made of cadmium. Because the cadmium rods absorb neutrons, they can control the rate that uranium-235 nuclei undergo fission. The rods are moved in or out to keep the fission rate constant. Heat energy given off by the reactor turns water into steam, which drives a turbine that generates electricity.

Fission reactors are built with many safeguards. These safeguards are designed to prevent the nuclear reaction from going out of control and to keep radiation from being released into the environment. Even so, serious nuclear accidents have occurred.

The most serious nuclear accident occurred on April 28, 1986, at a nuclear power plant in Chernobyl, Ukraine. The nuclear reactions went out of control, melting part of the inside of the reactor and releasing radioactivity. People died from radiation poisoning, and about 40,000 were evacuated from the area. The wind carried radioactive clouds caused by this accident over the entire world.

**Figure 23.10
Nuclear Fission Reactor** ▼

Steam turns a turbine attached to a generator, which converts kinetic into electrical energy.

Control rods in the reactor absorb neutrons from the fuel rods to regulate the speed of the nuclear reaction.

Steam turbine generator

Electricity

Condenser

Cold water from outside is piped through the condenser to change the steam back into water.

Cool water intake

Hot water outlet

Pump

Steam

Fuel rods

Reactor

Pump

Steam generator

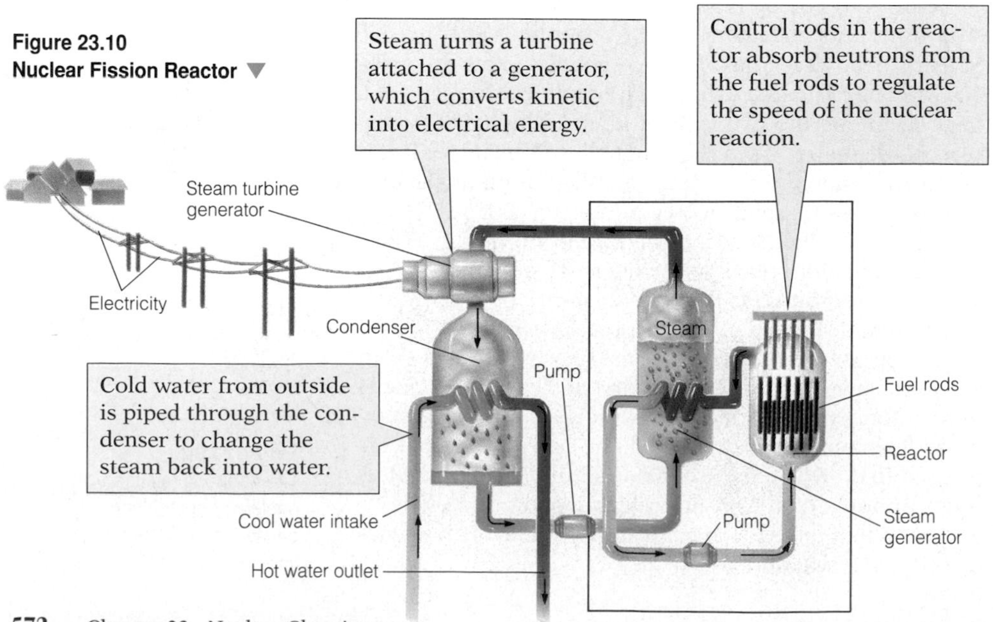

Portfolio

Ask students to find the information they need to make graphs comparing the number of nuclear power plants in their state, the state with the most nuclear power plants, and the total number of nuclear power plants across the nation. Students can keep their graphs in their portfolios.

Cooperative Learning

Have the class work in cooperative learning groups to debate the use of nuclear power plants. Have one group argue for limits, the other group for increased use. Each group should address issues like accidents, waste, cost, and the amount of electricity generated. Hold the debate open to the school and poll students on their opinions.

Nuclear Fusion

Within the sun, a different, more powerful type of nuclear reaction occurs. This reaction is called **nuclear fusion**. During nuclear fusion, two or more nuclei are joined or "fused" together. As the particles form a single nucleus, some mass is converted into energy.

Most of the sun's nuclear fuel is hydrogen. Hydrogen nuclei fuse to form helium in the extremely high temperatures of the sun. Nuclei of these light elements also combine to form heavier elements. Great amounts of heat are given off during fusion. Fusion in the sun is the source of the solar radiation reaching earth.

Unlike fission, fusion doesn't happen spontaneously. It occurs only at extremely high temperatures. For this reason, scientists haven't yet found a practical way of harnessing fusion energy on the earth. They have discovered, however, how to cause an uncontrolled fusion reaction to take place.

Consider This

Should New Nuclear Power Plants Be Built?

When the first nuclear power plants were built, experts said nuclear power would become our most important energy source. Since then, however, many questions have come up concerning the safety and cost of nuclear power. At present, nuclear energy supplies 16 percent of the power in the United States.

Supporters of nuclear power feel it has many advantages over other sources of energy. Nuclear-fuel supplies will last up to 1,000 years, much longer than fossil fuels. In addition, nuclear reactors don't normally produce air pollution as other sources of energy do.

However, critics point out that nuclear power is very dangerous. Although safety regulations for nuclear power plants have been tightened, accidents can still happen. A major accident could cause deaths, illnesses, and environmental damage. Another big problem is that the waste from nuclear reactors is highly radioactive for a long time.

Overall the costs of adding safeguards and disposing of waste make nuclear power much more expensive than anyone originally thought.

Think About It Can nuclear power plants be made safe enough? Is it worth the risks to build more of them? Are there other sources of energy that should be developed instead?

Write About It Write a paper stating your position for or against building new nuclear power plants. Include your reasons for choosing your position

Reteach

To help students understand why nuclear fusion is more powerful than nuclear fission, review page 562. Remind students that the binding energy is particularly high in atoms having few particles in the nucleus.

Critical Thinking

Compare and Contrast Ask students to compare and contrast nuclear fission and nuclear fusion. Ask the following questions:

▶ What elements are involved in fission? In fusion? (Fission—uranium-235, barium-141, krypton-90; fusion—hydrogen, helium)

▶ How does fission differ from fusion? (During fission, the nucleus splits; during fusion, two or more nuclei are joined together.)

Consider This

Think About It Answers will vary. Students should evaluate risks and benefits, such as cheap clean fuel, some kinds of reduced environmental damage, risk of nuclear accidents, and problems with disposal of nuclear waste. Students may mention wind power and solar energy as other sources.

Write About It Answers will vary, but students should give the reasons why they have chosen their position.

 The Living Textbook: Physical Science Sides 1-4

Chapter 13   Frame 02186
Sun's Nuclear Fusion (1 Frame)
Search:

573

TEACH ▪ Continued

Skills Development

Infer Have students think about the properties a substance must have in order to be contained in a magnetic bottle or a magnetic field. Ask students what they can infer about the particles in the substance. (They're charged.)

EVALUATE

WrapUp

Reinforce Using colored chalk, have a student make a diagram of nuclear fission and nuclear fusion reactions on the chalkboard. Have another student write an equation for the reactions. Ask a third student to describe each reaction in words.

Use Review Worksheet 23.3.

Check and Explain

1. Splitting the nucleus of U-235 causes the release of neutrons and energy, which causes a chain reaction in which more nuclei of U-235 are split. A lot of energy is released.

2. Nuclear fusion is the process by which two nuclei fuse to form a heavier nucleus, giving off large amounts of heat energy.

3. Both convert matter to energy; fission splits nuclei to release energy; fusion joins or fuses nuclei releasing energy.

4. One neutron smashes into the nucleus of uranium-235, and uranium-235 splits into barium-141, krypton-92, and three more neutrons.

Answer to Link

Once you push the first domino, the reaction goes to completion. You cannot stop it. Once a neutron is smashed into a U-235 atom and splits it, other neutrons are released that split other nuclei. In both cases, you have a chain reaction.

574

Integrating the Sciences

Life Science Explain to students that one of the problems associated with radioactive waste is the spread of radioactivity in increasing concentrations through the food chain. Have students find out about the process of biomagnification and make a diagram that shows how radioactivity spreads.

Art Connection

Many students will recognize the radiation hazard symbol. Ask a volunteer to draw it on the chalkboard. Discuss the symbol's meaning and explain that it is recognized all over the world. Suggest that students design labels that make use of the symbol, and explain where their labels would appear.

Figure 23.11
This drum of nuclear waste must be stored in a place where it won't pollute water or land. ▼

Physical Science LINK

Nuclear fission has been likened to a domino reaction. Obtain a set of dominos.
   1. Stand one domino on its short end and put another behind it. Push the first domino so that it makes the other one fall.
   2. Set up several dominos in a row, so you can push one and topple them all.
   How are the falling dominos like nuclear fission?

ACTIVITY

Fusion-Reactor Projects

For many years, scientists have tried to build a fusion reactor. The main problem they face is that no material can withstand the extremely high temperatures of a fusion reaction. In some experimental fusion reactors, called tokamaks, a powerful magnetic field confines the hot hydrogen nuclei in the center of the reactor. Unfortunately, these reactors and others like them use more energy than they produce. If these problems can be solved, fusion may one day be an important energy source. It is relatively clean, and the hydrogen used as fuel is plentiful.

Science and Society *Nuclear Waste*

Nuclear power plants, nuclear weapons plants, and uranium mines all produce tons of nuclear waste every year. Nuclear waste is very dangerous. It causes serious health problems, such as cancer and birth defects. In some cases, the waste will remain dangerous for as long as 200,000 years. How can nuclear waste be disposed of safely?

A truly safe method of disposal may never be found. Scientists are still considering which of several options is the safest. Possibilities include burying the waste under the seafloor, disposing of it in the Antarctic ice cap, shooting it into space, and burying it under mountains.

Burying the waste is favored by many because it is easiest and the least costly. However, if the nuclear waste were to leak into the ground water, it could poison the environment for many generations. Most nuclear waste is now stored in radiation-proof containers at temporary storage sites.

Check and Explain

1. What causes a nucleus of U-235 to undergo fission?

2. What is nuclear fusion?

3. **Compare and Contrast** How are fission and fusion reactors similar? How are they different?

4. **Communicate** In your own words, explain the following equation.
$$^{235}_{92}\text{U} + ^{1}_{0}\text{n} \rightarrow ^{141}_{56}\text{Ba} + ^{92}_{36}\text{Kr} + 3^{1}_{0}\text{n}$$

Check Your Vocabulary

1. alpha decay
2. binding energy
3. radioactivity
4. transmutation
5. nuclear fusion
6. beta decay
7. radioactive decay
8. gamma decay
9. half-life
10. nuclear fission

Write Your Vocabulary

Students' sentences should show that they know the meaning of each word as well as how to use it in a sentence.

Use Vocabulary Worksheet for Chapter 23.

Chapter 23 Review

Concept Summary

23.1 Radioactivity
▶ The source of radioactivity is the unstable nuclei of some atoms.
▶ The stability of a nucleus is determined by the number of protons and neutrons it contains.
▶ Most elements have isotopes that are radioactive.
▶ Unstable nuclei are radioactive. All nuclei with more than 83 protons are radioactive.

23.2 Radioactive Decay
▶ There are three kinds of radioactive decay. Alpha decay is the release of a helium nucleus. Beta decay is the release of a negatively charged particle with almost no mass. Gamma decay is the release of energy.

▶ Alpha and beta decay change one element into another.
▶ A half life is the period of time required for half of the mass of a radioactive material to decay. The decay rate depends on the radioactive element or isotope.
▶ Carbon-14 decay can be used to estimate the age of the remains of organisms.

23.3 Energy from the Nucleus
▶ During both nuclear fission and fusion, matter is converted into energy.
▶ Fission reactors control nuclear reactions and produce energy.
▶ During nuclear fusion, two light nuclei combine to form one heavier nucleus, releasing large amounts of energy.
▶ Fusion occurs only at extremely high temperatures.

Chapter Vocabulary

radioactivity (p. 561)   alpha decay (p. 566)   transmutation (p. 567)   nuclear
binding energy (p. 562)   beta decay (p. 566)   half-life (p. 568)   fusion (p. 573)
radioactive decay (p. 565)   gamma decay (p. 566)   nuclear fission (p. 571)

Check Your Vocabulary

Use the vocabulary words above to complete the following sentences correctly.

1. During ____ , a helium nucleus is released from an unstable nucleus.
2. Stable nuclei have a large amount of ____ per particle.
3. An element with unstable nuclei produces ____ .
4. The change of one element into another element is called ____ .
5. During ____ , hydrogen nuclei come together to form a helium nucleus.
6. A neutron changes into a proton during ____ decay.

7. The release of alpha particles is one kind of ____ .
8. The most energetic type of radioactive decay is ____ .
9. The ____ of a radioactive substance is a measure of its rate of decay.
10. When a nucleus of uranium-235 undergoes ____ , two smaller nuclei result.

Write Your Vocabulary

Write sentences using the vocabulary words above. Show that you know what each word means.

Check Your Knowledge

1. A stable nucleus will often have an equal number of protons and neutrons.

2. An unstable nucleus will decay, releasing radiation.

3. Isotopes are radioactive when they have too many or too few neutrons compared to protons.

4. During radioactive decay, the nucleus breaks down, giving off either particles or energy.

5. Gamma radiation can penetrate deep into tissues, causing ionization of atoms inside cells.

6. In transmutation, an element's atom loses or gains protons and becomes a different element.

7. Reactor-building materials have not yet been developed that can withstand the extremely high temperatures necessary for fusion.

8. True

9. False; the strong nuclear force

10. True

11. False; helium nucleus

12. False; beta radiation

13. True

14. False; fusion

15. False; less

Check Your Understanding

1. b, d, e, and f are transmutations.

2. The more protons in a nucleus, the greater the range of neutrons the nucleus can have.

3. Most radioactive nuclei have too many neutrons compared to protons. All nuclei with more than 83 protons are radioactive.

4. The lost mass was converted into energy.

5. a. alpha decay   b. beta decay

6. Without control rods, the rate of the chain reaction would increase until the energy released became more than the reactor's materials could contain, and a meltdown would occur.

7. The amount of helium in the sun increases because helium is a product of nuclear fusion, which constantly occurs on the sun.

8. Answers will vary. The reason some paths are curved and some are straight is that some particles are charged and some are not. Charged particles moving through a magnetic field will be deflected into curved paths.

Chapter 23 Review

Check Your Knowledge

Answer the following in complete sentences.

1. In a stable nucleus, how does the number of protons compare to the number of neutrons?

2. What happens to an unstable nucleus?

3. When are isotopes radioactive?

4. What happens during radioactive decay?

5. Why is gamma radiation dangerous to living things?

6. What happens to an element during transmutation?

7. What is the main problem in developing a fusion reactor?

Determine whether each statement is true or false. Write *true* if it is true. If it is false, change the underlined term to make the statement true.

8. The source of radioactivity is the <u>nuclei</u> of atoms.

9. Protons and neutrons are held together in a nucleus by <u>electrons</u>.

10. Carbon-12 and carbon-14 are <u>isotopes</u>.

11. Alpha decay produces an <u>electron</u>.

12. A sheet of aluminum will protect you from <u>gamma radiation</u>.

13. Alpha and beta decay cause <u>transmutations</u>.

14. During nuclear <u>fission</u>, hydrogen nuclei join to produce helium nuclei.

15. Experimental fusion reactors produce <u>more</u> energy than they use.

Check Your Understanding

Apply the concepts you have learned to answer each question.

1. **Classify** Which of the following nuclear changes is a transmutation?

   a. C-14 to C-12

   b. C-14 to N-14

   c. $_1^3H$ to $_1^2H$

   d. U-238 to Th-234

   e. $_{84}^{210}Po \rightarrow _{82}^{206}Pb + _2^4He$

   f. Ra-226 to Rn-222

2. As elements increase in atomic number, the number of isotopes they have increases. Explain why this is true.

3. **Generalize** What are the characteristics of radioactive substances?

4. **Infer** A nuclear reaction produces particles with less total mass than the starting material. It also produces energy. What can you infer?

5. **Find Causes** What kind of decay would cause each of the following nuclear changes?

   a. $_{88}^{226}Ra$ to $_{86}^{222}Rn$

   b. $_{82}^{214}Pb$ to $_{83}^{214}Bi$

6. **Predict** What might happen if technicians couldn't move control rods into a nuclear reactor?

7. **Infer** What is happening to the amount of helium in the sun?

8. **Mystery Photo** The photograph on page 560 shows the paths made by subatomic particles inside a bubble chamber. The particles come from nuclei bombarded with high-speed neutrons or protons produced by a particle accelerator. Why do you think some of the paths are curved and some are straight?

Develop Your Skills

1. Approximately 2 years
Year 0: 16 g
Year 2: 8 g
Year 4: 4 g
Year 6: 2 g
Year 8: 1 g
Year 10: 0.5 g
Year 12: 0.25 g

2. a. 10 g
b. 6
c. 7,640 years
d. No, because too much of the original carbon-14 will have decayed.

3. a. 25 mrem
b. 10 mrem
c. Outer space

Make Connections

1. Concept maps will vary. You may wish to have students do the map below. First draw the map on the board, then add a few key terms. Have students draw and complete the map.

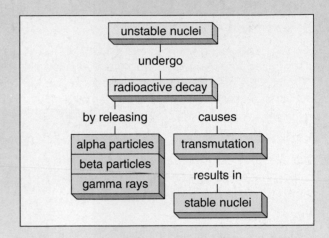

2. Radon is a product of uranium decay. It can cause lung cancer if it enters the lung tissue, because it will decay to Po, releasing alpha radiation that is particularly harmful to mucous membranes like those in the lungs. Test kits are available. The kit is left in the basement for a period of time, then sent to a lab for analysis. A homeowner can seal the basement walls to prevent seepage of radon gas.

3. Nuclear energy: major disadvantage is the danger from the wastes; wind, water, tides, geothermal energy, and solar radiation are all clean sources of energy, but are limited by geography—not all regions of the earth have access to each type.

4. Student reports will vary. Each should present clearly the goal of a specific fusion project. For example, is the project aimed at sustaining a plasma for the longest length of time, or at initiating fusion at the lowest temperature?

Develop Your Skills

Use the skills you have developed to complete each activity.

1. Calculate After 12 years, 0.25 g of a 16-g sample of a radioactive substance remains. What is its half-life?

2. Interpret Data The graph below shows the decay of carbon-14 over time.

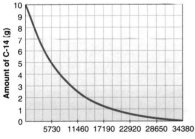

a. How much carbon-14 did the sample begin with?

b. How many half-lives pass before the amount of carbon-14 nears zero?

c. Estimate the age of the sample when it contains 4 g of carbon-14.

d. Do you think the age of an object older than 1 million years can be determined by carbon-14 dating? Explain.

3. Data Bank Use the information on page 643 to answer the following questions.

a. How much radiation does the average person receive every year from air, water, and food?

b. How much radiation do you receive on a 10-hr plane flight?

c. For most people, which is the greatest source of radiation exposure, television or outer space?

Make Connections

1. Link the Concepts Construct a concept map that shows how the following concepts in this chapter link together: alpha particles, stable nuclei, transmutation, beta particles, unstable nuclei, radioactive decay, gamma rays.

2. Science and Health Radon, a radioactive gas, is thought to cause some lung cancers. It is sometimes found in the basements of houses. Find the answers to the following questions about radon: Where does radon come from? Why might it cause lung cancer? How can people find out whether radon is present in their basements? What can people do to protect themselves from exposure to radon?

3. Science and Society Electricity is the main source of energy used in homes, factories, and businesses. Most of the electricity used in the United States comes from burning fossil fuels, such as oil and coal. The world's supply of these fuels is limited, and the power plants that burn them produce air pollution. How do each of the following sources of energy compare with the energy in fossil fuels? Radioactive elements, wind, flowing water, tides, heat from inside the earth, and solar radiation. Choose one and write a report about its advantages and disadvantages as an energy source.

4. Science and Technology What are the latest advances in nuclear fusion research? Are scientists any closer to creating a fusion reaction that generates more energy than it uses? Do library research to discover what fusion research is being done.

About the Literary Work

"Mother and Daughter" was adapted from the short story *Mother and Daughter* by Gary Soto, copyright 1990 by Harcourt, Brace, Jovanovich. Reprinted by permission of Harcourt, Brace, Jovanovich.

Description of Change

Passages depicting Mrs. Moreno's own childhood were edited from the text. Edited material primarily develops the idea that money had been scarce in previous generations of the Moreno family.

Rationale

The excerpt illustrates reactions of matter and solution chemistry by describing the use of fabric dye.

Vocabulary

sophisticated, bobby pin, ash

Teaching Strategies

Directed Inquiry

After students finish reading, discuss the story. Be sure to relate the story to the science lesson in this unit. Ask the following questions:

▶ What caused the dress to turn black? (Dipping it in the dye solution)

▶ What caused the dye to come out of the dress? (Getting wet again in the rain)

▶ Suppose the dance had been indoors. Is it likely that the dye would have run out of the dress? Why? (No, because the fabric wouldn't have been soaked with an additional solvent.)

Critical Thinking

Predict Challenge your students to think of occurrences other than rain that might have caused the dye to run from the dress. (Answers may vary. Students may mention getting water spilled on the dress and perspiration on the material.)

Generalize Discuss the differences between physical changes and chemical changes. Reinforce the idea that chemical changes alter the chemical composition of a substance. Physical changes do not produce new substances. Ask: Was dyeing the dress a physical or chemical change? Explain. (It was a physical change. Only the color of the dress changed. The color is a property of a dye solution, which leaves its color behind after evaporating. The dye came out of the dress when it got wet again.)

Science and Literature Connection

Mother and Daughter

The following excerpts are from the short story "Mother and Daughter" by Gary Soto

There was nothing funny about Yollie needing a new outfit for the eighth-grade fall dance. They couldn't afford one. . . . The best Mrs. Moreno could do was buy Yollie a pair of black shoes with velvet bows and fabric dye to color her white summer dress black.

"We can color your dress so it will look brand-new," her mother said brightly, shaking the bottle of dye as she ran hot water into a plastic dish tub. She poured the black liquid into the tub and stirred it with a pencil. Then, slowly and carefully, she lowered the dress into the tub.

Yollie couldn't stand to watch. She knew it wouldn't work. . . .

To Yollie's surprise, the dress came out shiny black. It looked brand-new and sophisticated, like what the people in New York wear. She beamed at her mother, who hugged Yollie and said, "See, what did I tell you?"

The dance was important to Yollie because she was in love with Ernie Castillo, the third-best speller in the class. She bathed, dressed, did her hair and nails, and primped until her mother yelled, "All right already." Yollie sprayed her neck and wrists with Mrs. Moreno's Avon perfume and bounced into the car.

Mrs. Moreno let Yollie out in front of the school. She waved and told her to have a good time but behave herself, then roared off, blue smoke trailing from the tail pipe of the old Nova . . .

The evening was warm but thick with clouds. Gusts of wind picked up the paper lanterns hanging in the trees and swung them, blurring the night with reds and yellows. The lanterns made the evening seem romantic, like a scene from a movie. Everyone danced, sipped punch, and stood in knots of threes and fours, talking. . . .

Yollie, who kept smoothing her dress down when the wind picked up, had her eye on Ernie. It turned out that Ernie had his mind on Yollie, too. He ate a handful of cookies nervously, then asked her for a dance.

"Sure," she said, nearly throwing herself into his arms.

They danced two fast ones before they got a slow one. As they circled under the lanterns, rain began falling, lightly at first. Yollie loved the sound of the raindrops ticking against the leaves. She leaned her head on Ernie's shoulder, though his sweater was scratchy. He felt warm and tender. Yollie could tell that he was in love, and with her, of course. The dance continued successfully, romantically, until it began to pour. . . .

The girls and boys raced into the cafeteria. Inside, the girls, drenched to the bone, hurried to the restrooms to brush their hair and dry themselves. One girl cried because her velvet dress was ruined.

Skills in Science

Reading Skills in Science

1. Rainwater that fell on the dress caused the dye to run out of the fabric.

2. The dye solution consisted of a black dye solute and a water solvent.

Writing Skills in Science

1. Gasoline reacts with oxygen in the engine to form exhaust containing carbon monoxide. Incomplete burning of gasoline or oil in the car engine produces a visible exhaust.

2. Answers may vary. Yollie immediately felt sorry for the girl in the velvet dress; the other girls did not even notice Yollie's ruined dress.

3. Yollie thought everyone would know she dyed an old dress, and that they would laugh. Her reaction was unreasonable because no one noticed or knew that she had worn an old dress. Also, her own reaction to the other rain-soaked dress was to feel sorry.

4. Answers may vary. Students may write endings to the story that depict Yollie staying at the dance and enjoying her time with Ernie.

Activities

Gathering Information Students' charts may include the madder plant (red dye), the crocus plant (yellow dye), the indigo plant (dark blue dye), the dogwood tree (black and brown dyes), and henna (an orange-brown dye).

Model The eggshell absorbs the yellow dye from the onion skin and water solution.

Yollie felt sorry for her and helped her dry the dress off with paper towels, but it was no use. The dress was ruined.

Yollie went to a mirror. She looked a little gray now that some of her mother's makeup had washed away but not as bad as some of the other girls. She combed her damp hair, careful not to pull too hard. She couldn't wait to get back to Ernie.

Yollie bent over to pick up a bobby pin, and shame spread across her face. A black puddle was forming at her feet. Drip, black drip. Drip, black drip. The dye was falling from her dress like black tears. Yollie stood up. Her dress was now the color of ash. She looked around the room. The other girls, unaware of Yollie's problem, were busy grooming themselves. What could she do? Everyone would laugh. They would know she dyed an old dress because she couldn't afford a new one. She hurried from the restroom with her head down, across the cafeteria floor and out the door. She raced through the storm, crying as the rain mixed with her tears and ran into twig-choked gutters.

Skills in Science

Reading Skills in Science

1. **Find the Main Idea** What caused the dye to come out of Yollie's dress?

2. **Classify** Identify the solvent and the solute in the dye solution used to change the color of the dress.

Writing Skills in Science

1. **Find Causes** After Mrs. Moreno dropped Yollie off, "there was blue smoke trailing from the tail pipe of the old Nova." What chemical reaction is producing this smoke?

2. **Compare and Contrast** How did Yollie's reaction to the girl's velvet dress ruined by the rain compare to the reaction of the others to Yollie's ruined dress?

3. **Finding Causes** What was Yollie's biggest concern when the dye washed off her dress? Do you think her reaction was reasonable. Explain.

4. **If . . . Then Arguments** If you were Yollie, would you have left the dance? Write an ending to the story describing what you would have done.

Activities

Gather Information Natural dyes have been used to dye fabrics and other materials for 5,000 years. Use reference tools to learn about plants that provide natural dyes. Make a chart that shows five different plants and how each is used for dyeing.

Model Place a raw egg and a handful of yellow onion skins in a pan of cold water. Boil the egg and the onion skins together for five minutes. Describe what happens to the egg shell?

Where to Read More

Adventures with Atoms and Molecules Book 3 by Robert C. Mebane and Thomas R. Rybolt. Hillside, New Jersey: Enslow Publishers, Inc., 1991. Thirty experiments demonstrate the properties and behavior of atoms and molecules.

Chemically Active! by Vicki Cobb. New York: J.B. Lippincott, 1985. Interesting experiments illustrate chemistry basics using common materials.

Directed Inquiry

Have students examine the photograph. Discuss the following:

▶ In what way is a microchip an individual piece of technology? How is it used in larger technology? (Students may answer that a single microchip, although extremely small, contains a great deal of information. Microchips placed on a wafer are able to perform many intricate tasks that are used in large pieces of electronic equipment. Accept all reasonable answers.)

▶ Ask students to identify the advantages of small size in microchip technology. (If microchips are small, then more information can fit in a small space. Accept all reasonable answers.)

Writing About the Photograph

Encourage students to think of a microchip as a small community of specialists, or a single small farm. In addition, ask students to imagine the wafer as a city of many communities or a farm community made of small farmers. Have students write an essay telling how the wafer operates like a city or a large farming community.

This unit explores technology as it relates to energy, chemistry, and the environment. Chapter 24 describes the process of generating electric power, comparing conventional energy sources with one another and describing the advantages and disadvantages of alternative energy technologies. The chapter closes with a discussion of energy conservation issues. Chapter 25 describes the properties and uses of hydrocarbons in petroleum and of petrochemical products such as plastics and synthetic fibers. The processes used in manufacturing metals, ceramics, glass, and other composite materials are also described. Lastly, the chapter explores ways in which technology damages and benefits the environment.

Unit 7
Technology
and
Resources

Chapters

24 Energy Use and Technology

25 Chemical Technology

Data Bank

Use the information on pages 634 to 643 to answer the questions about topics explored in this unit.

Inferring

If motor vehicles used electricity instead of gasoline, how would the usage of crude oil change?

Interpreting Data

Approximately what portion of the products made from crude oil is directly related to transportation?

Classifying

List the three largest individual consumers of industrial energy.

The photograph to the left shows how individual chips are placed on a wafer. What kinds of electronic devices might use a microchip wafer?

Data Bank Answers

Have students search the Data Bank on pages 634 to 643 for the answers to the questions on this page.

Inferring If motor vehicles ran on electricity, 46.7 percent of the crude oil now used for gasoline could be used for other purposes. The answer can be found using the circle graph, Products from One Barrel of Crude Oil, on page 636.

Interpreting Data About 60 percent of products made from crude oil are directly related to transportation. The answer is found in the circle graph, Products from One Barrel of Crude Oil, on page 636.

Classifying The three largest individual consumers of industrial energy are the metal industry, the chemical industry, and the petroleum and coal industry. The answer is found in the graphs, Breakdown of Energy Consumption in the United States, page 642.

Extension Ask students what portion of the total energy consumption in the United States goes for highway vehicles. (Highway vehicles account for about 19 percent of the total energy consumption.)

Answer to In-Text Question

Pacemakers, hearing aids, and other very small electronic devices might use microchip wafers.

CHAPTER 24

Overview

This chapter presents energy use and technology. The process of generating electric power is described and conventional energy sources are compared in the first section. The next section describes advantages and disadvantages of alternative energy technologies. A discussion of energy conservation issues completes the chapter.

Advance Planner

▶ Provide maps for the activity on TE pages 587 and 597.

▶ Provide shoe boxes, aluminum foil, long wooden skewers, hot dogs, and, if possible, other foods for SE Activity 24, page 595.

Skills Development Chart

Sections	Analyze	Communicate	Graph	Hypothesize	Infer	Observe	Research
24.1 Skills WarmUp Skills WorkOut					●		●
24.2 Skills WarmUp Skills WorkOut Activity				● 	●	● ● ●	
24.3 Skills WarmUp SkillBuilder Skills WorkOut	●	●	●			●	

Individual Needs

▶ **Limited English Proficiency Students** Have each student choose one commonly used source of electric power. Have them explain their energy source, using words and diagrams to explain all the steps involved in getting the electricity from the source to a user. Then have each student select an alternative source of electric power and, on a second journal page, describe how it produces electric power. Finally, have each student make a simple chart comparing and contrasting the renewability, risks, and benefits of the two sources of electrical power.

▶ **At-Risk Students** Have students work in groups to plan and carry out a plan for using energy more efficiently. One group, for example, might choose to recycle their soft drink cans by collecting cans throughout the week, weighing the cans, and bringing them to a recycling center. Another group might choose to recycle plastic milk and detergent containers. Groups should work together to choose a plan, describe the steps involved in carrying out the plan, and list possible environmental advantages that will result. Have groups meet to share and discuss their strategies.

▶ **Gifted Students** Have students work in groups of four to design and build a model of a solar-powered water distillation plant. Groups may assign specific tasks to their members: One student might prepare drawings showing what happens as the solar energy evaporates the water, another might prepare drawings showing what happens as the evaporated water is condensed. The third student might compute how much energy is used during each part of the distillation process. The fourth might show how the solar device could be used on cloudy days. If possible, have the group prepare demonstrations for the rest of the class.

Resource Bank

▶ **Bulletin Board** Encourage the class to discuss some newsworthy energy topics or controversies. Ask students to select three or four topics that have been discussed on television and radio and in the newspapers. Have them bring in stories and pictures relating to the topics. You might want to classify the contributions into categories or focus on one topic, for example: cost of energy, energy tax, energy reserve, energy problem, proposed solution.

▶ **Field Trip** Take students to a commercial or industrial building that uses a solar heating system. Ask the guide to show students how the system works. As a class activity, have students make a diagram to show how solar systems work.

Section	Core	Standard	Enriched
24.1 Generating and Using Electric Power pp. 583–588			
Section Features Skills WarmUp, p. 583 Skills WorkOut, p. 588	•	• •	• •
Blackline Masters Review Worksheet 24.1 Reteach Worksheet 24.1 Integrating Worksheet 24.1	• •	• •	•
Overhead Blackline Transparencies Overhead Blackline Master 23 and Student Worksheet	•	•	•
Color Transparencies Transparencies 84a, 84b	•	•	•
24.2 Alternative Energy Technologies pp. 589–595			
Section Features Skills WarmUp, p. 589 Career Corner, p. 593 Skills WorkOut, p. 594 Activity, p. 595	• • •	• • •	• • • •

Section	Core	Standard	Enriched
Blackline Masters Review Worksheet 24.2 Skills Worksheet 24.2	• •	• •	•
24.3 Energy Conservation Decisions pp. 596–600			
Section Features Skills WarmUp, p. 596 SkillBuilder, p. 597 Skills WorkOut, p. 599	• •	• • •	• • •
Blackline Masters Review Worksheet 24.3 Skills Worksheet 24.3 Integrating Worksheet 24.3 Vocabulary Worksheet 24	• •	• • • •	• • • •
Ancillary Options *One-Minute Readings,* p. 99	•	•	•
Color Transparencies Transparency 85	•	•	•
Laboratory Program Investigation 43	•	•	•

Bibliography

The following resources can be used for teaching the chapter. See page T-46 for supplier codes.

Library Resources

Dolan, Edward F., and Margaret Scariano. *Nuclear Waste: The 10,000 Year Challenge.* New York: Franklin Watts, 1990.

Fogel, Barbara R. *Energy Choices for the Future.* New York: Franklin Watts, 1985.

Gay, Kathlyn. *Garbage and Recycling.* Hillside, NJ: Enslow Publishers, Inc., 1991.

Herda, D. J., and Margaret L. Madden. *Energy Resources: Towards a Renewable Future.* New York: Franklin Watts, 1991.

Lee, Sally. *The Throwaway Society.* New York: Franklin Watts, 1990.

Pack, Janet. *Fueling the Future.* Chicago, IL: Children's Press, Inc., 1992.

Technology Resources

Software

Superstar Science. Mac, Win. LS.

CD-ROMs

An Odyssey of Discovery for Science Insights: Encourage students to explore the activity *Recycler* on the Earth and Space Disk. *SFAW.*

hip Physics. Mac. ESI.

Interactive Earth. SFAW.

Laserdiscs

Living Textbook. (See barcodes on pages in this chapter.) Optical Data.

Videos

Energy: The Fuels and Man. NGSES.

Energy: The Problems and the Future. Video or Film. NGSES.

Recycling: The Endless Circle. NGSES.

The Resource Revolution. CSWS.

Audio-Visual Resources

The World of Energy II. Filmstrips. NGSES.

Writing Connection

Have students study the photograph. Ask them to imagine that they are solar-powered robots with rows of tiny solar-energy collectors positioned on their shoulders. Ask students to write a description of how they feel when the morning sun strikes their solar collectors. Encourage them to be creative.

Themes in Science

Energy Explain that energy exists in many forms and can be changed from one form to another. For example, if a student makes a mistake on a paper and erases it rapidly, that part of the paper will feel warm. The student changed mechanical energy—erasing—into heat energy. Ask students for other examples of how energy can be changed from one form to another.

Introducing the Chapter

Have students read the description of the photograph. Ask if they agree or disagree with the description. Explain to students that the solar reflector concentrates light from the sun before it is turned into electric energy.

Directed Inquiry

Have students study the photograph. Ask:

▶ How would you describe the objects in the photograph? (Students may say that they look like buckets or shiny bowls.)

▶ What do you think these objects are? (Students may say they are solar energy collectors or reflectors.)

▶ What do you think happens to the sunlight that reaches the shiny surface? (As it reflects back and forth from the walls of the objects, it becomes concentrated.)

▶ How is concentrated sunlight used? (It's converted into electric energy.)

▶ What does energy from the sun have to do with the subject of the chapter? (Today, people are trying to develop technologies that use free, nonpolluting solar energy.)

Chapter Vocabulary

biomass	nonrenewable
fossil fuel	resources
geothermal	renewable resources
hydroelectric	solar cell
power	

Chapter 2/4 Energy Use and Technology

Chapter Sections

24.1 Generating and Using Electric Power

24.2 Alternative Energy Technologies

24.3 Energy Conservation Decisions

What do you see?

❝I think it is a solar energy collector. It absorbs energy from the sun. It is shiny because the light is reflecting off it. This technology is important because it helps save our natural resources. With it we use the energy from the sun instead of energy from the earth.❞

Elisa Shzu
Parkhill Junior High School
Dallas, Texas

To find out more about the photograph, look on page 602. As you read this chapter, you will learn about energy sources and how electric power is generated.

24.1 Generating and Using Electric Power

Objectives

▶ **Identify** how the sun's energy changes to form an energy pathway.

▶ **Describe** four ways of producing electricity.

▶ **Explain** how electricity from a power plant is delivered to the home.

▶ **Compare** and **contrast** the advantages and disadvantages of conventional energy sources.

▼ **ACTIVITY**

Inferring

Energy Sources

List all the things you did yesterday that required the use of some form of energy. Identify the energy sources you used.

SKILLS WARMUP

I magine that you lived 200 years ago. People had no telephones, washing machines, air conditioners, or sewing machines. They cooked over an open fire or on a wood-burning stove like the one shown in Figure 24.1. They scrubbed their clothes on stones in a river or on a washboard, and hung them in the open air to dry.

Today electric power makes your life easier and more comfortable. Furnaces, air conditioners, and fans keep you warm in winter and cool in summer. Appliances, such as washers and dryers, help you to do work. Radios, TVs, and CD players provide you with entertainment. What are the sources of the electric power that make all these things work? ①

Energy Pathways

Changes of the sun's energy from one form to another are called pathways of energy. For example, by heating the earth and its atmosphere, the sun creates the winds that circulate over the earth. A windmill may change the wind energy into mechanical energy that operates a water pump.

In some energy pathways, the sun's energy is stored for a very long time. For example, coal, oil, and natural gas are the remains of plants or other organisms that lived hundreds of millions of years ago. The energy stored in the plants and organisms that created these fuels originally came from the sun.

Figure 24.1
Wood burned inside this stove not only cooked food, it also was the main heat source for the entire room. ▼

Reteach

Before students study this page, have them read page 302 of Chapter 12 to review how generators produce electricity. Use Transparency 47. Remind students that a generator has a permanent magnet around the armature. The armature inside is a coil of wire. As mechanical energy turns the armature through the magnetic field of the magnet, current is induced in the coil.

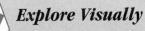

Explore Visually

Have students study pages 584 and 585. Ask:

▶ What energy source powers the plant in the illustration? (Moving water—mechanical energy)

▶ What kind of energy does the water behind the dam have? (Potential energy)

▶ How does water behind the dam provide mechanical energy? (It releases mechanical energy as it flows through pipes to the turbine.)

▶ What happens when water reaches the turbine? (It strikes the turbine blades, causing them to turn.)

▶ What makes the shaft of the generator turn? (Water hitting the turbine blades)

▶ When the generator shaft turns, what happens to the coil? (The coil turns inside a magnet, producing a current.)

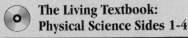

The Living Textbook: Physical Science Sides 1-4

Chapter 15   Frame 02614
Generating Electricity (24 Frames)
Search: Step:

STS Connection

Explain that since the early 1900s, people have nearly doubled their energy use every 20 years. Yet in the period between the late 1950s and late 1970s, people in the United States increased their energy use by 90 percent. Ask students if they can suggest why energy use increased so rapidly in this country. (Electric appliances became widespread; people used products that require a lot of energy to produce.)

Integrating the Sciences

Geology Explain to students that only certain places are suitable for building dams. Geologists and engineers must work together to determine the best locations. Dams are built on rivers between mountains where the terrain is steep and the sides of the mountains are used to confine the water. Have students research the terrain around the Grand Coulee Dam, Shasta Dam, or a local dam. Ask them what water source feeds the dam.

Electric Power

Most electricity is manufactured from other forms of energy. The electricity you use comes from a power plant. All power plants do the same thing. They convert mechanical energy into electric energy.

Electricity is made from many different energy sources. Some power plants use moving water as a source of mechanical energy. Others burn coal or oil to make steam. Steam pressure is used to turn a generator coil, which produces electricity.

**Figure 24.2
Electricity Production and Distribution** ▼

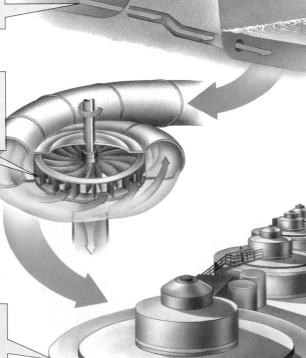

Energy Source
Mechanical energy is released as water from behind the dam moves through the pipes.

Turbine
The moving water strikes the blades of a turbine and turns the shaft of a generator connected to it.

Generator
Inside this housing, a coil connected to the turbine generates electricity as it rotates.

Electric power plants normally serve large areas. Study Figure 24.2 to learn how electricity is produced and supplied to homes and industry. Some of the electric energy must be transported great distances. Electricity travels quickly and efficiently through high-voltage wires called transmission lines. Like a network of roads, power lines carry electricity to farms, homes, and businesses in your community.

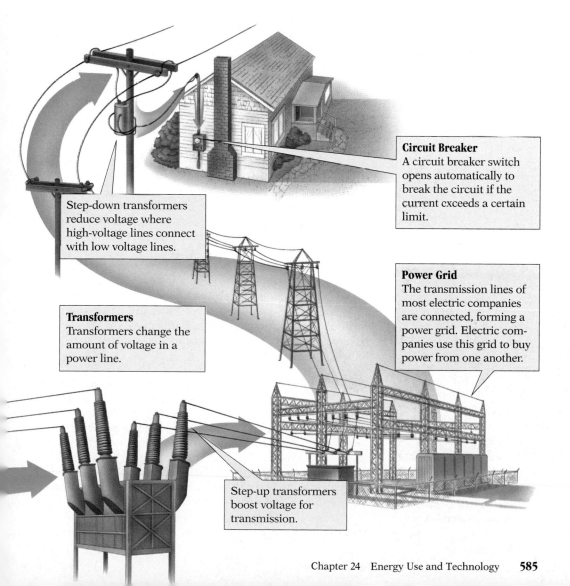

Step-down transformers reduce voltage where high-voltage lines connect with low voltage lines.

Transformers
Transformers change the amount of voltage in a power line.

Step-up transformers boost voltage for transmission.

Circuit Breaker
A circuit breaker switch opens automatically to break the circuit if the current exceeds a certain limit.

Power Grid
The transmission lines of most electric companies are connected, forming a power grid. Electric companies use this grid to buy power from one another.

TEACH ▪ *Continued*

Skills Development

Interpret Data Have students study Figure 24.3. Ask:

► Which of the five fuel sources provides the most energy for producing electricity? (Coal)

► Which fuel source provides the least? (Oil)

► What percent of our total energy is met by fossil fuels? (71 percent)

Portfolio

Ask students to update the Energy Inventory journals they started at the beginning of this section after reading pages 586 and 587.

Critical Thinking

Infer Ask students why hydroelectric power plants do not pollute. (No fuel is burned to release pollutants into the air; no nuclear wastes are produced.)

Answer to In-Text Question

① Total is 29%.

The Living Textbook:
Physical Science Sides 1-4

Chapter 15   Frame 02615
Hydroelectric Power (5 Frame)
Search: Step:

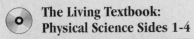

The Living Textbook:
Physical Science Sides 1-4

Chapter 4   Frame 01023
Nuclear Reactor (1 Frame)
Search:

586

Integrating the Sciences

Life Science Tell students that dams on major rivers in the Pacific Northwest block migrating salmon from making their way upstream to spawn. Engineers have built stepped waterfalls along some of these dams, including Bonneville Dam on the Columbia River near Portland, Oregon. Salmon and other migrating fish make their way upriver by leaping up a terrace of low waterfalls, called a *fish ladder*.

Earth Science Explain that coal is a form of sedimentary rock, which was formed as ancient plant remains were deposited and hardened under layers of silt and sand. Ask students to use references to define lignite, bituminous, and anthracite coal and to find out how each was formed.

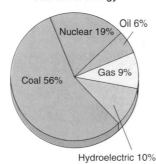

Sources of Energy

Nuclear 19%
Oil 6%
Coal 56%
Gas 9%
Hydroelectric 10%

Figure 24.3 ▲
What percent of the total fuel sources are water power and nuclear power? ①

Figure 24.4 ▲
After being buried and put under heat and pressure, plants like these became the coal we use today.

Sources of Electric Power

In the United States, utility companies use five energy sources to make most electricity—water, coal, oil, natural gas, and nuclear. The percentage contributed by each energy source is shown in Figure 24.3. Notice that coal, oil, and gas account for more than 70 percent of the total energy.

Hydroelectric Power Electricity generated by moving water from dams is called **hydroelectric power**. The sun provides heat energy that evaporates surface water from oceans, lakes, and streams. The water returns to the earth as rain or snow. Reservoirs behind dams built across river valleys collect and store the water.

The mechanical energy of the moving water as it leaves the dam is converted to electricity. The amount of kinetic energy in the falling water depends on the speed and the volume of the water available to turn the generators. About 10 percent of the electricity used in the United States is produced by hydroelectric power.

Generating electricity with water power is efficient and clean. Little energy is lost, and no pollutants are produced. Another advantage of hydroelectric power is its low cost. Although dams are expensive to build, hydroelectric plants have low operating costs.

The lakes, or reservoirs, behind the dams also provide water storage for irrigation and serve as recreational areas. However, building a dam changes a river forever. It floods low-lying areas upstream, destroying farmland and wildlife habitats. Dams may also block the migration and survival of some kinds of fish, such as salmon.

Fossil Fuels Fuels formed from the remains of ancient organisms are called **fossil fuels**. These plants and animals were buried under layers of mud and silt. Heat and pressure gradually transformed their organic compounds into concentrated chemical energy. Coal, oil, and natural gas are the three most common fossil fuels.

Fossil fuels are burned to heat water under pressure to create steam. The pressurized steam is the mechanical energy source that turns a turbine and generates electricity. Fossil fuels are used all over the world because they are relatively easy to get and are easy to transport.

Cooperative Learning

Have the class work in three cooperative groups. Have one group research the number of nuclear plants in the United States and plot the major ones on a map. Have the second group draw a nuclear reactor and how it works. Ask the third group to find detailed information on the benefits and risks of nuclear power. Have the groups share their information and make a bulletin board display on nuclear power for the school.

Answer to Link

The sun produces energy by the nuclear fusion. Four hydrogen nuclei are successively fused into one helium nucleus. This reaction forms a particle about 0.7% less massive than the four original particles. This "lost" mass is converted into energy according to the equation $E = mc^2$. Fusion reactors are still in the experimental stage and are not used as a source of electrical power.

Coal is the cheapest and most abundant energy source in the United States. However, coal is a dirty fuel. The smoke from burning coal contains large amounts of sulfur and carbon dioxide. Surface mining destroys the land environment. Drainage from surface mining pollutes water.

Oil is the major source of gasoline and other liquid fuels used for transportation and heat. The United States must import 40 to 45 percent of its oil supply. Burning oil also adds pollutants to the atmosphere, such as carbon dioxide, sulfur dioxide, and other gases. The production and transportation of oil can also pollute the environment, especially if an oil spill occurs.

Natural gas is the cleanest-burning fossil fuel. It generates fewer air pollutants and less carbon dioxide than other fossil fuels do. Gas is an efficient fuel and is used a great deal in industry, transportation, and power generation.

Nuclear Power Some electricity in the United States is produced by nuclear fission. A nuclear power plant is similar to a fossil-fuel plant—both produce heat that boils water to make steam. The fuel is very different, however. In a nuclear plant, fission of an unstable isotope of uranium or plutonium produces the heat.

Nuclear power plants have two main advantages over fossil-fuel plants. The energy stored in a small amount of nuclear fuel is enormous. For example, 1 kg of nuclear fuel contains nearly three million times the energy that is in 1 kg of coal. In addition, nuclear plants don't give off air pollutants.

Nuclear power plants have two major disadvantages. One disadvantage is the danger of nuclear accidents. Because nuclear power plants use radioactive material, accidents can release radioactive material into the environment that is extremely dangerous to living things. Accidents have occurred at nuclear reactors. The nuclear power industry has responded by developing safer reactor designs.

The disposal of nuclear wastes is another disadvantage and a serious problem facing the industry. Nuclear waste materials remain dangerously radioactive for thousands of years. Because the United States has no permanent storage facilities for these wastes, they are stored at the reactor sites.

Astronomy
LINK

The sun produces huge amounts of energy in the form of heat, light and radiation. Some of this energy is used on the earth to generate electricity.

Research how the sun produces energy. Describe the process used by the sun to produce energy. Is energy generated on the earth in the same way it's generated by the sun?

ACTIVITY

Figure 24.5 ▲
The stack of a nuclear power plant is a cooling tower that releases hot steam into the atmosphere.

Discuss

Have students think about the use of fossil fuels in the United States. Ask:

▶ What is the cheapest fossil fuel used in the United States? (Coal)

▶ Why doesn't the United States rely on coal for energy? (Smoke from burning coal contains pollutants; surface mining destroys the land and pollutes the water.)

▶ What are some of the problems with using oil? (The United States imports almost one-half of its oil supply; burning oil adds pollutants to the air; oil spills pollute oceans and shorelines.)

▶ What is the advantage of natural gas as a fuel? (It's the cleanest-burning fuel.)

Critical Thinking

Compare and Contrast Ask students to compare and contrast the three biggest sources of fuel in this country. Which is the cheapest? (Coal) Which is the cleanest? (Hydroelectric) Which is most dangerous to human health? (Nuclear)

Decision Making Have students list the major issues involved in using nuclear power to generate electricity. (Answers should reflect students' awareness of nuclear power as an inexpensive but dangerous power source.)

Reteach

Use Reteach Worksheet 24.1.

 The Living Textbook:
Physical Science Sides 1-4

Chapter 16   Frame 02716
Nuclear Cooling Towers (1 Frame)
Search:

587

Skills WorkOut

To help students research sources of energy, have them do the Skills WorkOut.
Answer Answers will vary, but should show that energy accounts for much of each item's cost.

Portfolio

Have students check their Energy Inventory journals against the information on this page. Have them add new examples.

EVALUATE

WrapUp

Reteach Most of the energy sources depend indirectly on the sun. Discuss how the energy from the sun can be converted to electricity.
Use Review Worksheet 24.1.

Check and Explain

1. There are several possible pathways. One involves the sun heating the atmosphere and causing winds. Wind turns the shaft of a generator in a windmill, producing electricity.

2. Hydroelectric power—moving water is converted into electricity; oil and coal—burned to produce mechanical energy, which powers a generator; nuclear energy—fission heats water to produce steam to power a generator.

3. The power plant generates electricity, which is carried on transmission lines. Transformers reduce the voltage for individual use.

4. Hydroelectric— clean, changes environment; oil—cheap, pollutes; gas—clean, nonrenewable; coal—cheap, pollutes; nuclear—clean, creates radioactive waste

Math Connection

Have students read this page and identify the number of megajoules needed for each step in the process of making a loaf of bread. Ask them to make a circle graph using this information.

Multicultural Perspectives

Point out that a change in an energy source has often changed the way people live. Ask students to make before-and-after posters showing how new energy sources affected a society different from their own. Possible subjects include life in Wales before and after people began to rely on coal for fuel or life in a Middle Eastern country before and after oil became important.

Science and You
Energy Cost of Your Lunch

The next time you eat your lunch, think of the cost of the energy needed to make it. The food you eat is at the end of a long chain of energy-consuming processes. These processes use far more energy than the food itself contains.

Take bread, for example. It takes 20 megajoules of energy to produce a 1-kg loaf of bread. Twenty percent of the energy is used to grow the wheat. Milling the wheat into flour uses about 15 percent, and baking uses about 65 percent. The same amount of energy is needed to drive a car a distance of 5 km.

Part of the energy consumed in growing food is used to operate farm machinery and for irrigation. The rest goes into the production of agricultural chemicals, animal feeds, and other farm supplies.

Processing and distributing food also uses large amounts of energy. For example, it takes energy to peel, mash, and strain grapes for grape juice. The packaging itself consumes a large amount of energy. To produce one aluminum pop-top can, almost 7 megajoules of energy are needed.

At the end of the chain, energy is used to light and heat the supermarket, and to keep food fresh. You use energy to take your food home, to cool it in your refrigerator, and to prepare it. The next time you eat lunch, think of all the ways energy was used to grow, package, and transport the food to you.

▼ ACTIVITY

Calculating

Cost of Food Processing

Find out how much energy is used daily by a food processing company. What is the energy cost per item of several kinds of food the company produces?

SKILLS WORKOUT

Check and Explain

1. Identify an energy pathway from the sun to electric power.

2. Name four sources of electric power and describe how each produces electricity.

3. **Define Operationally** Explain the process of making electricity and moving it from a power plant to the homes and buildings in your city.

4. **Compare and Contrast** In a table, list two advantages and two disadvantages of the five energy sources described in this section.

Social Studies Connection

The oil industry began in 1859 near Titusville, Pennsylvania. With the invention of cars and electric lights around 1900, demand for oil grew. Two world wars increased the demand. By the 1950s, oil had become one of America's main energy sources. About 80 percent of the world's oil is located in the Middle East and Latin America. By 1973, the United States imported 35 percent of its oil. Today it imports nearly 50 percent.

Writing Connection

Have students write a short story about a boy in a poor family who found a way to keep them warm in winter by using an alternative energy source. Ask some students to share their stories with the class.

Skills Objectives
Students should be able to:

Observe possible energy resources in their community.

Hypothesize about how fuels can be cost effective.

Communicate the role of the sun's energy in three energy sources by using a flowchart.

Infer why the sun can cook food.

Vocabulary
solar cell, biomass, geothermal

24.2 Alternative Energy Technologies

Objectives

▶ **Infer** ways to use solar energy in a home.

▶ **Relate** wind, geothermal, and tidal processes to the production of electricity.

▶ **Compare** and **contrast** the benefits of biomass and synthetic fuels.

▶ **Communicate** the role of the sun's energy in three alternative energy sources.

▼ **ACTIVITY**

Observing

New Energy Source

Imagine that your community wants to develop a new source of energy. What are some forms of energy you observe every day that could be tapped as an energy source? ·

SKILLS WARMUP

MOTIVATE

Skills WarmUp
To help students understand alternative energy technologies, have them do the Skills WarmUp.
Answer Answers will vary. Students may mention such ideas as burning garbage to produce fuel for steam generators, harnessing the power of waves, and using solar energy to heat houses.

Prior Knowledge

Gauge how much students know about alternative energy technologies by asking:

▶ Why are people looking for new sources of energy?

▶ What alternative energy sources have you heard of?

▶ Why don't we start using these sources right now?

Answer to In-Text Question

① Answers will vary, but students should show an awareness of energy consumption.

Until the eighteenth century, wind, water, and wood were the primary sources of energy. Dependence on fossil fuels began with the Industrial Revolution and the increased use of coal. Discoveries of oil and large pools of gas from the mid-1800s to the early 1900s made these convenient, inexpensive fossil fuels popular.

In 1973, a shortage of gasoline created long gas lines like the one in Figure 24.6. Periodic shortages of gasoline and other oil products since then made people aware of their dependence on oil. The need to supplement and eventually replace fossil fuels became a reality. Increased awareness of environmental problems also intensified the search for safer, more dependable alternate energy sources.

Alternative Energy Sources

Opinions vary on how long the present supply of fossil fuels will last. However, most experts admit that sooner or later the supply will run out. As fossil-fuel reserves are used up, the need for energy continues to grow. The modern lifestyle of many countries requires large amounts of energy.

Unfortunately, the world can't wait to run out of fossil fuels before finding other energy resources. What will those resources be? Some energy sources are more promising over the long term than others are.

Figure 24.6 ▲
People waiting in long lines like these were often limited in the amount of gas they could buy. How much gas do your parents buy each week? ①

TEACH

Skills Development

Infer Ask, Why do solar panels in the United States face south? (Southern exposures receive the most sun during the year in the northern hemisphere.)

Discuss

Point out that solar energy is widely available, but not widely used today. Engage students in a discussion about solar power. Ask:

▶ Where on the earth are most days the hottest? Where are most days the coldest? (Hottest at the equator; coldest far south and far north)

▶ If sunlight is free, why is solar energy so costly? (The cost of piping systems, storage tanks for heated water, pumps, electricity to run the pumps, and maintenance expenses make the cost of solar energy higher than purchasing fuel.)

▶ Where would it cost the most to use solar energy? Why? (In cold regions; they receive the least sun and would have to store energy the longest.)

▶ What might lower the cost of using solar energy? (Better technology or designs for collecting it and storing it)

Class Activity

Have students use reference sources to find out about other items powered by solar energy, such as spacecraft, cars, and calculators. They can report what they learn to the class.

The Living Textbook:
Physical Science Sides 1-4

Chapter 16   Frame 02718
Solar Panels (1 Frame)
Search: Step:

590

STS Connection

Explain that space satellites are equipped with solar cells that gather the sun's energy and use it to generate and store electric power. The electricity is used to operate instruments and computers aboard the satellite. Have students use reference sources to find out what these instruments enable satellites to do. Have students report their findings to the class.

Solar Power Solar energy is heat and light energy from the sun. For a long time, people have dreamed about harnessing this free, limitless, and nonpolluting source of energy. Today the technology exists to convert solar energy into both heat and electricity.

A **solar cell** is a device containing a semiconductor that converts sunlight directly into electricity. When sunlight strikes solar cells, like those shown in Figure 24.7, electrons flow from one part of the cell to another. This action produces electricity.

Solar energy is converted into heat by using an active solar heating system, such as the one used to heat houses in Figure 24.8. Flat-plate solar collectors trap heat from the sun's rays. Pipes filled with water heated by the solar collector carry the heat to other places in the house where it is used or stored for future use.

Figure 24.8 ▲
Solar collectors on a south-facing roof will absorb a maximum amount of energy from the sun.

The major disadvantage of using solar power for commercial use is cost. Harnessing solar energy is difficult. Sunlight isn't a concentrated form of energy. To collect this widely scattered energy, solar power plants need vast amounts of land and equipment. Also, exposure to sunlight varies with latitude, season, time of day, and weather conditions. Power plants need costly equipment to store solar energy for use when sunlight isn't available.

Advances in materials and design are making solar cells less expensive and more competitive with conventional energy sources. One breakthrough is "thin-film" solar technology. Perhaps you have a watch or a calculator that uses this inexpensive source of solar power. Thin-film modules don't convert solar energy very efficiently. However, their low cost makes it reasonable to use large numbers of them.

Figure 24.7 ▲
Large numbers of solar cells on panels are needed to heat a home.

Themes in Science

Patterns of Change/Cycles

Remind students that nutrients and energy are naturally recycled in the environment. Ask them what living things and fossil fuels have in common. (They are organic.) Point out that plant materials and animal wastes can be used as alternatives to fossil fuels.

Critical Thinking

Compare and Contrast Explain to students that California has many large wind farms that together provide enough energy to serve the needs of a major metropolitan area. Ask, How is a wind farm similar to a hydroelectric plant? How is it different? (Some answers include: Both convert mechanical energy to electric energy; one relies on wind, the other on water.)

Classify List the following fuel sources on the chalkboard. Have students identify which represent biomass and explain why: nuclear reactions, peat, wind, wood, cornhusks, hydrogen, water, nutshells, sunlight, coffee seed hulls. (Peat, wood, cornhusks, nutshells, coffee seed hulls; each of these materials are organic and can either be used as fuel or converted into another kind of fuel.)

Wind Generators Wind energy is used to generate electricity. Wind is caused by differences in temperature and atmospheric pressure at the earth's surface. Because the earth and its atmosphere are heated by the sun, wind energy is an indirect form of solar power.

Wind generators often feature two or three large turbine blades on top of a tall tower. Height is important because wind speed is greater and more constant high above the earth's surface.

Wind generators don't produce any air or water pollution. They can, however, be noisy. Large numbers of them can interfere with TV and microwave transmission.

A major disadvantage of wind power is its variable nature. To produce electricity efficiently, a steady wind speed of 19 to 24 km per hour is needed. These conditions don't always exist where wind power is needed. In the United States, the right conditions occur mainly in the mountains, along certain coastal areas, and on the Great Plains.

Figure 24.9 ▲
The shaft of the windmill connects the turbine blades to a coil in the generator. When wind turns the turbine, the generator produces electricity.

Figure 24.10 ▲
Biomass from waste materials is dried and compressed to form these pellets. The pellets are used as fuel source.

Biomass Organic matter that can be used as fuel is called **biomass**. Plant material in any form and organic wastes, such as garbage and manure, are also biomass.

When burned, most biomass releases at least half the energy of high-grade coal. Nearly any kind of dry biomass is easy to burn. Materials, such as sawdust, corncobs, and walnut shells make good fuels.

Biomass can also be converted into liquids and gases that burn. The action of bacteria on a mixture of sewage and water produces methane gas. Methane can be liquefied and used as a fuel.

An important advantage of biomass is that it is easily replenished. The main disadvantage is that it requires large areas of farmland. Land used to produce biomass won't be available for food crops.

 The Living Textbook: Physical Science Sides 1-4

Chapter 16   Frame 02756
Wind Generators (3 Frames)
Search: Step:

 The Living Textbook: Physical Science Sides 1-4

Chapter 16   Frame 02769
Refuse-Fired Power Plant (4 Frames)
Search: Step:

TEACH ▪ Continued

Discuss

Have a discussion about synthetic fuels. Ask the following questions:

▶ Can ethanol and methanol be considered renewable resources? Why? (Yes; they're made from plants.)

▶ In what way do ethanol and methanol improve on gasoline? (They burn cleaner.)

▶ Do you think kerogen and bitumen are as promising alternatives as ethanol and methanol? Explain. (Answers may vary, but should reflect students' awareness of the abundance of oil shale and tar sands, and the energy and waste involved in recovering oil from them.)

Class Activity

Point out to students that much geothermal activity occurs near the edges of tectonic plates. Then form two cooperative learning groups. Have one group draw a large world map and research the countries that use geothermal energy. Have the other group research the location of the tectonic plates and the activity that occurs near the plates' edges. Have the groups combine their information to make a bulletin board map showing the plates and the location of geothermal plants, and explaining how activity at the plates' edges creates heat.

**The Living Textbook:
Physical Science Sides 1-4**

Chapter 16   Frame 02761
Geothermal Activity (5 Frames)
Search: Step:

592

Synthetic Fuels Synthetic fuels are liquids and gases made from energy sources other than fossil fuels. Ethanol and methanol are both alcohols made from biomass. Gasohol is gasoline blended with ethanol.

Ethanol is made by fermenting corn or sugar cane. Methanol is made from wood. These synthetic fuels burn cleaner and produce less carbon dioxide than gasoline does.

Kerogen and bitumen are organic substances that can be converted into synthetic oil or gas. Kerogen is found in an oil-bearing shale. Bitumen is a thick, black substance in tar sands. Oil shale and tar sands are plentiful energy sources. However, to extract them requires large amounts of energy and water and produces mountains of waste rock.

Figure 24.12 ▲
This power station in Iceland uses geothermal steam to generate electricity.

Geothermal Energy Heat produced beneath the earth's surface is **geothermal** energy. Hot magma or molten rock in the earth's crust is the source of geothermal energy. Magma near the earth's surface heats the surrounding rock. The rocks heat underground water to form geothermal reservoirs.

Geothermal wells in the reservoirs bring a mixture of steam and hot water to the surface. After the water and impurities are removed from the steam, the steam is piped into turbine generators to produce electricity. Most of the hot water is used for heating buildings.

Geothermal energy is an almost limitless source of power, but it's practical only where the source of heat is close to the earth's surface. Environmentally, geothermal power appears to be less harmful than nuclear or fossil fuel plants. Also, geothermal plants require smaller areas of land than other electricity plants. Minerals dissolved in the hot water corrode turbines. The wastewater can damage soil.

Figure 24.11 ▲
The cornstalk is used as biomass that is burned. The corn is used to make ethanol, which is a fuel used in car engines.

Geography Connection

Explain to students that the Bay of Fundy between Nova Scotia and the Canadian mainland has the highest tidal range in the world—16 m between high and low tides. Point out the Bay of Fundy on a map or globe. The Canadian government has been building dams in the bay for a power plant. When the power plant is finished, it will provide power to cities in Canada and the United States.

Themes in Science

Energy Remind students that energy can be changed from one form to another. Tell them that for a tidal power plant to work, it must have a dam built across a narrow bay, just as a hydroelectric plant requires a dam built across a river. In both cases water is held back as potential energy, then released as mechanical energy.

Class Activity

Use tide tables from several areas in the country that would be good locations for tidal power generators. If possible, look at tide tables in foreign-country newspapers from a local newsstand. Have students correlate the time between high and low tide to the amount of time a tidal dam would be able to generate electricity. You may wish to have students make a chart to illustrate the tidal activity. Have students discuss why they think tidal power generators are a good or bad idea.

Career Corner

Discuss Invite an electrical engineer who designs computer systems to visit the class. Students should discuss with the guest how a computer works.

Tidal Power Recall that tides are the rise and fall of the ocean's surface caused by the gravitational pull on the water by the sun and the moon. The back and forth flow of ocean water near the shore can provide a source of energy that doesn't pollute and never runs out.

Tidal power is harnessed in much the same way as hydroelectric power is. A dam is used to control the flow of water, which turns a turbine. Tidal-power electric plants are practical only in narrow bays or estuaries. The difference between the level of the sea water and the water in the channel must be at least 5 m.

Building and maintaining a tidal power plant is very expensive. Also, the amount of electricity generated by a tidal power plant varies during the day, and from day to day and month to month. As a result, tidal power plants don't always generate electricity when it's most needed. One successful tidal power plant is in northern France on the Rance River estuary.

Career *Electrical Engineer*

Who Designs the Circuits in a Computer?

Electrical engineering is a broad field. Electrical engineers design and develop electric motors and other kinds of electric machinery. Some electrical engineers design power equipment and distribution systems that provide you with electricity.

Electrical engineers working in electronics develop, produce, and test electronic equipment, such as radios, TVs, telephone networks, and computers. Software engineers design automation systems for factories and controls for airplanes, spaceships, and other systems.

To be an electrical engineer requires good math skills and a knowledge of physics, chemistry, and electricity. You should be curious about mechanical operations and enjoy finding new ways of doing things. An interest in computers, model-building, and math games is useful. You also need to be able to analyze problems and to communicate your ideas, both in writing and in diagrams.

Electrical engineers must complete a bachelor's degree at a college or university. Some schools have cooperative education programs.

These programs allow you to alternate between taking classes and working as an engineering trainee.

In high school, you should take mathematics, chemistry, physics, and English.

The Living Textbook: Physical Science Sides 1-4

Chapter 9   Frame 01614
High and Low Tides (6 Frames)
Search: Step:

The Living Textbook: Physical Science Side 4

Chapter 25   Frame 14938
Decomposition of Water (Movie)
Search: Play:

TEACH ▪ *Continued*

Skills WorkOut

To help students hypothesize about the use of hydrogen as a cost efficient fuel, have them do the Skills WorkOut.

Answer Students' statements must be testable.

Critical Thinking

Decision Making Have students list the pros and cons of hydrogen fuel and solar energy. Ask:

▶ What issues are involved in using these energy sources? (Solar energy—needs a lot of land and costly equipment to store energy; hydrogen gas— explosive; fuel is expensive.)

▶ Which energy source would you develop? Explain. (Solar; safer than hydrogen; easier to control)

EVALUATE

WrapUp

Reinforce Consider the alternative sources of energy described in this section. Which ones depend on geography? Where could each be used? Discuss geographic issues that affect a community's choice of energy.

Use Review Worksheet 24.2.

Check and Explain

1. Heating the air, heating water, generating electricity

2. By driving turbines that turn the shaft of a generator

3. Advantages—biomass: availability, ease of burning, energy released; synthetics: created from biomass, availability; disadvantages—biomass: requires space; synthetics: create waste. Biomass has more advantages.

4. Flowcharts can show the sun, biomasses, wind energy.

594

STS Connection

Explain to students that hydrogen gas has other advantages. It can be burned like natural gas and shipped through pipelines. Tell them that some scientists think that advanced solar cells will make it possible to produce low-cost hydrogen fuel for cars. Engineers have already developed hydrogen-powered test cars.

Integrating the Sciences

Chemistry Explain that the process of electrolysis of water that separates oxygen and hydrogen uses more energy than is recovered when the hydrogen burns. Have students recall that the bond between hydrogen and oxygen is very strong. The energy used in electrolysis goes to breaking this bond and is not totally recoverable. Discuss the law of conservation of energy.

Science and Technology
The Hydrogen Stove

In the late 1970s, an energy experiment turned an ordinary house in Provo, Utah, into a "hydrogen homestead." Hydrogen gas operated the stove, oven, water heater, gas furnace, and outdoor barbecue. It also fueled a car and a lawn tractor.

In many ways, hydrogen is an ideal fuel. It can be made from ordinary water. You can burn hydrogen in a stove, a power plant, or an internal-combustion engine. When it burns, hydrogen produces no pollution. The only products are heat and water.

What prevents the widespread use of this ideal fuel? The biggest problem is cost. Breaking the strong chemical bonds between the hydrogen and oxygen atoms in water takes a great deal of energy. Making hydrogen from water uses more energy than the gas gives up when it recombines with oxygen. Recent advances in solar-cell technology might solve this problem. Thin-film solar cells are a cheap energy source.

Storing hydrogen safely is another problem. Hydrogen gas is very explosive. It reacts violently in air when ignited. The system used in the "hydrogen homestead" is probably the safest method available. The storage tank holds fine particles of a metal alloy that absorbs hydrogen like a sponge, forming a compound known as a metal hydride. Heating the tank releases the hydrogen gas slowly and safely.

▼ ACTIVITY

Hypothesizing

Hydrogen as Fuel

Use the library to find out more about the "hydrogen homestead." Write a hypothesis about why hydrogen was a success or failure as a cost-efficient fuel.

SKILLS WORKOUT

Check and Explain

1. Describe three ways to use solar energy in a conventional home.

2. Explain how technology uses wind, geothermal, and tidal processes to produce electricity.

3. **Compare and Contrast** List the advantages and disadvantages of using biomass and synthetic fuels. Which has the most advantages? Which has the most disadvantages?

4. **Communicate** Draw a flowchart that shows the role of the sun's energy in three alternative energy sources.

Prelab Discussion

Have students read the entire activity. Try to use the solar cooker at or near noon on a cloudless day. It will work faster if the air temperature is warm. Discuss the following points before beginning:

▶ What are some added ways to concentrate the heat in the shoe box? (You may wish to cover it with plastic wrap; you may also wish to place books under one end to angle it toward the sun.)

▶ Have students suggest a control that would test the effect of the sun's rays reflected by the aluminum foil.

Time 90 minutes   **Group** pairs

Materials

15 shoe boxes

10 m aluminum foil

15 long wooden skewers

15 hot dogs

scissors

Analysis

1. The temperature increased.
2. The sun
3. To reflect and concentrate the sun's rays
4. The foil lining causes more solar energy to reach the hot dog, decreasing the amount of time it takes to cook.

Conclusion

Conclusions depend on students' actual observations. Both direct incoming solar energy and reflected solar energy cooked the hot dog.

Everyday Application

Factors include air temperature, wind, season, time of day, latitude, and size and shape of the box.

Extension

Answers depend on the foods selected and actual observations. Because the cooking is done by radiation striking the surface of the food, students may see a connection between cooking time and relative surface area of the food.

Activity 24 *How do you make a solar hot-dog cooker?*

Skills Observe; Infer

Task 1 Prelab Prep
Collect the following items: shoe box, aluminum foil, scissors, long wooden skewer, and a hot dog.

Task 2 Data Record
Draw a table like the one shown. Record all of your observations in your table.

Table 24.1 Data Record

Time (Minutes)	Observations
10	
20	
30	
40	
50	
60	

Task 3 Procedure
1. Drape the foil inside the box so that it forms a concave shape as shown. Fold the edges of the foil over the top edges of the box to secure it in place. Make sure the shiny side of the foil faces up.
2. Make a small hole in the center of each end of the shoe box with the point of a pair of scissors. From the outside of the box, push the skewer through one of the holes.
3. Push the skewer through the length of the hot dog. Be sure the hot dog is centered on the skewer.
4. Push the skewer through the hole in the other end of the shoe box. The skewer should be firmly in place.
5. Put the shoe-box solar cooker in a sunny place. It needs to be in full sunlight for at least one hour.

6. Feel the hot dog every ten minutes and record your observations in your table.

Task 4 Analysis
1. What change did you observe in the temperature of the hot dog?
2. What was the source of the energy that caused this change?
3. What was the purpose of lining the box with aluminum foil?
4. What is the effect of the foil lining on the time required to cook the hot dog?

Task 5 Conclusion
Explain how your solar hot-dog cooker works. Identify the most important parts of the solar cooker.

Everyday Application

What factors affect how long it takes to cook a hot dog in a solar cooker? Suggest one or more ways to speed up the process.

Extension

Try cooking other kinds of food in your solar cooker. Identify foods that cook slower or faster than a hot dog. What do foods that cook at the same rate have in common?

MOTIVATE

STS Connection
Explain that since the Industrial Revolution in the nineteenth century, people have developed technologies that use—and waste—huge amounts of fossil fuels. In the United States alone, inefficient motors, lighting, and appliances waste nearly 75 percent of the energy used. Ask students to suggest how people can use technology to solve both energy waste and dependence on fossil fuels.

Writing Connection
Have students imagine they've been asked to speak to the Department of Energy. Department leaders want to hear the opinions of young Americans on the country's future energy use. Ask students to write the short speech they would make before department leaders. Tell them to identify two important points about energy that they want America's energy leaders to understand.

▼ **ACTIVITY**

Observing

Energy Map
Draw a diagram of your classroom. Label the places where energy is used. List some ways you or your school could save energy in that room. Share your list with the class.

SKILLS WARMUP

Table 24.2 Energy Sources

Renewable	Nonrenewable
Hydroelectric	Coal
Wind	Natural gas
Tides	Oil
Geothermal*	Uranium
Biomass	Oil shale
Ethanol/methanol†	Tar sands
Sunlight	

* Individual fields may run out
† Renewable when made from biomass

24.3 Energy Conservation Decisions

Objectives

▶ **Identify** three nonrenewable and three renewable sources of energy.

▶ **Analyze** the risks and benefits of four energy sources.

▶ **Infer** how conserving energy can affect natural resources.

▶ **Collect data** on personal energy conservation.

The United States has enough coal to last for several hundred years. What will happen to future generations when the coal supply runs out? Should the United States continue to rely on coal as a source of energy?

Someday you may be involved in making long-range energy decisions. There are several things you can do right now to conserve energy. You can save energy by turning off lights when they aren't needed or by taking a quick shower instead of a bath. Conserving energy is the cleanest, cheapest, and quickest way to stretch precious energy resources.

Nonrenewable and Renewable Energy

Energy sources not replaced by natural processes within the span of a person's lifetime are classified as **nonrenewable resources**. People are using fossil fuels at a rate that is thousands of times faster than the rate at which fossil fuels form. Although no one can predict exactly how long it will take, the world supply of coal, oil, and natural gas will eventually run out.

Natural resources replaced by ecological cycles or by natural chemical or physical processes are **renewable resources**. Look at Table 24.2. Solar energy is a renewable resource. It comes from nuclear fusion reactions in the sun's interior that will continue for billions of years. Hydroelectric power is also renewable. The energy of moving water is supplied by the natural water cycle that provides rain or snow. Which of the renewable energy sources listed are practical in your area?

Portfolio

Have students research the 1,300-kilometer Trans-Alaskan Pipeline. Ask them to draw a map of Alaska showing the route of the pipeline, the towns at either end of the pipeline, national parks and wildlife habitats, and bodies of water important to shipping Alaskan oil. Tell students to create a key for their maps. Have them keep the maps in their portfolios.

Cooperative Learning

Have the class work in two cooperative groups. Ask one group to explore the benefits of drilling for oil in Alaska's Brook Range or off the coast of California. Ask the other to explore the risks. Tell each group to gather information supporting their point of view and to organize the information into a class presentation. Each group can use photographs, drawings, maps, graphs, and charts.

Technology Risks and Benefits

Every energy technology or project has both risks and benefits. For example, oil companies wanted to build a gas pipeline from Alaska to the United States. Two benefits of the project were new jobs, and the availability of fuel where it was needed.

The project also carried risks. Drilling for oil in Alaska would upset the ecology of wilderness areas and displace wildlife. To pay for the project, oil companies were authorized to increase charges to their customers—before the pipeline was built. The cost of development is one kind of risk. A change in the environment is another kind of risk.

Risk-benefit analysis is used to evaluate the risks and benefits of a new technology. If a project carries more risks than benefits, it shouldn't be done. A technology is acceptable if the benefits outweigh the risks, and if consumers are willing to accept the risks.

SkillBuilder *Analyzing*

A Risk-Benefit Analysis

Imagine that you are in charge of an environmental-assessment group. Your group must decide whether or not a utility company should build a large dam and hydroelectric power plant on the Great Whale River in Quebec, Canada.

The plant is part of a $12.7 billion project that will generate 3,168 megawatts of electricity—enough to serve a city of 700,000 people. The project will create many needed jobs. The government says the project is essential to the economic growth of Quebec.

The project will reduce the flow of the Great Whale River by 85 percent. About 17,500 Native-Canadians who live in the wilderness area where the dam will be built will be affected. The supply of river fish, which is their main food source, will be greatly reduced. Also, the dam will flood their ancestral hunting grounds and destroy thousands of sacred sites.

1. List the benefits of building the hydroelectric power plant. Consider the benefits to people, the economy, and the environment. Rate each benefit as unimportant, important, or very important.

2. Use the same method to list and rate the risks to the people and the environment involved in building the power plant.

3. Compare your two lists. Do the benefits outweigh the risks? If not, are the people who will be affected the most by this project willing to accept the risks?

4. Use your risk-benefit analysis to make your decision.

Write a short report stating your decision about the power project. Be sure to include your reasons for making that decision.

Critical Thinking

Compare and Contrast Ask students if they use risk-benefit analysis to make decisions in their personal lives. Have them compare the technique they use to the one in the SkillBuilder. (Students should realize that they use risk-benefit analysis to make decisions; all sound decisions are made after weighing positive and negative consequences.)

SkillBuilder

Infer Have students read the analysis and infer benefits and risks not stated. An unstated benefit of economic growth might be improved health care. An unstated risk might be destroying the traditions of Native Canadians. Tell students to consider these ideas in their final analysis.

Answers

1. Students' lists may include providing energy, jobs, and a reservoir. Ratings will vary.

2. It will reduce the fish population, disturb hunting and sacred sites, and reduce river's flow by 85 percent. Specific ratings will vary.

3. Answers will vary, but students must realize that people will be able to vote on this project.

4. The risk-benefit analysis should be essential in making the final decision.

Emphasize that the report should include the decision and the reasons for it.

 **The Living Textbook: Physical Science Sides 1-4**

Chapter 17   Frame 03286
Renewable Resources (2 Frames)
Search: Step:

597

TEACH ▪ Continued

◆ Explore Visually

Have students study Figure 24.13. Ask:

▶ What three things can be done in the living room to conserve energy? (Cover windows to keep the room cool; turn off the TV set and lights when not in use; turn the thermostat down.)

▶ What four things could be done in the kitchen to save energy? (Turn off appliances not in use; let dishes air dry; use warm or cold water wash on clothes; wash only full loads of clothes and dishes; wash dishes by hand; cover windows to keep the room cool.)

▶ What are three ways to save energy in the bathroom? (Use a flow control on the shower; turn lights off when not in use; air dry clothes.)

◆ Portfolio

Have students compare their Energy Inventory journals that they started at the beginning of Section 24.1 against the picture on this page. Tell them to add any new energy uses they find.

Answer to In-Text Question

① **Accept all reasonable answers. Students might suggest specific ways of cutting down on hot water use, making sure electric lights and appliances are turned off when not in use, looking for places where warm air escapes from the home, maintaining and cleaning appliances.**

◆ Art Connection

Ask students to invent an energy-efficient home. Have them use what they know about passive solar energy, wind energy, conservation, and common living patterns to draw or describe the home in detail.

◆ Math Connection

Explain that the average American home uses the equivalent of 4,742 liters of oil a year. About half is used to heat rooms and water. The rest is used by refrigerators, air conditioners, lighting, and stoves. About half of this total energy use is waste. Ask students to calculate how many actual liters of oil are used to heat rooms and water. (1,185.5 liters)

Energy Conservation

Energy consumption in the United States can be divided among three main users—home, transportation, and industry. All three areas must be involved in reducing energy consumption.

Conservation is using less energy in order to preserve natural resources. It's important to use existing energy sources wisely while new sources and new technology are being developed. Using less fuel also protects other natural resources by reducing pollution.

Home Many energy conservation measures require only a change in personal or family habits. Look at Figure 24.13. What are some ways you can save energy at home? ①

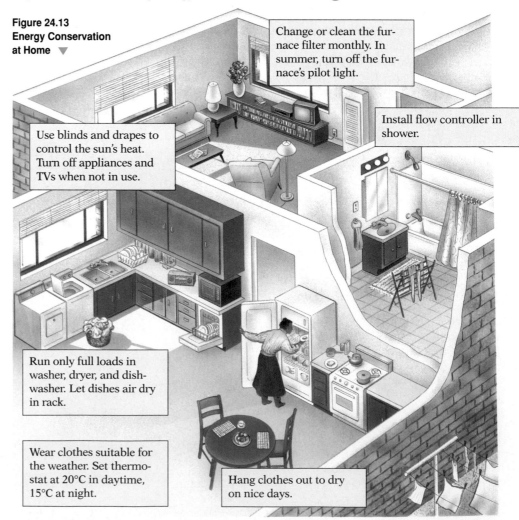

**Figure 24.13
Energy Conservation at Home** ▼

Change or clean the furnace filter monthly. In summer, turn off the furnace's pilot light.

Use blinds and drapes to control the sun's heat. Turn off appliances and TVs when not in use.

Install flow controller in shower.

Run only full loads in washer, dryer, and dishwasher. Let dishes air dry in rack.

Wear clothes suitable for the weather. Set thermostat at 20°C in daytime, 15°C at night.

Hang clothes out to dry on nice days.

Multicultural Perspectives

Explain that in China more than 270 million people use bicycles for everyday transportation. Other industrialized countries in which people rely heavily on bicycles for transportation include Japan, Denmark, and the Netherlands. Ask students to discuss ways that local governments could encourage more people to use bicycles.

Integrating the Sciences

Environmental Science Explain that in North America, the forest products industry uses its own wastes to generate about 75 percent of the energy it uses. The industry also cuts energy use through cogeneration: It uses steam energy to produce both electricity and pulp. Ask students to research renewable materials that can be used to power cogeneration systems.

Transportation Motor vehicles use 40 percent of the oil consumed in the United States. You can save some of this energy by riding a bicycle or walking whenever possible. Sharing rides with friends or using public transportation also saves energy. Automobile usage can be reduced by planning shopping trips in advance to combine errands. Eliminate automobile trips whenever possible.

Encourage your family to drive a small car that conserves fuel. Keep vehicles operating at peak efficiency with proper maintenance. Regular car tune-ups can improve mileage up to 10 percent. Clean engine filters, frequent oil changes, and proper tire pressure also increase gasoline efficiency.

Driving skills affect the fuel economy of a vehicle. Driving at moderate speeds saves energy. Most cars get about 20 percent more kilometers per liter at 88 km per hour than they do at 112 km per hour. Driving at a steady speed also saves energy. Sudden starts and stops and racing an engine waste gasoline.

Industry Industry is the biggest energy user. It also has the greatest potential for energy savings. Industries can save energy by doing many of the same things your family can do at home. For example, industries can add insulation and turn off lights.

The biggest energy savings in industry come from streamlining manufacturing processes and installing more efficient equipment. These changes are expensive to make. However, the investment can pay off in lower manufacturing costs.

Some industries are saving energy by burning wastes as fuel. Others recover waste heat from machinery and use it for space heating or other purposes. Industries can also conserve by a process called *cogeneration*. This process involves producing heat and electricity from the same fuel source. For example, power plants heat water as they operate. Instead of dumping the hot water, some power plants use it to heat their offices.

Many utilities are promoting energy conservation among their customers. Some utility companies will pay part of the bill when a business or a family makes improvements to save energy. By reducing demand for electric power, utility companies can save the cost of building and maintaining new power plants.

Figure 24.14 ▲
How does using public transportation save energy? ②

▼ ACTIVITY

Graphing

Energy Distribution

Make a circle graph to show the distribution of energy use for each of the following: Industry and business, 52%; Transportation, 26%; Homes, 22%. Label all the parts of your graph.

SKILLS WORKOUT

Skills WorkOut

To help students graph energy use, have them do the Skills WorkOut.

Answer Students' circle graphs will vary in design, size, use of color, and so on. Each graph should show three labeled sections. The section labeled for industry and business energy use should take up half the graph; the other sections should each take up approximately one-fourth.

Research

Explain to students that some electric vehicles are currently used in Europe and North America. These vans and cars run on batteries and give off no pollutants. Ask students to use recent periodicals to learn about the new developments in electric cars. Students can prepare a report or collage to share with the class.

Skills Development

Infer Have students think about cogeneration. Ask, How does producing electricity and heat from the same fuel source save money? (Companies can divide the cost of electricity and heat by the amount spent on only one fuel source.)

Portfolio

Tell students to review their Energy Inventory journals. On the last page of their journals, tell them to list things they plan to do to save energy.

Answer to In-Text Question

② Using public transportation saves gasoline because fewer cars are used.

TEACH ▪ Continued

Class Activity

Have students study and discuss Figure 24.15. Have each student bring one or two newspapers to class. They should stack the papers. Next, measure the stack. Ask students how tall the pine tree would be that produced this stack of paper. They can identify a local tree that is the same height. Discuss why recycling is important.

EVALUATE

WrapUp

Portfolio Ask students to write an essay describing life in the United States in 50 years if nonrenewable resources are used at the current rate. Ask them to include home, transportation, and industry in their descriptions.

Use Review Worksheet 24.3.

Decision Making

If you have classroom sets of *One-Minute Readings,* have students read Issue 58 "Energy: U.S. Consumption" on page 99. Discuss the questions.

Check and Explain

1. Nonrenewable—energy not replaced by natural processes in one lifetime; oil, gas, coal. Renewable—natural resources replaced constantly; solar, hydroelectric, and wind energy.

2. Check students' tables for reasonableness and evidence of weighing both sides.

3. Answers can include turning off lights and appliances, taking short showers instead of baths, using public transportation, and recycling.

4. Check students' answers for reasonableness.

Answer to In-Text Question
① It reuses our resources.

Cooperative Learning

Have students design an ad campaign encouraging people to recycle. Have the class work in four cooperative groups and assign one material—glass, plastic, aluminum, paper—to each group. Ask the groups to find statistics on the amount of their material that is wasted each day, month, and year and the amount of money and energy that can be saved through recycling. Have the groups meet and discuss their findings. Tell them to use the strongest information they found to produce a public service radio announcement and a public service poster advocating recycling. Encourage students to be persuasive.

Use Integrating Worksheet 24.3.

Figure 24.15 ▲
Each stack of newspapers represents a pine tree ten times its height. Explain why recycling is important. ①

Science and Society
Saving Energy by Recycling

An average family in the United States produces about 45 kg of trash every week! By recycling some of these materials instead of throwing them away, you can save energy and natural resources. Recycling also reduces pollution and the need for landfill space.

Recycling is any activity that keeps matter in use. One way to recycle is to find another use for a product. You can use discarded envelopes for phone messages or grocery lists, for example. Using products more than once for the same purpose is another form of recycling. Instead of throwing away old clothes, books, toys, or furniture, give them to someone who can use them.

One of the best ways to save energy is to take part in local recycling programs. Many communities have curbside pickup for items that can be recycled, such as aluminum cans, glass bottles, newspapers, and some plastics. In other places, you must take items to a collection center.

Each aluminum can you recycle saves the amount of energy in about 2 liters of gasoline. The energy you save by recycling a single glass bottle could light a 100-watt light bulb for four hours. Recycling paper saves about half the energy it takes to make paper from new materials. The results of saving paper are shown in Figure 24.15. What are some other ways you could recycle items instead of throwing them away?

Check and Explain

1. Explain the difference between nonrenewable and renewable resources. Identify three of each resource.

2. Make a table that compares the risks and benefits of developing one of the energy sources in this chapter. Which alternative is the most promising? Explain.

3. **Infer** List three ways you can conserve energy. How do these methods affect natural resources?

4. **Collect Data** Keep a record by listing all of the ways you conserve energy for one week. Organize your data into a table or chart.

Chapter 24 Review

Concept Summary

24.1 Generating and Using Electric Power

▶ Energy sources used to produce electricity are coal, oil, natural gas, moving water, and nuclear reactions.

▶ Electric power plants use mechanical energy to generate electric energy.

▶ High-voltage transmission lines carry electricity from a power plant over long distances to homes and industry.

24.2 Alternative Energy Technologies

▶ Solar power can be used to produce heat and electricity.

▶ Wind, geothermal steam, and the motion of the tides are alternative energy sources used to generate electricity.

▶ Dried organic material can be burned

as biomass fuel. Biomass fuels can be grown as crops or made from garbage.

▶ Synthetic fuels can be used in industry and automobiles instead of gasoline and other fuels made from oil.

24.3 Energy Conservation Decisions

▶ Nonrenewable resources aren't naturally replaced or regenerated in a person's lifetime. Renewable resources are easily replaced.

▶ Efforts to conserve energy can be made in business, industry, transportation, and at home.

▶ Risk-benefit analysis helps people to make better decisions about energy use by comparing the risks and benefits of an action.

Chapter Vocabulary

hydroelectric power (p. 586)	biomass (p. 591)	nonrenewable resources (p. 596)
fossil fuel (p. 586)	geothermal (p. 592)	renewable resources (p. 596)
solar cell (p. 590)		

Check Your Vocabulary

Use the vocabulary words above to complete the following sentences correctly.

1. Solar power can produce an electric current in a device called a(n) _____ .

2. Heat energy from hot magma beneath the earth's surface is _____ energy.

3. An energy source that is the remains of plants and animals that lived long ago and that changed over millions of years is a(n) _____ .

4. At a(n) _____ plant, water released through a dam turns a turbine that operates a generator.

5. Hydroelectric power, wind power, and solar power are examples of _____ energy sources.

6. Plant material and other organic matter used as fuel is called _____ .

7. Energy sources not replenished by natural biological, chemical, and physical processes are _____ energy sources.

Explain the differences between the words in each pair.

8. renewable, nonrenewable

9. geothermal, hydroelectric

10. fossil fuel, biomass

Write Your Vocabulary

Write sentences using the vocabulary words above. Show that you know what each word means.

Check Your Vocabulary

1. solar cell

2. geothermal

3. fossil fuel

4. hydroelectric power

5. renewable

6. biomass

7. nonrenewable

8. *Nonrenewable* energy sources are sources that are not replenished by natural biological, chemical, and physical processes, while *renewable* sources are constantly replenished by one of the above processes.

9. *Geothermal* energy is in the form of heat from molten rock below the earth's surface, while *hydroelectric* power is generated from moving water.

10. *Fossil* fuels are different from *biomass* in the age of the material: The organisms that have been converted to fossil fuels are very old, while biomass can be recently living material.

Write Your Vocabulary

Students' sentences should show that they know the meaning of each word as well as how to use it in a sentence.

Use Vocabulary Worksheet for Chapter 24.

Check Your Knowledge

1. Electricity is produced by converting solar energy into electrical energy; from generators turned by steam (from combustion of fossil fuels, geothermal energy, or the energy released in fission reactions); by water flowing downhill; and by wind.

2. Fossil fuels are substances created by the pressure and heat of layers of earth above buried animal and plant remains.

3. It is the electricity produced by generators turned by water falling over a dam.

4. Power station to step-up transformer to power grid/transmission lines to step-down transformer to house

5. The advantages include the large amount of energy stored in a small amount of fuel and the fact that nuclear plants do not produce air pollution. The disadvantages include the danger of accidents that release radioactive material, and the radioactive waste produced.

6. Geothermal power is produced when heat from molten rock heats ground water to create steam, used to turn turbines of generators.

7. Both take advantage of the energy of flowing water. However, a tidal power plant harnesses the energy of water flowing in and out with the tides, while hydroelectric power is generated by water flowing over a dam across a river.

8. It is important to develop alternative energy sources now because some day nonrenewable sources of energy will be used up.

9. Advantages: biomass contains a relatively large amount of energy, it can be converted into liquids and gases that burn, and it is easily replenished. Disadvantages: it requires that land be converted from food production, and it does not contain as much energy by volume as other energy sources.

10. turbine

11. limited

12. changes sunlight to electricity

13. biomass

Check Your Understanding

1. Paper, food scraps, wood

2. Thin-film solar cells are very inexpensive to produce.

3. Recycling saves energy because it takes less energy to produce some items from used items than it does to produce the same items from natural raw materials. Aluminum cans and glass bottles are two items that can be recycled with less energy than it takes to make them from raw materials.

4. a. It increases the amount of electricity produced.

   b. The reflectors are shaped so that the light is reflected from all points on the reflector to a single point.

   c. The heat can be used to make steam that is used to turn the turbines of a generator.

5. In a mountain location, solar energy would be the most likely source of heat and electricity. It is also possible that wind could be used to turn a windmill or a nearby stream could be used to turn a water wheel.

6. Risks/costs: too expensive, does not produce enough energy to meet needs, economic effects on traditional utilities who lose business. Benefits: solar energy does not pollute, is a renewable source, and could save money over the long term.

7. Student posters will vary. Each should imply some kind of inducement or incentive in its message.

Chapter 24 Review

Check Your Knowledge

Answer the following in complete sentences.

1. How is electricity produced?

2. What are fossil fuels? How are they formed?

3. What is hydroelectric power? How is it produced?

4. Trace the path of electricity from a power station to your home.

5. What are the advantages and disadvantages of nuclear power?

6. What is geothermal power? How is it produced?

7. How does a tidal power plant differ from a hydroelectric power plant? How are they similar?

8. Why is it important to develop alternative energy sources now?

9. What are two advantages to using biomass as an energy source? What are two possible disadvantages?

Choose the answer that best completes each sentence.

10. Some electric power plants use moving water or steam to turn a (power grid, turbine, circuit breaker, transformer).

11. Supplies of fossil fuels, such as coal and oil, are (unlimited, increasing, limited, widely available).

12. A solar cell (collects heat, changes sunlight to electricity, contains a generator, burns biomass).

13. Materials such as corncobs, sawdust, sewage, and manure are all forms of (fossil fuel, hydrogen, biomass, nuclear power).

Check Your Understanding

Apply the concepts you have learned to answer each question.

1. **Application** Identify three items in your home that could be used as biomass.

2. Explain the advantages of "thin-film" solar technology.

3. How does recycling save energy? Give two examples.

4. **Mystery Photo** The photograph on page 582 shows solar reflectors used to concentrate light from the sun. The energy from the concentrated sunlight is eventually converted into electric energy.

   a. Why is concentrating the sunlight important?

   b. How does the design of the reflectors work to concentrate light from the sun?

   c. What is another way energy from concentrated sunlight can be converted to electricity?

5. **Application** Imagine that you are an architect designing a vacation home. The home is to be built in a mountain area where there aren't any electric power lines. Describe how you would supply the home with heat, hot water, and electricity.

6. Prepare a risk-benefit analysis for converting your home or school to a solar-heating system from its present heating system.

7. Design a poster that motivates and shows people how they can save energy at home.

Develop Your Skills

1. a. autos, home heating, air conditioning
   b. Drive less, keep the air conditioner temperature in the home at 23°C in the summer and the heater thermostat at 20°C in the winter.

2. 10 kg of corn chips; in addition to the energy from the sun required to grow the corn, energy must be expended to process and package the product.

3. a. industry
   b. Metal processing; Recycling would be one solution.
   c. 74% of 25% of the total energy usage is consumed by highway vehicles. This is 19% of the total energy used. If all highway vehicles were cars, then one-half of 19%, or 9.5%, of total energy consumption would be saved.

Make Connections

1.

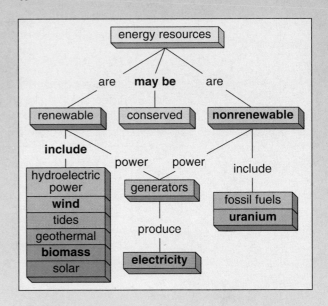

2. Student reports will vary. The crisis was caused by an embargo placed by the Organization of Petroleum Exporting Countries (OPEC), which drastically reduced the supply of petroleum entering the United States, driving up the price of gasoline and other fuels.

3. Student reports will vary. Note critical contrasts and comparisons with the energy used to meet today's needs.

4. Student plans and reports will vary, but should be based on needs specific to individual homes.

Develop Your Skills

1. Interpret Data The table below contains data about nonindustrial energy use in the United States.

Nonindustrial Energy Use

Transportation		Home Use	
Autos	29%	Heating and air conditioning	29%
Trucks	13%	Water heating	6%
Air conditioning	4%	Appliances	6%
Other	9%	Lighting	4%

a. What are the biggest nonindustrial energy users?

b. Based on the table, what actions could the average person take that would result in the greatest energy savings?

2. Infer Which do you think requires more energy to produce: 10 kg of corn on the cob or 10 kg of corn chips? Explain.

3. Data Bank Use the information on page 642 to answer the following questions.

a. What is the largest overall energy user in the United States?

b. What industrial process uses the most energy? What could be done to reduce the amount of energy used for this purpose?

c. About what percentage of the total energy could be saved if people drove their cars only half as much?

Make Connections

1. Link the Concepts Below is a concept map showing how some of the main concepts in this chapter link together. Only part of the map is filled in. Finish the map, using words and ideas from the chapter.

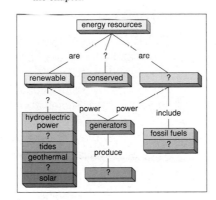

2. Science and Social Studies Research the energy crisis of the 1970s. Use articles from magazines and newspapers to find out why the energy crisis took place and how people felt about it. Report your findings to the class.

3. Science and Literature Many novels and short stories describe life in the United States before electric power. Read such a novel or story, and write a report about it. Discuss how the people in the story met their energy needs for heat, light, transportation, and other uses.

4. Science and You Develop an energy-savings plan for your home. Try the plan for one week, and write a report about your experiences.

CHAPTER 25

Overview

This chapter focuses on chemical technology. The first section identifies petroleum formation, sources, and refining processes. The second section includes a description of hydrocarbons and their properties and uses. It also discusses properties of petrochemical products such as plastics and synthetic fibers. The third section describes the processes used to make metals, ceramics, glass, and various composite materials. How technology affects the environment is presented in the last section.

Advance Planner

▶ Obtain copies of Helen Frankenthaler's paintings for TE page 611.

▶ Collect magazines for TE page 611.

▶ Supply small jars, self-locking thick plastic bags, safety goggles, while glue solution, and borax solution for SE Activity 25, page 620.

Skills Development Chart

Sections	Classify	Collect Data	Communicate	Hypothesize	Infer	Measure	Observe	Research
25.1 Skills WarmUp				●				
25.2 Skills WarmUp	●							
Skills WorkOut							●	
Consider This			●					●
25.3 Skills WarmUp	●							
Historical Notebook			●					●
Skills WorkOut		●						
Activity			●		●	●	●	
25.4 Skills WarmUp	●							

Individual Needs

▶ **Limited English Proficiency Students** Tape-record the definitions and pronunciations of the chapter's boldface terms. Tell students which figures and definitions in the text illustrate each term. Have them use the tape recorder to listen to the information about each term. Have students define the terms using their own words. Have them make their own tape recordings of their definitions. They can use this tape to review important chapter concepts.

▶ **At-Risk Students** Ask students to name five of their favorite possessions that involve technology. Have them write the name of each one at the top of a page in their portfolio. Have them list the main types of materials used to make each one, as covered in the chapter: plastics, metals, ceramics, glass, and composites. They should also add any natural materials, such as wood or cotton. Have them write a sentence or two for each material that identifies the material and explains why its properties are useful for that object.

▶ **Gifted Students** Ask students to create a technology timeline for metals, ceramics, glass, and plastics. Timelines should include the discovery or first use of the technologies, revolutionary uses for the rnaterials, important advances and developments, and so on. Encourage them to illustrate their timelines with photographs or drawings. Have them share their timelines with the class and prepare a short oral report about the items shown on the timeline.

Resource Bank

▶ **Bulletin Board** Place the title *Earth and Us: A Successful Team* at the top of the bulletin board. Underneath the title place three headings: *Air, Water,* and *Land.* Encourage students to write descriptions and contribute drawings, photographs, and articles about new technologies. The technologies might directly improve the quality of air, water, or land or they may replace older, more polluting technologies. They should also include stories about people's successful efforts to improve environmental quality.

Section	Core	Standard	Enriched	Section	Core	Standard	Enriched
25.1 Petroleum Fuels pp. 605–608				**25.3 Materials Science** pp. 614–620			
Section Features Skills WarmUp, p. 605	●	●	●	**Section Features** Skills WarmUp, p. 614 / Historical Notebook, p. 617 / Skills WorkOut, p. 618 / Activity, p. 620	●●●	●●●●	●●●●
Blackline Masters Review Worksheet 25.1 / Skills Worksheet 25.1 / Integrating Worksheet 25.1	●	●	●	**Blackline Masters** Review Worksheet 25.3 / Skills Worksheet 25.3	●	●	●
Overhead Blackline Transparencies Overhead Blackline Master 24 and Student Worksheet		●	●	**Color Transparencies** Transparency 87		●	●
Color Transparencies Transparency 86	●	●	●	**25.4 Technology and the Environment** pp. 621–628			
Laboratory Program Investigation 44	●	●	●	**Section Features** Skills WarmUp, p. 621	●	●	●
25.2 Petrochemical Products pp. 609–613				**Blackline Masters** Review Worksheet 25.4 / Skills Worksheet 25.4 / Integrating Worksheet 25.4 / Vocabulary Worksheet 25	●●●●	●●●	●●
Section Features Skills WarmUp, p. 609 / Skills WorkOut, p. 612 / Consider This, p. 612	●●	●●	●●	**Ancillary Options** *One-Minute Readings,* pp. 57–58, 62–64	●	●	●
Blackline Masters Review Worksheet 25.2 / Reteach Worksheet 25.2 / Integrating Worksheet 25.2	●●●	●●●	●	**Color Transparencies** Transparency 88	●	●	●

Bibliography

The following resources can be used for teaching the chapter. See page T-46 for supplier codes.

Library Resources

Bortz, Fred. Superstuff. New York: Franklin Watts, 1990.

Dolan, Edward F., and Margaret Scariano. Nuclear Waste: The 10,000 Year Challenge. New York: Franklin Watts, 1990.

Fogel, Barbara R. Energy Choices for the Future. New York: Franklin Watts, 1985.

Gay, Kathlyn. Garbage and Recycling. Hillside, NJ: Enslow Publishers, Inc., 1991.

Herda, D. J., and Margaret L. Madden. Energy Resources: Towards a Renewable Future. New York: Franklin Watts, 1991.

Johnson, Rebecca L. The Greenhouse Effect. Minneapolis, MN: Lerner Publications Company, 1990.

Lee, Sally. The Throwaway Society. New York: Franklin Watts, 1990.

Pack, Janet. Fueling the Future. Chicago, IL: Children's Press, Inc., 1992.

Technology Resources

Internet

PLANETDIARY at *http://www.planetdiary.com*
● Learn more about the atmosphere and about oil spills by clicking on *Phenomena Backgrounders.*

Software

Air Pollution. Mac, Dos. ESI.
Our Ozone Crisis. Mac, Dos, Win. ESI.
Water Pollution. Mac, Dos. ESI.

CD-ROMs

Interactive Earth. SFAW.

Laserdiscs

Living Textbook. (See barcodes on pages in this chapter.) Optical Data.

Videos

Pollution: The World at Risk. NGSES.

Audio-Visual Resources

Pollution: Problems and Prospects. Filmstrips. NGSES.
This World of Energy II. Filmstrips. NGSES.

Writing Connection

Ask students to imagine they're walking through a Middle Eastern bazaar. They've just taken a photograph of colorful, old ceramic bowls. Have them describe the appearance of the bowls, focusing on their color. They can try to imagine where the colors that were applied to the bowls came from.

Multicultural Perspectives

The patterns and styles of Native-American pottery pieces identify the tribes that made them. These patterns are used by archaeologists to trace the ancestry, location, and influence of different tribal groups. Ask students to do research on Native-American pottery styles and prepare a poster for classroom display.

Introducing the Chapter

Have students read the description of the photograph. Ask if they agree or disagree with the description.

Directed Inquiry

Have students study the photograph. Ask the following questions:

► What does this photograph show? (Students should recognize pottery.)

► How do you think this pottery was made? (Students should say that it was shaped from damp clay, then dried, and baked or fired in a hot oven.)

► What do you think would happen to the pottery if it were not fired? (It would not hold water and would soften when wet.)

► Do you think this is an old or a new technology? (Students should say it is old. In fact, it is one of the oldest of human technologies.)

► What does pottery have to do with the subject of this chapter? (It is an example of chemical technology because heat acting on substances in the clay and glazes changes them into different substances and makes the pottery waterproof.)

Chapter Vocabulary

acid rain	matrix
air pollution	metallurgy
ceramic	petrochemical
composite	petroleum
global warming	polymer
greenhouse effect	thermal pollution

Chapter 25 Chemical Technology

What do you see?

❝This is a picture of a ceramic bowl and plate on a table. The plate and bowl were probably shaped by hand out of wet clay and then glazed, baked, and painted. The pattern was carefully designed and painted onto the bowl and dish. These are no doubt ancient artifacts of some old civilization.❞

Katie Sherwin
Bethlehem Central
Middle School
Delmar, New York

To find out more about the photograph, look on page 630. As you read this chapter, you will learn about chemical technology.

Integrating the Sciences

Earth Science Explain that scientists think that petroleum and natural gas are formed in the same chemical reaction. The pressure and heat of sedimentary rock layers cause a substance called *kerogen* to form. Kerogen separates into oil and natural gas when heated. Since oil and gas are less dense than water, water trapped in underground rocks pushes the oil and gas up through cracks in the earth.

Themes in Science

Energy Remind students that changes in heat energy bring about phase changes in matter. Encourage students to identify examples of these changes.

Section Objectives
For a list of section objectives, see the Student Edition page.

Skills Objectives
Students should be able to:

Hypothesize why oil and water have different properties.

Interpret Data shown on the diagram of a fractionating tower.

Vocabulary
petroleum

25.1 Petroleum Fuels

Objectives

▶ **Identify** the source of petroleum.

▶ **Explain** how petroleum is refined.

▶ **Compare** and **contrast** the properties of various petroleum hydrocarbons.

▶ **Interpret** a diagram on the activity in a fractionating tower.

▼ **ACTIVITY**

Hypothesizing

Oil and Water Don't Mix

You know that oil floats on top of water. List five other ways that oil and water are different. Based on what you already know, write a hypothesis that explains why the two substances have different properties.

SKILLS WARMUP

Imagine filling the gas tank of a car with prehistoric sunlight! The gasoline that flows into a car's tank doesn't look like sunlight. However, gasoline contains energy that once was light. The light energy came from nuclear fusion reactions that occurred in the sun.

Light energy was absorbed by plants, algae, and microscopic animals. Through the process of photosynthesis, some living things converted light energy into stored chemical energy. When microscopic ocean organisms died, their buried remains still contained chemical energy. Over millions of years, some of the dead organisms were changed into crude oil.

Oil and Gas Formation

Crude oil and natural gas formed from the bodies of microscopic ocean organisms. These organisms had skeletons made of silica and soft parts made up of organic compounds. When ancient ocean organisms died, their remains often settled on the ocean floor. Similar organisms can be seen in Figure 25.1.

Clay and mud sediments also settled on the ocean floor. These sediments buried and compacted the remains of the organisms. Over time, the weight of many layers of sediment produced pressure and heat that changed the organic material into crude oil, or **petroleum**. Petroleum, a greenish-black oily liquid, is a mixture of hydrocarbons. Petroleum is usually found along with natural gas. Natural gas, a mixture of flammable gases, is mostly methane (CH_4).

Figure 25.1
These microscopic organisms, called diatoms, float freely in the ocean. They get energy from sunlight by the process of photosynthesis. ▼

MOTIVATE

Skills WarmUp

To help students understand petroleum fuels, have them do the Skills WarmUp.
Answer Students will probably mention that oil is less dense than water, pours more slowly than water, and is slipperier than water; that water can dissolve more things than oil can, and that water and oil will not form a solution, only an emulsion when an emulsifier is added. Students should hypothesize that oil and water have different properties because of their molecular structures.

Prior Knowledge

Gauge how much students know about petroleum fuels by asking the following questions:

▶ Where does gasoline come from?

▶ What does crude oil look like?

▶ How is petroleum like coal? How are coal and petroleum different?

TEACH

Discuss

Ask students to look at Figure 25.2. Remind them that nonporous rock lies on top of oil traps and seals them like a lid. Ask:

▶ How would you describe a non-porous rock? (The rock has no openings for oil to seep through.)

▶ What do you think would happen to the oil if the cap rock were porous? (Oil migrates into surrounding rock layers.)

Critical Thinking

Find Causes Have students study Figure 25.2. to notice where natural gas collects. Ask, Why would natural gas collect in a pocket above the petroleum? (Natural gas is less dense than petroleum, so the gas would rise to the top.)

Infer Ask students to study Figure 25.3 to notice where petroleum reserves are located. Ask, Where do you think it would be most expensive to drill for oil? Explain. (Offshore; building a rig, housing workers, shipping in equipment, food, and other supplies would be expensive.)

Integrated Learning

Use Integrating Worksheet 25.1.

Answer to In-Text Question

① **Coastal areas, offshore areas, the Great Plains, and the Ohio Valley area**

**The Living Textbook:
Physical Science Sides 1-4**

Chapter 16   Frame 02672
Stratigraphy (1 Frame)
Search:

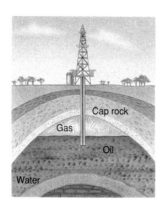

Figure 25.2 ▲
The amount of natural gas in a trap varies. Small amounts of natural gas are usually burned off as waste.

Petroleum Deposits

Recall that hydrocarbons are organic molecules that contain only hydrogen and carbon. The carbon atoms are attached to other carbon atoms to form long or short chains. Petroleum is a mixture of long-chain and short-chain hydrocarbons. Hydrocarbons in petroleum include gasoline, kerosene, wax, and lubricating oil.

Petroleum deposits often form in "traps," like the one shown in Figure 25.2. A trap is a geologic structure of porous and nonporous rock. A nonporous rock, such as shale, is called a cap rock because it lies on top of the trap. Because the petroleum can't flow through the cap rock, it collects in the lower layers of porous rock.

By drilling a hole through the cap rock, the petroleum can be removed from the trap. A well-pipe is inserted through the hole into the oil-saturated rock. Pressure caused by underground water pushes the petroleum toward the surface through the well pipe. If there isn't enough water pressure, pumps draw the petroleum up to the surface.

Some natural gas is dissolved in the liquid petroleum. Often the natural gas collects in a pocket above the petroleum deposit. The map in Figure 25.3 shows the locations of known petroleum and natural gas deposits in the United States.

Natural gas and
petroleum fields

Figure 25.3 ▲
What kind of land surfaces have oil deposits? Use an atlas to help you find the answer. ①

Social Studies Connection

From the 1950s to the 1980s, oil changed the way people lived in the United States. Improved roads, inexpensive cars, and cheap fuel enabled urbanites to move to the suburbs. Between 1950 and 1976, suburban population grew by 85 million. In turn, shopping centers in the suburbs grew from 8 in 1946 to 20,000 in the 1980s. Ask students to list aspects of their towns shaped by the car and availability of inexpensive gas.

STS Connection

Explain that petrochemical engineers use a process called *cracking* to make high-quality gasoline. In this process, heat and pressure are used to weaken the molecular bonds of heavy fractions. The molecules crack, or break, into simpler molecules that form lighter fractions. These lighter fractions produce high-quality or high-octane gasoline that burns smoothly.

Directed Inquiry

Have students read the page and study Figure 25.4. Ask:

▶ What does the fractional distillation process of petroleum do? (Separates crude oil into groups of hydrocarbons with similar properties)

▶ What is each group of hydrocarbons called? (A fraction)

▶ Heated crude oil is piped into a fractionating tower. What happens inside the tower? (The hydrocarbons vaporize, rise, and condense, or become liquid at different temperature levels. Pipes carry the different liquids to separate holding tanks.)

▶ What gases are piped from the tower? (Methane, propane, and butane)

▶ At what temperature range is most gasoline obtained? (0°C to 200°C)

▶ What fraction condenses between 180°C to 270°C? (Kerosene and solvents)

▶ From what temperature range is heating oil and diesel fuel obtained? (260°C to 370°C)

▶ Which fraction is the densest? (Asphalt and other residues drained off the bottom at temperatures over 460°C.)

Petroleum Refining

Petroleum contains many different kinds of hydrocarbons. A process called *fractional distillation* separates hydrocarbons with similar properties into groups. Each group of petroleum hydrocarbons is called a fraction.

Pumps transport petroleum into the bottom of a fractionating tower. At the bottom, which is the hottest part of the tower, most of the hydrocarbons vaporize and begin to rise. As the vapor rises, it starts to cool. Each fraction condenses, or cools to a liquid, within a certain temperature range. The temperature ranges are shown in Figure 25.4. As a result, each fraction condenses at a different height in the tower. As each fraction becomes liquid, pipes carry it from the tower to holding tanks.

Figure 25.4
A fractionating tower refines crude oil. Which fractions do you use every day? ▼ ②

Answer to In-Text Question

② Answers will vary, but should include gasoline, oils, and greases that enable cars and buses to run.

Below 0°C
Methane and other gaseous fractions are piped from the tower. The fractions are cooled to liquids and used as fuel or in the chemical industry.

Fractionating Tower

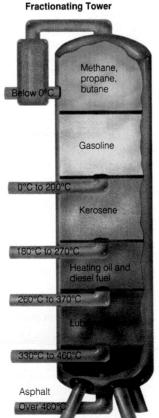

Methane, propane, butane — Below 0°C

Gasoline

0°C to 200°C

Kerosene

180°C to 270°C

Heating oil and diesel fuel

260°C to 370°C

Lub

330°C to 460°C

Asphalt — Over 460°C

260°C to 370°C
This gas-oil fraction is processed into heating oil and diesel fuel. Some of these hydrocarbons are also processed into gasoline.

0°C to 200°C
This fraction of petroleum contains hydrocarbons that are processed into gasoline. Gasoline accounts for nearly half of all petroleum products.

330°C to 460°C
This fraction includes lubricating oils and greases that are used to decrease friction in the moving parts of machinery.

180°C to 270°C
Kerosene and solvents form this fraction. Kerosene is mixed with gasoline to make jet fuel. Solvents are used in industry.

Over 460°C
Asphalt and other heavy residues remain as liquids and are drained off. Asphalt is used in roofing materials and to pave roads.

 The Living Textbook: Physical Science Sides 1-4

Chapter 16   Frame 02669
Fractional Distillation (1 Frame)
Search:

EVALUATE

WrapUp

Reinforce Discuss the cycle of energy changes starting with the sun and microscopic organisms, and ending with the burning of gasoline in a car. Talk about why petroleum is a nonrenewable resource. Students may want to make a diagram showing the cycle.

Use Review Worksheet 25.1.

Check and Explain

1. Microscopic ocean organisms die, settle on the ocean floor, and are buried under mud and clay sediments. The weight of the overlaying sediments produces pressure and heat that change the organisms into petroleum.

2. Heat causes petroleum to vaporize, which is part of the process of separating hydrocarbons with similar properties.

3. Asphalt is a heavy fraction used for roofing and paving streets; heating and lubricating fractions are lighter and can be burned for heat or used to decrease friction on moving machinery parts.

4. Lubricating oils and greases; methane

Answers to In-Text Questions

① The earth will have no petroleum reserves left. Other energy sources will have to be used.

② In 2060, the needle will point to "E."

**The Living Textbook:
Physical Science Sides 1-4**

Chapter 16   Frame 02670
Fractions of Oil Data (1 Frame)
Search:

⊞ *Math Connection*

Explain to students that the United States has 25.9 billion barrels of oil reserves and produces about 7.6 million barrels of oil a day. The United States uses about 6.3 billion barrels of oil a year. Ask students to calculate the annual oil shortfall in the United States. (About 3.5 billion barrels) Ask students how long it would take to deplete U.S. oil reserves if we did not import oil. (About 7 1/2 years)

⊞ *Social Studies Connection*

In the 1970s, the United States bought nearly one-third of its oil from the Middle East. In 1973, the Organization of Petroleum Exporting Countries (OPEC) was formed. OPEC is a group of 13 nations that depend on oil exports. In the United States, gas prices jumped from about 35 cents to $2 a gallon. Ask students to research the impact of oil prices on the auto industry in the United States.

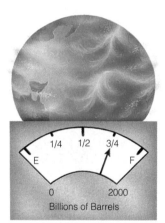

Earth's Fuel Gauge

Figure 25.5 ▲

Read the gauge showing the amount of petroleum remaining on the earth. What happens when it registers "Empty"? ①

🜂 Science and Society *Petroleum Reserves*

How can you tell if a car is low on gas? The gas gauge indicates how much fuel is in the gas tank. When the needle points to "F," the fuel tank holds its maximum amount of fuel. As the engine uses fuel, the needle moves toward "E." Soon it's time to refill the tank.

Suppose you were to use a gauge to show how much petroleum the earth has in reserve. What would the gauge show? To construct such a gauge, you need to know two things: how much petroleum was in the earth when its tank was "full" and how much of this petroleum has been used.

An optimistic estimate of the earth's total petroleum reserve suggests that at one time there were about 2,000 billion barrels. Of this amount, only half has been discovered. About 500 billion barrels of petroleum are already used up. Observable geologic structures suggest that 1,000 billion barrels of petroleum still remain undiscovered. Environmental protection laws prohibit tapping some of the remaining reserves. Some undiscovered reserves may be located on protected land or water. Some reserves are too deep in the earth, near expensive real estate, or not large enough to be profitable.

If you include both the known and the possible petroleum reserves, "F" on your gauge would equal about 2,000 billion barrels of petroleum. If you subtract the 500 billion barrels that have been used, the needle would point to about "3/4" full. About 20 billion barrels of petroleum are extracted from the ground each year. At this rate, the needle on your gauge will point to a little over "1/2" by the year 2010. Where will the needle point to in 2060? ②

Check and Explain

1. How is petroleum formed?

2. Why is heat important for refining petroleum?

3. **Compare and Contrast** How do the uses of asphalt differ from those of heating oil or lubricating oil?

4. **Interpret Data** Look at the fractionating tower on page 607. Which substances condense at the highest temperatures? The lowest temperatures?

Themes in Science

Scale and Structure Explain to students that the arrangements of electrons in hydrocarbon molecules determine the chemical properties of petrochemicals. Different chemical reactions cause molecules to form different monomers and polymers.

Integrating the Sciences

Chemistry Explain that monomers are small molecules of carbon, hydrogen, nitrogen, and oxygen atoms. In some cases, monomers have atoms of sulfur, silicon, chlorine, and fluorine. Point out that some polymer chains may have more than one million monomer links.
Use Integrating Worksheet 25.2.

Section Objectives
For a list of section objectives, see the Student Edition page.

Skills Objectives
Students should be able to:

Classify items made of petroleum and other substances.

Observe which synthetic fabrics are used to make clothing.

Make a Model of the arrangement of polymers in synthetic fiber.

Vocabulary
petrochemical, polymer

25.2 Petrochemical Products

Objectives

▶ **List** examples of products made from petrochemicals.

▶ **Identify** the characteristics of a polymer

▶ **Compare** and **contrast** the properties of plastics and synthetic fibers.

▶ **Make a model** of the arrangement of molecules in a synthetic fiber.

▼ **ACTIVITY**

Classifying

Petroleum Products

Make two lists. First, list six common items that are made from petroleum. Next, list six items that aren't made from petroleum. Add or subtract items from your lists as you learn more in this chapter.

SKILLS WARMUP

What does the sole of your sneaker have in common with a plastic chair, nylon fabric, antifreeze, paint, and the ink on this page? Like the items in Figure 25.6, all of these materials are made from petroleum! Recall that petroleum is made up of groups, or fractions, that contain different hydrocarbons. Some fractions, such as fuel oil and gasoline, can be used without being broken down further. Other fractions are combined with various chemical substances to produce synthetic materials. Synthetic materials and chemical substances produced from petroleum are called **petrochemicals.**

Properties of Petrochemicals

Recall that hydrocarbon molecules can be broken apart and rejoined to form petrochemicals with different properties. Dyes, plastics, synthetic fibers, and rubber substitutes are petrochemicals with complex structures. They are formed only by controlled chemical reactions.

Plastics and synthetic fibers are made of chains of many small molecules. Each small molecule is called a *monomer*. A chain of linked monomers forms a large molecule called a **polymer**. Each polymer may contain hundreds or thousands of monomers.

The properties of each petrochemical are due to its molecular structure and composition. For example, hard plastics contain a rigid framework of polymers. Plastics that stretch contain "bunched up" polymers that lengthen when pulled. Fibers contain polymers that run in the same direction and can slide past each other.

Figure 25.6
The nylon fibers of the fanny pack and the paint in the bucket are made from petroleum. What other things that you use are made from petroleum? ▼ ③

MOTIVATE

Skills WarmUp

To help students understand petrochemical products, have them do the Skills WarmUp.
Answer Answers will vary. Students will probably list liquids, such as motor oil, gasoline, and kerosene, and materials, such as synthetic fabrics and plastics.

Misconceptions

Students may think that petroleum is used only to make fuels, such as gasoline. They may underestimate the number of other products that come from petroleum. Explain that petrochemical products include fabrics, soaps, packaging, and computer parts, to name a few.

Answer to In-Text Question

③ **Answers include plastic products, such as combs, portable radios, pens, and auto parts.**

The Living Textbook:
Physical Science Sides 1-4

Chapter 16   Frame 02671
Products from Crude Oil (1 Frame)
Search:

609

Directed Inquiry

Have students read the text and study the photographs on this page. Ask the following questions:

▶ What are the properties of polystyrene? (Light weight, low density)

▶ Which object serves as a model of molecules in plastics? Why? (The chain of paper clips, because it represents linked monomers that make up polymers.)

▶ What are the properties of PVC plastics? (Strong, rigid, heat resistant)

Skills Development

Classify List the following plastic products on the board and have students identify the kind of plastic used in the product. Hint: Tell students to think about the properties of each type of plastic and identify several uses. Plastic pipe (PVC); plastic wire insulation (polystyrene); plastic mug (PVC); thin plastic dispenser cup (polystyrene); imitation leather (PVC)

Ancillary Options

If you are using CEPUP modules in your classroom for additional hands-on activities, experiments, and exercises, have students do Activities one through eight in *Plastics in Our Lives.*

Enrich

Use Enrich Worksheet 25.2.

Answer to Link

1. polyethylene terephthalate
2. high-density polyethylene
3. polyvinyl chloride
4. low-density polyethylene
5. polypropylene
6. polystyrene
7. all other resins and layered materials

Plastics are sorted by type before they are recycled. Many plastics are incompatible and if mixed will yield a low-quality recycled material.

Language Arts Connection

Have students find the meaning and source of the word *plastic.* (From the Greek *plastikos,* meaning "able to be shaped") Then ask students to suggest how the word describes the objects on this page.

Social Studies Connection

Explain that early phonograph records were made from natural substances like tree resin that had properties similar to plastic. Point out that celluloid was discovered in the 1860s. It was the first widely used plastic material and is used today to make film and table-tennis balls.

Plastics

Dozens of objects in your home and school are made from plastic. Some items contain many different plastics. For example, a telephone has a base and receiver made from a hard, shock-resistant plastic. The coiled wires that connect the receiver and base are covered with a flexible plastic that can uncoil and then return to its coiled shape. A third kind of plastic covers the wires that connect the base to the wall jack.

Air injected into plastic makes a soft and pliable foam. Artificial sponges are made of plastic foam with an open-cell structure that can hold water. Plastics with a closed-cell structure are stiff and hold very little water.

Polymers

All plastics are made from polymers. In a polymer, monomer units are connected in a chain. What represents the monomers in this model of a polymer? Plastics like those in the sandal are classified by the kind of polymer from which they are made. ▼

PVC Plastics ▲

Acetylene and chlorine gas combine to form a monomer called vinyl chloride. Vinyl chloride monomers join together to form the polymer called polyvinyl chloride, or PVC. PVC is a strong, rigid, heat-resistant plastic used to make many useful products. Cups, dishes, pipes, rain gutters, and rainwear are PVC products.

Polystyrene Plastics

Acetylene and benzene combine to form the monomer called styrene. When styrene monomers join together, they form polystyrene, a lightweight, low-density plastic. Water absorbed by a diver's wet suit, which is made of polystyrene, is kept warm by the diver's body. The diver is kept warm by the suit.

▼

Synthetic Fibers

The polymers that make up synthetic fibers, such as nylon, rayon, and polyester, are long, straight chains of monomers. The chains line up next to each other in a side-by-side arrangement. Bonding forces between neighboring chains keep the polymers close together. However, the polymers can slide past each other. This sliding action produces a long, thin arrangement of molecules called a strand or fiber.

You can see the strands that make up nylon in Figure 25.7. The strands can be produced in different thicknesses and woven together in various ways to produce many kinds of nylon fabric. For example, nylon is used to make a stretchable fabric for stockings. Thin strands of nylon can be tightly woven to make fabrics that are wind-resistant and water-repellent. Unlike natural fibers, synthetic fibers like nylon don't break down easily.

Figure 25.7
The petrochemical liquids in the beaker combine to make a polymer that forms a nylon fiber. Which items owe their brilliant color to petrochemical dyes? ▼ ①

Dyes

Some petrochemicals add color to clothing, cosmetics, and other products. These colorful chemicals are called dyes. Until the 1850s, most dyes came from plants or animals. The blue dye called indigo was made from plants. The dye called royal purple came from shellfish. Today most dyes are made from petrochemicals.

Petrochemical dyes offer several advantages over natural dyes. Petrochemical dyes have a consistent color and are cheap to produce. In addition, petrochemical dyes have a wider range of color, and work on a wider variety of materials than natural dyes do.

Pharmaceuticals

In industrial nations like the United States, many drugs, or pharmaceuticals, are made from petrochemicals. For example, the active ingredient in aspirin was once extracted from the bark of willow trees. Today this active ingredient is manufactured from coal tar.

TEACH ▪ *Continued*

Skills WorkOut

To help students observe clothing labels for cleaning suggestions, have them do the Skills WorkOut.
Answer Answers will vary, but will probably include rayon, nylon, and cotton/polyester blends. Most synthetic fabrics are machine washable and can be dried in a dryer.

Research

Ask students to use references to learn how solvents can harm their health. Have students list three solvents and the physical damage they can cause.

Consider This

Research Ask students to research biodegradable plastics in order to find out more about photodegradable plastics and plastics that degrade because they contain substances, such as cornstarch additives and oxidizing chemicals.
Think About It Using recyclable plastic would use less of the world's petroleum reserves.
Write About It Be sure students give reasons that support the position they choose.

Integrating the Sciences

Environmental Science Explain that petrochemical solvents are partly responsible for buildings becoming "sick," or filled with indoor pollutants. Explain that chemicals used in household cleaners, polishes, paints and thinners, varnishes, spot removers, and other products pollute the air. Some irritate the respiratory organs. Others may be cancer causing.

Tell students that there are several ways to keep the air inside a home clean. One is to keep fresh air flowing into the building so pollutants don't build up to dangerous levels. Houseplants can also rid the air of some toxins. Ask students to suggest other ways to reduce indoor air pollution.

▼ ACTIVITY

Observing

Washable?

Look at clothing labels to see what synthetic fabrics they contain. Make a list of synthetic fabrics worn by the entire class. Which fabrics are the most common? What are the manufacturer's suggestions for cleaning each kind of fabric?

SKILLS WORKOUT

Solvents

Have you ever tried to clean out a brush that contained enamel paint, or fingernail polish? If so, you know that these substances don't wash out with soap and water. To remove materials that won't dissolve in water, such as oil paint or lacquer, you need to use a petrochemical solvent. When you write with a felt-tip marker, the odor you smell is that of the petrochemical solvent used to thin the ink. Some kinds of petrochemical solvents are paint thinner, ammonia, acetone, and benzene.

Petrochemical solvents are used in the manufacture of pharmaceuticals, cosmetics, textiles, and computer chips. Some petrochemical solvents are used in the dry-cleaning process. Cleaning solvents easily dissolve body oils, oily food, and ink stains from cloth. Petrochemical solvents give off fumes that can be hazardous to health. All solvents should be used in a well-ventilated room, and disposed of properly.

Consider This

Are Biodegradable Plastics Good for the Environment?

Most solid wastes, including plastics, end up buried in landfills. They remain in the landfill without ever being recycled into the environment. By mixing plastic polymers with substances that break down easily, a material called biodegradable plastic is produced.

Supporters of biodegradable plastic think that it should be used for making disposable items. They say that, unlike regular plastic, the biodegradable plastics will decompose more readily into recyclable materials and are therefore better for the environment.

Opponents of biodegradable plastic feel that this product is more of a hazard than a help. They claim that very little of this material will break down in a landfill. They also think that marketing biodegradable plastics interferes with efforts to recycle other plastics. Consumers may choose to buy disposable containers instead of those designed to be recycled.

Think About It Which strategy would use less of the world's petroleum reserve—using biodegradable plastic or recycling plastic?

Write About It Write a paper stating your position for or against the use of biodegradable plastics. Include your reasons for choosing your position. Share your position with the class.

Cooperative Learning

Have the class work in two cooperative learning groups to prepare a report on local plastic recycling. Ask one group to talk to the manager of the local recycling center. Have them find out how much plastic is recycled monthly and the type of process used. Ask the other group to write to a manufacturer that receives plastic flakes and find out what products they make and where they are sold. Students can report their findings.

Science and You *Plastic Recycling*

What do the letters *PET* and *HDPE* mean to you? If you sort and recycle plastics, you may already know the answer! These letters identify two of the most commonly recycled plastics. The clear plastic PET, which stands for polyethylene terephthalate, is used to make carbonated-beverage containers. The translucent plastic HDPE, or high-density polyethylene, is used in milk and juice containers.

To help identify recyclable plastics, the containers are marked with a code. The code is either printed on the package label or molded into the plastic itself. Look at Figure 25.8. The code appears as a number within a triangle that is formed by three arrows. The number 1 identifies a PET container. The number 2 identifies an HDPE container.

A recycling plant sorts the containers it accepts. Unwanted materials, such as metal caps, are removed from the plastic. Machines cut the plastic containers into small, confetti-like flakes. The plastic flakes are washed and sorted again to remove contaminants. After drying, the plastic flakes are packaged and transported to manufacturers that use recycled plastics.

Recycled plastic flakes have many uses. For example, after they've been processed, flakes can be used as an insulating material in articles such as sleeping bags. Plastic flakes can also be bonded together to form a material that can be substituted for lumber. This wood substitute doesn't rot or break down easily. Manufacturers hope that plastic lumber will someday replace the wood used to build things like decks, picnic tables, and piers.

Figure 25.8 ▲
The number 1 in a triangle is the code for a recyclable, clear plastic called polyethylene terephthalate, or PET. Where can you see this code? ①

Check and Explain

1. List five examples of products made from petrochemicals.

2. What is a polymer?

3. **Compare and Contrast** How are the properties of plastics and synthetic fibers similar? How do they differ?

4. **Make a Model** Design a model of the arrangement of the polymers in a synthetic fiber.

Discuss

Students may wonder about recycling plastics at home. Ask:

▶ What kinds of different plastic containers does your family use? (Answers should reflect a variety of products.)

▶ How might each kind of plastic affect the recycling process? (Sorting containers takes time, different containers would have to be shipped to their origins.)

EVALUATE

WrapUp

Reteach Have pairs of students choose a classroom object that contains petrochemicals. Ask each pair to consider the answers to the following questions: From its properties, what might the object's molecular structure be like? What are some other uses for the material the object is made of? What substance could be used to make the object if petroleum reserves ran out? Ask each pair to point out its object and call on other students to answer the questions.

Use Review Worksheet 25.2.

Check and Explain

1. Answers may include plastic furniture, nylon, antifreeze, paint, ink, telephones, sandals, plates, cups, fabrics, dyes, and medicines.

2. A chain of linked monomers

3. Similar: made of polymers in which monomers are linked in a chain; different: hard plastics have a rigid frame of polymers; fibers have straight-chain polymers that can slide past one another.

4. Models should show long, straight chains of monomers lined up next to each other.

Answer to In-Text Question

① At the center of the container bottom

25.3

Section Objectives
For a list of section objectives, see the Student Edition page.

Skills Objectives
Students should be able to:

Classify building materials as plant or animal product, ceramic, plastic, or unknown.

Collect Data for a table showing the properties of plastics, metals, ceramics, and composites.

Infer what kinds of materials would be needed for the space shuttle.

Vocabulary
metallurgy, ceramic, composite, matrix

MOTIVATE

Skills WarmUp
To help students understand materials science, have them do the Skills WarmUp.
Answer Answers will vary. Students will probably list wooden boards (plant), window glass (ceramic), bricks (ceramic), nails (metal), vinyl tile (plastic), sheet rock (ceramic).

Prior Knowledge
Gauge how much students know about materials science by asking the following questions:

▶ Why is metallurgy so important to people?

▶ What's the difference between iron and steel?

▶ What are some properties of ceramics and glass that make them useful materials?

Answer to In-Text Question
① Nails, water pipe, screws, brace for holding wire, outlet box

614

Social Studies Connection
Explain that the Bronze Age followed the Stone Age, in which people used stone to make weapons and tools. Tell students that during the Bronze Age people learned to make and use bronze for cups, vases, sculptures, jewelry, axes and other objects. The earliest Bronze Age occurred in 3500 B.C. in Mesopotamia. Ask students what they would call the age they live in. (They may say the Oil Age or the Plastic Age.)

Integrating the Sciences
Earth Science Point out that the richest iron ores are the iron oxides, which are composed of iron and oxygen. These ores—hematite and magnetite—are about 70 percent iron. Explain that silver comes mostly from copper and lead ores, and that copper comes from ores that contain less than 4 percent copper.

▼ **ACTIVITY**

Classifying

Building Materials

Make a list of 12 materials you would need to build a house. Classify each building material as a plant or animal product, metal, ceramic, plastic, or substance of unknown origin. Some items may fall into more than one group.

SKILLS WARMUP

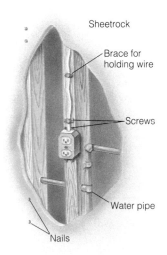

Sheetrock

Brace for holding wire

Screws

Water pipe

Nails

Figure 25.9 ▲
What metal items can you identify in this drawing of the inside of the wall of a building?
①

25.3 Materials Science

Objectives

▶ **Describe** metallurgy and explain its importance.

▶ **Describe** how steel is made.

▶ **Compare** and **contrast** the processes for making ceramics and glass.

▶ **Infer** the properties of a composite material.

How many objects do you use every day that are made from metal? You have many metal objects inside your home, such as kitchen utensils, appliances, and light fixtures. Your home also has many hidden metal parts.

If you could look behind the walls, as in Figure 25.9, you'd find steel nails, brackets, and screws that hold the frame of your home together. You'd also find pipes and electric wires made of copper. You might even observe a metal-foil backing on fiberglass wall insulation.

Metallurgy

The complete process of taking metals from the earth and making them into useful products is called **metallurgy** (MEHT uh LUR jee). Many familiar metals, such as iron, silver, and copper, look very different when they come out of the earth as an ore. A metal ore is a naturally occurring compound or mixture from which a metal is removed. For example, iron ore contains iron, oxygen, sulfur, and sand.

After an ore deposit is found, the ore is mined and brought to the surface. The metal is separated from the ore. Once the metal is refined, it can be mixed with other materials or shaped into usable forms.

Metallurgy is so important to human society that periods of history have been named for metals. For example, the Bronze Age began approximately 3500 B.C. with the discovery of bronze. Bronze is an alloy of copper and tin and is very strong. It can be easily shaped into tools. The Iron Age began approximately 1000 B.C., when iron tools and weapons were developed.

From Iron Ore to Steel

Steel-making is a step-by-step process that begins with the location of iron-ore deposits. After the ore is mined, the refining process begins. Follow the steps of the steel-making process in Figure 25.10.

Figure 25.10
The Steel-making Process ▼

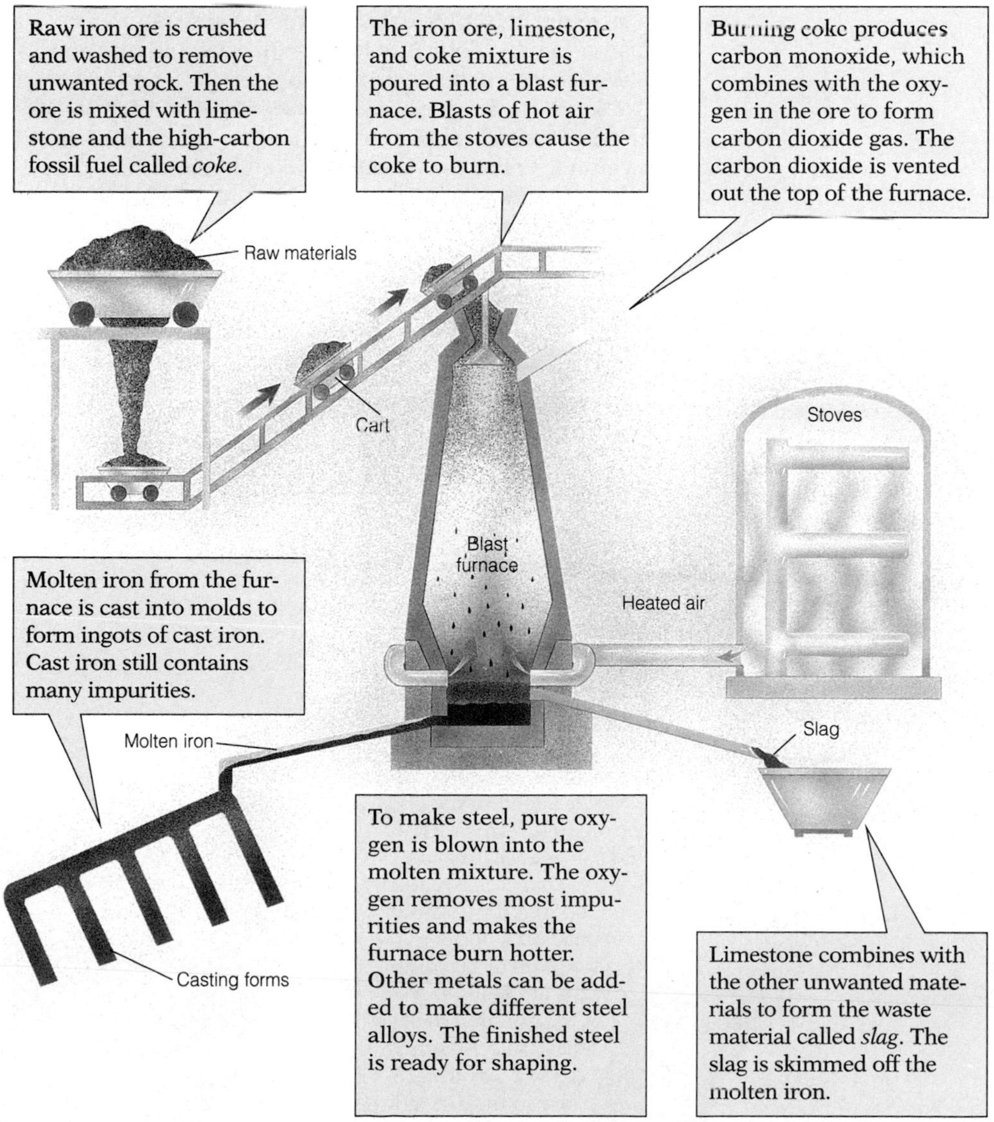

Raw iron ore is crushed and washed to remove unwanted rock. Then the ore is mixed with limestone and the high-carbon fossil fuel called *coke*.

The iron ore, limestone, and coke mixture is poured into a blast furnace. Blasts of hot air from the stoves cause the coke to burn.

Burning coke produces carbon monoxide, which combines with the oxygen in the ore to form carbon dioxide gas. The carbon dioxide is vented out the top of the furnace.

Raw materials

Cart

Molten iron from the furnace is cast into molds to form ingots of cast iron. Cast iron still contains many impurities.

Molten iron

Casting forms

Blast furnace

Heated air

Stoves

Slag

To make steel, pure oxygen is blown into the molten mixture. The oxygen removes most impurities and makes the furnace burn hotter. Other metals can be added to make different steel alloys. The finished steel is ready for shaping.

Limestone combines with the other unwanted materials to form the waste material called *slag*. The slag is skimmed off the molten iron.

TEACH ▪ Continued

Discuss

Explain that ceramics, plastics, and metals have a wide range of uses. Ask the following questions:

▶ What is a ceramic? (An object made of clay or earth materials that is shaped and fired.)

▶ What properties make ceramics so useful? (Good insulators, water resistant, withstand high temperatures)

Directed Inquiry

Have students study the photographs on this page. Ask the following questions:

▶ What raw materials are used to make ceramics? (Silicate minerals and clays)

▶ How are clay and mineral powders able to be shaped? (By adding water)

▶ What is a potter's wheel used for? (To shape wet clay into round or circular forms)

▶ How is a clay object turned into a ceramic? (It's fired in a kiln or oven where intense heat burns off impurities and causes physical and chemical reactions. Heat hardens and brings out the color of the paint.)

▶ If all dishes were made from plastic or metal, why would a knowledge of ceramics still be important? (Ceramics are used to make many things other than dishes.)

Answer to In-Text Question

① Bricks, cement, tiles, bathtubs, sinks, some abrasives

Multicultural Perspectives

Explain to students that in 1974 archaeologists found an "army" of 6,000 life-sized terra cotta figures made to guard the tomb of Qin Shi Huangdi, the emperor of China in 200 B.C. Some scholars think it took hundreds of thousands of people more than 30 years to make the soldiers, archers, officers, and horses that guard the tomb. Explain that the figures are so detailed you can see eyebrows, fabric folds, and mustaches.

Integrating the Sciences

Environmental Science Point out that some ceramic glazes contain uranium oxides that give off dangerous amounts of radiation. These glazes, which are often yellow or orange, were banned in 1978. Consumers are also warned to avoid serving food in some lead glaze earthenware from Italy, Spain, China, and Mexico.

Ceramics

Clay and other earth materials that are shaped and fired at high temperatures form materials called **ceramics** [seh RAM ihks]. You are probably familiar with many different kinds of ceramics. The earthenware in flower pots is a ceramic. Earthenware is made of a coarse red clay. Fine china and porcelain statues are also ceramics. Porcelain is made of very fine clay and has a smooth and glassy appearance.

Ceramics are good insulators, are resistant to water, and can withstand high temperatures. Spark plugs have a ceramic collar that is subject to high temperatures and also acts as an electric insulator. What are some other uses for ceramics? ①

Ceramic Clay

Silicate minerals and clays used in ceramics are mined from the earth. These materials are crushed into a fine powder. Different kinds and amounts of clay and mineral powders determine what kind of object will be made. Bowls, plates, and vases are just a few examples of objects made from ceramic clay. ▼

Clay Shapes ▲

Water added to the powder mixture forms a clay that can be easily shaped. Ceramic shapes are made by hand, poured into a mold, or formed on a potter's wheel. Round or circular objects are easily shaped on the spinning potter's wheel. After shaping, the wet clay objects dry in the air and harden.

Firing

After the dry object is painted, it is fired in a kiln. Firing is a method of high-temperature heating. During firing, the intense heat in the kiln burns off impurities and causes physical and chemical reactions to take place. Firing hardens the clay and brings out the color of the paint. The clay changes to ceramic. After firing, the object can be glazed. ▼

Glass

What happens if you drop a porcelain cup or dish? It shatters just like glass! Porcelain and glass have many similar properties. They are both brittle, heat resistant, and poor conductors of electricity.

The raw materials used in glass are sand, limestone, and a sodium compound called soda. These materials are ground into a powder and blended together. The amount of each ingredient detemines if the glass is heat-resistant, shatterproof, or common plate glass.

To make glass, the powdered materials are heated and melted into a thick liquid. The liquid is continually stirred to allow waste products to bubble off. After several days, the hot liquid glass is removed from the furnace and shaped. Plate glass is made by squeezing molten glass between rollers to form sheets. Dishes are pressed in a mold. Bottles and similar containers are blown or injected into molds to give them their hollow shape.

Historical Notebook

Ceramic Pottery

Thousands of years ago, people on different continents learned to make ceramic pottery. Some of this ancient pottery still exists. The characteristics of the pottery give clues to the techniques and materials that were used to make it.

In ancient Africa, people made two-color ceramic pots. They buried part of the pot in the ashes of a fire. The clay that was buried in the ashes produced a black ceramic, while the part exposed to the air turned red.

In ancient America, people also made two-colored ceramic vessels and figurines. The ancient Americans, however, colored their ceramics with paint. The paints were made using pigments from local mineral deposits.

About 2,000 years ago in China, people discovered how to make the smooth, glassy ceramic known as porcelain. They used a local white clay called kaolin. Objects made from this very

fine clay were fired at very high temperatures. The shiny porcelain surface is a glass that forms from the melted mineral crystals in kaolin clay.

1. How could the area in which people lived affect the kinds of ceramics they made?

2. Why do you think pottery might be important in studying about ancient cultures?

3. Choose a geographic area and do library research on the kinds of ceramics made there in ancient or modern times. Write a one-page report.

TEACH ▪ *Continued*

Skills WorkOut

To help students collect data about the properties of materials, have them do the Skills WorkOut.

Answer Answers will vary, but should include only personal observations.

Reteach

Review the properties of plastics and ceramics as you discuss this page. Have students draw a line to divide a sheet of paper in half lengthwise. Have them list the properties of plastics on the left and the properties of ceramics on the right. Be sure students realize that composites are materials woven or blended together so that the desired properties of both materials are used.

Answers to In-Text Questions

① **The fibers are fiberglass and the matrix is a clear plastic.**

② **Curtains, insulation, lightweight canoes, football and baseball helmets, and certain yarns**

Art Connection

Point out that composite materials are designed to meet special needs. Ask students to imagine a composite that would fill a need in their lives, such as indestructible books that weigh less than a pound. Encourage students to draw a picture showing their composites in use. Have them label the materials used in their composites.

▼ ACTIVITY

Collecting Data

Material Witness

Make a table that contains information about the properties of plastics, metals, ceramics, and composites. All the information included in this table must be obtained from your personal observation of these materials. Compare your list with a classmate.

SKILLS WORKOUT

Figure 25.11
The body of this automobile is made of fiberglass similar to the sample. Can you identify the fibers and the matrix in the fiberglass sample? ▼ ①

Composites

Special materials, called **composites**, were developed and manufactured for their properties. Composites are made up of fibers that are embedded in a layer of material called a **matrix**. The matrix material determines such properties as density, resistance to heat, and ability to conduct electricity. The fibers determine such properties as the strength and flexibility of the composite.

The choice of the matrix material and of the fiber depends on how the composite will be used. If the composite must be heat resistant, ceramics are the best choice for the matrix. Carbon-based fibers are strong and can withstand temperature extremes. Composites made with carbon-based fibers are used to construct some parts for aircraft and space vehicles. Plastics are strong, lightweight, and resist corrosion. However, plastics can't withstand extreme heat. Plastics are used as a matrix in composites like fiberglass.

Fiberglass is a strong and lightweight composite. It is a good material for building and repairing boat hulls and automobile bodies. The fibers are thin strands of glass. Glass fibers are inexpensive, strong, and easy to handle. Plastic polymers, such as polyester, are used as the matrix.

Fiberglass is commonly used as an insulating material. There are air spaces between the glass fibers so heat travels slowly through the material. Also, glass is a poor conductor of heat, so the heat does not escape. Look closely at the fiberglass in Figure 25.11. It looks like fabric covered with a transparent coating. Actually, the fabric is made from glass fibers that have been woven and matted together. The matrix is hardened plastic. What are some other uses of fiberglass? ②

Science and Technology *Ceramic Engines*

As petroleum use increases, people are more concerned about the supply of fossil fuel. Automakers are looking for ways to make more energy-efficient, nonpolluting vehicles. New developments in ceramic technology may help automakers to build better cars.

The internal-combustion engine used in most cars isn't very fuel efficient. Only about one third of the energy from the burning gasoline is used to move the car. The remaining two thirds of the energy is carried away as waste heat.

By replacing some of the metal parts with parts made of ceramics or ceramic composites, the car's fuel efficiency could be improved. A car with ceramic parts would be lighter than a car with metal parts. A lighter car would use less energy. Also, ceramic engine parts could withstand higher temperatures. As a result, cars with ceramic parts wouldn't need a cooling system. The extra heat could be used to produce more engine power.

Ceramics developed for space vehicles may be used to design a more energy-efficient automobile engine. Ceramics, such as silicon carbide and silicon nitride, developed for the space shuttle shown in Figure 25.12, could be used in gas-turbine engines. As the cost for producing space-age ceramics decreases, ceramics are more likely to be molded into the car engines of the future.

Figure 25.12 ▲

The space shuttle uses high-tech ceramic materials to withstand extreme temperature changes that are caused by friction as the shuttle re-enters the earth's atmosphere.

Check and Explain

1. What is metallurgy? Why is it important?

2. Describe how steel is made from iron ore. Explain the purpose of each step in the process.

3. **Compare and Contrast** How are the processes used for making ceramics and glass similar? How are they different?

4. **Infer** Imagine that you're an engineer designing a composite material for the space shuttle. You need a strong, lightweight, and heat-resistant composite. What kind of materials would you use for the fiber? What would you use for the matrix? Explain.

Time 40 minutes   Group pairs

Materials

30 small jars

15 thick, plastic self-lock bags

30 safety goggles

300 mL 50% white-glue solution

100 mL 4% borax solution

Analysis

1. Before combining them, both solutions are nonviscous liquids. The polymer is milky, and smells like glue. The borax solution is clear and odorless. The product is rubbery, with a doughy, translucent color. Descriptions of color will vary.

2. A chemical reaction takes place.

Conclusion

The borax caused the individual polyvinyl acetate molecules to link together forming the solid product. Check students' drawings for accuracy.

Everyday Application

As the glue dries, the polymer molecules bind together and to the objects being glued.

Prelab Discussion

Have students read the entire activity before beginning. Explain to students that their careful observations of the polymer will be important. Demonstrate the techniques for smelling a sample and for observing a liquid's texture without touching it.

Activity 25 *How can the properties of a polymer be changed?*

Skills   Measure; Observe; Infer

Task 1 Prelab Prep

Collect the following items: safety goggles, 2 identical small-size jars, 15 mL of 50 percent white-glue solution, 5 mL of 4 percent borax solution, 1 thick, plastic self-lock bag.

Task 2 Data Record

Draw a data table like the one below.

Task 3 Procedure

1. Pour 15 mL of the white-glue solution into one of the small jars. Observe the solution and record your observations in the data table. Include the solution's color, odor, and texture. To observe texture, gently swirl the jar without touching the solution. You can smell the solution by gently fanning air from the top of the jar toward your nose. **CAUTION! Handle glass jar carefully to avoid breakage.**

2. Fill the other jar with 5 mL of the borax solution. **CAUTION! Do not touch the borax solution.** Record your observations of the borax solution in the data table. Include the solution's color, odor, and texture. To observe texture, gently swirl the jar without touching the solution. You can smell the solution by gently fanning air from the top of the jar toward your nose.

3. Pour the white-glue solution from the jar into the bag.

4. Pour the borax solution from the other jar into the bag. Seal the bag.

5. Knead the solutions through the bag until they are evenly mixed. No excess liquid should remain.

6. Remove the product from the bag and knead it with your hands. After you've finished, wash your hands.

7. Record your observations of the product in the data table. Include the product's color, odor, and texture.

Task 4 Analysis

1. How are the properties of the solutions and the product similar? How are they different?

2. Describe what happens to the molecules when two substances that are mixed together form a product with properties that are different than both substances.

Task 5 Conclusion

The 50 percent white-glue solution contains many individual molecules of the polymer polyvinyl acetate. Write a paragraph explaining what you think happened to the polymer molecules after they were mixed with borax solution to produce the changes you observed. What role did the borax play? Make *before* and *after* drawings to illustrate your ideas.

Everyday Application

You probably use white glue to stick things together. In terms of a polymer and what you learned from this activity, explain how glue sticks things together.

Table 25.1

Substance	Color	Odor	Texture
Glue solution			
Borax solution			
Product			

Themes in Science
Systems and Interactions
Explain to students that changes in one part of the environment affect the whole environment. For example, pollution of air or water affects living organisms that depend on air and water to live. Ask students to cite other examples.

Integrating the Sciences
Environmental Science Air pollution contains particulates, or tiny dust particles, produced in part by burning fossil fuels. Particulates can aggravate asthma and bronchitis and may cause cancer. In 1970, the Environmental Protection Agency regulated the level of particulates in the air. Have students consult a local newspaper or environmental agency to find out the average daily particulate readings. Have students report their findings.

Section Objectives
For a list of section objectives, see the Student Edition page.

Skills Objectives
Students should be able to:

Classify 20 items they use as recyclable or degradable.

Communicate how local water quality is controlled.

Infer how air pollution affects water and land quality.

Vocabulary
air pollution, greenhouse effect, global warming, acid rain, thermal pollution

25.4 Technology and the Environment

Objectives

▶ **Identify** two causes of air, water, and land pollution.

▶ **Explain** how waste disposal affects the environment.

▶ **Communicate** how technology creates and solves water pollution problems.

▶ **Infer** how air pollution affects water quality and land quality.

▼ **ACTIVITY**

Classifying

Separating Refuse

List 15 items that you used today. Classify each item as either recyclable or degradable. What items did you list that don't fall into either group?

SKILLS WARMUP

MOTIVATE

Skills WarmUp
To help students identify recyclable and degradable materials, have them do the Skills WarmUp.
Answer Possible answers include paper, metals, and glass as recyclable. Degradable items include those made of wood, leather, natural fibers, and some metals. Items in neither category include plastics and synthetic fabrics.

Misconceptions
Students may think that technology is either all bad or all good. Encourage students to see the relationship between technology and the environment as a complex one with problems that can't easily be solved.

Look around your classroom. The desks, walls, books, and even your clothes are all manufactured by some industrial process. Industrial processes use natural resources and energy. Both the school bus you ride on and the street are made of petroleum products. The quality of the air, water, and land is affected by human activity. It is also affected by natural processes.

The next time you smell car exhaust, watch oily water run off the street, or see dirt erode from a hill, think about where these substances are headed. The earth is a closed system. It recycles its natural resources.

Air Quality

The air you breathe is a mixture of nitrogen, oxygen, argon, carbon dioxide, and trace amounts of helium, neon, and several other gases. Air also contains water vapor. Pure air contains only the gases and water vapor needed for the earth's environment to be healthy.

Too often air contains pollutants. Pollutants are substances, or even energy, that harm living things. Some pollutants in the atmosphere can change the earth's overall temperature and affect climate.

A high concentration of pollutants in the air is called **air pollution**. Some air pollution comes from natural sources, such as the dust and smoke from volcanic eruptions and forest fires. However, most air pollution is caused by human activity. For example, automobile exhaust and industrial smoke release chemical pollutants.

Figure 25.13 ▲
The quality of the air in the earth's atmosphere depends on human activity.

Research

Have students use references to learn about the temperature inversion that occurred in Donora, Pennsylvania, in 1948. Have them find out how many days it lasted and how many people died as a result.

Explore Visually

Have students read the text and study Figure 25.13. Then ask:

▶ What are the common greenhouse gases? (Carbon dioxide, methane, nitrous oxide)

▶ Where do greenhouse gases collect? (In the upper atmosphere)

▶ What do greenhouse gases do? (Trap heat energy from the sun in the lower atmosphere)

▶ Where do most temperature inversions occur? (In large industrial areas)

Integrating the Sciences

Environmental Science Explain that some scientists estimate if people add greenhouse gases to the atmosphere at the current rate, the average world temperature will increase 1°C by the year 2025. But scientists disagree on the effects of global warming. Some think that global warming could cause ice caps to melt, raising ocean levels and flooding coastal areas. Others think that higher temperatures could cause more ocean water to evaporate. Increased water vapor could mean heavier snows for the polar regions, increasing the size of the ice caps. More water vapor could also result in heavier cloud cover that may cause global temperatures to drop.

Temperature Inversion Normally, the temperature of the air is warmer near the ground than it is at high altitudes. However, sometimes a blanket of cold air is trapped beneath a thick layer of warm air. This reversed layering of air is called a *temperature inversion*.

During a temperature inversion, air near the ground doesn't circulate. Pollutants released by cars and industry build up in the cold air at the surface. The air quality becomes unhealthy. Temperature inversions may last for several weeks.

Greenhouse Effect Why does the air temperature inside a car increase when the windows are closed on a sunny day? As sunlight passes through the windows, the car's interior absorbs and radiates heat energy. Air inside the closed car is warmed by the heat energy. Trapping heat energy from sunlight is called the **greenhouse effect**.

The greenhouse effect also happens globally. Look at Figure 25.13. Gases, such as carbon dioxide, methane, and nitrous oxide, build up in the atmosphere. These gases, called greenhouse gases, trap energy in the lowest layer of the earth's atmosphere.

Many scientists are concerned about a global greenhouse effect increasing temperatures worldwide. The increase of the earth's atmospheric temperature due to the greenhouse effect is called **global warming**. If average global temperatures increase even a few degrees, worldwide climate changes might occur. Rainfall patterns could change and cause the types and amount of plant life in many areas to change.

Figure 25.13 The Greenhouse Effect ▼

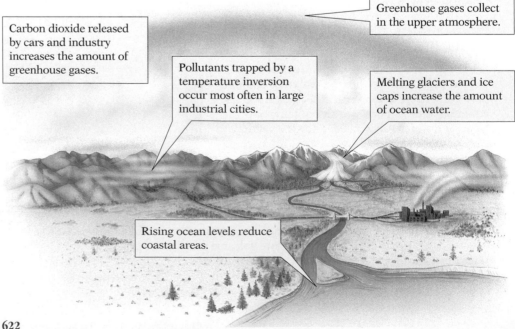

Carbon dioxide released by cars and industry increases the amount of greenhouse gases.

Greenhouse gases collect in the upper atmosphere.

Pollutants trapped by a temperature inversion occur most often in large industrial cities.

Melting glaciers and ice caps increase the amount of ocean water.

Rising ocean levels reduce coastal areas.

Portfolio

Explain to students that the EPA regularly measures air quality in each state and in major cities nationwide. Have students find out the EPA rating of their community or region, and identify the pollutants measured. Have students organize their findings in a circle graph or bar graph and keep the graphs in their portfolios.

Cooperative Learning

Point out to students that many devices help detect or limit air pollution. Have students work in three cooperative learning groups and pick one of the following antipollution devices: scrubbers, catalytic converters, or carbon monoxide detectors. Have each group research the device and how it works. Have the groups prepare illustrated reports on their devices and present them to the class.

Directed Inquiry

Have students read this page and study the photographs. Ask the following questions:

▶ What does industrial smog contain? (Sulfur oxide and solid particles released when factories burn fossil fuels; they combine with moisture in the air.)

▶ What does industrial smog look like? (Like a grayish haze)

▶ What does photochemical smog contain? (Formaldehyde, ozone, and other pollutants from cars and power plants)

▶ What part does sunlight play in creating photochemical smog? (Sunlight combines nitrogen oxide and hydrocarbons to form the chemical compounds in photochemical smog.)

▶ What does photochemical smog look like? (Like a brownish-orange haze)

▶ What are scrubbers? (Devices attached to smokestacks to remove pollutants from smoke before it is released)

▶ How do scrubbers work? (They trap solid particles and gases as they pass through a fine water mist.)

▶ **Infer** How are the numbers in Table 25.2 related to the use of devices like scrubbers? (Such standards result in the use of more pollution-control devices.)

Decision Making

If you have classroom sets of *One-Minute Readings*, have students read Issue 37 "Catalysis and City Air Pollution" on pages 62 and 63. Discuss the questions.

Smog Smog, a major contributor to air pollution, is a mixture of chemical fumes, suspended particles, and fog. Two kinds of smog are photochemical smog and industrial smog. Photochemical smog contains formaldehyde (for MAL duh HYD), ozone, and other pollutants from cars and power plants. Industrial smog contains sulfur oxide and solid particles that are released when fossil fuels are burned. Air pollutant levels set by the Environmental Protection Agency (EPA) protect human health and control pollution.

Industrial Smog ▲
When factories burn coal or oil, they release pollutants that combine with moisture in the air to form industrial smog. Industrial smog appears as a grayish haze and usually forms over heavily industrialized cities.

Photochemical Smog ▶
The action of sunlight on nitrogen oxide and hydrocarbons combines them to form the chemical compounds in photochemical smog. Photochemical smog appears as a brownish-orange haze in the air, and usually occurs over large cities.

Table 25.2
U.S. Air Quality Standards

Air Pollutant	Concentration (ppm)
Sulfur oxides	0.14
Carbon monoxide	35.00
Ozone	0.12
Hydro-carbons	0.24

Scrubbers
To meet EPA standards, scrubbers are attached to smokestacks to remove pollutants from smoke before it is released. Solid particles and gases are trapped as they pass through a fine water mist in the scrubber. The pollutant-laden waste water is processed into sludge, which is used in bricks. ◀

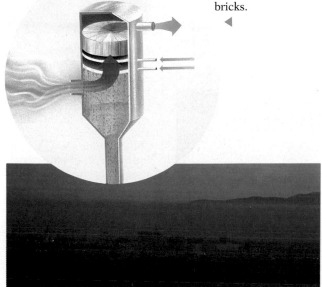

TEACH ▪ *Continued*

Directed Inquiry

Have students study the text and photographs on this page. Ask:

▶ Where is freshwater found? (It is in ice caps, glaciers, lakes, rivers, ponds, and underground.)

▶ What is the water cycle? (The natural recycling of water by means of evaporation, condensation, and precipitation.)

▶ Why are oil spills dangerous? (They damage beaches and water environments and kill wildlife; it takes years to restore ocean environments.)

▶ What is acid rain? (Sulfur oxides, nitrogen oxides, and increased amounts of carbon dioxide released by burning fossil fuels combine with water in the atmosphere to form sulfuric and nitric acids. When these acids lower the pH of rainwater below 5.7, acid rain forms.)

▶ How does acid rain damage plants? (The leaves of plants are damaged so that photosynthesis can't take place.)

▶ How does acid rain damage buildings and statues? (It dissolves marble and limestone.)

▶ What signs of pollution do you see in your environment? (Answers may include examples of air and water pollution.)

Decision Making

If you have classroom sets of *One-Minute Readings*, have students read Issue 36 "Acid Rain" on pages 60 and 61 as well as Issue 38 "Oil Pollution" on page 64. Discuss the questions.

Math Connection

Explain that the earth's supply of fresh water is limited. Point out that 97 percent of the world's water is undrinkable ocean water. The remaining 3 percent is fresh water. Of this 3 percent, about 2 percent is frozen in glaciers and ice caps. The remaining 1 percent is found in the air, in lakes, rivers, and underground. Ask students to use this information to make a circle graph showing the amount of fresh water that is readily available.

Art Connection

Explain that sulfur oxides pollute the air in Athens, Greece, which contains a wealth of marble temples and sculptures from around 400 B.C. The sulfur oxides in the air are changing the marble into gypsum, which cracks and peels away. Explain to students that some statues have been removed to museums and cement replicas have been put in their places.

Water Quality

Do you know where the water you use comes from? Freshwater is stored in the ice caps, in glaciers, lakes, rivers, and ponds, or underground in the spaces between rocks. Actually the earth's total freshwater supply is limited. Water is constantly being recycled from surface water that evaporates, then condenses in the atmosphere, and returns to the earth as precipitation. This cycle of evaporation, condensation, and precipitation is called the water cycle.

Oil Spills

Ocean oil spills come from ruptured oil tankers, oil rig drilling accidents, and oil dumped into rivers. Oil spills damage beaches and kill fish, birds, and marine mammals. It takes many years for an unhealthy river or ocean environment to rebuild. ▼

Acid Rain ▲

When sulfur oxides and nitrogen oxides are released by burning fossil fuels, they combine with water in the atmosphere to form sulfuric and nitric acids. If enough of these acids are present to lower the pH of pure rainwater to below 5.7, **acid rain** forms. Leaves of trees and plants are damaged by acid rain. Photosynthesis can't take place, and many plants die.

Effects of Acid Rain

Acid rain reacts with the marble and limestone in buildings and statues. Historic buildings and monuments have been damaged by acid rain. Acid rain also weakens the exposed metal in bridges and automobiles. ▼

Integrating the Sciences

Environmental Science Explain to students that a healthy lake has a balance of nutrients and organisms. But when excess nutrients from pollution flow into a lake, they enable more algae to grow. When these organisms die, bacteria in the lake use oxygen to break them down. The more plants that grow, the more die, resulting in more bacteria and less oxygen. Ask students to describe the effects of decreased oxygen on other organisms.

The quality of fresh water depends on the chemicals and waste material, or pollutants, dumped into surface waters and onto the ground. Water pollution is any physical or chemical change in water that harms organisms. Water pollutants often spread throughout an entire river system. Sometimes pollutants can become concentrated in small lakes and ponds.

Thermal Pollution ▲

An increase in water temperature that harms living organisms is called **thermal pollution**. Thermal pollution occurs when large amounts of hot waste water from power plants and refineries are dumped into surface water. Fish and microscopic organisms that live in the water die from lack of oxygen that results from the higher temperatures.

Chemical Pollution ▶

Chemicals that make water unsafe for drinking cause water pollution. Water runoff from streets contains asbestos and oil from cars, and salt used on icy roads. Mercury from processing plastics and nitrates from sewage plants are also water pollutants.

**Table 25.3
EPA Water Quality Standards**

Toxic Chemical	Concentration (ppm)
arsenic	50
lead	50
mercury	2
nitrate	10,000
selenium	10
2,4-D fertilizer	100

Water Standards ▲

EPA standards were set in the 1970s to control water safety. Industries were no longer allowed to dump unprocessed waste water into rivers and lakes. Farms were required to control water contaminated with animal waste and fertilizers.

Pollution from Runoff

Many lakes become clogged by plants that feed on sewage, industrial waste, and fertilizer runoff from cities and farms. An overgrowth of plant life reduces the oxygen supply in the water. Fish and other organisms die from lack of oxygen. The lakes become polluted. ▼

Have students read the text and study the photographs on this page. Ask:

▶ What is water pollution? (Any physical or chemical change in water that harms organisms)

▶ What is thermal pollution? (An increase in water temperature that harms living organisms)

▶ What causes thermal pollution? (Power plants and refineries that dump hot water into surface waters)

▶ What is the result of thermal pollution? (Fish and microscopic organisms in the water die from a lack of oxygen caused by increased water temperature.)

▶ What causes chemical pollution? (Runoff from roads, sewage plants, and industrial plants)

▶ What are some sources of chemicals that pollute the water supply? (Salt spread on icy roads, asbestos and oil from cars, mercury from processing plastics, and nitrates from sewage plants all make untreated water unsafe for drinking.)

▶ How are lakes affected by pollution? (Sewage, industrial waste, and fertilizers contain nutrients that cause the number of lake plants to increase. Increased plant growth reduces the amount of oxygen in the water, causing fish and other organisms to die.)

▶ What effect does the EPA Water Quality Standard have? (It controls the amount of unprocessed waste and contaminated water released into rivers and lakes.)

Directed Inquiry

Have students study the photographs and read the text. Ask:

▶ What happens to the garbage your city dumps each day? (Answers will vary, but most would say the garbage is dumped and plowed into the soil.)

▶ What are the problems with dump sites? (Future use is limited. Some materials, such as plastics, take years to break down. Chemicals pollute the ground water and make the soil unsuitable for agriculture.)

▶ What is strip mining? (Removing coal and ores close to the surface by stripping away top layers of dirt and rock)

▶ What are some effects of strip mining? (Topsoil erodes into streams and rivers, chemicals concentrate in the soil, and many plants and animals die.)

▶ Why is drilling or transporting oil a problem? (Oil may be spilled, damaging the environment.)

Decision Making

If you have classroom sets of *One-Minute Readings*, have students read Issue 33 "Waste Disposal" on page 57. Discuss the questions.

Integrated Learning

Use Integrating Worksheet 25.4.

Geography Connection

Explain to students that the Trans-Alaska Pipeline skirts the edge of the Arctic National Wildlife Refuge, a huge area of mountains and tundra that contains oil. Point out that business interests want permission to drill for oil on refuge lands. Have students find the Arctic National Wildlife Refuge on a map. Ask them to use an atlas to find out about the characteristics of this land and its wildlife.

Integrating the Sciences

Environmental Science Industry and farming in the United States produce the equivalent of 18 metric tons of trash per person each year. At home and work, people throw away the equivalent of 2 kilograms of trash per American each day. Tell students that 42 percent of this waste is paper; 18 percent is glass, metal, and plastic; 16 percent is yard waste; and 7 percent is food waste. Ask students to discuss ways they can help reduce waste.

Land Quality

How much garbage did you produce today? Does your home have wood doors? Perhaps your classroom is heated by oil or coal. Everything you use affects the quality of the land. When you throw away an empty carton or an apple core, you add to the garbage pile. Whenever lumber is cut from a forest, or oil and coal are brought to the surface, land quality is affected in some way.

Litter ▲
The garbage, or litter, your city dumps each day adds up to a staggering amount each year. Dumping and burying garbage often limit future use of the dump site. Some kinds of litter, such as plastics, take years to break down into safe, usable substances. Chemicals make the soil unsuitable for agriculture.

Strip Mining ▲
A process called strip mining removes coal and ores that are close to the earth's surface. The top layers of rock and dirt are stripped away and pushed aside. Nutrient-rich topsoil erodes into streams and rivers. Harmful chemicals concentrate in the soil. Plants and animals are unable to survive.

Oil Transport
◀ Oil from Alaska is transported through pipelines that are above the ground. Because the frozen tundra in Alaska is a fragile land environment, it is easily damaged by oil spilled during transport and drilling.

Hazardous Wastes Waste materials that are poisonous, or toxic, to people and animals are called hazardous wastes. Wastes are created when the products you use are manufactured. Your standard of living depends on these products.

Proper disposal of hazardous wastes is vital to all living things. Some toxic wastes are made harmless, or detoxified, by treating them so they are no longer poisonous. Other toxic wastes are collected and stored in places where they can't get into the environment.

One process for disposing of toxic waste chemicals is called deep-well injection, shown in Figure 25.16. Toxic waste is pumped into the ground where it is trapped between two layers of impermeable rock that it can't penetrate. Wastes remain in deep-wells for many years.

Nuclear Waste Disposal of radioactive waste from nuclear reactors and mining sites presents a problem. Some radioactive isotopes have a long half-life and are dangerous for thousands of years. Permanent disposal is needed for hun-

Figure 25.15 ▲
Nuclear waste is transported long distances to a disposal site.

dreds of metric tons of nuclear waste being kept in temporary storage sites.

One disposal method is to mix the radioactive wastes with molten glass. The waste hardens and is sealed in containers like the one shown in Figure 25.15. Some containers are buried in hardened rock deposits located in remote areas. Transporting nuclear waste is a major concern for many communities.

Figure 25.16   Deep-well Injection ▼
Waste chemicals injected into the ground can move slowly to other underground areas.

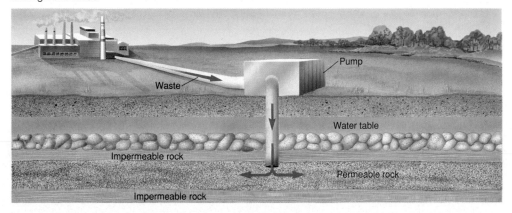

Pump

Waste

Water table

Impermeable rock

Permeable rock

Impermeable rock

Skills Development

Classify Ask students to read the text and classify the main sources of pollution that nearly destroyed Lake Erie. (Hazardous wastes, chemical pollution, and runoff)

EVALUATE

WrapUp

Portfolio Although the car is only one source of environmental pollution, it is an important one. Ask students to write a description of the effects cars have on air, water, and land quality. They should use the information in this section and be as specific as possible. Have students suggest solutions—both technological and nontechnological—for each environmental problem caused by the automobile.

Use Review Worksheet 25.4.

Check and Explain

1. From the burning of fossil fuels and release of chemical pollutants from cars and factories; the action of sunlight or the interaction with moisture produces pollutants.

2. Dumping hazardous wastes changes the land and water resources, making them unsafe for people, animals, and plants.

3. Possible answers include reservoirs, lakes, and rivers. Answers should focus on the process of removing chemical pollutants, sewage, and other wastes.

4. Pollutants in the air combine with moisture to form sulfuric and nitric acids, creating acid rain. This rain damages plants, affects the pH level of lakes and soil, which can harm or kill organisms.

Answer to In-Text Question

① **Industrial pollutants**

Cooperative Learning

Explain to students that people all over the country have cleaned up waterways including New York's Hudson River, Texas beaches, Washington's Puget Sound, and the Delaware River Basin. Have students work in cooperative learning groups to gather information on one of these projects or write to organizations, such as Greenpeace or the Cousteau Society to learn about current cleanups. Ask students to report their findings.

Science and Society   *River on Fire!*

How can a river burn? In 1969, near the city of Cleveland, Ohio, that's actually what happened. The water at the mouth of the Cuyahoga River, which flows into Lake Erie, caught fire and burned! At the time of the fire, Lake Erie was so polluted that fish and other organisms were dying by the thousands.

At 64 meters deep, Lake Erie is the shallowest of the Great Lakes. Lake Erie could not contain all the waste dumped into it. Fertilizers and phosphates from detergents caused a thick growth of algae and other plants. The excess plant material caused the growth of bacteria that used up the lake's oxygen. Fish and other organisms died from lack of oxygen.

The fire so horrified the people and the governments in the Lake Erie area that steps were immediately taken to clean up the lake. New laws were passed to keep industries from dumping hazardous wastes into the lake. New sewage treatment plants were built that cleaned up 90 percent of the organic wastes. Detergents that contained phosphates were banned. Farmers were encouraged to reduce their use of fertilizers. People were educated about pollution and how to reduce it in their own homes.

The amount of new pollutants entering the lake was drastically reduced. Lake Erie was able to clean itself through biological and chemical processes that occur naturally in a lake. People can swim and fish in Lake Erie once again.

Figure 25.17 ▲
The inset photo shows the algae growth that clogged Lake Erie. What kinds of pollutants do you think caused the lake to catch fire? ①

Check and Explain

1. What causes smog to form?

2. How does hazardous waste disposal harm the quality of land and water?

3. **Communicate** Research the source of your community's water supply. Explain how the quality of the water is controlled.

4. **Infer** How are water quality and land quality directly affected by air pollution? Explain.

Check Your Vocabulary

1. matrix
2. petroleum
3. air pollution
4. polymer
5. petrochemical
6. metallurgy
7. ceramic
8. thermal pollution
9. composite
10. greenhouse effect
11. acid rain
12. global warming

Write Your Vocabulary

Students' sentences should show that they know the meaning of each word as well as how to use it in a sentence.

Use Vocabulary Worksheet for Chapter 25.

Chapter 25 Review

Concept Summary

25.1 Petroleum Fuels
▶ Petroleum is formed from the remains of microscopic ocean organisms.
▶ Fractional distillation is used to separate crude oil into usable products.

25.2 Petrochemical Products
▶ Products containing plastics, synthetic fibers, dyes, and solvents are made from petrochemicals.
▶ Petrochemicals are composed of hydrocarbon molecules called monomers that combine to form chainlike molecules called polymers.

25.3 Materials Science
▶ Metallurgy is taking metals from the earth and making them into products.

▶ To make steel, iron ore is combined with limestone and coke in a blast furnace and then treated with oxygen.
▶ Ceramic and glass are made from earth materials that are heated to high temperatures.
▶ Composites are fibers that are embedded in a matrix.

25.4 Technology and the Environment
▶ The quality of air, water, and land is reduced by pollution.
▶ Pollutants are substances or energy that harm living things.
▶ Methods of disposing of hazardous waste materials, trash, and nuclear waste affect land quality.

Chapter Vocabulary

petroleum (p. 605)
petrochemical (p. 609)
polymer (p. 609)
metallurgy (p. 614)

ceramic (p. 616)
composite (p. 618)
matrix (p. 618)
air pollution (p. 621)

greenhouse effect (p. 622)
global warming (p. 622)
acid rain (p. 624)
thermal pollution (p. 625)

Check Your Vocabulary

Use the vocabulary words above to complete the following sentences correctly.

1. Fiberglass contains glass fibers embedded in a plastic ____.
2. The remains of microscopic ocean organisms were changed into ____.
3. A high concentration of pollutants in the air is called ____.
4. Monomers can form a larger molecule called a(n) ____.
5. A chemical substance made from petroleum is called a(n) ____.
6. Mining and processing metal-containing ore rocks is part of ____.
7. A hard, glasslike substance made from earth materials is a(n) ____.

8. Hot water released by industrial plants causes ____.
9. A material made of fibers embedded in a solid matrix is a(n) ____.
10. Trapping heat energy from sunlight is called the ____.
11. Water in the atmosphere combines with pollutants to form ____.
12. An increase of the greenhouse effect could cause ____.

Write Your Vocabulary

Write sentences using the vocabulary words above. Show that you know what each word means.

Check Your Knowledge

1. Petroleum is a liquid mixture of hydrocarbons that is formed from the remains of fossilized organisms that have been heated and compacted under layers of sedimentary rock.

2. Acid rain damages the leaves of plants, making them unable to carry out photosynthesis. It lowers the pH of lakes and rivers, killing aquatic organisms.

3. Crude oil is heated at the bottom of a tower until it vaporizes. As the vapor rises, it cools, with different compounds condensing out at different heights. By collecting the condensed product at different heights, the original crude oil is separated into many useful compounds.

4. Examples may vary but may include fuels, plastics, synthetic fibers, dyes, pharmaceuticals, and solvents.

5. A polymer is a chainlike molecule made up of repeating smaller molecules called *monomers*.

6. Water is pumped around the reactor to cool it. When this water is released into the environment, it is called *thermal pollution* because it is too warm for some plants and animals.

7. Litter from homes, businesses, and schools; strip mining; oil spills; hazardous wastes from manufacturing processes; and nuclear waste from nuclear power plants and mining sites

8. Metal-containing ore is pulverized, and then treated with other chemicals and heated to separate the pure metals from the ore.

9. A well is drilled into the trap, and oil is either forced out by natural water pressure or is pumped to the surface.

10. False; ocean organisms
11. True
12. False; non-toxic
13. True
14. True
15. False; porous

Check Your Understanding

1. Heat is used to evaporate the petroleum so it can be separated into its components.

2. Many products can be made from petroleum because it contains many different hydrocarbon compounds.

3. After undergoing a chemical reaction, the substance and the polymer are combined into a new compound with properties different from either one alone.

4. a. Students may answer that vitrification is partial because the pottery is not totally glassy.

   b. The pigments show evidence of firing because they are shiny.

5. The ash released into the atmosphere will block some of the sun's energy, and result in reducing the earth's average temperature.

6. Answers will vary. In general, the technology involves ways to cut down on the pollution at its source. (Examples might include catalytic converters on cars, cogeneration, scrubbing, and improved fuel efficiency overall.)

7. Ceramics are able to withstand extremely high temperatures and are excellent insulators.

Chapter 25 Review

Check Your Knowledge

Answer the following in complete sentences.

1. Explain what petroleum is and how it forms.

2. Describe how acid rain is harmful to the environment.

3. Explain what a fractionating tower does and how it works.

4. Give four examples of petrochemicals and describe how each is used.

5. Describe the structure of a polymer.

6. Explain how industrial plants can pollute the water around them.

7. Name five kinds of land pollution. Identify the source of each one.

8. Explain how pure metals are obtained from ore.

9. How is oil removed from a trap?

Determine whether each statement is true or false. Write *true* if it is true. If it is false, change the underlined term to make the statement true.

10. Petroleum forms from the remains of <u>land plants</u>.

11. Petroleum contains a mixture of <u>hydrocarbons</u>.

12. When hazardous wastes are <u>toxic</u>, they are no longer poisonous.

13. PVC plastics are made from chemicals that come from <u>petroleum</u>.

14. Composites are made up of <u>fibers</u> embedded in a matrix.

15. Petroleum collects in the <u>nonporous</u> rock layers below a cap rock.

Check Your Understanding

Apply the concepts you have learned to answer each question.

1. What is the role of heat in a fractionating tower?

2. Why can so many different products be made from petrochemicals?

3. **Critical Thinking** How can a substance combine with a polymer to form a product, such as a fiber, that isn't like the substance or the polymer?

4. **Mystery Photo** The photograph on page 604 shows North African pottery from the 1800s. The pottery is made from clay and other earth materials fired at a very high temperature. The heat turns the clay into a hard, glassy substance by a process called vitrification. Vitrification can be total or partial depending on the temperature.

   a. Do you think this pottery has undergone total or partial vitrification? Explain.

   b. Do you think the color designs on the pottery surface were added before or after firing? Explain.

5. **Application** Volcanic ash was released from Mt. Pinatubo in 1990. What effect might this have on global warming?

6. **Critical Thinking** Advances in technology are responsible for smog, acid rain, thermal pollution, and water pollution. What are some kinds of technology being applied to solve these problems?

7. **Application** Ceramics are used to make such items as fireplace tiles and baking sheets. What properties of ceramics make them useful for these purposes?

Develop Your Skills

1. a. around the year 2000

    b. Accept all logical responses. The amount of petroleum produced in the year 2015 will be less than the amount of petroleum produced in the late 1980s. The amount of petroleum available per person depends on the population concerned at that time, assuming that the amount produced is equal to the amount available.

2. Buried toxic wastes can leak into ground water. Seismic activity can compromise a storage location that was thought to be securely sealed. Future generations might unknowingly dig into buried wastes.

3. a. 1.3%; 28.6%; 3.8%

    b. A 10% reduction in gasoline usage would reduce the consumption of oil by about 5%. (About half of each barrel of crude oil goes to the production of gasoline. Assuming all gasoline is used for driving, if driving is cut back by one-tenth, then half of that portion, or one-twentieth, represents the overall reduction.)

Make Connections

1. Concept maps will vary. You may wish to have students do the map below. First draw the map on the board, then add a few key terms. Have students draw and complete the map.

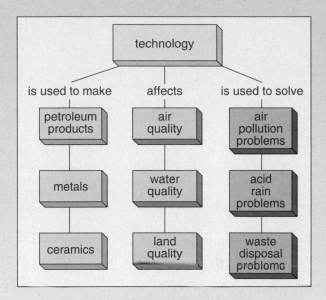

2. Student reports will vary. Most will be familiar through news reports with the connection of Middle East oil reserves and the area's political climate, as well as leverage applied by embargoes imposed by Western powers.

3. Student reports will vary. Both cultures worked and fashioned pure gold, though the Egyptians used alloys in their creations.

4. Student posters will vary. Economic benefits include money gained by selling recyclables to companies that can use them; lower production costs from using recycled instead of virgin materials. Environmental benefits include reduction of waste in landfills; conservation of natural resources as recycled materials are used as input for manufacturing.

5. Student reports will vary. Student reports should include local or county recycling efforts and some information on local dump sites.

Develop Your Skills

Use the skills you have developed in this chapter to complete each activity.

1. Interpret Data The graph shows data about world petroleum production.

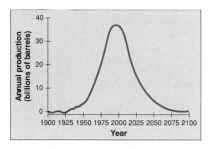

a. In what year is the world's petroleum production expected to peak?

b. When you are thirty, will there be more or less petroleum per person than when you were born? Explain.

2. Infer Injecting toxic wastes in deep wells, and burying nuclear waste deep in the ground are current disposal methods. How might these practices harm the environment?

3. Data Bank Use the information on page 636 to answer the following questions.

a. What percentage of a barrel of crude oil will be used for lubricants? Fuel oil? Petrochemicals?

b. Estimate the percentage of a barrel of crude oil that would be saved if everybody reduced their driving by 10 percent.

Make Connections

1. Link the Concepts Make your own concept map to show how some of the main concepts in this chapter link together. Use words and ideas you find in the chapter.

2. Science and Social Studies The largest petroleum deposits are located in just a few countries of the world. Do library research to find out where these petroleum deposits are located and investigate their impact on politics and the global economy. Write a report or prepare a class presentation to share what you learn.

3. Science and Art Ancient civilizations from all over the world used metallurgy to create distinctive art and jewelry. Do library research on the metallurgy of an ancient culture, such as the Egyptians or the Incas. How did they get metal, and what techniques did they use to make the objects? Write a paper or prepare a poster report for the class.

4. Science and You Investigate plastic recycling in your community. Make a poster to tell people how they can recycle plastic items instead of throwing them away. Include information about the economic and environmental benefits of recycling.

5. Science and Society Many household products contain toxic or hazardous substances. When you throw these items in the trash, they may end up in a landfill that isn't prepared to contain hazardous waste. Research the efforts your community is making to separate these items from household trash. Give an oral report

About the Literary Work

"M.C. Higgins the Great" was adapted from the novel *M.C. Higgins the Great* by Virginia Hamilton, copyright 1974 by Macmillan Publishing Company. Reprinted by permission of Macmillan Publishing Company.

Description of Change

Long passages detailing M.C. Higgins' relationship with his family and other members of the community were edited out of this short section of the text.

Rationale

The selection focuses on the negative impact that strip mining has on the ecology of the region and its inhabitants.

Vocabulary

subsoil, nestled, coal seam, summits, cropland

Teaching Strategies

Directed Inquiry

After students finish reading, discuss the story. Be sure to relate the story to the science lesson in this unit. Ask the following questions:

▶ How is the need for a natural resource causing changes on Sarah's Mountain? (People are strip-mining coal.)

▶ Is this natural resource renewable or nonrenewable? (Nonrenewable)

▶ What is coal used for? (Coal is burned to produce heat and electricity.)

Skills Development

Classify Often an individual's opinion depends on personal experiences. Have students classify each of the following individuals as most likely *for* or *against* the mining of Sarah's Mountain: a forest ranger who works in the region, a factory owner whose facility is powered by electricity, a person who lives near the mountain, a local resident who is hired by the mining company, shareholders in the mining company, a farmer whose farm lies at the base of the mountain, a resort owner whose property lies near the mountain's summit. (*For*—factory owner, local resident hired by mining company, shareholders; *against*—forest ranger, person who lives near the mountain, farmer, resort owner)

Critical Thinking

Compare and Contrast Have students imagine they are members of the community within Sarah's Mountain. A town meeting will be held to decide whether the mining company should be allowed to mine the coal seam. Ask:

▶ What arguments would be used by supporters of the mining project? (Mining would increase town revenues, provide new jobs, reduce electrical costs in the community)

▶ What arguments would be used by opponents of the project? (Mining would destroy the environment, increase community dependence on a nonrenewable resource, have a negative impact on the local ecosystem, interfere with the farm industry at the base of the mountain, and destroy homes.)

Science and Literature Connection

M.C. Higgins the Great

The following excerpts are from the novel M.C. Higgins the Great *by Virginia Hamilton*

Two years ago bulldozers had come to make a cut at the top of Sarah's Mountain. They began uprooting trees and pushing subsoil in a huge pile to get at the coal. As the pile grew enormous, so had M.C.'s fear of it. He had nightmares in which the heap came tumbling down. Over and over again, it buried his family on the side of the mountain.

But his dreams hadn't come true. The spoil heap didn't fall. Slowly his nightmares had ceased and his fear faded within. But then something would remind him, like the chance to get off the mountainside with the dude's coming . . .

To the north and east had been ranges of hills with farmhouses nestled in draws and lower valleys. But now the hills looked as if some gray-brown snake had curled itself along their ridges. The snake loops were mining cuts just like the one across Sarah's Mountain, only they were a continuous gash. They went on and on, following fifty miles of a coal seam. As far as M.C.'s eyes could see, the summits of hills had been shredded away into rock and ruin which spilled down into cropland at the base of the hills.

Glad I don't have to see it, M.C. thought. He turned away riverward, where the hills in front of Sarah's rolled and folded, green and perfect.

"Now that's beauty-*ful*, I'll tell you," the dude said, gazing after M.C. He breathed in deeply, as if he would swallow the sight of the rich river land. "It's like a picture-painting but ever so much better because it's so real. Hills, untouched. Not a thing like it where I come from."

M.C. felt suddenly better, proud of his hills. . . .

"Now you lead and I'll follow."

At once M.C. struck out along the top of Sarah's until he came to where a road began, twisting down into the mining cut. The walk along the road was not hard and soon they were standing in the cut, with seventy feet of a sheer wall to their backs...

"Was all this wall a coal seam at one time?" Lewis asked him.

M.C. sighed inwardly. He didn't want to talk about it. He wanted to get down to home. But he found himself answering, his hands moving, scratching his neck and arms: "Only about ten feet at the bottom of it was ever coal. The rest was just trees and rocks and soils."

Skills in Science

Reading Skills in Science

1. The author opposed the mining of Sarah's Mountain. Answers may vary. Students may cite the author's description of the debris left by the bulldozers, and the dangers to M.C.'s sister by the blasting.

2. The rock and the ruin from the tops of the hills spilled into the cropland at the base of the hills.

Writing Skills in Science

1. Letters will vary. Some students may express dismay and anger at the destruction of the mountain and its unique ecosystem; students may suggest restrictions on strip mining.

2. Stories will vary. Passages will probably describe destruction of M.C.'s home and the loss of his personal possessions.

Activities

Collect Data Answers may vary. Students should note laws that account for environmental and human concerns—for example, regulations governing the restoration of the land.

Communicate Collages and reports should include coal seams, equipment used to uproot trees and push subsoil, and strip-mined areas.

"Lordy," the dude said, shaking his head. "Sixty feet of mountain gone for ten foot of coal. I tell you, there ought-a be a law."

"They take most of the dirt and rocks away in trucks," M.C. said. "But a big pile they just push over the edge of the road with the trees. Then they blasted that coal."

"They didn't!" the dude said.

"Yessir," M.C. said. "We were just playing down around the house when there was a bursting noise. Some rock and coal hit the back of the house real hard. It fell around my sister on her tricycle. Knock holes in her spokes, too. It fell all around her and she never was touched."

"That surely was a blessing," the dude said.

"Yessir," M.C. said.

Skills in Science

Reading Skills in Science

1. **Detect the Writer's Mood** How do you think the author of this selection feels about the mining of Sarah's Mountain? Support your answer with evidence from the selection.

2. **Predict** How do you think the mining on and near Sarah's Mountain affected the farms along the base of the hills?

Writing Skills in Science

1. **Reason and Conclude** Imagine you are M.C. Higgins. Write a letter to your elected officials expressing your opinion regarding the mining of Sarah's Mountain. Give reasons for your opinion and for any action that you think should be taken.

2. **Predict** Suppose M.C.'s nightmares came true and the spoil heap suddenly fell down upon his home. Write a short story describing what happens.

Activities

Collect Data In a library, research various methods of mining coal and the laws regulating the environmental aspects of coal-mining in the United States. How do the laws apply to the mining described in the selection?

Communicate Use photos from magazines to make a collage that illustrates the activity in the selection. Give an oral report on your collage.

Where to Read More

Save the Earth by Betty Miles. New York: Alfred Knopf, Inc., 1991. This handbook provides an overview of environmental problems and offers suggestions on how students can help protect the earth.

Restoring Our Earth by Lawrence Pringle. Hillside, N.J.: Enslow Publishing, 1987. This text examines the ecological restoration of prairies, marshes, forests, rivers, and other ecosystems damaged by humans.

Periodic Table of Elements

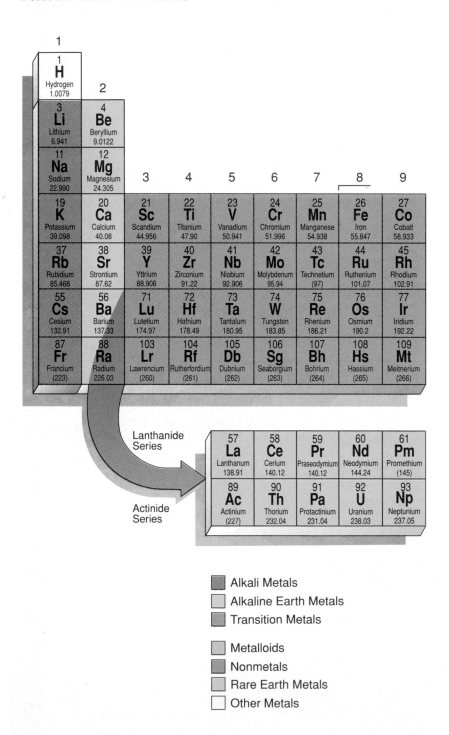

Legend	
■	Alkali Metals
□	Alkaline Earth Metals
■	Transition Metals
■	Metalloids
■	Nonmetals
■	Rare Earth Metals
□	Other Metals

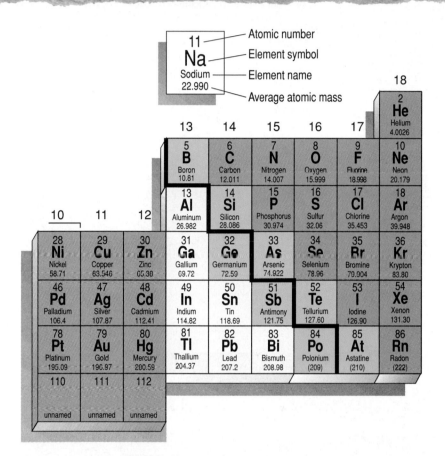

		Atomic number
11		
Na		Element symbol
Sodium		Element name
22.990		Average atomic mass

	13	14	15	16	17	18
						2 He Helium 4.0026
	5 B Boron 10.81	6 C Carbon 12.011	7 N Nitrogen 14.007	8 O Oxygen 15.999	9 F Fluorine 18.998	10 Ne Neon 20.179

10	11	12						
			13 Al Aluminum 26.982	14 Si Silicon 28.086	15 P Phosphorus 30.974	16 S Sulfur 32.06	17 Cl Chlorine 35.453	18 Ar Argon 39.948
28 Ni Nickel 58.71	29 Cu Copper 63.546	30 Zn Zinc 65.38	31 Ga Gallium 69.72	32 Ge Germanium 72.59	33 As Arsenic 74.922	34 Se Selenium 78.96	35 Br Bromine 79.904	36 Kr Krypton 83.80
46 Pd Palladium 106.4	47 Ag Silver 107.87	48 Cd Cadmium 112.41	49 In Indium 114.82	50 Sn Tin 118.69	51 Sb Antimony 121.75	52 Te Tellurium 127.60	53 I Iodine 126.90	54 Xe Xenon 131.30
78 Pt Platinum 195.09	79 Au Gold 196.97	80 Hg Mercury 200.59	81 Tl Thallium 204.37	82 Pb Lead 207.2	83 Bi Bismuth 208.98	84 Po Polonium (209)	85 At Astatine (210)	86 Rn Radon (222)
110 unnamed	111 unnamed	112 unnamed						

62 Sm Samarium 150.4	63 Eu Europium 151.96	64 Gd Gadolinium 157.25	65 Tb Terbium 158.93	66 Dy Dysprosium 162.50	67 Ho Holmium 164.93	68 Er Erbium 167.26	69 Tm Thulium 168.93	70 Yb Ytterbium 173.04
94 Pu Plutonium (244)	95 Am Americium (243)	96 Cm Curium (247)	97 Bk Berkelium (247)	98 Cf Californium (247)	99 Es Einsteinium (254)	100 Fm Fermium (257)	101 Md Mendelevium (258)	102 No Nobelium (259)

Surface Gravity of Bodies in the Solar System

Body	Surface Gravity
Sun	27.90
Jupiter	2.54
Saturn	1.06
Neptune	1.20
Uranus	0.92
Earth	1.00
Venus	0.92
Mars	0.38
Pluto	0.07
Mercury	0.38

*The surface gravity of each body is based on the surface gravity of Earth, which is expressed as 1.00.

Products from One Barrel of Crude Oil

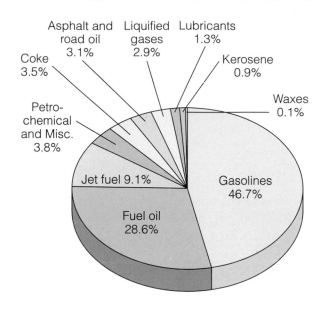

Asphalt and road oil 3.1%
Liquified gases 2.9%
Lubricants 1.3%
Coke 3.5%
Kerosene 0.9%
Waxes 0.1%
Petro-chemical and Misc. 3.8%
Jet fuel 9.1%
Gasolines 46.7%
Fuel oil 28.6%

Development of the Computer

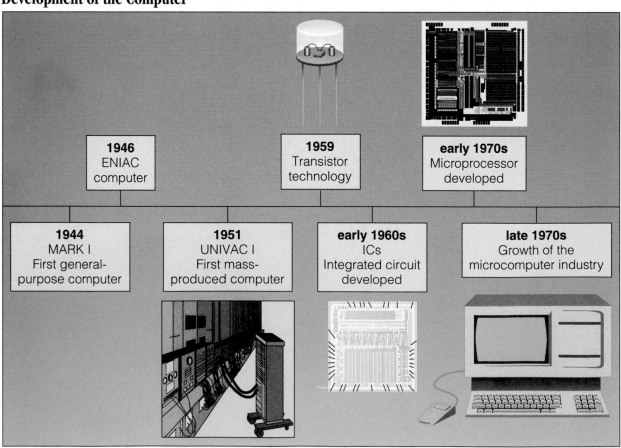

1944 MARK I First general-purpose computer

1946 ENIAC computer

1951 UNIVAC I First mass-produced computer

1959 Transistor technology

early 1960s ICs Integrated circuit developed

early 1970s Microprocessor developed

late 1970s Growth of the microcomputer industry

Size of Atoms and Ions of Elements in Periods 2 and 3

Atomic Number	Element	Radius of Atom (nanometers)	Ion	Radius of Ion (nanometers)
3	Lithium	0.123	Li⁺	0.060
4	Beryllium	0.089	Be²⁺	0.031
5	Boron	0.080	B³⁺	0.020
6	Carbon	0.077	C⁴⁺	0.015
7	Nitrogen	0.070	N³⁻	0.171
8	Oxygen	0.066	O²⁻	0.140
9	Fluorine	0.064	F⁻	0.136
11	Sodium	0.157	Na⁺	0.095
12	Magnesium	0.136	Mg²⁺	0.065
13	Aluminum	0.125	Al³⁺	0.050
14	Silicon	0.117	Si⁴⁺	0.041
15	Phosphorus	0.110	P³⁻	0.212
16	Sulfur	0.104	S²⁻	0.184
17	Chlorine	0.099	Cl⁻	0.181

Energy Production

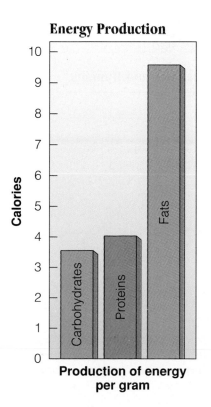

Calories

Carbohydrates, Proteins, Fats

Production of energy per gram

Average Maximum Daily Temperatures

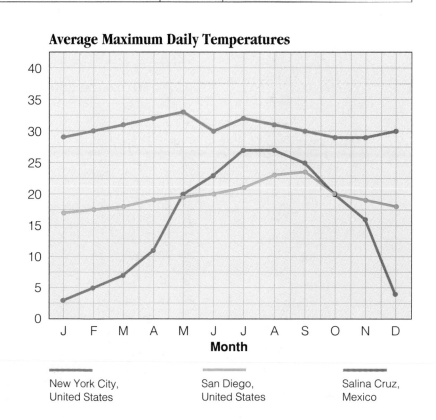

Month

J F M A M J J A S O N D

New York City, United States

San Diego, United States

Salina Cruz, Mexico

Top Speed of Some Animals in Air

Animal	Speed (km/hr)
Spine-tailed swift	170
Pigeon	96
Hawk moth	53
Monarch butterfly	32
Honeybee	18

Top Speed of Some Animals on Land

Animal	Speed (km/hr)
Cheetah	112
Prong-horned antelope	96
Jackrabbit	72
Ostrich	48
Human	43

Top Speed of Some Animals in Water

Animal	Speed (km/hr)
Sailfish	96
Flying fish	64
Dolphin	59
Trout	24
Human	8

Activity Series of Metals

Most Active

Lithium

Potassium

Barium

Calcium

Sodium

Magnesium

Aluminum

Zinc

Iron

Nickel

Tin

Lead

Copper

Mercury

Silver

Gold

Least Active

Radio-Band Frequencies

Type	Wave	Frequency
Short wave (AM)		2,300–26,100 kHz
Medium wave (AM)		525–1,700 kHz
Long wave (AM)		150–300 kHz
VHF (FM)		87–108 kHz

Mechanical Efficiency of Machines and Humans

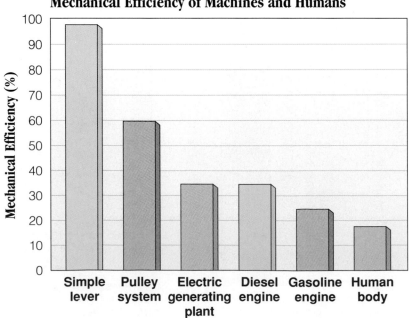

Sound Spectrum

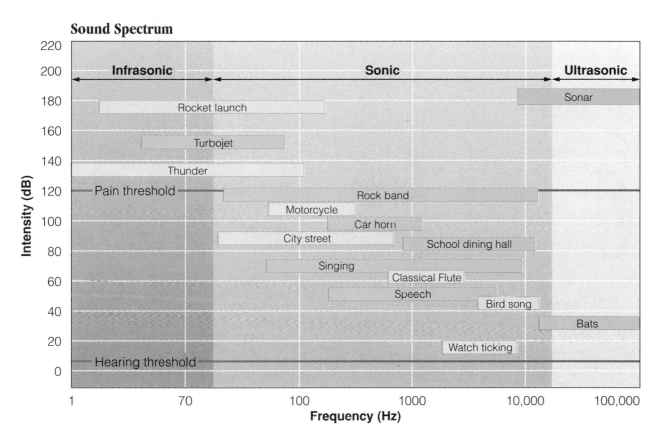

Electric Conductivity of Metals at 20° C

Material	% IACS*
Aluminum	65
Arsenic	5
Copper	100
Gold	77
Iron	18
Lead	8
Magnesium	39
Nickel	25
Platinum	16
Silver	108
Zinc	29

*International Annealed Copper Standard
A value of 100% is given to copper when it is at a specific conductive state.

Magnetic Declination in the United States

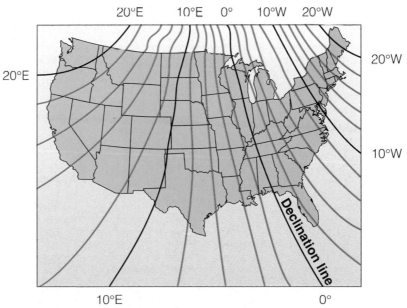

Each of the lines on this magnetic map shows the number of degrees a magnetic compass varies from true or geographic north. East declination means the compass needle is pulled to the east of true north. West declination means the compass needle is pulled to the west of true north.

Normal Body Temperatures of Some Animals

Canada jay
43°C

King penguin
37.7°C

Indian python
28.6°C

Large-mouthed black bass
24°C

Lungless salamander
14.8°C

Domestic rabbit
38.5°C

Human
37°C

Saltwater crocodile
25.6°C

Spiny anteater
23.3°C

Ascaphus frog
10°C

Color Wheel

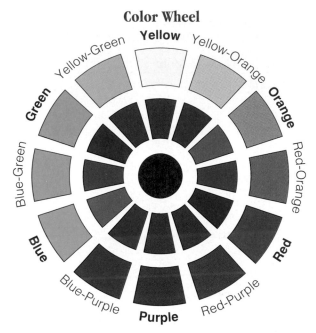

Yellow
Yellow-Green
Yellow-Orange
Green
Orange
Blue-Green
Red-Orange
Blue
Red
Blue-Purple
Red-Purple
Purple

The colors shown in the inner circle are obtained when the colors opposite each other in the outer circle are mixed together.

Air Pollutant Sources from Combustion

Pollutant	Major Source
Carbon monoxide	Transportation (68.4%)
Sulfur oxides	Power Plants/Heating (73.4.%)
Hydrocarbons	Transportation (60%)
Nitrogen oxides	Transportation (49.1%)
Particulates	Power Plants/Heating (42%)

Speed of Sound

Material	Speed of Sound (m/s)
Air (0°C)	331
Helium (0°C)	965
Ethyl alcohol (25°C)	1207
Water (25°C)	1498
Copper	3800
Tempered glass	5170

Properties of Common Elements

Element	Symbol	Atomic Number	Atomic Mass	Melting Point (°C)	Boiling Point (°C)	Density (g/cm³)	Specific Heat (J/kg°C)
Aluminum	Al	13	26.982	660	2467	2.7	899
Arsenic	As	33	74.922	817	613	5.7	330
Bromine	Br	35	79.904	−7	59	3.1	472
Calcium	Ca	20	40.08	839	1484	1.6	652
Carbon	C	6	12.011	3550	4827	2.3	711
Chlorine	Cl	17	35.453	−101	−35	0.0032	477
Chromium	Cr	24	51.996	1857	2672	7.2	447
Copper	Cu	29	63.546	1083	2567	8.96	385
*Einsteinium	Es	99	(252)	—	—	—	823
Fluorine	F	9	18.998	−220	−189	0.00179	823
Gold	Au	79	196.966	1064	3080	19.3	130
Helium	He	2	4.003	−272	−269	0.00018	5,183
Hydrogen	H	1	1.008	−259	−253	0.00009	14,253
Iodine	I	53	126.904	114	184	4.93	426
Iron	Fe	26	55.847	1535	2750	7.87	443
Lead	Pb	82	207.2	328	1740	11.35	159
Lithium	Li	3	6.941	181	1342	0.53	3,553
Magnesium	Mg	12	24.305	649	1090	1.74	1,016
Mercury	Hg	80	200.59	−39	357	13.55	138
Neon	Ne	10	20.179	−249	−246	0.0009	1,028
Nickel	Ni	28	58.71	1453	2732	8.9	443
Nitrogen	N	7	14.007	−210	−196	0.0013	1,041
Oxygen	O	8	15.999	−218	−183	0.00143	915
Phosphorus	P	15	30.974	44	280	1.82	757
Platinum	Pt	78	195.09	1772	3827	21.45	133
Potassium	K	19	39.098	63	760	0.862	752
Silicon	Si	14	28.086	1410	2355	2.3	702
Sodium	Na	11	22.990	98	883	0.97	1,225
Sulfur	S	16	32.06	113	445	2.07	732
Tin	Sn	50	118.69	232	2270	7.31	213
Uranium	U	92	238.029	1132	3818	19.0	117
Zinc	Zn	30	65.38	420	907	7.133	389

*Some data is unavailable (—).

Data Bank

Comparison of Fluorescent and Incandescent Light Bulbs

Fluorescent			Incandescent		
Fluorescent Lamp Type and Wattage	Light Output (lumens)*	Lamp Life (hrs)	Incandescent Bulbs Type and Wattage All 130 Volt	Light Output (lumens)*	Lamp Life (hrs)
6 watt	230	11,000	25 watt	172	6,250
8 watt	310	11,000	60 watt	650	2,500
14 watt	600	11,000	150 watt	2080	1,875
20 watt	1110	13,000	200 watt	2847	1,875
8 watt	263	9,000	40 watt	350	3,750
14 watt	521	9,000	64 watt	504	7,500
18 watt	740	9,000	75 watt	730	7,500
40 watt	2480	17,500	2/100 watt	2496	1,875
19 watt	610	17,500	60 watt	650	2,500
22 watt	740	17,500	75 watt	730	6,250
32 watt	1495	17,500	100 watt	1248	1,875
7 watt	400	10,500	40 watt	350	2,750
9 watt	600	10,500	60 watt	650	2,500
13 watt	900	10,500	75 watt	730	6,250

*Approximate lumens at 40% of lamp life.

Breakdown of Energy Consumption in the United States

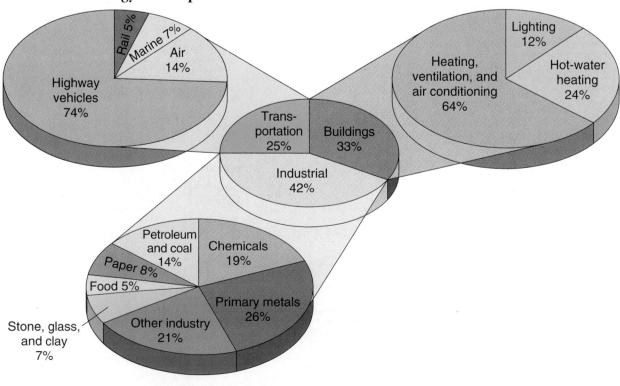

Radiation Exposure in the United States

Source of radiation	Average dose
Cosmic radiation (from space)	40 mrem/year
TV and computer screens	4 mrem/year (2 hours of viewing per day)
Living in a brick or stone house	40 mrem/year
Dental X-ray (whole mouth)	910 mrem
Air travel	2 mrem per 2-hour flight
Air, water, food	25 mrem/year
Rocks and soil	55 mrem/year
Smoke detectors, luminous watch dials	2 mrem/year

*The unit for radiation is the *rem*. A millirem, or *mrem*, is $\frac{1}{1,000}$ of a rem. The U.S. Council on Radiation Protection recommends limiting radiation from all sources to 500 *mrem* per year.

Elements in the Earth's Crust (in percent)

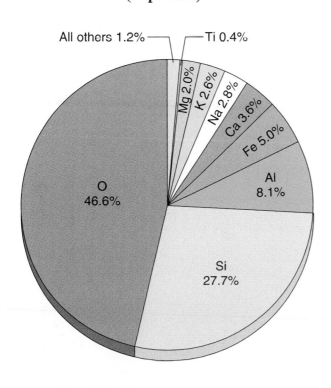

All others 1.2% — Ti 0.4%
Mg 2.0%
K 2.6%
Na 2.8%
Ca 3.6%
Fe 5.0%
Al 8.1%
O 46.6%
Si 27.7%

The pH Scale

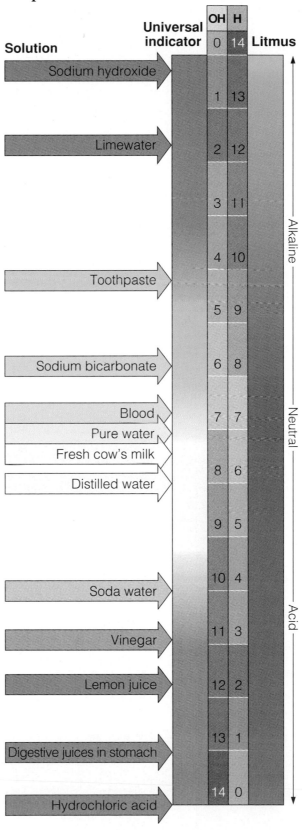

Solution — Universal indicator — Litmus

Solution	OH	H	
Sodium hydroxide	0	14	Alkaline
	1	13	
Limewater	2	12	
	3	11	
	4	10	
Toothpaste			
	5	9	
Sodium bicarbonate	6	8	
Blood	7	7	Neutral
Pure water			
Fresh cow's milk			
Distilled water	8	6	
	9	5	
Soda water	10	4	Acid
Vinegar	11	3	
Lemon juice	12	2	
Digestive juices in stomach	13	1	
Hydrochloric acid	14	0	

Math Appendix

Symbols

α = alpha particle	f = frequency	M.A. = mechanical advantage
β = beta particle	G = universal gravity	N = newton
γ = gamma ray	G.P.E. = gravitational potential energy	P = power
λ = wavelength	g = acceleration due to gravity (9.8 m/s^2)	P.E. = potential energy
Ω = ohm		p = pressure
a = acceleration	h = height	R = resistance
A = amps	Hz = hertz	r = angle of reflection
A = area	I = electric current	T = temperature
c = speed of light	i = angle of incidence	t = time
°C = degree Celsius	J = joule	v = velocity
d = density	K.E. = kinetic energy	V = volt
d = distance	kWh = kilowatt hour	v = volume
E = effort	l = length	W = watt
°F = degree Fahrenheit	m = mass	w = weight
F = force	m = meter	W = work

Formulas

Chapter 1

density

$$\text{density} = \frac{\text{mass}}{\text{volume}}$$

$$d = \frac{m}{v}$$

Chapter 2

acceleration

$$\text{acc.} = \frac{\text{final velocity} - \text{initial velocity}}{\text{time}}$$

$$a = \frac{v_f - v_i}{t}$$

velocity

$$\text{velocity} = \frac{\text{distance}}{\text{time}}$$

$$v = \frac{d}{t}$$

kinetic energy

$$\text{kinetic energy} = \frac{1}{2} \times \text{mass} \times \text{velocity}^2$$

$$\text{K.E.} = \frac{1}{2}mv^2$$

joule

$$\text{joule} = 1 \text{ newton-meter}$$
$$= \text{newton} \times \text{meter}$$
$$\text{J} = 1 \text{ N·m}$$

gravitational potential energy

$$\text{gravitational potential energy} = \text{mass} \times \text{gravity} \times \text{height}$$
$$\text{G.P.E.} = mgh$$

weight

$$\text{weight} = \text{mass} \times \text{gravity}$$
$$w = mg$$

Chapter 3

newton

$$\text{newton} = 1 \text{ kilogram} \times \frac{\text{meter}}{\text{second}^2}$$

$$\text{N} = 1 \text{ kg} \cdot \frac{m}{s^2}$$

force

$$\text{force} = \text{mass} \times \text{acceleration}$$
$$F = ma$$

momentum

$$\text{momentum} = \text{mass} \times \text{velocity}$$
$$\text{momentum} = mv$$

Chapter 4

pressure

$$\text{pressure} = \frac{\text{force}}{\text{area}}$$

$$p = \frac{F}{A}$$

Chapter 5

work	work = force x distance
	$W = \mathbf{F} \times d$
power	$power = \dfrac{work}{time}$
	$P = \dfrac{W}{t}$
mechanical advantage	mechanical advantage
	$= \dfrac{resistance\ force}{effort\ force}$
	$M.A. = \dfrac{R}{E}$
mechanical efficiency	mechanical efficiency
	$= \dfrac{work\ output}{work\ input} \times 100\%$
	$efficiency = \dfrac{W_{out}}{W_{in}} \times 100\%$

Chapter 6

Charles' Law	As pressure (p) increases, volume (v) decreases.
Boyle's Law	As temperature (T) increases, volume (v) increases.

Chapter 9

temperature conversions	$°F = \dfrac{9}{5} °C + 32$
	$°C = \dfrac{5}{9} (°F - 32)$
heat	heat = mass × specific heat × temperature change
	$heat = m \times specific\ heat \times (T_2 - T_1)$

Chapter 11

current	$current = \dfrac{voltage}{resistance}$
	$I = \dfrac{V}{R}$
electric power	electric power = volt × current
	$P = VI$
volt	volt = current × resistance
	$V = IR$
energy	energy = power × time
	energy = Pt

Chapter 14

wave speed	speed = frequency × wavelength
	$speed = f\lambda$
wave reflection	angle of incidence = angle of reflection
	$i = r$

Practice Problems

Chapter 1

1. You are given the following information: mass = 48 g; volume = 24 cm³. What is the density of this substance?

2. What is the density of a rock if its mass is 36 g and its volume is 12 cm³?

3. If a block of wood has a density of 0.6 g/cm³ and a mass of 120 g, what is its volume?

4. Calculate the mass of a substance which has a volume of 35 cm³ and a density of 0.5 g/cm³.

5. If you have a gold brick that is 2 cm by 3 cm by 4 cm and has a density of 19.3 g/cm³, what is its mass?

6. What is the density of an object that has a mass of 25 g and a volume of 10 cm³?

Chapter 2

1. A car is stopped at a red light. When the light turns green, it accelerates to 30 m/s in 15 s. What is the car's acceleration?

2. You took a car trip with your family to visit relatives who live 750 km away. The trip took 8 h. What was your average speed in km/h?

3. If you travel 50 km due east in 2 h, what is your velocity ?

4. A train goes from 20 m/s to 40 m/s in 5 min. What is the train's acceleration in m/s²?

5. A train takes 10 min to slow down to 10 m/s from 40 m/s. What is its acceleration?

6. The traffic on the highway you are traveling moves at 90 km/h. At this rate, how long will it take you to travel 450 km?

7. If a runner maintains a speed of 2.5 m/s, how far can he run in 15 s? In an hour?

8. You pedal your 20 kg bicycle at 3 m/s. What is the kinetic energy of your bicycle?

9. You are pedaling your bicycle at 3 m/s. If you add your mass in kg to the 20 kg bicycle, what is the kinetic energy of both you and the bicycle?

Answers to Practice Problems

Chapter 1

1. 2 g/cm³
2. 3 g/cm³
3. 200 cm³
4. 17.5 g
5. 463.2 g
6. 2.5 g/cm³

Chapter 2

1. 2 m/s²
2. 93.75 km/h
3. 25 km/h
4. 0.07 m/s²
5. − 0.05 m/s²
6. 5 h
7. 37.5 m; 9000 m
8. 90 kg · m/s
9. Answers will average between 300–360 kg · m/s.

Chapter 2 *Continued*

10. **9 m/s**

11. **0.08 kg**

12. **600 m**

13. **11 760 kg · m/s**

14. **617.4 N**

15. **102.9 N**

Chapter 3

1. **686 N**

2. **60 kg**

3. **1000 m/s^2**

4. **2 m/s^2**

5. **150 000 kg · m/s**

6. **50 000 kg · m/s**

7. **50 kg**

8. **40 m/s**

Chapter 4

1. **75 N**

2. **4 N/m^2**

3. **0.4 m^2**

4. **8750 N/m^2**

5. **250 000 N/m^2**

Chapter 5

1. **2 J**

2. **0.4 *W***

3. **3000 J**

4. **6400 J**

5. **100 N**

6. **4500 J; 150 *W***

7. **200 *W***

8. **M.A. = 3**

9. **280 N**

10. **80 N**

11. **67%**

12. **500 N**

13. **6000 J; 75%**

Chapter 6

1. **9 mL**

2. **18 mL**

3. **divided by 2**

646

10. While ice skating, a 50 kg student has a kinetic energy of 2025 J. What is the student's velocity?

11. A baseball thrown at a velocity of 40 m/s has a kinetic energy of 64 joules, what is its mass?

12. A ball has a potential energy of 150 kg m and a mass of 0.25 kg. How high is the ball from the ground?

13. What is the gravitational potential energy of a 60 kg skier at the top of a hill that is 20 m high?

14. A rock has a mass of 63 kg. What is its weight on the earth?

15. Suppose you took a rock with a mass of 63 kg to the moon where the gravitational force is 1/6 that of the earth. What would the rock weigh on the moon?

Chapter 3

1. What is a person's weight in newtons if she has a mass of 70 kg?

2. If a person weighs 588 N, what is his mass?

3. Imagine that you throw a baseball that weighs 0.1 kg with a force of 100 N, what is the acceleration of the baseball?

4. An arrow leaves the bow with a force of 500 N. The mass of the arrow is 250 g. What is its acceleration?

5. A 5,000 kg car is moving with a velocity of 30 m/s, what is its momentum?

6. What is the momentum of a 2,500 kg boulder rolling down a hill at a velocity of 20 m/s?

7. A rolling ball has a velocity of 5 m/s and a momentum of 250 kg·m/s. What is the mass of the ball?

8. A train has a momentum of 400 000 kg·m/s and a mass of 10,000 kg. What is its velocity?

Chapter 4

1. If a pressure of 15 N/m^2 is applied over an area of 5 m^2, what is the force?

2. You are given the following information: Force = 20 N; Area = 5 m^2. Find pressure.

3. Find the cross-section area of a concrete piling if the force required to drive it into the ground is 10 N with a pressure of 25 N/m^2.

4. A person weighing 350 N is standing up. The area of the bottom of her feet is 0.04 m^2. What pressure is being exerted onto the ground, in N/m^2?

5. A bullet hits a target with a force of 500 N. The hole it leaves has an area of 0.002 m^2. What pressure did the bullet apply to the target?

Chapter 5

1. If Maria uses 4 N of force to lift a box onto a shelf 0.5 m high, how much work did she do?

2. Joanne did 2 J of work in 5 s. How much power did she use?

3. How much work is required to push a 300 N box 10 m across the floor?

4. Suppose you weigh 300 N and you carry your books, which weigh 20 N, to your class on the fourth floor. Each flight of stairs is 5 m high. How much work did you do?

5. If a person does 200 J of work by lifting a box 2 m off the floor, how much does the box weigh?

6. A 450-N person ran up a flight of stairs which was 10 m high. How much work did the person do? If it took 30 s, what was the person's power?

7. What is the power of a motorboat that can do 5000 J of work in 25 s?

8. What is the mechanical advantage of a lever if the effort force is 15 N and the resistance force is 45 N?

9. A lever has a mechanical advantage of 7. If John applies 40 N of effort force, how much resistance force can he overcome?

10. If a machine has a mechanical advantage of 3, how much effort force is required to overcome a resistance force of 240 N?

11. If you need to put 12 N of work into a machine to get 8 N of work out, what is the mechanical efficiency of this machine?

12. A machine has an efficiency of 80%. If you need to get a work output of 400 N, how much work must you put in?

13. A machine can lift 1,500 kg to a height of 4 m, but it uses 8,000 J to do so. What is the work output of the machine? What is its mechanical efficiency?

Chapter 6

1. You are given the following information: initial pressure) × (initial volume) = (final pressure) × (final volume); initial pressure = 3.0 N/m^2; initial volume = 12 mL; final pressure = 4.0 N/m^2. Calculate the final volume.

2. If a sample of gas has an initial volume of 30 mL at a pressure of 1.2 N/m^2, what is the final volume if the pressure is increased to 2.0 N/m^2, assuming no change in the temperature?

3. If you double the pressure on a specific amount of gas, what happens to its volume, assuming there is no temperature change?

4. If the volume of a 50 mL sample of gas at 2.1 N/m² of pressure is reduced to 30 mL, what is the final pressure?

5. Suppose you use all of the air from a filled balloon to blow up a toy that is only one half the size of the balloon. How will the pressure inside that toy compare to the original pressure in the balloon?

Chapter 9

1. If today's air temperature is 41°F, what is the air temperature in °C.

2. What is the approximate temperature in °F of 20°C?

3. You take your temperature with a thermometer that measures in degrees Celsius. Your temperature is 40°C. Are you sick? What is your temperature in °F?

4. A radiator with a mass of 50 kg has an initial temperature of 95 °C and a final temperature of 50°C. Its specific heat is 448 J/kg°C. How much heat energy did it give off?

5. How much heat is required to raise the temperature of 0.5 kg of water from 20°C to 30°C ? The specific heat of water is 4,190 J/kg°C.

6. How much heat is needed to raise the temperature of 2 kg of copper by 5°C (specific heat of copper = 387 J/kg °C)

7. A 10 kg mass of an unknown substance gives off 180 200 J/kg°C of heat when it cools 20° C. What is its specific heat?

8. How much heat is needed to raise the temperature of 0.05 kg of iron from 20°C to 35°C? (specific heat of iron = 448 J/kg °C)

Chapter 11

1. What is the current used by a toaster that has a resistance of 12 ohms and uses 120 volts?

2. What is the resistance of a light bulb if it uses 0.5 amps of current and 110 volts?

3. What is the voltage of a battery that can create a 1.5 amp current through a 8 ohm resistor?

4. What is the voltage in a circuit that uses 5 amps of current across a 10 ohm resistor?

5. If a 4 amp circuit has a resistance of 3 ohms, what is the voltage?

6. If a stereo draws 0.5 amps of current when plugged into a 120 volt outlet, how much power does it use?

7. How much power does a 1.5-volt battery have if it can produce a 0.05-amp current?

8. A 100-W light bulb was left on in your room while you were at school for 8 h. How much energy was wasted?

9. Suppose the electric company in your area charges $.08 per kWh, how much did it cost to use 8,000 W?

Chapter 14

1. You are at the beach watching the waves roll in. You time them and determine that they hit the beach every 5 s and that the crests are 15 m apart. What is the speed of these waves?

2. The speed of sound in air is 340 m/s. If the frequency of the middle C note is 256 Hz, what is its wavelength?

3. What is the frequency of a sound wave that has a wavelength of 0.017 m?

4. What is the wavelength of a sound wave with a frequency of 20 Hz?

5. The speed of light is 3.00 x 10⁸ m/s. Calculate the frequency of a wavelength that is 30 m.

6. A photographer wants to light up an object using light bounced off a blank wall. If the object is at a 45° angle to the wall, at what angle should she direct the spotlight towards the wall?

4. 3.5 N/m²

5. doubled

Chapter 9

1. 5°C

2. 68°F

3. yes; 104°F

4. 1 008 000 J

5. 20 950 J

6. 3870 J

7. 901 J/kg°C

8. 336 J

Chapter 11

1. 10 amps

2. 220 ohms

3. 12 volts

4. 50 volts

5. 12 volts

6. 60 *W*

7. 0.075 *W*

8. 8000 *W*h or 8 k*W*h

9. $ 0.06

Chapter 14

1. 3 m/s

2. 1.33 m

3. 20 000 Hz

4. 17 m

5. 10 000 000 Hz

6. 45° angle

Glossary

A simple, phonetic spelling is given for words in this book that may be unfamiliar or hard to pronounce.

Stressed syllables are printed in capital letters. Sometimes a word has two stressed syllables. The syllable with the primary stress is printed in FULL capitals. The syllable with the secondary stress is printed in SMALL capitals.

Most of the time, the phonetic spelling can be interpreted without referring to the key. The key below gives the pronunciations for letters that are commonly used for more than one sound.

Example: *Bioluminescence* is pronounced BY oh LOO muh NES uhns.

Pronunciation Key

a	c**a**t	ih	p**i**n
ah	h**o**t	oh	gr**o**w
ai	c**a**re	oo	r**u**le, m**u**sic
aw	**a**ll	ow	n**ow**
ay	s**ay**, **a**ge	oy	v**oi**ce
ee	m**ee**t	u	p**u**t
eh	l**e**t	uh	s**u**n, **a**bout
eye	**i**ce or b**y**	ur	t**er**m

absolute zero   The temperature at which molecules do not move; the lowest temperature matter can have. Abbreviated: 0 K. (p. 211)

acceleration   A change in velocity, or the rate at which this change occurs. (p. 39)

acid   A chemically active substance low on the pH scale that gives up hydrogen ions (H+) in a water solution. (p. 527)

acid rain   Rainwater polluted with sulfuric acid, nitric acid, or both. (p. 624)

activation energy   Energy required to start a chemical reaction. (p. 504)

air pollution   A high concentration of harmful gases and solids in the air. (p. 621)

airfoil   An object, such as a plane's wing, with one flat and one curved surface that causes a pressure difference and a reaction force when moving through air. (p. 98)

alpha decay   Radioactive decay in which alpha particles are released from the nucleus of an atom. (p. 566)

ampere   (AM peer) SI unit of electric current. Abbreviated: A, or amps. (p. 270)

amplitude   (AM pluh tood) The distance in a transverse wave between the line of origin and each crest or trough. (p. 344)

applied science   The use of science or technical knowledge to achieve a practical purpose; technology. (p. 21)

astigmatism   A vision disorder in which an imperfectly shaped cornea unevenly bends light entering the eye. (p. 439)

atom   The smallest particle of an element with all the properties of the element that can combine with other atoms to form a molecule. (p. 157)

base   A chemically active substance high on the pH scale that gives up hydroxide ions (OH-) in a water solution. (p. 527)

basic   Having the characteristics of a base or containing a base. (p. 528)

beta decay   Radioactive decay in which beta particles are released from the nucleus of an atom. (p. 566)

binding energy   Energy of the force that holds protons and neutrons together. (p. 562)

bioluminescence   (BY oh LOO muh NES uhns) The emission of light by living things. (p. 434)

biomass   Organic matter that can be used as fuel. (p. 591)

boiling point   The temperature at which a substance changes from a liquid to a gas. (p. 223)

Boyle's Law   The principle stating that the pressure of gas in a confined space increases when the volume of the gas is reduced, if its temperature is kept constant. (p. 143)

buoyant force   The upward force acting on an object in a fluid. Buoyant force equals the weight of the fluid displaced by the object. (p. 91)

calorie   The amount of heat needed to raise the temperature of 1g of water 1° C. (p. 217)

carbohydrate   (kar boh HY drayt) An organic compound of carbon, hydrogen, and oxygen, such as a starch or sugar, with a ratio of hydrogen and oxygen atoms that is two to one. (p. 545)

catalyst (CAT uh lihst)   A substance that initiates or speeds up a chemical reaction without being used up in the process. (p. 506)

central heating system   A network of wires, pipes, ducts, and vents that transfers heat throughout a building from a central location. (p. 231)

centripetal acceleration   (sehn TRIP uh tuhl) Acceleration caused by movement in a circle. (p. 43)

centripetal force   The force necessary to keep an object moving in a circle and that is directed inward toward the center. (p. 68)

ceramic   Material made by firing clay or other substance at a high temperature. (p. 616)

charge   Electric force of a proton, electron, or an object having an unequal number of protons and electrons. (p. 257)

Charles' Law   The principle stating that the volume of a gas increases as its temperature is increased, if its pressure remains constant. (p. 144)

chemical bond   The attractive force that holds atoms or ions together. (p. 467)

chemical change   Change in the chemical identity of a substance. (p. 149)

chemical equation   A combination of chemical symbols and formulas that represent a chemical reaction. (p. 494)

chemical reaction   Interaction between substances in which existing chemical bonds break and new bonds form, creating one or more new substances. (p. 489)

circuit   A closed, continuous path through which electric current flows. (p. 267)

cochlea   (KOHK lee uh) The coil-shaped organ in the inner ear that is lined with hair cells that detect motion, sound waves, and send a nerve impulse to the brain. (p. 386)

coefficient   (KOH uh FIHSH uhnt) The number in a chemical equation that shows how many atoms or molecules of a substance are involved in a reaction. (p. 496)

cogeneration   An energy-saving process in which heat and electricity are produced and utilized from the same fuel source. (p. 599)

colloid   (KAHL oyd) A mixture with particles larger than those in a solution and smaller than those in a suspension. Colloids are not completely homogeneous, but are less heterogeneous than suspensions. (p. 523)

combustion   Any type of chemical reaction with oxygen that gives off heat or light. (p. 244)

compass   An instrument for determining direction with a magnetized needle that aligns itself with the earth's magnetic field. (p. 290)

composite   Material made of fibers that are embedded in a matrix. (p. 618)

compound machine   A system of two or more simple machines. (p. 120)

compound   A substance made of two or more chemically combined elements. (p. 168)

compression   Part of a longitudinal wave where the particles of matter through which the energy wave is moving are pressed together. (p. 337)

concave   A surface that is curved or rounded inward, like the inside surface of a bowl. (p. 443)

concentration   The amount of solute relative to the amount of solvent. (p. 520)

conduction   The transfer of heat energy or electrons between objects in direct contact. (pp. 213, 262)

conductor   A substance through which electric charges or heat can move easily. (p. 263)

constant   The factor that is kept the same in a controlled experiment. (p. 7)

constructive interference   The interaction of energy waves in which the same parts of two waves match up so that the amplitudes of the waves add to each other. (pp. 376–377)

controlled experiment   An experiment with two test groups: an experimental group and a control group. (p. 7)

convection   The transfer of heat energy by the movement of a fluid. (p. 214)

convex   A surface that is curved or rounded outward like the surface of a ball. (p. 443)

cornea   The transparent structure that covers the pupil and the iris of the eye. (p. 438)

covalent bond   (koh VAY lent) A type of chemical bond formed between nonmetals in which atoms share one or more electrons. (pp. 469, 478)

crest   The highest point of a transverse wave. Indicates the amount of energy in the wave. (p. 336)

crystal lattice   The structure of an ionic solid in which an orderly three- dimensional pattern of atoms is repeated over and over. (p. 474)

cubic meter   The basic SI unit of volume; space occupied by a cube 1 m x 1 m x 1 m. Abbreviated: m^3. (p. 12)

 data   Information from which analyses and conclusions can be made. (p. 3)

deceleration   A decrease in velocity over a period of time. (p. 40)

decibel   The unit used to measure sound intensity. Abbreviated: dB. (p. 367)

decomposition reaction   A chemical reaction in which a single reactant breaks down into simpler parts, such as elements. (p. 500)

density   The measure of how much mass exists in a given volume; density = mass/volume. (p. 13)

destructive interference   The interaction of waves in which the same parts of each wave do not match. The amplitudes of the waves subtract from each other. (p. 376)

diffraction   Bending of a wave as a result of the interaction between the wave and the edge of an object. (p. 350)

diode   A vacuum tube through which electrons flow in only one direction. (p. 310)

Doppler effect   A change in wave frequency, and therefore the pitch of a sound, caused by movement of either the source or the receiver. (p. 369)

double-replacement reaction   A chemical reaction in which two different ions trade places between different ionic compounds, forming two new compounds. (p. 501)

drag   The force that opposes the movement of an object through a fluid. (p. 99)

E   **echolocation**   (EK oh loh KAY shuhn) The method used by animals to locate objects by sending and receiving high-frequency sound waves . (p. 402)

electric current   Flow of electric charge. Abbreviated: I. (p. 267)

electromagnet   A magnet made of a soft-iron core surrounded by a coil of wire through which an electric current is passed. (p. 294)

electromagnetic induction   The process of producing an electric current by moving a magnetic field through a wire coil without touching it. (p. 300)

electromagnetic spectrum   The entire range of visible and invisible electromagnetic waves. (p. 428)

electron   A subatomic particle with a negative charge located outside of an atom's nucleus. (p. 158)

electronics   The specialized field of physics dealing with behavior and control of electrons. (p. 309)

element   Matter that cannot be changed into a simpler form by any ordinary physical or chemical process. (p. 157)

emulsifier   (ee MUHL sih FY er) A substance that helps to disperse tiny particles of liquid throughout another substance. (p. 526)

endothermic reaction   (EN duh THER mihk) Any chemical reaction that absorbs energy. (p. 492)

energy   The ability to cause change or do work. (pp. 45– 46)

enzyme   A biological catalyst that controls the rate of a specific chemical reaction in a living thing. (p. 508)

exothermic reaction   (EK suh THER mihk) A chemical reaction that releases energy. (p. 492)

F   **fluid**   Any substance that tends to flow or to conform to the outline of its container, such as a liquid or a gas. (p. 85)

fluorescent   Referring to light produced by electrons colliding with gas particles in a tube coated with phosphor. (p. 434)

focal length   The distance from a lens to the point where light rays that pass through the lens are focused. (p. 446)

force   The push or pull on an object that causes motion or change. (p. 55)

fossil fuel   Fuel, such as oil, formed naturally from the remains of ancient organisms over millions of years. (p. 586)

frame of reference   A place or object that is assumed to be fixed and by which the movement of other objects is determined. (p. 31)

frequency   (FREE kwuhn see) The number of wavelengths that pass a point in a given time. (p. 344)

friction   The force of resistance that occurs when movement takes place between any two objects or substances that make contact. (p. 57)

fulcrum   The fixed point of a lever. (p. 117)

G   **gamma decay**   Radioactive decay in which no matter is released, but which releases energy called gamma radiation, or gamma rays. (p. 566)

gamma ray   The electromagnetic wave with the shortest wavelength that is emitted by radioactive materials during a nuclear reaction. (p. 420)

gas   Matter having no definite shape and no definite volume. (p. 142)

geothermal   Relating to the heat produced beneath the earth's surface. (p. 592)

global warming   The increase of the earth's atmospheric temperature as a result of the greenhouse effect. (p. 622)

greenhouse effect   A process that traps energy from the sun by allowing radiant energy to enter a given space, but prevents heat energy from escaping. (p. 622)

 half-life   The amount of time it takes for half the atoms of a quantity of a radioactive isotope to decay. (p. 568)

halogen   Any one of the five elements in Group 17 of the periodic table (fluorine, chlorine, bromine, iodine, and astatine) that can combine with a metal to form a salt. (p. 197)

hardware   The equipment and components that make up a computer, such as a central processing unit, main storage, input devices, and output devices. (p. 323)

heat energy   A form of energy produced by vibration of molecules that can be absorbed, given up, or transferred between substances. (p. 209)

hertz   The unit used to measure the frequency of waves. Abbreviated: Hz. (p. 368)

heterogeneous mixture   A mixture in which the components are not evenly mixed so that different parts of the mixture have different compositions. (p. 176)

hologram   A three-dimensional picture formed on photographic film by the interference pattern of a split beam of laser light. (p. 456)

homogeneous mixture   A mixture in which the components are evenly mixed so that every part of the mixture is the same as any other. Same as *solution*. (p. 176)

hydrocarbon   (hy druh KAR buhn) An organic compound that contains only hydrogen and carbon atoms. (p. 539)

hydroelectric power   Electricity generated by the power of moving water. (p. 586)

 illuminated   An object or substance that is visible because it is reflecting light. (p. 433)

incandescent   Light produced by a heated object that glows. (p. 434)

inclined plane   A slanted-surface, simple machine that is used to raise or lower an object. (p. 116)

induction   The transfer of electrons between objects that are not in direct contact. (p. 262)

inertia   The tendency of an object to remain at rest or in motion until acted upon by an external force. (p. 61)

infrared   Invisible electromagnetic waves with wavelengths slightly longer than red light. Infrared waves have a penetrating heating effect. (p. 420)

inner ear   The part of a human ear that contains the cochlea and the semicircular canals. (p. 386)

insulation   (ihn suh LAY shuhn) A substance that slows the transfer of heat. (p. 236)

insulator   A substance through which electric charges or heat can't move readily. (p. 263)

integrated circuit   A tiny electric circuit that contains transistors, diodes, and resistors usually located on a small piece of silicon. (p. 313)

interference   The effect of two or more waves interacting. (p. 352)

internal energy   The total amount of energy a substance contains. (p. 209)

internal reflection   The reflection of light off the inner surface of an object, as in a tube or optical fiber. (p. 457)

Ion   An atom or group of atoms having an electric charge as a result of losing or gaining one or more electrons. (p. 170)

ionic bond   (eye AHN ihk) A chemical bond between a metal and a nonmetal in which electrons are transferred from one atom to another. (pp. 469, 471)

iris   The colored portion of the eye that surrounds the pupil. (p. 437)

isomer   (EYE suh mur) An organic compound that has the same chemical formula for which more than one structure is possible. (p. 541)

isotope   (EYE soh tohp) Atoms of the same element that have different numbers of neutrons, and therefore different atomic masses. (p. 161)

joule   (JOOL) The metric unit that measures work or energy. Abbreviated: J. (p. 108)

Kelvin   The SI temperature scale using units equivalent to Celsius degrees and beginning at absolute zero. (p. 211)

kilogram   The basic SI unit of mass. Abbreviated: kg. (p. 13)

kinetic energy   (KUH neht ihk) The energy of motion. Abbreviated: K.E. (p. 47)

laser   A device that produces coherent light of one wavelength that does not spread out as it travels. An acronym for **L**ight **A**mplification by **S**timulated **E**missions of **R**adiation. (p. 455)

Law of Conservation of Mass and Energy The principle that the amount of matter and energy in the universe cannot be created or destroyed. (p. 124)

lens A curved transparent object that forms an image by refracting light passing through it. (p. 446)

lever A simple machine that does work by moving around a fixed point. (p. 117)

lift Upward force acting on an airfoil moving through air. (p. 98)

lipid (LIH pihd) An organic compound, such as fat or oil, that has long hydrocarbon chains and does not dissolve in water. (p. 547)

liquid Matter having definite volume but not definite shape. A fluid. (p. 141)

liter A metric unit of volume. Abbreviated: L. (p. 12)

longitudinal wave (lahn juh TOOD uh nuhl) An energy wave consisting of a series of compressions and rarefactions that moves through a medium in the same direction the wave is travelling. (p. 337)

luminous (LOO muh nuhs) Referring to an object that produces light. (p. 433)

luster A property of metal that enables it to reflect light from the surface. (p. 189)

M **machine** A device that makes work easier by changing the direction or distance an object moves, or by reducing the amount of force needed to do work. (p. 112)

magnetic domain Magnetic regions in which the poles of individual atoms line up and group together. (p. 289)

magnetic field The area of magnetic force surrounding a magnet. (p. 288)

magnetic pole One of the two ends of a magnet where magnetic force is strongest. (p. 288)

malleability (MAL ee uh BIL uh tee) The ability to be flattened, bent, and shaped without breaking; a property of metals. (p. 189)

mass The scientific measurement of the amount of matter that an object contains. Abbreviation: *m*. (p. 13)

matrix Material in which another material or substance is embedded in a composite. (p. 618)

matter Any object or substance that has mass and takes up space. (p. 135)

mechanical advantage The advantage gained by using a machine to transmit force. Mechanical advantage = resistance force/effort force. Abbreviated: M.A. (p. 113)

mechanical efficiency The measurement that compares a machine's work output with its work input. Mechanical efficiency = work output/work input x 100% (p. 114)

melting point The temperature at which a substance changes from a solid to a liquid. (p. 224)

metalloid An element that has the properties of both a metal and a nonmetal. (p. 187)

metallurgy (MEHT uh LUR jee) The process and science of taking metals from the earth and making them into useful products. (p. 614)

meter The basic SI unit of length. Abbreviated: m. (p. 12)

microprocessor An integrated circuit that can hold all of a computer's problem-solving capabilities on one small silicon chip. (p. 322)

middle ear The part of the human ear between the eardrum and the oval window containing the hammer, anvil, and stirrup. (p. 386)

molecule Two or more chemically bonded atoms; the smallest part of a compound having all the properties of the compound. (p. 170)

momentum The product of the mass and velocity of an object. Momentum = mass x velocity. (p. 67)

N **neutralization** A process in which bases and acids react to form products that are neither acids nor bases. (p. 527)

neutron (NOO trahn) A subatomic particle located in an atom's nucleus that has no electric charge and that has a mass similar to that of a proton. (p. 160)

newton The basic SI unit of force. Abbreviated: N. (p. 56)

noise An unwanted sound that may disturb or threaten mental or physical health. (p. 394)

nonrenewable resource A natural resource, such as oil or natural gas, that can't be replaced by natural cycles or processes within a human lifetime. (p. 596)

nuclear fission Splitting of an atom's nucleus into two smaller nuclei, releasing a large amount of energy. (p. 571)

nuclear force The force within the nucleus of the atom that holds the parts of the nucleus together. (p. 78)

nuclear fusion Joining of two or more atoms' nuclei, which releases an enormous amount of energy. (p. 573)

nucleus The central region of an atom where neutrons and protons are located. (p. 159)

ohm (OHM) The SI unit of resistance force. Abbreviated: Ω. (p. 271)

opaque (oh PAYK) Referring to a material that absorbs most light that strikes it. (p. 423)

optic nerve Nerve fibers connecting the rods and cones of the retina to the brain. (p. 438)

optical fiber A thin, flexible, glass or plastic fiber that transmits light throughout its length by internal reflection. (p. 457)

ore A mineral containing a relatively large amount of a metal compound. (p. 192)

organic compound A carbon compound that occurs naturally in all living things. (p. 537)

outer ear The part of the human ear that is visible from the exterior, and includes the ear canal and the eardrum. (p. 386)

overtone One of the higher pitched tones produced when a note is sounded and that contributes to the timbre of the sound. (p. 391)

 particle model The idea stating that all matter is made of tiny particles which are in constant motion. (p. 135)

periodic Describing a regular, repeating pattern, such as the periodic table of the elements or the periodic phases of the moon. (p. 183)

permanent magnet A magnet that retains its magnetism after the magnetizing force is removed. (p. 289)

petrochemicals (peh troh KEHM ih cuhls) Synthetic materials and chemical substances produced from petroleum. (p. 609)

petroleum A dark, oily, liquid mixture of hydrocarbons formed from organic material over millions of years; crude oil. (p. 605)

pH A measurement that shows how acidic or basic a solution is. (p. 529)

photoelectric effect The release of electrons by certain substances, such as metals, when struck by high-energy light. (p. 411)

photon (FOH tahn) The packet of light energy given off by an atom. (p. 409)

photosynthesis (FOH toh SIHN theh suhs) A chemical process by which plants use water, carbon dioxide, and energy from the sun to make oxygen and glucose for energy. (p. 552)

physical change A change in a substance's physical properties but not in its chemical identity. (p. 147)

pitch The property of sound determined by the frequency of the sound waves producing it; highness or lowness of sound. (pp. 367–368)

plasma (PLAZ muh) The fourth phase of matter having unique properties and formed at very high temperatures. (p. 145)

polarized Referring to light waves that are parallel, usually as a result of passing through a special filter. (p. 410)

polyatomic ion A group of covalently bonded atoms that has an electric charge due to losing or gaining one or more electrons. (p. 480)

polymer (PAHL ih mur) A large molecule made of a chain of many smaller units connected by covalent bonds. (pp. 541, 609)

potential energy Energy due to the position of an object or the chemical bonds in a substance. Abbreviated: P.E. (p. 46)

power The rate at which work is done, measured in watts. Power = work/time. (p. 109)

pressure The force exerted on a surface. Pressure = force/area. (p. 85)

product A substance produced by a chemical reaction. (p. 495)

protein (PROH teen) An organic compound existing as a large, complex molecule made of amino acids. (p. 548)

proton A subatomic particle with a positive charge located in the nucleus of an atom. (p. 159)

pulley A simple machine made of a rope wrapped around a grooved wheel. (p. 119)

pupil The opening through which light enters the eye. (p. 437)

R-value The measurement of a material's ability to stop the flow of heat. (p. 236)

radiation The transfer of energy by infrared rays. (p. 215)

radioactive decay The process by which an unstable nucleus of a radioactive element breaks down spontaneously. (p. 565)

radioactivity The release of particles and energy from the nucleus of an atom. (p. 561)

rarefaction (RAIR uh FAK shun) Part of a longitudinal wave where the particles of matter through which the wave is moving are spread apart. (p. 337)

reactant   (ree AK tuhnt) The raw material in a chemical reaction; shown on the left side of a chemical equation. (pp. 494–495)

real image   An image formed by converging light rays. (p. 442)

rectifier   A vacuum tube diode that changes alternating current into direct current. (p. 310)

reflection   The action of a wave when it bounces off a surface. Also, the image formed by light rays reflected off a surface. (pp. 349, 441)

refraction   Bending of a wave caused by the change of speed that occurs when the wave moves from one medium to another. (pp. 351, 445)

refrigerant   A chemical that evaporates at a low temperature and removes heat as it changes from a liquid to a gas; used in cooling systems. (p. 241)

renewable resource   A natural resource that is replaced continuously by natural cycles or processes. (p. 596)

resistance   The force opposing the flow of electric current. Abbreviated: R. (p. 271)

resonance   (REZ uh nehnts) The vibration of an object at its natural frequency. (p. 378)

respiration   The chemical process in living organisms during which oxygen reacts with glucose to produce carbon dioxide, water, and energy in the form of ATP. (pp. 554–555)

retina   The inner layer of the back of the eye where light-sensitive cells are located. (p. 438)

salt   An ionic compound made of a metal and a nonmetal and formed when an acid and a base react. (p. 529)

saturated hydrocarbon   Hydrocarbon in which all carbon atoms are joined by single covalent bonds. (p. 541)

saturated   Referring to a solution that contains as much of the solute as can be dissolved at a given temperature and pressure. (pp. 520-521)

scientific notation   The method of expressing a very large or very small number by multiplying a number between 1 and 10 by some power of 10. (p. 14)

sclera   The visible white part of the eye surrounding the iris. (p. 437)

semiconductor   Material whose electric conductivity is between that of a conductor and that of an insulator. (p. 312)

silt   Very fine particles of earth material. (p. 522)

simple machine   A machine that does work in one movement. (p. 116)

single-replacement reaction   A chemical reaction in which atoms of one element replace atoms of another element in a compound, producing a different element and a different compound. (p. 501)

smog   A type of air pollution consisting primarily of smoke and fog. (p. 623)

software   Programs that instruct computer hardware to perform certain tasks. (p. 324)

solar cell   A device containing a semiconductor that converts sunlight into electricity. (p. 590)

solid   Matter having definite shape and a definite volume. (p. 141)

solubility   The ability of a substance to dissolve in another substance. (p. 519)

solute   The component of a solution that is dissolved in the solvent. (p. 515)

solution   A mixture in which the components are evenly mixed so that every part of the mixture is the same as any other. Same as *homogeneous mixture*. (p. 515)

solvent   A component of a solution in which the solute is dissolved. (p. 515)

sonar   The technique of using ultrasonic waves to locate underwater objects. Acronym for **so**und **n**avigation **a**nd **r**anging. (p. 400)

sonogram   The image created by ultrasonic waves reflected off the soft tissue of living organism. (p. 399)

sound wave   The longitudinal wave in matter that can be heard, produced by a vibrating object. (p. 359)

specific heat   The amount of heat necessary to raise the temperature of 1 g of a substance 1°C. (p. 216)

speed   The distance travelled in a given amount of time. (p. 34)

strong force   A nuclear force that holds protons and neutrons together by holding their quarks together. (p. 78)

substituted hydrocarbon   A hydrocarbon in which at least one hydrogen atom is replaced by another functional group. (p. 542)

supersaturated   Referring to a solution that contains more solute than could normally be dissolved at a given temperature and pressure. (pp. 520-521)

suspension   Mixture in which some particles are relatively large and will settle out when the mixture is not moving. (p. 522)

synthesis reaction   A chemical reaction in which two substances combine to form a third, more complex substance. Also called combination or composition reaction. (p. 500)

T   **technology**   The use of scientific or technical knowledge to solve a problem or to achieve a practical purpose; applied science. (p. 21)

temperature   The amount of heat energy in a substance, determined by the average kinetic energy of the molecules in the substance. (p. 209)

terminal velocity   The maximum velocity of a falling object, occurring when the force of friction equals the force of gravity. (pp. 57–58)

thermal expansion   An increase in the volume of a substance due to an increase in heat energy. (p. 225)

thermal pollution   An increase in water temperature that harms living things. (p. 625)

thrust   Force that moves an object forward. (pp. 98–99)

timbre   (TIM bur) The quality of a sound determined by the combination of different frequencies of the sound waves that make up the sound. (p. 370)

transistor   A semiconducting device that contains layered n-type and p-type semiconducting materials. (p. 313)

translucent   (tranz LOOS uhnt) Referring to a material that transmits some light but scatters it so that a sharp image is not seen. (p. 423)

transmutation   (trans myoo TAY shun) The process in which an element changes into a different element, such as by radioactive decay. (p. 567)

transparent   Describing a material that transmits almost all the light rays that strike it. (p. 423)

transverse wave   Wave in which matter moves at a right angle to the direction of the wave. (p. 336)

trough   The lowest point of a transverse wave. (p. 336)

turbine   A set of curved blades mounted on a long shaft that is turned by the flow of a fluid, such as steam. Used to generate electricity. (p. 247)

U   **ultrasound**   A sound with a wave frequency greater than those within the range of human hearing. (p. 398)

ultraviolet   Relating to invisible electromagnetic waves with wavelengths shorter than visible violet light and longer than X-rays. (p. 420)

universal force   One of the four forces common throughout the universe: gravitational, nuclear, electric, or magnetic. (p. 73)

universal solvent   Water, so called because of its ability to dissolve many substances. (p. 517)

unsaturated   Referring to a solution that contains less solute than can be dissolved at a given temperature and pressure. (pp. 520-521)

unsaturated hydrocarbon   A hydrocarbon that contains at least one double or triple covalent bond in its chain of carbon atoms. (p. 541)

V   **vacuum tube**   An early electronic device that consists of a glass vacuum bulb, a filament, and a plate. Used to control electrons. (p. 310)

variable   The factor that is changed in a controlled experiment. (p. 7)

velocity   (veh LAHS uh tee) The speed and direction of movement. (p. 34)

virtual image   An image, such as one seen in a plane mirror, formed by light rays that do not actually pass where the image appears. (p. 442)

volt   The SI unit of voltage. Abbreviated: V. (p. 270)

voltage   The amount of electric energy available to move a charge. (p. 270)

volume   The amount of space occupied by an object or substance. (p. 12)

W   **watt**   The basic SI unit of power; one watt equals one joule per second. Abbreviated: W. (p. 109)

wave   Disturbance that transfers energy through matter or space. (p. 335)

wavelength   The distance between two like parts of a wave, such as crests. (p. 343)

weak force   The nuclear force that holds together the particles within protons and neutrons. (p. 78)

work   Force acting upon an object in the direction the object moves. Work = force x distance. (p. 107)

work input   The amount of work put into a machine. (p. 114)

work output   The amount of work produced by a machine. (p. 114)

X   **X-ray**   A high energy electromagnetic wave that can travel through matter and has a wavelength of .001 nm to 10 nm. (p. 420)

Index

Note: Boldfaced page numbers refer to definitions. Italicized page numbers refer to figures.

external-combustion, *246,* 246-247
gasoline, *245,* 245-246
gas-turbine, 619
internal-combustion, *245,* 245-246, 619
solar-powered, 247
turbines, 247-248, 584, 591
workings of, 244
Heating systems
central, 231-234, *232, 233, 234,* 248
insulation, *236,* 236, 237, 238
solar, 234-235, *235*
Heat pumps, *234,* 234
Heat transfer
climate and, *218-219,* 218-219
conduction and, *213,* 213, 215
convection and, *214,* 214, 215
measuring, 216-217
methods of, *213,* 213
radiation and, *215,* 215
Helium (He)
density of, 198
hydrogen and, 197, 573
light of, 435
oxygen and, 199
properties of, 165, *197*
uses of, 198-199
Helium-3, 162
Henry, Joseph, 300
Hertz (Hz), 344, 368, 387, 398, 418
Hertz, Heinrich, 344
Heterogeneous mixtures, **176,** *176*
Hologram, **456,** *456*
Holography, *456,* 456
Homogeneous mixtures, **176,** *176,* 515, 516, 522
Homogenized milk, 525
Horsepower (hp), 109
Hot-water heating, *232,* 232
Human body. *See also* Hearing; Vision
acids in stomach of, 554
bones of, 365
cooling system of, *240,* 240
copper in, 167
digestion and, 125, 508, 545
ear, 86, *386,* 386
electric activity in, *79,* 79
electric charge in, 259
electricity safety and, 282
energy conversion in, 125
eye, 426, *437,* 437-438, *438,* 440
iron in, 167
metabolic rate and, 556
pH of blood in, *531,* 531
radiation on, 569
sound energy and, 365
temperature of, 125
trace elements in, 167
water in, 125
Hummingbirds, *101,* 101
Hydrocarbons, **539**-541, *540, 542,* 542

Hydrochloric acid, 502, 530
Hydroelectric power, **586**
Hydrogen (H)
atomic mass of, 162
atom of, 469
in bubble chamber, 163
chemical bonds and, *467,* 467
chlorine and, *491,* 491
covalent bonds and, *479*
helium and, 197, 573
nonmetals and, 197, 198
as nuclear fuel, 573
oxygen and, 169, *171,* 171
properties of, *197,* 197
stove, 594
in water, *467,* 467
Hydrogen chloride (HCl), *479, 491,* 491, 501
Hydrogen peroxide, 151, *467,* 467
Hydrogen stove, 594
Hydroxyls, 542
Hypothesis, **5**

Illuminated objects, *433,* 433
Images, 442, 446, 447, 454
Impressionism, *427,* 427
Impurities, 312
Incandescent light, **434**-435, 436
Incident rays, **441**
Inclined plane, **116,** *116*
Indicator, 530
Indium (In), *195,* 195
Induction, **262,** *262*
Industrial smog, 623
Inertia, 60-**61**
Inferring, **4,** *4*
Infrared rays, **420,** *420*
Inner ear, **386**
Input devices, computer, *323,* 323
Insolubility, 520-521
Insulation, **236,** *236,* 237, 238
Insulators
ceramics as, 616
electric, 137
fiberglass as, 618
heat, 238
materials for, 221
plastics as, 137, 263
static electricity and, *263,* 263
Integrated circuits, **313,** *313*
Intensity, *366,* 366, 412
Interference
constructive, *352,* 352, *376,* 376-377
deconstructive, *352,* 352, *376,* 376-377
definition of, **352**
of light waves, 424
of sound waves, *376,* 376-377
of waves, *352,* 352
Internal-combustion engines, *245,* 245-246, 619

Internal energy, **209**
Internal reflection, **457**
Intertidal zone, *88*
Invertase, 508
Invisible electromagnetic spectrum, 419-420, *420*
Iodine (I), *166,* 167, *197,* 197
Iodine-131, 563
Iodized table salt, 175, 191, 529
Ion-exchange process, 477
Ion-exchange resins, 477
Ionic bonds
crystal lattice and, *474,* 474
definition of, **471**
electrons in, 469, 471
electron transfer and, 471
formation of, *472-473,* 472-473
ions in, *475,* 475-476, 477
sodium chloride and, *472-473,* 472-473
Ionic compounds, **170,** *170,* 474, 476, 484
Ionic solids, 474, 476
Ions
in alkali metals, 191, 475
chlorine, *472-473,* 472-473
in covalent bonds, 480
definition of, **170**
dissolved, 476
in halogens, 475
in ionic bonds, *475,* 475-476, 477
in ionic compounds, *170,* 170
magnesium, *475,* 475, 477
nitrogen, *475,* 475
nonmetals and, 194
in plasma, 476
polyatomic, *480,* 480
in rare-earth metals, 475
size of, 475
sodium, *472-473,* 472-473
Iris, **437,** *438,* 438, 449
Iron (Fe)
carbon in, 193
copper sulfate and, *501,* 501
in human body, 167
ore, *615,* 615
properties of, 165
sulfur and, 500
tools, 614
Iron Age, 614
Iron nails, 175
Iron sulfide (FeS), 500
Isomers, **541,** *541*
Isotopes
atoms and, *161,* 161
of carbon compounds, *161*
definition of, **161,** *163*
radioactive, 161, **563,** *563,* 569

Joule, **108,** 209, 279
Joule, James Prescott, 210
Joules per second (J/s), 279

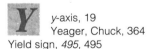

Illustrations

Patric Gnan
pgs. 86-87, 215, 218

Precision Graphics
pgs. xi, xv, 17,18, 19, 20, 29, 31, 35, 36, 38, 40, 42b, 53, 56, 65b, 68, 83, 90, 92, 105, 129, 143b, 144b, 155, 181, 183, 184, 199, 203, 211, 222, 224, 229, 251, 274, 280, 285, 307, 321, 325, 329, 342, 343, 344, 345, 349, 352, 357, 362, 366, 368, 370, 376, 383, 395, 407, 411, 412, 415, 416, 417, 418-419, 424, 431, 443, 446, 447, 450, 487, 513, 530, 531, 535, 546, 547, 548, 554, 559, 562, 567, 577, 586, 595, 603, 606b, 631, 636, 637, 638, 639, 640, 641, 642, 643

Rolin Graphics
pgs. iii, iv-v, 4, 7, 26, 42c, 43b, 50a, 57, 5, 65a, 71a, 85, 94, 96, 97, 116, 117, 118, 119, 121, 122, 123, 126, 151, 157, 162, 168, 170b, 174, 186-187, 191, 192, 195, 196, 197, 212, 213, 214, 217, 223, 231, 232, 233, 234, 235, 240, 242, 245, 246, 262, 268, 269, 288, 289, 293, 294, 296, 297, 301, 302, 303, 312, 317, 318, 336, 337, 338, 351, 360-361, 364, 369, 386, 387, 391, 400-401, 404, 413, 421, 427, 439, 442, 456, 457, 468, 472-473, 474, 477, 479, 480, 481, 484, 493, 495, 504, 506, 509, 523, 572, 596, 607, 606a, 614, 615, 623, 627, 634-635

Larry Hughston
pgs. 74-75, 76

Michael Maydak
pgs. vii, 264-265, 437, 568

Jane McCreary
pgs. 330-331, 374, 380, 462-463

Barbara Melodia
All reflective artwork for unit and chapter openers, half-page activity bars, chapter review bars, icons for WarmUp, WorkOut, and STS Features.

DJ Simison
pgs. 130-131, 204-205

Nadine Sokol
pgs. 140, 141, 142, 143a, 144a

Margo Stahl-Pronk
pgs. 32-33, 47, 48, 88-89, 372, 373, 551, 552-553

Doug Roy
pg. 120

Sarah Woodward
pgs. v, vii, 8, 9, 132, 158, 159, 160, 161, 170a, 171, 475, 491, 496, 500, 501, 540, 566, 571, 584-585, 598

Acknowledgments

Photographs

Title Page i Robert L. Dunne/Bruce Coleman Inc.; i-L Ken Karp*; i-C Bill Ross/AllStock-TR Ellis Herwig/Stock, Boston

Contents iii Don Carroll/The Image Bank; ivBL Phil Degginger/Bruce Coleman Inc.; ivCL Lee Boltin; ivTR Ken Karp*; vBL GHP Studio*; vBR Ken Karp*; vi-vii Ken Karp*; viBL Ted Levin/Earth Scenes; viTC David Parker/Science Photo Library/ Photo Researchers; viTL Jeff Hornbaker; viiBC Louis Bencze/AllStock; viiBR Stanley Breeden/DRK Photos; viiiBR Robert Winslow/Tom Stack & Associates; viiiBL GHP Studio*; viiiCL Science Photo Library/Photo Researchers; viiiTL Dan McCoy/Rainbow; ixBL Nick Pavloff*; ixBLC The Granger Collection; ixBR GHP Studio*; ixBRC The Granger Collection; ixTR Robert Shafer/Tony Stone Worldwide; xi Agence Vandystadt/Allsport; xiiB National Museum of American History/Smithsonian Institution; xiiT Elliott Smith*; xiii Ken Karp*; xivC James E. Lloyd/Animals, Animals; xivL Ken Karp*; xivR GHP Studio*

Unit 1 xvi 1 Nuridsany & Perennou/Photo Researchers

Chapter 1 2 John Cancalosi/Peter Arnold, Inc.; 3B GHP Studio*; 3C GHP Studio*; 4B Ken Karp*; 5 Ken Karp*; 10 Stacy Pick/Stock, Boston; 12L GHP Studio*; 12R Ken Karp*; 13L Ken Karp*; 13R Ken Karp*; 14 Ken Karp*; 21 James A. Sugar/Woodfin Camp & Associates; 22B CERN/Science Photo Library/Photo Researchers; 22C Kodansha/The Image Bank; 22T Richard Nowitz/Phototake; 23B Takeshi Takahara/Photo Researchers; 23C T. J. Florian/Rainbow; 23TL Ken Eward/Science Source/Photo Researchers; 23TR Jean Claude Revy/Phototake; 25L Erich Lessing/Art Resource; 25R Lee Boltin; 26 Ken Karp*

Chapter 2 30 © Roger Hessmeyer/Starlight; 31B W. Eastep/The Stock Market; 31T W. Eastep/The Stock Market; 34B Gabor Demjen/Stock, Boston; 34T Elliott Smith*; 36 John Eastcott-Yva Momatiuk/DRK Photos; 39 Agence Vandystadt/Allsport; 41 Vince Streano/The Stock Market; 42 Anna & Manat Shah/Animals, Animals; 43T Michael J. Howell/Stock, Boston; 45 Steve Elmore/Tom Stack & Associates; 46 Eberhard Grames-Bilderberd/The Stock Market; 47B John Gillmoure/The Stock Market; 49B John Running/Stock, Boston; 49T Z. Leszczynski/Earth Scenes; 50 Ken Karp*

Chapter 3 54 John M. Roberts/The Stock Market; 55 Elliott Smith*; 59 David Madison; 60 Elliott Smith*; 61 Elliott Smith*; 62B GHP Studio*; 62L Tony Duffy-Priscilla Rouse/Allsport; 62TR Stephen Hilson/AllStock; 63 Ken Karp*; 67 Calspan for the National Highway Traffic Safety Administration; 70 NASA; 71B Focus on Sports; 72 Bill Ross/AllStock; 77B Craig Davis/Sygma; 77T Wes Thompson /The Stock Market; 78B Robert Winslow/Tom Stack & Associates; 78C Hank Morgan/Rainbow; 78T Richard Nowitz/The Stock Market; 79 L. Steinmark/Custom Medical Stock Photo; 80 Ken Karp*

Chapter 4 84 Phototake; 88L Bob Abraham/The Stock Market; 88R Mike Severns/Tom Stack & Associates; 89L Doug Perrine/DRK Photos; 89R Dr. Paul A. Zahl/Photo Researchers; 91 Kevin Schafer-Martha Hill/AllStock; 93 Ken Karp*; 94 Jack Fields/Photo Researchers; 95 Robert Azzi/Woodfin Camp & Associates; 96 Ken Karp*; 97B Elliott Smith*; 97T Elliott Smith*; 98 Paul Chauncey/The Stock Market; 100B Wayne Lankinen/DRK Photos; 100R Keith H. Murakami/Tom Stack & Associates; 101L Michael Fogden/Bruce Coleman Inc.; 101R A.E. Zuckerman/Tom Stack & Associates; 102B GHP Studio*; 102C GHP Studio*; 102T GHP Studio*

Chapter 5 106 Bernard Van Berg/The Image Bank; 107 Elliott Smith*; 108 Elliott Smith*; 109L Charles Gupton/AllStock; 109R Elliott Smith*; 113 GHP Studio*; 114 Nick Pavloff*; 120T GHP Studio*; 123T; NASA; 124B GHP Studio*; 124C GHP Studio*; 124T GHP Studio*; 125 Don Carroll/The Image Bank; 126 Ken Karp*; 130-131 Ken Karp*

Unit 2 132-133 Masa Uemura/AllStock

Chapter 6 134 Manfred Kage/Peter Arnold, Inc.; 135 NASA; 136BCL Erich Lessing/Art Resource; 136BL Lee Boltin; 136BR Erich Lessing/Art Resource; 136CRB Ken Karp*; 136CRT Janice Sheldon*; 136TL Phil Degginger/Bruce Coleman Inc.; 137BC Lee Boltin; 137BR Ken Karp*; 137L Ken Karp*; 137TC Ken Karp* 137TR; Stephen Frisch*; 138C Ken Karp*; 138L Fred Ward/Black Star; 138R GHP Studio*; 139C Joe Bator/The Stock Market; 139L Karl Hartmann-Sachs/Phototake; 139TR Fred Ward/Black Star; 141CR Ken Karp*; 141L Karl Hartmann-Sachs/Phototake; 142B GHP Studio*; 145 NASA; 146 GHP Studio*; 147 D. P. Hershkowitz/Bruce Coleman Inc.; 148C L. L. T. Rhodes/Earth Scenes; 149B James E. Lloyd/Animals, Animals; 149L Colin Milkins/Oxford Scientific Films/Earth Scenes; 149R Steve Elmore/The Stock Market; 150 Lawrence Migdale*; 151T CNRI-Science Photo Library/Photo Researchers; 152 Ken Karp*

Chapter 7 156 Bryan Peterson/The Stock Market; 158L GHP Studio*; 158R GHP Studio*; 159L GHP Studio*; 159R GHP Studio*; 163 David Parker-Science Photo Library/Photo Researchers; 165BC Ken Karp*; 165BR Tui De Roy/Bruce Coleman Inc.; 165R GHP Studio*; 165TC GHP Studio*; 165TR Wayland Lee*; 166B Ken Karp*; 166BC Ken Karp*; 166CT Ken Karp*; 166T Ken Karp*; 168B Ken Karp*; 168C Ken Karp*; 168I Ken Karp*; 169BC GHP Studio*; 169L Stephen Frisch*; 169R Runk-Schoenberger/Grant Heilman Photography; 169TC Breck P. Kent/Earth Scenes; 170B Ken Karp*; 170T Ken Karp*; 172 Elliott Smith*; 173 Bob Daemmrich/Stock, Boston; 174B Ken Karp*; 174C Ken Karp*; 174T Ken Karp*; 175BL Ken Karp*; 175C Ken Karp*; 175R Ken Karp*; 175TL Ken Karp*; 176C Farrell Grehan/Photo Researchers; 176L Ken Karp*; 176R GHP Studio*; 178 Ken Karp*

Chapter 8 182 Brenda Tharp; 188 Yoav Levy/Phototake; 189 GHP Studio*; 190 Nick Pavloff*; 191BL Ken Karp*; 191BR Cindy Lewis; 191TL Ken Karp*; 191TR GHP Studio*; 192BL Joseph Nettis/Photo Researchers; 192BR Stacy Pick/Stock, Boston; 192TL Ken Karp*; 192TR Phototake; 193 Seth Joel/Woodfin Camp & Associates; 194 Dan McCoy/Rainbow; 195BL Stephen Frisch*; 195BR GHP Studio*; 195TL GHP Studio*; 195TR Breck P. Kent/Earth Scenes; 196BL Ken Karp*; 196BR Ken Karp*; 196TL GHP Studio*; 196TR NASA; 197BL CNRI/Phototake; 197BR Ellis Herwig/Stock, Boston; 197TL Elliott Smith*; 197TR Ted Mahieu/The Stock Market; 199 David Lawrence/The Stock Market; 200 Ken Karp*; 204-205 M. Angelo/Westlight

Unit 3 206 GHP Studio*; 206-207 Gerald & Buff Corsi/Tom Stack & Associates

Chapter 9 208 Chuck O'Rear/Westlight; 209 David Madison/DUOMO; 210 Tim Davis*; 216 Ken Karp*; 219B Salmoiraghi/The Stock Market; 219T Gerald & Buff Corsi/Tom Stack & Associates; 221 Ken Karp*; 225C Ken Karp*; 225L Robert Mathena/Fundamental Photographs; 225R Ken Karp*

Chapter 10 230 Phillip A. Harrington/Fran Heyl Associates; 236B Anne Dowie*; 236T Anne Dowie*; 238 Ken Karp*; 241 Nick Pavloff*; 247 Greg Vaughn/Tom Stack & Associates; 252-253 GHP Studio*; 254 T. J. Florian/Rainbow; 254-255 Cameron Davidson/Bruce Coleman Inc.

Chapter 11 256 Bob O'Shaughnessy/The Stock Market; 257 Ken Karp*; 258B Ken Karp*; 258TL Ken Karp*; 258TR Ken Karp*; 260 Ken Karp*; 261 GHP Studio*; 263L GHP Studio*; 263R GHP Studio*; 267 Ken Karp*; 270L Ken Karp*; 270R Ken Karp*; 271 Ken Karp*; 272 Nick Pavloff*; 275B Ken Karp*; 275T Ken Karp*; 276 Ken Karp*; 277 Ken Karp*; 281B Stephen Frisch*; 281C Stephen Frisch*; 281T Stephen Frisch*

Chapter 12 286 CNRI-Science Photo Library/Photo; Researchers 287; GHP Studio*; 288 Ken Karp*; 289B The Granger Collection; 289T The Granger Collection; 291 NASA; 292B GHP Studio*; 292CL Bill Ross/Westlight; 292CR W. Cody/Westlight; 292T Linda K. Moore/Rainbow; 298 Chromosohm/Sohm/AllStock; 299 Ken Karp*; 300 Rich Buzzelli/Tom Stack & Associates; 304 GHP Studio*

Chapter 13 308 David Parker-Science Photo Library/Photo Researchers; 309 Elliott Smith*; 313BL Ken Karp*; 313BR David Parker-Science Photo Library/Photo Researchers; 313R David Parker-Science Photo Library/Photo Researchers; 313T Ken Karp*; 314T

Ross Ehlert/Woodfin Camp & Associates; 321 Ken Karp*; 322 UPI/Bettmann; 324 Peter Menzel/Stock, Boston; 330-331 GHP Studio*

Unit 5 332 Ken Karp*; 332-333 Frank Siteman/Rainbow

Chapter 14 334 W. Maehl/AllStock; 336 Ken Karp*; 339 Jeff Hornbaker; 340 Ken Karp*; 341 Steve Lissau/Rainbow; 346 Roy Giles/Tony Stone Worldwide; 347B Tony Stone Worldwide; 347T Charles O'Rear/Westlight; 348 Jonathan Blair/Woodfin Camp & Associates; 350 Baron Wolman; 351L Ken Karp*; 353 Baron Wolman; 354L Dick Luria-Science Source/Photo Researchers; 354R Pix Elation/Fran Heyl Associates

Chapter 15 358 Mark Richards*; 359 Tim Davis*; 364 Tony Stone Worldwide; 367C GHP Studio*; 367L GHP Studio*; 367R GHP Studio*; 370L Anne Dowie*; 370R Anne Dowie*; 376 Baron Wolman; 377L Ken Karp*; 377R Runk-Schoenberger/Grant Heilman Photography; 379 Lawrence Manning/Tony Stone Worldwide; 380 Ken Karp*

Chapter 16 384 © Lennart Nilsson from `Behold Man', Little, Brown & Co., Boston; 385 Doug Menuez/Stock, Boston; 388 Robert Shafer/Tony Stone Worldwide; 389 Gabe Palmer/The Stock Market; 390C Ken Karp*; 390L Ken Karp*; 390R Mark Richards*; 392B Anne Dowie*; 392R Andrea Brizzi/The Stock Market; 392TL Ken Karp*; 393C Anne Dowie*; 393L Ken Karp*; 393R Ken Karp*; 397 Ken Karp*; 398 Martin Rogers/Stock, Boston; 399 Howard Sochurek/The Stock Market; 401 Rod Catanach/Woods Hole Oceanographic Institute; 402TL Kelvin Aitken/Peter Arnold, Inc.; 402TR Stephen J. Krasemann/DRK Photos; 403B Dwight R. Kuhn/DRK Photos; 403R Stanley Breeden/DRK Photos; 403TL Stephen Dalton/Photo Researchers

Chapter 17 408 A.M. Rosario/The Image Bank; 410 Kodansha/The Image Bank; 415 Ken Karp*; 417 Runk-Schoenberger/Grant Heilman Photography; 420B David Pollack/The Stock Market; 420C Stuart L. Craig Jr./Bruce Coleman Inc.; 420T NASA; 422 Louis Bencze/AllStock; 423C Ken Karp*; 423L Ken Karp*; 423R Ken Karp*; 424C Ken Karp*; 424L Anne Dowie*; 425 John Livzey/AllStock; 426L Ken Karp*; 426R Ken Karp*; 427 Giraudon/Art Resource; 428 Lawrence Migdale*

Chapter 18 432 Michael Furman/The Stock Market; 433 Mary Clay/Tom Stack & Associates; 434BL Robert L. Dunne/Bruce Coleman Inc.; 434BR Wallace Kirkland/Animals, Animals; 434L Ken Karp*; 434TC Ken Karp*; 435CB Spencer Grant/Stock, Boston; 435CR Kent Knudson/Stock, Boston; 435L Ken Karp*; 435TR Don & Pat Valenti/DRK Photos; 440 Elliott Smith*; 441 Don & Pat Valenti/DRK Photos; 443B Ken Karp*; 443T Ken Karp*; 445 Phillip A. Harrington/Fran Heyl Associates; 446 Ted Levin/Earth Scenes; 447 Ken Karp*; 448L Anne Dowie*; 448C Anne Dowie*; 448R Anne Dowie*; 449B Ken Karp*; 449T Harry Pulschen/Custom Medical Stock Photo; 450 Ken Karp*; 451 Ken Karp*; 456R Yoav Levy/Phototake; 456T Philippe Plailly/Science Photo Library/Photo Researchers; 457BR Doug Armand/Tony Stone Worldwide; 457R Chuck O'Rear/Woodfin Camp & Associates; 458 Chuck O'Rear/Woodfin Camp & Associates; 462 Ken Karp*; 462-463 Renee Lynn*

Unit 6 464 Stephen Frisch*; 464-465 GHP Studio*

Chapter 19 466 William McCoy/Rainbow; 467 Ken Karp*; 469 Dr. A. Lesk, Laboratory of Molecular Biology-Science Photo Library/Photo Researchers; 471 Craig Aurness/Woodfin Camp & Associates; 474R OMIKRON/Science Source/Photo Researchers; 478 Anne Dowie*; 481 GHP Studio*; 483L Marty Cordano/DRK Photos; 483R Pat O'Hara/DRK Photos; 484 Ken Karp*

Chapter 20 488 Craig Aurness/ Westlight; 489B GHP Studio*; 489T GHP Studio*; 490B Ken Karp*; 490CL Ken Karp*; 490R GHP Studio*; 490TC Ken Karp*; 492B Ken Karp*; 492T Richard Pasley/Stock, Boston; 498 NASA; 499 Stephen Frisch*; 503 Ken Karp*; 505B Ken Karp*; 505CR Ken Karp*; 505TL Elliott Smith*; 505TR Ken Karp*; 507 Anne Dowie*; 508 John Colwell/Grant Heilman Photography; 510 Ken Karp*

Chapter 21 514 Jon Brenneis/Photo 20-20; 515 Holt Studios/Earth Scenes; 516 Elliott Smith*; 517 Ken Karp*; 518C GHP Studio*; 518CL Ken Karp*; 518R Ken Karp*; 518TL Ken Karp*; 519 Elliott Smith*; 521 Bohdan Hrynewych/Stock, Boston; 522 Tom Till/DRK Photos; 524B Charles Derby/Photo Researchers; 524T Dan McCoy/Rainbow; 525 Seth H. Goltzer/The Stock Market; 527 Elliott Smith*; 528 Ken Karp*; 529 Ken Karp*; 532 Ken Karp*

Chapter 22 536 J. Gross, Biozentrum-Science Photo Library/Photo Researchers, Inc.; 537 John Gerlach/DRK Photos; 538 Anne Dowie*; 542 GHP Studio*; 544 Ken Karp*; 545 Mike King/Tony Stone Worldwide; 546 GHP Studio*; 547 GHP Studio*; 548 GHP Studio*; 549 Anne Dowie*; 555 Science Photo Library/Photo Researchers; 556 Anne Dowie*

Chapter 23 560 Patrice Loiez, CERN/Science Photo Library/Photo Researchers; 561 Shopper/Stock, Boston; 564C Photo Researchers; 564T Dan Budnik/Woodfin Camp & Associates; 565 Art Resource; 569B Biophoto Associates/Science Source/Photo Researchers; 569T Biophoto Associates/Photo Researchers; 570 Ken Karp*; 573 Zefa-Streichan/The Stock Market; 574 Jeff Zaruba/The Stock Market; 578-579 Chuck O'Rear/Westlight; 578C GHP Studio*; 578T GHP Studio*; 579 GHP Studio*

Unit 7 580 Mark Sherman; 580-581 Barry L. Runk/Grant Heilman Photography

Chapter 24 582 Dan McCoy/Rainbow; 583 C. H. Currier/The Bettmann Archive 586; James H. Carmichael/Bruce Coleman Inc.; 587 Jan Staller/The Stock Market; 589 Gabe Palmer/The Stock Market; 590B Dewitt Jones/Woodfin Camp & Associates; 590T Bernard Pierre Wolff/Photo Researchers Inc.; 591B Kunio Owaki/The Stock Market; 591T Torin Boyd; 592B Robert Frerch/Woodfin Camp & Associates; 592C Greg Vaughn/Tom Stack & Associates; 592T Simon Fraser/Science Photo Library/Photo Researchers Inc.; 593 Sepp Seitz/Woodfin Camp & Associates; 595 Ken Karp*; 599 Jim Pickerell/Westlight; 600 Heartland All Species Project

Chapter 25 604 Lisl Dennis/The Image Bank; 605B Tom Stack/Tom Stack & Associates; 605C Eric Grave/Phototake; 609B GHP Studio*; 609T GHP Studio*; 610B GHP Studio*; 610D GHP Studio*; 610L GHP Studio*; 610R GHP Studio*; 611C GHP Studio*; 611L Stephen Frisch*; 611R GHP Studio*; 612 GHP Studio*; 613 GHP Studio*; 616BL GHP Studio*; 616C Geoffrey Clifford/Woodfin Camp & Associates; 616CL GHP Studio*; 616R Tim Davis*; 617 Stephen Trimble/DRK Photos; 618B Ron Kimball; 618C Herb Charles Ohlmeyer/Fran Heyl Associates; 619 NASA; 620 Ken Karp*; 621 NASA; 623B Marc Muench/AllStock; 623T M. Gottschalk/Westlight; 624BL Gary Braasch/AllStock; 624C David M. Dennis/Tom Stack & Associates; 624R Gary Milburn/Tom Stack & Associates; 624TL Tom Walker/AllStock; 625L Tom Carroll/Phototake; 626B Thomas Kitchin/Tom Stack & Associates; 626R Tom Bean/AllStock; 626T Ray Pfortner/Peter Arnold, Inc.; 627T Matt McVay/Black Star; 628C Robert Winslow/Tom Stack & Associates; 628T Ivan Massar/Black Star; 632 GHP Studio*; 632-633 GHP Studio*

* Photographed expressly for Addison-Wesley, Inc.

Science and Literature

Unit 1 From *The Boy Who Reversed Himself* by William Sleator. Copyright © 1986 by William Sleator. Used by permission of Dutton Children's Books, a division of Penguin Books USA Inc.

Unit 2 From *Invitation to the Game* by Monica Hughes. Copyright © 1990 by Monica Hughes. Published in Canada by HarperCollins Publishers Ltd. Reprinted by permission of Simon and Schuster Books for Young Readers, HarperCollins Publishers Ltd., Toronto and Reed Consumer Books.

Unit 3 From *Child of the Owl* by Laurence Yep. Copyright © 1977 by Laurence Yep. Reprinted by permission of HarperCollins Publishers.

Unit 4 From *Genie With The Light Blue Hair* by Ellen Conford. Copyright © 1989 by Conford Enterprises Ltd. Used by permission of Bantam Books, a division of Bantam Doubleday Dell Publishing Group, Inc.

Unit 5 From *Blue Tights* by Rita Williams-Garcia. Copyright © 1988 by Rita Williams-Garcia. Reprinted by permission of Penguin Books USA Inc.

Unit 6 From "Mother and Daughter," *Baseball in April and Other Stories* by Gary Soto. Copyright © 1990 by Gary Soto. Reprinted by permission of Harcourt Brace and Company.

Unit 7 Reprinted with permission of Macmillan Publishing Company from *M.C. Higgins, The Great* by Virginia Hamilton. Copyright © 1974 by Virginia Hamilton.